BUSINESS STATISTICS

The McGraw-Hill Education Series in Operations and Decision Sciences

Third Edition

BUSINESS STATISTICS
Communicating with Numbers

Sanjiv Jaggia   Alison Kelly
California Polytechnic   *Suffolk University*
State University

McGraw Hill Education

BUSINESS STATISTICS

2 3 4 5 6 7 8 9 GPC 21 20 19

ISBN   9-781-26028837-7
MHID   1-260-28837-4

Cover Image: @ *McGraw-Hill Education*

mheducation.com/highered

Dedicated to Chandrika, Minori, John, Megan, and Matthew

Sanjiv Jaggia

Courtesy of Sanjiv Jaggia

Sanjiv Jaggia is the associate dean of graduate programs and a professor of economics and finance at California Polytechnic State University in San Luis Obispo, California. After earning a Ph.D. from Indiana University, Bloomington, in 1990, Dr. Jaggia spent 17 years at Suffolk University, Boston. In 2003, he became a Chartered Financial Analyst (CFA®). Dr. Jaggia's research interests include empirical finance, statistics, and econometrics. He has published extensively in research journals, including the *Journal of Empirical Finance, Review of Economics and Statistics, Journal of Business and Economic Statistics, Journal of Applied Econometrics,* and *Journal of Econometrics*. Dr. Jaggia's ability to communicate in the classroom has been acknowledged by several teaching awards. In 2007, he traded one coast for the other and now lives in San Luis Obispo, California, with his wife and daughter. In his spare time, he enjoys cooking, hiking, and listening to a wide range of music.

Alison Kelly

Courtesy of Alison Kelly

Alison Kelly is a professor of economics at Suffolk University in Boston, Massachusetts. She received her B.A. degree from the College of the Holy Cross in Worcester, Massachusetts; her M.A. degree from the University of Southern California in Los Angeles; and her Ph.D. from Boston College in Chestnut Hill, Massachusetts. Dr. Kelly has published in journals such as the *American Journal of Agricultural Economics, Journal of Macroeconomics, Review of Income and Wealth, Applied Financial Economics*, and *Contemporary Economic Policy*. She is a Chartered Financial Analyst (CFA®) and teaches review courses in quantitative methods to candidates preparing to take the CFA exam. Dr. Kelly has also served as a consultant for a number of companies; her most recent work focused on how large financial institutions satisfy requirements mandated by the Dodd-Frank Act. She resides in Hamilton, Massachusetts, with her husband and two children.

A Unique Emphasis on Communicating with Numbers Makes Business Statistics Relevant to Students

We wrote *Business Statistics: Communicating with Numbers* because we saw a need for a contemporary, core statistics text that sparked student interest and bridged the gap between how statistics is taught and how practitioners think about and apply statistical methods. Throughout the text, the emphasis is on communicating with numbers rather than on number crunching. In every chapter, students are exposed to statistical information conveyed in written form. By incorporating the perspective of practitioners, it has been our goal to make the subject matter more relevant and the presentation of material more straightforward for students. Although the text is application-oriented and practical, it is also mathematically sound and uses notation that is generally accepted for the topic being covered.

From our years of experience in the classroom, we have found that an effective way to make statistics interesting is to use timely applications. For these reasons, examples in *Business Statistics* come from all walks of life, including business, economics, sports, health, housing, the environment, polling, and psychology. By carefully matching examples with statistical methods, students learn to appreciate the relevance of statistics in our world today, and perhaps, end up learning statistics without realizing they are doing so.

*This is probably the **best book** I have seen in terms of explaining concepts.*
Brad McDonald, *Northern Illinois University*

*The book is **well written, more readable and interesting than most stats texts,** and effective in explaining concepts. The examples and cases are particularly good and effective teaching tools.*
Andrew Koch, *James Madison University*

***Clarity and brevity are the most important things I look for**—this text has both in abundance.*
Michael Gordinier, *Washington University, St. Louis*

Continuing Key Features

The third edition of *Business Statistics* reinforces and expands six core features that were well-received in earlier editions.

Integrated Introductory Cases. Each chapter begins with an interesting and relevant introductory case. The case is threaded throughout the chapter, and once the relevant statistical tools have been covered, a synopsis—a short summary of findings—is provided. The introductory case often serves as the basis of several examples in other chapters.

Writing with Statistics. Interpreting results and conveying information effectively is critical to effective decision making in a business environment. Students are taught how to take the data, apply it, and convey the information in a meaningful way.

Unique Coverage of Regression Analysis. Relevant coverage of regression without repetition is an important hallmark of this text.

Written as Taught. Topics are presented the way they are taught in class, beginning with the intuition and explanation and concluding with the application.

Integration of Microsoft Excel®. Students are taught to develop an understanding of the concepts and how to derive the calculation; then Excel is used as a tool to perform the cumbersome calculations. In addition, guidelines for using Minitab, SPSS, and JMP are provided in chapter appendices.

Connect®. *Connect* is an online system that gives students the tools they need to be successful in the course. Through guided examples and LearnSmart adaptive study tools, students receive guidance and practice to help them master the topics.

*I really like the case studies and the **emphasis on writing.** We are making a big effort to incorporate more business writing in our core courses, so that meshes well.*

Elizabeth Haran, *Salem State University*

*For a statistical analyst, your analytical skill is only as good as your communication skill. Writing with statistics **reinforces the importance of communication** and provides students with concrete examples to follow.*

Jun Liu, *Georgia Southern University*

Features New to the Third Edition

The third edition of *Business Statistics* features a number of improvements suggested by many reviewers and users of earlier editions. The following are the major changes.

Integration of R. R is a powerful software that merges the convenience of statistical packages with the power of coding. We feel that there are several good reasons for learning R in a Business Statistics class. First, R is open source as well as cross-platform compatible. This means that there is zero cost to download R, and it can be run on Windows, Mac OS X, or Linux. Second, with the availability of several data analysis tools for conventional and modern statistical models, R is easy to use. Third, R is wildly popular and quickly becoming one of the most powerful programming languages for data analytics. It is estimated that R has about 2 million users, and many of these users regularly interact on discussion forums. And finally, employers find knowledge of R very attractive in prospective hires. Leading firms like the New York Times, Google, Facebook, Bank of America, Pfizer, and Merck are all using R. For these reasons, in addition to Excel, we now provide R instructions in all relevant sections of the text; however, for those instructors who prefer to focus only on Excel, the R instructions sections are easily skipped.

Focus on the *p*-Value Approach. In the earlier editions of *Business Statistics*, we stressed both the *p*-value approach and the critical value approach in all chapters related to hypothesis testing. We have found that students often get confused with the mechanics of implementing a hypothesis test with both approaches. While the critical value approach is attractive when a computer is unavailable and all calculations must be done by hand, most researchers and practitioners favor the *p*-value approach since virtually every statistical software package reports *p*-values. We also surveyed users of *Business Statistics*, and the decision was unanimous: focus on the *p*-value approach. So this is what we have done throughout the text. A discussion of the critical value methodology is now provided in the appendix to Chapter 9.

Here are a few other noteworthy changes:

- Dozens of new examples, exercises, introductory cases, and case studies have been added.
- Many Learning Outcomes have been streamlined or rewritten for the sake of simplicity and consistency.
- In Chapter 1 (Statistics and Data), structured data, unstructured data, and big data are introduced, and the section on online data sources has been revised.
- In Chapter 4 (Introduction to Probability), the Writing with Statistics example now examines marijuana legalization in the United States.
- In Chapter 6 (Continuous Probability Distributions), the normal distribution is covered in one section, rather than two sections.
- In Chapter 7 (Sampling and Sampling Distributions), a discussion of the Trump election coupled with social-desirability bias has been added.
- In Chapter 14 (Regression Analysis), the estimation of a simple linear regression and a multiple linear regression is covered in one section, rather than two sections.

***Business Statistics* Coupled with Connect.** Since both of us use Connect in our classes, we have attempted to make the technology component seamless with the text itself. We have reviewed every Connect exercise, and during this process, we have painstakingly evaluated rounding rules and revised tolerance levels. The positive feedback from users of the earlier editions has been well worth the effort. In addition, we have reviewed every LearnSmart probe. Instructors who teach in an online or hybrid environment will especially appreciate our Connect product.

Students Learn Through Real-World Cases and Business Examples . . .

Integrated Introductory Cases

Each chapter opens with a real-life case study that forms the basis for several examples within the chapter. The questions included in the examples create a roadmap for mastering the most important learning outcomes within the chapter. A synopsis of each chapter's introductory case is presented when the last of these examples has been discussed. Instructors of distance learners may find these introductory cases particularly useful.

Mark Bowden/Getty Images RF

SYNOPSIS OF INTRODUCTORY CASE

Growth and value are two fundamental styles in stock and mutual fund investing. Proponents of growth investing believe that companies that are growing faster than their peers are trendsetters and will be able to maintain their superior growth. By investing in the stocks of these companies, they expect their investment to grow at a rate faster than the overall stock market. By comparison, value investors focus on the stocks of companies that are trading at a discount relative to the overall market or a specific sector. Investors of value stocks believe that these stocks are undervalued and that their price will increase once their true value is recognized by other investors. The debate between growth and value investing is age-old, and which style dominates depends on the sample period used for the analysis.

©Ingram Publishing RF

An analysis of annual return data for Vanguard's Growth Index mutual fund (Growth) and Vanguard's Value Index mutual fund (Value) for the years 2007 through 2016 provides important information for an investor trying to determine whether to invest in a growth mutual fund, a value mutual fund, or both types of mutual funds. Over this period, the mean return for the Growth fund of 10.09% is greater than the mean return for the Value fund of 7.56%. While the mean return typically represents the reward of investing, it does not incorporate the risk of

INTRODUCTORY CASE

Investment Decision

Jacqueline Brennan works as a financial advisor at a large investment firm. She meets with an inexperienced investor who has some questions regarding two approaches to mutual fund investing: growth investing versus value investing. The investor has heard that growth funds invest in companies whose stock prices are expected to grow at a faster rate, relative to the overall stock market, and value funds invest in companies whose stock prices are below their true worth. The investor has also heard that the main component of investment return is through capital appreciation in growth funds and through dividend income in value funds. The investor shows Jacqueline the annual return data for Vanguard's Growth Index mutual fund (henceforth, Growth) and Vanguard's Value Index mutual fund (henceforth, Value). Table 3.1 shows the annual return data for these two mutual funds for the years 2007–2016.

*In all of these chapters, **the opening case leads directly into the application questions** that students will have regarding the material. Having a strong and related case will certainly provide more benefit to the student, as context leads to improved learning.*

Alan Chow, *University of South Alabama*

This is an excellent approach. *The student gradually gets the idea that he can look at a problem—one which might be fairly complex—and break it down into root components. He learns that a little bit of math could go a long way, and even more math is even more beneficial to evaluating the problem.*

Dane Peterson, *Missouri State University*

and Build Skills to Communicate Results

Writing with Statistics

One of our most important innovations is the inclusion of a sample report within every chapter (except Chapter 1). Our intent is to show students how to convey statistical information in written form to those who may not know detailed statistical methods. For example, such a report may be needed as input for managerial decision making in sales, marketing, or company planning. Several similar writing exercises are provided at the end of each chapter. Each chapter also includes a synopsis that addresses questions raised from the introductory case. This serves as a shorter writing sample for students. Instructors of large sections may find these reports useful for incorporating writing into their statistics courses.

> Writing with statistics shows that statistics **is more than number crunching.**
> Greg Cameron,
> *Brigham Young University*

> *These technical writing examples provide a **very useful example of how to make statistics work and turn it into a report** that will be useful to an organization. I will strive to have my students learn from these examples.*
> Bruce P. Christensen,
> *Weber State University*

WRITING WITH STATISTICS

Professor Lang is a professor of economics at Salem State University. She has been teaching a course in Principles of Economics for over 25 years. Professor Lang has never graded on a curve since she believes that relative grading may unduly penalize (benefit) a good (poor) student in an unusually strong (weak) class. She always uses an absolute scale for making grades, as shown in the two left columns of Table 6.5.

TABLE 6.5 Grading Scales with Absolute Grading versus Relative Grading

Absolute Grading		Relative Grading	
Grade	Score	Grade	Probability
A	92 and above	A	0.10
B	78 up to 92	B	0.35
C	64 up to 78	C	0.40
D	58 up to 64	D	0.10
F	Below 58	F	0.05

©Image Source, all rights reserved. RF

A colleague of Professor Lang's has convinced her to move to relative grading, since it corrects for unanticipated problems. Professor Lang decides to experiment with grading based on the relative scale as shown in the two right columns of Table 6.5. Using this relative grading scheme, the top 10% of students will get A's, the next 35% B's, and so on. Based on her years of teaching experience, Professor Lang believes that the scores in her course follow a normal distribution with a mean of 78.6 and a standard deviation of 12.4.

Professor Lang wants to use the above information to

1. Calculate probabilities based on the absolute scale. Compare these probabilities to the relative scale.
2. Calculate the range of scores for various grades based on the relative scale. Compare these ranges to the absolute scale.
3. Determine which grading scale makes it harder to get higher grades.

Many teachers would confess that grading is one of the most difficult tasks of their profession. Two common grading systems used in higher education are relative and absolute. Relative grading systems are norm-referenced or curve-based, in which a grade is based on the student's relative position in class. Absolute grading systems, on the other hand, are criterion-referenced, in which a grade is related to the student's absolute performance in class. In short, with absolute grading, the student's score is compared to a predetermined scale, whereas with relative grading, the score is compared to the scores of other students in the class.

Let X represent a grade in Professor Lang's class, which is normally distributed with a mean of 78.6 and a standard deviation of 12.4. This information is used to derive the grade probabilities based on the absolute scale. For instance, the probability of receiving an A is derived as $P(X \geq 92) = P(Z \geq 1.08) = 0.14$. Other probabilities, derived similarly, are presented in Table 6.A.

TABLE 6.A Probabilities Based on Absolute Scale and Relative Scale

Grade	Probability Based on Absolute Scale	Probability Based on Relative Scale
A	0.14	0.10
B	0.38	0.35
C	0.36	0.40
D	0.07	0.10
F	0.05	0.05

Sample Report—Absolute Grading versus Relative Grading

> This is an **excellent approach. . . .** The ability to translate numerical information into words that others can understand is critical.
> Scott Bailey, *Troy University*

> **Excellent.** Students need to become better writers.
> Bob Nauss, *University of Missouri, St. Louis*

Unique Coverage and Presentation . . .

Unique Coverage of Regression Analysis

Our coverage of regression analysis is more extensive than that of the vast majority of texts. This focus reflects the topic's growing use in practice. We combine simple and multiple regression in one chapter, which we believe is a seamless grouping and eliminates needless repetition. Three more in-depth chapters cover statistical inference, nonlinear relationships, dummy variables, and binary choice models.

Chapter 14: Regression Analysis
Chapter 15: Inference with Regression Models
Chapter 16: Regression Models for Nonlinear Relationships
Chapter 17: Regression Models with Dummy Variables

> *By comparing this chapter with other books, I think that this is one of the best explanations about regression I have seen.*
> Cecilia Maldonado, *Georgia Southwestern State University*

> *The authors have put forth a novel and innovative way to present regression which in and of itself should make instructors take a long and hard look at this book.* **Students should find this book very readable and a good companion for their course.**
> Harvey A. Singer, *George Mason University*

Inclusion of Important Topics

In our teaching outside the classroom, we have found that several fundamental topics important to business are not covered by the majority of traditional texts. For example, most books do not integrate the geometric mean, mean-variance analysis, and the Sharpe ratio with descriptive statistics. Similarly, the discussion of probability concepts generally does not include odds ratios, risk aversion, and the analysis of portfolio returns. We incorporate these important topics in the text because practitioners tend to use them on a regular basis.

> *The inclusion of material used on a regular basis by investment professionals adds real-world credibility to the text and course and better prepares students for the real world.*
> Bob Gillette, *University of Kentucky*

THE SHARPE RATIO

The Sharpe ratio measures the extra reward per unit of risk. The Sharpe ratio for an investment I is computed as

$$\frac{\bar{x}_I - \bar{R}_f}{s_I},$$

where $\bar{x}_I$ is the mean return for the investment, $\bar{R}_f$ is the mean return for a risk-free asset such as a Treasury bill (T-bill), and s_I is the standard deviation for the investment.

Written as Taught

We introduce topics just the way we teach them; that is, the relevant tools follow the opening application. Our roadmap for solving problems is

1. Start with intuition
2. Introduce mathematical rigor, and
3. Produce computer output that confirms results.

We use worked examples throughout the text to illustrate how to apply concepts to solve real-world problems.

> *This is **easy for students to follow** and I do get the feeling . . . the sections are spoken language.*
> Zhen Zhu, *University of Central Oklahoma*

that Make the Content More Effective

Integration of Microsoft Excel®, and now, R

We prefer that students first focus on and absorb the statistical material before replicating their results with a computer. Solving each application manually provides students with a deeper understanding of the relevant concept. However, we recognize that, primarily due to cumbersome calculations or the need for statistical tables, embedding computer output is necessary. Microsoft Excel and R are the primary software packages used in this text. We chose Excel and R over other statistical packages based on their widespread use and reviewer feedback. For instructors who prefer to focus only on Excel, the R instructions sections are easily skipped. We provide brief guidelines for using Minitab, SPSS, and JMP in chapter appendices.

Using Excel

We use Excel's **BINOM.DIST** function to calculate binomial probabilities. In order to find $P(X = x)$, we enter "=BINOM.DIST(x, n, p, 0)" where x is the number of successes, n is the number of trials, and p is the probability of success. If we enter a "1" for the last argument in the function, then Excel returns $P(X \le x)$.

a. In order to find the probability that exactly 70 American adults are Facebook users, $P(X = 70)$, we enter "=BINOM.DIST(70, 100, 0.68, 0)" and Excel returns 0.0791.

b. In order to find the probability that no more than 70 American adults are Facebook users, $P(X \le 70)$, we enter "=BINOM.DIST(70, 100, 0.68, 1)" and Excel returns 0.7007.

c. In order to find the probability that at least 70 American adults are Facebook users, $P(X \ge 70) = 1 - P(X \le 69)$, we enter "=1−BINOM.DIST(69, 100, 0.68, 1)" and Excel returns 0.3784.

Using R

We use R's **dbinom** and **pbinom** functions to calculate binomial probabilities. In order to calculate $P(X = x)$, we enter "dbinom(x, n, p)" where x is the number of successes, n is the number of trials, and p is the probability of success. In order to calculate $P(X \le x)$, we enter "pbinom(x, n, p)".

a. In order to find $P(X = 70)$, we enter:

```
> dbinom(70, 100, 0.68)
```

And R returns: 0.07907911.

b. In order to find $P(X \le 70)$, we enter:

```
> pbinom(70, 100, 0.68)
```

And R returns: 0.7006736.

c. In order to find $P(X \ge 70) = 1 - P(X \le 69)$, we enter:

```
> 1 - pbinom(69, 100, 0.68)
```

And R returns: 0.3784055.

---

*. . . does a solid job of building the intuition behind the concepts and **then adding mathematical rigor to these ideas** before finally verifying the results with Excel.*

Matthew Dean,
University of Southern Maine

Real-World Exercises and Case Studies that Reinforce the Material

Mechanical and Applied Exercises

Chapter exercises are a well-balanced blend of mechanical, computational-type problems followed by more ambitious, interpretive-type problems. We have found that simpler drill problems tend to build students' confidence prior to tackling more difficult applied problems. Moreover, we repeatedly use many data sets—including house prices, rents, stock returns, salaries, and debt—in various chapters of the text. For instance, students first use these real data to calculate summary measures, make statistical inferences with confidence intervals and hypothesis tests, and finally, perform regression analysis.

Applied exercises from *The Wall Street Journal, Kiplinger's, Fortune, The New York Times, USA Today*; various websites—Census.gov, Zillow.com, Finance.yahoo.com, ESPN.com; and more.

a. State the null and the alternative hypotheses for the test.

b. Calculate the value of the test statistic and the p-value.

c. Use $\alpha = 0.01$ to determine if the average breaking distance differs from 120 feet.

Customers at Costco spend an average of $130 per trip (*The Wall Street Journal*, October 6, 2010). One of Costco's rivals would like to determine whether its customers spend more per trip. A survey of the receipts of 25 customers found that the sample mean was $135.25. Assume that the population standard deviation is $10.50 and that spending follows a normal distribution.

a. Specify the null and alternative hypotheses to test whether average spending at the rival's store is more than $130.

b. Calculate the value of the test statistic and the p-value.

c. At the 5% significance level, what is the conclusion to the test?

24. In May 2008, CNN reported that sports utility vehicles (SUVs) are plunging toward the "endangered" list. Due to the uncertainty of oil prices and environmental concerns, consumers are replacing gas-guzzling vehicles with fuel-efficient smaller cars. As a result, there has been a big drop in the demand for new as well as used SUVs. A sales manager of a used car dealership for SUVs believes that it takes more than 90 days, on average, to sell an SUV. In order to test his claim, he samples 40 recently sold SUVs and finds that it took an average of 95 days to sell an SUV. He believes that the population standard deviation is fairly stable at 20 days.

a. State the null and the alternative hypotheses to test if the bottling process is inaccurate.

b. What is the value of the test statistic and the p-value?

c. At $\alpha = 0.05$, what is the conclusion to the hypothesis test? Make a recommendation to the bottler.

27. **FILE** *MV_Houses.* A realtor in Mission Viejo, California, believes that the average price of a house is more than $500,000.

a. State the null and the alternative hypotheses for the test.

b. The data accompanying this exercise show house prices. (Data are in $1,000s.) Assume the population standard deviation is $100 (in $1,000s). What is the value of the test statistic and the p-value?

c. At $\alpha = 0.05$, what is the conclusion to the test? Is the realtor's claim supported by the data?

28. **FILE** *Home_Depot.* The data accompanying this exercise show the weekly stock price for Home Depot. Assume that stock prices are normally distributed with a population standard deviation of $3.

a. State the null and the alternative hypotheses in order to test whether or not the average weekly stock price differs from $30.

b. Find the value of the test statistic and the p-value.

c. At $\alpha = 0.05$, can you conclude that the average weekly stock price does not equal $30?

29. **FILE** *Hourly_Wage.* An economist wants to test if the average hourly wage is less than $22. Assume that the population standard deviation is $6.

a. State the null and the alternative hypotheses for

I especially like the introductory cases, the quality of the end-of-section problems, and the writing examples.

Dave Leupp, *University of Colorado at Colorado Springs*

Their exercises and problems are excellent!

Erl Sorensen, *Bentley University*

Features that Go Beyond the Typical

Conceptual Review

At the end of each chapter, we present a conceptual review that provides a more holistic approach to reviewing the material. This section revisits the learning outcomes and provides the most important definitions, interpretations, and formulas.

CONCEPTUAL REVIEW

LO 5.1 Describe a discrete random variable and its probability distribution.

A **random variable** summarizes outcomes of an experiment with numerical values. A **discrete random variable** assumes a countable number of distinct values, whereas a **continuous random variable** is characterized by uncountable values in an interval.

The **probability mass function** for a discrete random variable X is a list of the values of X with the associated probabilities; that is, the list of all possible pairs $(x, P(X = x))$. The **cumulative distribution function** of X is defined as $P(X \leq x)$.

LO 5.2 Calculate and interpret summary measures for a discrete random variable.

For a discrete random variable X with values $x_1, x_2, x_3, \ldots$, which occur with probabilities $P(X = x_i)$, the **expected value** of X is calculated as $E(X) = \mu = \Sigma x_i P(X = x_i)$. We interpret the expected value as the long-run average value of the random variable over infinitely many independent repetitions of an experiment. Measures of dispersion indicate whether the values of X are clustered about μ or widely scattered from μ. The variance of X is calculated as $Var(X) = \sigma^2 = \Sigma(x_i - \mu)^2 P(X = x_i)$. The standard deviation of X is $SD(X) = \sigma = \sqrt{\sigma^2}$.

In general, a **risk-averse consumer** expects a reward for taking risk. A risk-averse consumer may decline a risky prospect even if it offers a positive expected gain. A **risk-neutral consumer** completely ignores risk and always accepts a prospect that offers a positive expected gain. Finally, **a risk-loving consumer** may accept a risky prospect even if the expected gain is negative.

LO 5.3 Calculate and interpret summary measures to evaluate portfolio returns.

Portfolio return R_p is represented as a linear combination of the individual returns. The **expected return** for a portfolio with two assets is $E(R_p) = w_A E(R_A) + w_B E(R_B)$, where R_A and R_B represent asset returns and w_A and w_B are the corresponding portfolio weights. The **variance** for the portfolio is $Var(R_p) = w_A^2 \sigma_A^2 + w_B^2 \sigma_B^2 + 2w_A w_B \sigma_{AB}$, or equivalently, $Var(R_p) = w_A^2 \sigma_A^2 + w_B^2 \sigma_B^2 + 2w_A w_B \rho_{AB} \sigma_A \sigma_B$.

Most texts basically list what one should have learned but don't add much to that. You do a good job of reminding the reader of what was covered and what was most important about it.

Andrew Koch, *James Madison University*

They have gone beyond the typical [summarizing formulas] and I like the structure. This is a very strong feature of this text.

Virginia M. Miori, *St. Joseph's University*

 **connect**®

McGraw-Hill Connect® is a highly reliable, easy-to-use homework and learning management solution that utilizes learning science and award-winning adaptive tools to improve student results.

Homework and Adaptive Learning

- Connect's assignments help students contextualize what they've learned through application, so they can better understand the material and think critically.
- Connect will create a personalized study path customized to individual student needs through SmartBook®.
- SmartBook helps students study more efficiently by delivering an interactive reading experience through adaptive highlighting and review.

Over **7 billion questions** have been answered, making McGraw-Hill Education products more intelligent, reliable, and precise.

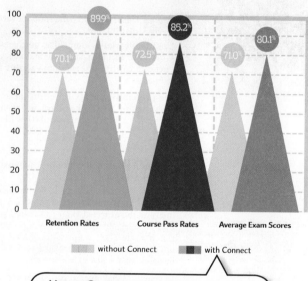

Connect's Impact on Retention Rates, Pass Rates, and Average Exam Scores

Using **Connect** improves retention rates by **19.8%**, passing rates by **12.7%**, and exam scores by **9.1%**.

73% of instructors who use **Connect** require it; instructor satisfaction **increases** by 28% when **Connect** is required.

Quality Content and Learning Resources

- Connect content is authored by the world's best subject matter experts, and is available to your class through a simple and intuitive interface.
- The Connect eBook makes it easy for students to access their reading material on smartphones and tablets. They can study on the go and don't need internet access to use the eBook as a reference, with full functionality.
- Multimedia content such as videos, simulations, and games drive student engagement and critical thinking skills.

Robust Analytics and Reporting

- Connect Insight® generates easy-to-read reports on individual students, the class as a whole, and on specific assignments.

- The Connect Insight dashboard delivers data on performance, study behavior, and effort. Instructors can quickly identify students who struggle and focus on material that the class has yet to master.

- Connect automatically grades assignments and quizzes, providing easy-to-read reports on individual and class performance.

Impact on Final Course Grade Distribution

without Connect		with Connect
22.9%	A	31.0%
27.4%	B	34.3%
22.9%	C	18.7%
11.5%	D	6.1%
15.4%	F	9.9%

> More students earn **As** and **Bs** when they use **Connect**.

Trusted Service and Support

- Connect integrates with your LMS to provide single sign-on and automatic syncing of grades. Integration with Blackboard®, D2L®, and Canvas also provides automatic syncing of the course calendar and assignment-level linking.

- Connect offers comprehensive service, support, and training throughout every phase of your implementation.

- If you're looking for some guidance on how to use Connect, or want to learn tips and tricks from super users, you can find tutorials as you work. Our Digital Faculty Consultants and Student Ambassadors offer insight into how to achieve the results you want with Connect.

www.mheducation.com/connect

What Resources are Available for Instructors?

Instructor Library

The *Connect* Instructor Library is your repository for additional resources to improve student engagement in and out of class. You can select and use any asset that enhances your lecture. The *Connect* Instructor Library includes:

- PowerPoint presentations
- Excel Data Files
- Test Bank
- Instructor's Solutions Manual
- Digital Image Library

Tegrity Campus: Lectures 24/7

Tegrity Campus is integrated in *Connect* to help make your class time available 24/7. With Tegrity, you can capture each one of your lectures in a searchable format for students to review when they study and complete assignments using *Connect*. With a simple one-click start-and-stop process, you can capture everything that is presented to students during your lecture from your computer, including audio. Students can replay any part of any class with easy-to-use browser-based viewing on a PC or Mac.

Educators know that the more students can see, hear, and experience class resources, the better they learn. In fact, studies prove it. With *Tegrity Campus*, students quickly recall key moments by using *Tegrity Campus*'s unique search feature. This search helps students efficiently find what they need, when they need it, across an entire semester of class recordings. Help turn all your students' study time into learning moments immediately supported by your lecture. To learn more about *Tegrity*, watch a two-minute Flash demo at http://tegritycampus.mhhe.com.

ALEKS

ALEKS

ALEKS is an assessment and learning program that provides individualized instruction in Business Statistics, Business Math, and Accounting. Available online in partnership with McGraw-Hill Education, ALEKS interacts with students much like a skilled human tutor, with the ability to assess precisely a student's knowledge and provide instruction on the exact topics the student is most ready to learn. By providing topics to meet individual students' needs, allowing students to move between explanation and practice, correcting and analyzing errors, and defining terms, ALEKS helps students to master course content quickly and easily.

ALEKS also includes an instructor module with powerful, assignment-driven features and extensive content flexibility. ALEKS simplifies course management and allows instructors to spend less time with administrative tasks and more time directing student learning. To learn more about ALEKS, visit www.aleks.com.

MegaStat® for Microsoft Excel®

MegaStat® by J. B. Orris of Butler University is a full-featured Excel add-in that is available online through the *MegaStat* website at **www.mhhe.com/megastat** or through an access card packaged with the text. It works with Excel 2016, 2013, and 2010 (and Excel: Mac 2016). On the website, students have 10 days to successfully download and install *MegaStat* on their local computer. Once installed, *MegaStat* will remain active in Excel with no expiration date or time limitations. The software performs statistical analyses within an Excel workbook. It does basic functions, such as descriptive statistics, frequency distributions, and probability calculations, as well as hypothesis testing, ANOVA, and regression. *MegaStat* output is carefully formatted, and its ease-of-use features include Auto Expand for quick data selection and Auto Label detect. Since *MegaStat* is easy to use, students can focus on learning statistics without being distracted by the software. *MegaStat* is always available from Excel's main menu. Selecting a menu item pops up a dialog box. Screencam tutorials are included that provide a walkthrough of major business statistics topics. Help files are built in, and an introductory user's manual is also included.

What Resources are Available for Students?

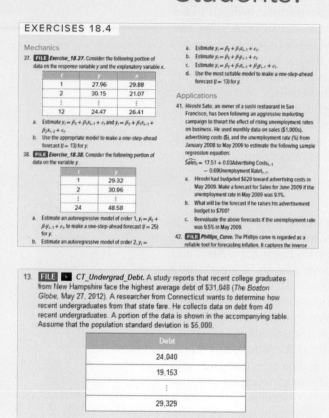

Integration of Excel Data Sets. A convenient feature is the inclusion of an Excel data file link in many problems using data files in their calculation. The link allows students to easily launch into Excel, work the problem, and return to *Connect* to key in the answer and receive feedback on their results.

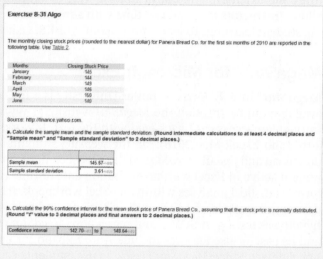

Guided Examples. These narrated video walkthroughs provide students with step-by-step guidelines for solving selected exercises similar to those contained in the text. The student is given personalized instruction on how to solve a problem by applying the concepts presented in the chapter. The video shows the steps to take to work through an exercise. Students can go through each example multiple times if needed.

The *Connect* Student Resource page is the place for students to access additional resources. The Student Resource page offers students quick access to the recommended study tools, data files, and helpful tutorials on statistical programs.

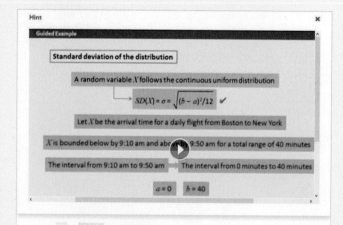

McGraw-Hill Customer Care Contact Information

At McGraw-Hill, we understand that getting the most from new technology can be challenging. That's why our services don't stop after you purchase our products. You can e-mail our product specialists 24 hours a day to get product training online. Or you can search our knowledge bank of frequently asked questions on our support website.

For customer support, call **800-331-5094** or visit **www.mhhe.com/support**. One of our technical support analysts will be able to assist you in a timely fashion.

ACKNOWLEDGMENTS

We would like to acknowledge the following people for providing useful comments and suggestions for past and present editions of all aspects of *Business Statistics*.

John Affisco
Hofstra University

Mehdi Afiat
College of Southern Nevada

Mohammad Ahmadi
University of Tennessee—Chattanooga

Sung Ahn
Washington State University

Mohammad Ahsanullah
Rider University

Imam Alam
University of Northern Iowa

Mostafa Aminzadeh
Towson University

Ardavan Asef-Vaziri
California State University

Antenah Ayanso
Brock University

Scott Bailey
Troy University

Jayanta Bandyopadhyay
Central Michigan University

Samir Barman
University of Oklahoma

Douglas Barrett
University of North Alabama

John Beyers
University of Maryland

Arnab Bisi
Purdue University—West Lafayette

Gary Black
University of Southern Indiana

Randy Boan
Aims Community College

Matthew Bognar
University of Iowa

Juan Cabrera
Ramapo College of New Jersey

Scott Callan
Bentley University

Gregory Cameron
Brigham Young University

Kathleen Campbell
St. Joseph's University

Alan Cannon
University of Texas—Arlington

Michael Cervetti
University of Memphis

Samathy Chandrashekar
Salisbury University

Gary Huaite Chao
University of Pennsylvania—Kutztown

Sangit Chatterjee
Northeastern University

Leida Chen
California Polytechnic State University

Anna Chernobai
Syracuse University

Alan Chesen
Wright State University

Juyan Cho
Colorado State University—Pueblo

Alan Chow
University of South Alabama

Bruce Christensen
Weber State University

Howard Clayton
Auburn University

Robert Collins
Marquette University

M. Halim Dalgin
Kutztown University

Tom Davis
University of Dayton

Matthew Dean
University of Maine

Jason Delaney
University of Arkansas—Little Rock

Ferdinand DiFurio
Tennessee Tech University

Matt Dobra
UMUC

Luca Donno
University of Miami

Joan Donohue
University of South Carolina

David Doorn
University of Minnesota

James Dunne
University of Dayton

Mike Easley
University of New Orleans

Erick Elder
University of Arkansas—Little Rock

Ashraf ElHoubi
Lamar University

Roman Erenshteyn
Goldey-Beacom College

Grace Esimai
University of Texas—Arlington

Soheila Fardanesh
Towson University

Carol Flannery
University of Texas—Dallas

Sydney Fletcher
Mississippi Gulf Coast Community College

Andrew Flight
Portland State University

Samuel Frame
Cal Poly San Luis Obispo

Priya Francisco
Purdue University

Vickie Fry
Westmoreland County Community College

Ed Gallo
Sinclair Community College

Glenn Gilbreath
Virginia Commonwealth University

Robert Gillette
University of Kentucky

Xiaoning Gilliam
Texas Tech University

Mark Gius
Quinnipiac University

Malcolm Gold
Saint Mary's University of Minnesota

Michael Gordinier
Washington University

Deborah Gougeon
University of Scranton

Don Gren
Salt Lake Community College

Thomas G. Groleau
  Carthage College
Babita Gupta
  CSU Monterey Bay
Robert Hammond
  *North Carolina State
  University*
Jim Han
  Florida Atlantic University
Elizabeth Haran
  Salem State University
Jack Harshbarger
  Montreat College
Edward Hartono
  *University of Alabama—
  Huntsville*
Clifford Hawley
  West Virginia University
Santhi Heejebu
  Cornell College
Paul Hong
  University of Toledo
Ping-Hung Hsieh
  Oregon State University
Marc Isaacson
  Augsburg College
Mohammad Jamal
  *Northern Virginia
  Community College*
Robin James
  Harper College
Molly Jensen
  University of Arkansas
Craig Johnson
  *Brigham Young University—
  Idaho*
Janine Sanders Jones
  University of St. Thomas
Vivian Jones
  *Bethune—Cookman
  University*
Jerzy Kamburowski
  University of Toledo
Howard Kaplon
  Towson University
Krishna Kasibhatla
  *North Carolina A&T State
  University*
Mohammad Kazemi
  *University of North
  Carolina—Charlotte*
Ken Kelley
  University of Notre Dame
Lara Khansa
  Virginia Tech
Esther C. Klein
  St. Francis College
Ronald Klimberg
  St. Joseph's University

Andrew Koch
  James Madison University
Subhash Kochar
  Portland State University
Brandon Koford
  Weber University
Randy Kolb
  St. Cloud State University
Vadim Kutsyy
  San Jose State University
Francis Laatsch
  *University of Southern
  Mississippi*
David Larson
  University of South Alabama
John Lawrence
  *California State University—
  Fullerton*
Shari Lawrence
  Nicholls State University
Radu Lazar
  University of Maryland
David Leupp
  *University of Colorado—
  Colorado Springs*
Carel Ligeon
  *Auburn University—
  Montgomery*
Carin Lightner
  *North Carolina A&T State
  University*
Constance Lightner
  Fayetteville State University
Scott Lindsey
  Dixie State College of Utah
Ken Linna
  *Auburn University—
  Montgomery*
Andy Litteral
  University of Richmond
Jun Liu
  Georgia Southern University
Chung-Ping Loh
  University of North Florida
Salvador Lopez
  University of West Georgia
John Loucks
  St. Edward's University
Cecilia Maldonado
  *Georgia Southwestern State
  University*
Farooq Malik
  *University of Southern
  Mississippi*
Ken Mayer
  *University of Nebraska—
  Omaha*
Bradley McDonald
  Northern Illinois University

Elaine McGivern
  Duquesne University
John McKenzie
  Babson University
Norbert Michel
  Nicholls State University
John Miller
  *Sam Houston State
  University*
Virginia Miori
  St. Joseph's University
Prakash Mirchandani
  University of Pittsburgh
Jason Molitierno
  Sacred Heart University
Elizabeth Moliski
  University of Texas—Austin
Joseph Mollick
  *Texas A&M University—
  Corpus Christi*
James Moran
  Oregon State University
Khosrow Moshirvaziri
  *California State University—
  Long Beach*
Tariq Mughal
  University of Utah
Patricia Mullins
  *University of Wisconsin—
  Madison*
Kusum Mundra
  Rutgers University—Newark
Anthony Narsing
  Macon State College
Robert Nauss
  *University of Missouri—
  St. Louis*
Satish Nayak
  *University of Missouri—
  St. Louis*
Thang Nguyen
  *California State University—
  Long Beach*
Mohammad Oskoorouchi
  *California State University—
  San Marcos*
Barb Osyk
  University of Akron
Bhavik Pathak
  *Indiana University
  South Bend*
Scott Paulsen
  Illinois Central College
James Payne
  Calhoun Community College
Norman Pence
  *Metropolitan State College
  of Denver*

Dane Peterson
  Missouri State University
Joseph Petry
  *University of Illinois—
  Urbana/Champaign*
Courtney Pham
  Missouri State University
Martha Pilcher
  University of Washington
Cathy Poliak
  *University of Wisconsin—
  Milwaukee*
Simcha Pollack
  St. John's University
Hamid Pourmohammadi
  *California State University—
  Dominguez Hills*
Tammy Prater
  Alabama State University
Zbigniew H. Przasnyski
  *Loyola Marymount
  University*
Manying Qiu
  Virginia State University
Troy Quast
  *Sam Houston State
  University*
Michael Racer
  University of Memphis
Srikant Raghavan
  *Lawrence Technological
  University*
Bharatendra Rai
  *University of Massachusetts—
  Dartmouth*
Michael Aaron Ratajczyk
  *Saint Mary's University of
  Minnesota*
Tony Ratcliffe
  James Madison University
David Ravetch
  University of California
Bruce Reinig
  San Diego State University
Darlene Riedemann
  Eastern Illinois University
David Roach
  Arkansas Tech University
Carolyn Rochelle
  *East Tennessee State
  University*
Alfredo Romero
  *North Carolina A&T State
  University*
Ann Rothermel
  University of Akron
Jeff Rummel
  Emory University
Deborah Rumsey
  The Ohio State University

Stephen Russell
  Weber State University
William Rybolt
  Babson College
Fati Salimian
  Salisbury University
Fatollah Salimian
  Perdue School of Business
Samuel Sarri
  College of Southern Nevada
Jim Schmidt
  *University of Nebraska—
  Lincoln*
Patrick Scholten
  Bentley University
Bonnie Schroeder
  Ohio State University
Pali Sen
  University of North Florida
Donald Sexton
  Columbia University
Vijay Shah
  *West Virginia University—
  Parkersburg*
Dmitriy Shaltayev
  *Christopher Newport
  University*
Soheil Sibdari
  *University of Massachusetts—
  Dartmouth*
Prodosh Simlai
  University of North Dakota
Harvey Singer
  George Mason University
Harry Sink
  *North Carolina A&T State
  University*
Don Skousen
  Salt Lake Community College
Robert Smidt
  *California Polytechnic State
  University*
Gary Smith
  Florida State University
Antoinette Somers
  Wayne State University
Ryan Songstad
  Augustana College
Erland Sorensen
  Bentley University
Arun Kumar Srinivasan
  *Indiana University—
  Southeast*
Scott Stevens
  James Madison University
Alicia Strandberg
  Temple University
Linda Sturges
  Suny Maritime College

Wendi Sun
  Rockland Trust
Bedassa Tadesse
  University of Minnesota
Pandu Tadikamalta
  University of Pittsburgh
Roberto Duncan Tarabay
  *University of Wisconsin—
  Madison*
Faye Teer
  James Madison University
Deborah Tesch
  Xavier University
Patrick Thompson
  University of Florida
Satish Thosar
  University of Redlands
Ricardo Tovar-Silos
  Lamar University
Quoc Hung Tran
  *Bridgewater State
  University*
Elzbieta Trybus
  *California State University—
  Northridge*
Fan Tseng
  *University of Alabama—
  Huntsville*
Silvanus Udoka
  *North Carolina A&T State
  University*
Shawn Ulrick
  Georgetown University
Bulent Uyar
  University of Northern Iowa
Ahmad Vakil
  Tobin College of Business
Tim Vaughan
  *University of Wisconsin—
  Eau Claire*
Raja Velu
  Syracuse University
Holly Verhasselt
  *University of Houston—
  Victoria*
Zhaowei Wang
  Citizens Bank
Rachel Webb
  Portland State University
Kyle Wells
  Dixie State College
Alan Wheeler
  *University of Missouri—
  St. Louis*
Mary Whiteside
  *University of Texas—
  Arlington*
Blake Whitten
  University of Iowa

Rick Wing
  San Francisco State University
Jan Wolcott
  Wichita State University
Rongning Wu
  Baruch College
John Yarber
  Northeast Mississippi Community College
John C. Yi
  St. Joseph's University
Kanghyun Yoon
  University of Central Oklahoma

Mark Zaporowski
  Canisius College
Ali Zargar
  San Jose State University
Dewit Zerom
  California State University
Eugene Zhang
  Midwestern State University
Ye Zhang
  Indiana University—Purdue University—Indianapolis

Yi Zhang
  California State University—Fullerton
Yulin Zhang
  San Jose State University
Wencang Zhou
  Baruch College
Zhen Zhu
  University of Central Oklahoma

The editorial staff of McGraw-Hill Education are deserving of our gratitude for their guidance throughout this project, especially Noelle Bathurst, Pat Frederickson, Ryan McAndrews, Harper Christopher, Daryl Horrocks, and Egzon Shaquiri.

We would also like to thank Kate Belotti, Alex Firsov, Claudia Sison, and Morgan Sperry for their outstanding research assistance.

BRIEF CONTENTS

CONTENTS

PART THREE
Probability and Probability Distributions

CHAPTER 4

INTRODUCTION TO PROBABILITY *114*

CHAPTER 5

DISCRETE PROBABILITY DISTRIBUTIONS *160*

CHAPTER 6

CONTINUOUS PROBABILITY DISTRIBUTIONS *204*

BUSINESS STATISTICS

1

Statistics and Data

Every day we are bombarded with data and claims. The analysis of data and the conclusions made from data are part of the field of statistics. A proper understanding of statistics is essential in understanding more of the real world around us, including business, sports, politics, health, social interactions—just about any area of contemporary human activity. In this first chapter, we will differentiate between sound statistical conclusions and questionable conclusions. We will also introduce some important terms, which are referenced throughout the text, that will help us describe different aspects of statistics and their practical importance. You are probably familiar with some of these terms already, from reading or hearing about opinion polls, surveys, and the all-pervasive product ads. Our goal is to place what you already know about these uses of statistics within a framework that we then use for explaining where they came from and what they really mean. A major portion of this chapter is also devoted to a discussion of variables and types of measurement scales. As we will see in later chapters, we need to distinguish between different variables and measurement scales in order to choose the appropriate statistical methods for analyzing data.

INTRODUCTORY CASE

Tween Survey

Luke McCaffrey owns a ski resort two hours outside Boston, Massachusetts, and is in need of a new marketing manager. He is a fairly tough interviewer and believes that the person in this position should have a basic understanding of data fundamentals, including some background with statistical methods. Luke is particularly interested in serving the needs of the "tween" population (children aged 8 to 12 years old). He believes that tween spending power has grown over the past few years, and he wants their skiing experience to be memorable so that they want to return. At the end of last year's ski season, Luke asked 20 tweens four specific questions.

Q1. On your car drive to the resort, which radio station was playing?

Q2. On a scale of 1 to 4, rate the quality of the food at the resort (where 1 is poor, 2 is fair, 3 is good, and 4 is excellent).

Q3. Presently, the main dining area closes at 3:00 pm. What time do you think it should close?

Q4. How much of your *own* money did you spend at the lodge today?

The responses to these questions are shown in Table 1.1

TABLE 1.1 Tween Responses to Resort Survey

Tween	Q1	Q2	Q3	Q4	Tween	Q1	Q2	Q3	Q4
1	JAMN94.5	4	5:00 pm	20	11	JAMN94.5	3	3:00 pm	0
2	MIX104.1	2	5:00 pm	10	12	JAMN94.5	4	4:00 pm	5
3	KISS108	2	4:30 pm	10	13	KISS108	2	4:30 pm	5
4	JAMN94.5	3	4:00 pm	0	14	KISS108	2	5:00 pm	10
5	KISS108	1	3:30 pm	0	15	KISS108	3	4:00 pm	5
6	JAMN94.5	1	6:00 pm	25	16	JAMN94.5	3	6:00 pm	20
7	KISS108	2	6:00 pm	15	17	KISS108	2	5:00 pm	15
8	KISS108	3	5:00 pm	10	18	MIX104.1	4	6:00 pm	15
9	KISS108	2	4:30 pm	10	19	KISS108	1	5:00 pm	25
10	KISS108	3	4:30 pm	20	20	KISS108	2	4:30 pm	10

Luke asks each job applicant to use the information to:

1. Summarize the results of the survey.

2. Provide management with suggestions for improvement.

A synopsis from the job applicant with the best answers is provided at the end of Section 1.3.

1.1 THE RELEVANCE OF STATISTICS

In order to make intelligent decisions in a world full of uncertainty, we all have to understand statistics—the language of data. Data are usually compilations of facts, figures, or other contents, both numerical and nonnumerical. Insights from data enable businesses to make better decisions, such as deepening customer engagement, optimizing operations, preventing threats and fraud, and capitalizing on new sources of revenue. We must understand statistics or risk making uninformed decisions and costly mistakes. A knowledge of statistics also provides the necessary tools to differentiate between sound statistical conclusions and questionable conclusions drawn from an insufficient number of data points, "bad" data points, incomplete data points, or just misinformation. Consider the following examples.

Example 1. After Washington, DC, had record amounts of snow in the winter of 2010, the headline of a newspaper asked, "What global warming?"

Problem with conclusion: The existence or nonexistence of climate change cannot be based on one year's worth of data. Instead, we must examine long-term trends and analyze decades' worth of data.

Example 2. A gambler predicts that his next roll of the dice will be a lucky 7 because he did not get that outcome on the last three rolls.

Problem with conclusion: As we will see later in the text when we discuss probability, the probability of rolling a 7 stays constant with each roll of the dice. It does not become more likely if it did not appear on the last roll or, in fact, any number of preceding rolls.

Example 3. On January 10, 2010, nine days prior to a special election to fill the U.S. Senate seat that was vacated due to the death of Ted Kennedy, a *Boston Globe* poll gave the Democratic candidate, Martha Coakley, a 15-point lead over the Republican candidate, Scott Brown. On January 19, 2010, Brown won 52% of the vote, compared to Coakley's 47%, and became a U.S. senator for Massachusetts.

Problem with conclusion: Critics accused the *Globe*, which had endorsed Coakley, of purposely running a bad poll to discourage voters from coming out for Brown. In reality, by the time the *Globe* released the poll, it contained old information from January 2–6, 2010. Even more problematic was that the poll included people who said that they were unlikely to vote!

Example 4. Starbucks Corp., the world's largest coffee-shop operator, reported that sales at stores open at least a year climbed 4% at home and abroad in the quarter ended December 27, 2009. Chief Financial Officer Troy Alstead said that "the U.S. is back in a good track and the international business has similarly picked up. . . . Traffic is really coming back. It's a good sign for what we're going to see for the rest of the year." (www.bloomberg.com, January 20, 2010)

Problem with conclusion: In order to calculate same-store sales growth, which compares how much each store in the chain is selling compared with a year ago, we remove stores that have closed. Given that Starbucks closed more than 800 stores over the past few years to counter large sales declines, it is likely that the sales increases in many of the stores were caused by traffic from nearby, recently closed stores. In this case, same-store sales growth may overstate the overall health of Starbucks.

Example 5. Researchers at the University of Pennsylvania Medical Center found that infants who sleep with a nightlight are much more likely to develop myopia later in life (*Nature*, May 1999).

Problem with conclusion: This example appears to commit the *correlation-to-causation fallacy.* Even if two variables are highly correlated, one does not necessarily cause the other. *Spurious correlation* can make two variables appear closely related when no causal relation exists. Spurious correlation between two variables is not based on any demonstrable relationship, but rather can be explained by confounding factors. For instance, the fact that the cost of a hamburger is correlated with how much people spend on a computer is explained by a confounding factor called inflation, which makes both the hamburger and the computer costs grow over time. In a follow-up study regarding myopia, researchers at The Ohio State University found no link between infants who sleep with a nightlight and the development of myopia (*Nature*, March 2000). They did, however, find strong links between parental myopia and the development of child myopia, and between parental myopia and the parents' use of a nightlight in their children's room. So the confounding factor for both conditions (the use of a nightlight and the development of child myopia) is parental myopia. See www.tylervigen.com/spurious-correlations for some outrageous examples of spurious correlation.

Note the diversity of the sources of these examples—the environment, psychology, polling, business, and health. We could easily include others, from sports, sociology, the physical sciences, and elsewhere. Data and data interpretation show up in virtually every facet of life, sometimes spuriously. All of the preceding examples basically misuse data to add credibility to an argument. A solid understanding of statistics provides you with tools to react intelligently to information that you read or hear.

1.2 WHAT IS STATISTICS?

LO 1.2

In the broadest sense, we can define the study of statistics as the methodology of extracting useful information from a data set. Three steps are essential for doing good statistics. First, we have to find the right data, which are both complete and lacking any misrepresentation. Second, we must use the appropriate statistical tools, depending on the data at hand. Finally, an important ingredient of a well-executed statistical analysis is to clearly communicate numerical information into written language.

Differentiate between descriptive statistics and inferential statistics.

We generally divide the study of statistics into two branches: descriptive statistics and inferential statistics. **Descriptive statistics** refers to the summary of important aspects of a data set. This includes collecting data, organizing the data, and then presenting the data in the form of charts and tables. In addition, we often calculate numerical measures that summarize, for instance, the data's typical value and the data's variability. Today, the techniques encountered in descriptive statistics account for the most visible application of statistics—the abundance of quantitative information that is collected and published in our society every day. The unemployment rate, the president's approval rating, the Dow Jones Industrial Average, batting averages, the crime rate, and the divorce rate are but a few of the many "statistics" that can be found in a reputable newspaper on a frequent, if not daily, basis. Yet, despite the familiarity of descriptive statistics, these methods represent only a minor portion of the body of statistical applications.

The phenomenal growth in statistics is mainly in the field called inferential statistics. Generally, **inferential statistics** refers to drawing conclusions about a large set of data—called a **population**—based on a smaller set of **sample** data. A population is defined as all members of a specified group (not necessarily people), whereas a sample is a subset of that particular population. In most statistical applications, we must rely on sample data in order to make inferences about various characteristics of the population. For example, a 2016 Gallup survey found that only 50% of Millennials plan to be with their current job for more than a year. Researchers use this sample result, called a **sample statistic**, in an attempt to estimate the corresponding unknown **population parameter**. In this case, the parameter of interest is the percentage of *all* Millennials who plan to be with their current job for more than a year. It is generally not feasible to obtain population data and calculate the relevant parameter directly, due to prohibitive costs and/or practicality, as discussed next.

> ### POPULATION VERSUS SAMPLE
> A population consists of all items of interest in a statistical problem. A sample is a subset of the population. We analyze sample data and calculate a sample statistic to make inferences about the unknown population parameter.

The Need for Sampling

A major portion of inferential statistics is concerned with the problem of estimating population parameters or testing hypotheses about such parameters. If we have access to data that encompass the entire population, then we would know the values of the parameters. Generally, however, we are unable to use population data for two main reasons.

- **Obtaining information on the entire population is expensive**. Consider how the monthly unemployment rate in the United States is calculated by the Bureau of Labor Statistics (BLS). Is it reasonable to assume that the BLS counts every unemployed person each month? The answer is a resounding NO! In order to do this, every home in the country would have to be contacted. Given that there are approximately 160 million individuals in the labor force, not only would this process cost too much, it would take an inordinate amount of time. Instead, the BLS conducts a monthly sample survey of about 60,000 households to measure the extent of unemployment in the United States.

- **It is impossible to examine every member of the population**. Suppose we are interested in the average length of life of a Duracell AAA battery. If we tested the duration of each Duracell AAA battery, then in the end, all batteries would be dead and the answer to the original question would be useless.

Cross-Sectional and Time Series Data

Sample data are generally collected in one of two ways. **Cross-sectional data** refers to data collected by recording a characteristic of many subjects at the same point in time, or without regard to differences in time. Subjects might include individuals, households, firms, industries, regions, and countries. The tween data set presented in Table 1.1 in the introductory case is an example of cross-sectional data because it contains tween responses to four questions at the end of the ski season. It is unlikely that all 20 tweens took the questionnaire at exactly the same time, but the differences in time are of no relevance in this example. Other examples of cross-sectional data include the recorded scores of students in a class, the sale prices of single-family homes sold last month, the current price of gasoline in different states in the United States, and the starting salaries of recent business graduates from The Ohio State University.

Time series data refers to data collected over several time periods focusing on certain groups of people, specific events, or objects. Time series can include hourly, daily, weekly, monthly, quarterly, or annual observations. Examples of time series data include the hourly body temperature of a patient in a hospital's intensive care unit, the daily price of General Electric stock in the first quarter of 2015, the weekly exchange rate between the U.S. dollar and the euro over the past six months, the monthly sales of cars at a dealership in 2016, and the annual growth rate of India in the last decade.

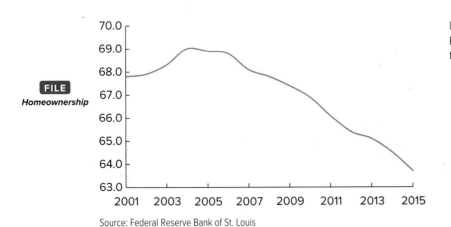

FIGURE 1.1 Homeownership Rate (%) in the United States from 2001 through 2015

Source: Federal Reserve Bank of St. Louis

Figure 1.1 shows a plot of the national homeownership rate in the United States from 2001 through 2015. According to the U.S. Census Bureau, the national homeownership rate in the first quarter of 2016 plummeted to 63.6% from a high of 69.4% in 2004. An obvious explanation for the decline in homeownership is the stricter lending practices caused by the housing market crash in 2007 that precipitated a banking crisis and the Great Recession. This decline can also be attributed to home prices outpacing wages in the sample period.

> ### CROSS-SECTIONAL DATA AND TIME SERIES DATA
> Cross-sectional data contain values of a characteristic of many subjects at the same point or approximately the same point in time. Time series data contain values of a characteristic of a subject over time.

Structured and Unstructured Data

As mentioned earlier, consumers and businesses are increasingly turning to data to make decisions. When you hear the word "data," you probably imagine lots of numbers and perhaps some charts and graphs as well. In reality, data can come in multiple forms. For example, information exchange in social networking services such as Facebook, LinkedIn, Twitter, YouTube, and blogs also constitutes data. In order to better understand the various forms of data, we make a distinction between structured data and unstructured data.

The term **structured data** generally refers to data that has a well-defined length and format. Structured data reside in a predefined row-column format. Examples of structured data include numbers, dates, and groups of words and numbers called strings. Structured data generally consist of numerical information that is objective. In other words, structured data are not open to interpretation. The data set that appears in Table 1.1 from the introductory case is an example of structured data.

Unlike structured data, **unstructured data** (or unmodeled data) do not conform to a predefined row-column format. They tend to be textual (e.g., written reports, e-mail messages, doctor's notes, or open-ended survey responses) or have multimedia contents (e.g., photographs, videos, and audio data). Even though these data may have some implied structure (e.g., a report title, an e-mail's subject line, or a time stamp on a photograph), they are still considered unstructured because they do not conform to a row-column model required in most database systems. Social media data, such as those that appear on Facebook, LinkedIn, Twitter, YouTube, and blogs, are examples of unstructured data.

Big Data

Nowadays, businesses and organizations generate and gather more and more data at an increasing pace. The term **big data** is a catchphrase, meaning a massive volume of both structured and unstructured data that are extremely difficult to manage, process, and analyze using traditional data processing tools. Despite the challenges, big data presents great opportunities to glean intelligence from data that affects company revenues, margins, and organizational efficiency.

Big data, however, do not necessarily imply complete (population) data. Take, for example, the analysis of all Facebook users. It certainly involves big data, but if we consider all Internet users in the world, Facebook data are only a very large sample. There are many Internet users who do not use Facebook, so the data on Facebook do not represent the population. Even if we define the population as pertaining to those who use online social media, Facebook is still one of many social media services that consumers use. Therefore, Facebook data would still just be considered a large sample.

In addition, we may choose not to use a big data set in its entirety even when it is available. Sometimes it is just inconvenient to analyze a very large data set because it is computationally burdensome, even with a modern, high-capacity computer system. Other times, the additional benefits of working with a big data set may not justify its associated additional resource costs. In sum, we often choose to work with a small data set, which, in a sense, is a sample drawn from big data.

> STRUCTURED DATA, UNSTRUCTURED DATA, AND BIG DATA
>
> Structured data reside in a predefined row-column format, while unstructured data do not conform to a predefined row-column format. The term big data is used to describe a massive volume of both structured and unstructured data that are extremely difficult to manage, process, and analyze using traditional data processing tools. The availability of big data, however, does not necessarily imply complete (population) data.

In this textbook, we will not cover specialized tools to manage, process, and analyze big data. Instead, we will focus on structured data. Text analytics and other sophisticated tools to analyze unstructured data are beyond the scope of this textbook.

Data on the Web

©Comstock Images/Jupiter Images RF

At every moment, data are being generated at an increasing velocity from countless sources in an overwhelming volume. Many experts believe that 90% of the data in the world today were created in the last two years alone. Not surprisingly, businesses continue to grapple with how to best ingest, understand, and operationalize large volumes of data. We access much of the data in this textbook by simply using a search engine like Google. These search engines direct us to data-providing websites. For instance, searching for economic data may lead you to the Bureau of Economic Analysis (www.bea.gov), the Bureau of Labor Statistics (www.bls.gov/data), the Federal Reserve Economic Data (research.stlouisfed.org), and the U.S. Census Bureau (www.census.gov/data.html). These websites provide data on inflation, unemployment, GDP, and much more, including useful international data. The National Climatic Data Center (www.ncdc.noaa.gov/data-access) provides a large collection of environmental, meteorological, and climate data. Similarly, transportation data can be found at www.its-rde.net. The University of Michigan has compiled sentiment data found at www.sca.isr.umich.edu. Several cities in the United States have publicly available data in categories such as finance, community and economic development, education, and crime. For example, the Chicago data portal data.cityofchicago.org provides a large volume of city-specific data. Excellent world development indicator data are available at data.worldbank.org. The happiness index data for most countries are available at www.happyplanetindex.org/data.

Private corporations also make data available on their websites. For example, Yahoo Finance (www.finance.yahoo.com) and Google Finance (www.google.com/finance) list data such as stock prices, mutual fund performance, and international market data. Zillow (www.zillow.com/) supplies data for recent home sales, monthly rent, mortgage rates, and so forth. Similarly, www.espn.go.com offers comprehensive sports data on both professional and college teams. Finally, *The Wall Street Journal*, *The New York Times*, *USA Today*, *The Economist*, *Business Week*, *Forbes*, and *Fortune* are all reputable publications that provide all sorts of data. We would like to point out that all of the above data sources represent only a fraction of publicly available data.

EXERCISES 1.2

1. It came as a big surprise when Apple's touch screen iPhone 4, considered by many to be the best smartphone ever, was found to have a problem (*The New York Times*, June 24, 2010). Users complained of weak reception, and sometimes even dropped calls, when they cradled the phone in their hands in a particular way. A quick survey at a local store found that 2% of iPhone 4 users experienced this reception problem.
   a. Describe the relevant population.
   b. Does 2% denote the population parameter or the sample statistic?

2. Many people regard video games as an obsession for youngsters, but, in fact, the average age of a video game player is 35 years (Reuters.com, August 21, 2009). Is the value 35 likely the actual or the estimated average age of the population? Explain.

3. An accounting professor wants to know the average GPA of the students enrolled in her class. She looks up information on Blackboard about the students enrolled in her class and computes the average GPA as 3.29.
   a. Describe the relevant population.
   b. Does the value 3.29 represent the population parameter or the sample statistic?

4. Business graduates in the United States with a marketing concentration earn high salaries. According to the Bureau of Labor Statistics, the average annual salary for marketing managers was $140,660 in 2015.
   a. What is the relevant population?
   b. Do you think the average salary of $140,660 was computed from the population? Explain.

5. Research suggests that depression significantly increases the risk of developing dementia later in life (*BBC News*, July 6, 2010). In a study involving 949 elderly persons, it was reported that 22% of those who had depression went on to develop dementia, compared to only 17% of those who did not have depression.

   a. Describe the relevant population and the sample.
   b. Do the numbers 22% and 17% represent population parameters or sample statistics?

6. Go to www.finance.yahoo.com/ to get a current stock quote for General Electric, Co. (ticker symbol = GE). Then, click on historical prices to record the monthly adjusted close price of General Electric stock in 2016. Create a table that uses this information. What type of data do these numbers represent? Comment on the data.

7. Ask 20 of your friends whether they live in a dormitory, a rental unit, or other form of accommodation. Also find out their approximate monthly lodging expenses. Create a table that uses this information. What type of data do these numbers represent? Comment on the data.

8. Go to www.zillow.com/ and find the sale price data of 20 single-family homes sold in Las Vegas, Nevada, in the last 30 days. In the data set, include the sale price, the number of bedrooms, the square footage, and the age of the house. What type of data do these numbers represent? Comment on the data.

9. The Federal Reserve Bank of St. Louis is a good source for downloading economic data. Go to research.stlouisfed.org/fred2/ to extract quarterly data on gross private saving (GPSAVE) from 2012 to 2015 (16 observations). Create a table that uses this information. Plot the data over time and comment on the savings trend in the United States.

10. Go to the U.S. Census Bureau website at www.census.gov/ and extract the most recent median household income for Alabama, Arizona, California, Florida, Georgia, Indiana, Iowa, Maine, Massachusetts, Minnesota, Mississippi, New Mexico, North Dakota, and Washington. What type of data do these numbers represent? Comment on the regional differences in income.

11. Go to *The New York Times* website at www.nytimes.com/ and review the front page. Would you consider the data on the page to be structured or unstructured? Explain.

12. Conduct an online search to compare price and fuel economy of small hybrid vehicles such as Toyota Prius, Ford Fusion, and Chevrolet Volt. Would the resulting data be structured or unstructured? Explain.

13. Ask your peers about their online social media usage. In particular collect information on (a) whether they use Facebook, Instagram, and Snapchat, (b) how often they use each social media service, and (c) their overall satisfaction with each of these services using a 5-point numerical scale where 1 represents totally unsatisfied and 5 represents totally satisfied. Are the resulting data structured or unstructured? Are the data cross-sectional or time series?

14. Conduct an online search for a weekly car rental in Seattle, Washington, and Portland, Oregon, for different car types and rental car companies for the year 2017. Are the data structured or unstructured? Are the data cross-sectional or time series?

1.3 VARIABLES AND SCALES OF MEASUREMENT

Describe variables and types of measurement scales.

When we conduct a statistical investigation, we invariably focus on people, objects, or events with particular characteristics. When a characteristic of interest differs in kind or degree among various observations, then the characteristic can be termed a **variable**. We further categorize a variable as either qualitative or quantitative. For a **qualitative variable**, we use labels or names to identify the distinguishing characteristic of each observation. For instance, the 2010 Census asked each respondent to indicate gender on the form. Each respondent chose either male or female. Gender is a qualitative variable. Other examples of qualitative variables include race, profession, type of business, the manufacturer of a car, and so on.

A variable that assumes meaningful numerical values is called a **quantitative variable**. Quantitative variables, in turn, are either discrete or continuous. A **discrete variable** assumes a countable number of values. Consider the number of children in a family or the number of points scored in a basketball game. We may observe values such as 3 children in a family or 90 points being scored in a basketball game, but we will not observe 1.3 children or 92.5 scored points. The values that a discrete variable assumes need not be whole numbers. For example, the price of a stock for a particular firm is a discrete variable. The stock price may take on a value of $20.37 or $20.38, but it cannot take on a value between these two points. Finally, a discrete variable may assume an infinite number of values, but these values are countable; that is, they can be presented as a sequence x_1, x_2, x_3, and so on. The number of cars that cross the Golden Gate Bridge on a Saturday is a discrete variable. Theoretically, this variable assumes the values 0, 1, 2, . . .

A **continuous variable** is characterized by uncountable values within an interval. Weight, height, time, and investment return are all examples of continuous variables. For example, an unlimited number of values occur between the weights of 100 and 101 pounds, such as 100.3, 100.625, 100.8342, and so on. In practice, however, continuous variables may be measured in discrete values. We may report a newborn's weight (a continuous variable) in discrete terms as 6 pounds 10 ounces and another newborn's weight in similar discrete terms as 6 pounds 11 ounces.

QUALITATIVE VARIABLES VERSUS QUANTITATIVE VARIABLES

A variable is a general characteristic being observed on a set of people, objects, or events, where each observation varies in kind or degree. Labels or names are used to categorize the distinguishing characteristics of a qualitative variable; eventually, these attributes may be coded into numbers for purposes of data processing. A quantitative variable assumes meaningful numerical values, and can be further categorized as either discrete or continuous. A discrete variable assumes a countable number of values, whereas a continuous variable is characterized by uncountable values within an interval.

In order to choose the appropriate statistical methods for summarizing and analyzing data, we need to distinguish between different measurement scales. All data measurements can be classified into one of four major categories: nominal, ordinal, interval, and ratio. Nominal and ordinal scales are used for qualitative variables, whereas interval and ratio scales are used for quantitative variables. We discuss these scales in ascending order of sophistication.

The Nominal Scale

The **nominal scale** represents the least sophisticated level of measurement. If we are presented with nominal data, all we can do is categorize or group the data. The values in the data set differ merely by name or label. Consider the following example.

Each company listed in Table 1.2 is a member of the Dow Jones Industrial Average (DJIA). The DJIA is a stock market index that shows how 30 large, publicly owned companies based in the United States have traded during a standard trading session in the stock market. Table 1.2 also shows where stocks of these companies are traded: on either the National Association of Securities Dealers Automated Quotations (Nasdaq) or the New York Stock Exchange (NYSE). These data are classified as nominal scale since we are simply able to group or categorize them. Specifically, only four stocks are traded on Nasdaq, whereas the remaining 26 are traded on the NYSE.

©ymgerman/Shutterstock RF

TABLE 1.2 Companies of the DJIA and Exchange Where Stock Is Traded

Company	Exchange	Company	Exchange
3M (MMM)	NYSE	Intel (INTC)	Nasdaq
American Express (AXP)	NYSE	Johnson & Johnson (JNJ)	NYSE
Apple (AAPL)	Nasdaq	JPMorgan Chase (JPM)	NYSE
Boeing (BA)	NYSE	McDonald's (MCD)	NYSE
Caterpillar (CAT)	NYSE	Merck (MRK)	NYSE
Chevron (CVX)	NYSE	Microsoft (MFST)	Nasdaq
Cisco (CSCO)	Nasdaq	Nike (NKE)	NYSE
Coca-Cola (KO)	NYSE	Pfizer (PFE)	NYSE
Disney (DIS)	NYSE	Procter & Gamble (PG)	NYSE
Dupont (DD)	NYSE	Travelers (TRV)	NYSE
ExxonMobil (XOM)	NYSE	United Health (UNH)	NYSE
General Electric (GE)	NYSE	United Tech. Corp. (UTX)	NYSE
Goldman Sachs (GS)	NYSE	Verizon (VZ)	NYSE
Home Depot (HD)	NYSE	Visa (V)	NYSE
IBM (IBM)	NYSE	Walmart (WMT)	NYSE

Source: Money.CNN.com information retrieved March 21, 2015.

Often we substitute *numbers* for the particular qualitative characteristic or trait that we are grouping. One reason why we do this is for ease of exposition; always referring to the National Association of Securities Dealers Automated Quotations, or even Nasdaq, becomes awkward and unwieldy. In addition, as we will see later in the text, statistical analysis is greatly facilitated by using numbers instead of names. For example, we might use the number 0 to show that a company's stock is traded on Nasdaq and the number 1 to show that a company's stock is traded on the NYSE. In tabular form:

Exchange	Number of Companies Trading on Exchange
0	4
1	26

The Ordinal Scale

Compared to the nominal scale, the **ordinal scale** reflects a stronger level of measurement. With ordinal data we are able to both *categorize* and *rank* the data with respect to some characteristic or trait. The weakness with ordinal data is that we cannot interpret the difference between the ranked values because the actual numbers used are arbitrary. For example, suppose you are asked to classify the service at a particular hotel as excellent, good, fair, or poor. A standard way to record the ratings is

Category	Rating
Excellent	4
Good	3
Fair	2
Poor	1

Here the value attached to excellent (4) is higher than the value attached to good (3), indicating that the response of excellent is preferred to good. However, another representation of the ratings might be

Category	Rating
Excellent	100
Good	80
Fair	70
Poor	40

Excellent still receives a higher value than good, but now the difference between the two categories is 20 (100 − 80), as compared to a difference of 1 (4 − 3) when we use the first classification. In other words, *differences between categories are meaningless with ordinal data.* (We also should note that we could reverse the ordering so that, for instance, excellent equals 40 and poor equals 100; this renumbering would not change the nature of the data.)

EXAMPLE 1.1

In the introductory case, four questions were posed to tweens. The first question (Q1) asked tweens to name the radio station that they listened to on the ride to the resort, and the second question (Q2) asked tweens to rate the food quality at the resort on a scale of 1 to 4. The tweens' responses to these questions are shown in Table 1.1 in the introductory case.

a. What is the scale of measurement of the radio station data?

b. How are the data based on the ratings of the food quality similar to the radio station data? How are the data different?

c. Summarize the tweens' responses to Q1 and Q2 in tabular form. How can the resort use the information from these responses?

SOLUTION:

a. When asked which radio station played on the car ride to the resort, tweens responded with one of the following answers: JAMN94.5, MIX104.1, or KISS108. These are nominal data—the values in the data differ merely in name or label.

b. Since we can both categorize and rank the food quality data, we classify these responses as ordinal data. Ordinal data are similar to nominal data in the sense that we can categorize the data. The main difference between ordinal and nominal data is that the categories of ordinal data are ranked. A rating of 4 is better than a rating of 3. With the radio station data, we cannot say that KISS108 is ranked higher than MIX104.1; some tweens may argue otherwise, but we simply categorize nominal data without ranking.

c. With respect to the radio station data (Q1), we can assign 1 to JAMN94.5, 2 to MIX104.1, and 3 to KISS108. Counting the responses that fall into each category, we find that six tweens listened to 1, two listened to 2, and 12 listened to 3, or in tabular form:

Radio Station	Number of Tweens
1	6
2	2
3	12

Twelve of the 20 tweens, or 60%, listened to KISS108. This information could prove useful to the management of the resort as they make decisions as to where to allocate their advertising dollars. If the resort could only choose to advertise at one radio station, it would appear that KISS108 would be the wise choice.

Given the food quality responses (Q2), we find that three of the tweens rated food quality with a 4, six tweens rated food quality with a 3, eight tweens rated food quality with a 2, and three tweens rated food quality with a 1. In tabular form:

Rating	Number of Tweens
4	3
3	6
2	8
1	3

The food quality results may be of concern to management. Just as many tweens rated the food quality as excellent as compared to poor. Moreover, the majority $[(8 + 3)/20 = 55\%]$ felt that the food was, at best, fair. Perhaps a more extensive survey that focuses solely on food quality would reveal the reason for their apparent dissatisfaction.

As mentioned earlier, nominal and ordinal scales are used for *qualitative variables*. Values corresponding to a qualitative variable are typically expressed in words but are coded into numbers for purposes of data processing. When summarizing the results of a qualitative variable, we typically count the number or calculate the percentage of persons or objects that fall into each possible category. With a qualitative variable, we are unable to perform meaningful arithmetic operations such as adding and subtracting.

The Interval Scale

With data that are measured on an **interval scale**, not only can we categorize and rank the data, we are also assured that the differences between scale values are meaningful. Thus, the arithmetic operations of addition and subtraction are meaningful. The Fahrenheit scale for temperatures is an example of an interval scale. Not only is 60 degrees Fahrenheit hotter than 50 degrees Fahrenheit, the same difference of 10 degrees also exists between 90 and 80 degrees Fahrenheit.

The main drawback of data on an interval scale is that the value of zero is arbitrarily chosen; the zero point of an interval scale does not reflect a complete absence of what is being measured. No specific meaning is attached to zero degrees Fahrenheit other than to say it is 10 degrees colder than 10 degrees Fahrenheit. With an arbitrary zero point, meaningful ratios cannot be constructed. For instance, it is senseless to say that 80 degrees is twice as hot as 40 degrees; in other words, the ratio 80/40 has no meaning.

The Ratio Scale

The **ratio scale** represents the strongest level of measurement. Ratio data have all the characteristics of interval data as well as a *true zero* point, which allows us to interpret the ratios of values. A ratio scale is used to measure many types of data in business analysis. Variables such as sales, profits, and inventory levels are expressed as ratio data. A meaningful zero allows us to state, for example, that profits for firm A are double those of firm B. Measurements such as weight, time, and distance are also measured on a ratio scale since zero is meaningful.

Unlike qualitative data, arithmetic operations are valid on interval- and ratio-scaled values. In later chapters, we will calculate summary measures for the typical value and the variability of quantitative variables; we cannot calculate these measures if the variable is qualitative in nature.

EXAMPLE 1.2

In the last two questions from the introductory case's survey (Q3 and Q4), the 20 tweens were asked: "What time should the main dining area close?" and "How much of your *own* money did you spend at the lodge today?" Their responses appear in Table 1.1 in the introductory case.

a. How are the time data classified? In what ways do the time data differ from ordinal data? What is a potential weakness of this measurement scale?

b. What is the measurement scale of the money data? Why is it considered the strongest form of data?

c. In what ways is the information from Q3 and Q4 useful for the resort?

SOLUTION:

a. Clock time responses, such as 3:00 pm and 3:30 pm, or 5:30 pm and 6:00 pm, are on an interval scale. Interval data are a stronger measurement scale than ordinal data because differences between interval-scaled values are meaningful. In this particular example, we can say that 3:30 pm is 30 minutes later than 3:00 pm and 6:00 pm is 30 minutes later than 5:30 pm. The weakness with interval data is that the value of zero is arbitrary. Here, with the clock time responses, we have no apparent zero point; however, we could always arbitrarily define a zero point, say, at 12:00 am. Thus, although differences are comparable with interval data, ratios are meaningless due to the arbitrariness of the zero point. In other words, it is senseless to form the ratio 6:00 pm/3:00 pm and conclude that 6:00 pm is twice as long a time period as 3:00 pm.

b. Since the tweens' responses are in dollar amounts, this is ratio data. The ratio scale is the strongest form of data because we can categorize and rank values as well as calculate meaningful differences. Moreover, since there is a natural zero point, valid ratios can also be calculated. For example, the data show that three tweens spent $20. These tweens spent four times as much as the three tweens that spent $5 ($20/$5 = 4).

c. A review of the clock time responses (Q3) in Table 1.1 shows that the vast majority of the tweens would like the dining area to remain open later. In fact, only one tween feels that the dining area should close at 3:00 pm. An inspection of the money responses (Q4) in Table 1.1 indicates that only three of the 20 tweens did not spend any of his/her own money. This is very important information. It does appear that the discretionary spending of this age group is significant. The resort would be wise to cater to some of their preferences.

SYNOPSIS OF INTRODUCTORY CASE

A preliminary survey of tween preferences conducted by the management of a ski resort two hours outside Boston, Massachusetts, revealed some interesting information.

- Tweens were first asked to name the radio station that they listened to on the way to the resort. The responses show that 60% of the tweens listened to KISS108. If the resort wishes to contact tweens using this medium, it may want to direct its advertising dollars to this station.

- Next, the tweens were asked to rate the food quality at the resort on a scale of 1 to 4 (where 1 is poor, 2 is fair, 3 is good, and 4 is excellent). The survey results with respect to food quality are disturbing. The majority of the tweens, 55% (11/20), felt that the food was, at best, fair. A more extensive study focusing on food quality appears necessary.

- Tweens were then asked what time the main dining area should close, given a present closing time of 3:00 pm. The data suggest that the vast majority of the tweens (19 out of 20) would like the dining area to remain open later.

©Dennis Welsh/UpperCut Images/Getty Images RF

- Finally, the tweens were asked to report the amount of their *own* money that they spent at the lodge. The resort is likely pleased with the responses to this question because 17 of the 20 tweens spent their own money at the lodge. This finding appears consistent with the belief that tween spending is growing.

EXERCISES 1.3

15. Which of the following variables are qualitative and which are quantitative? If the variable is quantitative, then specify whether the variable is discrete or continuous.
    a. Points scored in a football game.
    b. Racial composition of a high school classroom.
    c. Heights of 15-year-olds.

16. Which of the following variables are qualitative and which are quantitative? If the variable is quantitative, then specify whether the variable is discrete or continuous.
    a. Colors of cars in a mall parking lot.
    b. Time it takes each student to complete a final exam.
    c. The number of patrons who frequent a restaurant.

17. In each of the following scenarios, define the type of measurement scale.
    a. A kindergarten teacher marks whether each student is a boy or a girl.
    b. A ski resort records the daily temperature during the month of January.
    c. A restaurant surveys its customers about the quality of its waiting staff on a scale of 1 to 4, where 1 is poor and 4 is excellent.

18. In each of the following scenarios, define the type of measurement scale.
    a. An investor collects data on the weekly closing price of gold throughout a year.

b. An analyst assigns a sample of bond issues to one of the following credit ratings, given in descending order of credit quality (increasing probability of default): AAA, AA, BBB, BB, CC, D.

c. The dean of the business school at a local university categorizes students by major (i.e., accounting, finance, marketing, etc.) to help in determining class offerings in the future.

19. In each of the following scenarios, define the type of measurement scale.

a. A meteorologist records the amount of monthly rainfall over the past year.

b. A sociologist notes the birth year of 50 individuals.

c. An investor monitors the daily stock price of BP following the 2010 oil disaster in the Gulf of Mexico.

20. A professor records the majors of her 30 students as follows:

Accounting	Economics	Undecided	Finance	Management
Management	Finance	Marketing	Economics	Management
Marketing	Finance	Marketing	Accounting	Finance
Finance	Undecided	Management	Undecided	Economics
Economics	Accounting	Management	Undecided	Economics
Accounting	Economics	Management	Accounting	Economics

a. What is the measurement scale of these data?

b. Summarize the results in tabular form.

c. What information can be extracted from the data?

21. **FILE** *DOW_Characteristics*. The accompanying table shows a portion of the 30 companies that comprise the Dow Jones Industrial Average (DJIA). The second column shows the year that the company joined the DJIA (Year). The third column shows each company's Morningstar rating (Rating). (Five stars is the best rating that a company can receive, indicating that the company's stock price is undervalued and thus a very good buy. One star is the worst rating a company can be given, implying that the stock price is overvalued and a bad buy.) Finally, the fourth column shows each company's stock price as of March 17, 2017 (Price in $).

Company	Year	Rating	Price
3M (MMM)	1976	**	192.36
American Express (AMX)	1982	***	79.25
⋮	⋮	⋮	⋮
Wal-Mart (WMT)	1991	****	69.89

Source: Morningstar ratings retrieved from www.morningstar.com on March 17, 2017; stock prices retrieved from www.finance.yahoo.com.

a. What is the measurement scale of the Year data? What are the strengths of this type of data? What are the weaknesses?

b. What is the measurement scale of Morningstar's star-based rating system? Summarize Morningstar's star-based rating system for the companies in tabular form. Let 5 denote *****, 4 denote ****, and so on. What information can be extracted from these data?

c. What is the measurement scale of the Stock Price data? What are its strengths?

CONCEPTUAL REVIEW

LO 1.1 Describe the importance of statistics.

A proper understanding of statistical ideas and concepts helps us understand more of the real world around us, including issues in business, sports, politics, health, and social interactions. We must understand statistics or risk making bad decisions and costly mistakes. A knowledge of statistics also provides the necessary tools to differentiate between sound statistical conclusions and questionable conclusions drawn from an insufficient number of data points, "bad" data points, incomplete data points, or just misinformation.

LO 1.2 Differentiate between descriptive statistics and inferential statistics.

The study of statistics is generally divided into two branches: descriptive statistics and inferential statistics. **Descriptive statistics** refers to the summary of a data set in the form of tables, graphs, and/or the calculation of numerical measures. **Inferential statistics** refers to extracting useful information from a **sample** to draw conclusions about a **population**. A **population** consists of all items of interest in a statistical problem; a **sample** is a subset of that population.

In general, we use sample data rather than population data for two main reasons: (1) obtaining information on the entire population is expensive and/or (2) it is impossible to examine every item of the population.

LO 1.3 Explain the various data types.

Cross-sectional data contain values of a characteristic of many subjects at the same point in time or without regard to differences in time. **Time series data** contain values of a characteristic of a subject over time.

Structured data conform but **unstructured data** do not conform to a predefined row-column format.

Big data is a term used to describe a massive volume of both structured and unstructured data that are extremely difficult to manage, process, and analyze using traditional data processing tools. Big data, however, does not necessary imply complete (population) data.

LO 1.4 Describe variables and types of measurement scales.

A variable is categorized as either qualitative or quantitative. For a **qualitative variable**, we use labels or names to identify the distinguishing characteristic of each observation. A **quantitative variable** assumes meaningful numerical values and can be further categorized as either **discrete** or **continuous**. A discrete variable assumes a countable number of values, whereas a continuous variable is characterized by uncountable values within an interval.

All data measurements can be classified into one of four major categories.

- The **nominal scale** represents the least sophisticated level of measurement. The values on a nominal scale differ merely by name or label. These values are then simply categorized or grouped by name.
- The values on an **ordinal scale** can be categorized *and* ranked; however, differences between the ranked values are meaningless.
- The **interval scale** is a stronger measurement scale as compared to nominal and ordinal scales. Values on the interval scale can be categorized and ranked, and differences between values are meaningful. The main drawback of the interval scale is that the value of zero is arbitrarily chosen; this implies that ratios constructed from interval-scaled values bear no significance.
- The **ratio scale** represents the strongest level of measurement. Ratio data have all the characteristics of interval data as well as a true zero point; thus, as its name implies, meaningful ratios can be calculated with values on the ratio scale.

Nominal and ordinal scales are used for qualitative variables. When summarizing the results of qualitative data, we typically count the number or calculate the percentage of persons or objects that fall into each possible category. Interval and ratio scales are used for quantitative variables. Unlike qualitative variables, arithmetic operations are valid on quantitative variables.

2 Tabular and Graphical Methods

LEARNING OBJECTIVES

After reading this chapter you should be able to:

LO **2.1** Summarize qualitative data by constructing a frequency distribution.

LO **2.2** Construct and interpret a pie chart and a bar chart.

LO **2.3** Summarize quantitative data by constructing a frequency distribution.

LO **2.4** Construct and interpret a histogram, a polygon, and an ogive.

LO **2.5** Construct and interpret a stem-and-leaf diagram.

LO **2.6** Construct and interpret a scatterplot.

People often have difficulty processing information provided by data in its raw form. A useful way of interpreting data effectively is through data visualization. In this chapter, we present several tabular and graphical tools that can help us organize and present data. We first make a table referred to as a frequency distribution using qualitative data. For visual representations of qualitative data, we construct a pie chart or a bar chart. For quantitative data, we again make a frequency distribution. In addition to giving us an overall picture of where the data tend to cluster, a frequency distribution using quantitative data also shows us how the data are spread out from the lowest value to the highest value. For visual representations of quantitative data, we construct a histogram, a polygon, an ogive, and a stem-and-leaf diagram. Finally, we show how to construct a scatterplot, which graphically depicts the relationship between two quantitative variables. We will find that a scatterplot is a very useful tool when conducting correlation and regression analysis, topics discussed in depth later in the text.

©Mitch Diamond/Photodisc/Getty Images RF

INTRODUCTORY CASE

House Prices in Southern California

Mission Viejo, a city located in Southern California, was named the safest city in California and the third-safest city in the nation (CQPress.com, November 23, 2009). Matthew Edwards, a relocation specialist for a real estate firm in Mission Viejo, often relays this piece of information to clients unfamiliar with the many benefits that the city offers. Recently, a client from Seattle, Washington, asked Matthew for a summary of recent sales. The client is particularly interested in the availability of houses in the $500,000 range. Table 2.1 shows the sale price for 36 single-family houses in Mission Viejo during June 2010.

TABLE 2.1 Recent Sale Price of Houses in Mission Viejo, CA, for June 2010 (data in $1,000s)

430	670	530	521	669	445
520	417	525	350	660	412
460	533	430	399	702	735
475	525	330	560	540	537
670	538	575	440	460	630
521	370	555	425	588	430

Source: www.zillow.com.

Matthew wants to use the sample information to

1. Make summary statements concerning the range of house prices.
2. Comment on where house prices tend to cluster.
3. Calculate appropriate percentages in order to compare house prices in Mission Viejo, California, to those in Seattle, Washington.

A synopsis of this case is provided in Section 2.2.

2.1 SUMMARIZING QUALITATIVE DATA

Summarize qualitative data by constructing a frequency distribution.

As we discussed in Chapter 1, nominal and ordinal data are types of qualitative data. Nominal data typically consist of observations that represent labels or names; information related to gender or race are examples. Nominal data are considered the least sophisticated form of data since all we can do with the data is categorize it. Ordinal data are stronger in the sense that we can categorize and order the data. Examples of ordinal data include the ratings of a product or a professor, where 1 represents the worst and 4 represents the best. In order to organize qualitative data, it is often useful to construct a **frequency distribution**.

FREQUENCY DISTRIBUTION FOR QUALITATIVE DATA

A frequency distribution for qualitative data groups data into categories and records the number of observations that fall into each category.

To illustrate the construction of a frequency distribution with nominal data, Table 2.2 shows the weather for the month of February (2010) in Seattle, Washington.

TABLE 2.2 Seattle Weather, February 2010

Sunday	Monday	Tuesday	Wednesday	Thursday	Friday	Saturday
	1 Rainy	2 Rainy	3 Rainy	4 Rainy	5 Rainy	6 Rainy
7 Rainy	8 Rainy	9 Cloudy	10 Rainy	11 Rainy	12 Rainy	13 Rainy
14 Rainy	15 Rainy	16 Rainy	17 Sunny	18 Sunny	19 Sunny	20 Sunny
21 Sunny	22 Sunny	23 Rainy	24 Rainy	25 Rainy	26 Rainy	27 Rainy
28 Sunny						

Source: www.wunderground.com.

©sbk_20d pictures/Moment/Getty Images RF

We first note that the weather in Seattle is categorized as cloudy, rainy, or sunny. The first column in Table 2.3 lists these categories. Initially, we use a "tally" column to record the number of days that fall into each category. Since the first eight days of February were rainy days, we place the first eight tally marks in the rainy category; the ninth day of February was cloudy, so we place one tally mark in the cloudy category, and so on. Finally, we convert each category's total tally count into its respective numerical value in the frequency column. Since only one tally mark appears in the cloudy category, we record the value 1 as its frequency. Note that if we sum the frequency column, we obtain the sample size. A frequency distribution in its final form does not include the tally column.

TABLE 2.3 Frequency Distribution for Seattle Weather, February 2010

Weather	Tally	Frequency
Cloudy	I	1
Rainy	⊞⊞⊞⊞ ⊞⊞⊞⊞ ⊞⊞⊞⊞ ⊞⊞⊞⊞	20
Sunny	⊞⊞⊞⊞ II	7
		Total = 28 days

From the frequency distribution, we can now readily observe that the most common type of day in February was rainy since this type of day occurs with the highest frequency. In many applications, we want to compare data sets that differ in size. For example, we might want to compare the weather in February to the weather in March. However, February has 28 days (except during a leap year) and March has 31 days. In this instance, we would convert the frequency distribution to a **relative frequency distribution**. We calculate each category's relative frequency by dividing the respective category's frequency by the total number of observations. The sum of the relative frequencies should equal one, or a value very close to one due to rounding.

In Table 2.4, we convert the frequency distribution from Table 2.3 into a relative frequency distribution. Similarly, we obtain the relative frequency distribution for the month of March; the raw data for March are not shown. March had 3 cloudy days, 18 rainy days, and 10 sunny days. Each of these frequencies was then divided by 31, the number of days in the month of March.

TABLE 2.4 Relative Frequency Distribution for Seattle Weather

Weather	February 2010: Relative Frequency	March 2010: Relative Frequency
Cloudy	1/28 = 0.036	3/31 = 0.097
Rainy	20/28 = 0.714	18/31 = 0.581
Sunny	7/28 = 0.250	10/31 = 0.323
	Total = 1	Total = 1 (subject to rounding)

Source: www.wunderground.com.

We can easily convert relative frequencies into percentages by multiplying by 100. For instance, the percent of cloudy days in February and March equals 3.6% and 9.7%, respectively. From the relative frequency distribution, we can now conclude that the weather in Seattle in both February and March was predominantly rainy. However, the weather in March was a bit nicer in that approximately 32% of the days were sunny, as opposed to only 25% of the days in February.

> ### CALCULATING RELATIVE AND PERCENT FREQUENCIES
> The relative frequency for each category in a frequency distribution equals the proportion (fraction) of observations in each category. A category's relative frequency is calculated by dividing the frequency by the total number of observations. The sum of the relative frequencies should equal one.
>
> The percent frequency for each category in a frequency distribution equals the percent (%) of observations in each category; it equals the relative frequency of the category multiplied by 100.

Pie Charts and Bar Charts

LO 2.2

We can visualize the information found in frequency distributions by constructing various graphs. Graphical representations often portray the data more dramatically, as well as simplify interpretation. A **pie chart** and a **bar chart** are two widely used graphical representations for qualitative data.

Construct and interpret a pie chart and a bar chart.

> ### GRAPHICAL DISPLAY OF QUALITATIVE DATA: PIE CHART
> A pie chart is a segmented circle whose segments portray the relative frequencies of the categories of some qualitative variable.

A pie chart is best explained by using an example. Consider Example 2.1.

EXAMPLE 2.1

Is America having a "marriage crisis?" The answer depends on whom you ask, but nearly every study focuses on the women's liberation movement of the late 1960s and 1970s. As more and more women earned college degrees, they entered the workforce and delayed motherhood. Marriage became less necessary for their economic survival. No matter what the reason for the decline in marriage, here are some facts. In 1960, 71% of all adults in the United States were married. Today, barely half of all adults are married, just 52%. Table 2.5 shows the proportions of all adults who were married, widowed, divorced, or single in 1960 compared to those same proportions in 2010. Construct pie charts to graphically depict marital status in the United States in these two time periods.

TABLE 2.5 Marital Status, 1960 versus 2010

Marital Status	1960	2010
Married	0.71	0.52
Single	0.15	0.28
Divorced	0.05	0.14
Widowed	0.09	0.06

Note: Proportions for each year rounded so that they summed to one.

Source: Pew Research Center analysis of Decennial Census (1960–2000) and American Community Survey data (2008, 2010).

SOLUTION: In order to construct a pie chart, we first draw a circle. We then cut the circle into slices, or sectors such that each sector is proportional to the size of the category we wish to display. For instance, Table 2.5 shows that married adults accounted for 0.71 in 1960. Since a circle contains 360 degrees, the portion of the circle representing married adults encompasses $0.71 \times 360 = 255.6$ degrees. Similar calculations for the other three categories yield:

Single: $0.15 \times 360 = 54$ degrees

Divorced: $0.05 \times 360 = 18$ degrees

Widowed: $0.09 \times 360 = 32.4$ degrees

The same methodology can be used to construct a pie chart for marital status in 2010. Figure 2.1 shows the resulting pie charts.

FIGURE 2.1 Pie charts for marital status

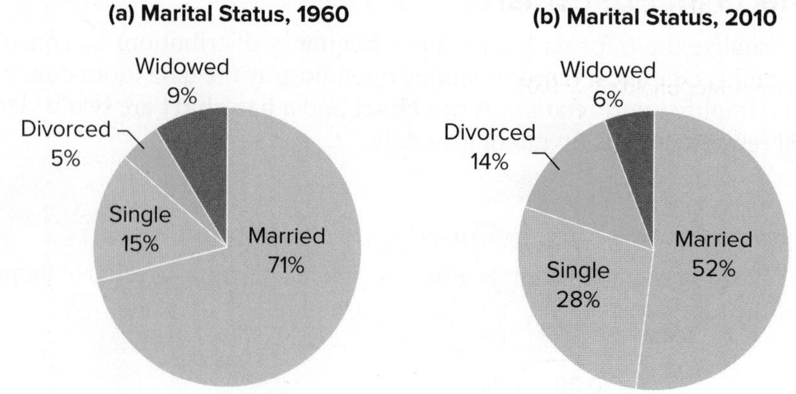

(a) Marital Status, 1960

(b) Marital Status, 2010

Another way to graphically depict qualitative data is to construct a **bar chart**.

> ## GRAPHICAL DISPLAY OF QUALITATIVE DATA: BAR CHART
> A bar chart depicts the frequency or the relative frequency for each category of the qualitative variable as a series of horizontal or vertical bars, the lengths of which are proportional to the values that are to be depicted.

We first discuss a vertical bar chart, sometimes referred to as a column chart. Here, we place each category on the horizontal axis and mark the vertical axis with an appropriate range of values for either frequency or relative frequency. The height of each bar is equal to the frequency or the relative frequency of the corresponding category. Typically, we leave space between categories to improve clarity.

Figure 2.2 shows a relative frequency bar chart for the marital status example. It is particularly useful because we can group marital status by year, emphasizing the decline in the proportion of U.S. adults who are married and the rise in the proportion of U.S. adults who are single.

FIGURE 2.2
Marital status of U.S. adults, 1960 versus 2010

For a horizontal bar chart, we simply place each category on the vertical axis and mark the horizontal axis with an appropriate range of values for either frequency or relative frequency. For example, a recent poll asked more than 1,000 Americans: "When traveling in a non-English-speaking country, which word or phrase is most important to know in that country's language?" (Source: *Vanity Fair*, January 2, 2012). Figure 2.3 shows the results of the poll. The phrase "Thank you" earned the largest percentage of votes (38%). Fortunately, only 1% of Americans believed that the phrase "Where is McDonald's?" was of vital importance. The proportions in Figure 2.3 do not sum to one because we exclude those that responded with uncommon words or phrases.

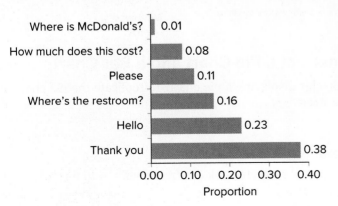

FIGURE 2.3
Results to question: "When traveling in a non-English-speaking country, which word or phrase is most important to know in that country's language?"

Cautionary Comments When Constructing or Interpreting Charts or Graphs

As with many of the statistical methods that we examine throughout this text, the possibility exists for unintentional, as well as purposeful, distortions of graphical information. As a careful researcher, you should follow these basic guidelines:

- The simplest graph should be used for a given set of data. Strive for clarity and avoid unnecessary adornments.

- Axes should be clearly marked with the numbers of their respective scales; each axis should be labeled.

- When creating a bar chart, each bar should be of the same width. Differing bar widths create distortions. The same principle holds in the next section when we discuss histograms.

Crude_Oil

- The vertical axis should not be given a very high value as an upper limit. In these instances, the data may appear compressed so that an increase (or decrease) of the data is not as apparent as it perhaps should be. For example, Figure 2.4(a) plots the daily price for a barrel of crude oil for the first quarter of 2011. Due to Middle East unrest, the price of crude oil rose from a low of $83.13 per barrel to a high of $106.19 per barrel, or approximately 28% $\left(= \frac{106.19 - 83.13}{83.13}\right)$. However, since Figure 2.4(a) uses a high value as an upper limit on the vertical axis ($325), the rise in price appears dampened.

JNJ

- The vertical axis should not be stretched so that an increase (or decrease) of the data appears more pronounced than warranted. For example, Figure 2.4(b) charts the daily closing stock price for Johnson & Johnson (JNJ) for the week of April 4, 2011. It is true that the stock price declined over the week from a high of $60.15 to a low of $59.46; this amounts to a $0.69 decrease or an approximate 1% decline. However, since the vertical axis is stretched, the drop in stock price appears more dramatic.

FIGURE 2.4 Misleading scales on vertical axes

(a) Vertical axis with high upper limit

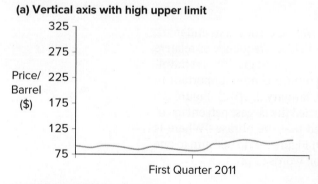

Source: U.S. Energy Information Administration.

(b) Stretched vertical axis

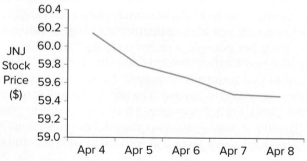

Source: www.finance.yahoo.com.

Using Excel to Construct a Pie Chart and a Bar Chart

Excel offers various options for displaying a pie chart. To replicate the pie chart in Figure 2.1(a), follow these steps:

A Pie Chart

Marital_Status

A. **FILE** Open *Marital_Status* (Table 2.5).

B. Select the category names and respective relative frequencies from the year 1960. Leave out the heading (top row).

C. From the menu, choose **Insert > Pie > 2-D Pie** and choose the graph on the top left. (If you are having trouble finding this option after selecting **Insert**, look for the circle above Charts.)

D. In order to add category names and their respective percentages, select the '+' sign that appears to the right of the pie chart.

A Bar Chart

Excel provides many options for showing a bar chart. To replicate the bar chart in Figure 2.2, follow these steps:

A. **FILE** Open *Marital_Status* (Table 2.5).

B. Select the category names and respective relative frequencies for the years 1960 and 2010. Leave out the heading (top row).

C. Choose **Insert > Column > 2-D Column**. From the options given, choose the graph on the top left. (If you are having trouble finding this option after selecting **Insert**, look for the vertical bars above Charts.)

D. In the legend to the right of the bar chart, Excel labels the data for the year 1960 as "Series 1" and the data for the year 2010 as "Series 2" by default. In order to edit the legend, select the legend and choose **Design > Select Data**. From the *Legend Entries*, select "Series 1," then select *Edit*, and under *Series Name*, type the new name of 1960. Follow the same steps to rename "Series 2" to 2010.

FILE
Marital_Status

Using R to Construct a Pie Chart

Before following all R instructions, make sure that you have read Appendix A ("Getting Started with R"). We assume that you have downloaded R and RStudio, and that you know how to import an Excel file.

Throughout the textbook, our goal is to provide the simplest way to obtain the relevant output. Like Excel, R has many built-in formulas or functions. We denote all function names in **boldface** and all options within a function in *italics*.

Here we replicate the pie chart in Figure 2.1(a).

A. Import the *Marital_Status* data into a data frame (table) in R.

B. We create a pie chart using the **pie** function. As outlined in Appendix A, we are able to choose variables from a data frame by attaching the expression $'variable name' to the data frame. For options within the function, we use *labels* to indicate the names for each category and *main* to designate a title. For readability purposes, we have used a few lines to show the command; however, you may enter the entire command in one line. Enter:

FILE
Marital_Status

```
> pie(Marital_Status$'1960',
    labels = Marital_Status$'Marital Status',
    main = "Marital Status, 1960")
```

Or, if you want to break the command into parts, R prompts you to finish the command with plus symbols (+) in lines following the first line as shown here:

```
> pie(Marital_Status$'1960',
  + labels = Marital_Status$'Marital Status',
  + main = "Marital Status, 1960")
```

It is possible to construct a bar chart in R, but that is a bit more involved. Due to its complexity, we have not included instructions. If you're interested, research the **barplot** function in R.

EXERCISES 2.1

1. A local restaurant is committed to providing its patrons with the best dining experience possible. On a recent survey, the restaurant asked patrons to rate the quality of their entrées. The responses ranged from 1 to 5, where 1 indicated a disappointing entrée and 5 indicated an exceptional entrée. The results of the survey are as follows:

3	5	4	4	3	2	3	3	2	5	5	5
5	3	3	2	1	4	5	5	4	2	5	5
5	4	4	3	1	5	2	1	5	4	4	4

a. Construct frequency and relative frequency distributions that summarize the survey's results.

b. Are patrons generally satisfied with the quality of their entrées? Explain.

2. First-time patients at North Shore Family Practice are required to fill out a questionnaire that gives the doctor an overall idea of each patient's health. The first question is: "In general, what is the quality of your health?" The patient chooses Excellent, Good, Fair, or Poor. Over the past month, the responses to this question from first-time patients were:

Fair	Good	Fair	Excellent
Good	Good	Good	Poor
Excellent	Excellent	Poor	Good
Fair	Good	Good	Good
Good	Poor	Fair	Excellent
Excellent	Good	Good	Good

a. Construct frequency and relative frequency distributions that summarize the responses to the questionnaire.

b. What is the most common response to the questionnaire? How would you characterize the health of first-time patients at this medical practice?

3. A survey asked chief executives at leading U.S. firms the following question: "Where do you expect the U.S. economy to be 12 months from now?" A representative sample of their responses appears below:

Same	Same	Same	Better	Worse
Same	Same	Better	Same	Worse
Same	Better	Same	Better	Same
Worse	Same	Same	Same	Worse
Same	Same	Same	Better	Same

a. Construct frequency and relative frequency distributions that summarize the responses to the survey. Where did most chief executives expect the U.S. economy to be in 12 months?

b. Construct a pie chart and a bar chart to summarize your results.

4. AccuWeather.com reported the following weather delays at these major U.S. airline hubs for July 21, 2010:

City	Delay	City	Delay
Atlanta	PM Delays	Mpls./St. Paul	None
Chicago	None	New York	All Day Delays
Dallas/Ft. Worth	None	Orlando	None
Denver	All Day Delays	Philadelphia	All Day Delays
Detroit	AM Delays	Phoenix	None
Houston	All Day Delays	Salt Lake City	None
Las Vegas	All Day Delays	San Francisco	AM Delays
Los Angeles	AM Delays	Seattle	None
Miami	AM Delays	Washington	All Day Delays

a. Construct frequency and relative frequency distributions that summarize the delays at major U.S. hubs. What was the most common type of delay? Explain.

b. Construct a pie chart and a bar chart to summarize your results.

5. Fifty pro-football rookies were rated on a scale of 1 to 5, based on performance at a training camp as well as on past performance. A ranking of 1 indicated a poor prospect whereas a ranking of 5 indicated an excellent prospect. The following frequency distribution was constructed.

Rating	Frequency
1	4
2	10
3	14
4	18
5	4

a. How many of the rookies received a rating of 4 or better? How many of the rookies received a rating of 2 or worse?

b. Construct the corresponding relative frequency distribution. What percent received a rating of 5?

c. Construct a bar chart for these data.

6. A recent survey asked 5,324 individuals: "What's most important to you when choosing where to live?" The responses are shown in the following relative frequency distribution.

Response	Relative Frequency
Good jobs	0.37
Affordable homes	0.15
Top schools	0.11
Low crime	0.23
Things to do	0.14

a. Construct the corresponding frequency distribution. How many of the respondents chose "low crime" as the most important criterion when choosing where to live?

b. Construct a bar chart for the frequency distribution found in part a.

7. What is the perfect summer trip? A National Geographic Kids survey (*AAA Horizons*, April 2007) asked this question to 316 children ages 8 to 14. Their responses are given in the following frequency distribution.

Top Vacation Choice	Frequency
Cruises	140
Beaches	68
Amusement Parks	68
Big Cities	20
Lakes	12
Summer Camp	8

a. Construct a relative frequency distribution. What percentage of the responses cited "Cruises" as the perfect summer trip?

b. Construct a bar chart for these data.

8. The following table lists U.S. revenue (in $ billions) of the major car-rental companies.

Car-Rental Company	Revenue in 2009
Enterprise	$10.7
Hertz	4.7
Avis Budget	4.0
Dollar Thrifty	1.5
Other	1.0

Source: *The Wall Street Journal*, July 30, 2010.

a. Compute the relative market share of the car-rental companies.

b. Hertz accounted for what percentage of sales?

c. Construct a pie chart for these data.

9. In a CBS News survey, 829 respondents were provided with a list of major events and asked which event would happen first. The events and their responses are summarized in the following percent frequency table.

Cure for cancer found	40%
End of dependence on oil	27%
Signs of life in outer space	12%
Peace in Middle East	8%
Other	6%
None will happen	7%

Source: *Vanity Fair*, December 2009.

a. Construct a pie chart and a bar chart for these data.

b. How many people think that a cure for cancer will be found first?

10. A 2010 poll conducted by NBC asked respondents who would win Super Bowl XLV in 2011. The responses by 20,825 people are summarized in the following table.

Team	Number of Votes
Atlanta Falcons	4,040
New Orleans Saints	1,880
Houston Texans	1,791
Dallas Cowboys	1,631
Minnesota Vikings	1,438
Indianapolis Colts	1,149
Pittsburgh Steelers	1,141
New England Patriots	1,095
Green Bay Packers	1,076
Others	

a. How many responses were for "Others"?

b. The Green Bay Packers won Super Bowl XLV, defeating the Pittsburgh Steelers by the score of 31–25. What proportion of respondents felt that the Green Bay Packers would win?

c. Construct a bar chart for these data using relative frequencies.

11. In a USA TODAY/Gallup Poll, respondents favored Barack Obama over Mitt Romney in terms of likeability, 60% to 30% (*Los Angeles Times,* July 28, 2012). The following bar chart summarizes the responses.

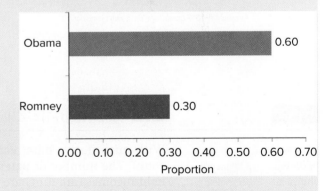

a. What percentage of respondents favored neither Obama nor Romney in terms of likeability?

b. Suppose this survey was based on 500 respondents. How many respondents favored Obama over Romney?

12. The accompanying figure plots the monthly stock price of Caterpillar, Inc., from July 2009 through March 2011. The stock has experienced tremendous growth over this time

period, almost tripling in price. Does the figure reflect this growth? If not, why not?

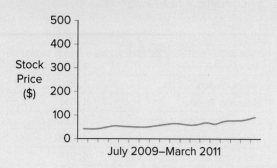

13. A recent survey of 992 people asked: In which professional sport—football, boxing, hockey, or martial arts—is an athlete most likely to sustain an injury that will affect the athlete after he or she retires? (*Vanity Fair*, January 29, 2012.) The following pie chart summarizes the responses.

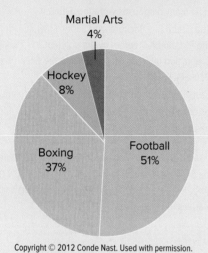

a. According to this survey, in which sport was an athlete most likely to sustain an injury with lifelong consequences? In which sport was an athlete least likely to sustain an injury with lifelong consequences?

b. How many respondents believed that professional hockey players were most likely to sustain an injury with lifelong consequences?

14. Annual sales at a small pharmaceutical firm have been rather stagnant over the most recent five-year period, exhibiting only 1.2% growth over this time frame. A research analyst prepares the accompanying graph for inclusion in a sales report.

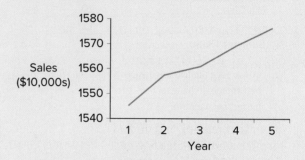

Does this graph accurately reflect what has happened to sales over the last five years? If not, why not?

2.2 SUMMARIZING QUANTITATIVE DATA

Summarize quantitative data by constructing a frequency distribution.

With quantitative data, each observation represents a meaningful amount or count. The number of patents held by pharmaceutical firms (count) and household incomes (amount) are examples of quantitative data. Although different in nature from qualitative data, we still use a **frequency distribution** to summarize quantitative data.

Before discussing the mechanics of constructing a frequency distribution, we find it useful to first examine one in its final form, using the house-price data from the introductory case to this chapter. We converted the raw data (the actual values) from Table 2.1 into a frequency distribution with five intervals or **classes**, each of width 100, as shown in Table 2.6. We see, for instance, that four houses sold in the first class, where prices ranged from $300,000 up to $400,000. The data are more manageable using a frequency distribution, but some detail is lost because we no longer see the actual values.

TABLE 2.6 Frequency Distribution for House-Price Data

Class (in $1,000s)	Frequency
300 up to 400	4
400 up to 500	11
500 up to 600	14
600 up to 700	5
700 up to 800	2
	Total = 36

EXAMPLE 2.2

Based on the frequency distribution in Table 2.6, what is the price range over this time period? Over what price range did the majority of the houses sell?

SOLUTION: The frequency distribution shows that house prices ranged from $300,000 up to $800,000 over this time period. The most houses (14) sold in the $500,000 up to $600,000 range. Note that only four houses sold in the lowest price range and only two houses sold at the highest price range.

It turns out that reading and understanding a frequency distribution is actually easier than forming one. When we constructed a frequency distribution with qualitative data, the raw data could be categorized in a well-defined way. With quantitative data, we must make certain decisions about the number of classes, as well as the width of each class. We do not apply concrete rules when we define the classes in Table 2.6; however, we are able to follow several guidelines.

Guidelines for Constructing a Frequency Distribution

TABLE 2.7 Too Many Classes in a Distribution

Class (in $1,000s)	Frequency
325 up to 350	2
350 up to 375	1
375 up to 400	1
400 up to 425	3
425 up to 450	5
450 up to 475	3
475 up to 500	0
500 up to 525	5
525 up to 550	5
550 up to 575	3
575 up to 600	1
600 up to 625	0
625 up to 650	1
650 up to 675	4
675 up to 700	0
700 up to 725	1
725 up to 750	1
	Total = 36

- *Classes are mutually exclusive.* In other words, classes do not overlap. Each observation falls into one, and only one, class. For instance, suppose a value of 400 appeared in Table 2.1. Given the class divisions in Table 2.6, we would have included this observation in the second class interval. Mathematically, the second class interval is expressed as $400 \leq Price < 500$. Alternatively, we can define the second interval as $400 < Price \leq 500$, in which case the value 400 is included in the previous class interval. In short, no matter the specification of the classes, the observation is included in only one of the classes.
- *Classes are exhaustive.* The total number of classes covers the entire sample (or population). In Table 2.6, if we had left off the last class, 700 up to 800, then we would be omitting two observations from the sample.
- *The total number of classes in a frequency distribution usually ranges from 5 to 20.* Smaller data sets tend to have fewer classes than larger data sets. Recall that the goal of constructing a frequency distribution is to summarize the data in a form that accurately depicts the group as a whole. If we have too many classes, then this advantage of the frequency distribution is lost. For instance, suppose we create a frequency distribution for the house-price data with 17 classes, each of width 25, as shown in Table 2.7. Technically, this is a valid frequency distribution, but the summarization advantage of the frequency distribution is lost because there are too many class intervals. Similarly, if the frequency distribution has too few classes, then considerable accuracy and detail are lost. Consider a frequency distribution of the house-price data with three classes, each of width 150, as shown in Table 2.8.

TABLE 2.8 Too Few Classes in a Distribution

Class (in $1,000s)	Frequency
300 up to 450	12
450 up to 600	17
600 up to 750	7
	Total = 36

Again, this is a valid frequency distribution. However, we cannot tell whether the 17 houses that sold for $450,000 up to $600,000 fall closer to the price of $450,000, fall closer to the price of $600,000, or are evenly spread within the interval. With only three classes in the frequency distribution, too much detail is lost.

• Once we choose the number of classes for a raw data set, we can then *approximate the width of each class* by using the formula

$$\frac{\text{Largest value} - \text{Smallest value}}{\text{Number of classes}}.$$

Generally, the width of each class is the same for each class interval. If the class width varied, comparisons between the numbers of observations in different intervals would be misleading.

• It is preferable to *define class limits that are easy to recognize and interpret*. Suppose we conclude, as we do in Table 2.6, that we should have five classes in the frequency distribution for the house-price data. Applying the class-width formula with the largest value of 735 and the smallest value of 330 (from Table 2.1) yields $\frac{735 - 330}{5} = 81$. Table 2.9 shows the frequency distribution with five classes and a class width of 81.

TABLE 2.9 Cumbersome Class Width in a Distribution

Class (in $1,000s)	Frequency
330 up to 411	4
411 up to 492	11
492 up to 573	12
573 up to 654	3
654 up to 735	6
	Total = 36

Again, this is a valid frequency distribution, but it proves unwieldy. Recall that one major goal in forming a frequency distribution is to provide more clarity in interpreting the data. Grouping the data in this manner actually makes analyzing the data more difficult. In order to facilitate interpretation of the frequency distribution, it is best to define class limits with ease of recognition in mind. To this end, and as initially shown in Table 2.6, we set the lower limit of the first class at 300 (rather than 330) and obtain the remaining class limits by successively adding 100 (rather than 81).

Once we have clearly defined the classes for a particular data set, the next step is to count and record the number of data points that fall into each class. As we did with the construction of a qualitative frequency distribution, we usually include a tally column to aid in counting (see Table 2.10), but then we remove this column in the final presentation of the frequency distribution. For instance, in Table 2.1, the first data point, 430, falls in the second class, so we place a tally mark in the second class; the next value of 520 falls in the third class, so we place a tally mark in the third class, and so on. The frequency column shows the numerical value of the respective tally count. Since four tally marks appear in the first class, we record the value 4 as its frequency—the number of observations that fall into the first class. One way to ensure that we have included all the data points in the frequency distribution is to sum the frequency column. This sum should always equal the population or sample size.

TABLE 2.10 Constructing Frequency Distributions for the House-Price Data

Class (in $1,000s)	Tally	Frequency	Cumulative Frequency
300 up to 400	IIII	4	4
400 up to 500	HHH HHH I	11	4 + 11 = 15
500 up to 600	HHH HHH IIII	14	4 + 11 + 14 = 29
600 up to 700	HHH	5	4 + 11 + 14 + 5 = 34
700 up to 800	II	2	4 + 11 + 14 + 5 + 2 = 36
		Total = 36	

A frequency distribution indicates how many observations fall within some range. However, we might want to know how many observations fall below the upper limit of a particular class. In these cases, our needs are better served with a **cumulative frequency distribution**.

The last column of Table 2.10 shows values for cumulative frequency. The cumulative frequency of the first class is the same as the frequency of the first class—that is, the value 4. However, the interpretation is different. With respect to the frequency column, the value 4 tells us that four of the houses sold in the $300,000 up to $400,000 range. For the cumulative frequency column, the value 4 tells us that four of the houses sold for less than $400,000. To obtain the cumulative frequency for the second class we add its frequency, 11, with the preceding frequency, 4, and obtain 15. This tells us that 15 of the houses sold for less than $500,000. We solve for the cumulative frequencies of the remaining classes in a like manner. Note that the cumulative frequency of the last class is equal to the sample size of 36. This indicates that all 36 houses sold for less than $800,000.

> **FREQUENCY AND CUMULATIVE FREQUENCY DISTRIBUTIONS FOR QUANTITATIVE DATA**
>
> For quantitative data, a frequency distribution groups data into intervals called classes and records the number of observations that falls into each class. A cumulative frequency distribution records the number of observations that fall below the upper limit of each class.

> **EXAMPLE 2.3**
>
> Using Table 2.10, how many of the houses sold in the $500,000 up to $600,000 range? How many of the houses sold for less than $600,000?
>
> **SOLUTION:** From the frequency distribution, we find that 14 houses sold in the $500,000 up to $600,000 range. In order to find the number of houses that sold for less than $600,000, we use the cumulative frequency distribution. We readily observe that 29 of the houses sold for less than $600,000.

Suppose we want to compare house prices in Mission Viejo, California, to house prices in another region of the United States. Just as for qualitative data, when making comparisons between two quantitative data sets—especially if the data sets differ in size—a **relative frequency distribution** tends to provide more meaningful information than a frequency distribution.

The second column of Table 2.11 shows the construction of a relative frequency distribution from the frequency distribution in Table 2.10. We take each class's frequency and divide by the total number of observations. For instance, we observed four houses that sold in the lowest range of $300,000 up to $400,000. We take the class frequency of 4 and divide by the sample size, 36, and obtain 0.11. Equivalently, we can say 11% of the houses sold in this price range. We make similar calculations for each class and note that when we sum the column of relative frequencies, we should get a value of one (or, due to rounding, a number very close to one).

TABLE 2.11 Constructing Relative Frequency Distributions for House-Price Data

Class (in $1,000s)	Relative Frequency	Cumulative Relative Frequency
300 up to 400	4/36 = 0.11	0.11
400 up to 500	11/36 = 0.31	0.11 + 0.31 = 0.42
500 up to 600	14/36 = 0.39	0.11 + 0.31 + 0.39 = 0.81
600 up to 700	5/36 = 0.14	0.11 + 0.31 + 0.39 + 0.14 = 0.95
700 up to 800	2/36 = 0.06	0.11 + 0.31 + 0.39 + 0.17 + 0.06 ≈ 1
	Total = 1 (subject to rounding)	

The last column of Table 2.11 shows the **cumulative relative frequency distribution**. The cumulative relative frequency for a particular class indicates the proportion (fraction) of the observations that falls below the upper limit of that particular class. We can calculate the cumulative relative frequency of each class in one of two ways: (1) We can sum successive relative frequencies, or (2) we can divide each class's cumulative frequency by the sample size. In Table 2.11 we show the first way. The value for the first class is the same as the value for its relative frequency—that is, 0.11. For the second class, we add 0.31 to 0.11 and obtain 0.42; this value indicates that 42% of the house prices were less than $500,000. We continue calculating cumulative relative frequencies in this manner until we reach the last class. Here, we get the value one, which means that 100% of the houses sold for less than $800,000.

RELATIVE AND CUMULATIVE RELATIVE FREQUENCY DISTRIBUTIONS

For quantitative data, a relative frequency distribution identifies the proportion (or the fraction) of observations that falls into each class—that is,

$$\text{Class relative frequency} = \frac{\text{Class frequency}}{\text{Total number of observations}}.$$

A cumulative relative frequency distribution records the proportion (or the fraction) of observations that fall below the upper limit of each class.

EXAMPLE 2.4

Using Table 2.11, what percent of the houses sold for at least $500,000 but not more than $600,000? What percent of the houses sold for less than $600,000? What percent of the houses sold for $600,000 or more?

SOLUTION: The relative frequency distribution indicates that 39% of the houses sold for at least $500,000 but not more than $600,000. Further, the cumulative relative frequency distribution indicates that 81% of the houses sold for less than $600,000. This result implies that 19% sold for $600,000 or more.

SYNOPSIS OF INTRODUCTORY CASE

During June 2010, Matthew Edwards reviewed the selling prices of 36 house sales in Mission Viejo, California, for a client from Seattle, Washington. After constructing various frequency distributions, he is able to make the following summary conclusions. House prices ranged from $300,000 up to $800,000 over this time period. Most of the houses (14) sold in the $500,000 up to $600,000 range, which is, more or less, the client's price range. Twenty-nine of the houses sold for less than $600,000. Converting the data into percentages so the client can make comparisons with home sales in the Seattle area, Matthew found that 39% of the houses sold for $500,000 up to $600,000. Moreover, 81% of the houses sold for less than $600,000, which implies that 19% sold for $600,000 or more.

©Brand X Pictures/Stockbyte/Getty Images RF

Histograms, Polygons, and Ogives

LO 2.4

A **histogram** and a **polygon** are graphical depictions of frequency and relative frequency distributions. The advantage of a visual display is that we can quickly see where most of the observations tend to cluster, as well as the spread and shape of the data. For instance, a histogram and a polygon may reveal whether or not the distribution has a symmetric shape.

Construct and interpret a histogram, a polygon, and an ogive.

> **GRAPHICAL DISPLAY OF QUANTITATIVE DATA: A HISTOGRAM**
>
> A histogram is a series of rectangles where the width and height of each rectangle represent the class width and frequency (or relative frequency) of the respective class.

For quantitative data, a histogram is essentially the counterpart to the vertical bar chart we use for qualitative data. When constructing a histogram, we mark off the class limits along the horizontal axis. The height of each bar represents either the frequency or the relative frequency for each class. No gaps appear between the interval limits. Figure 2.5 shows a histogram for the frequency distribution of house prices shown in Table 2.6. A casual inspection of the histogram reveals that the selling price of houses in this sample ranged from $300,000 to $800,000; however, the most common house price fell in the $500,000 to $600,000 range.

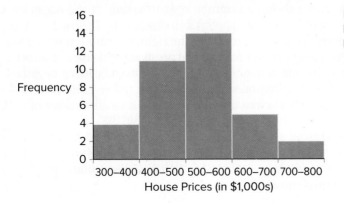

FIGURE 2.5
Frequency histogram for house prices

The only difference between a frequency histogram and a relative frequency histogram is the unit of measurement on the vertical axis. For the frequency histogram, we use the frequency of each class to represent the height; for the relative frequency histogram we use the proportion (or the fraction) of each class to represent the height. In a relative frequency histogram, the area of any rectangle is proportional to the relative frequency of observations falling into that class. Figure 2.6 shows the relative frequency histogram for house prices.

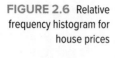

FIGURE 2.6 Relative frequency histogram for house prices

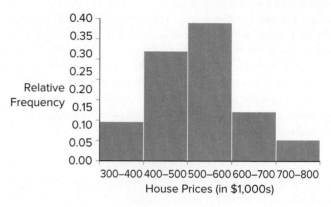

In general, the shape of most data distributions can be categorized as either symmetric or skewed. A symmetric distribution is one that is a mirror image of itself on both sides of its center. That is, the location of values below the center correspond to those above the center. As we will see in later chapters, the smoothed histogram for many data sets approximates a bell-shaped curve, which is indicative of the well-known normal distribution. If the distribution is not symmetric, then it is either positively skewed or negatively skewed.

FIGURE 2.7 Histograms with differing shapes

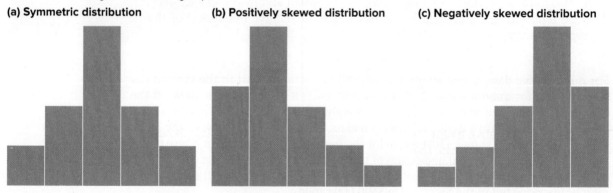

The histogram in Figure 2.7(a) shows a symmetric distribution. If the edges were smoothed, this histogram would look somewhat bell-shaped. In Figure 2.7(b), the histogram shows a positively skewed, or skewed to the right, distribution with a long tail extending to the right. This attribute reflects the presence of a small number of relatively large values. Finally, the histogram in Figure 2.7(c) indicates a negatively skewed, or skewed to the left, distribution since it has a long tail extending off to the left. Data that follow a negatively skewed distribution have a small number of relatively small values.

Though not nearly as skewed as the data exhibited in Figure 2.7(b), the house-price data in Figure 2.6 exhibit slight positive skew. This is the result of a few, relatively expensive homes in the city. It is common for distributions of house prices and incomes to exhibit positive skewness.

A polygon provides another convenient way of depicting a frequency distribution. It too gives a general idea of the shape of a distribution. Like the histogram, we place either the frequency or the relative frequency of the distribution on the y-axis, and the upper and lower limits of each class on the x-axis. We plot the midpoint of each class with its corresponding frequency or relative frequency. We then connect neighboring points with a straight line.

GRAPHICAL DISPLAY OF QUANTITATIVE DATA: A POLYGON

A polygon connects a series of neighboring points where each point represents the midpoint of a particular class and its associated frequency or relative frequency.

If we choose to construct a polygon for the house-price data, we first calculate the midpoint of each interval; thus, the midpoint for the first interval is $\frac{300 + 400}{2} = 350$, and similarly, the midpoints for the remaining intervals are 450, 550, 650, and 750. We treat each midpoint as the x-coordinate and the respective frequency (or relative frequency) as the y-coordinate. After plotting the points, we connect neighboring points. In order to close off the graph at each end, we add one interval below the lowest interval (so, 200 up to 300 with midpoint 250) and one interval above the highest interval (so, 800 up to 900 with midpoint 850) and assign each of these classes zero frequencies. Table 2.12 shows the relevant coordinates for plotting a polygon using the house-price data. We chose to use relative frequency to represent the y-coordinate.

TABLE 2.12 Coordinates for Plotting Relative Frequency Polygon

Classes	x-coordinate (midpoint)	y-coordinate (relative frequency)
(Lower end)	250	0
300–400	350	0.11
400–500	450	0.31
500–600	550	0.39
600–700	650	0.14
700–800	750	0.06
(Upper end)	850	0

Figure 2.8 plots a relative frequency polygon for the house-price data. Here the distribution appears to approximate the bell-shaped distribution discussed earlier. Only a careful inspection of the right tail suggests that the data are slightly positively skewed.

FIGURE 2.8
Polygon for the house-price data

In many instances, we might want to convey information by plotting an **ogive** (pronounced "ojive").

> GRAPHICAL DISPLAY OF QUANTITATIVE DATA: AN OGIVE
>
> An ogive connects a series of neighboring points where each point represents the upper limit of a particular class and its associated cumulative frequency or cumulative relative frequency.

An ogive differs from a polygon in that we use the upper limit of each class as the x-coordinate and the cumulative frequency or cumulative relative frequency of the corresponding class as the y-coordinate. After plotting the points, we connect neighboring points. Lastly, we close the ogive only at the lower end by intersecting the x-axis at the lower limit of the first class. Table 2.13 shows the relevant coordinates for plotting an ogive using the house-price data. We choose to use cumulative relative frequency as the y-coordinate since the resulting graph tends to have more interpretive appeal. The use of cumulative frequency would not change the shape of the ogive, just the unit of measurement on the y-axis.

TABLE 2.13 Coordinates for the Ogive for the House-Price Data

Classes	x-coordinate (upper limit)	y-coordinate (cumulative relative frequency)
(Lower end)	300	0
300–400	400	0.11
400–500	500	0.42
500–600	600	0.81
600–700	700	0.95
700–800	800	1

Figure 2.9 plots the ogive for the house-price data. In general, we can use an ogive to approximate the proportion of values that are less than a specified value on the horizontal axis. Consider an application to the house-price data in Example 2.5.

FIGURE 2.9
Ogive for the house-price data

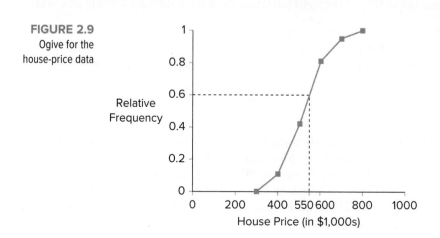

EXAMPLE 2.5

Using Figure 2.9, approximate the percentage of houses that sold for less than $550,000.

SOLUTION: Draw a vertical line that starts at 550 and intersects the ogive. Then follow the line to the vertical axis and read the value. You can conclude that approximately 60% of the houses sold for less than $550,000.

Using Excel to Construct a Histogram, a Polygon, and an Ogive

A Histogram Constructed from Raw Data

In general, Excel offers two different ways to construct a histogram, depending on whether we have access to the raw data or the frequency distribution. We first replicate Figure 2.5 using the house-price data from Table 2.1 where the data are in raw form. We then replicate Figure 2.5 using the house-price data from Table 2.6 where the data have been converted to a frequency distribution.

A. **FILE** Open *MV_Houses* (Table 2.1).

B. In a column next to the data, enter the values of the upper limits of each class, or in this example, 400, 500, 600, 700, and 800; label this column as Class Limits. The reason for these entries is explained in step D. The house-price data and the class limits (as well as the resulting frequency distribution and histogram) are shown in Figure 2.10.

FILE

MV_Houses

FIGURE 2.10 Constructing a histogram from raw data with Excel

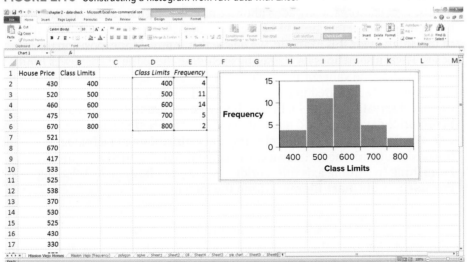

C. From the menu choose **Data > Data Analysis > Histogram > OK**. (*Note:* If you do not see the **Data Analysis** option under **Data**, you must *add in* this option. From the menu choose **File > Options > Add-Ins** and choose **Go** at the bottom of the dialog box. Select the box to the left of **Analysis Toolpak**, and then click **OK**. If you have installed this option properly, you should now see **Data Analysis** under **Data**.)

D. In the *Histogram* dialog box (see Figure 2.11), under *Input Range*, select the House Price data. Excel uses the term "bins" for the class limits. If we leave the *Bin Range* box empty, Excel creates evenly distributed intervals using the minimum and maximum values of the input range as end points. This methodology is rarely satisfactory. In order to construct a histogram that is more informative, we use the upper limit of each class as the bin values. Under *Bin Range*, we select the Class Limits data. (Check the *Labels* box if you have included the names House Price and Class Limits as part of the selection.) Under *Output Options,* we choose **Chart Output**, then click **OK**.

FIGURE 2.11 Excel's dialog box for a histogram

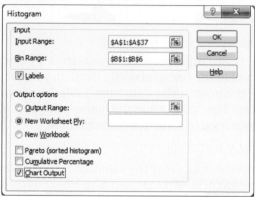

E. Since Excel leaves spaces between the rectangles, we right-click on any of the rectangles, choose **Format Data Series** and change the *Gap Width* to 0, then choose **Close**. In the event that the given class limits do not include all the data points, Excel automatically adds another interval labeled "More" to the resulting frequency distribution and histogram. Since we observe zero observations in this interval for this example, we delete this interval for expositional purposes. Excel also defines its classes by excluding the value of the lower limit and including the value of the upper class limit for each interval. For example, if the value 400 appeared in the house-price data, Excel would have accounted for this observation in the first class. If any upper-limit value appeared in the house-price data, we would have adjusted the class limits in the *Bin Range* to 399, 499, and so on, so that Excel's frequency distribution and histogram would be consistent with those that we constructed in Table 2.10 and Figure 2.5. Formatting (regarding axis titles, gridlines, etc.) can be done by selecting **Format > Add Chart Element** from the menu.

A Histogram Constructed from a Frequency Distribution

Suppose we do not have the raw data for house prices, but we have the frequency distribution reported in Table 2.6.

MV_Frequency

A. **FILE** Open *MV_Frequency* (Table 2.6).

B. Select the classes and respective frequencies. See Figure 2.12.

C. From the menu choose **Insert > Column > 2-D Column** and choose the graph on the top left. (If you are having trouble finding this option after selecting **Insert**, look for the vertical bars above Charts.)

FIGURE 2.12 Constructing a histogram from a frequency distribution with Excel

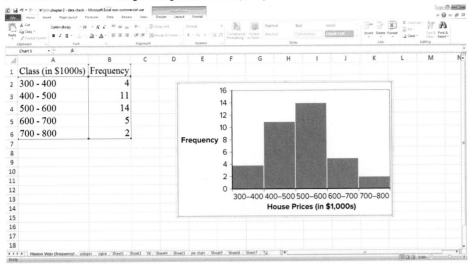

D. In order to remove the spaces between the rectangles, right-click on any of the rectangles, choose **Format Data Series** and change the *Gap Width* to 0, then choose **Close**.

E. Formatting (regarding axis titles, gridlines, etc.) can be done by selecting **Format > Add Chart Element** from the menu.

A Polygon

We replicate the polygon in Figure 2.8.

A. Open *Polygon* (this is a simplified version of the data in Table 2.12).

B. Select the values in the *x* and *y* columns and choose **Insert > Scatter.** Select the box at the middle right. (If you are having trouble finding this option after selecting **Insert**, look for the graph with data points above Charts.)

C. Formatting (regarding axis titles, gridlines, etc.) can be done by selecting **Format > Add Chart Element** from the menu.

FILE
Polygon

An Ogive

We replicate the polygon in Figure 2.9.

A. Open *Ogive* (this is a simplified version of the data in Table 2.13).

B. Select the values in the *x* and *y* columns and choose **Insert > Scatter.** Select the box at the middle right. (If you are having trouble finding this option after selecting **Insert**, look for the graph with data points above Charts.)

C. Formatting (regarding axis titles, gridlines, etc.) can be done by selecting **Format > Add Chart Element** from the menu.

FILE
Ogive

Using R to Construct a Histogram, a Polygon, and an Ogive

A Histogram

We replicate the histogram in Figure 2.5.

A. Import the **MV_Houses** data into a data frame (table) in R.

FILE
MV_Houses

B. We make a histogram using the **hist** function. For options within the function, we use *breaks* to denote the number of distinct intervals, *main* to designate a title, and *xlab* to label the *x*-axis. Enter:

```
> hist(MV_Houses$'House Price', breaks = 5, main =
  "Histogram", xlab = "House Prices (in $1,000s)")
```

A Polygon

We replicate the polygon in Figure 2.8.

A. Import the **Polygon** data into a data frame (table) in R.

B. We make a scatterplot using the **plot** function. For options within the function, we use *ylab* and *xlab* to label the *y*-axis and the *x*-axis, respectively. Enter:

```
> plot(Polygon$'y' ~ Polygon$'x', ylab="Relative
  Frequency", xlab="House Prices (in $1,000s)")
```

C. We add lines to the scatterplot using the **lines** function. Enter:

```
> lines(Polygon$'y' ~ Polygon$'x')
```

An Ogive

We replicate the ogive in Figure 2.9.

A. Import the **Ogive** data into a data frame (table) in R.

B. Since the commands for the ogive are identical to the ones for the polygon, we are brief. Enter:

```
> plot(Ogive$'y' ~ Ogive$'x', ylab="Relative Frequency",
  xlab="House Prices (in $1,000s)")
> lines(Ogive$'y' ~ Ogive$'x')
```

EXERCISES 2.2

Mechanics

15. Consider the following data set:

4	10	8	7	6	10	11	14	13	14
3	9	8	5	7	6	10	3	11	11
8	8	4	5	5	12	12	3	8	8

a. Construct the frequency distribution using classes of 3 up to 5, 5 up to 7, etc.

b. Construct relative frequency, cumulative frequency, and cumulative relative frequency distributions.

c. How many of the observations are at least 7 but less than 9? How many of the observations are less than 9?

d. What percentage of the observations are at least 7 but less than 9? What percentage of the observations are less than 9?

e. Graph the relative frequency histogram.

f. Graph the ogive.

16. Consider the following data set:

4	10	8	7	6	10	11	14	13	14
3	9	8	5	7	6	10	3	11	11
8	8	4	5	5	12	12	3	8	8
10	−9	28	14	−5	9	11	5	8	−3
33	−4	2	3	22	25	5	29	26	0
−8	−5	0	15	−4	35	21	15	19	23
4	6	−2	12	24	36	15	3	−5	2

a. Construct the frequency distribution using classes of −10 up to 0, 0 up to 10, etc. How many of the observations are at least 10 but less than 20?

b. Construct the relative frequency distribution and the cumulative relative frequency distribution. What percent of the observations are at least 10 but less than 20? What percent of the observations are less than 20?

c. Graph the relative frequency polygon. Is the distribution symmetric? If not, then how is it skewed?

17. Consider the following frequency distribution:

Class	Frequency
10 up to 20	12
20 up to 30	15
30 up to 40	25
40 up to 50	4

a. Construct the relative frequency distribution. Graph the relative frequency histogram.

b. Construct the cumulative frequency distribution and the cumulative relative frequency distribution.

c. What percent of the observations are at least 30 but less than 40? What percent of the observations are less than 40?

18. Consider the following frequency distribution:

Class	Frequency
1,000 up to 1,100	2
1,100 up to 1,200	7
1,200 up to 1,300	3
1,300 up to 1,400	4

a. Construct the relative frequency distribution. What percent of the observations are at least 1,100 but less than 1,200?

b. Construct the cumulative frequency distribution and the cumulative relative frequency distribution. How many of the observations are less than 1,300?

c. Graph the frequency histogram.

19. Consider the following cumulative frequency distribution:

Class	Cumulative Frequency
15 up to 25	30
25 up to 35	50
35 up to 45	120
45 up to 55	130

a. Construct the frequency distribution. How many observations are at least 35 but less than 45?

b. Graph the frequency histogram.

c. What percent of the observations are less than 45?

20. Consider the following relative frequency distribution:

Class	Relative Frequency
−20 up to −10	0.04
−10 up to 0	0.28
0 up to 10	0.26
10 up to 20	0.22
20 up to 30	0.20

a. Suppose this relative frequency distribution is based on a sample of 50 observations. Construct the frequency distribution. How many of the observations are at least −10 but less than 0?

b. Construct the cumulative frequency distribution. How many of the observations are less than 20?

c. Graph the relative frequency polygon.

21. Consider the following cumulative relative frequency distribution.

Class	Cumulative Relative Frequency
150 up to 200	0.10
200 up to 250	0.35
250 up to 300	0.70
300 up to 350	1

a. Construct the relative frequency distribution. What percent of the observations are at least 250 but less than 300?

b. Graph the ogive.

Applications

22. *Kiplinger's* (August 2007) lists the assets (in billions of $) for the 20 largest stock mutual funds (ranked by size) as follows:

99.8	49.7	86.3	109.2	56.9
88.2	44.1	58.8	176.7	49.9
61.4	128.8	53.6	95.2	92.5
55.0	96.5	45.3	73.0	70.9

a. Construct the frequency distribution using classes of 40 up to 70, 70 up to 100, etc.

b. Construct the relative frequency distribution, the cumulative frequency distribution, and the cumulative relative frequency distribution.

c. How many of the funds had assets of at least $100 but less than $130 (in billions)? How many of the funds had assets less than $160 (in billions)?

d. What percent of the funds had assets of at least $70 but less than $100 (in billions)? What percent of the funds had assets less than $130 (in billions)?

e. Construct the frequency histogram. Comment on the shape of the distribution.

23. The number of text messages sent by 25 13-year-olds over the past month are as follows:

630	516	892	643	627	510	937	909	654
817	760	715	605	975	888	912	952	701
744	793	852	504	562	670	685		

a. Construct the frequency distribution using classes of 500 up to 600, 600 up to 700, etc.

b. Construct the relative frequency distribution, the cumulative frequency distribution, and the cumulative relative frequency distribution.

c. How many of the 13-year-olds sent at least 600 but less than 700 text messages? How many sent less than 800 text messages?

d. What percent of the 13-year-olds sent at least 500 but less than 600 text messages? What percent of the 13-year-olds sent less than 700 text messages?

e. Graph the relative frequency polygon. Comment on the shape of the distribution.

24. AccuWeather.com listed the following high temperatures (in degrees Fahrenheit) for 33 European cities on July 21, 2010.

75	92	81	85	90	73	94	95	81	64	85
62	84	85	81	86	90	79	74	90	91	95
88	87	81	73	76	86	90	83	75	92	83

a. Construct the frequency distribution using classes of 60 up to 70, 70 up to 80, etc.

b. Construct the relative frequency, the cumulative frequency, and the cumulative relative frequency distributions.

c. How many of the cities had high temperatures less than 80°?

d. What percent of the cities had high temperatures of at least 80° but less than 90°? What percent of the cities had high temperatures less than 90°?

e. Construct the relative frequency polygon. Comment on the shape of the distribution.

25. The following relative frequency distribution summarizes the ages of women who had a child in the last year.

Ages	Relative Frequency
15 up to 20	0.10
20 up to 25	0.25
25 up to 30	0.28
30 up to 35	0.24
35 up to 40	0.11
40 up to 45	0.02

Source: *The Statistical Abstract of the United States, 2010.*

a. Assume the relative frequency distribution is based on a sample of 2,000 women. Construct the frequency, the cumulative frequency, and the cumulative relative frequency distributions.

b. What percent of the women were at least 25 but less than 30 years old? What percent of the women were younger than 35 years old?

c. Graph the relative frequency polygon. Comment on the shape of the distribution.

d. Graph the ogive. Using the graph, approximate the age of the middle 50% of the distribution.

26. Fifty cities provided information on vacancy rates (in percent) in local apartments in the following frequency distribution.

Vacancy Rate (in percent)	Frequency
0 up to 3	5
3 up to 6	10
6 up to 9	20
9 up to 12	10
12 up to 15	5

a. Construct the relative frequency distribution, the cumulative frequency distribution, and the cumulative relative frequency distribution.

b. How many of the cities had a vacancy rate less than 12%? What percent of the cities had a vacancy rate of at least 6% but less than 9%? What percent of the cities had a vacancy rate of less than 9%?

c. Graph the frequency histogram. Comment on the shape of the distribution.

27. The manager of a nightclub near a local university recorded the ages of the last 100 guests in the following cumulative frequency distribution.

Ages	Cumulative Frequency
18 up to 22	45
22 up to 26	70
26 up to 30	85
30 up to 34	96
34 up to 38	100

a.   Construct the frequency, the relative frequency, and the cumulative relative frequency distributions.

b.   How many of the guests were at least 26 but less than 30 years old? What percent of the guests were at least 22 but less than 26 years old? What percent of the guests were younger than 34 years old? What percent were 34 years or older?

c.   Graph the frequency histogram. Comment on the shape of the distribution.

28. The following relative frequency histogram summarizes the median household income for the 50 states in the United States (*U.S. Census*, 2010).

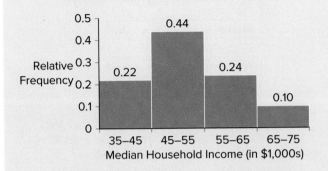

a.   Is the distribution symmetric? If not, is it positively or negatively skewed?

b.   What percentage of the states had median household income between $45,000 and $55,000?

c.   What percentage of the states had median household income between $35,000 and $55,000?

29. The following ogive summarizes the median household income for the 50 states in the United States (*U.S. Census*, 2010).

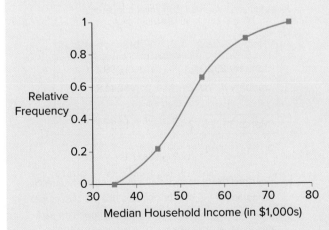

a.   Approximate the percentage of states with median household income less than $50,000.

b.   Approximate the percentage of states with median household income more than $60,000.

30. The following histogram summarizes Apple Inc.'s monthly stock price for the years 2007 through 2011 (http://finance.yahoo.com, data retrieved April 20, 2012).

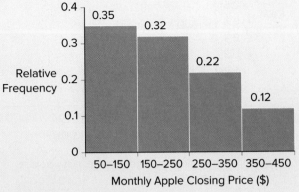

a.   Is the distribution symmetric? If not, is it positively or negatively skewed?

b.   Over this five-year period, approximate the minimum monthly stock price and the maximum monthly stock price.

c.   Over this five-year period, which class had the highest relative frequency?

31. The following histogram summarizes the salaries (in $1,000,000s) for the 30 highest-paid players in the National Basketball Association (NBA) for the 2012 season (www.nba.com, data retrieved March 2012).

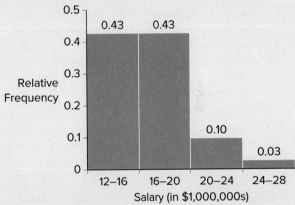

a.   Is the distribution symmetric? If not, is it positively or negatively skewed?

b.   How many NBA players earned between $20,000,000 and $24,000,000?

c.   Approximately how many NBA players earned between $12,000,000 and $20,000,000?

32. The following ogive summarizes the salary (in $1,000,000s) for the 30 highest-paid players in the National Basketball Association (NBA) for the 2012 season (www.nba.com, data retrieved March 2012).

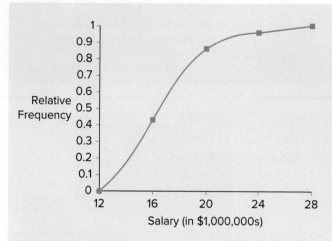

Relative Frequency (y-axis: 0 to 1)
Salary (in $1,000,000s) (x-axis: 12, 16, 20, 24, 28)

a. Approximate the percentage of salaries that were less than $18,000,000.

b. Approximate the number of salaries that were more than $14,000,000.

33. **FILE** *Math_SAT.* The following table lists a portion of the average math SAT scores for each state for the year 2009.

State	SAT
Alabama	552
Alaska	516
⋮	⋮
Wyoming	568

Source: www.collegeboard.com.

a. Construct the frequency distribution and graph the frequency histogram using classes of 450 to 500, 501 to 550, etc. Comment on the shape of the distribution. How many of the states had scores between 551 and 600?

b. Construct the relative frequency, the cumulative frequency, and the cumulative relative frequency distributions.

c. How many of the states had math SAT scores of 550 or less?

d. What percent of the states had math SAT scores between 551 and 600? What percent of the states had mean SAT scores of 550 or less?

34. **FILE** *Census.* The accompanying table shows a portion of median house values (in $) for the 50 states as reported by the U.S. Census Bureau in 2010.

State	House Value
Alabama	117600
Alaska	229100
⋮	⋮
Wyoming	174000

a. Construct the frequency distribution and graph the frequency histogram for the median house values. Use six classes with upper limits of $100,000, $200,000, etc.

b. Is the distribution symmetric? If not, is it positively or negatively skewed?

c. Which class interval had the highest frequency?

d. What percentage of the states had median house values between $300,000 and $400,000?

e. How many of the states had median house values less than $300,000?

35. **FILE** *Gas_Prices.* The accompanying table shows a portion of the average price (in $) for a gallon of gas for the 50 states during April 2012.

State	Price
Alabama	4.36
Alaska	3.79
⋮	⋮
Wyoming	3.63

Source: www.AAA.com, data retrieved April 16, 2012.

a. Construct the frequency distribution and graph the frequency histogram for the average gas prices. Use six classes with upper limits of $3.70, $3.90, etc.

b. Is the distribution symmetric? If not, is it positively or negatively skewed?

c. Which class interval had the highest frequency?

d. Graph the ogive. Approximate the percentage of states that had average gas prices of $3.90 or less. Approximate the number of states that had average gas prices greater than $3.90.

36. **FILE** *DJIA_2012.* For the first three months of 2012, the stock market put up its best first-quarter performance in over a decade (Money.cnn.com, April 9, 2012). The accompanying table shows a portion of the daily price index for the Dow Jones Industrial Average (DJIA) over this period.

Day	DJIA
January 3, 2012	12397
January 4, 2012	12418
⋮	⋮
March 31, 2012	13212

Source: Finance.yahoo.com, data retrieved April 20, 2012.

a. Construct the frequency distribution and the frequency histogram for the DJIA price index. Use five classes with upper limits of 12,500, 12,750, etc. On how many days during this quarter was the DJIA less than 12,500?

b. Graph the relative frequency polygon. Is the distribution symmetric? If not, is it positively or negatively skewed?

c. Graph the ogive. Approximate the percentage of days that the DJIA was less than 13,000.

Construct and interpret a stem-and-leaf diagram.

John Tukey (1915–2000), a well-known statistician, provided another visual method for displaying quantitative data. A **stem-and-leaf diagram** is often a preliminary step when analyzing a data set. It is useful in that it gives an overall picture of where the data are centered and how the data are dispersed from the center.

> GRAPHICAL DISPLAY OF QUANTITATIVE DATA: A STEM-AND-LEAF DIAGRAM
>
> A stem-and-leaf diagram is constructed by separating each value of a data set into two parts: a *stem*, which consists of the leftmost digits, and a *leaf*, which consists of the last digit.

The best way to explain a stem-and-leaf diagram is to show an example.

EXAMPLE 2.6

Table 2.14 shows the ages of the 25 wealthiest people in the world in 2010. Construct and interpret a stem-and-leaf diagram.

TABLE 2.14 Wealthiest People in the World, 2010

Name	Age	Name	Age
Carlos Slim Helu	70	Li Ka-shing	81
William Gates III	54	Jim Walton	62
Warren Buffet	79	Alice Walton	60
Mukesh Ambani	52	Liliane Bettencourt	87
Lakshmi Mittal	59	S. Robson Walton	66
Lawrence Ellison	65	Prince Alwaleed Alsaud	54
Bernard Arnault	61	David Thomson	52
Eike Batista	53	Michael Otto	66
Amancio Ortega	74	Lee Shau Kee	82
Karl Albrecht	90	Michael Bloomberg	68
Ingvar Kamprad	83	Sergey Brin	36
Christy Walton	55	Charles Koch	74
Stefan Persson	62		

Reprinted by permission of Forbes Media LLC © 2011.

FILE
Wealthiest_People

SOLUTION: For each age, we first decide that the number in the tens spot will denote the stem, thus leaving the number in the ones spot as the leaf. We then identify the lowest and highest values in the data set. Sergey Brin is the youngest member of this group at 36 years of age (stem: 3, leaf: 6) and Karl Albrecht is the oldest at 90 years of age (stem: 9, leaf: 0). These values give us the first and last values in the stem. This means our stems will be 3, 4, 5, 6, 7, 8, and 9, as shown in Panel A of Table 2.15.

TABLE 2.15 Constructing a Stem-and-Leaf Diagram for Example 2.6

Panel A		Panel B		Panel C	
Stem	Leaf	Stem	Leaf	Stem	Leaf
3		3	6	3	6
4		4		4	
5		5	4 2 9 3 5 4 2	5	2 2 3 4 4 5 9
6		6	5 1 2 2 0 6 6 8	6	0 1 2 2 5 6 6 8
7	0	7	0 9 4 4	7	0 4 4 9
8		8	3 1 7 2	8	1 2 3 7
9		9	0	9	0

We then begin with the wealthiest man in the world, Carlos Slim Helu, whose age of 70 gives us a stem of 7 and a leaf of 0. We place a 0 in the row corresponding to a stem of 7, as shown in Panel A of Table 2.15. We continue this process with all the other ages and obtain the values in Panel B. Finally, in Panel C we arrange each individual leaf row in ascending order; this is the stem-and-leaf diagram in its final form.

The stem-and-leaf diagram (Panel C) presents the original 25 values in a more organized form. From the diagram we can readily observe that the ages range from 36 to 90. Wealthy individuals in their sixties make up the greatest group in the sample with eight members, while those in their fifties place a close second, accounting for seven members. We also note that the distribution is not perfectly symmetric. A stem-and-leaf diagram is similar to a histogram turned on its side with the added benefit of retaining the original values.

EXERCISES 2.3

Mechanics

37. Consider the following data set:

5.4	4.6	3.5	2.8	2.6	5.5	5.5	2.3	3.2	4.2
4.0	3.0	3.6	4.5	4.7	4.2	3.3	3.2	4.2	3.4

Construct a stem-and-leaf diagram. Is the distribution symmetric? Explain.

38. Consider the following data set:

−64	−52	−73	−82	−85	−80	−79	−65	−50	−71
−80	−85	−75	−65	−77	−87	−72	−83	−73	−80

Construct a stem-and-leaf diagram. Is the distribution symmetric? Explain.

Applications

39. A sample of patients arriving at Overbrook Hospital's emergency room recorded the following body temperature readings over the weekend:

100.4	99.6	101.5	99.8	102.1	101.2	102.3	101.2	102.2	102.4
101.6	101.5	99.7	102.0	101.0	102.5	100.5	101.3	101.2	102.2

Construct and interpret a stem-and-leaf diagram.

40. Suppose the following high temperatures were recorded for major cities in the contiguous United States for a day in July.

84	92	96	91	96	94	93	82	81	76
90	95	84	90	84	98	94	90	83	78
88	96	106	78	92	98	91	84	80	94
94	93	107	87	77	99	94	73	74	92

Construct and interpret a stem-and-leaf diagram.

41. A police officer is concerned with excessive speeds on a portion of Interstate 90 with a posted speed limit of 65 miles per hour. Using his radar gun, he records the following speeds for 25 cars and trucks:

66	72	73	82	80	81	79	65	70	71
80	75	75	65	67	67	72	73	73	80
81	78	71	70	70					

Construct a stem-and-leaf diagram. Are the officer's concerns warranted?

42. Spain was the winner of the 2010 World Cup, beating the Netherlands by a score of 1–0. The ages of the players from both teams were as follows:

Spain									
29	25	23	30	32	25	29	30	26	29
21	28	24	21	27	22	25	21	23	24
Netherlands									
27	22	26	30	35	33	29	25	27	25
35	27	27	26	23	25	23	24	26	39

Construct a stem-and-leaf diagram for each country. Comment on similarities and differences between the two data sets.

2.4 SCATTERPLOTS

All of the tabular and graphical tools presented thus far have focused on describing one variable. However, in many instances we are interested in the relationship between two variables. People in virtually every discipline examine how one variable may systematically influence another variable. Consider, for instance, how

Construct and interpret a scatterplot.

- Incomes vary with education.
- Sales vary with advertising expenditures.
- Stock prices vary with corporate profits.
- Crop yields vary with the use of fertilizer.
- Cholesterol levels vary with dietary intake.
- Price varies with reliability.

When examining the relationship between two quantitative variables, a **scatterplot** often proves to be a powerful first step in any analysis.

GRAPHICAL DISPLAY OF TWO QUANTITATIVE VARIABLES: A SCATTERPLOT

A scatterplot is a graphical tool that helps in determining whether or not two quantitative variables are related in some systematic way. Each point in the diagram represents a pair of observed values of the two variables.

When constructing a scatterplot, we generally refer to one of the variables as x and represent it on the horizontal axis and the other variable as y and represent it on the vertical axis. We then plot each pairing: (x_1, y_1), (x_2, y_2), and so on. Once the data are plotted, the graph may reveal that

- A linear relationship exists between the two variables;
- A nonlinear relationship exists between the two variables; or
- No relationship exists between the two variables.

For example, Figure 2.13(a) shows points on a scatterplot clustered together along a line with a negative slope; we infer that the two variables have a negative linear relationship. Part (b) depicts a positive nonlinear relationship; as x increases, y tends to increase at an increasing rate. The points in part (c) are scattered with no apparent pattern; thus, there is no relationship between the two variables.

FIGURE 2.13 Scatterplots depicting relationships between two variables

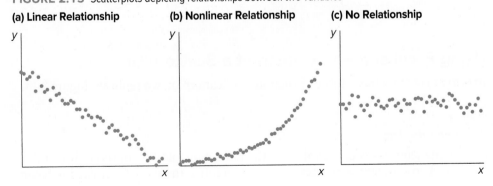

(a) Linear Relationship **(b) Nonlinear Relationship** **(c) No Relationship**

In order to illustrate a scatterplot, consider the following example.

EXAMPLE 2.7

A social scientist wants to analyze the relationship between educational attainment and income. He collects the data shown in Table 2.16, where Education and Income refer to an individual's years of higher education and annual income in thousands of dollars, respectively. Construct and interpret a scatterplot.

Edu_Inc

TABLE 2.16 Education and Income for Eight Individuals

Individual	Education	Income
1	3	45
2	4	56
3	6	85
4	2	35
5	5	55
6	4	48
7	8	100
8	0	38

SOLUTION: We let x and y denote Education and Income, respectively. We plot the first individual's pairing as (3, 45), the second individual's pairing as (4, 56), and so on. The graph should resemble Figure 2.14.

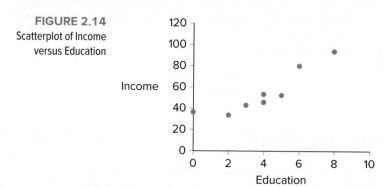

FIGURE 2.14
Scatterplot of Income versus Education

As expected, we observe a positive relationship between the two variables; that is, when Education increases, Income tends to increase.

Using Excel and R to Construct a Scatterplot

In order to demonstrate the construction of a scatterplot, we replicate Figure 2.14.

Using Excel

Edu_Inc

A. Open **Edu_Inc**.

B. Simultaneously select the values in the Education and Income columns, and then choose **Insert > Scatter**. Select the graph at the top left. (If you are having trouble finding this option after selecting **Insert**, look for the graph with data points above Charts.)

C. Formatting (regarding axis titles, gridlines, etc.) can be done by selecting **Format** > **Add Chart Element** from the menu.

Using R

A. Import the **Edu_Inc** data into a data frame (table) in R.

Edu_Inc

B. Since we used the **plot** function in Section 2.2, we simply provide the command. Enter:

```
> plot(Edu_Inc$'Income' ~ Edu_Inc$'Education', ylab =
  "Income", xlab = "Education")
```

EXERCISES 2.4

Mechanics

43. Construct a scatterplot with the following data. Describe the relationship between x and y.

x	3	7	12	5	6
y	22	10	5	14	12

44. Construct a scatterplot with the following data. Does a linear relationship exist between x and y?

x	10	4	6	3	7
y	3	2	6	6	4

45. Construct a scatterplot with the following data. Describe the relationship between x and y.

x	1	2	3	4	5	6	7	8
y	22	20	18	10	5	4	3	2

Applications

46. A statistics instructor wants to examine whether a relationship exists between the hours a student spends studying for the final exam (Hours) and a student's grade on the final exam (Grade). She takes a sample of eight students.

Hours	8	2	3	8	10	15	25	5
Grade	75	47	50	80	85	88	93	55

Construct a scatterplot. What conclusions can you draw from the scatterplot?

47. A study offers evidence that the more weight a woman gains during pregnancy, the higher the risk of having a high-birth-weight baby, defined as at least 8 pounds, 13 ounces, or 4 kilograms (*The Wall Street Journal*, August 5, 2010). High-birth-weight babies are more likely to be obese in adulthood. The weight gain (in kilograms) of eight mothers and the birth weight of their newborns (in kilograms) are recorded in the accompanying table.

Mother's Weight Gain	Newborn's Birth Weight
18	4.0
7	2.5
8	3.0
22	4.5
21	4.0
9	3.5
8	3.0
10	3.5

Construct a scatterplot. Do the results support the findings of the study?

48. In order to diversify risk, investors are often encouraged to invest in assets whose returns have either a negative

relationship or no relationship. The annual return data (in %) on two assets is shown in the accompanying table.

Return A	Return B
−20	8
−5	5
18	−1
15	−2
−12	2

Construct a scatterplot. In order to diversify risk, would the investor be wise to include both of these assets in her portfolio? Explain.

49. In an attempt to determine whether a relationship exists between the price of a home (in $1,000s) and the number of days it takes to sell the home, a real estate agent collects data on the recent sales of eight homes.

Price	Days to Sell Home
265	136
225	125
160	120
325	140
430	145
515	150
180	122
423	145

Construct a scatterplot. What can the realtor conclude?

WRITING WITH STATISTICS

©Rubberball/Getty Images RF

The tabular and graphical tools introduced in this chapter are the starting point for most studies and reports that involve statistics. They can help you organize data so you can see patterns and trends in the data, which can then be analyzed by the methods described in later chapters of this text. In this section, we present an example of using tabular and graphical methods in a sample report. Each of the remaining chapters contains a sample report incorporating the concepts developed in that respective chapter.

Camilla Walford is a newly hired journalist for a national newspaper. One of her first tasks is to analyze gas prices in the United States during the week of the Fourth of July holiday. She collects average gas prices (in $ per gallon) for the 48 contiguous states and the District of Columbia (DC), a portion of which is shown in Table 2.17.

TABLE 2.17 U.S. Gas Prices, July 2, 2010

FILE
Gas_Prices_2010

State	Price
Alabama	2.59
Arkansas	2.60
⋮	⋮
Wyoming	2.77

Source: *AAA's Daily Fuel Gauge Report*, July 2, 2010.

Camilla wants to use the sample information to

1. Construct frequency distributions to summarize the data.
2. Make summary statements concerning gas prices.
3. Convey the information from the distributions into graphical form.

Historically, in the United States, many people choose to take some time off during the Fourth of July holiday period and travel to the beach, the lake, or the mountains. The roads tend to be heavily traveled, making the cost of gas a concern. The following report provides an analysis of gas prices across the nation over this holiday period.

The analysis focuses on the average gas price for the 48 contiguous states and the District of Columbia (henceforth, referenced as 49 states for ease of exposition). The range of gas prices is from a low of $2.52 per gallon (South Carolina) to a high of $3.15 per gallon (California). To find out how gas prices are distributed between these extremes, the data have been organized into several frequency distributions as shown in Table 2.A. For instance, most states (17 of the 49) have an average gas price between $2.70 and $2.80 per gallon.

TABLE 2.A Frequency Distributions for Gas Prices in the United States, July 2, 2010

Average Price ($ per gallon)	Frequency	Relative Frequency	Cumulative Frequency	Cumulative Relative Frequency
2.50 up to 2.60	5	0.10	5	0.10
2.60 up to 2.70	13	0.27	18	0.37
2.70 up to 2.80	17	0.35	35	0.72
2.80 up to 2.90	8	0.16	43	0.88
2.90 up to 3.00	4	0.08	47	0.96
3.00 up to 3.10	1	0.02	48	0.98
3.10 up to 3.20	1	0.02	49	1.00
	Sample Size = 49			

Equivalently, looking at the relative frequency column, 35% of the states have an average price in this range. The cumulative frequency column indicates that 35 states have an average price less than $2.80 per gallon. Finally, the last column shows that the average price in 72% of the states (approximately three-quarters of the sample) is less than $2.80 per gallon. Figure 2.A shows a histogram for gas prices, which graphs the frequency distribution from Table 2.A. This graph reinforces the fact that the average price of gas nationwide is between $2.50 and $3.20 per gallon. Moreover, gas prices are positively skewed since the distribution runs off to the right; only two states (California and Washington) have gas prices that are more than $3.00 per gallon.

FIGURE 2.A Histogram of average gas prices nationwide

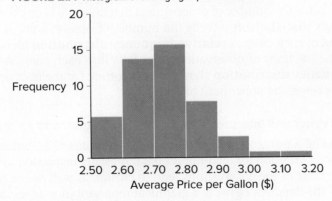

Another useful visual representation of the data is an ogive, shown in Figure 2.B. The ogive graphs the cumulative relative frequency distribution from Table 2.A. The ogive is useful for approximating the "middle" price. If we draw a horizontal line to the ogive at the 0.5 relative frequency mark, it intersects the plot at a point corresponding on the horizontal axis to a "middle price" of approximately $2.75. This indicates that gas stations in approximately half of the states charged below this price and half charged above it.

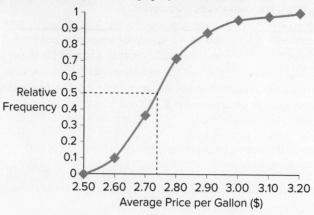

FIGURE 2.B Ogive of average gas prices nationwide

CONCEPTUAL REVIEW

LO 2.1 Summarize qualitative data by constructing a frequency distribution.

For qualitative data, a **frequency distribution** groups data into categories and records the number of observations that fall into each category. A **relative frequency distribution** shows the proportion (or the fraction) of observations in each category.

LO 2.2 Construct and interpret a pie chart and a bar chart.

Graphically, we can show a frequency distribution for qualitative data by constructing a **pie chart** or a **bar chart**. A pie chart is a segmented circle that clearly portrays the categories of some qualitative variable. A bar chart depicts the frequency or the relative frequency for each category of the qualitative variable as a series of horizontal or vertical bars, the lengths of which are proportional to the values that are to be depicted.

LO 2.3 Summarize quantitative data by constructing a frequency distribution.

For quantitative data, a **frequency distribution** groups data into intervals called classes, and records the number of observations that falls into each class. A **cumulative frequency distribution** records the number of observations that falls below the upper limit of each class. A **relative frequency distribution** identifies the proportion (or the fraction) of observations that falls into each class. A **cumulative relative frequency distribution** shows the proportion (or the fraction) of observations that falls below the upper limit of each class.

LO 2.4 Construct and interpret a histogram, a polygon, and an ogive.

A **histogram** and a **polygon** are graphical representations of a frequency or a relative frequency distribution for quantitative data. A casual inspection of these graphs reveals where most of the observations tend to cluster, as well as the general shape and spread of the data. An **ogive** is a graphical representation of a cumulative frequency or cumulative relative frequency distribution.

LO 2.5 Construct and interpret a stem-and-leaf diagram.

A **stem-and-leaf diagram** is another visual method of displaying quantitative data. It is constructed by separating each value of a data set into a *stem*, which consists of the leftmost digits, and a *leaf*, which consists of the last digit. Like a histogram and a polygon, a stem-and-leaf diagram gives an overall picture of where the data are centered and how the data are dispersed from the center.

LO 2.6 **Construct and interpret a scatterplot.**

A **scatterplot** is a graphical tool that helps in determining whether or not two quantitative variables are related in some systematic way. Each point in the diagram represents a pair of observed values of the two variables.

ADDITIONAL EXERCISES AND CASE STUDIES

Exercises

50. A 2003 survey by the Centers for Disease Control and Prevention concluded that smoking is forbidden in nearly 75% of U.S. households (*The Boston Globe*, May 25, 2007). The survey gathered responses from at least 900 households in each state. When residents of Utah were asked whether or not smoking was allowed in their households, a representative sample of responses was as follows:

No	No	No	No	No	No	Yes	No	No	No
No	Yes	No	No	No	No	No	No	No	No

When a similar survey was taken in Kentucky, a representative sample of responses was as follows:

No	No	Yes	No	Yes	No	Yes	Yes	No	No
No	Yes	Yes	No	Yes	No	No	Yes	Yes	No

a. Construct a relative frequency distribution that summarizes the responses of residents from Utah and Kentucky. Comment on the results.

b. Construct a bar chart that summarizes the results for each state.

51. Patrons at a local restaurant were asked to rate their recent experience at the restaurant with respect to its advertised atmosphere of upbeat, comfortable, and clean. Possible responses included Outstanding, Good, OK, and Horrible. The following table shows the responses of 28 patrons:

Horrible	OK	Horrible	Horrible
OK	OK	Horrible	Horrible
Horrible	OK	Horrible	Good
Horrible	Good	Good	Good
Horrible	OK	Horrible	OK
Good	Good	Horrible	Good
Horrible	OK	Horrible	Good

a. Construct a relative frequency distribution that summarizes the responses of the patrons. Briefly summarize your findings. What recommendations would you make to the owner of the restaurant?

b. Construct a pie chart and a bar chart for these data.

52. A survey conducted by CBS News asked parents about the professions they would want their children to pursue. Parents' preferences (in %) are summarized in the following table.

Profession	Parents' Preference
Doctor, banker, lawyer, or president	65
Internet mogul	13
Humanitarian-aid worker	6
Athlete	9
Movie star, rock star	2
Other	5

Source: *Vanity Fair*, December 2009.

a. Construct a pie chart and a bar chart for these data.

b. How many parents wanted their children to become athletes if the results were based on 550 responses?

53. The one-year return (in %) for 24 mutual funds is as follows:

−14.5	−5.0	−3.7	2.5	−7.9	−11.2
4.8	−16.8	9.0	6.5	8.2	5.3
−12.2	15.9	18.2	25.4	3.4	−1.4
5.5	−4.2	−0.5	6.0	−2.4	10.5

a. Construct the frequency distribution using classes of −20 up to −10, −10 up to 0, etc.

b. Construct the relative frequency, the cumulative frequency, and the cumulative relative frequency distributions.

c. How many of the funds had returns of at least 0% but less than 10%? How many of the funds had returns of 10% or more?

d. What percentage of the funds had returns of at least 10% but less than 20%? What percent of the funds had returns less than 20%?

54. *The Statistical Abstract of the United States, 2010* provided the following frequency distribution of the number of people (in 1,000s) who live below the poverty level by region.

Region	Number of People
Northeast	6,166
Midwest	7,237
South	15,501
West	8,372

a. Construct the relative frequency distribution. What percentage of people who live below the poverty level live in the Midwest?

b. Construct a pie chart and a bar chart for these data.

55. *Money* magazine (January 2007) reported that an average of 77 million adults in the United States make financial resolutions at the beginning of a new year. Consider the following frequency distribution, which reports the top financial resolutions of 1,026 Americans (MONEY/ICR poll conducted November 8–12, 2006).

Financial Resolution	Frequency
Saving more	328
Paying down debt	257
Making more income	154
Spending less	133
Investing more	103
Saving for a large purchase	41
Don't know	10

a. Construct the relative frequency distribution. What percentage of the respondents indicated that paying down debt was their top financial resolution?

b. Graph the bar chart.

56. A recent poll of 3,057 individuals asked: "What's the longest vacation you plan to take this summer?" The following relative frequency distribution summarizes the results.

Response	Relative Frequency
A few days	0.21
A few long weekends	0.18
One week	0.36
Two weeks	0.25

a. Construct the frequency distribution. How many people are going to take a one-week vacation this summer?

b. Graph the pie chart.

57. A survey conducted by CBS News asked 1,026 respondents: "What would you do with an unexpected tax refund?" The responses (in %) are summarized in the following table.

Pay off debts	47
Put it in the bank	30
Spend it	11
I never get a refund	10
Other	2

Copyright © CBS News Archives. Used with permission.

a. Graph the bar chart.

b. How many people will spend the tax refund?

58. The following table reports the number of people as well as the number of people living below the poverty level across regions in the U.S. for the year 2013. (All numbers are in 1,000s.)

Region	Total	Below Poverty Level
Northeast	55,478	7,046
Midwest	66,785	8,590
South	116,961	18,870
West	73,742	10,812

Source: www.census.gov/hhes/www/poverty/data/incpovhlth/2013/table3.pdf, data retrieved March 23, 2015.

a. Graph and interpret the pie chart that summarizes the proportion of people living in each region.

b. Graph and interpret the pie chart that summarizes the proportion of people living below the poverty level in each region. Is this pie chart consistent with the one you constructed in part (a); that is, in those regions that are relatively less populated, is the proportion of people living below the poverty level less?

59. The manager at a water park constructed the following frequency distribution to summarize attendance in July and August.

Attendance	Frequency
1,000 up to 1,250	5
1,250 up to 1,500	6
1,500 up to 1,750	10
1,750 up to 2,000	20
2,000 up to 2,250	15
2,250 up to 2,500	4

a. Construct the relative frequency, cumulative frequency, and cumulative relative frequency distributions.

b. What is the most likely attendance range? How many times was attendance less than 2,000 people?

c. What percentage of the time was attendance at least 1,750 but less than 2,000 people? What percentage of the time was attendance less than 1,750 people? What percentage of the time was attendance 1,750 or more?

d. Graph the relative frequency histogram. Comment on the shape of the distribution.

60. *The Wall Street Journal* (August 28, 2006) asked its readers: "Ideally, how many days a week, if any, would you work from home?" The following relative frequency distribution summarizes the responses from 3,478 readers.

Days Working from Home	Relative Frequency
0	0.12
1	0.18
2	0.30
3	0.15
4	0.07
5	0.19

Graph the pie chart and the bar chart to summarize the data.

61. A researcher conducts a mileage economy test involving 80 cars. The frequency distribution describing average miles per gallon (mpg) appears in the following table.

Average mpg	Frequency
15 up to 20	15
20 up to 25	30
25 up to 30	15
30 up to 35	10
35 up to 40	7
40 up to 45	3

a. Construct the relative frequency, cumulative frequency, and cumulative relative frequency distributions.

b. How many of the cars got less than 30 mpg? What percentage of the cars got at least 20 but less than 25 mpg? What percentage of the cars got less than 35 mpg? What percent got 35 mpg or more?

c. Graph the relative frequency histogram. Comment on the shape of the distribution.

62. **FILE** *Wealthiest_Americans.* The accompanying table lists a portion of the ages and net worth (in $ billions) of the wealthiest people in America.

Name	Age	Net Worth
William Gates III	53	50.0
Warren Buffet	79	40.0
⋮	⋮	⋮
Philip Knight	71	9.5

Source: *Forbes*, Special Report, September 2009.

a. What percentage of the wealthiest people in America had net worth more than $20 billion?

b. What percentage of the wealthiest people in America had net worth between $10 billion and $20 billion?

c. Construct a stem-and-leaf diagram on age. Comment on the shape of the distribution.

63. **FILE** *DOW_PEG.* The price-to-earnings growth ratio, or PEG ratio, is the market's valuation of a company relative to its earnings prospects. A PEG ratio of 1 indicates that the stock's price is in line with growth expectations. A PEG ratio less than 1 suggests that the stock of the company is undervalued (typical of value stocks), whereas a PEG ratio greater than 1 suggests the stock is overvalued (typical of growth stocks). The accompanying table shows a portion of PEG ratios of companies listed on the Dow Jones Industrial Average.

Company	PEG Ratio
3M (MMM)	1.4
Alcoa (AA)	0.9
⋮	⋮
Walt Disney (DIS)	1.2

Source: www.finance.yahoo, data retrieved April 13, 2011.

Construct the stem-and-leaf diagram on the PEG ratio. Interpret your findings.

64. The following table lists the sale price (in $1,000s) and type of 20 recently sold houses in New Jersey.

Price	Type	Price	Type
305	Ranch	568	Colonial
450	Colonial	385	Other
389	Contemporary	310	Contemporary
525	Other	450	Colonial
300	Ranch	400	Other
330	Contemporary	359	Ranch
355	Contemporary	379	Ranch
405	Colonial	509	Colonial
365	Ranch	435	Colonial
415	Ranch	510	Other

a. Construct a frequency distribution for types of houses sold in New Jersey. Interpret the results.

b. Construct a frequency distribution for house prices sold in New Jersey. Use six classes, starting with 300, each with a width of 50. Interpret the results.

65. A manager of a local retail store analyzes the relationship between Advertising (in $100s) and Sales (in $1,000s) by reviewing the store's data for the previous six months. Construct a scatterplot and comment on whether or not a relationship exists.

Advertising	Sales
20	15
25	18
30	20
22	16
27	19
26	20

66. The following table lists the National Basketball Association's (NBA's) leading scorers, their average minutes per game (MPG), and their average points per game (PPG) for 2008:

Player	MPG	PPG
D. Wade	38.6	30.2
L. James	37.7	28.4
K. Bryant	36.1	26.8
D. Nowitzki	37.3	25.9
D. Granger	36.2	25.8
K. Durant	39.0	25.3
C. Paul	38.5	22.8
C. Anthony	34.5	22.8
C. Bosh	38.0	22.7
B. Roy	37.2	22.6

Source: www.espn.com.

Construct and interpret a scatterplot of PPG against MPG. Does a relationship exist between the two variables?

CASE STUDIES

CASE STUDY 2.1 There are six broad sectors that comprise the Dow Jones Industrial Average (DJIA). These are the areas in which the company conducts its primary business. The following table shows a portion of the 30 companies that comprise the DJIA and each company's sector.

FILE

DJIA_Sector

Data for Case Study 2.1 Companies and Sectors of the DJIA

Company	Sector
3M (MMM)	Manufacturing
American Express (AXP)	Finance
⋮	⋮
Walmart (WMT)	Consumer

Source: www.money.cnn.com/data/dow30/, information retrieved March 21, 2015.

In a report, use the sample information to

1. Construct the frequency distribution and the relative frequency distribution for the sectors that comprise the DJIA. Use pie charts for data visualization.

2. Discuss how the various sectors are represented in the DJIA.

CASE STUDY 2.2 When reviewing the overall strength of a particular firm, financial analysts typically examine the net profit margin. This statistic is generally calculated as the ratio of a firm's net profit after taxes (net income) to its revenue, expressed as a percentage. For example, a 20% net profit margin means that a firm has a net income of $0.20 for each dollar of sales. A net profit margin can even be negative if the firm has a negative net income. In general, the higher the net profit margin, the more effective the firm is at converting revenue into actual profit. The net profit margin serves as a good way of comparing firms in the same industry, since such firms generally are subject to the same business conditions. However, financial analysts also use the net profit margin to compare firms in different industries in order to gauge which firms are relatively more profitable. The accompanying table shows a portion of net profit margins (in %) for a sample of clothing retailers.

Data for Case Study 2.2 Net Profit Margin for Clothing Retailers

Firm	Net Profit Margin
Abercrombie & Fitch	1.58
Aéropostale	10.64
⋮	⋮
Wet Seal	16.15

Source: www.finance.yahoo.com, data retrieved July 2010.

In a report, use the sample information to

1. Provide a brief definition of net profit margin and explain why it is an important statistic.

2. Construct appropriate tables (frequency distribution, relative frequency distribution, etc.) and graphs that summarize the clothing industry's net profit margin. Use −5, 0, 5, and so on, for the upper limits of the classes for the distributions.

3. Discuss where the data tend to cluster and how the data are spread from the lowest value to the highest value.

4. Comment on the net profit margin of the clothing industry, as compared to the beverage industry's net profit margin of approximately 10.9% (Source: biz.yahoo, July 2010).

CASE STUDY 2.3   The following table lists a portion of U.S. life expectancy (in years) for the 50 states.

Data for Case Study 2.3 Life Expectancy by State, 2010–2011

Rank	State	Life Expectancy
1	Hawaii	81.5
2	Minnesota	80.9
⋮	⋮	⋮
50	Mississippi	74.8

Source: en.wikipedia.org/wiki/List_of_U.S._states_by_life_expectancy, data retrieved April 25, 2012.

In a report, use the sample information to

1. Construct appropriate tables (frequency distribution, relative frequency distribution, etc.) and graphs to summarize life expectancy in the United States. Use 75, 76.5, 78, and so on, for the upper limits of the classes for the distributions.

2. Discuss where the data tend to cluster and how the data are spread from the lowest value to the highest value.

3. Comment on the shape of the distribution.

APPENDIX 2.1   Guidelines for Other Software Packages

The following section provides brief commands for Minitab, SPSS, and JMP. Copy and paste the specified data file into the relevant software spreadsheet prior to following the commands.

Minitab

Pie Chart

Marital_Status

A. (Replicating Figure 2.1) From the menu, choose **Graph > Pie Chart**. Select **Chart values from a table**, select Marital Status as the **Categorical variable**, and 1960 and 2010 as the **Summary variables**.

B. Choose **Labels**. Select **Titles/Footnotes** and enter Marital Status, 1960 versus 2010. Then select **Slice Labels** and select **Category name** and **Percent**.

C. Choose **Multiple Graphs**, and then select **On the same graph**.

Bar Chart

Marital_Status

A. (Replicating Figure 2.2) From the menu, choose **Graph > Bar Chart**. From **Bars Represent** select **Values from a Table**, and from **Two-way Table** select **Cluster**.

B. In the *Bar Chart—Two-Way Table—Cluster* dialog box, select 1960 and 2010 as **Graph variables**. Select Marital Status as **Row labels**. Under **Table Arrangement**, choose **Rows are outermost categories and columns are innermost**.

Histogram

From Raw Data:

MV_Houses

A. (Replicating Figure 2.5) From the menu, choose **Graph > Histogram > Simple**. Click **OK**.

B. Select House Price as **Graph Variables**. Click **OK**.

C. Double-click *x*-axis and select **Edit Scale**. Under **Major Tick Positions**, choose **Position of Ticks** and enter 300 400 500 600 700 800. Under **Scale Range**, deselect **Auto** for *Minimum* and enter 300. Then deselect **Auto** for *Maximum* and enter 800. Select the **Binning** tab. Under **Interval Type**, select **Cutpoint**. Under **Interval Definition**, select **Midpoint/Cutpoint Definitions** and enter 300 400 500 600 700 800.

From a Frequency Distribution:

MV_Frequency

A. (Replicating Figure 2.5) From the menu, choose **Graph > Bar Chart**. From **Bars Represent** select **A function of a variable**, and from **One Y** select **Simple**. Click **OK**.

B. Under **Function** select **Sum**. Under **Graph variables** select **Frequency,** and under **Categorical variable** select **Class (in $1,000s)**.

C. Double-click *x*-axis. Under **Space Between Scale Categories**, deselect **Gap between Cluster** and enter 0.

Polygon

Polygon

A. (Replicating Figure 2.8) From the menu, choose **Graph > Scatterplot > With Connect Line**.

B. Under **Y variables** select y, and under **X variables** select x.

Ogive

A. (Replicating Figure 2.9) From the menu, choose **Graph > Scatterplot > With Connect Line**.

B. Under **Y variables** select y, and under **X variables** select x.

FILE
Ogive

Scatterplot

A. (Replicating Figure 2.14) From the menu, choose **Graph > Scatterplot > Simple**.

B. Under **Y variables** select Income, and under **X variables** select Education.

FILE
Edu_Inc

SPSS

Pie Chart

A. (Replicating Figure 2.1) From the menu, choose **Graphs > Legacy Dialogs > Pie**. Under **Data in Chart Are**, select **Values of individual cases**. Click **Define**.

B. Under **Slices Represent**, select 1960. Under **Slices Labels**, select **Variable**, then select Marital Status.

C. Double-click on the graph to open **Chart Editor**, and then choose **Elements > Show Data Labels**. In the **Properties** dialog box, under **Displayed** select Percent and Marital Status.

FILE
Marital_Status

Bar Chart

A. (Replicating Figure 2.2) From the menu, choose **Graphs > Legacy Dialogs > Bar**. Choose **Clustered**. Under **Data in Chart Are**, select **Values of individual cases**. Click **Define**.

B. Under **Bars Represent**, select 1960 and 2010. Under **Category Labels**, select **Variable**, then select Marital Status.

FILE
Marital_Status

Histogram

A. (Replicating Figure 2.5) From the menu, choose **Graphs > Legacy Dialogs > Histogram**. Under **Variable**, select HousePrice.

B. In the Output window, double-click on Frequency (y-axis title), choose the **Scale** tab, and under **Range**, enter 0 as **Minimum**, 15 as **Maximum**, and 5 as **Major Increment**. Then click **Apply**.

C. Double-click on the bars. Choose the **Binning** tab, and under **X Axis**, select **Custom** and **Interval width**, and enter 100 for the interval width. Then click **Apply**.

FILE
MV_Houses

Polygon

A. (Replicating Figure 2.8) From the menu, choose **Graphs > Legacy Dialogs > Scatter/Dot**. Choose **Simple Scatter** and then click **Define**.

B. Under **Y Axis** select y, and under **X Axis** select x. Click **OK**.

C. In the Output window, double-click on the graph to open the **Chart Editor**, then from the menu choose **Elements > Interpolation Line**.

FILE
Polygon

Ogive

A. (Replicating Figure 2.9) From the menu, choose **Graphs > Legacy Dialogs > Scatter/Dot**. Choose **Simple Scatter**. Then click **Define**.

B. Under **Y Axis**, select y, and under **X Axis**, select x. Click **OK**.

FILE
Ogive

C. In the Output window, double-click on the graph to open the **Chart Editor**, then from the menu choose **Elements > Interpolation Line**. Then click **Apply**. From the menu choose **Edit > Select X Axis**. Choose the **Scale** tab, and under **Range**, enter 300 as **Minimum**, 800 as **Maximum**, 100 as **Major Increment**, and 300 as **Origin**. Then click **Apply**.

Scatterplot

Edu_Inc

A. (Replicating Figure 2.14) From the menu, choose **Graphs > Legacy Dialogs > Scatter/Dot**. Choose **Simple Scatter**. Then click **Define**.
B. Under **Y Axis**, select Income, and under **X Axis**, select Education. Click **OK**.
C. In the Output window, double-click on the graph to open the **Chart Editor**. From the menu, choose **Edit > Select Y Axis**. Under **Range**, enter 0 as **Minimum**, 120 as **Maximum**, and 20 as **Major Increment**. Then click **Apply**. From the menu choose **Edit > Select X Axis**. Choose the **Scale** tab, and under **Range**, enter 0 as **Minimum**, 10 as **Maximum**, and 2 as **Major Increment**. Then click **Apply**.

JMP

Pie Chart

Marital_Status

(Replicating Figure 2.1) From the menu, choose **Graph > Chart**. Under **Select Columns**, select Marital Status, and then under **Cast Selected Columns into Roles**, select **Categories, X, Levels**. Under **Select Columns**, select 1960 and 2010, and then select **Statistics > % of Total**. Under **Options**, choose **Pie Chart**. In order to add percentages to the pie chart, click the red arrow next to **Chart > Label Options > Label by Percent of Total Values**.

Bar Chart

Marital_Status

(Replicating Figure 2.2) From the menu, choose **Graph > Chart**. Under **Select Columns**, select **Marital Status**, and then under **Cast Selected Columns into Roles**, select **Categories, X, Levels**. Under Select Columns, select 1960 and 2010, and select **Statistics > Data**. Under **Options**, select **Overlay** and **Bar Chart**.

Histogram

MV_Houses

A. (Replicating Figure 2.5) From the menu, choose **Analyze > Distribution**. Under **Select Columns**, select House Price, then under **Cast Selected Columns into Roles**, select **Y, columns**.
B. Right-click on the *y*-axis and select **Axis Settings**. For **Minimum**, enter 300; for **Maximum** enter 800; and for **Increment**, enter 100. (JMP automatically produces a histogram in a vertical layout. In order to change the layout to horizontal, click the red arrow next to **House Price > Display Options > Horizontal Layout**.)

Polygon

Polygon

A. (Replicating Figure 2.8) From the menu, choose **Graph > Overlay Plot**. Under **Select Columns**, select x, and then under **Cast Selected Columns into Roles**, select **X**. Under **Select Columns**, select y, and then under **Cast Selected Columns into Roles**, select **Y**.
B. Click on the red triangle next to the title **Overlay Plot**. Select **Y Options > Connect Points**.

Ogive

A. (Replicating Figure 2.9) From the menu, choose **Graph > Overlay Plot**. Under **Select Columns**, select x, and then under **Cast Selected Columns into Roles**, select **X**. Under **Select Columns**, select y, and then under **Cast Selected Columns into Roles**, select **Y**.

B. Click on the red triangle next to the title **Overlay Plot**. Select **Y Options > Connect Points**.

Ogive

Scatterplot

(Replicating Figure 2.14) From the menu, choose **Graph > Overlay Plot**. Under **Select Columns**, select Education, and then under **Cast Selected Columns into Roles**, select **X**. Under **Select Columns**, select Income, and then under **Cast Selected Columns into Roles**, select **Y**.

Edu_Inc

3 Numerical Descriptive Measures

LEARNING OBJECTIVES

After reading this chapter you should be able to:

LO **3.1** Calculate and interpret measures of central location.

LO **3.2** Interpret a percentile and a boxplot.

LO **3.3** Calculate and interpret a geometric mean return and an average growth rate.

LO **3.4** Calculate and interpret measures of dispersion.

LO **3.5** Explain mean-variance analysis and the Sharpe ratio.

LO **3.6** Apply Chebyshev's theorem, the empirical rule, and z-scores.

LO **3.7** Calculate summary measures for grouped data.

LO **3.8** Calculate and interpret measures of association.

In Chapter 2, we used tables and graphs in order to extract meaningful information from data. In this chapter, we focus on numerical descriptive measures. These measures provide precise, objectively determined values that are easy to calculate, interpret, and compare with one another. We first calculate several measures of central location, which attempt to find a typical or central value for the data. In addition to analyzing the center, we examine how the data vary around the center. Measures of dispersion gauge the underlying variability of the data. We use measures of central location and dispersion to introduce some popular applications, including the Sharpe ratio, Chebyshev's theorem, the empirical rule, and the z-score. Finally, we discuss measures of association that examine the linear relationship between two variables. These measures assess whether two variables have a positive linear relationship, a negative linear relationship, or no linear relationship.

©Mark Bowden/Getty Images RF

INTRODUCTORY CASE

Investment Decision

Jacqueline Brennan works as a financial advisor at a large investment firm. She meets with an inexperienced investor who has some questions regarding two approaches to mutual fund investing: growth investing versus value investing. The investor has heard that growth funds invest in companies whose stock prices are expected to grow at a faster rate, relative to the overall stock market, and value funds invest in companies whose stock prices are below their true worth. The investor has also heard that the main component of investment return is through capital appreciation in growth funds and through dividend income in value funds. The investor shows Jacqueline the annual return data for Vanguard's Growth Index mutual fund (henceforth, Growth) and Vanguard's Value Index mutual fund (henceforth, Value). Table 3.1 shows the annual return data for these two mutual funds for the years 2007–2016.

TABLE 3.1 Returns (in percent) for the Growth and the Value Funds

Year	Growth	Value	Year	Growth	Value
2007	12.56	0.09	2012	16.89	15.00
2008	−38.32	−35.97	2013	32.16	32.85
2009	36.29	19.58	2014	13.47	13.05
2010	16.96	14.28	2015	3.17	−1.03
2011	1.71	1.00	2016	5.99	16.75

Source: finance.yahoo.com, data retrieved February 17, 2017.

In addition to clarifying the style differences in growth investing versus value investing, Jacqueline will use the above sample information to

1. Calculate and interpret the typical return for these two mutual funds.
2. Calculate and interpret the investment risk for these two mutual funds.
3. Determine which mutual fund provides the greater return relative to risk.

A synopsis of this case is provided at the end of Section 3.5.

Calculate and interpret
measures of central location.

The term *central location* relates to the way quantitative data tend to cluster around some middle or central value. Measures of central location attempt to find a typical or central value that describes the data. Examples include finding a typical value that describes the return on an investment, the number of defects in a production process, the salary of a business graduate, the rental price in a neighborhood, the number of customers at a local convenience store, and so on.

The Mean

The **arithmetic mean** is the primary measure of central location. Generally, we refer to the arithmetic mean as simply the **mean** or the **average**. In order to calculate the mean of a data set, we simply add up the values of all the data points and divide by the number of data points in the population or sample.

EXAMPLE 3.1

Let's use the data in Table 3.1 in the introductory case to calculate and interpret the mean return for the Growth mutual fund and the mean return for the Value mutual fund.

SOLUTION: Let's start with the mean return for the Growth mutual fund. We first add all the returns and then divide by the number of returns as follows:

$$\text{Growth mutual fund mean return} = \frac{12.56 + (-38.32) + \cdots + 5.99}{10}$$

$$= \frac{100.88}{10} = 10.09\%.$$

Similarly, we calculate the mean return for the Value mutual fund as:

$$\text{Value mutual fund mean return} = \frac{0.09 + (-35.97) + \cdots + 16.75}{10}$$

$$= \frac{75.60}{10} = 7.56\%.$$

Thus, over the 10-year period 2007–2016, the mean return for the Growth mutual fund was greater than the mean return for the Value mutual fund, or equivalently, 10.09% > 7.56%. These means represent typical annual returns resulting from one-year investments. We will see throughout this chapter, however, that we would be ill-advised to invest in a mutual fund solely on the basis of its average return.

All of us have calculated a mean before. What might be new for some of us is the notation used to express the mean as a formula. For instance, when calculating the mean return for the Growth mutual fund, we let $x_1 = 12.56$, $x_2 = -38.32$, and so on, and let n represent the number of observations in the sample. So our calculation for the mean can be written as

$$\text{Mean} = \frac{x_1 + x_2 + \cdots + x_{10}}{n}.$$

The mean of the sample is referred to as $\bar{x}$ (pronounced x-bar). Also, we can denote the numerator of this formula using summation notation, which yields the following compact formula for the **sample mean**: $\bar{x} = \frac{\Sigma x_i}{n}$. We should also point out that if we had all the return data for this mutual fund, instead of just the data for the past 10 years, then we would have been able to calculate the **population mean** μ as $\mu = \frac{\Sigma x_i}{N}$, where μ is the Greek letter mu (pronounced as "mew") and N is the number of observations in the population.

MEASURE OF CENTRAL LOCATION: THE MEAN

For sample values $x_1, x_2, \ldots, x_n$, the sample mean $\bar{x}$ is computed as

$$\bar{x} = \frac{\Sigma x_i}{n}.$$

For population values $x_1, x_2, \ldots, x_N$, the population mean μ is computed as

$$\mu = \frac{\Sigma x_i}{N}.$$

The calculation method is identical for the sample mean and the population mean except that the sample mean uses n observations and the population mean uses N observations, where $n < N$. We refer to the population mean as a **parameter** and the sample mean as a **statistic**. Since the population mean is generally unknown, we often use the sample mean to estimate the population mean.

The mean is used extensively in statistics. However, it can give a misleading description of the center of the distribution in the presence of extremely small or large values, also referred to as **outliers**.

The mean is the most commonly used measure of central location. One weakness of this measure is that it is unduly influenced by outliers.

Example 3.2 highlights the main weakness of the mean.

EXAMPLE 3.2

Seven people work at Acetech, a small technology firm in Seattle. Their salaries (in $) over the past year are listed in Table 3.2. Compute the mean salary for this firm and discuss whether it accurately indicates a typical value.

TABLE 3.2 Salaries of Employees at Acetech

Title	Salary
Administrative Assistant	40,000
Research Assistant	40,000
Computer Programmer	65,000
Senior Research Associate	90,000
Senior Sales Associate	145,000
Chief Financial Officer	150,000
President (and owner)	550,000

SOLUTION: Since the salaries of all employees of Acetech are included in Table 3.2, we calculate the population mean salary as:

$$\mu = \frac{\Sigma x_i}{N} = \frac{40,000 + 40,000 + \cdots + 550,000}{7} = 154,286.$$

It is true that the mean salary for this firm is $154,286, but this value does not reflect the typical salary at this firm. In fact, six of the seven employees earn less than $154,286. This example highlights the main weakness of the mean — that is, it is very sensitive to extreme observations (extremely large or extremely small values), or outliers.

The Median

Since the mean can be affected by outliers, we often also calculate the **median** as a measure of central location. The median is the middle value of a data set. It divides the data in half; an equal number of observations lie above and below the median. Many government publications and other data sources publish both the mean and the median in order to accurately portray a data set's typical value. If the values of the mean and the median differ significantly, then it is likely that the data set contains outliers. For instance, in 2015 the U.S. Census Bureau determined that the median income for American households was $52,353, whereas the mean income was $71,932. It is well documented that a small number of households in the United States have income considerably higher than the typical American household income. As a result, these top-earning households influence the mean by pushing its value significantly above the value of the median.

MEASURE OF CENTRAL LOCATION: THE MEDIAN

The median is the middle value of a data set. The data are arranged in ascending order (smallest to largest) and the median is calculated as

- The middle value if the number of observations is odd, or
- The average of the two middle values if the number of observations is even.

The median is especially useful when outliers are present.

EXAMPLE 3.3

Use the data in Table 3.2 to calculate the median salary of employees at Acetech.

SOLUTION: In Table 3.2, the data are already arranged in ascending order. We reproduce the salaries along with their relative positions.

Position:	1	2	3	4	5	6	7
Value:	40,000	40,000	65,000	90,000	145,000	150,000	550,000

Given seven salaries, the median occupies the 4th position. Thus, the median is $90,000. Three salaries are less than $90,000 and three salaries are greater than $90,000. As compared to the mean income of $154,286, the median in this case better reflects the typical salary.

EXAMPLE 3.4

Use the data in Table 3.1 in the introductory case to calculate and interpret the median returns for the Growth and the Value mutual funds.

SOLUTION: Let's start with the median return for the Growth mutual fund. We first arrange the data in ascending order:

Position:	1	2	3	4	5	6	7	8	9	10
Value:	−38.32	1.71	3.17	5.99	12.56	13.47	16.89	16.96	32.16	36.29

Given 10 observations, the median is the average of the values in the 5th and 6th positions. These values are 12.56 and 13.47, so the median is $\frac{12.56 + 13.47}{2} = 13.02$. Over the period 2007–2016, the Growth mutual fund had a median return of 13.02%, which indicates that 5 years had returns less than 13.02% and 5 years had returns greater than 13.02%. For the Growth mutual fund, the median return of 13.02% differs from the mean return of 10.09% by approximately 3 percentage points. For the Value mutual fund, a similar comparison of these two measures of central location reveals a bigger gap. The median return of 13.67% (calculations not shown) is more than 6 percentage points greater than the mean return of 7.56%. This result is not surprising since a casual inspection of the data reveals that the relative magnitude of very small values is larger for the Value mutual fund. In order to give a more transparent description of a data's center, it is wise to report both the mean and the median.

The Mode

The **mode** of a data set is the value that occurs most frequently. A data set can have more than one mode, or even no mode. For instance, if we try to calculate the mode return for either the Growth mutual fund or the Value mutual fund in Table 3.1, we see that no value in either mutual fund occurs more than once. Thus, there is no mode value for either mutual fund. If a data set has one mode, then we say it is unimodal. If two or more modes exist, then the data set is multimodal; it is common to call it bimodal in the case of two modes. Generally, the mode's usefulness as a measure of central location tends to diminish with data sets that have more than three modes.

> ### MEASURE OF CENTRAL LOCATION: THE MODE
> The mode is the most frequently occurring value in a data set. A data set may have no mode or more than one mode.

EXAMPLE 3.5

Use the data in Table 3.2 to calculate the modal salary for employees at Acetech.

SOLUTION: The salary $40,000 is earned by two employees. Every other salary occurs just once. So $40,000 is the modal salary. Just because a value occurs with the most frequency does not guarantee that it best reflects the center of the data. It is true that the modal salary at Acetech is $40,000, but most employees earn considerably more than this amount.

In the preceding examples, we used measures of central location to describe quantitative data. However, in many instances we want to summarize qualitative data, where the mode is the only meaningful measure of central location.

EXAMPLE 3.6

Kenneth Forbes is a manager at the University of Wisconsin campus bookstore. There has been a recent surge in the sale of women's sweatshirts, which are available in three sizes: Small (S), Medium (M), and Large (L). Kenneth notes that the campus bookstore sold 10 sweatshirts over the weekend in the following sizes:

©Sebastian Pfeutze/Taxi/Getty Images

S	L	L	M	S	L	M	L	L	M

Comment on the data set and use the appropriate measure of central location that best reflects the typical size of a sweatshirt.

SOLUTION: This data set is an example of qualitative data. Here, the mode is the only relevant measure of central location. The modal size is L since it appears 5 times, as compared to S and M, which appear 2 and 3 times, respectively. Often, when examining issues relating to the demand for a product, such as replenishing stock, the mode tends to be the most relevant measure of central location.

The Weighted Mean

So far we have focused on applications where each observation in the data contributed equally to the mean. The **weighted mean** is relevant when some observations contribute more than others. For example, a student is often evaluated on the basis of the weighted mean since the score on the final exam is typically worth more than the score on the midterm.

> ### MEASURE OF CENTRAL LOCATION: THE WEIGHTED MEAN
>
> Let $w_1, w_2, \ldots, w_n$ denote the weights of the sample observations $x_1, x_2, \ldots, x_n$ such that $w_1 + w_2 + \cdots + w_n = 1$. The weighted mean for the sample is computed as
> $$\bar{x} = \Sigma w_i x_i.$$
> The weighted mean for the population is computed similarly.

EXAMPLE 3.7

A student scores 60 on Exam 1, 70 on Exam 2, and 80 on Exam 3. What is the student's average score for the course if Exams 1, 2, and 3 are worth 25%, 25%, and 50% of the grade, respectively?

SOLUTION: We define the weights as $w_1 = 0.25$, $w_2 = 0.25$, and $w_3 = 0.50$. We compute the average score as $\bar{x} = \Sigma w_i x_i = 0.25(60) + 0.25(70) + 0.50(80) = 72.50$. Note that the unweighted mean is only 70 because it does not incorporate the higher weight given to the score on Exam 3.

Using Excel and R to Calculate Measures of Central Location

In general, Excel and R offer a couple of ways to calculate most of the descriptive measures that we discuss in this chapter. To illustrate, we follow the these steps to calculate the mean for the Growth mutual fund.

Using Excel's Formula Option

Excel provides built-in formulas for virtually every summary measure that we may need. To illustrate, we follow these steps to calculate the mean for the fund.

A. Open the **Growth_Value** data (Table 3.1).

B. From the menu choose **Formulas > Insert Function**. In the *Insert Function* dialog box, choose **Statistical** under *Select a Category*. Here you will see a list of all the relevant summary measures that Excel calculates.

C. Since we want to calculate the mean return for the Growth mutual fund, under *Select a Function,* choose **AVERAGE**. Click **OK**.

D. See Figure 3.1. In the *Average* dialog box, click on the box to the right of *Number 1* and then select the Growth data. Click **OK**. You should see the value 10.088, which, when rounded to two decimal places, equals the value that we calculated manually. In order to calculate the median and the mode, we repeat these steps, but we choose MEDIAN and MODE as the functions instead of AVERAGE.

FILE
Growth_Value

FIGURE 3.1 Excel's AVERAGE dialog box

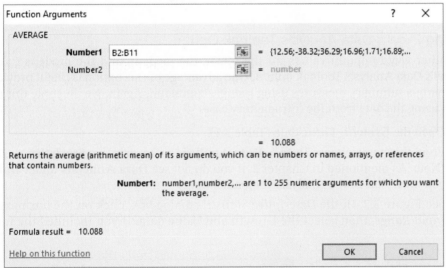

Once you get familiar with Excel's function names, an easier way to perform these calculations is to select an empty cell in the spreadsheet and input "=Function Name(array)", where you replace Function Name with Excel's syntax for that particular function and select the relevant data for the array or input the cell designations. For example, if we want to calculate the mean return for the Growth mutual fund, and we know that the data occupy cells B2 through B11 on the spreadsheet, we input "=AVERAGE(B2:B11)". After choosing <Enter>, Excel returns the function result in the cell. When introducing new functions later in this chapter and other chapters, we will follow this format. The first and second columns of Table 3.3 show various descriptive measures and corresponding function names in Excel. We will refer back to Table 3.3 on numerous occasions in this chapter.

TABLE 3.3 Descriptive Measures and Corresponding Function Names in Excel and R

Descriptive Measure	Excel	R
Location		
Mean	=AVERAGE(array)	mean(datafile\$'varname')[a]
Median	=MEDIAN(array)	median(datafile\$'varname')
Mode	=MODE(array)	NA[b]
Minimum	=MIN(array)	min(datafile\$'varname')
Maximum	=MAX(array)	max(datafile\$'varname')
Multiple measures	NA	summary(datafile)
Dispersion		
Range	=MAX(array)-MIN(array)	range(datafile\$'varname')[c]
Mean Absolute Deviation	=AVEDEV(array)	mad(datafile\$'varname')[d]
Sample Variance	=VAR.S(array)	var(datafile\$'varname')
Sample Standard Deviation	=STDEV.S(array)	sd(datafile\$'varname')
Population Variance	=VAR.P(array)	NA
Population Standard Deviation	=STDEV.P(array)	NA
Association		
Sample Covariance	=COVARIANCE.S(array1,array2)	cov(datafile)
Population Covariance	=COVARIANCE.P(array1,array2)	NA
Correlation	=CORREL(array1,array2)	cor(datafile)

[a]Within the parentheses, datafile refers to the name of the data file and varname refers to the variable name within the data file.

[b]NA denotes that a simple function is not readily available.

[c]Since R returns the minimum and maximum values, the range is easily calculated by taking the difference.

[d]By default, R calculates the median absolute deviation, rather than the mean absolute deviation. The "aad" function uses the mean rather than the median in the calculation of MAD, but it requires the installation of the "lsr" package.

Using Excel's Data Analysis Toolpak Option

Another way to obtain values for the mean, the median, and the mode is to use Excel's Data Analysis Toolpak option. One advantage of this option is that it provides numerous summary measures using a single command. Again, we illustrate this option using the data from the introductory case.

FILE
Growth_Value

A. Open the ***Growth_Value*** data (Table 3.1).

B. From the menu, choose **Data > Data Analysis > Descriptive Statistics > OK**. (Note: As mentioned in Chapter 2, if you do not see **Data Analysis** under **Data**, you must *Add-in* the Analysis Toolpak option.)

C. See Figure 3.2. In the *Descriptive Statistics* dialog box, click on the box next to *Input Range*, then select the Growth and Value data. If you included the fund

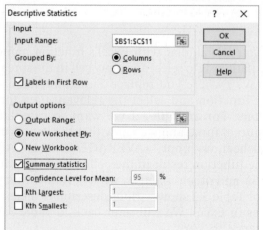

FIGURE 3.2 Excel's Descriptive Statistics dialog box

names when you highlighted the data, make sure you click on the option next to *Labels in First Row*. Click the box in front of *Summary Statistics*. Then click **OK**.

D. Table 3.4 presents the Excel output. If the output is difficult to read, highlight the output and choose **Home > Format > Column > Autofit Selection**. As noted earlier, Excel provides numerous summary measures; we have put the measures of central location in boldface. (Measures of dispersion are also in boldface; we analyze these measures in more detail shortly.) Note that Excel reports the mode as #N/A, which means no value is available; this is consistent with our finding that no value in the data appeared more than once.

TABLE 3.4 Excel's Output Using Descriptive Statistics Dialog Box

Growth		Value	
Mean	**10.088**	**Mean**	**7.56**
Standard Error	6.46609616	Standard Error	5.837290277
Median	**13.015**	**Median**	**13.665**
Mode	**#N/A**	**Mode**	**#N/A**
Standard Deviation	**20.44759144**	**Standard Deviation**	**18.45913264**
Sample Variance	**418.1039956**	**Sample Variance**	**340.7395778**
Kurtosis	3.416405191	Kurtosis	3.262709799
Skewness	−1.380719627	Skewness	−1.418700256
Range	74.61	Range	68.82
Minimum	−38.32	Minimum	−35.97
Maximum	36.29	Maximum	32.85
Sum	100.88	Sum	75.6
Count	10	Count	10

Using R

Before following all R instructions, make sure that you have read Appendix A ("Getting Started with R"). We assume that you have downloaded R and RStudio, and that you know how to import an Excel file.

Throughout the text, our goal is to provide the simplest way to obtain the relevant output. Like Excel, R has many built-in formulas or functions. We denote all function names in **boldface** and all options within a function in *italics*. The first and third columns of Table 3.3 show various descriptive measures and corresponding function names in R.

A. Import the *Growth_Value* data into a data frame (table) in R.

B. The **mean** function will return the mean for a specified variable in a data frame. As outlined in Appendix A, we are able to choose variables from a data frame by attaching the expression $'variable name' to the data frame. In order to find the mean for the Growth mutual fund, enter:

```
> mean(Growth_Value$'Growth')
```

And R returns: 10.088.

FILE
Growth_Value

C. The **summary** function will return the minimum, first quartile, median, mean, third quartile, and maximum values for each variable in a data frame. Enter:

```
> summary(Growth_Value)
```

And R returns:

Year*	Growth	Value
Min. :2007	Min. :-38.320	Min. :-35.9700
1st Qu.:2009	1st Qu.: 3.875	1st Qu.: 0.3175
Median :2012	Median : 13.015	Median : 13.6650
Mean :2012	Mean : 10.088	Mean : 7.5600
3rd Qu.:2014	3rd Qu.: 16.942	3rd Qu.: 16.3125
Max. :2016	Max. : 36.290	Max. : 32.8500

*Note that nonnumerical (usually categorical) data will produce results that are often not meaningful. In this example, the summary statistics for the variable Year are not useful. Also, the values for the first and third quartiles differ from the ones that we will calculate in Section 3.2; the reasons for the differences will be addressed in Section 3.2.

Note on Symmetry

In Chapter 2, we used histograms to discuss **symmetry** and **skewness**. Recall that the distribution is symmetric if one side of the histogram is a mirror image of the other side. For a symmetric and unimodal distribution, the mean, the median, and the mode are equal. In business applications, it is common to encounter data that are skewed. The mean is usually greater than the median when the data are positively skewed and less than the median when the data are negatively skewed. We would also like to comment on the numerical measure of skewness that Excel reports in Table 3.4, even though we will not discuss its calculation. A skewness coefficient of zero indicates the data values are evenly distributed on both sides of the mean. A positive skewness coefficient implies that extreme values are concentrated in the right tail of the distribution, pulling the mean up, relative to the median, and the bulk of values lie to the left of the mean. Similarly, a negative skewness coefficient implies that extreme values are concentrated in the left tail of the distribution, pulling the mean down, relative to the median, and the bulk of values lie to the right of the mean. For both mutual funds, we see that the returns are negatively skewed.

EXERCISES 3.1

Mechanics

1. Given the following observations from a sample, calculate the mean, the median, and the mode.

8	10	9	12	12

2. Given the following observations from a sample, calculate the mean, the median, and the mode.

−4	0	−6	1	−3	−4

3. Given the following observations from a population, calculate the mean, the median, and the mode.

150	257	55	110	110	43	201	125	55

4. Given the following observations from a population, calculate the mean, the median, and the mode.

20	15	25	20	10	15	25	20	15

Applications

5. At a small firm in Boston, seven employees were asked to report their one-way commute time (in minutes) into the city. Their responses were the following.

20	35	90	45	40	35	50

   a. How long was the shortest commute? The longest commute?

   b. Calculate the mean, the median, and the mode.

6. In order to get an idea on current buying trends, a real estate agent collects data on 10 recent house sales in the area. Specifically, she notes the number of bedrooms in each house as follows:

3	4	3	3	5	2	4	2	5	3

a. Calculate the mean, the median, and the mode.
b. Which measure of central location best reflects the typical value with respect to the number of bedrooms in recent house sales?

7. The following table shows the 10 highest-paid chief executive officers of the last decade.

Name	Firm	Compensation (in $ millions)
Lawrence Ellison	Oracle	1,835.7
Barry Diller	IAC, Expedia	1,142.9
Ray Irani	Occidental Petroleum	857.1
Steve Jobs	Apple	748.8
Richard Fairbank	Capital One	568.5
Angelo Mozilo	Countrywide	528.6
Eugene Isenberg	Nabors Industries	518.0
Terry Semel	Yahoo	489.6
Henry Silverman	Cendant	481.2
William McGuire	UnitedHealth Group	469.3

Source: *The Wall Street Journal*, July 27, 2010.

a. Calculate the mean compensation for the 10 highest-paid chief executive officers.
b. Does the mean accurately reflect the center of the data? Explain.

8. An investor bought common stock of Microsoft Corporation on three occasions at the following prices.

Date	Price Per Share	Number of Shares
January 2009	19.58	70
July 2009	24.06	80
December 2009	29.54	50

Calculate the average price per share at which the investor bought these shares.

9. You score 90 on the midterm, 60 on the final, and 80 on the class project. What is your average score if the midterm is worth 30%, the final is worth 50%, and the class project is worth 20%?

10. An investor bought common stock of Apple Inc. on three occasions at the following prices.

Date	Price Per Share
January 2016	94.81
July 2016	102.67
December 2016	115.32

a. What is the average price per share if the investor had bought 100 shares in January, 60 in July, and 40 in December?
b. What is the average price per share if the investor had bought 40 shares in January, 60 in July, and 100 in December?

11. **FILE** *ERA.* One important statistic in baseball is a pitcher's earned run average, or ERA. This number represents the average number of earned runs given up by the pitcher per nine innings. The following table lists a portion of the ERAs for pitchers playing for the New York Yankees and the Baltimore Orioles as of July 22, 2010.

New York Yankees	ERA	Baltimore Orioles	ERA
Sabathia	3.13	Guthrie	4.58
Pettitte	2.88	Millwood	5.77
⋮	⋮	⋮	⋮

Source: www.mlb.com.

a. Calculate the mean and the median ERAs for the New York Yankees.
b. Calculate the mean and the median ERAs for the Baltimore Orioles.
c. Based solely on your calculations above, which team is likely to have the better winning record? Explain.

12. **FILE** *Largest_Corporations.* The following table shows Fortune 500's rankings of America's 10 largest corporations for 2010. Next to each corporation is its market capitalization (in $ billions as of March 26, 2010) and its total return (in %) to investors for the year 2009.

Company	Mkt. Cap.	Total Return
Walmart	209	−2.7
Exxon Mobil	314	−12.6
Chevron	149	8.1
General Electric	196	−0.4
Bank of America	180	7.3
ConocoPhillips	78	2.9
AT&T	155	4.8
Ford Motor	47	336.7
JP Morgan Chase	188	19.9
Hewlett-Packard	125	43.1

Source: money.cnn.com, data retrieved May 3, 2010.

a. Calculate the mean and the median for market capitalization.
b. Calculate the mean and the median for total return.
c. For each variable (market capitalization and total return), comment on which measure better reflects central location.

13. **FILE** *MV_Houses.* The following table shows a portion of the sale price (in $1,000s) for 36 homes sold in Mission Viejo, CA, during June 2010.

Number	Price
1	430
2	520
⋮	⋮
36	430

Calculate the mean, the median, and the mode.

14. **FILE** *Gas_Prices_2012.* The accompanying table shows a portion of the average price of gas (in $ per gallon) for the 50 states in the United States.

State	Price
Alabama	4.36
Alaska	3.79
⋮	⋮
Wyoming	3.63

Source: AAA.com, data retrieved April 16, 2012.

Find the mean, the median, and the mode for the price per gallon in the U.S.

15. **FILE** *Life_Expectancy.* The following table lists a portion of U.S. life expectancy (in years) for the 50 states.

Rank	State	Life Expectancy
1	Hawaii	81.5
2	Alaska	80.9
⋮	⋮	⋮
50	Mississippi	74.8

Source: en.wikipedia.org/wiki/List_of_U.S._states_by_life _expectancy, data retrieved April 25, 2012.

Find the mean, the median, and the mode of life expectancy.

3.2 PERCENTILES AND BOXPLOTS

Interpret a percentile and a boxplot.

As discussed earlier, the median is a measure of central location that divides the data in half; that is, half of the data points fall below the median and half fall above the median. The median is also called the 50th percentile. In many instances, we are interested in a **percentile** other than the 50th percentile. Here we discuss calculating and interpreting percentiles. Generally, percentiles are calculated for large data sets; for ease of exposition, we show their use with a small data set. In addition, we construct a boxplot, which is, more or less, a visual representation of particular percentiles. It also helps us identify outliers and skewness in the data.

Percentiles provide detailed information about how data are spread over the interval from the smallest value to the largest value. You have probably been exposed to percentiles. For example, the SAT is the most widely used test in the undergraduate admissions process. Scores on the math portion of the SAT range from 200 to 800. Suppose you obtained a raw score of 650 on this section of the test. It may not be readily apparent how you did relative to other students that took the same test. However, if you know that the raw score corresponds to the 75th percentile, then you know that approximately 75% of students had scores lower than your score and approximately 25% of students had scores higher than your score.

PERCENTILES

In general, the pth percentile divides a data set into two parts:

- Approximately p percent of the observations have values less than the pth percentile.
- Approximately $(100 - p)$ percent of the observations have values greater than the pth percentile.

Calculating the *p*th Percentile

A. First arrange the data in ascending order (smallest to largest).

B. Locate the approximate position of the percentile by calculating L_p:

$$L_p = (n + 1)\frac{p}{100},$$

where L_p indicates the location of the desired *p*th percentile and *n* is the sample size; for the population percentile, replace *n* with *N*. For example, we set $p = 50$ for the median because it is the 50th percentile.

C. Once you find the value for L_p, observe whether or not L_p is an integer:

- If L_p is an integer, then L_p denotes the location of the *p*th percentile. For instance, if L_{20} is equal to 2, then the 20th percentile is equal to the second observation in the ordered data set.

- If L_p is not an integer, we need to interpolate between two observations to approximate the desired percentile. So if L_{20} is equal to 2.25, then we need to interpolate 25% of the distance between the second and third observations in order to find the 20th percentile.

EXAMPLE 3.8

Consider the information presented in the introductory case of this chapter. Calculate and interpret the 25th and the 75th percentiles for the Growth mutual fund.

SOLUTION: The first step is to arrange the data in ascending order:

Position:	1	2	3	4	5	6	7	8	9	10
Value:	−38.32	1.71	3.17	5.99	12.56	13.47	16.89	16.96	32.16	36.29

For the 25th percentile: $L_{25} = (n + 1)\frac{p}{100} = (10 + 1)\frac{25}{100} = 2.75$. So, the 25th percentile is located 75% of the distance between the second and third observations; it is calculated as

$$1.71 + 0.75(3.17 - 1.71) = 1.71 + 1.10 = 2.81.$$

Thus, approximately 25% of the returns were less than 2.81%, and approximately 75% of the returns were greater than 2.81%.

For the 75th percentile: $L_{75} = (n + 1)\frac{p}{100} = (10 + 1)\frac{75}{100} = 8.25$. So, the 75th percentile is located 25% of the distance between the eighth and ninth observations; it is calculated as

$$16.96 + .25(32.16 - 16.96) = 16.96 + 3.80 = 20.76.$$

Thus, approximately 75% of the returns were less than 20.76%, and approximately 25% of the returns were greater than 20.76%.

Earlier, we calculated the median or the 50th percentile for the Growth mutual fund and obtained a value of 13.02%. When we calculate the 25th, the 50th, and the 75th percentiles for a data set, we have effectively divided the data into four equal parts, or quarters. Thus, the 25th percentile is also referred to as the first quartile (Q1), the 50th percentile is referred to as the second quartile (Q2), and the 75th percentile is referred to as the third quartile (Q3).

Note on Calculating Percentiles

As mentioned in the introduction, the use of percentiles is most meaningful for large data sets. The use of a small data set in this section is simply for expositional purposes. In addition, software packages, like Excel and R, use different algorithms to calculate percentiles. Differences in values tend to be more dramatic with small sample sizes. With larger sample sizes, the differences, if any, tend to be negligible.

Constructing and Interpreting a Boxplot

The minimum value (Min), the quartiles (Q1, Q2, and Q3), and the maximum value (Max) are often referred to as the five-number summary of a data set. Table 3.5 shows the five-number summary for the Growth mutual fund. A **boxplot**, also referred to as a box-and-whisker plot, is a convenient way to graphically display the five-number summary of a data set.

TABLE 3.5 Summary Values for the Growth Mutual Fund

Min	Q1	Q2	Q3	Max
−38.32	2.81	13.02	20.76	36.29

Boxplots are particularly useful when comparing similar information gathered at another place or time. They are also an effective tool for identifying outliers and skewness. In Section 3.1, we discussed that the mean is unduly influenced by outliers. Sometimes outliers may indicate bad data due to incorrectly recorded observations or incorrectly included observations in the data set. In such cases, the relevant observations should be corrected or simply deleted from the data set. Alternatively, outliers may just be due to random variations, in which case the relevant observations should remain in the data set. In any event, it is important to be able to identify potential outliers so that one can take corrective actions, if needed.

In order to construct a boxplot, we follow these steps.

A. Plot the five-number summary values in ascending order on the horizontal axis.

B. Draw a box encompassing the first and third quartiles.

C. Draw a dashed vertical line in the box at the median.

D. To determine if a given observation is an outlier, first calculate the difference between Q3 and Q1. This difference is called the **interquartile range** or IQR. Therefore, the length of the box is equal to the IQR and the span of the box contains the middle half of the data. Draw a line ("whisker") that extends from Q1 to the minimum data value that is not farther than $1.5 \times$ IQR from Q1. Similarly, draw a line that extends from Q3 to the maximum data value that is not farther than $1.5 \times$ IQR from Q3.

E. Use an asterisk (or comparable symbol) to indicate points that are farther than $1.5 \times$ IQR from the box. These points are considered outliers.

Consider the boxplot in Figure 3.3 for illustration. In the figure, the left whisker extends from Q1 to Min since Min is not farther than $1.5 \times$ IQR from Q1. The right whisker, on the other hand, does not extend from Q3 to Max since there is an observation that is farther than $1.5 \times$ IQR from Q3. The asterisk on the right indicates that this observation is considered an outlier.

Boxplots are also used to informally gauge the shape of the distribution. Symmetry is implied if the median is in the center of the box and the left and right whiskers are equidistant from their respective quartiles. If the median is left of center and the right whisker is longer than the left whisker, then the distribution is positively skewed. Similarly, if the median is right of center and the left whisker is longer than the right whisker, then the distribution is negatively skewed. If outliers exist, we need to include them when comparing the lengths of the left and right whiskers. From Figure 3.3, we note that the median is located to the left of center and that an outlier exists on the right side. Here the right whisker is longer than the left whisker, and, if the outlier is included, then the right whisker becomes even longer. This indicates that the underlying distribution is positively skewed.

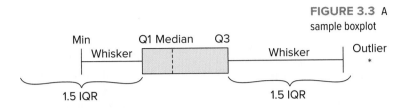

FIGURE 3.3 A sample boxplot

EXAMPLE 3.9

Use the information in Table 3.5 to construct and interpret the boxplot for the Growth mutual fund.

SOLUTION: Based on the information in Table 3.5, we calculate the IQR as the difference between Q3 and Q1, or IQR = 20.76 − 2.81 = 17.95. We then calculate $1.5 \times$ IQR = 1.5×17.95 = 26.93. The distance between Q1 and the smallest value, 2.81 − (−38.32) = 41.13, exceeds the limit of 26.93, thus the value −38.32 is considered an outlier and will be designated as such. The next smallest value in the data set is 1.71. The distance between Q1 and this value, 2.81 − 1.71 = 1.10, is well within the limit of 26.93, so the left whisker will extend up to the point 1.71. The distance between the largest value and Q3, 36.29 − 20.76 = 15.53, is also within the limit of 26.93, so the right whisker will extend to the maximum value of 36.29. See Figure 3.4.

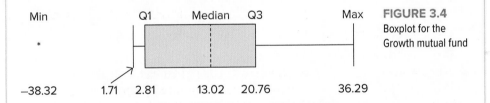

FIGURE 3.4
Boxplot for the Growth mutual fund

From this boxplot we can quickly grasp several points concerning the distribution of returns for the Growth mutual fund. First, returns range from −38.32% to 36.29%, with about half being less than 13.02% and half being greater than 13.02%. We make two further observations: (1) the median is off-center within the box, being located to the right of center, and (2) the outlier on the left side implies that if the left whisker were to continue to this outlier, the left whisker would be longer than the right whisker. These two observations suggest the distribution is negatively skewed.

Using R to Construct a Boxplot

Since a boxplot is an effective way to compare the distributions of two variables, we will construct boxplots using the return information for the Growth and Value mutual funds.

A. Import the **Growth_Value** data into a data frame (table) in R.

FILE
Growth_Value

B. We create a boxplot using the **boxplot** function. For options within the function, we use *xlab* to label the *x*-axis, *names* to label each variable, and *horizontal* to construct a horizontal boxplot, rather than a vertical boxplot. Enter:

```
> boxplot(Growth_Value$'Growth', Growth_Value$'Value',
   xlab="Annual Returns, 2007-2016 (in percent)", names
   =c("Growth","Value"), horizontal = TRUE)
```

Figure 3.5 shows the output that R returns.

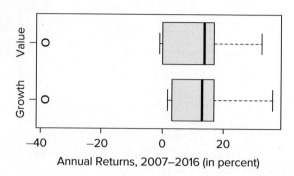

FIGURE 3.5 Boxplots of annual returns for the Growth and Value mutual funds, 2007–2016

Over this 10-year period, it appears that the return behavior for these two mutual funds has been similar. We already found that the median returns for both funds were close (13.02% for the Growth fund versus 13.67% for the Value mutual fund), and this is indicated by the bold and wider vertical lines in Figure 3.5. Also, each fund has one outlier on the left-hand side, as indicated by the circle. This finding, plus the fact that the median falls to the right of center in the interquartile range, suggests that both distributions are negatively skewed. This is not surprising because we found in Section 3.1 that each fund had a negative skewness coefficient. Finally, it seems like the Growth mutual fund has returns that are slightly more spread out than the Value mutual fund. We explore this concept of dispersion in Section 3.4.

EXERCISES 3.2

Mechanics

16. Calculate the 20th, 50th, and 80th percentiles for the following data set:

120	215	187	343	268	196	312

17. Calculate the 20th, 40th, and 70th percentiles for the following data set:

−300	−257	−325	−234	−297	−362	−255

18. Consider the following boxplot.

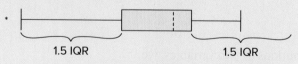

a. Does the boxplot indicate possible outliers in the data?
b. Comment on the skewness of the underlying distribution.

19. Consider the following boxplot.

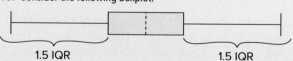

a. Does the boxplot indicate possible outliers in the data?
b. Comment on the skewness of the underlying distribution.

20. Consider the following five-point summary that was obtained from a data set with 200 observations.

Min	Q1	Median	Q3	Max
34	54	66	78	98

a. Interpret Q1 and Q3.
b. Calculate the interquartile range. Determine whether any outliers exist.
c. Is the distribution symmetric? If not, comment on its skewness.

21. Consider the following five-point summary that was obtained from a data set with 500 observations.

Min	Q1	Median	Q3	Max
125	200	300	550	1300

a. Interpret Q1 and Q3.
b. Calculate the interquartile range. Determine whether any outliers exist.
c. Is the distribution symmetric? If not, comment on its skewness.

Applications

22. Consider the return data (in percent) for the Value mutual fund in Table 3.1.
a. Calculate and interpret the 25th, 50th, and 75th percentiles.
b. Calculate the interquartile range. Are there any outliers?
c. Is the distribution symmetric? If not, comment on its skewness.

23. Scores on the final in a statistics class are as follows.

75	25	75	52	80	85	80	99	90	60
86	92	40	74	72	55	87	70	85	70

a. Calculate and interpret the 25th, 50th, and 75th percentiles.
b. Calculate the interquartile range. Are there any outliers?
c. Is the distribution symmetric? If not, comment on its skewness.

24. **FILE** *Census.* The accompanying table shows a portion of median household income (Income in $) and median house value (House Value in $) for the 50 states in 2010.

State	Income	House Value
Alabama	42081	117600
Alaska	66521	229100
⋮	⋮	⋮
Wyoming	53802	174000

Source: 2010 U.S. Census.

a. Construct a boxplot for household income and use it to identify outliers, if any, and comment on skewness.
b. Construct a boxplot for median house value and use it to identify outliers, if any, and comment on skewness.

25. **FILE** *PE_Ratio.* A price-earnings ratio or P/E ratio is calculated as a firm's share price compared to the income or profit earned by the firm per share. Generally, a high P/E ratio suggests that investors are expecting higher earnings growth in the future compared to companies with a lower P/E ratio. The accompanying table shows a portion of companies that comprise the Dow Jones Industrial Average (DJIA) and their P/E ratios as of May 17, 2012 (at the time data were retrieved, the P/E ratio for Bank of America was not available).

Company	P/E Ratio
3M (MMM)	14
Alcoa (AA)	24
⋮	⋮
Walt Disney (DIS)	14

a. Calculate and interpret the 25th, 50th, and 75th percentiles.
b. Construct a boxplot. Are there any outliers? Is the distribution symmetric? If not, comment on its skewness.

3.3 THE GEOMETRIC MEAN

LO 3.3

The **geometric mean** is a multiplicative average, as opposed to an additive average (the arithmetic mean). It is the relevant measure when evaluating investment returns over several years, as well as when calculating average growth rates.

Calculate and interpret a geometric mean return and an average growth rate.

The Geometric Mean Return

Suppose you invested $1,000 in a stock that had a 10% return in 2016 and a −10% return in 2017. The arithmetic mean suggests that by the end of year 2017, you would be right back where you started with $1,000 worth of stock. It is true that the arithmetic mean return over the two-year period is 0% $\left(\bar{x} = \frac{0.10 + (-0.10)}{2} = 0 \right)$; however, the arithmetic mean ignores the effects of compounding. As shown in Table 3.6, the value of your investment at the end of two years is $990, a loss of $10. The geometric mean **return** accurately captures a negative annual return from the two-year investment period.

TABLE 3.6 End of Year Holdings Given an Initial Investment of $1,000

Year	Return %	Value at the End of Year
2016	10	1,000 + 1,000(0.10) = 1,100
2017	−10	1,100 + 1,100(−0.10) = 990

THE GEOMETRIC MEAN RETURN

For multiperiod returns $R_1, R_2, \ldots, R_n$, the geometric mean return G_R is computed as

$$G_R = \sqrt[n]{(1 + R_1)(1 + R_2) \cdots (1 + R_n)} - 1,$$

where n is the number of multiperiod returns.

Let us revisit the above case where you invested $1,000 in a stock that had a 10% return in 2016 and a −10% return in 2017. The geometric mean is computed as

$$G_R = \sqrt[2]{(1 + 0.10)(1 + (-0.10))} - 1 = ((1.10)(0.90))^{1/2} - 1 = -0.005, \text{ or } -0.5\%.$$

We interpret the geometric mean return as the **annualized return** that you will earn from a two-year investment period. Table 3.7 shows that with the computed annualized return of −0.5%, the end investment value is the same as shown in Table 3.6.

TABLE 3.7 End-of-Year Holdings Given an Initial Investment of $1,000

Year	Annualized Return	Value at the End of Year
2016	−0.5	1,000 + 1,000(−0.005) = 995
2017	−0.5	995 + 995(−0.005) = 990

EXAMPLE 3.10

Use the data in Table 3.1 to calculate the geometric mean for the Growth and the Value mutual funds.

SOLUTION:

$$\text{Growth: } G_R = \sqrt[10]{(1 + 0.1256)(1 - 0.3832) \cdots (1 + 0.0599)} - 1$$

$$= (2.1576)^{1/10} - 1 = 0.0799, \text{ or } 7.99\%.$$

$$\text{Value: } G_R = \sqrt[10]{(1 + 0.0009)(1 - 0.3597) \cdots (1 + 0.1675)} - 1$$

$$= (1.7653)^{1/10} - 1 = 0.0585, \text{ or } 5.85\%.$$

Therefore, for the 10-year period, the annualized return for the Growth mutual fund is higher than that of the Value mutual fund, 7.99% > 5.85%.

Arithmetic Mean versus Geometric Mean

An issue that begs for explanation is the relevance of the arithmetic mean and the geometric mean as summary measures for financial returns. Both means are relevant descriptive measures for annual return; however, each has a different interpretation. The arithmetic mean is appropriate for analyzing a one-year investment, whereas the geometric mean is appropriate for analyzing a multiyear investment.

For the Growth mutual fund, the arithmetic mean return of 10.09% is the average annual return for summarizing returns with an investment horizon of one year. Its geometric mean return of 7.99% is the average annual return when the investment horizon is 10 years. For illustration, we can think of the arithmetic mean return as the relevant metric for an investor who is saving/investing to buy a house in about a year's time. The geometric mean return is the relevant metric for an investor who is saving for retirement.

The Average Growth Rate

We also use the geometric mean when we calculate an **average growth rate**.

THE AVERAGE GROWTH RATE

For growth rates $g_1, g_2, \ldots, g_n$, the average growth rate G_g is computed as:

$$G_g = \sqrt[n]{(1 + g_1)(1 + g_2) \cdots (1 + g_n)} - 1$$

where n is the number of multiperiod growth rates.

EXAMPLE 3.11

Table 3.8 shows sales for Adidas (in millions of €) for the years 2011 through 2015.

TABLE 3.8 Sales for Adidas (in millions of €), 2011–2015

Year	2011	2012	2013	2014	2015
Sales	13,322	14,883	14,203	14,534	16,915

Source: Annual Report of Adidas Group, data retrieved February 22, 2017.

Calculate the growth rates for 2011–2012, 2012–2013, 2013–2014, and 2014–2015 and use them to compute the average growth rate.

SOLUTION: The growth rates for Adidas for four years are computed as:

- 2011–2012: $\dfrac{14{,}883 - 13{,}322}{13{,}322} = 0.1172$

- 2012–2013: $\dfrac{14{,}203 - 14{,}883}{14{,}883} = -0.0457$

- 2013–2014: $\dfrac{14{,}534 - 14{,}203}{14{,}203} = 0.0233$

- 2014–2015: $\dfrac{16{,}915 - 14{,}534}{14{,}534} = 0.1638$

Therefore,

$$G_g = \sqrt[4]{(1 + 0.1172)(1 - 0.0457)(1 + 0.0233)(1 + 0.1638)} - 1$$

$$= 1.2697^{1/4} - 1 = 0.0615, \text{ or } 6.15\%.$$

Sales for Adidas from 2011 to 2015 had an average growth rate of 6.15% per year.

There is a simpler way to compute the average growth rate when the underlying values of the series are given. In the above example, it is cumbersome to first calculate the relevant growth rates and then use them to compute the average growth rate.

AN ALTERNATIVE FORMULA FOR THE AVERAGE GROWTH RATE

For observations $x_1, x_2, \ldots, x_n$, the average growth rate G_g is computed as

$$G_g = \sqrt[n-1]{\frac{x_n}{x_{n-1}} \frac{x_{n-1}}{x_{n-2}} \frac{x_{n-2}}{x_{n-3}} \cdots \frac{x_2}{x_1}} - 1 = \sqrt[n-1]{\frac{x_n}{x_1}} - 1,$$

where $n - 1$ is the number of distinct growth rates. Note that only the first and last observations are needed in the time series due to cancellations in the formula.

EXAMPLE 3.12

Calculate the average growth rate for Adidas directly from the sales data in Table 3.8.

SOLUTION: Using the first and last observations from the time series consisting of five observations, we calculate

$$G_g = \sqrt[n-1]{\frac{x_n}{x_1}} - 1 = \sqrt[5-1]{\frac{16,915}{13,322}} - 1 = 1.2697^{1/4} - 1 = 0.0615, \text{ or } 6.15\%,$$

which is the same as in Example 3.11.

EXERCISES 3.3

Mechanics

26. Given the following investment returns, calculate the geometric mean return.

| 4% | 8% | −5% | 6% |

27. Given the following investment returns, calculate the geometric mean return.

| −3% | 2% | −5% | 2.7% | 3.1% |

28. The returns for a pharmaceutical firm are 10% in Year 1, 5% in Year 2, and −15% in Year 3. What is the annualized return for the period?

29. The returns from an investment are 2% in Year 1, 5% in Year 2, and 1.8% in the first half of Year 3. Calculate the annualized return for the entire period.

30. The returns for an auto firm are 5% in Year 1 and 3% in the first quarter of Year 2. Calculate the annualized return for the period.

31. Consider the following observations for a time series:

Year 1	Year 2	Year 3	Year 4
90	110	150	160

   a. Calculate the growth rates for Year 1–Year 2, Year 2–Year 3, and Year 3–Year 4.
   b. Calculate the average growth rate.

32. Consider the following observations for a time series:

Year 1	Year 2	Year 3	Year 4
1,200	1,280	1,380	1,520

   a. Calculate the growth rates for Year 1–Year 2, Year 2–Year 3, and Year 3–Year 4.
   b. Calculate the average growth rate.

33. Calculate the average growth rate from the following growth rates.

| 2.5% | 3.6% | 1.8% | 2.2% | 5.2% |

Applications

34. Suppose at the beginning of 2012 you decide to invest $1,000 in Vanguard's European Stock Index mutual fund. The following table shows the returns (in %) for the years 2012–2015.

Year	Annual Return
2012	17.3
2013	19.6
2014	6.8
2015	8.2

Source: finance.yahoo.com.

   a. Calculate and interpret the arithmetic mean return.
   b. Calculate and interpret the geometric mean return.
   c. How much money would you have accumulated by the end of 2015?

35. Home Depot and Lowe's are the two largest home improvement retailers in the U.S. The following table shows the total revenue (in $ billions) for each retailer for the years 2008–2010.

Year	Home Depot	Lowe's
2008	77.35	48.28
2009	71.29	48.23
2010	66.18	47.22

Source: Annual Reports of Home Depot, Inc., and Lowe's Companies Inc.

a. Calculate the growth rate for 2008–2009 and 2009–2010 for each retailer.
b. Calculate the average growth rate for each retailer.

36. Suppose at the beginning of 2012 you decide to invest $20,000 in Driehaus' Emerging Markets Growth mutual fund. The following table shows the returns (in %) for the years 2012–2016.

Year	Annual Return
2012	19.5
2013	8.9
2014	−6.0
2015	−10.5
2016	5.9

Source: finance.yahoo.com.

a. Calculate and interpret the arithmetic mean return.
b. Calculate and interpret the geometric mean return.
c. How much money would you have accumulated by the end of 2016?

37. The following table shows the total revenue (in $ billions) for Walmart Stores, Inc., and Target Corp. for the years 2008–2010.

Year	2008	2009	2010
Walmart	379.8	404.3	408.2
Target	63.4	65.0	65.3

Source: Annual Reports of Walmart Stores, Inc., and Target Corp.

a. Calculate the average growth rate for each firm.
b. Which firm had the higher growth rate over the 2008–2010 period?

38. The following table shows sales for Nike (in $ millions) for the years 2011 through 2015.

Year	2011	2012	2013	2014	2015
Sales	20,117	23,331	25,313	27,799	30,601

Source: Annual Reports of Nike, Inc.

a. Use the growth rates for 2011–2012, 2012–2013, 2013–2014, and 2014–2015 to calculate the average growth rate.
b. Calculate the average growth rate directly from sales.

3.4 MEASURES OF DISPERSION

LO 3.4

Calculate and interpret measures of dispersion.

In Section 3.1, we focused on measures of central location in an attempt to find a typical or central value that describes the data. It is also important to analyze how the data vary around the center. Recall that over the 10-year period 2007–2016, the average returns for the Growth and Value mutual funds were 10.09% and 7.56%, respectively. As an investor, you might ask why anyone would put money in the Value mutual fund when, on average, this fund has a lower return. The answer to this question will become readily apparent once we analyze measures of variability or dispersion.

Table 3.9 shows each fund's minimum and maximum returns, as well as each fund's average return, over this time period. Note that the minimum and the maximum values for the Growth mutual fund are more extreme compared to the Value mutual fund; that is, the minimum value is smaller (−38.32% < −35.97%) and the maximum value is larger (36.29% > 32.85%). This indicates that returns for the Growth mutual fund may be more dispersed from the mean. The comparison of the funds illustrates that the average is not sufficient when summarizing a data set; that is, it fails to describe the underlying variability of the data.

TABLE 3.9 Select Measures for the Growth and Value Mutual Funds, 2007–2016

	Minimum Return	Average Return	Maximum Return
Growth	−38.32%	10.09%	36.29%
Value	−35.97%	7.56%	32.85%

We now discuss several measures of dispersion that gauge the variability of a data set. Each measure is a numerical value that equals zero if all data values are identical, and increases as data values become more diverse.

Range

The **range** is the simplest measure of dispersion; it is the difference between the maximum value and the minimum value in a data set.

> ### MEASURE OF DISPERSION: THE RANGE
> The range is calculated by taking the difference between the maximum value (Max) and minimum value (Min) in a data set:
> $$\text{Range} = \text{Max} - \text{Min}$$

EXAMPLE 3.13

Use the data in Table 3.9 to calculate the range for the Growth and the Value mutual funds.

SOLUTION:
Growth: $36.29\% - (-38.32\%) = 74.61\%$
Value: $32.85\% - (-35.97\%) = 68.82\%$

The Growth mutual fund has the higher value for the range, indicating that it has more dispersion with respect to its minimum and maximum values.

The range is not considered a good measure of dispersion because it focuses solely on the extreme values and ignores every other observation in the data set. While the interquartile range, $\text{IQR} = \text{Q3} - \text{Q1}$, discussed in Section 3.2, does not depend on extreme values, this measure still does not incorporate all the data.

The Mean Absolute Deviation

A good measure of dispersion should consider differences of all observations from the mean. If we simply average all differences from the mean, the positives and the negatives will cancel out, even though they both contribute to dispersion, and the resulting average will equal zero. The **mean absolute deviation** (MAD) is an average of the absolute differences between the observations and the mean.

> ### MEASURE OF DISPERSION: THE MEAN ABSOLUTE DEVIATION (MAD)
> For sample values, $x_1, x_2, \ldots, x_n$, the sample MAD is computed as
> $$\text{Sample MAD} = \frac{\Sigma|x_i - \bar{x}|}{n}.$$
> For population values, $x_1, x_2, \ldots, x_N$, the population MAD is computed as
> $$\text{Population MAD} = \frac{\Sigma|x_i - \mu|}{N}.$$

EXAMPLE 3.14

Use the data in Table 3.1 to calculate MAD for the Growth and the Value mutual funds.

SOLUTION: We first compute MAD for the Growth mutual fund. The second column in Table 3.10 shows differences from the sample mean, $\bar{x} = 10.09$. As mentioned earlier, the sum of these differences equals zero (or a number very close to zero due to rounding). The third column shows the absolute value of each deviation from the mean. Summing these values yields the numerator for the MAD formula.

TABLE 3.10 MAD Calculations for the Growth Mutual Fund

x_i	$x_i - \bar{x}$	$|x_i - \bar{x}|$
12.56	$12.56 - 10.09 = 2.47$	2.47
−38.32	$-38.32 - 10.09 = -48.41$	48.41
⋮	⋮	⋮
5.99	$5.99 - 10.09 = -4.10$	4.10
	Total = 0 (subject to rounding)	Total = 135.60

For the Growth mutual fund: $\text{MAD} = \frac{\Sigma|x_i - \bar{x}|}{n} = \frac{135.60}{10} = 13.56$.

Similar calculations for the Value mutual fund yield: $\text{MAD} = \frac{\Sigma|x_i - \bar{x}|}{n} = \frac{132.30}{10} = 13.23$.

The Value mutual fund has a slightly smaller value for MAD than the Growth mutual fund, again indicating a less dispersed data set.

The Variance and the Standard Deviation

The **variance** and the **standard deviation** are the two most widely used measures of dispersion. Instead of calculating the average of the absolute differences from the mean, as in MAD, we calculate the average of the squared differences from the mean. The squaring of differences from the mean emphasizes larger differences more than smaller ones; MAD weighs large and small differences equally.

The variance is defined as the average of the squared differences between the observations and the mean. The formula for the variance differs depending on whether we have a sample or a population. Also, whatever the units of the original data, the variance has squared units. In order to return to the original units of measurement, we take the positive square root of variance, which gives us the standard deviation.

MEASURES OF DISPERSION: THE VARIANCE AND THE STANDARD DEVIATION

For sample values $x_1, x_2, \ldots, x_n$, the sample variance s^2 and the sample standard deviation s are computed as

$$s^2 = \frac{\Sigma(x_i - \bar{x})^2}{n - 1} \quad \text{and} \quad s = \sqrt{s^2}.$$

For population values $x_1, x_2, \ldots, x_N$, the population variance σ^2 (the Greek letter sigma, squared) and the population standard deviation σ are computed as

$$\sigma^2 = \frac{\Sigma(x_i - \mu)^2}{N} \quad \text{and} \quad \sigma = \sqrt{\sigma^2}.$$

Note: The sample variance uses $n - 1$ rather than n in the denominator to ensure that the sample variance is an unbiased estimator for the population variance. The concept of an unbiased estimator is discussed in Appendix 7.2. We explore statistical inference for the population variance in more detail in Chapter 11.

EXAMPLE 3.15

Use the data in Table 3.1 to calculate the sample variance and the sample standard deviation for the Growth and Value mutual funds. Express the answers in the correct units of measurement.

SOLUTION: We will show the calculations for the Growth mutual fund, which has a mean return of 10.09%. The second column in Table 3.11 shows each return less the mean. The third column shows the square of each deviation from the mean. Summing these values yields the numerator for the sample variance formula.

TABLE 3.11 Sample Variance Calculation for the Growth Fund

x_i	$x_i - \bar{x}$	$(x_i - \bar{x})^2$
12.56	$12.56 - 10.09 = 2.47$	$(2.47)^2 = 6.10$
−38.32	$-38.32 - 10.09 = -48.41$	$(-48.41)^2 = 2343.53$
⋮	⋮	⋮
5.99	$5.99 - 10.09 = -4.10$	$(-4.10)^2 = 16.81$
	Total = 0 (subject to rounding)	Total = 3762.94

For the Growth mutual fund: $s^2 = \frac{\Sigma(x_i - \bar{x})^2}{n-1} = \frac{3{,}762.94}{10-1} = 418.10(\%)^2$. Note that the units of measurement are squared. The sample standard deviation is $s = \sqrt{418.10} = 20.45(\%)$.

Similar calculations for the Value mutual fund yield

$$s^2 = \frac{\Sigma(x_i - \bar{x})^2}{n-1} = \frac{3{,}066.66}{10-1} = 340.74(\%)^2 \text{ and } s = \sqrt{340.74} = 18.46(\%).$$

Based on all measures of dispersion discussed thus far, we can conclude that the Value mutual fund is less dispersed than the Growth mutual fund. With financial data, standard deviation tends to be the most common measure of risk. Therefore, the investment risk of the Value mutual fund is lower than that of the Growth mutual fund over this 10-year period.

The Coefficient of Variation

In some instances, analysis entails comparing the variability of two or more data sets that have different means or units of measurement. The **coefficient of variation** (**CV**) serves as a relative measure of dispersion and adjusts for differences in the magnitudes of the means. Calculated by dividing a data set's standard deviation by its mean, CV is a unitless measure that allows for direct comparisons of mean-adjusted dispersion across different data sets.

MEASURE OF DISPERSION: THE COEFFICIENT OF VARIATION (CV)

The coefficient of variation (CV) for a data set is calculated by dividing the standard deviation by the mean. For a sample, it is calculated as $s/\bar{x}$. For a population, it is calculated as μ/σ.

EXAMPLE 3.16

Calculate and interpret the coefficient of variation for the Growth and the Value mutual funds.

SOLUTION: We use the sample means and the sample standard deviations computed earlier.

$$\text{Growth: CV} = \frac{s}{\bar{x}} = \frac{20.45\%}{10.09\%} = 2.03.$$

$$\text{Value: CV} = \frac{s}{\bar{x}} = \frac{18.46\%}{7.56\%} = 2.44.$$

Even though all other measures of variability show that returns for the Growth mutual fund are more dispersed than returns for the Value mutual fund, the coefficient of variation indicates that returns for the Value mutual fund have more relative dispersion.

Using Excel and R to Calculate Measures of Dispersion

Table 3.3 in Section 3.1 shows the function names for various measures of dispersion in Excel and R. To illustrate, we provide instructions to find the sample standard deviation for the Growth fund.

Using Excel's Formula Option

We open the **Growth_Value** data file and insert "=STDEV.S(B2:B11)". Excel returns a value of 20.45, which matches the value that we calculated by hand.

FILE
Growth_Value

Using Excel's Data Analysis Toolpak Option

In Section 3.1, we also discussed using Excel's Data Analysis Toolpak option for calculating summary measures. For measures of dispersion, Excel treats the data as a sample and calculates the range, the sample variance, and the sample standard deviation. These values for the Growth and the Value mutual funds are shown in boldface in Table 3.4.

Using R

A. Import the **Growth_Value** data into a data frame (table) in R.

B. The **sd** function will return the sample standard deviation for a specified variable in a data frame. Enter:

```
> sd(Growth_Value$'Growth')
```

And R returns: 20.44759.

EXERCISES 3.4

Mechanics

39. Consider the following population data:

34	42	12	10	22

   a. Calculate the range.
   b. Calculate MAD.
   c. Calculate the population variance.
   d. Calculate the population standard deviation.

40. Consider the following population data:

0	−4	2	−8	10

   a. Calculate the range.
   b. Calculate MAD.
   c. Calculate the population variance.
   d. Calculate the population standard deviation.

41. Consider the following sample data:

40	48	32	52	38	42

   a. Calculate the range.
   b. Calculate MAD.
   c. Calculate the sample variance.
   d. Calculate the sample standard deviation.

42. Consider the following sample data:

−10	12	−8	−2	−6	8

   a. Calculate the range.
   b. Calculate MAD.
   c. Calculate the sample variance and the sample standard deviation.

Applications

43. The Department of Transportation (DOT) fields thousands of complaints about airlines each year. The DOT categorizes and tallies complaints, and then periodically publishes rankings of airline performance. The following table presents the 2006 results for the 10 largest U.S. airlines.

Airline	Complaints*	Airline	Complaints*
Southwest	1.82	Northwest	8.84
JetBlue	3.98	Delta	10.35
Alaska	5.24	American	10.87
AirTran	6.24	US	13.59
Continental	8.83	United	13.60

Source: Department of Transportation; *per million passengers.

   a. Which airline fielded the least amount of complaints? Which airline fielded the most? Calculate the range.
   b. Calculate the mean and the median number of complaints for this sample.
   c. Calculate the variance and the standard deviation.

44. The monthly closing stock prices (rounded to the nearest dollar) for Starbucks Corp. and Panera Bread Co. for the first six months of 2016 are reported in the following table.

Month	Starbucks Corp.	Panera Bread Co.
January 2016	61	194
February 2016	58	207
March 2016	60	205
April 2016	55	215
May 2016	57	219
June 2016	58	212

Source: finance.yahoo.com.

   a. Calculate the sample variance and the sample standard deviation for each firm's stock price.
   b. Which firm's stock price had greater variability as measured by the standard deviation?
   c. Which firm's stock price had the greater relative dispersion?

45. **FILE** *AnnArbor_Rental.* Real estate investment in college towns continues to promise good returns (*The Wall Street Journal*, September 24, 2010). Marcela Treisman works for an investment firm in Michigan. Her assignment is to analyze the rental market in Ann Arbor, which is home to the University of Michigan. She gathers data on monthly rent for 2011 along with the square footage of 40 homes. A portion of the data is shown in the accompanying table.

Monthly Rent	Square Footage
645	500
675	648
⋮	⋮
2,400	2,700

Source: www.zillow.com.

   a. Calculate the mean and the standard deviation for monthly rent.
   b. Calculate the mean and the standard deviation for square footage.
   c. Which sample data exhibit greater relative dispersion?

46. **FILE** *Largest_Corporations.* The accompanying data file shows the Fortune 500 rankings of America's largest corporations for 2010. Next to each corporation are its market capitalization (in $ billions as of March 26, 2010) and its total return (in %) to investors for the year 2009.

   a. Calculate the coefficient of variation for market capitalization.

   b. Calculate the coefficient of variation for total return.

   c. Which sample data exhibit greater relative dispersion?

47. **FILE** *Census.* The accompanying data file shows, among other variables, median household income and median house value for the 50 states.

   a. Compute and discuss the range of household income and house value.

   b. Compute the sample MAD and the sample standard deviation of household income and house value.

   c. Discuss why we cannot directly compare the sample MAD and the standard deviations of the two data sets.

3.5 MEAN-VARIANCE ANALYSIS AND THE SHARPE RATIO

LO 3.5

Explain mean-variance analysis and the Sharpe ratio.

In the introduction to Section 3.4, we asked why any rational investor would invest in the Value mutual fund over the Growth mutual fund since the average return for the Value mutual fund over the 2007–2016 period was 7.56%, whereas the average return for the Growth mutual fund was 10.09%. It turns out that, in general, investments with higher returns also carry higher risk. Investments include financial assets such as stocks, bonds, and mutual funds. The average return represents an investor's reward, whereas variance, or equivalently standard deviation, corresponds to risk.

According to mean-variance analysis, we can measure performance of any risky asset solely on the basis of the average and the variance of its returns.

> **MEAN-VARIANCE ANALYSIS**
>
> Mean-variance analysis postulates that the performance of an asset is measured by its rate of return, and this rate of return is evaluated in terms of its reward (mean) and risk (variance). In general, investments with higher average returns are also associated with higher risk.

Consider Table 3.12, which summarizes the mean and the variance for the Growth and Value mutual funds. It is true that an investment in the Growth mutual fund rather than the Value mutual fund provided an investor with a higher reward over this 10-year period, as measured by the mean return. However, this same investor encountered more risk, as measured by the variance.

TABLE 3.12 Mean-Variance Analysis for the Two Mutual Funds, 2007–2016

Fund	Mean Return %	Variance %^{2}
Growth	10.09	418.10
Value	7.56	340.74

A discussion of mean-variance analysis seems almost incomplete without mention of the **Sharpe ratio**. Nobel Laureate William Sharpe developed what he originally referred to as the "reward-to-variability" ratio. However, academics and finance professionals prefer to call it the "Sharpe ratio." The Sharpe ratio is used to characterize how well the return of an asset compensates for the risk that the investor takes. Investors are often advised to pick investments that have high Sharpe ratios.

The Sharpe ratio is defined with the reward specified in terms of the population mean and the variability specified in terms of the population standard deviation. However, we often compute the Sharpe ratio in terms of the sample mean and the sample standard deviation, where the return is usually expressed as a percent and not a decimal.

THE SHARPE RATIO

The Sharpe ratio measures the extra reward per unit of risk. The Sharpe ratio for an investment I is computed as

$$\frac{\bar{x}_I - \bar{R}_f}{s_I},$$

where $\bar{x}_I$ is the mean return for the investment, $\bar{R}_f$ is the mean return for a risk-free asset such as a Treasury bill (T-bill), and s_I is the standard deviation for the investment.

The numerator of the Sharpe ratio measures the extra reward that investors receive for the added risk taken—this difference is often called excess return. The higher the Sharpe ratio, the better the investment compensates its investors for risk.

EXAMPLE 3.17

Calculate and interpret the Sharpe ratios for the Growth and the Value mutual funds given that the return on a 1-year T-bill is 2%.

SOLUTION: Since the return on a 1-year T-bill is 2%, $\bar{R}_f = 2$. Plugging in the values of the relevant means and standard deviations into the Sharpe ratio yields

Sharpe ratio for the Growth mutual fund: $\dfrac{\bar{x}_I - \bar{R}_f}{s_I} = \dfrac{10.09 - 2}{20.45} = 0.40.$

Sharpe ratio for the Value mutual fund: $\dfrac{\bar{x}_I - \bar{R}_f}{s_I} = \dfrac{7.56 - 2}{18.46} = 0.30.$

We had earlier shown that the Growth mutual fund had a higher return, which is good, along with a higher variance, which is bad. We can use the Sharpe ratio to make a valid comparison between the funds. The Growth mutual fund provides a higher Sharpe ratio than the Value mutual fund (0.40 > 0.30); therefore, the Growth mutual fund offered more reward per unit of risk compared to the Value mutual fund.

SYNOPSIS OF INTRODUCTORY CASE

Growth and value are two fundamental styles in stock and mutual fund investing. Proponents of growth investing believe that companies that are growing faster than their peers are trendsetters and will be able to maintain their superior growth. By investing in the stocks of these companies, they expect their investment to grow at a rate faster than the overall stock market. By comparison, value investors focus on the stocks of companies that are trading at a discount relative to the overall market or a specific sector. Investors of value stocks believe that these stocks are undervalued and that their price will increase once their true value is recognized by other investors. The debate between growth and value investing is age-old, and which style dominates depends on the sample period used for the analysis.

©Ingram Publishing RF

An analysis of annual return data for Vanguard's Growth Index mutual fund (Growth) and Vanguard's Value Index mutual fund (Value) for the years 2007 through 2016 provides important information for an investor trying to determine whether to invest in a growth mutual fund, a value mutual fund, or both types of mutual funds. Over this period, the mean return for the Growth fund of 10.09% is greater than the mean return for the Value fund of 7.56%. While the mean return typically represents the reward of investing, it does not incorporate the risk of investing.

Standard deviation tends to be the most common measure of risk with financial data. Since the standard deviation for the Growth fund (20.45%) is greater than the standard deviation for the Value fund (18.46%), the Growth fund is likelier to have returns farther above and below its mean. Finally, given a risk-free rate of 2%, the Sharpe ratio for the Growth fund is 0.40 compared to that for the Value fund of 0.30, indicating that the Growth fund provides more reward per unit of risk. Assuming that the behavior of these returns will continue, the investor will favor investing in Growth over Value. A commonly used disclaimer, however, states that past performance is no guarantee of future results. Since the two styles often complement each other, it might be advisable for the investor to add diversity to his portfolio by using them together.

EXERCISES 3.5

Mechanics

48. Consider the following data for two investments, A and B:

Investment A:	$\bar{x} = 10\%$ and $s = 5\%$
Investment B:	$\bar{x} = 15\%$ and $s = 10\%$

a. Which investment provides the higher return? Which investment provides less risk? Explain.

b. Given a risk-free rate of 1.4%, calculate the Sharpe ratio for each investment. Which investment provides the higher reward per unit of risk? Explain.

49. Consider the following data for two investments, A and B:

Investment A:	$\bar{x} = 8\%$ and $s = 5\%$
Investment B:	$\bar{x} = 10\%$ and $s = 7\%$

a. Which investment provides the higher return? Which investment provides less risk? Explain.

b. Given a risk-free rate of 2%, calculate the Sharpe ratio for each investment. Which investment provides the higher reward per unit of risk? Explain.

50. Consider the following returns for two investments, A and B, over the past four years:

Investment 1:	2%	8%	−4%	6%
Investment 2:	6%	12%	−8%	10%

a. Which investment provides the higher return?

b. Which investment provides less risk?

c. Given a risk-free rate of 1.2%, calculate the Sharpe ratio for each investment. Which investment has performed better? Explain.

Applications

51. The following table shows the annual returns (in %) and summary measures for the Vanguard Energy Fund and the Vanguard Health Care Fund from 2005 through 2009.

Year	Energy	Health Care
2005	44.60	15.41
2006	19.68	10.87
2007	37.00	4.43
2008	−42.87	−18.45
2009	38.36	20.96
	$\bar{x}_{Energy} = 19.35$ $s_{Energy} = 35.99$	$\bar{x}_{Health} = 6.64$ $s_{Health} = 15.28$

Source: finance.yahoo.com.

a. Which fund had the higher average return?
b. Which fund was riskier over this time period?
c. Given a risk-free rate of 3%, which fund has the higher Sharpe ratio? What does this ratio imply?

52. The following table shows the annual returns (in %) for the Fidelity Latin America Fund and the Fidelity Canada Fund from 2005 through 2009.

Year	Latin America	Canada
2005	55.17	27.89
2006	44.33	15.04
2007	43.71	35.02
2008	−54.64	−42.64
2009	91.60	39.63

Source: finance.yahoo.com.

a. Which fund had the higher average return?
b. Which fund was riskier over this time period?
c. Given a risk-free rate of 3%, which fund has the higher Sharpe ratio? What does this ratio imply?

53. **FILE** *Fidelity_Select.* The accompanying table shows a portion of the annual return (in %) for the Fidelity Select Technology Fund and Fidelity Select Energy Fund from 2000 through 2016.

Year	Technology	Energy
2000	−32.30	31.77
2001	−31.70	−11.97
⋮	⋮	⋮
2016	11.94	33.84

Source: finance.yahoo.com.

a. Compare the sample means and the sample standard deviations of the two funds.
b. Use a risk-free rate of 2% to compare the Sharpe ratios of the two funds.

3.6 ANALYSIS OF RELATIVE LOCATION

Apply Chebyshev's theorem, the empirical rule, and z-scores.

The mean and the standard deviation are the most extensively used measures of central location and dispersion, respectively. Unlike the mean, it is not easy to interpret the standard deviation intuitively. All we can say is that a low value for the standard deviation indicates that the data points are close to the mean, while a high value for the standard deviation indicates that the data are spread out. In this section, we will use Chebyshev's theorem and the empirical rule to make precise statements regarding the percentage of data values that fall within a specified number of standard deviations from the mean. We will also use the mean and the standard deviation to compute z-scores that measure the relative location of a value within a data set; z-scores are also used to detect outliers.

Chebyshev's Theorem

As we will see in more detail in later chapters, it is important to be able to use the standard deviation to make statements about the proportion of observations that fall within certain intervals. Fortunately, a Russian mathematician named Pavroty

Chebyshev (1821–1894) found bounds for the proportion of the data that lie within a specified number of standard deviations from the mean.

> ### CHEBYSHEV'S THEOREM
> For any data set, the proportion of observations that lie within k standard deviations from the mean is at least $1 - 1/k^2$, where k is any number greater than 1.

This theorem holds both for a sample and for a population. For example, it implies that at least 0.75, or 75%, of the observations fall within $k = 2$ standard deviations from the mean. Similarly, at least 0.89, or 89%, of the observations fall within $k = 3$ standard deviations from the mean.

> ### EXAMPLE 3.18
>
> A large lecture class has 280 students. The professor has announced that the mean score on an exam is 74 with a standard deviation of 8. At least how many students scored within 58 and 90?
>
> **SOLUTION:** The score 58 is two standard deviations below the mean ($\bar{x} - 2s = 74 - (2 \times 8) = 58$), while the score 90 is two standard deviations above the mean ($\bar{x} + 2s = 74 + (2 \times 8) = 90$). Using Chebyshev's theorem and $k = 2$, we have $1 - 1/2^2 = 0.75$. In other words, Chebyshev's theorem asserts that at least 75% of the scores will fall within 58 and 90. Therefore, at least 75% of 280 students, or 0.75(280) = 210 students, scored within 58 and 90.

The main advantage of Chebyshev's theorem is that it applies to all data sets, regardless of the shape of the distribution. However, it results in conservative bounds for the percentage of observations falling in a particular interval. The actual percentage of observations lying in the interval may in fact be much larger.

The Empirical Rule

If we know that our data are drawn from a relatively symmetric and bell-shaped distribution—perhaps by a visual inspection of its histogram—then we can make more precise statements about the percentage of observations that fall within certain intervals. Symmetry and bell-shape are characteristics of the normal distribution, a topic that we discuss in Chapter 6. The normal distribution is often used as an approximation for many real-world applications. The **empirical rule** is illustrated in Figure 3.6. It provides the approximate percentage of observations that fall within 1, 2, or 3 standard deviations from the mean.

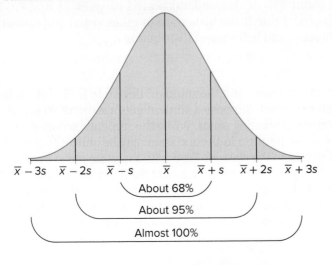

FIGURE 3.6
Graphical description of the empirical rule

THE EMPIRICAL RULE

Given a sample mean $\bar{x}$, a sample standard deviation s, and a relatively symmetric and bell-shaped distribution:

- Approximately 68% of all observations fall in the interval $\bar{x} \pm s$,
- Approximately 95% of all observations fall in the interval $\bar{x} \pm 2s$, and
- Almost all observations fall in the interval $\bar{x} \pm 3s$.

EXAMPLE 3.19

Let's revisit Example 3.18 regarding a large lecture class with 280 students with a mean score of 74 and a standard deviation of 8. Assume that the distribution is symmetric and bell-shaped.

a. Approximately how many students scored within 58 and 90?

b. Approximately how many students scored more than 90?

SOLUTION:

a. As shown in Example 3.18, the score 58 is two standard deviations below the mean, while the score 90 is two standard deviations above the mean. The empirical rule states that approximately 95% of the observations fall within two standard deviations of the mean. Therefore, about 95% of 280 students, or 0.95(280) = 266 students, scored within 58 and 90.

b. We know that the score 90 is two standard deviations above the mean. Since approximately 95% of the observations fall within two standard deviations of the mean, we can infer that 5% of the observations fall outside the interval. Therefore, given the symmetry of the distribution, about half of 5%, or 2.5%, of 280 students scored above 90. Equivalently, about 7 students (0.025 × 280) scored above 90 on the exam. If the professor uses a cutoff score above 90 for an A, then only seven students in the class are expected to get an A.

The main difference between Chebyshev's theorem and the empirical rule is that Chebyshev's theorem applies to all data sets, whereas the empirical rule is appropriate when the distribution is symmetric and bell-shaped. In the preceding two examples, while Chebyshev's theorem asserts that at least 75% of the students scored between 58 and 90, we are able to make a more precise statement with the empirical rule that suggests that about 95% of the students scored between 58 and 90. It is preferable to use the empirical rule if the histogram or other visual and numerical measures suggest a symmetric and bell-shaped distribution.

z-Scores

It is often instructive to use the mean and the standard deviation to find the relative location of values within a data set. Suppose a student gets a score of 90 on her accounting exam and 90 on her marketing exam. While the student's scores are identical in both classes, her relative position in these classes may be quite different. What if the mean score was different in the classes? Even with the same mean scores, what if the standard deviation was different in the classes? Both the mean and the standard deviation are needed to find the relative position of this student in both classes.

We use the **z-score** to find the relative position of a sample value within the data set by dividing the deviation of the sample value from the mean by the standard deviation.

A z-score is a unitless measure since its numerator and the denominator have the same units, which cancel out with each other. It measures the distance of a given sample value from the mean in terms of standard deviations. For example, a z-score of 2 implies that the given sample value is 2 standard deviations above the mean. Similarly, a z-score of −1.5 implies that the given sample value is 1.5 standard deviations below the mean. Converting sample data into z-scores is also called **standardizing** the data.

EXAMPLE 3.20

The mean and the standard deviation of scores on an accounting exam are 74 and 8, respectively. The mean and standard deviation of scores on a marketing exam are 78 and 10, respectively. Find the z-scores for a student who scores 90 in both classes.

SOLUTION: The z-score in the accounting class is $z = \frac{90 - 74}{8} = 2$. Similarly, the z-score in the marketing class is $z = \frac{90 - 78}{10} = 1.2$. Therefore, the student has fared relatively better in accounting since she is two standard deviations above the mean, as compared to marketing where she is only 1.2 standard deviations above the mean.

In Section 3.2, we used boxplots as an effective tool to identify outliers. If the data are relatively symmetric and bell-shaped, we can also use z-scores to detect outliers. Since almost all observations fall within three standard deviations of the mean, it is common to treat an observation as an outlier if its z-score is more than 3 or less than −3. Such observations must be reviewed to determine if they should remain in the data set.

EXAMPLE 3.21

Consider the information presented in the introductory case of this chapter. Use z-scores to determine if there are outliers in the Growth mutual fund data. Is this result consistent with the boxplot constructed in Figure 3.4?

SOLUTION: The smallest and the largest observations in the data set are −38.32 and 36.29, respectively. The z-score for the smallest observation is $z = \frac{-38.32 - 10.09}{20.45} = -2.37$ and the z-score for the largest observation is $z = \frac{36.29 - 10.09}{20.45} = 1.28$. Since the absolute value of both z-scores is less than 3, it would suggest that there are no outliers in the Growth mutual fund data. However, the boxplot in Figure 3.4 in Section 3.2 indicates that there is an outlier. How do we resolve this apparent inconsistency? Remember that z-scores are reliable indicators of outliers when the distribution is relatively bell-shaped and symmetric. Since the Growth mutual fund data are shown to be negatively skewed, we are better served identifying outliers in this case with a boxplot.

EXERCISES 3.6

Mechanics

54. A data set has a mean of 80 and a standard deviation of 5.
    a. Using Chebyshev's theorem, what percentage of the observations fall between 70 and 90?
    b. Using Chebyshev's theorem, what percentage of the observations fall between 65 and 95?

55. A data set has a mean of 1,500 and a standard deviation of 100.
    a. Using Chebyshev's theorem, what percentage of the observations fall between 1,300 and 1,700?
    b. Using Chebyshev's theorem, what percentage of the observations fall between 1,100 and 1,900?

56. A data set has a mean of 500 and a standard deviation of 25.
    a. Using Chebyshev's theorem, find the interval that encompasses at least 75% of the data.
    b. Using Chebyshev's theorem, find the interval that encompasses at least 89% of the data.

57. Data are drawn from a bell-shaped distribution with a mean of 20 and a standard deviation of 2.
    a. Approximately what percentage of the observations fall between 18 and 22?
    b. Approximately what percentage of the observations fall between 16 and 24?
    c. Approximately what percentage of the observations are less than 16?

58. Consider a bell-shaped distribution with a mean of 750 and a standard deviation of 50. There are 500 observations in the data set.
    a. Approximately what percentage of the observations are less than 700?
    b. Approximately how many observations are less than 700?

59. Data are drawn from a bell-shaped distribution with a mean of 25 and a standard deviation of 4. There are 1,000 observations in the data set.
    a. Approximately what percentage of the observations are less than 33?
    b. Approximately how many observations are less than 33?

60. Data are drawn from a bell-shaped distribution with a mean of 5 and a standard deviation of 2.5.
    a. Approximately what percentage of the observations are positive?
    b. Approximately what percentage of the observations are not positive?

61. Data are drawn from a bell-shaped distribution with a mean of 50 and a standard deviation of 12. There are 250 observations in the data set. Approximately how many observations are more than 74?

62. Consider a sample with six observations of 6, 9, 12, 10, 9, and 8. Compute the z-scores for each sample observation.

63. Consider a sample with 10 observations of −3, 8, 4, 2, −4, 15, 6, 0, −4, and 5. Use z-scores to determine if there are any outliers in the data; assume a bell-shaped distribution.

Applications

64. A sample of the salaries of assistant professors on the business faculty at a local university revealed a mean income of $72,000 with a standard deviation of $3,000.
    a. Using Chebyshev's theorem, what percentage of the faculty earns at least $66,000 but no more than $78,000?
    b. Using Chebyshev's theorem, what percentage of the faculty earns at least $63,000 but no more than $81,000?

65. The historical returns on a portfolio had an average return of 8% and a standard deviation of 12%. Assume that returns on this portfolio follow a bell-shaped distribution.
    a. Approximately what percentage of returns were greater than 20%?
    b. Approximately what percentage of returns were below −16%?

66. It is often assumed that IQ scores follow a bell-shaped distribution with a mean of 100 and a standard deviation of 16.
    a. Approximately what percentage of scores are between 84 and 116?
    b. Approximately what percentage of scores are less than 68?
    c. Approximately what percentage of scores are more than 116?

67. An investment strategy has an expected return of 8% and a standard deviation of 6%. Assume investment returns are bell-shaped.
    a. How likely is it to earn a return between 2% and 14%?
    b. How likely is it to earn a return greater than 14%?
    c. How likely is it to earn a return below −4%?

68. On average, an American professional football game lasts about three hours, even though the ball is actually in play only 11 minutes (www.sportsgrid.com, January 14, 2014). Let the standard deviation be 0.4 hour.
    a. Use Chebyshev's theorem to approximate the proportion of games that last between 2.2 hours and 3.8 hours.
    b. Assume a bell-shaped distribution to approximate the proportion of games that last between 2.2 hours and 3.8 hours.

69. **FILE** *Census.* The accompanying data file shows, among other variables, median household income and median house value for the 50 states in 2010. Assume that income and house value data are bell-shaped.
    a. Use z-scores to determine if there are any outliers in the household income data.
    b. Use z-scores to determine if there are any outliers in the house value data.

70. **FILE** *Fidelity_Select.* The accompanying data file shows the annual return (in percent) for the Fidelity Select Technology Fund and the Fidelity Select Energy Fund from 2000 through 2016. Assume that the return data are bell-shaped.

a. Use z-scores to determine if there are any outliers in the technology return data.
b. Use z-scores to determine if there are any outliers in the energy return data.

3.7 SUMMARIZING GROUPED DATA

LO **3.7**

The mean and the variance are the most widely used descriptive measures in statistics. However, the formulas in Sections 3.1 and 3.4 apply to ungrouped or raw data. In many instances, we access data that are in the form of a frequency distribution or grouped data. This is especially true of secondary data, such as data we obtain from government publications. When data are grouped or aggregated, the formulas for the mean and the variance must be modified.

Calculate summary measures for grouped data.

> ### THE MEAN AND THE VARIANCE FOR A FREQUENCY DISTRIBUTION
>
> - Sample: $\bar{x} = \dfrac{\Sigma m_i f_i}{n}$ and $s^2 = \dfrac{\Sigma(m_i - \bar{x})^2 f_i}{n-1}$
>
> - Population: $\mu = \dfrac{\Sigma m_i f_i}{N}$ and $\sigma^2 = \dfrac{\Sigma(m_i - \mu)^2 f_i}{N}$,
>
> where m_i and f_i are the midpoint and the frequency of the ith class, respectively. The standard deviation is the positive square root of the variance.

We note that by aggregating, some of the data information is lost. Therefore, unlike in the case of raw data, we can only compute approximate values for the summary measures with grouped data.

EXAMPLE 3.22

Recall the frequency distribution of house prices (in $1,000s) that we constructed in Chapter 2.

Class	Frequency
300 up to 400	4
400 up to 500	11
500 up to 600	14
600 up to 700	5
700 up to 800	2

a. Calculate the average house price.
b. Calculate the sample variance and the sample standard deviation.

SOLUTION: Table 3.13 shows the frequency f_i and the midpoint m_i for each class in the second and third columns, respectively.

TABLE 3.13 The Sample Mean and the Sample Variance Calculation for Grouped Data

Class	f_i	m_i	$m_i f_i$	$(m_i - \bar{x})^2 f_i$
300 up to 400	4	350	1400	$(350 - 522)^2 \times 4 = 118{,}336$
400 up to 500	11	450	4950	$(450 - 522)^2 \times 11 = 57{,}024$
500 up to 600	14	550	7700	$(550 - 522)^2 \times 14 = 10{,}976$
600 up to 700	5	650	3250	$(650 - 522)^2 \times 5 = 81{,}920$
700 up to 800	2	750	1500	$(750 - 522)^2 \times 2 = 103{,}968$
Total	36		18800	372,224

a. For the mean, we multiply each class's midpoint by its respective frequency, as shown in the fourth column of Table 3.13. Finally, we sum the fourth column and divide by the sample size. Or,

$$\bar{x} = \frac{\Sigma m_i f_i}{n} = \frac{18{,}800}{36} = 522.$$ The average house price is thus $522,000.

b. For the sample variance, we first calculate the sum of the weighted squared differences from the mean. The fifth column in Table 3.13 shows the appropriate calculations for each class. Summing the values in the fifth column yields the numerator for the variance formula. Thus, we calculate the variance as

$$s^2 = \frac{\Sigma (m_i - \bar{x})^2 f_i}{n - 1} = \frac{372{,}224}{36 - 1} = 10{,}635.$$

The standard deviation is simply the positive square root of the sample variance, or $s = \sqrt{10{,}635} = 103.13$. The standard deviation for house price is thus $103,130.

Many times, the data from secondary sources are distributed in the form of a relative frequency distribution rather than a frequency distribution. In order to use the formulas for the mean and variance for grouped data, first convert the relative frequency distribution into a frequency distribution, as discussed in Section 2.2 of Chapter 2.

EXERCISES 3.7

Mechanics

71. Consider the following frequency distribution.

Class	Frequency
2 up to 4	20
4 up to 6	60
6 up to 8	80
8 up to 10	20

a. Calculate the population mean.
b. Calculate the population variance and the population standard deviation.

72. Consider the following frequency distribution.

Class	Frequency
50 up to 60	10
60 up to 70	15
70 up to 80	8
80 up to 100	2

a. Calculate the sample mean.
b. Calculate the sample variance and the sample standard deviation.

73. The following relative frequency distribution was constructed from a population of 200. Calculate the population mean, the population variance, and the population standard deviation.

Class	Relative Frequency
−20 up to −10	0.35
−10 up to 0	0.20
0 up to 10	0.40
10 up to 20	0.05

74. The following relative frequency distribution was constructed from a sample of 50. Calculate the sample mean, the sample variance, and the sample standard deviation.

Class	Relative Frequency
0 up to 2	0.34
2 up to 4	0.20
4 up to 6	0.40
6 up to 8	0.06

Applications

75. Fifty cities provided information on vacancy rates (in %) for local apartments in the following frequency distribution.

Vacancy Rate	Frequency
0 up to 3	5
3 up to 6	5
6 up to 9	10
9 up to 12	20
12 up to 15	10

a. Calculate the average vacancy rate.
b. Calculate the variance and the standard deviation for this sample.

76. A local hospital provided the following frequency distribution summarizing the weights of babies (in pounds) delivered over the month of January.

Weight	Number of Babies
2 up to 4	3
4 up to 6	8
6 up to 8	25
8 up to 10	30
10 up to 12	4

a. Calculate the mean weight.
b. Calculate the variance and the standard deviation for this sample.

77. A researcher conducts a mileage economy test involving 80 cars. The accompanying frequency distribution summarizes the results concerning miles per gallon (MPG).

MPG	Frequency
15 up to 20	15
20 up to 25	30
25 up to 30	15
30 up to 35	10
35 up to 40	7
40 up to 45	3

a. Calculate the mean mpg.
b. Calculate the variance and the standard deviation.

78. The Boston Security Analysts Society, Inc. (BSAS) is a nonprofit association that serves as a forum for the exchange of ideas for the investment community. Suppose the ages of its members are based on the following frequency distribution.

Age	Frequency
21–31	11
32–42	44
43–53	26
54–64	7

a. Calculate the mean age.
b. Calculate the sample variance and the sample standard deviation.

79. The National Sporting Goods Association (NSGA) conducted a survey of the ages of people who purchased athletic footwear in 2009. The ages are summarized in the following percent frequency distribution.

Age of Purchaser	Percent
Under 14 years old	19
14 to 17 years old	6
18 to 24 years old	10
25 to 34 years old	13
35 to 44 years old	14
45 to 64 years old	25
65 years old and over	13

Suppose the survey was based on 100 individuals. Calculate the average age of this distribution. Calculate the sample standard deviation. Use 10 as the midpoint of the first class and 75 as the midpoint of the last class.

3.8 MEASURES OF ASSOCIATION

In Chapter 2, we introduced the idea of a scatterplot to visually assess whether two variables had some type of linear relationship. In this section, we present two numerical measures of association that quantify the direction and strength of the linear relationship between two variables, x and y. It is important to point out that these measures are not appropriate when the underlying relationship between the variables is nonlinear.

An objective numerical measure that reveals the direction of the linear relationship between two variables is called the **covariance**. We use s_{xy} to refer to a sample covariance, and σ_{xy} to refer to a population covariance.

MEASURE OF ASSOCIATION: THE COVARIANCE

The covariance shows the direction of the linear relationship between two variables. For values $(x_1, y_1), (x_2, y_2), \ldots, (x_n, y_n)$, the sample covariance s_{xy} is computed as

$$s_{xy} = \frac{\Sigma(x_i - \bar{x})(y_i - \bar{y})}{n - 1}.$$

For values $(x_1, y_1), (x_2, y_2), \ldots, (x_N, y_N)$, the population covariance σ_{xy} is computed as

$$\sigma_{xy} = \frac{\Sigma(x_i - \mu_x)(y_i - \mu_y)}{N}.$$

Note: As in the case of the sample variance, the sample covariance uses $n - 1$ rather than n in the denominator.

The covariance can assume a negative value, a positive value, or a value of zero.

- A negative value for covariance indicates a negative linear relationship between the two variables; on average, if x is above its mean, then y tends to be below its mean, and vice versa.

- A positive value for covariance indicates a positive linear relationship between the two variables; on average, if x is above its mean, then y tends to be above its mean, and vice versa.

- The covariance is zero if y and x have no linear relationship.

The covariance is difficult to interpret because it is sensitive to the units of measurement. That is, the covariance between two variables might be 100 and the covariance between another two variables might be 100,000, yet all we can conclude is that both sets of variables are positively related. We cannot comment on the strength of the relationships. An easier measure to interpret is the **correlation coefficient**; it describes both the direction and the strength of the linear relationship between x and y. We use r_{xy} to refer to a sample correlation coefficient and ρ_{xy} (the Greek letter rho) to refer to a population correlation coefficient.

MEASURE OF ASSOCIATION: THE CORRELATION COEFFICIENT

The correlation coefficient shows the direction and the strength of the linear relationship between two variables. The sample correlation coefficient is computed as $r_{xy} = \dfrac{s_{xy}}{s_x s_y}$, and the population correlation coefficient is computed as $\rho_{xy} = \dfrac{\sigma_{xy}}{\sigma_x \sigma_y}$.

The correlation coefficient is unit-free since the units in the numerator cancel with those in the denominator. The value of the correlation coefficient falls between -1 and 1. A perfect positive relationship exists if it equals 1, and a perfect negative relationship exists if it equals −1. Other values for the correlation coefficient must be interpreted with reference to −1, 0, or 1. For instance, a correlation coefficient equal to −0.80 indicates a strong negative relationship, whereas a correlation coefficient equal to 0.12 indicates a weak positive relationship.

EXAMPLE 3.23

Use the data in Table 3.1 to calculate and interpret the covariance and the correlation coefficient for the Growth (x) and Value (y) mutual funds. Recall that $\bar{x} = 10.09$, $s_x = 20.45$, $\bar{y} = 7.56$, and $s_y = 18.46$.

SOLUTION: As a first step, Figure 3.7 shows a scatterplot of the return data for the Growth and Value mutual funds; scatterplots were introduced in Section 2.4. It appears that there is a positive linear relationship between the two mutual fund returns.

FIGURE 3.7 Scatterplot of return data for the Growth and Value mutual funds

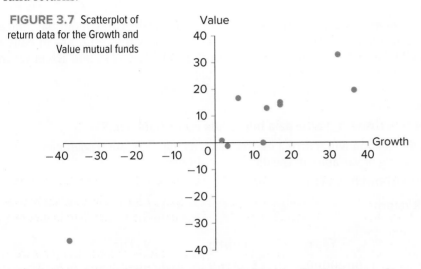

Table 3.14 shows the return data for each fund in the first two columns. The third column shows the product of differences from the mean.

TABLE 3.14 Covariance Calculation for the Growth and Value Mutual Funds

x_i	y_i	$(x_i - \bar{x})(y_i - \bar{y})$
12.56	0.09	$(12.56 - 10.09)(0.09 - 7.56) = -18.45$
−38.32	−35.97	$(-38.32 - 10.09)(-35.97 - 7.56) = 2{,}107.29$
⋮	⋮	⋮
5.99	16.75	$(5.99 - 10.09)(16.75 - 7.56) = -37.68$
		Total = 3,153.96

Summing the values in the third column yields the numerator for the covariance formula. Thus, we calculate the covariance as

$$s_{xy} = \frac{\Sigma(x_i - \bar{x})(y_i - \bar{y})}{n - 1} = \frac{3{,}153.96}{10 - 1} = 350.44.$$

The covariance of 350.44 indicates that the variables have a positive linear relationship. In other words, on average, when one fund's return is above its mean, the other fund's return is above its mean, and vice versa. The covariance is used to compute the correlation coefficient as

$$r_{xy} = \frac{s_{xy}}{s_x s_y} = \frac{350.44}{(20.45)(18.46)} = 0.93.$$

The correlation coefficient of 0.93 indicates a strong positive linear relationship. In order to diversify the risk in an investor's portfolio, an investor is often advised to invest in assets (such as stocks, bonds, and mutual funds) whose returns are not strongly correlated. If asset returns do not have a strong positive correlation, then if one investment does poorly, the other may still do well.

Growth_Value

Using Excel and R to Calculate Measures of Association

Table 3.3 in Section 3.1 provides function names for Excel and R for finding the covariance and the correlation coefficient. To illustrate, we provide instructions for finding the correlation coefficient between the returns for the Growth and Value mutual funds.

Using Excel

Open the **Growth_Value** data file. Note that the data for the Growth mutual fund are in cells B2 through B11 (array1) and the data for the Value fund are in cells C2 through C11 (array2). We enter "=CORREL(B2:B11, C2:C11)", and Excel returns 0.93; this is the value that we calculated manually.

Using R

A. Import the **Growth_Value** data into a data frame (table) in R.
B. The **cor** function will return a matrix that lists the correlation coefficient for each pairing of variables in the data frame. Enter:

```
> cor(Growth_Value)
```

And R returns:

	Year	Growth	Value
Year	1.0000000	0.1597169	0.4290143
Growth	0.1597169	1.0000000	**0.9284542**
Value	0.4290143	**0.9284542**	1.0000000

We are interested in the correlation coefficient between Growth and Value, which appears twice in this matrix (see boldface values). We also see the value 1 down the diagonal of the matrix, which just measures the correlation between each variable and itself. Finally, the correlation coefficient between Year and Growth and Year and Value is meaningless in this application.

EXERCISES 3.8

Mechanics

80. Consider the following sample data:

x	−2	0	3	4	7
y	−2	−3	−8	−9	−10

a. Calculate the covariance.
b. Calculate and interpret the correlation coefficient.

81. Consider the following sample data:

x	12	18	20	22	25
y	15	20	25	22	27

a. Calculate the covariance.
b. Calculate and interpret the correlation coefficient.

Applications

82. In an attempt to determine whether a linear relationship exists between the price of a home (x in $1,000s) and the number of days it takes to sell the home (y), a real estate agent collected the following data from recent sales in his city.

x	y	x	y
265	136	430	145
225	125	515	121
160	120	180	122
325	140	423	145

a. Calculate the covariance. What kind of linear relationship exists?
b. Calculate and interpret the correlation coefficient.

83. The following table shows the annual returns (in %) for T. Rowe Price's Value and International Stock funds for the time period 2005–2009.

Year	Value Fund	International Fund
2005	6.30	16.27
2006	19.75	19.26
2007	0.75	13.43
2008	−39.76	−48.02
2009	37.15	52.20

a. Calculate and interpret the covariance between the returns.
b. Calculate and interpret the correlation coefficient.

84. A social scientist wants to analyze the relationship between educational attainment and salary. He interviews eight people. The accompanying table shows each person's years of higher education (Education in years) and corresponding salary (Salary in $1,000s).

Education	3	4	6	2	5	4	8	0
Salary	40	53	60	35	55	50	80	35

a. Calculate the covariance. What kind of linear relationship exists?
b. Calculate and interpret the correlation coefficient.

85. The director of graduate admissions at a local university is analyzing the relationship between scores on the Graduate Record Examination (GRE) and subsequent performance in graduate school, as measured by a student's grade point average (GPA). She uses a sample of 10 students who graduated within the past five years.

GRE	GPA
1,500	3.4
1,400	3.5
1,000	3.0
1,050	2.9
1,100	3.0
1,250	3.3
800	2.7
850	2.8
950	3.2
1,350	3.3

a. Calculate and interpret the covariance.
b. Calculate and interpret the correlation coefficient. Does an applicant's GRE score seem to be a good indicator of subsequent performance in graduate school?

86. **FILE** *Census.* Access the data accompanying this exercise.
a. Compute and interpret the correlation coefficient for household income and house value.
b. Compute and interpret the correlation coefficient for household income and the percentage of the residents who are foreign born.
c. Compute and interpret the correlation coefficient for household income and the percentage of the residents who are without a high school diploma.

87. **FILE** *Happiness_Age.* Many attempts have been made to relate happiness with various factors. One such study relates happiness with age and finds that holding everything else constant, people are least happy when they are in their mid-40s (*The Economist*, December 16, 2010). Data are collected on a respondent's age and his/her perception of well-being on a scale from 0 to 100; a portion of the data is presented in the accompanying table.

Age	Happiness
49	62
51	66
⋮	⋮
69	72

a. Calculate and interpret the correlation coefficient between age and happiness.
b. Construct a scatterplot to point out a flaw with the above correlation analysis.

WRITING WITH STATISTICS

Many environmental groups and politicians are suggesting a return to the federal 55-mile-per-hour (mph) speed limit on America's highways. They argue that not only will a lower national speed limit reduce greenhouse emissions, it will also increase traffic safety.

Cameron Grinnell believes that a lower speed limit will not increase traffic safety. He believes that traffic safety is based on the variability of the speeds with which people are driving, rather than the average speed. The person who drives 20 mph below the pace of traffic is often as much a safety menace as the speeder. Cameron gathers the speeds of 40 cars from a highway with a speed limit of 55 mph (Highway 1) and the speeds of 40 cars from a highway with a speed limit of 65 mph (Highway 2). A portion of the data is shown in Table 3.15.

©Mike Watson Images/moodboard/Getty Images Plus/ Getty Images RF

FILE
Highway_Speeds

TABLE 3.15 Speed of Cars from Highway 1 and Highway 2

Highway 1	Highway 2
60	70
55	65
⋮	⋮
52	65

Cameron would like to use the above sample information to

1. Compute and interpret the typical speed on these highways.

2. Compute and interpret the variability of speed on these highways.

3. Discuss if the reduction in the speed limit to 55 mph would increase safety on the highways.

Sample Report— Analyzing Speed Limits

Recently, many concerned citizens have lobbied for a return to the federal 55-mile-per-hour (mph) speed limit on America's highways. The reduction may lower gas emissions and save consumers on gasoline costs, but whether it will increase traffic safety is not clear. Many researchers believe that traffic safety is based on the variability of the speed rather than the average speed with which people are driving—the more variability in speed, the more dangerous the roads. Is there less variability in speed on a highway with a 55-mph speed limit as opposed to a 65-mph speed limit?

To compare average speeds, as well as the variability of speeds on highways, the speeds of 40 cars were recorded on a highway with a 55-mph speed limit (Highway 1) and on a highway with a 65-mph speed limit (Highway 2). Table 3.A shows the most relevant descriptive measures for the analysis.

TABLE 3.A Summary Measures for Highway 1 and Highway 2

	Highway 1	Highway 2
Mean	57	66
Median	56	66
Mode	50	70
Minimum	45	60
Maximum	74	70
Standard deviation	7.0	3.0
Coefficient of variation	0.12	0.05
Number of cars	40	40

The average speed of a car on Highway 1 was 57 mph, as opposed to 66 mph on Highway 2. On Highway 1, half of the 40 cars drove faster than 56 mph and half drove slower than 56 mph, as measured by the median; the median for Highway 2 was 66 mph. The mode shows that the most common speeds on Highway 1 and Highway 2 were 50 mph and 70 mph, respectively. Based on each measure of central location, Highway 2 experiences higher speeds as compared to Highway 1.

While measures of central location typically represent where the data cluster, these measures do not relay information about the variability in the data. The range of speeds is 29 mph for Highway 1 as compared to a range of just 10 mph for Highway 2. Generally, standard deviation is a more credible measure of dispersion, since range is based entirely on the minimum and the maximum values. The standard deviation for Highway 1 is substantially greater than the standard deviation for Highway 2 (7.0 mph > 3.0 mph). Therefore, the speeds on Highway 1 are more variable than the speeds on Highway 2. Even adjusting for differences in the magnitudes of the means by calculating the coefficient of variation, the speeds on Highway 1 are still more dispersed than on Highway 2 (0.12 > 0.05).

On average, it is true that the speeds on Highway 2 are higher than the speeds on Highway 1; however, the variability of speeds is greater on Highway 1. If traffic safety improves when the variability of speeds declines, then the data suggest that a return to a federal 55-mph speed limit may not enhance the well-being of highway travelers.

CONCEPTUAL REVIEW

LO 3.1 Calculate and interpret measures of central location.

The mean (average) is the most widely used measure of central location. The **sample mean** and the **population mean** are computed as $\bar{x} = \frac{\Sigma x_i}{n}$ and $\mu = \frac{\Sigma x_i}{N}$, respectively. One weakness of the mean is that it is unduly influenced by **outliers**—extremely small or large values.

The **median** is the middle value of a data set and is especially useful when outliers are present. We arrange the data in ascending order (smallest to largest) and find the median as the middle value if the number of observations is odd, or the average of the two middle values if the number of observations is even.

The **mode** is the value in the data set that occurs with the most frequency. A data set may have no mode or more than one mode. If the data are qualitative, then the mode is the only meaningful measure of central location.

LO 3.2 Interpret a percentile and a boxplot.

Percentiles provide detailed information about how the data are spread over the interval from the smallest value to the largest value. In general, the pth percentile divides the data set into two parts, where approximately p percent of the observations have values less than the pth percentile and the rest have values greater than the pth percentile. The 25th percentile is also referred to as the first quartile (Q1), the 50th percentile is referred to as the second quartile (Q2), and the 75th percentile is referred to as the third quartile (Q3).

A **boxplot** displays the five-number summary (the minimum value, Q1, Q2, Q3, and the maximum value) for the data set. Boxplots are particularly useful when comparing similar information gathered at another place or time. They are also used as an effective tool for identifying outliers and skewness.

Calculate and interpret a geometric mean return and an average growth rate.

The **geometric mean** is the multiplicative average of a data set. In general, the geometric mean is smaller than the arithmetic mean and is less sensitive to outliers. The geometric mean is relevant when summarizing financial returns over several years. For multiperiod returns $R_1, R_2, \ldots, R_n$, the **geometric mean return** is computed as $G_R = \sqrt[n]{(1 + R_1)(1 + R_2) \cdots (1 + R_n)} - 1$, where n is the number of multiperiod returns.

The geometric mean is also used when summarizing **average growth rates**. For growth rates $g_1, g_2, \ldots, g_n$, the average growth rate is computed as $G_g = \sqrt[n]{(1 + g_1)(1 + g_2) \cdots (1 + g_n)} - 1$, where n is the number of multiperiod growth rates. When the underlying values of the series are given, there is a simpler way to compute the average growth rate. For observations $x_1, x_2, \ldots, x_n$, the average growth rate is computed as $G_g = \sqrt[n-1]{\frac{x_n}{x_1}} - 1$, where $n - 1$ is the number of distinct growth rates.

LO 3.4 **Calculate and interpret measures of dispersion.**

The **range** is the difference between the maximum and the minimum values in a data set.

The **mean absolute deviation** (MAD) is an average of the absolute differences between the observations and the mean of a data set. The sample MAD and the population MAD are computed as $\text{MAD} = \frac{\Sigma |x_i - \bar{x}|}{n}$ and $\text{MAD} = \frac{\Sigma |x_i - \mu|}{N}$, respectively.

The **variance** and the **standard deviation**, which are based on squared differences from the mean, are the two most widely used measures of dispersion. The sample variance s^2 and the sample standard deviation s are computed as $s^2 = \frac{\Sigma(x_i - \bar{x})^2}{n - 1}$ and $s = \sqrt{s^2}$, respectively. The population variance σ^2 and the population standard deviation σ are computed as $\sigma^2 = \frac{\Sigma(x_i - \mu)^2}{N}$ and $\sigma = \sqrt{\sigma^2}$, respectively. Whatever the units of the original data, the variance has squared units. By calculating the standard deviation, we return to the original units of measurement.

The **coefficient of variation CV** is a relative measure of dispersion. The CV allows comparisons of variability between data sets with different means or different units of measurement. The sample CV and the population CV are computed as $\text{CV} = \frac{s}{\bar{x}}$ and $\text{CV} = \frac{\sigma}{\mu}$, respectively.

LO 3.5 **Explain mean-variance analysis and the Sharpe ratio.**

Mean-variance analysis postulates that we measure the performance of an asset by its rate of return and evaluate this rate of return in terms of its reward (mean) and risk (variance). In general, investments with higher average returns are also associated with higher risk.

The **Sharpe ratio** measures extra reward per unit of risk. The Sharpe ratio for an investment I is computed as $\frac{\bar{x}_I - \bar{R}_f}{s_I}$ separate subscript a bit from division sign, where $\bar{R}_f$ denotes the mean return on a risk-free asset. The higher the Sharpe ratio, the better the investment compensates its investors for risk.

LO 3.6 **Apply Chebyshev's theorem, the empirical rule, and z-scores.**

Chebyshev's theorem dictates that for any data set, the proportion of observations that lie within k standard deviations from the mean will be at least $1 - 1/k^2$, where k is any number greater than 1.

Given a sample mean $\bar{x}$, a sample standard deviation s, and a bell-shaped distribution, the **empirical rule** dictates that

- Approximately 68% of all observations fall in the interval $\bar{x} \pm s$,
- Approximately 95% of all observations fall in the interval $\bar{x} \pm 2s$, and
- Almost all observations fall in the interval $\bar{x} \pm 3s$.

A **z-score**, calculated as $(x - \bar{x})/s$, measures the relative location of the sample value x. For a relatively symmetric and bell-shaped distribution, it is also used to detect outliers.

LO 3.7 **Calculate summary measures for grouped data.**

When analyzing grouped data, the formulas for the mean and the variance are modified as follows:

- The sample mean and the population mean are computed as $\bar{x} = \frac{\Sigma m_i f_i}{n}$ and $\mu = \frac{\Sigma m_i f_i}{N}$, respectively.
- The sample variance and the population variance are computed as $s^2 = \frac{\Sigma (m_i - \bar{x})^2 f_i}{n-1}$ and $\sigma^2 = \frac{\Sigma (m_i - \mu)^2 f_i}{N}$, respectively. As always, the standard deviation is calculated as the positive square root of the variance.

LO 3.8 **Calculate and interpret measures of association.**

The **covariance** and the **correlation coefficient** are measures of association that assess the direction and strength of a linear relationship between two variables, x and y. The sample covariance s_{xy} and the population covariance σ_{xy} are computed as $s_{xy} = \frac{\Sigma (x_i - \bar{x})(y_i - \bar{y})}{n-1}$ and $\sigma_{xy} = \frac{\Sigma (x_i - \mu_x)(y_i - \mu_y)}{N}$, respectively. The sample correlation coefficient r_{xy} and the population correlation coefficient ρ_{xy} are computed as $r_{xy} = \frac{s_{xy}}{s_x s_y}$ and $\rho_{xy} = \frac{\sigma_{xy}}{\sigma_x \sigma_y}$, respectively.

ADDITIONAL EXERCISES AND CASE STUDIES

Exercises

88. The following table lists the sales (in $ millions) of the top Italian restaurant chains in 2009.

Restaurant	Sales
Olive Garden	3,300
Carrabba's Italian Grill	629
Romano's Macaroni Grill	583
Maggiano's	366
Carino's Italian Grill	356
Buca di Beppo	220
Bertucci's	210

Source: *The Boston Globe*, July 31, 2010.

Calculate the mean, the median, and the mode. Which measure of central tendency best reflects typical sales? Explain.

89. The following table shows the annual returns (in percent) for Fidelity's Electronic and Utilities funds.

Year	Electronic	Utilities
2005	13.23	9.36
2006	1.97	32.33
2007	2.77	21.03
2008	−50.00	−35.21
2009	81.65	14.71

Source: www.finance.yahoo.com.

a. Calculate the sample mean, the sample variance, and the sample standard deviation for each fund.
b. Which fund had the higher average return?
c. Which fund was riskier over this time period? Use both the standard deviation and the coefficient of variation in your explanation.

d. Given a risk-free rate of 4%, which fund has the higher Sharpe ratio? What does this ratio imply?

90. The manager at a water park constructed the following frequency distribution to summarize attendance for 60 days in July and August.

Attendance	Frequency
1,000 up to 1,250	5
1,250 up to 1,500	6
1,500 up to 1,750	10
1,750 up to 2,000	20
2,000 up to 2,250	15
2,250 up to 2,500	4

a. Calculate the mean attendance.
b. Calculate the variance and the standard deviation.

91. Monthly stock prices (in $) for two competing firms are as follows.

Month	Firm A	Firm B
January	28	21
February	31	24
March	32	24
April	35	27
May	34	25
June	28	20

a. Calculate the sample mean, the sample variance, and the sample standard deviation for each firm's stock price.
b. Which firm had the higher average stock price over the time period?
c. Which firm's stock price had greater variability as measured by the standard deviation? Which firm's stock price had the greater relative dispersion?

92. The following table shows the revenues (in $ millions) for The Gap and American Eagle Outfitters for the years 2008–2010.

Year	Gap	American Eagle
2008	15.73	3.06
2009	14.53	2.99
2010	14.20	2.99

Source: Annual Reports for Gap, Inc., and American Eagle Outfitters, Inc.

a. Calculate the average growth rate for each firm.
b. Which firm had the higher growth rate over the 2008–2010 period?

93. Annual growth rates for individual firms in the toy industry tend to fluctuate dramatically, depending on consumers' tastes and current fads. Consider the following growth rates (in %) for two firms in this industry, Hasbro and Mattel.

Year	2005	2006	2007	2008	2009
Hasbro	3.0	2.1	21.8	4.8	1.2
Mattel	1.5	9.1	5.7	−0.1	−8.2

Source: Annual Reports for Hasbro, Inc., and Mattel Inc.

a. Calculate the geometric mean growth rate for each firm.
b. Use the standard deviation to evaluate the variability for each firm.
c. Which firm had the higher geometric mean growth rate? Which firm's growth rate had greater variability?

94. The National Sporting Goods Association (NSGA) conducted a survey of the ages of individuals that purchased skateboarding footwear. The ages of this survey are summarized in the following percent frequency distribution.

Age of User	Percent
Under 14 years old	35
14 to 17 years old	41
18 to 24 years old	15
25 to 34 years old	4
35 to 44 years old	4
45 to 64 years old	1

Suppose the survey was based on a sample of 200 individuals. Calculate the mean and the standard deviation of the age of individuals that purchased skateboarding shoes. Use 10 as the midpoint of the first class.

95. A manager of a local retail store analyzes the relationship between advertising (in $100s) and sales (in $1,000s) by reviewing the store's data for the previous six months.

Advertising	Sales
20	15
25	18
30	20
22	16
27	19
26	20

a. Calculate the mean of advertising and the mean of sales.
b. Calculate the standard deviation of advertising and the standard deviation of sales.
c. Calculate and interpret the covariance between advertising and sales.

d. Calculate and interpret the correlation coefficient.

96. The following table shows the annual returns (in %) for two of Putnam's mutual funds: the Voyager Growth Fund and the George Putnam Balanced Fund.

Year	Growth	Balanced
2011	−17.76	2.71
2012	14.39	12.36
2013	43.93	17.76
2014	9.55	10.48
2015	4.25	−1.11

Source: www.finance.yahoo.com.

a. Calculate and interpret the covariance.
b. Calculate and interpret the correlation coefficient.

97. **FILE** *Debt_Payments.* An economist wishes to summarize sample data from 26 metropolitan areas in the United States. The following table lists a portion of each area's 2010–2011 median income (Income in $1,000s) as well as the monthly unemployment rate (in %) and average consumer debt (in $) for August 2010.

Metropolitan Area	Income	Unemployment	Debt
Washington, D.C.	103.50	6.3	1285
Seattle	81.70	8.5	1135
⋮	⋮	⋮	⋮
Pittsburgh	63.00	8.3	763

Source: eFannieMae.com reports 2010–2011 area median incomes; www.bls.gov gives monthly unemployment rates for August 2010; Experian.com collected average monthly consumer debt payments in August 2010 and published the data in November 2010.

Compute summary measures for income, the monthly unemployment rate, and average consumer debt. Interpret these summary measures.

98. **FILE** *Car_Theft.* The accompanying table shows a portion of the number of cases of car thefts for the 50 states during 2010.

State	Car Theft
Alabama	658
Alaska	280
⋮	⋮
Wyoming	84

Source: www.fbi.gov.

a. Calculate the mean, the median, and the mode for the number of car thefts.
b. Use z-scores to determine if there are any outliers in the data. Are you surprised by the result?

99. **FILE** *Quarterback_Salaries.* American football is the highest paying sport on a per-game basis. Given that the quarterback is considered the most important player on an NFL team, he is typically well-compensated. Consider a portion of the following quarterback salary data (in $ millions) in 2009.

Name	Salary
Philip Rivers	25.5566
Jay Cutler	22.0441
⋮	⋮
Tony Romo	0.6260

Source: www.nfl.com.

a. Compute and interpret the mean and the median salary for a quarterback.
b. Compute and interpret the range and the standard deviation for quarterback salaries.

100. **FILE** *Gambling.* The accompanying table shows a portion of the number of cases of crime related to gambling (Gambling) and offenses against the family and children (Family Abuse) for the 50 states in the United States during 2010.

State	Gambling	Family Abuse
Alabama	47	1022
Alaska	10	315
⋮	⋮	⋮
Wyoming	0	194

Source: www.fbi.gov.

a. Construct a boxplot for gambling and use it to identify outliers, if any.
b. Construct a boxplot for abuse and use it to identify outliers, if any.
c. Calculate and interpret the sample correlation coefficient between gambling and family abuse.

101. **FILE** *Gas_Prices_2012.* The accompanying table shows a portion of the average price of gas (in $ per gallon) for the 50 states during April 2012.

State	Price
Alabama	4.36
Alaska	3.79
⋮	⋮
Wyoming	3.63

Source: AAA.com, data retrieved April 16, 2012.

a. Construct a boxplot for the gasoline price and use it to identify outliers, if any.
b. Confirm your analysis by using z-scores to determine if there are any outliers in the gasoline price.

CASE STUDIES

CASE STUDY 3.1   An article in *The Wall Street Journal* (July 11, 2008) outlined a number of reasons as to why the 16 teams in Major League Baseball's National League (NL) are inferior to the 14 teams in the American League (AL). One reason for the imbalance pointed to the disparity in opening-day payrolls: the average AL payroll is greater than the NL average. A portion of the data showing opening-day payroll (in $) for each team is shown in the accompanying table.

MLB_Salaries

Data for Case Study 3.1 Major League Baseball's Opening-Day Payrolls, 2010

American League	Payroll	National League	Payroll
New York Yankees	206333389	Chicago Cubs	146609000
Boston Red Sox	162447333	Philadelphia Phillies	141928379
⋮	⋮	⋮	⋮

Source: www.bizofbaseball.com.

In a report, use the sample information to

1. Discuss the mean and the median of AL and NL opening-day salaries and comment on skewness.
2. Compare the range and the standard deviation of AL and NL opening-day salaries.
3. Use these summary measures to comment on the findings in *The Wall Street Journal*.

CASE STUDY 3.2   Five years after graduating from college, Lucia Li feels that she is finally ready to invest some of her earnings. She has eliminated her credit card debt and has established an emergency fund. Her parents have been pleased with the performance of their mutual fund investments with Janus Capital Group. She has narrowed her search down to two mutual funds:

The Janus Balanced Fund (JANBX): This "core" fund consists of stocks and bonds and its goal is diversification. It has historically produced solid long-term returns through different market cycles.

The Janus Overseas Fund (JAOSX): This fund invests in overseas companies based on their individual merits instead of their geography or industry sector.

The following table reports a portion of the annual returns (in percent) for these two funds from 2000–2016.

Data for Case Study 3.2 Returns (in percent) for Janus Funds

FILE
Janus_Funds

Year	Balanced	Overseas
2000	−2.16	−18.57
2001	−5.04	−23.11
⋮	⋮	⋮
2016	4.51	−6.91

Source: finance.yahoo.com, data retrieved March 1, 2017.

In a report, use the sample information to

1. Calculate measures of central location to describe the similarities and the differences in these two funds' returns.
2. Calculate measures of dispersion to assess the risk of each fund.
3. Calculate and interpret measures of correlation between the two funds.

CASE STUDY 3.3 Due to a crisis in subprime lending, obtaining a mortgage has become difficult even for people with solid credit. In a report by the Associated Press (August 25, 2007), sales of existing homes fell for a 5th consecutive month, while home prices dropped for a record 12th month in July 2007. Mayan Horowitz, a research analyst for QuantExperts, wishes to study how the mortgage crunch has impacted the once-booming market of Florida. He collects data on the sale prices (in $1,000s) of 25 single-family homes in Fort Myers, Florida, in January 2007 and collects another sample in July 2007. For a valid comparison, he samples only three-bedroom homes, each with 1,500 square feet or less of space on a lot size of 10,000 square feet or less. A portion of the data is shown in the accompanying table.

Data for Case Study 3.3 Home Prices (in $1,000s) in January 2007 and July 2007

Number	January	July
1	100	136
2	190	235
⋮	⋮	⋮
25	200	180

Source: www.zillow.com.

In a report, use the sample information to

1. Compare the mean, the median, and the mode in each of the two sample periods.
2. Compare the standard deviation and the coefficient of variation in each of the two sample periods.
3. Discuss significant changes in the housing market in Fort Myers over the 6-month period.

CASE STUDY 3.4 Nike's Online Annual Report provides total revenues (in millions of $) for the Western Europe and Greater China regions for the years 2011 through 2015 as follows:

Data for Case Study 3.4
(a) Nike Revenues in Western Europe and Greater China (in millions of $)

	2011	2012	2013	2014	2015
Western Europe	3,868	4,144	4,128	4,979	5,709
Greater China	2,060	2,539	2,453	2,602	3,067

Source: Nike Inc. Annual Reports.

Adidas' Online Annual Report provides total revenues (in millions of €) for the Western Europe and Greater China regions for the years 2011 through 2015 as follows:

Data for Case Study 3.4
(b) Adidas Revenues in Western Europe and Greater China (in millions of €)

	2011	2012	2013	2014	2015
Western Europe	3,922	4,076	3,800	3,793	4,539
Greater China	1,229	1,562	1,655	1,776	2,449

Source: Adidas Group Annual Reports.

In a report, use the sample information to

1. Summarize the growth rates in Western Europe and Greater China for Nike.
2. Summarize the growth rates in Western Europe and Greater China for Adidas.
3. Discuss the similarities and the differences of the growth rates in the two companies.

APPENDIX 3.1 Guidelines for Other Software Packages

The following section provides brief commands for Minitab, SPSS, and JMP. More detailed instructions can be found on McGraw-Hill's Connect or through your instructor. Copy and paste the specified data file into the relevant software spreadsheet prior to following the commands.

Minitab

Calculating Summary Measures

Growth_Value

A. (Replicating Table 3.4) From the menu, choose **Stat > Basic Statistics > Display Descriptive Statistics.** Then, under **Variables**, select Growth and Value. Click **Statistics**.

B. Choose the summary measures that you wish to calculate, such as Mean, Standard deviation, etc.

Constructing a Boxplot

Growth_Value

A. (Replicating Figure 3.4) From the menu, choose **Graph > Boxplot > One Y > Simple**.

B. Under **Graph variables**, select Growth. Click on **Data View**. Choose **Interquartile range box**, **Outlier symbols**, **Individual symbols**, and **Median connect line**.

C. Click on **Scale** and select the **Transpose value and category scales** box.

Calculating the Covariance and the Correlation Coefficient

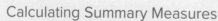
Growth_Value

(Replicating Example 3.23) From the menu, choose **Stat > Basic Statistics > Covariance** (choose **Correlation** to calculate the correlation coefficient). Under **Variables**, select Growth and Value.

SPSS

Calculating Summary Measures

Growth_Value

A. (Replicating Table 3.4) From the menu, choose **Analyze > Descriptive Statistics > Descriptives**.

B. Under **Variables**, select Growth and Value. Choose **Options**. Select the summary measures that you wish to calculate, such as Mean, Std. deviation, etc.

Calculating the Covariance and the Correlation Coefficient

Growth_Value

A. (Replicating Example 3.23) From the menu, choose **Analyze > Correlate > Bivariate**.

B. Under **Variables**, select Growth and Value. Under **Correlation Coefficients**, select **Pearson**. Choose **Options**. Under **Statistics**, select **Cross-product deviations and covariances**.

JMP

Calculating Summary Measures and Constructing a Boxplot

(Replicating Table 3.4 and Figure 3.4) From the menu, choose **Analyze > Distribution**. Under **Select Columns**, select Growth and Value, and under **Cast Selected Columns into Roles**, choose **Y, Columns**.

FILE
Growth_Value

Calculating the Covariance and the Correlation Coefficient

A. (Replicating Example 3.23) From the menu, choose **Analyze > Multivariate Methods > Multivariate**. Under **Select Columns**, select Growth and Value, and under **Cast Selected Columns into Roles**, select **Y, Columns**.

B. Click the red triangle beside **Multivariate**. Select **Covariance Matrix**.

FILE
Growth_Value

4 Introduction to Probability

Every day we make choices about issues in the presence of uncertainty. Uncertainty describes a situation where a variety of events are possible. Usually, we either implicitly or explicitly assign probabilities to these events and plan or act accordingly. For instance, we read the paper, watch the news, or check the Internet to determine the likelihood of rain and whether we should carry an umbrella. Retailers strengthen their sales force before the end-of-year holiday season in anticipation of an increase in shoppers. The Federal Reserve cuts interest rates when it believes the economy is at risk for weak growth and raises interest rates when it feels that inflation is the greater risk. By figuring out the chances of various events, we are better prepared to make the more desirable choices. This chapter presents the essential probability tools needed to frame and address many real-world issues involving uncertainty. Probability theory turns out to be the very foundation for statistical inference, and numerous concepts introduced in this chapter are essential for understanding later chapters.

©Fab Fernandez/Image Source/Getty Images RF

INTRODUCTORY CASE

Sportswear Brands

Annabel Gonzalez is chief retail analyst at Longmeadow Consultants, a marketing firm. One aspect of her job is to track sports-apparel sales and uncover any particular trends that may be unfolding in the industry. Recently, she has been following Under Armour, Inc., the pioneer in the compression-gear market. Compression garments are meant to keep moisture away from a wearer's body during athletic activities in warm and cool weather. Under Armour has experienced exponential growth since the firm went public in November 2005. However, Nike, Inc., and Adidas Group, with 18% and 10% market shares, respectively, have aggressively entered the compression-gear market (*The Wall Street Journal*, October 23, 2007).

As part of her analysis, Annabel would first like to examine whether the age of the customer matters when buying compression clothing. Her initial feeling is that the Under Armour brand attracts a younger customer, whereas the more established companies, Nike and Adidas, draw an older clientele. She believes this information is relevant to advertisers and retailers in the sporting goods industry, as well as to some in the financial community. She collects data on 600 recent purchases in the compression-gear market. She cross-classifies the data by age group and brand name, as shown in Table 4.1.

TABLE 4.1 Purchases of Compression Garments Based on Age and Brand Name

Age Group	Brand Name		
	Under Armour	Nike	Adidas
Under 35 years	174	132	90
35 years and older	54	72	78

Annabel wants to use the sample information to

1. Calculate and interpret relevant probabilities concerning brand name and age.

2. Determine whether the appeal of the Under Armour brand is mostly to younger customers.

A synopsis of this case is provided at the end of Section 4.3.

Describe fundamental
probability concepts.

Since many choices we make involve some degree of uncertainty, we are better prepared for the eventual outcome if we can use probabilities to describe which events
are likely and which are unlikely. A **probability** is defined as follows.

> A probability is a numerical value that measures the likelihood that an event
> occurs. This value is between zero and one, where a value of zero indicates
> *impossible* events and a value of one indicates *definite* events.

In order to define an event and assign the appropriate probability to it, it is useful to
first establish some terminology and impose some structure on the situation.

An **experiment** is a process that leads to one of several possible outcomes. The diversity of the outcomes of an experiment is due to the uncertainty of the real world.
When you purchase a new computer, there is no guarantee as to how long it will last
before any repair work is needed. It may need repair in the first year, in the second
year, or after two years. You can think of this as an experiment because the actual
outcome will be determined only over time. Other examples of an experiment include whether a roll of a fair die will result in a value of 1, 2, 3, 4, 5, or 6; whether the
toss of a coin results in heads or tails; whether a project is finished early, on time, or
late; whether the economy will improve, stay the same, or deteriorate; and whether a
ball game will end in a win, loss, or tie.

A **sample space**, denoted by S, of an experiment contains all possible outcomes
of the experiment. For example, suppose the sample space representing the letter
grade in a course is given by $S = \{A, B, C, D, F\}$. The sample space for an experiment
need not be unique. For example, in the above experiment, we can also define the
sample space with just P (pass) and F (fail) outcomes; that is, $S = \{P, F\}$. Note that if
the teacher also gives out an I (incomplete) grade, then neither of the sample spaces
defined above are valid because they do not contain all possible outcomes of the
experiment.

> An experiment is a process that leads to one of several possible outcomes. A
> sample space, denoted S, of an experiment contains all possible outcomes of
> the experiment.

EXAMPLE 4.1

A snowboarder competing in the Winter Olympic Games is trying to assess her
probability of earning a medal in her event, the ladies' halfpipe. Construct the
appropriate sample space.

SOLUTION: The athlete's attempt to predict her chances of earning a medal is an
experiment because, until the Winter Games occur, the outcome is unknown.
We formalize an experiment by constructing its sample space. The athlete's
competition has four possible outcomes: gold medal, silver medal, bronze
medal, and no medal. We formally write the sample space as $S = \{$gold, silver,
bronze, no medal$\}$.

Events

An **event** is a subset of the sample space. A simple event consists of just one of the possible outcomes of an experiment. Getting an A in a course is an example of a simple event. An event may also contain several outcomes of an experiment. For example, we can define an event as getting a passing grade in a course; this event is formed by the subset of outcomes A, B, C, and D.

> An event is any subset of outcomes of the experiment. It is called a simple event if it contains a single outcome.

Let us define two events from Example 4.1, where one event represents "earning a medal" and the other denotes "failing to earn a medal." These events are **exhaustive** because they include all outcomes in the sample space. In the earlier grade-distribution example, the events of getting grades A and B are not exhaustive events because they do not include many feasible grades in the sample space. However, the events P and F, defined as "pass" and "fail," respectively, are exhaustive.

Another important probability concept concerns **mutually exclusive** events. For two mutually exclusive events, the occurrence of one event precludes the occurrence of the other. Suppose we define the two events "at least earning a silver medal" (outcomes of gold and silver) and "at most earning a silver medal" (outcomes of silver, bronze, no medal). These two events are exhaustive because no outcome of the experiment is omitted. However, in this case, the events are not mutually exclusive because the outcome "silver" appears in both events. Going back to the grade-distribution example, while the events of getting grades A and B are not exhaustive, they are mutually exclusive, since you cannot possibly get an A as well as a B in the same course. However, getting grades P and F are mutually exclusive and exhaustive. Similarly, the events defined as "at least earning a silver medal" and "at most earning a bronze medal" are mutually exclusive and exhaustive.

> Events are exhaustive if all possible outcomes of an experiment belong to the events. Events are mutually exclusive if they do not share any common outcome of an experiment.

For any experiment, we can define events based on one or more outcomes of the experiment and also combine events to form new events. The **union** of two events, denoted $A \cup B$, is the event consisting of all outcomes in A or B. A useful way to illustrate these concepts is through the use of a Venn diagram, named after the British mathematician John Venn (1834–1923). Figure 4.1 shows a Venn diagram where the rectangle represents the sample space S and the two circles represent events A and B. The union $A \cup B$ is the portion in the Venn diagram that is included in either A or B.

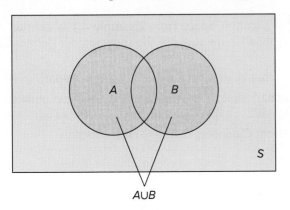

FIGURE 4.1
The union of two events, $A \cup B$

The **intersection** of two events, denoted $A \cap B$, is the event consisting of all outcomes in A and B. Figure 4.2 depicts the intersection of two events A and B. The intersection $A \cap B$ is the portion in the Venn diagram that is included in both A and B.

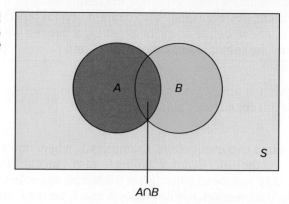

FIGURE 4.2
The intersection of two events, $A \cap B$

The **complement** of event A, denoted A^c, is the event consisting of all outcomes in the sample space S that are not in A. In Figure 4.3, A^c is everything in S that is not included in A.

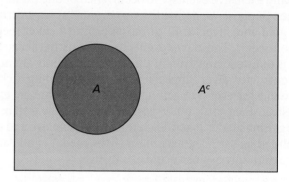

FIGURE 4.3
The complement of an event, A^c

COMBINING EVENTS

- The union of two events, denoted $A \cup B$, is the event consisting of all outcomes in A or B.
- The intersection of two events, denoted $A \cap B$, is the event consisting of all outcomes in A and B.
- The complement of event A, denoted A^c, is the event consisting of all outcomes in the sample space S that are not in A.

EXAMPLE 4.2

Recall that the snowboarder's sample space from Example 4.1 is defined as $S = \{$gold, silver, bronze, no medal$\}$. Now suppose the snowboarder defines the following three events:

- $A = \{$gold, silver, bronze$\}$; that is, event A denotes earning a medal;
- $B = \{$silver, bronze, no medal$\}$; that is, event B denotes earning at most a silver medal; and
- $C = \{$no medal$\}$; that is, event C denotes failing to earn a medal.

a. Find $A \cup B$ and $B \cup C$.
b. Find $A \cap B$ and $A \cap C$.
c. Find B^c.

SOLUTION:

a. The union of A and B denotes all outcomes common to A or B; here, the event $A \cup B = \{$gold, silver, bronze, no medal$\}$. Note that there is no double counting of the outcomes "silver" or "bronze" in $A \cup B$. Similarly, we have the event $B \cup C = \{$silver, bronze, no medal$\}$.

b. The intersection of A and B denotes all outcomes common to A and B; here, the event $A \cap B = \{$silver, bronze$\}$. The event $A \cap C = \varnothing$, where $\varnothing$ denotes the null (empty) set; no common outcomes appear in both A and C.

c. The complement of B denotes all outcomes in S that are not in B; here, the event $B^c = \{$gold$\}$.

Assigning Probabilities

Now that we have described a valid sample space and the various ways in which we can define events from that sample space, we are ready to assign probabilities. When we arrive at a probability, we generally are able to categorize the probability as a subjective probability, an empirical probability, or a classical probability. Regardless of the method used, there are two defining properties of probability.

> ### THE TWO DEFINING PROPERTIES OF PROBABILITY
>
> 1. The probability of any event A is a value between 0 and 1; that is, $0 \leq P(A) \leq 1$.
> 2. The sum of the probabilities of any list of mutually exclusive and exhaustive events equals 1.

Suppose the snowboarder from Example 4.1 believes that there is a 10% chance that she will earn a gold medal, a 15% chance that she will earn a silver medal, a 20% chance that she will earn a bronze medal, and a 55% chance that she will fail to earn a medal. She has assigned a **subjective probability** to each of the simple events. She made a personal assessment of these probabilities without referencing any data.

The snowboarder believes that the most likely outcome is failing to earn a medal since she gives that outcome the greatest chance of occurring at 55%. When formally writing out the probability that an event occurs, we generally construct a probability statement. Here, the probability statement might take the form: $P(\{$no medal$\}) = 0.55$, where $P($"event"$)$ represents the probability that a given event occurs. Table 4.2 summarizes these events and their respective subjective probabilities. Note that here the events are mutually exclusive and exhaustive.

TABLE 4.2 Snowboarder's Subjective Probabilities

Event	Probability
Gold	0.10
Silver	0.15
Bronze	0.20
No medal	0.55

Reading from the table we can readily see, for instance, that she assesses that there is a 15% chance that she will earn a silver medal, or $P(\{$silver$\}) = 0.15$. We should note that all the probabilities are between the values of zero and one, and they add up to one, thus meeting the defining properties of probability.

Suppose the snowboarder wants to calculate the probability of earning a medal. In Example 4.2, we defined "earning a medal" as event A, so the probability statement takes the form $P(A)$. We calculate this probability by summing the probabilities of the outcomes in A, or equivalently,

$$P(A) = P(\{gold\}) + P(\{silver\}) + P(\{bronze\}) = 0.10 + 0.15 + 0.20 = 0.45.$$

EXAMPLE 4.3

Given the events in Example 4.2 and the probabilities in Table 4.2, calculate the following probabilities.

a. $P(B \cup C)$

b. $P(A \cap C)$

c. $P(B^c)$

SOLUTION:

a. The probability that event B or event C occurs is

$$P(B \cup C) = P(\{silver\}) + P(\{bronze\}) + P(\{no\ medal\})$$
$$= 0.15 + 0.20 + 0.55 = 0.90.$$

b. The probability that event A and event C occur is

$$P(A \cap C) = 0;\ \text{recall that there are no common outcomes in } A \text{ and } C.$$

c. The probability that the complement of B occurs is

$$P(B^c) = P(\{gold\}) = 0.10.$$

In many instances, we calculate probabilities by referencing data based on the observed outcomes of an experiment. The **empirical probability** of an event is the observed relative frequency with which an event occurs. The experiment must be repeated a large number of times for empirical probabilities to be accurate.

EXAMPLE 4.4

The frequency distribution in Table 4.3 summarizes the ages of the richest 400 Americans. Suppose we randomly select one of these individuals.

a. What is the probability that the individual is at least 50 but less than 60 years old?

b. What is the probability that the individual is younger than 60 years old?

c. What is the probability that the individual is at least 80 years old?

TABLE 4.3 Frequency Distribution of Ages of 400 Richest Americans

Ages	Frequency
< 40	13
40 up to 50	24
50 up to 60	67
60 up to 70	113
70 up to 80	117
80 up to 90	55
≥ 90	11

Source: www.forbes.com, 2016 Ranking.

SOLUTION: In Table 4.3a, we first label each outcome with letter notation; for instance, the outcome "< 40" is denoted as event A. Next we calculate the relative frequency of each event and use the relative frequency to denote the probability of the event.

TABLE 4.3a Relative Frequency Distribution of Ages of 400 Richest Americans

Ages	Event	Frequency	Relative Frequency
< 40	A	13	13/400 = 0.0325
40 up to 50	B	24	0.0600
50 up to 60	C	67	0.1675
60 up to 70	D	113	0.2825
70 up to 80	E	117	0.2925
80 up to 90	F	55	0.1375
≥ 90	G	11	0.0275

a. The probability that an individual is at least 50 but less than 60 years old is

$$P(C) = \frac{67}{400} = 0.1675.$$

b. The probability that an individual is younger than 60 years old is

$$P(A \cup B \cup C) = \frac{13 + 24 + 67}{400} = 0.26.$$

c. The probability that an individual is at least 80 years old is

$$P(F \cup G) = \frac{55 + 11}{400} = 0.17.$$

In a more narrow range of well-defined problems, we can sometimes deduce probabilities by reasoning about the problem. The resulting probability is a **classical probability**. Classical probabilities are often used in games of chance. They are based on the assumption that all outcomes of an experiment are equally likely. Therefore, the classical probability of an event is computed as the number of outcomes belonging to the event divided by the total number of outcomes.

EXAMPLE 4.5

Suppose our experiment consists of rolling a six-sided die. Then we can define the appropriate sample space as $S = \{1, 2, 3, 4, 5, 6\}$.

a. What is the probability that we roll a 2?
b. What is the probability that we roll a 2 or 5?
c. What is the probability that we roll an even number?

SOLUTION: Here we recognize that each outcome is equally likely. So with 6 possible outcomes, each outcome has a 1/6 chance of occurring.

a. The probability that we roll a 2, $P(\{2\})$, is thus 1/6.
b. The probability that we roll a 2 or 5, $P(\{2\}) + P(\{5\})$, is $1/6 + 1/6 = 1/3$.
c. The probability that we roll an even number, $P(\{2\}) + P(\{4\}) + P(\{6\})$, is $1/6 + 1/6 + 1/6 = 1/2$.

According to the famous **law of large numbers**, the empirical probability approaches the classical probability if the experiment is run a very large number of times. Consider, for example, flipping a fair coin 10 times. It is possible that heads may not show up exactly 5 times and, therefore, the relative frequency may not be 0.5. However, if we flip the fair coin a very large number of times, heads will show up approximately 1/2 of the time. This would make the empirical probability equal the classical probability of 0.50.

Probabilities Expressed as Odds

©Gene J. Puskar/AP Images

Even though we tend to report the probability of an event occurring as a number between 0 and 1, alternative approaches to expressing probabilities include percentages and odds. Specifically, in wagering it is common to state probabilities in terms of odds. For instance, at the start of the 2008–2009 football season, the Pittsburgh Steelers were not one of the strong favorites to win the Super Bowl, with odds for winning of 1:24 (*Betfair* website). In other words, an individual who bet $1 on the Steelers winning the Super Bowl prior to the season would have won $24 in profits. Since the bettor also receives the original stake back, for every $1 staked in the wager, he/she would have gotten back $25. We can convert the odds ratio into a probability by using the following generalization.

Thus, with odds for winning the Super Bowl of 1:24, we can solve for the probability of the Steelers winning as: $1/(1 + 24) = 1/25$ or 0.04. Moreover, the bet's anticipated profit is $0 because (0.04 probability of winning) × ($24 profit if the wager is won) + (0.96 probability of losing) × (−$1 if the wager is lost) = 0.96 + (−0.96) = 0.

This is an example of an expected value calculation, which we discuss further in Chapter 5. We would also like to point out that sports betting odds are usually displayed in various formats, including American, British, or European formats; the details are beyond the scope of this chapter.

EXAMPLE 4.6

Days prior to the 2009 Super Bowl, the Pittsburgh Steelers' odds for beating the Arizona Cardinals increased to approximately 2:1. What was the probability of the Steelers winning just prior to the Super Bowl?

SOLUTION: The probability that the Steelers would win the Super Bowl rose to

$$\frac{a}{a + b} = \frac{2}{2 + 1} = 0.67.$$

(Note: The Steelers did win the Super Bowl, but just barely, scoring the winning touchdown with 35 seconds left in the game.)

Similarly, we can convert a probability to an odds ratio using the following generalization:

CONVERTING A PROBABILITY TO AN ODDS RATIO

If $P(A)$ denotes the probability of an event A occurring, and $P(A)$ does not equal zero or one, then:

The odds *for* A occurring equal $\dfrac{P(A)}{1 - P(A)}$, and

The odds *against* A occurring equal $\dfrac{1 - P(A)}{P(A)}$.

EXAMPLE 4.7

The summer of 2008 proved to be another difficult period for travelers. New York's Kennedy Airport topped the list with the lowest on-time arrival rate: the likelihood that a plane arrived on-time occurred only 56% of the time (*The Wall Street Journal*, September 9, 2008). Travelers at Atlanta's Hartsfield–Jackson Airport fared a bit better, where the on-time arrival rate was 74%.

a. Calculate the odds for a plane arriving on-time at New York's Kennedy Airport.

b. Calculate the odds for a plane arriving on-time at Atlanta's Hartsfield–Jackson Airport.

SOLUTION:

a. With an on-time arrival probability of 0.56 for New York's Kennedy Airport we find

$$\frac{P(\{\text{on-time}\})}{1 - P(\{\text{on-time}\})} = \frac{0.56}{1 - 0.56} = \frac{0.56}{0.44} = 1.27.$$

Therefore, we would report the odds for arriving on-time in New York as 1.27 to 1. Note that given the odds for arriving on-time as 1.27:1, we can deduce $P(\{\text{on-time}\})$ as

$$\frac{1.27}{2.27} = 0.56.$$

b. With an on-time arrival probability of 0.74 for Atlanta's Hartsfield–Jackson Airport, we find

$$\frac{P(\{\text{on-time}\})}{1 - P(\{\text{on-time}\})} = \frac{0.74}{1 - 0.74} = \frac{0.74}{0.26} = 2.85.$$

Therefore, we report the odds for arriving on-time in Atlanta as 2.85 to 1.

EXERCISES 4.1

Mechanics

1. Determine whether the following probabilities are best categorized as subjective, empirical, or classical probabilities.
   a. Before flipping a fair coin, Sunil assesses that he has a 50% chance of obtaining tails.
   b. At the beginning of the semester, John believes he has a 90% chance of receiving straight A's.
   c. A political reporter announces that there is a 40% chance that the next person to come out of the conference room will be a Republican, since there are 60 Republicans and 90 Democrats in the room.

2. Express each of the probabilities in the preceding question as
   a. odds assessed by Sunil for obtaining tails.
   b. odds assessed by John for receiving straight A's.
   c. odds assessed by the reporter for a Republican coming out of the room.

3. A sample space S yields five equally likely events, $A, B, C, D,$ and E.
   a. Find $P(D)$.
   b. Find $P(B^c)$.
   c. Find $P(A \cup C \cup E)$.

4. You roll a die with the sample space $S = \{1, 2, 3, 4, 5, 6\}$. You define A as $\{1, 2, 3\}$, B as $\{1, 2, 3, 5, 6\}$, C as $\{4, 6\}$, and D as $\{4, 5, 6\}$. Determine which of the following events are exhaustive and/or mutually exclusive.
   a. A and B
   b. A and C
   c. A and D
   d. B and C

5. A sample space, S, yields four simple events, $A, B, C,$ and D, such that $P(A) = 0.35$, $P(B) = 0.10$, and $P(C) = 0.25$.
   a. Find $P(D)$.
   b. Find $P(C^c)$.
   c. Find $P(A \cup B)$.

Applications

6. Survey data, based on 65,000 mobile phone subscribers, shows that 44% of the subscribers use smartphones (*Forbes*, December 15, 2011). Based on this information, you infer that the probability that a mobile phone subscriber uses a smartphone is 0.44. Would you consider this probability estimate accurate? Would you label this probability as subjective, empirical, or classical?

7. Jane Peterson has taken Amtrak to travel from New York to Washington, DC, on six occasions, of which three times the train was late. Therefore, Jane tells her friends that the probability that this train will arrive on time is 0.50. Would you label this probability as empirical or classical? Why would this probability not be accurate?

8. Consider the following scenarios to determine if the mentioned combination of attributes represents a union or an intersection.
   a. A marketing firm is looking for a candidate with a business degree and at least five years of work experience.
   b. A family has decided to purchase Toyota or Honda.

9. Consider the following scenarios to determine if the mentioned combination of attributes represents a union or an intersection.
   a. There are two courses that seem interesting to you, and you would be happy if you can take at least one of them.
   b. There are two courses that seem interesting to you, and you would be happy if you can take both of them.

10. You apply for a position at two firms. Let event A represent the outcome of getting an offer from the first firm and event B represent the outcome of getting an offer from the second firm.
    a. Explain why events A and B are not exhaustive.
    b. Explain why events A and B are not mutually exclusive.

11. An alarming number of U.S. adults are either overweight or obese. The distinction between overweight and obese is made on the basis of body mass index (BMI), expressed as weight/height^2. An adult is considered overweight if the BMI is 25 or more but less than 30. An obese adult will have a BMI of 30 or greater. According to a January 2012 article in the *Journal of the American Medical Association*, 33.1% of the adult population in the United States is overweight and 35.7% is obese. Use this information to answer the following questions.
    a. What is the probability that a randomly selected adult is either overweight or obese?
    b. What is the probability that a randomly selected adult is neither overweight nor obese?
    c. Are the events "overweight" and "obese" exhaustive?
    d. Are the events "overweight" and "obese" mutually exclusive?

12. Many communities are finding it more and more difficult to fill municipal positions such as town administrators, finance directors, and treasurers. The following table shows the proportion of municipal managers by age group in the United States for the years 1971 and 2006.

Age	1971	2006
Under 30	0.26	0.01
30 to 40	0.45	0.12
41 to 50	0.21	0.28
51 to 60	0.05	0.48
Over 60	0.03	0.11

Source: *The International City-County Management Association.*

a. In 1971, what was the probability that a municipal manager was 40 years old or younger? In 2006, what was the probability that a municipal manager was 40 years old or younger?

b. In 1971, what was the probability that a municipal manager was 51 years old or older? In 2006, what was the probability that a municipal manager was 51 years old or older?

c. What trends in ages can you detect from municipal managers in 1971 versus municipal managers in 2006?

13. At four community health centers on Cape Cod, Massachusetts, 15,164 patients were asked to respond to questions designed to detect depression (*The Boston Globe*, June 11, 2008). The survey produced the following results.

Diagnosis	Number
Mild	3,257
Moderate	1,546
Moderately Severe	975
Severe	773
No Depression	8,613

a. What is the probability that a randomly selected patient suffered from mild depression?

b. What is the probability that a randomly selected patient did not suffer from depression?

c. What is the probability that a randomly selected patient suffered from moderately severe to severe depression?

d. Given that the national figure for moderately severe to severe depression is approximately 6.7%, does it appear that there is a higher rate of depression in this summer resort community? Explain.

14. On Sunday, July 11, 2010, Spain and the Netherlands played in the 2010 World Cup Final in Johannesburg. On the eve of the final, many betting lines were offering Spain's odds for winning at 15:8 (*Oddschecker* website).

a. Spain won the World Cup. Suppose you had bet $1,000 on Spain. What was your net gain? If Spain had lost, what would have been your net loss?

b. What was the implied probability of Spain winning the final?

15. Prior to the Academy Awards ceremony in 2009, the United Kingdom bookmaker Ladbrokes reported the following odds for winning an Oscar in the category of best actress (*The Wall Street Journal*, February 20, 2009).

Best Actress	Movie	Odds
Anne Hathaway	*Rachel Getting Married*	2:11
Angelina Jolie	*Changeling*	1:20
Melissa Leo	*Frozen River*	1:33
Meryl Streep	*Doubt*	3:10
Kate Winslet	*The Reader*	5:2

a. Express the odds for each actress winning as a probability.

b. According to your calculations, which actress was most likely to win an Oscar? Kate Winslet won her first Oscar on February 22, 2009. Was your prediction realized?

4.2 RULES OF PROBABILITY

In the previous section, we discussed how the probability of an event is assigned. Here we present various rules used to combine probabilities of events.

The Complement Rule

The **complement rule** follows from one of the defining properties of probability: the sum of probabilities assigned to simple events in a sample space must equal one. Note that since S is a collection of all possible outcomes of the experiment (nothing else can happen), $P(S) = 1$. Let's revisit the sample space that we constructed when we rolled a six-sided die: $S = \{1, 2, 3, 4, 5, 6\}$. Suppose event A is defined as an even-numbered outcome or $A = \{2, 4, 6\}$. We then know that the complement of A, A^c, is the set consisting of $\{1, 3, 5\}$. Moreover, we can deduce that $P(A) = 1/2$ and $P(A^c) = 1/2$, so $P(A) + P(A^c) = 1$. Rearranging this equation, we obtain the complement rule: $P(A^c) = 1 - P(A)$.

> ### THE COMPLEMENT RULE
> The complement rule states that the probability of the complement of an event, $P(A^c)$, is equal to one minus the probability of the event; that is, $P(A^c) = 1 - P(A)$.

The complement rule is quite straightforward and rather simple, but it is widely used and powerful.

EXAMPLE 4.8

According to the 2010 U.S. Census, 37% of women ages 25 to 34 have earned at least a college degree, as compared with 30% of men in the same age group.

a. What is the probability that a randomly selected woman between the ages of 25 to 34 does not have a college degree?

b. What is the probability that a randomly selected man between the ages of 25 to 34 does not have a college degree?

SOLUTION:

a. Let's define A as the event that a randomly selected woman between the ages of 25 and 34 has a college degree; thus, $P(A) = 0.37$. In this problem, we are interested in the complement of A. So $P(A^c) = 1 - P(A) = 1 - 0.37 = 0.63$.

b. Similarly, we define B as the event that a randomly selected man between the ages of 25 to 34 has a college degree, so $P(B) = 0.30$. Thus, $P(B^c) = 1 - P(B) = 1 - 0.30 = 0.70$.

The Addition Rule

The **addition rule** allows us to find the probability of the union of two events. Suppose we want to find the probability that either A occurs or B occurs, so in probability terms, $P(A \cup B)$. We reproduce the Venn diagram, used earlier in Figure 4.1, to help in exposition. Figure 4.4 shows a sample space S with the two events A and B. Recall that the union, $A \cup B$, is the portion in the Venn diagram that is included in either A or B. The intersection, $A \cap B$, is the portion in the Venn diagram that is included in both A and B.

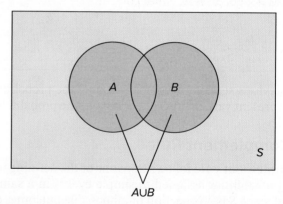

FIGURE 4.4
Finding the probability of the union of two events, $P(A \cup B)$

$A \cup B$

If we try to obtain $P(A \cup B)$ by simply summing $P(A)$ with $P(B)$, then we overstate the probability because we double-count the probability of the intersection of A and B, $P(A \cap B)$. When implementing the addition rule, we sum $P(A)$ and $P(B)$ and then subtract $P(A \cap B)$ from this sum.

THE ADDITION RULE

The addition rule states that the probability that A or B occurs, or that at least one of these events occurs, is equal to the probability that A occurs, plus the probability that B occurs, minus the probability that both A and B occur. Equivalently,

$$P(A \cup B) = P(A) + P(B) - P(A \cap B).$$

EXAMPLE 4.9

Anthony feels that he has a 75% chance of getting an A in Statistics and a 55% chance of getting an A in Managerial Economics. He also believes he has a 40% chance of getting an A in both classes.

a. What is the probability that he gets an A in at least one of these courses?

b. What is the probability that he does not get an A in either of these courses?

SOLUTION:

a. Let $P(A_S)$ correspond to the probability of getting an A in Statistics and $P(A_M)$ correspond to the probability of getting an A in Managerial Economics. Thus, $P(A_S) = 0.75$ and $P(A_M) = 0.55$. In addition, there is a 40% chance that Anthony gets an A in both classes; that is, $P(A_S \cap A_M) = 0.40$. In order to find the probability that he receives an A in at least one of these courses, we calculate:

$$P(A_S \cup A_M) = P(A_S) + P(A_M) - P(A_S \cap A_M) = 0.75 + 0.55 - 0.40 = 0.90.$$

b. The probability that he does not receive an A in either of these two courses is actually the complement of the union of the two events; that is, $P((A_S \cup A_M)^c)$. We calculated the union in part a, so using the complement rule we have

$$P((A_S \cup A_M)^c) = 1 - P(A_S \cup A_M) = 1 - 0.90 = 0.10.$$

An alternative expression that correctly captures the required probability is $P((A_S \cup A_M)^c) = P(A_S^c \cap A_M^c)$. A common mistake is to calculate the probability as $P((A_S \cap A_M)^c) = 1 - P(A_S \cap A_M) = 1 - 0.40 = 0.60$, which simply indicates that there is a 60% chance that Anthony will not get an A in both courses. This is clearly not the required probability that Anthony does not get an A in either course.

The Addition Rule for Mutually Exclusive Events

As mentioned earlier, mutually exclusive events do not share any outcome of an experiment. Figure 4.5 shows the Venn diagram for two mutually exclusive events; note that the circles do not intersect.

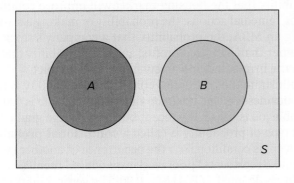

FIGURE 4.5
Mutually exclusive events

For mutually exclusive events A and B, the probability of their intersection is zero; that is, $P(A \cap B) = 0$. We need not concern ourselves with double-counting, and, therefore, the probability of the union is simply the sum of the two probabilities.

THE ADDITION RULE FOR MUTUALLY EXCLUSIVE EVENTS

If A and B are mutually exclusive events, then $P(A \cap B) = 0$ and, therefore, the addition rule simplifies to $P(A \cup B) = P(A) + P(B)$.

EXAMPLE 4.10

Samantha Greene, a college senior, contemplates her future immediately after graduation. She thinks there is a 25% chance that she will join the Peace Corps and teach English in Madagascar for the next few years. Alternatively, she believes there is a 35% chance that she will enroll in a full-time law school program in the United States.

a. What is the probability that she joins the Peace Corps or enrolls in law school?

b. What is the probability that she does not choose either of these options?

SOLUTION:

a. We can write the probability that Samantha joins the Peace Corps as $P(A) = 0.25$ and the probability that she enrolls in law school as $P(B) = 0.35$. Immediately after college, Samantha cannot choose both of these options. This implies that these events are mutually exclusive, so $P(A \cap B) = 0$. Thus, when solving for the probability that Samantha joins the Peace Corps or enrolls in law school, $P(A \cup B)$, we can simply sum $P(A)$ and $P(B)$: $P(A \cup B) = P(A) + P(B) = 0.25 + 0.35 = 0.60$.

b. In order to find the probability that she does not choose either of these options, we need to recognize that this probability is the complement of the union of the two events; that is, $P((A \cup B)^c)$. Therefore, using the complement rule, we have

$$P((A \cup B)^c) = 1 - P(A \cup B) = 1 - 0.60 = 0.40.$$

Conditional Probability

In business applications, the probability of interest is often a conditional probability. Examples include the probability that the housing market will improve conditional on the Federal Reserve taking remedial actions; the probability of making a six-figure salary conditional on getting an MBA; the probability that a company's stock price will go up conditional on higher-than-expected profits; and the probability that sales will improve conditional on the firm launching a new innovative product.

Let's use an example to illustrate the concept of conditional probability. Suppose the probability that a recent business college graduate finds a suitable job is 0.80. The probability of finding a suitable job is 0.90 if the recent business college graduate has prior work experience. This type of probability is called a **conditional probability**, where the probability of an event is conditional on the occurrence of another event. If A represents "finding a job" and B represents "prior work experience," then $P(A) = 0.80$ and the conditional probability is denoted as $P(A|B) = 0.90$. The vertical mark | means "given that," and the conditional probability is typically read as "the probability of A given B." In the above example, the probability of finding a suitable job increases from 0.80 to 0.90 when conditioned on prior work experience. In general, the conditional probability, $P(A|B)$, is greater than the **unconditional probability**, $P(A)$, if B exerts a positive influence on A. Similarly, $P(A|B)$ is less than $P(A)$ when B exerts a negative influence on A. Finally, if B exerts no influence on A, then $P(A|B)$ equals $P(A)$. It is common to refer to "unconditional probability" simply as "probability."

As we will see later, it is important that we write the event that has already occurred after the vertical mark, since in most instances $P(A|B) \neq P(B|A)$. In the above example $P(B|A)$ would represent the probability of prior work experience conditional on having found a job.

We again rely on the Venn diagram in Figure 4.6 to explain the conditional probability.

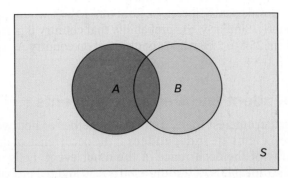

FIGURE 4.6
Finding the conditional probability, $P(A|B)$

Since $P(A|B)$ represents the probability of A conditional on B (B has occurred), the original sample space S reduces to B. The conditional probability $P(A|B)$ is based on the portion of A that is included in B. It is derived as the ratio of the probability of the intersection of A and B to the probability of B.

CONDITIONAL PROBABILITY

Given two events A and B, each with a positive probability of occurring, the probability that A occurs given that B has occurred (A conditioned on B) is equal to $P(A|B) = \frac{P(A \cap B)}{P(B)}$. Similarly, the probability that B occurs given that A has occurred (B conditioned on A) is equal to $P(B|A) = \frac{P(A \cap B)}{P(A)}$.

EXAMPLE 4.11

Economic globalization is defined as the integration of national economies into the international economy through trade, foreign direct investment, capital flows, migration, and the spread of technology. Although globalization is generally viewed favorably, it also increases the vulnerability of a country to economic conditions of the other country. An economist predicts a 60% chance that country A will perform poorly and a 25% chance that country B will perform poorly. There is also a 16% chance that both countries will perform poorly.

a. What is the probability that country A performs poorly given that country B performs poorly?

b. What is the probability that country B performs poorly given that country A performs poorly?

c. Interpret your findings.

SOLUTION: We first write down the available information in probability terms. Defining A as "country A performing poorly" and B as "country B performing poorly," we have the following information: $P(A) = 0.60$, $P(B) = 0.25$, and $P(A \cap B) = 0.16$.

a. $P(A|B) = \dfrac{P(A \cap B)}{P(B)} = \dfrac{0.16}{0.25} = 0.64$

b. $P(B|A) = \dfrac{P(A \cap B)}{P(A)} = \dfrac{0.16}{0.60} = 0.27$

c. It appears that globalization has definitely made these countries vulnerable to the economic woes of the other country. The probability that country A performs poorly increases from 60% to 64% when country B has performed poorly. Similarly, the probability that country B performs poorly increases from 25% to 27% when conditioned on country A performing poorly.

LO **4.3**

Distinguish between independent and dependent events.

Independent and Dependent Events

Of particular interest to researchers is whether or not two events influence one another. Two events are **independent** if the occurrence of one event does not affect the probability of the occurrence of the other event. Let's revisit the earlier example where the probability of finding a job is 0.80 and the probability of finding a job given prior work experience is 0.90. Prior work experience exerts a positive influence on finding a job because the conditional probability, $P(A|B) = 0.90$, exceeds the probability, $P(A) = 0.80$. Now consider the probability of finding a job given that your neighbor has bought a red car. Obviously, your neighbor's decision to buy a red car has no influence on your probability of finding a job, which remains at 0.80.

Events are considered **dependent** if the occurrence of one is related to the probability of the occurrence of the other. We generally test for the independence of two events by comparing the conditional probability of one event, for instance $P(A|B)$, to the probability, $P(A)$. If these two probabilities are the same, we say that the two events, A and B, are independent; if the probabilities differ, the two events are dependent.

INDEPENDENT VERSUS DEPENDENT EVENTS

Two events, A and B, are independent if $P(A|B) = P(A)$ or, equivalently, $P(B|A) = P(B)$. Otherwise, the events are dependent.

EXAMPLE 4.12

Suppose that for a given year there is a 2% chance that your desktop computer will crash and a 6% chance that your laptop computer will crash. Moreover, there is a 0.12% chance that both computers will crash. Is the reliability of the two computers independent of each other?

SOLUTION: Let event D represent the outcome that your desktop crashes and event L represent the outcome that your laptop crashes. Therefore, $P(D) = 0.02$, $P(L) = 0.06$, and $P(D \cap L) = 0.0012$. The reliability of the two computers is independent because

$$P(D|L) = \frac{P(D \cap L)}{P(L)} = \frac{0.0012}{0.06} = 0.02 = P(D).$$

In other words, if your laptop crashes, it does not alter the probability that your desktop also crashes. Equivalently,

$$P(L \mid D) = \frac{P(D \cap L)}{P(D)} = \frac{0.0012}{0.02} = 0.06 = P(L).$$

The Multiplication Rule

In some situations, we are interested in finding the probability that two events, A and B, both occur; that is, $P(A \cap B)$. In order to obtain this probability, we can rearrange the formula for conditional probability to derive $P(A \cap B)$. For instance, from $P(A \mid B) = \frac{P(A \cap B)}{P(B)}$, we can easily derive $P(A \cap B) = P(A \mid B)P(B)$. Similarly, from $P(B \mid A) = \frac{P(A \cap B)}{P(A)}$, we derive $P(A \cap B) = P(B \mid A)P(A)$. Since we calculate the product of two probabilities to find $P(A \cap B)$, we refer to it as the **multiplication rule** for probabilities.

> ### THE MULTIPLICATION RULE
>
> The multiplication rule states that the probability that A and B both occur is equal to the probability that A occurs given that B has occurred, times the probability that B occurs; that is, $P(A \cap B) = P(A \mid B)P(B)$. Equivalently, we can also arrive at this probability as $P(A \cap B) = P(B \mid A)P(A)$.

EXAMPLE 4.13

A stockbroker knows from past experience that the probability that a client owns stocks is 0.60 and the probability that a client owns bonds is 0.50. The probability that the client owns bonds if he/she already owns stocks is 0.55.

a. What is the probability that the client owns both of these securities?

b. Given that the client owns bonds, what is the probability that the client owns stocks?

SOLUTION:

a. Let S correspond to the event that a client owns stocks and B correspond to the event that a client owns bonds. Thus, the probabilities that the client owns stocks and that the client owns bonds are $P(S) = 0.60$ and $P(B) = 0.50$, respectively. The conditional probability that the client owns bonds given that he/she owns stocks is $P(B \mid S) = 0.55$. We calculate the probability that the client owns both of these securities as $P(S \cap B) = P(B \mid S)P(S) = 0.55 \times 0.60 = 0.33$.

b. We need to calculate the conditional probability that the client owns stocks given that he/she owns bonds, or $P(S \mid B)$. Using the formula for conditional probability and the answer from part a, we find
$$P(S \mid B) = \frac{P(S \cap B)}{P(B)} = \frac{0.33}{0.50} = 0.06.$$

The Multiplication Rule for Independent Events

We know that two events, A and B, are independent if $P(A \mid B) = P(A)$. With independent events, the multiplication rule $P(A \cap B) = P(A \mid B)P(B)$ simplifies to $P(A \cap B) = P(A)P(B)$. We can also use this rule to determine whether or not two events are independent. That is, two events are independent if the probability $P(A \cap B)$ equals the product of their probabilities, $P(A)P(B)$. In Example 4.12, we were given the probabilities $P(D) = 0.02$, $P(L) = 0.06$, and $P(D \cap L) = 0.0012$. Consistent with the earlier result, events D and L are independent because $P(D \cap L) = 0.0012$ equals $P(D)P(L) = 0.02 \times 0.06 = 0.0012$.

THE MULTIPLICATION RULE FOR INDEPENDENT EVENTS

If A and B are independent events, then the probability that A and B both occur equals the product of the probability of A and the probability of B; that is, $P(A \cap B) = P(A)P(B)$.

EXAMPLE 4.14

The probability of passing the Level 1 CFA (Chartered Financial Analyst) exam is 0.50 for John Campbell and 0.80 for Linda Lee. The prospect of John's passing the exam is completely unrelated to Linda's success on the exam.

a. What is the probability that both John and Linda pass the exam?

b. What is the probability that at least one of them passes the exam?

SOLUTION: We can write the probabilities that John passes the exam and that Linda passes the exam as $P(J) = 0.50$ and $P(L) = 0.80$, respectively.

a. Since we are told that John's chances of passing the exam are not influenced by Linda's success at the exam, we can conclude that these events are independent, so $P(J) = P(J|L) = 0.50$ and $P(L) = P(L|J) = 0.80$. Thus, when solving for the probability that both John and Linda pass the exam, we calculate the product of the probabilities: $P(J \cap L) = P(J) \times P(L) = 0.50 \times 0.80 = 0.40$.

b. We calculate the probability that at least one of them passes the exam as $P(J \cup L) = P(J) + P(L) - P(J \cap L) = 0.50 + 0.80 - 0.40 = 0.90$.

EXERCISES 4.2

Mechanics

16. Let $P(A) = 0.65$, $P(B) = 0.30$, and $P(A|B) = 0.45$.
    a. Calculate $P(A \cap B)$.
    b. Calculate $P(A \cup B)$.
    c. Calculate $P(B|A)$.

17. Let $P(A) = 0.55$, $P(B) = 0.30$, and $P(A \cap B) = 0.10$.
    a. Calculate $P(A|B)$.
    b. Calculate $P(A \cup B)$.
    c. Calculate $P((A \cup B)^c)$.

18. Let A and B be mutually exclusive events with $P(A) = 0.25$ and $P(B) = 0.30$.
    a. Calculate $P(A \cap B)$.
    b. Calculate $P(A \cup B)$.
    c. Calculate $P(A|B)$.

19. Let A and B be independent events with $P(A) = 0.40$ and $P(B) = 0.50$.
    a. Calculate $P(A \cap B)$.
    b. Calculate $P((A \cup B)^c)$.
    c. Calculate $P(A|B)$.

20. Let $P(A) = 0.65$, $P(B) = 0.30$, and $P(A|B) = 0.45$.
    a. Are A and B independent events? Explain.
    b. Are A and B mutually exclusive events? Explain.
    c. What is the probability that neither A nor B takes place?

21. Let $P(A) = 0.15$, $P(B) = 0.10$, and $P(A \cap B) = 0.05$.
    a. Are A and B independent events? Explain.
    b. Are A and B mutually exclusive events? Explain.
    c. What is the probability that neither A nor B takes place?

22. Consider the following probabilities: $P(A) = 0.25$, $P(B^c) = 0.40$, and $P(A \cap B) = 0.08$. Find:
    a. $P(B)$
    b. $P(A|B)$
    c. $P(B|A)$

23. Consider the following probabilities: $P(A^c) = 0.30$, $P(B) = 0.60$, and $P(A \cap B^c) = 0.24$. Find:
    a. $P(A|B^c)$
    b. $P(B^c|A)$
    c. Are A and B independent events? Explain.

24. Consider the following probabilities: $P(A) = 0.40$, $P(B) = 0.50$, and $P(A^c \cap B^c) = 0.24$. Find:
    a. $P(A^c|B^c)$
    b. $P(A^c \cup B^c)$
    c. $P(A \cup B)$

Applications

25. Survey data, based on 65,000 mobile phone subscribers, show that 44% of the subscribers use smartphones (*Forbes*, December 15, 2011). Moreover, 51% of smartphone users are women.
    a. Find the probability that a mobile phone subscriber is a woman who uses a smartphone.
    b. Find the probability that a mobile phone subscriber is a man who uses a smartphone.

26. Only 20% of students in a college ever go to their professor during office hours. Of those who go, 30% seek minor clarification and 70% seek major clarification.
    a. What is the probability that a student goes to the professor during her office hours for a minor clarification?
    b. What is the probability that a student goes to the professor during her office hours for a major clarification?

27. The probabilities that stock A will rise in price is 0.40 and that stock B will rise in price is 0.60. Further, if stock B rises in price, the probability that stock A will also rise in price is 0.50.
    a. What is the probability that at least one of the stocks will rise in price?
    b. Are events A and B mutually exclusive? Explain.
    c. Are events A and B independent? Explain.

28. Despite government bailouts and stimulus money, unemployment in the United States had not decreased significantly as economists had expected (*U.S. News & World Report,* July 2, 2010). Many analysts predicted only an 18% chance of a reduction in U.S. unemployment. However, if Europe slipped back into a recession, the probability of a reduction in U.S. unemployment would drop to 0.06.
    a. What is the probability that there is not a reduction in U.S. unemployment?

    b. Assume there is an 8% chance that Europe slips back into a recession. What is the probability that there is not a reduction in U.S. unemployment and that Europe slips into a recession?

29. Dr. Miriam Johnson has been teaching accounting for over 20 years. From her experience, she knows that 60% of her students do homework regularly. Moreover, 95% of the students who do their homework regularly pass the course. She also knows that 85% of her students pass the course.
    a. What is the probability that a student will do homework regularly and also pass the course?
    b. What is the probability that a student will neither do homework regularly nor will pass the course?
    c. Are the events "pass the course" and "do homework regularly" mutually exclusive? Explain.
    d. Are the events "pass the course" and "do homework regularly" independent? Explain.

30. Records show that 5% of all college students are foreign students who also smoke. It is also known that 50% of all foreign college students smoke. What percent of the students at this university are foreign?

31. An analyst estimates that the probability of default on a seven-year AA-rated bond is 0.06, while that on a seven-year A-rated bond is 0.13. The probability that they will both default is 0.04.
    a. What is the probability that at least one of the bonds defaults?
    b. What is the probability that neither the seven-year AA-rated bond nor the seven-year A-rated bond defaults?
    c. Given that the seven-year AA-rated bond defaults, what is the probability that the seven-year A-rated bond also defaults?

32. Mike Danes has been delayed in going to the annual sales event at one of his favorite apparel stores. His friend has just texted him that there are only 20 shirts left, of which 8 are in size M, 10 in size L, and 2 in size XL. Also 9 of the shirts are white, 5 are blue, and the remaining are of mixed colors. Mike is interested in getting a white or a blue shirt in size L. Define the events A = Getting a white or a blue shirt and B = Getting a shirt in size L.
    a. Find $P(A)$, $P(A^c)$, and $P(B)$.
    b. Are the events A and B mutually exclusive? Explain.
    c. Would you describe Mike's preference by the events $A \cup B$ or $A \cap B$?

33. In general, shopping online is supposed to be more convenient than going to stores. However, according to a Harris Interactive poll, 87% of people have experienced problems with an online transaction (*The Wall Street Journal*, October 2, 2007). Forty-two percent of people who

experienced a problem abandoned the transaction or switched to a competitor's website. Fifty-three percent of people who experienced problems contacted customer-service representatives.

a. What proportion of people did not experience problems with an online transaction?

b. What proportion of people experienced problems with an online transaction and abandoned the transaction or switched to a competitor's website?

c. What proportion of people experienced problems with an online transaction and contacted customer-service representatives?

34. A manufacturing firm just received a shipment of 20 assembly parts, of slightly varied sizes, from a vendor. The manager knows that there are only 15 parts in the shipment that would be suitable. He examines these parts one at a time.

a. Find the probability that the first part is suitable.

b. If the first part is suitable, find the probability that the second part is also suitable.

c. If the first part is suitable, find the probability that the second part is not suitable.

35. Apple products have become a household name in America, with 51% of all households owning at least one Apple product (*CNN*, March 19, 2012). In the Midwest, the likelihood of owning an Apple product is 61% for households with kids and 48% for households without kids. Suppose there are 1,200 households in a representative community, of which 820 are with kids and the rest are without kids.

a. Are the events "household with kids" and "household without kids" mutually exclusive and exhaustive? Explain.

b. What is the probability that a household is without kids?

c. What is the probability that a household is with kids and owns an Apple product?

d. What is the probability that a household is without kids and does not own an Apple product?

36. Despite the repeated effort by the government to reform how Wall Street pays its executives, some of the nation's biggest banks are continuing to pay out bonuses nearly as large as those in the best years before the Great Recession (*The Washington Post*, January 15, 2010). It is known that 10 out of 15 members of the board of directors of a company were in favor of the bonus. Suppose two members were randomly selected by the media.

a. What is the probability that both of them were in favor of the bonus?

b. What is the probability that neither of them was in favor of the bonus?

37. Christine Wong has asked Dave and Mike to help her move into a new apartment on Sunday morning. She has asked them both, in case one of them does not show up. From past experience, Christine knows that there is a 40% chance that Dave will not show up and a 30% chance that Mike will not show up. Dave and Mike do not know each other and their decisions can be assumed to be independent.

a. What is the probability that both Dave and Mike will show up?

b. What is the probability that at least one of them will show up?

c. What is the probability that neither Dave nor Mike will show up?

38. According to the Census's Population Survey, the percentage of children with two parents at home is the highest for Asians and lowest for blacks (*USA TODAY*, February 26, 2009). It is reported that 85% of Asian, 78% of white, 70% of Hispanic, and 38% of black children have two parents at home. Suppose there are 500 students in a representative school, of which 280 are white, 50 are Asian, 100 are Hispanic, and 70 are black.

a. Are the events "Asians" and "black" mutually exclusive and exhaustive? Explain.

b. What is the probability that a child is not white?

c. What is the probability that a child is white and has both parents at home?

d. What is the probability that a child is Asian and does not have both parents at home?

39. A study shows that unemployment does not impact white-collar and blue-collar workers equally (*Newsweek*, April 20, 2009). According to the Bureau of Labor Statistics report, while the national unemployment rate is 8.5%, it is only 4.3% for those with a college degree. It is fair to assume that 27% of people in the labor force are college educated. You have just heard that another worker in a large firm has been laid off. What is the probability that the worker is college educated?

40. According to a survey by two United Nations agencies and a nongovernmental organization, two in every three women in the Indian capital of New Delhi are likely to face some form of sexual harassment in a year (*BBC World News*, July 9, 2010). The study also reports that women who use public transportation are especially vulnerable. Suppose the corresponding probability of harassment for women who use public transportation is 0.82. It is also known that 28% of women use public transportation.

a. What is the probability that a woman takes public transportation and also faces sexual harassment?

b. If a woman is sexually harassed, what is the probability that she had taken public transportation?

41. According to results from the Spine Patient Outcomes Research Trial, or SPORT, surgery for a painful, common back condition resulted in significantly reduced back pain and better physical function than treatment with drugs and physical therapy (*The Wall Street Journal*, February 21, 2008). SPORT followed 803 patients, of whom 398 ended up getting surgery. After two years, of those who had surgery, 63% said they had a major

improvement in their condition, compared with 29% among those who received nonsurgical treatment.

a. What is the probability that a patient had surgery? What is the probability that a patient did not have surgery?

b. What is the probability that a patient had surgery and experienced a major improvement in his or her condition?

c. What is the probability that a patient received nonsurgical treatment and experienced a major improvement in his or her condition?

42. A study challenges the media narrative that foreclosures are dangerously widespread (*The New York Times,* March 2, 2009). According to this study, 62% of all foreclosures were centered in only four states, namely, Arizona, California, Florida, and Nevada. The national average rate of foreclosures in 2008 was 0.79%. What percent of the homes in the United States were foreclosed in 2008 and also centered in Arizona, California, Florida, or Nevada?

4.3 CONTINGENCY TABLES AND PROBABILITIES

LO 4.4

In Chapter 2 we learned that it is often useful to construct a frequency distribution when organizing qualitative data. While it is true that a frequency distribution is an effective tool for summarizing one variable, it is often the case that we want to examine or compare two qualitative variables. On these occasions, a **contingency table** proves very useful. Contingency tables are widely used in marketing and biomedical research, as well as in the social sciences.

Calculate and interpret probabilities from a contingency table.

A CONTINGENCY TABLE

A contingency table generally shows frequencies for two qualitative (categorical) variables, x and y, where each cell represents a mutually exclusive combination of the pair of x and y values.

Table 4.4, first presented in the introductory case study of this chapter, is an example of a contingency table where the qualitative variables of interest, x and y, are Age Group and Brand Name, respectively. Age Group has two possible categories: (1) under 35 years and (2) 35 years and older; Brand Name, has three possible categories: (1) Under Armour, (2) Nike, and (3) Adidas.

TABLE 4.4 Purchases of Compression Garments Based on Age and Brand Name

Age Group	Brand Name		
	Under Armour	Nike	Adidas
Under 35 years	174	132	90
35 years and older	54	72	78

Each cell in Table 4.4 represents a frequency; for example, there are 174 customers under the age of 35 who purchase an Under Armour product, whereas there are 54 customers at least 35 years old who purchase an Under Armour product. Recall that we estimate an empirical probability by calculating the relative frequency of the occurrence of the event. To make calculating these probabilities less cumbersome, it is often useful to denote each event with letter notation and calculate totals for each column and row as shown in Table 4.4a.

TABLE 4.4a A Contingency Table Labeled Using Event Notation

Age Group	Brand Name			Total
	B_1	B_2	B_3	
A	174	132	90	396
A^c	54	72	78	204
Total	228	204	168	600

Thus, let events A and A^c correspond to "under 35 years" and "35 years and older," respectively; similarly, let events B_1, B_2, and B_3 correspond to "Under Armour," "Nike," and "Adidas," respectively. In addition, after calculating row totals, it is now easier to recognize that 396 of the customers are under 35 years old and 204 of the customers are at least 35 years old. Similarly, column totals indicate that 228 customers purchase Under Armour, 204 purchase Nike, and 168 purchase Adidas. Finally, the frequency corresponding to the cell in the last column and the last row is 600. This value represents the sample size; that is, the total number of customers in the sample. We arrive at this value by either summing the values in the last column (396 + 204) or summing the values in the last row (228 + 204 + 168).

The following example illustrates how to calculate probabilities when the data are presented in the form of a contingency table.

EXAMPLE 4.15

Using the information in Table 4.4a, answer the following questions.

a. What is the probability that a randomly selected customer is younger than 35 years old?

b. What is the probability that a randomly selected customer purchases an Under Armour garment?

c. What is the probability that a customer is younger than 35 years old and purchases an Under Armour garment?

d. What is the probability that a customer is either younger than 35 years old or purchases an Under Armour garment?

e. What is the probability that a customer is under 35 years of age, given that the customer purchases an Under Armour garment?

SOLUTION:

a. $P(A) = \frac{396}{600} = 0.66$; there is a 66% chance that a randomly selected customer is less than 35 years old.

b. $P(B_1) = \frac{228}{600} = 0.38$; there is a 38% chance that a randomly selected customer purchases an Under Armour garment.

c. $P(A \cap B_1) = \frac{174}{600} = 0.29$; there is a 29% chance that a randomly selected customer is younger than 35 years old and purchases an Under Armour garment.

d. $P(A \cup B_1) = \frac{174 + 132 + 90 + 54}{600} = \frac{450}{600} = 0.75$; there is a 75% chance that a randomly selected customer is either younger than 35 years old or purchases an Under Armour garment. Alternatively, we can use the addition rule to solve this problem as $P(A \cup B_1) = P(A) + P(B_1) - P(A \cap B_1) = 0.66 + 0.38 - 0.29 = 0.75$.

e. We wish to calculate the conditional probability, $P(A \mid B_1)$. When the information is in the form of a contingency table, calculating a conditional probability is rather straightforward. We are given the information that the customer purchases an Under Armour garment, so the sample space shrinks from 600 customers to 228 customers. We can ignore all customers that make Nike or Adidas purchases, or all outcomes in events B_2 and B_3. Thus, of the 228 customers who make an Under Armour purchase, 174 of them are under 35 years of age. Therefore, the probability that a customer is under 35 years of age given that the customer makes an Under Armour purchase is calculated as $P(A \mid B_1) = \frac{174}{228} = 0.76$. Alternatively, we can use the conditional probability formula to solve the problem as $P(A \mid B_1) = \frac{P(A \cap B_1)}{P(B_1)} = \frac{174/600}{228/600} = \frac{174}{228} = 0.76$.

Arguably, a more convenient way of calculating relevant probabilities is to convert the contingency table to a **joint probability table**. The frequency in each cell is divided by the number of outcomes in the sample space, which in this example is 600 customers. Table 4.4b shows the results.

TABLE 4.4b Converting a Contingency Table to a Joint Probability Table

| Age Group | Brand Name | | | Total |
	B_1	B_2	B_3	
A	0.29	0.22	0.15	0.66
A^c	0.09	0.12	0.13	0.34
Total	0.38	0.34	0.28	1.00

The values in the interior of the table represent the probabilities of the intersection of two events, also referred to as **joint probabilities**. For instance, the probability that a randomly selected person is under 35 years of age and makes an Under Armour purchase, denoted $P(A \cap B_1)$, is 0.29. Similarly, we can readily read from this table that 12% of the customers purchase a Nike garment and are at least 35 years old, or $P(A^c \cap B_2) = 0.12$.

The values in the margins of Table 4.4b represent unconditional probabilities. These probabilities are also referred to as **marginal probabilities**. For example, the probability that a randomly selected customer is under 35 years of age, $P(A)$, is simply 0.66. Also, the probability of purchasing a Nike garment, $P(B_2)$, is 0.34.

Note that the conditional probability is basically the ratio of a joint probability to an unconditional probability. Since $P(A|B_1) = \frac{P(A \cap B_1)}{P(B_1)}$, the numerator is the joint probability, $P(A \cap B_1)$, and the denominator is the unconditional probability, $P(B_1)$. Let's refer back to the probability that we calculated earlier; that is, the probability that a customer is under 35 years of age, given that the customer purchases an Under Armour product. This conditional probability is easily computed as $P(A|B_1) = \frac{P(A \cap B_1)}{P(B_1)} = \frac{0.29}{0.38} = 0.76$.

EXAMPLE 4.16

Given the information in Table 4.4b, what is the probability that a customer purchases an Under Armour product, given that the customer is under 35 years of age?

SOLUTION: Now we are solving for $P(B_1|A)$. So

$$P(B_1|A) = \frac{P(A \cap B_1)}{P(A)} = \frac{0.29}{0.66} = 0.44.$$

Note that $P(B_1|A) = 0.44 \neq P(A|B_1) = 0.76$.

EXAMPLE 4.17

Determine whether the events "under 35 years old" and "Under Armour" are independent.

SOLUTION: In order to determine whether two events are independent, we compare an event's conditional probability to its unconditional probability; that is, events A and B are independent if $P(A|B) = P(A)$. In the Under Armour example, we have already found that $P(A|B_1) = 0.76$. In other words, there is a 76% chance that a customer is under 35 years old given that the customer purchases an Under Armour product. We compare this conditional probability to its unconditional probability, $P(A) = 0.66$. Since these probabilities differ, the events "under 35 years old" and "Under Armour" are not independent events. We could have compared $P(B_1 | A)$ to $P(B_1)$ and found that $0.44 \neq 0.38$, which leads us to the same conclusion that the events are dependent. As discussed in the preceding section, an alternative approach is to compare the joint probability with the product of the two unconditional probabilities. Events are independent if $P(A \cap B_1) = P(A)P(B_1)$. In this example, $P(A \cap B_1) = 0.29$ does not equal $P(A)P(B_1) = 0.66 \times 0.38 = 0.25$, so the two events are not independent.

It is important to note that the conclusions about independence, such as the one made in Example 4.17, are informal since they are based on empirical probabilities computed from given sample information. In the preceding example, these probabilities will change if a different sample of 600 customers is used. Formal tests of independence are discussed in Chapter 12.

SYNOPSIS OF INTRODUCTORY CASE

©Digital Vision/Photodisc/Getty Images RF

After careful analysis of the contingency table representing customer purchases of compression garments based on age and brand name, several interesting remarks can be made. From a sample of 600 customers, it appears that the majority of the customers who purchase these products tend to be younger: 66% of the customers were younger than 35 years old, whereas 34% were at least 35 years old. It is true that more customers chose to purchase Under Armour garments (with 38% of purchases) as compared to Nike or Adidas garments (with 34% and 28% of purchases, respectively). However, given that Under Armour was the pioneer in the compression-gear market, this company should be concerned with the competition posed by Nike and Adidas. Further inspection of the contingency table reveals that if a customer was under 35 years old, the chance of the customer purchasing an Under Armour garment rises to about 44%. This result indicates that the age of a customer seems to influence the brand name purchased. In other words, 38% of the customers choose to buy Under Armour products, but as soon as the attention is confined to those customers who are under 35 years old, the likelihood of a purchase from Under Armour rises to about 44%. The information that the Under Armour brand appeals to younger customers is relevant not only to Under Armour and how the firm may focus its advertising efforts, but also to competitors and retailers in the compression garment market.

EXERCISES 4.3

Mechanics

43. Consider the following contingency table.

	B	B^C
A	26	34
A^c	14	26

a. Convert the contingency table into a joint probability table.
b. What is the probability that A occurs?
c. What is the probability that A and B occur?
d. Given that B has occurred, what is the probability that A occurs?

e. Given that A^c has occurred, what is the probability that B occurs?
f. Are A and B mutually exclusive events? Explain.
g. Are A and B independent events? Explain.

44. Consider the following joint probability table.

	B_1	B_2	B_3	B_4
A	0.09	0.22	0.15	0.20
A^c	0.03	0.10	0.09	0.12

a. What is the probability that A occurs?
b. What is the probability that B_2 occurs?

c. What is the probability that A^c and B_4 occur?

d. What is the probability that A or B_3 occurs?

e. Given that B_2 has occurred, what is the probability that A occurs?

f. Given that A has occurred, what is the probability that B_4 occurs?

Applications

45. According to an online survey by Harris Interactive for job site CareerBuilder.com, more than half of IT (information technology) workers say they have fallen asleep at work (*InformationWeek*, September 27, 2007). Sixty-four percent of government workers admitted to falling asleep on the job. Consider the following contingency table that is representative of the survey results.

	Job Category	
Slept on the Job?	IT Professional	Government Professional
Yes	155	256
No	145	144

a. Convert the contingency table into a joint probability table.

b. What is the probability that a randomly selected worker is an IT professional?

c. What is the probability that a randomly selected worker slept on the job?

d. If a randomly selected worker slept on the job, what is the probability that he/she is an IT professional?

e. If a randomly selected worker is a government professional, what is the probability that he/she slept on the job?

f. Are the events "IT Professional" and "Slept on the Job" independent? Explain using probabilities.

46. A report suggests that business majors spend the least amount of time on course work than all other college students (*The New York Times*, November 17, 2011). A provost of a university decides to conduct a survey where students are asked if they study hard, defined by spending at least 20 hours per week on course work. Of 120 business majors included in the survey, 20 said that they studied hard, as compared to 48 out of 150 nonbusiness majors who said that they studied hard.

a. Construct a contingency table that shows the frequencies for the qualitative variables Major (business or nonbusiness) and Study Hard (yes or no).

b. Find the probability that a business major spends less than 20 hours per week on course work.

c. What is the probability that a student studies hard?

d. If a student spends at least 20 hours on course work, what is the probability that he/she is a business major? What is the corresponding probability that he/she is a nonbusiness major?

47. A poll asked 16- to 21-year-olds whether or not they are likely to serve in the U.S. military. The following joint probability table, cross-classified by gender and race, reports the proportion of those polled who responded that they are likely or very likely to serve in the active-duty military.

	Race		
Gender	Hispanic	Black	White
Male	0.335	0.205	0.165
Female	0.145	0.105	0.045

Source: Defense Human Resources Activity telephone poll of 3,228 Americans conducted October through December 2005.

a. What is the probability that a randomly selected respondent is female?

b. What is the probability that a randomly selected respondent is Hispanic?

c. Given that a respondent is female, what is the probability that she is Hispanic?

d. Given that a respondent is white, what is the probability that the respondent is male?

e. Are the events "Male" and "White" independent? Explain using probabilities.

48. According to a Michigan State University researcher, Americans are becoming increasingly polarized on issues pertaining to the environment (msutoday.msu.edu, April 19, 2011). It is reported that 70% of Democrats see signs of global warming as compared to only 30% of Republicans who feel the same. Suppose the survey was based on 400 Democrats and 400 Republicans.

a. Construct a contingency table that shows frequencies for the qualitative variables Political Affiliation (Democrat or Republican) and Global Warming (yes or no).

b. Find the probability that a Republican sees signs of global warming.

c. Find the probability that a person does not see signs of global warming.

d. If a person sees signs of global warming, what is the probability that this person is a Democrat?

49. Merck & Co. conducted a study to test the promise of its experimental AIDS vaccine (*The Boston Globe,* September 22, 2007). Volunteers in the study were all free of the human immunodeficiency virus (HIV), which causes AIDS, at the start of the study, but all were at high risk for getting the virus. Volunteers were given either the vaccine or a dummy shot; 24 of 741 volunteers who got the vaccine became infected with HIV, whereas 21 of 762 volunteers who got the dummy shot became infected with HIV. The following table summarizes the results of the study.

	Vaccinated	Dummy Shot
Infected	24	21
Not Infected	717	741

a. Convert the contingency table into a joint probability table.

b. What is the probability that a randomly selected volunteer got vaccinated?

c. What is the probability that a randomly selected volunteer became infected with the HIV virus?

d. If the randomly selected volunteer was vaccinated, what is the probability that he/she got infected?

e. Are the events "Vaccinated" and "Infected" independent? Explain using probabilities. Given your answer, is it surprising that Merck & Co. ended enrollment and vaccination of volunteers in the study? Explain.

50. More and more households are struggling to pay utility bills given high heating costs (*The Wall Street Journal*, February 14, 2008). Particularly hard hit are households with homes heated with propane or heating oil. Many of these households are spending twice as much to stay warm this winter compared to those who heat with natural gas or electricity. A representative sample of 500 households was taken to investigate if the type of heating influences whether or not a household is delinquent in paying its utility bill. The following table reports the results.

| Delinquent in Payment? | Type of Heating | | | |
	Natural Gas	Electricity	Heating Oil	Propane
Yes	50	20	15	10
No	240	130	20	15

a. What is the probability that a randomly selected household uses heating oil?

b. What is the probability that a randomly selected household is delinquent in paying its utility bill?

c. What is the probability that a randomly selected household uses heating oil and is delinquent in paying its utility bill?

d. Given that a household uses heating oil, what is the probability that it is delinquent in paying its utility bill?

e. Given that a household is delinquent in paying its utility bill, what is the probability that the household uses electricity?

f. Are the events "Heating Oil" and "Delinquent in Payment" independent? Explain using probabilities.

51. The research team at a leading perfume company is trying to test the market for its newly introduced perfume. In particular the team wishes to look for gender and international differences in the preference for this perfume. They sample 2,500 people internationally and each person in the sample is asked to try the new perfume and list his/her preference. The following table reports the results.

Preference	Gender	America	Europe	Asia
Like it	Men	210	150	120
	Women	370	310	180
Don't like it	Men	290	150	80
	Women	330	190	120

a. What is the probability that a randomly selected man likes the perfume?

b. What is the probability that a randomly selected Asian likes the perfume?

c. What is the probability that a randomly selected European woman does not like the perfume?

d. What is the probability that a randomly selected American man does not like the perfume?

e. Are the events "Men" and "Like Perfume" independent in (i) America, (ii) Europe, and (iii) Asia? Explain using probabilities.

f. Internationally, are the events "Men" and "Like Perfume" independent? Explain using probabilities.

4.4 THE TOTAL PROBABILITY RULE AND BAYES' THEOREM

In this section, we present two important rules in probability theory: the total probability rule and Bayes' theorem. The **total probability rule** is a useful tool for breaking the computation of a probability into distinct cases. **Bayes' theorem** uses this rule to update the probability of an event that has been affected by a new piece of evidence.

Apply the total probability rule.

The Total Probability Rule

Sometimes the probability of an event is not readily apparent from the given information. The total probability rule expresses the probability of an event in terms of joint or conditional probabilities. Let $P(A)$ denote the probability of an event of interest. We can express $P(A)$ as the sum of probabilities of the intersections of A with some mutually exclusive and exhaustive events corresponding to an experiment. For instance, consider event B and its complement B^c. Figure 4.7 shows the sample space partitioned entirely into these two mutually exclusive and exhaustive events. The circle, representing event A, consists entirely of its intersections with B and B^c. According to the total probability rule, $P(A)$ equals the sum of $P(A \cap B)$ and $P(A \cap B^c)$.

FIGURE 4.7
The total probability rule:
$P(A) = P(A \cap B) + P(A \cap B^c)$

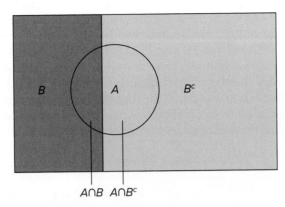

$A \cap B$ $A \cap B^c$

Oftentimes the joint probabilities needed to compute the total probability are not explicitly specified. Therefore, we use the multiplication rule to derive these probabilities from the conditional probabilities as $P(A \cap B) = P(A|B)P(B)$ and $P(A \cap B^c) = P(A|B^c)P(B^c)$.

THE TOTAL PROBABILITY RULE CONDITIONAL ON TWO EVENTS

The total probability rule expresses the probability of an event, A, in terms of probabilities of the intersection of A with any mutually exclusive and exhaustive events. The total probability rule based on two events, B and B^c, is

$$P(A) = P(A \cap B) + P(A \cap B^c),$$

or equivalently,

$$P(A) = P(A|B)P(B) + P(A|B^c)P(B^c).$$

An intuitive way to express the total probability rule is with the help of a **probability tree**. Whenever an experiment can be broken down into stages, with a different aspect of the result observed at each stage, we can use a probability tree to represent the various possible sequences of observations. We also use an alternative tabular method for computing the probability $P(A)$. The following example illustrates the mechanics of a probability tree and the tabular method.

EXAMPLE 4.18

Even though a certain statistics professor does not require attendance as part of a student's overall grade, she has noticed that those who regularly attend class have a higher tendency to get a final grade of A. The professor calculates that there is an 80% chance that a student attends class regularly. Moreover, given that a student attends class regularly, there is a 35% chance that the student receives an A grade; however, if a student does not attend class regularly, there is only a 5% chance of an A grade. Use this information to answer the following questions.

a. What is the probability that a student does not attend class regularly?

b. What is the probability that a student attends class regularly and receives an A grade?

c. What is the probability that a student does not attend class regularly and receives an A grade?

d. What is the probability that a student receives an A grade?

SOLUTION: We first let A correspond to the event that a student receives an A grade and R correspond to the event that a student attends class regularly. From the preceding information, we then have the following probabilities: $P(R) = 0.80$, $P(A|R) = 0.35$, and $P(A|R^c) = 0.05$. Figure 4.8 shows a probability tree that consists of nodes (junctions) and branches (lines) where the initial node O is called the origin. The branches emanating from O represent the possible outcomes that may occur at the first stage. Thus, at stage 1 we have events R and R^c originating from O. These events become the nodes at the second stage. The sum of the probabilities coming from any particular node is equal to one.

FIGURE 4.8 Probability tree for class attendance and final grade in statistics

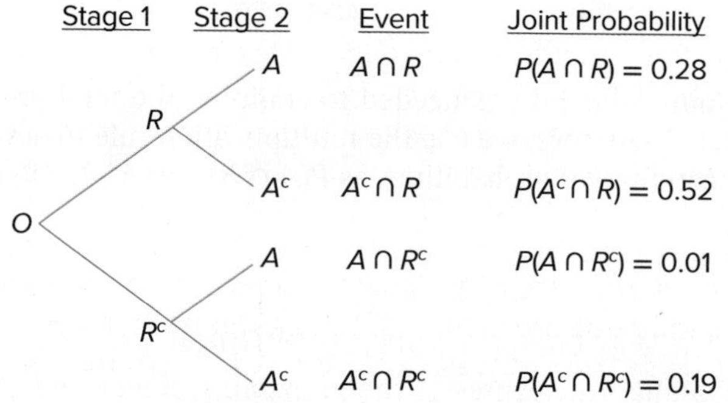

Stage 1	Stage 2	Event	Joint Probability
	A	$A \cap R$	$P(A \cap R) = 0.28$
R	A^c	$A^c \cap R$	$P(A^c \cap R) = 0.52$
R^c	A	$A \cap R^c$	$P(A \cap R^c) = 0.01$
	A^c	$A^c \cap R^c$	$P(A^c \cap R^c) = 0.19$

a. Using the complement rule, if we know that there is an 80% chance that a student attends class regularly, $P(R) = 0.80$, then the probability that a student does not attend class regularly is found as $P(R^c) = 1 - P(R) = 1 - 0.80 = 0.20$.

In order to arrive at a subsequent stage, and deduce the corresponding probabilities, we use the information obtained from the previous stage. For instance, given that a student attends class regularly, there is a 35% chance that the student receives an A grade; that is, $P(A|R) = 0.35$. Given that a student regularly attends class, the likelihood of not receiving an A grade is 65% because $P(A^c|R) = 1 - P(A|R) = 0.65$. Similarly, given $P(A|R^c) = 0.05$, we compute $P(A^c|R^c) = 1 - P(A|R^c) = 1 - 0.05 = 0.95$. Any path through branches of the tree from the origin to a terminal node defines the intersection of the earlier two events. Thus, following the top branches, we arrive at the event $A \cap R$, meaning that a student attends class regularly and receives an A grade. The probability of this event is the product of the probabilities attached to the branches forming that path; here we are simply applying the multiplication rule. Now we are prepared to answer parts b and c.

b. Multiplying the probabilities attached to the top branches, we obtain $P(A \cap R) = P(A|R)P(R) = 0.35 \times 0.80 = 0.28$; there is a 28% chance that a student attends class regularly and receives an A grade.

c. In order to find the probability that a student does not attend class regularly and receives an A grade, we compute $P(A \cap R^c) = P(A|R^c)P(R^c) = 0.05 \times 0.20 = 0.01$.

d. The probability that a student receives an A grade, $P(A)$, is not explicitly given in Example 4.18. However, we can sum the relevant joint probabilities in parts b and c to obtain this probability:

$$P(A) = P(A \cap R) + P(A \cap R^c) = 0.28 + 0.01 = 0.29.$$

An alternative method uses a tabular representation of probabilities. Table 4.5 contains all relevant probabilities that are directly or indirectly specified in Example 4.18.

TABLE 4.5 Tabular Method for Computing $P(A)$

Unconditional Probability	Conditional Probability	Joint Probability
$P(R) = 0.80$	$P(A \mid R) = 0.35$	$P(A \cap R) = P(A \mid R) P(R) = 0.28$
$P(R^c) = 0.20$	$P(A \mid R^c) = 0.05$	$P(A \cap R^c) = P(A \mid R^c) P(R^c) = 0.01$
$P(R) + P(R^c) = 1$		$P(A) = P(A \cap R) + P(A \cap R^c) = 0.29$

As we saw earlier, each joint probability is computed as a product of its conditional probability and the corresponding unconditional probability; that is, $P(A \cap R) = P(A \mid R)P(R) = 0.35 \times 0.80 = 0.28$. Similarly, $P(A \cap R^c) = P(A \mid R^c)P(R^c) = 0.05 \times 0.20 = 0.01$. Therefore, $P(A) = P(A \cap R) + P(A \cap R^c) = 0.29$.

Bayes' Theorem

LO **4.6**

Apply Bayes' theorem.

The total probability rule is also needed to derive Bayes' theorem, developed by the Reverend Thomas Bayes (1702–1761). Bayes' theorem is a procedure for updating probabilities based on new information. The original probability is an unconditional probability called a **prior probability**, in the sense that it reflects only what we know now before the arrival of any new information. On the basis of new information, we update the prior probability to arrive at a conditional probability called a **posterior probability**.

Suppose we know that 99% of the individuals who take a lie detector test tell the truth. Therefore, the prior probability of telling the truth is 0.99. Suppose an individual takes the lie detector test and the results indicate that the individual lied. Bayes' theorem updates a prior probability to compute a posterior probability, which in the above example is essentially a conditional probability based on the information that the lie detector has detected a lie.

Let $P(B)$ denote the prior probability and $P(B \mid A)$ the posterior probability. Note that the posterior probability is conditional on event A, representing new information. Recall the conditional probability formula from Section 4.2:

$$P(B \mid A) = \frac{P(A \cap B)}{P(A)}.$$

In some instances, we may have to evaluate $P(B \mid A)$, but we do not have explicit information on $P(A \cap B)$ or $P(A)$. However, given information on $P(B)$, $P(A \mid B)$, and $P(A \mid B^c)$, we can use the total probability rule and the multiplication rule to find $P(B \mid A)$ as follows:

$$P(B \mid A) = \frac{P(A \cap B)}{P(A)} = \frac{P(A \cap B)}{P(A \cap B) + P(A \cap B^c)} = \frac{P(A \mid B)P(B)}{P(A \mid B)P(B) + P(A \mid B^c)P(B^c)}.$$

BAYES' THEOREM

The posterior probability $P(B \mid A)$ can be found using the information on the prior probability $P(B)$ along with the conditional probabilities $P(A \mid B)$ and $P(A \mid B^c)$ as

$$P(B \mid A) = \frac{P(A \cap B)}{P(A)} = \frac{P(A \cap B)}{P(A \cap B) + P(A \cap B^c)} = \frac{P(A \mid B)P(B)}{P(A \mid B)P(B) + P(A \mid B^c)P(B^c)}.$$

In the above formula, we have used Bayes' theorem to update the prior probability $P(B)$ to the posterior probability $P(B \mid A)$. Equivalently, we can use Bayes' theorem to update the prior probability $P(A)$ to derive the posterior probability $P(A \mid B)$ by interchanging the events A and B in the above formula.

EXAMPLE 4.19

In a lie-detector test, an individual is asked to answer a series of questions while connected to a polygraph (lie detector). This instrument measures and records several physiological responses of the individual on the basis that false answers will produce distinctive measurements. Assume that 99% of the individuals who go in for a polygraph test tell the truth. These tests are considered to be 95% reliable. In other words, there is a 95% chance that the test will detect a lie if an individual actually lies. Let there also be a 0.5% chance that the test erroneously detects a lie even when the individual is telling the truth. An individual has just taken a polygraph test and the test has detected a lie. What is the probability that the individual was actually telling the truth?

SOLUTION: First we define some events and their associated probabilities. Let D and T correspond to the events that the polygraph detects a lie and that an individual is telling the truth, respectively. We are given that $P(T) = 0.99$, implying that $P(T^c) = 1 - 0.99 = 0.01$. In addition, we formulate $P(D|T^c) = 0.95$ and $P(D|T) = 0.005$. We need to find $P(T|D)$ when we are not explicitly given $P(D \cap T)$ and $P(D)$. We can use Bayes' theorem to find

$$P(T|D) = \frac{P(D \cap T)}{P(D)} = \frac{P(D \cap T)}{P(D \cap T) + P(D \cap T^c)} = \frac{P(D|T)P(T)}{P(D|T)P(T) + P(D|T^c)P(T^c)}.$$

Although we can use this formula to solve the problem directly, it is often easier to solve it systematically with the help of the following table.

TABLE 4.6 Computing Posterior Probabilities for Example 4.19

Prior Probability	Conditional Probability	Joint Probability	Posterior Probability
$P(T) = 0.99$	$P(D|T) = 0.005$	$P(D \cap T) = 0.00495$	$P(T|D) = 0.34256$
$P(T^c) = 0.01$	$P(D|T^c) = 0.95$	$P(D \cap T^c) = 0.00950$	$P(T^c|D) = 0.65744$
$P(T) + P(T^c) = 1$		$P(D) = 0.01445$	$P(T|D) + P(T^c|D) = 1$

The first column presents prior probabilities and the second column shows related conditional probabilities. We first compute the denominator of Bayes' theorem by using the total probability rule, $P(D) = P(D \cap T) + P(D \cap T^c)$. Joint probabilities are calculated as products of conditional probabilities with their corresponding prior probabilities. For instance, in Table 4.6, in order to obtain $P(D \cap T)$, we multiply $P(D|T)$ with $P(T)$, which yields $P(D \cap T) = 0.005 \times 0.99 = 0.00495$. Similarly, we find $P(D \cap T^c) = 0.95 \times 0.01 = 0.00950$. Thus, according to the total probability rule, $P(D) = 0.00495 + 0.00950 = 0.01445$. Finally, $P(T|D) = \frac{P(D \cap T)}{P(D \cap T) + P(D \cap T^c)} = \frac{0.00495}{0.01445} = 0.34256$. The prior probability of an individual telling the truth is 0.99. However, given the new information that the polygraph detected the individual telling a lie, the posterior probability of this individual telling the truth is now revised downward to 0.34256.

So far we have used the total probability rule as well as Bayes' theorem based on two mutually exclusive and exhaustive events, namely, B and B^c. We can easily extend the analysis to include n mutually exclusive and exhaustive events, $B_1, B_2, \ldots, B_n$.

EXTENSIONS OF THE TOTAL PROBABILITY RULE AND BAYES' THEOREM

If $B_1, B_2, \ldots B_n$ represent n mutually exclusive and exhaustive events, then the total probability rule extends to

$$P(A) = P(A \cap B_1) + P(A \cap B_2) + \cdots + P(A \cap B_n),$$

or equivalently,

$$P(A) = P(A \mid B_1)P(B_1) + P(A \mid B_2)P(B_2) + \cdots + P(A \mid B_n)P(B_n).$$

Similarly, Bayes' theorem, for any $i = 1, 2, \ldots, n$, extends to

$$P(B_i \mid A) = \frac{P(A \cap B_i)}{P(A \cap B_1) + P(A \cap B_2) + \cdots + P(A \cap B_n)},$$

or equivalently,

$$P(B_i \mid A) = \frac{P(A \mid B_i)P(B_i)}{P(A \mid B_1)P(B_1) + P(A \mid B_2)P(B_2) + \cdots + P(A \mid B_n)P(B_n)}.$$

EXAMPLE 4.20

Scott Myers is a security analyst for a telecommunications firm called Webtalk. Although he is optimistic about the firm's future, he is concerned that its stock price will be considerably affected by the condition of credit flow in the economy. He believes that the probability is 0.20 that credit flow will improve significantly, 0.50 that it will improve only marginally, and 0.30 that it will not improve at all. He also estimates that the probability that the stock price of Webtalk will go up is 0.90 with significant improvement in credit flow in the economy, 0.40 with marginal improvement in credit flow in the economy, and 0.10 with no improvement in credit flow in the economy.

a. Based on Scott's estimates, what is the probability that the stock price of Webtalk goes up?

b. If we know that the stock price of Webtalk has gone up, what is the probability that credit flow in the economy has improved significantly?

SOLUTION: As always, we first define the relevant events and their associated probabilities. Let S, M, and N denote significant, marginal, and no improvement in credit flow, respectively. Then $P(S) = 0.20$, $P(M) = 0.50$, and $P(N) = 0.30$. In addition, if we allow G to denote an increase in stock price, we formulate $P(G \mid S) = 0.90$, $P(G \mid M) = 0.40$, and $P(G \mid N) = 0.10$. We need to calculate $P(G)$ in part a and $P(S \mid G)$ in part b. Table 4.7 aids in assigning probabilities.

TABLE 4.7 Computing Posterior Probabilities for Example 4.20

Prior Probability	Conditional Probability	Joint Probability	Posterior Probability
$P(S) = 0.20$	$P(G \mid S) = 0.90$	$P(G \cap S) = 0.18$	$P(S \mid G) = 0.4390$
$P(M) = 0.50$	$P(G \mid M) = 0.40$	$P(G \cap M) = 0.20$	$P(M \mid G) = 0.4878$
$P(N) = 0.30$	$P(G \mid N) = 0.10$	$P(G \cap N) = 0.03$	$P(N \mid G) = 0.0732$
$P(S) + P(M) + P(N) = 1$		$P(G) = 0.41$	$P(S \mid G) + P(M \mid G) + P(N \mid G) = 1$

a. In order to calculate $P(G)$, we use the total probability rule, $P(G) = P(G \cap S) + P(G \cap M) + P(G \cap N)$. The joint probabilities are calculated as products of conditional probabilities with their corresponding prior probabilities. For instance, in Table 4.7, $P(G \cap S) = P(G \mid S)P(S) = 0.90 \times 0.20 = 0.18$. Therefore, the probability that the stock price of Webtalk goes up equals $P(G) = 0.18 + 0.20 + 0.03 = 0.41$.

b. According to Bayes' theorem, $P(S|G) = \frac{P(G \cap S)}{P(G)} = \frac{P(G \cap S)}{P(G \cap S) + P(G \cap M) + P(G \cap N)}$. We use the total probability rule in the denominator to find $P(G) = 0.18 + 0.20 + 0.03 = 0.41$. Therefore, $P(S|G) = \frac{P(G \cap S)}{P(G)} = \frac{0.18}{0.41} = 0.4390$. Note that the prior probability of a significant improvement in credit flow is revised upward from 0.20 to a posterior probability of 0.4390.

EXERCISES 4.4

Mechanics

52. Let $P(B) = 0.60$, $P(A|B) = 0.80$, and $P(A|B^c) = 0.10$. Calculate the following probabilities:

   a. $P(B^c)$

   b. $P(A \cap B)$ and $P(A \cap B^c)$

   c. $P(A)$

   d. $P(B|A)$

53. Let $P(A) = 0.70$, $P(B|A) = 0.55$, and $P(B|A^c) = 0.10$. Use a probability tree to calculate the following probabilities:

   a. $P(A^c)$

   b. $P(A \cap B)$ and $P(A^c \cap B)$

   c. $P(B)$

   d. $P(A|B)$

54. Complete the following probability table.

Prior Probability	Conditional Probability	Joint Probability	Posterior Probability
$P(A) = 0.30$	$P(B|A) = 0.25$	$P(A \cap B) =$	$P(A|B) =$
$P(A^c) =$	$P(B|A^c) = 0.80$	$P(A^c \cap B) =$	$P(A^c|B) =$
Total $=$		$P(B) =$	Total $=$

55. Complete the following probability table.

Prior Probability	Conditional Probability	Joint Probability	Posterior Probability
$P(B) = 0.85$	$P(A|B) = 0.05$	$P(A \cap B) =$	$P(B|A) =$
$P(B^c) =$	$P(A|B^c) = 0.80$	$P(A \cap B^c) =$	$P(B^c|A) =$
Total $=$		$P(A) =$	Total $=$

56. Let a sample space be partitioned into three mutually exclusive and exhaustive events, B_1, B_2, and B_3. Complete the following probability table.

Prior Probabilities	Conditional Probabilities	Joint Probabilities	Posterior Probabilities
$P(B_1) = 0.10$	$P(A|B_1) = 0.40$	$P(A \cap B_1) =$	$P(B_1|A) =$
$P(B_2) =$	$P(A|B_2) = 0.60$	$P(A \cap B_2) =$	$P(B_2|A) =$
$P(B_3) = 0.30$	$P(A|B_3) = 0.80$	$P(A \cap B_3) =$	$P(B_3|A) =$
Total $=$		$P(A) =$	Total $=$

Applications

57. Christine has always been weak in mathematics. Based on her performance prior to the final exam in Calculus, there is a 40% chance that she will fail the course if she does not have a tutor. With a tutor, her probability of failing decreases to 10%. There is only a 50% chance that she will find a tutor at such short notice.

   a. What is the probability that Christine fails the course?

   b. Christine ends up failing the course. What is the probability that she had found a tutor?

58. An analyst expects that 20% of all publicly traded companies will experience a decline in earnings next year. The analyst has developed a ratio to help forecast this decline. If the company is headed for a decline, there is a 70% chance that this ratio will be negative. If the company is not headed for a decline, there is a 15% chance that the ratio will be negative. The analyst randomly selects a company and its ratio is negative. What is the posterior probability that the company will experience a decline?

59. The State Police are trying to crack down on speeding on a particular portion of the Massachusetts Turnpike. To aid in this pursuit, they have purchased a new radar gun that promises greater consistency and reliability. Specifically, the gun advertises ± one-mile-per-hour accuracy 98% of the time; that is, there is a 0.98 probability that the gun will detect a speeder, if the driver is actually speeding. Assume there is a 1% chance that the gun erroneously detects a speeder even when the driver is below the speed limit. Suppose that 95% of the drivers drive below the speed limit on this stretch of the Massachusetts Turnpike.

   a. What is the probability that the gun detects speeding and the driver was speeding?

   b. What is the probability that the gun detects speeding and the driver was not speeding?

   c. Suppose the police stop a driver because the gun detects speeding. What is the probability that the driver was actually driving below the speed limit?

60. According to a study, cell phones are the main medium for teenagers to stay connected with friends and family (*CNN*, March 19, 2012). It is estimated that 90% of older teens and 60% of younger teens own a cell phone. Suppose 70% of all teens are older teens.

   a. What is the implied probability that a teen owns a cell phone?

   b. Given that a teen owns a cell phone, what is the probability that he/she is an older teen?

c. Given that the teen owns a cell phone, what is the probability that he/she is a younger teen?

61. According to data from the *National Health and Nutrition Examination Survey*, 33% of white, 49.6% of black, 43% of Hispanic, and 8.9% of Asian women are obese. In a representative town, 48% of women are white, 19% are black, 26% are Hispanic, and the remaining 7% are Asian.

   a. Find the probability that a randomly selected woman in this town is obese.

   b. Given that a woman is obese, what is the probability that she is white?

   c. Given that a woman is obese, what is the probability that she is black?

   d. Given that a woman is obese, what is the probability that she is Asian?

62. A crucial game of the Los Angeles Lakers basketball team depends on the health of their key player. According to his doctor's report, there is a 40% chance that he will be fully fit to play, a 30% chance that he will be somewhat fit to play, and a 30% chance that he will not be able to play at all. The coach has estimated the chances of winning at 80% if the player is fully fit, 60% if he is somewhat fit, and 40% if he is unable to play.

   a. What is the probability that the Lakers will win the game?

   b. You have just heard that the Lakers won the game. What is the probability that the key player had been fully fit to play in the game?

63. An analyst thinks that next year there is a 20% chance that the world economy will be good, a 50% chance that it will be neutral, and a 30% chance that it will be poor. She also predicts probabilities that the performance of a start-up firm, Creative Ideas, will be good, neutral, or poor for each of the economic states of the world economy. The following table presents probabilities for three states of the world economy and the corresponding conditional probabilities for Creative Ideas.

State of the World Economy	Probability of Economic State	Performance of Creative Ideas	Conditional Probability of Creative Ideas
Good	0.20	Good	0.60
		Neutral	0.30
		Poor	0.10
Neutral	0.50	Good	0.40
		Neutral	0.30
		Poor	0.30
Poor	0.30	Good	0.20
		Neutral	0.30
		Poor	0.50

   a. What is the probability that the performance of the world economy will be neutral and that of Creative Ideas will be poor?

   b. What is the probability that the performance of Creative Ideas will be poor?

   c. The performance of Creative Ideas was poor. What is the probability that the performance of the world economy had also been poor?

4.5 COUNTING RULES

LO 4.7

In several areas of statistics, including the binomial distribution discussed in the next chapter, the calculation of probabilities involves defining and counting outcomes. Here we discuss principles and shortcuts for counting. Specifically, we explore the factorial, combination, and permutation notations. We then find that in certain circumstances counting rules can aid in calculating the probability of an event.

Use a counting rule to calculate the probability of an event.

When we are interested in counting the arrangements of a given set of n items, we use the **factorial formula**, denoted $n!$. In other words, given n items, there are $n!$ ways of arranging them. We apply the factorial when there are no groups—we are only arranging a given set of n items.

THE FACTORIAL FORMULA

The number of ways to assign every member of a group of size n to n slots is calculated using the factorial formula:

$$n! = n \times (n-1) \times (n-2) \times (n-3) \times \cdots \times 1$$

By definition, $0! = 1$.

EXAMPLE 4.21

A little-league coach has nine players on his team and he has to assign each of the players to one of nine positions (pitcher, catcher, first base, etc.). In how many ways can the assignments be made?

SOLUTION: The first player may be assigned to nine different positions. Then eight positions remain. The second player can be assigned to eight different positions. The third player can be assigned to seven different positions, and so on, until the ninth and last player can be assigned in only one way. The total number of different assignments is equal to $9! = 9 \times 8 \times \cdots \times 1 = 362,880$.

The **combination** and **permutation formulas** apply to two groups of predetermined size. We apply the combination formula when the order of the arrangement does not matter, whereas we use the permutation formula when the order is important. Generally, we look for a specific reference to "order" being important when employing the permutation formula.

THE COMBINATION FORMULA

The number of ways to choose x objects from a total of n objects, where the order in which the x objects are listed *does not matter*, is calculated using the combination formula:

$$_nC_x = \binom{n}{x} = \frac{n!}{(n-x)!x!}$$

EXAMPLE 4.22

The little-league coach from Example 4.21 recruits three more players so that his team has backups in case of injury. Now his team totals 12.

a. How many ways can the coach select nine players from the 12-player roster?

b. If each of the lineups from part a is equally likely, what is the probability that the coach selects a particular lineup?

SOLUTION:

a. This is a combination problem because we are simply interested in placing 9 players on the field. We have no concern, for instance, as to whether a player pitches, catches, or plays first base. In other words, the order in which the players are selected is not important. We make use of the combination formula as follows:

$$_{12}C_9 = \binom{12}{9} = \frac{12!}{(12-9)! \times 9!} = \frac{12 \times 11 \times \cdots \times 1}{(3 \times 2 \times 1) \times (9 \times 8 \times \cdots \times 1)} = 220.$$

b. Given that each lineup in part a is equally likely, the probability that any one lineup occurs is $1/220 = 0.0045$.

THE PERMUTATION FORMULA

The number of ways to choose x objects from a total of n objects, where the order in which the x objects is listed *does matter*, is calculated using the permutation formula:

$$_nP_x = \frac{n!}{(n-x)!}$$

EXAMPLE 4.23

Now suppose the little league coach from Example 4.22 recognizes that the nine positions of baseball are quite different. It matters whether one player is pitching or whether that same player is in the outfield.

a. In how many ways can the coach assign his 12-player roster to the nine different positions?

b. If each of the lineups from part a are equally likely, what is the probability that the coach selects a particular lineup?

SOLUTION:

a. This is a permutation problem because the order in which the coach assigns the positions matters. For example, a lineup that has one player playing in the outfield is different from a lineup that has that same player pitching. We calculate the answer as follows:

$$_{12}P_9 = \frac{12!}{(12-9)!} = \frac{12 \times 11 \times \cdots \times 1}{3 \times 2 \times 1} = 79,833,600.$$

Comparing the answers we obtained from Examples 4.22 and 4.23, we see there is a big difference between the number of arrangements when the position of the player does not matter versus the number of arrangements when the position is important.

b. Given that each lineup in part a is equally likely, the probability that any one lineup occurs is $1/79,833,600 \approx 0.0000$; that is, the probability approaches zero.

EXERCISES 4.5

Mechanics

64. Calculate the following values.
    a. 8! and 6!
    b. $_8C_6$
    c. $_8P_6$

65. Calculate the following values.
    a. 7! and 3!
    b. $_7C_3$
    c. $_7P_3$

Applications

66. At a local elementary school, a principal is making random class assignments for her 8 teachers. Each teacher must be assigned to exactly one job. In how many ways can the assignments be made?

67. Twenty cancer patients volunteer for a clinical trial. Ten of the patients will receive a placebo and 10 will receive the trial drug. In how many different ways can the researchers select 10 patients to receive the trial drug from the total of 20?

68. There are 10 players on the local basketball team. The coach decides to randomly pick 5 players to start the game.
    a. In how many different ways can the coach select 5 players to start the game if order does not matter?
    b. In how many different ways can the coach select 5 players to start the game if order (the type of position, i.e., point guard, center, etc.) matters?

69. A horse-racing fan is contemplating the many different outcomes in an eight-horse race.

   a. How many different outcomes are possible if only the first three places are considered and ranking (first, second, and third) is important?

   b. If each of the outcomes in part a is equally likely, what is the probability of selecting the winning outcome?

   c. How many different outcomes are possible if only the first three places are considered and ranking (first, second, and third) is not important?

   d. If each of the outcomes in part c is equally likely, what is the probability of selecting the winning outcome?

70. Jacqueline Fibbe manages 10 employees at a small ice cream store in Beverly Farms, MA. She assigns three employees for each eight-hour shift.

   a. If order is not important, in how many different ways can she select three employees from the total of 10 for each eight-hour shift?

   b. Megan H. is one of the 10 employees. If the assignment of employees is random, how many of the shifts in part a will include Megan H.?

71. David Barnes and his fiancée Valerie Shah are visiting Hawaii. At the Hawaiian Cultural Center in Honolulu, they are told that 2 out of a group of 8 people will be randomly picked for a free lesson of a Tahitian dance.

   a. What is the probability that both David and Valerie get picked for the Tahitian dance lesson?

   b. What is the probability that Valerie gets picked before David for the Tahitian dance lesson?

WRITING WITH STATISTICS

©Seastock/Shutterstock RF

Support for marijuana legalization in the United States has grown remarkably over the past few decades. In 1969, when the question was first presented, only 12% of Americans were in favor of its legalization. This support had increased to over 25% by the late 1970s. While support was stagnant from 1981 to 1997, the turn of the century brought a renewed interest in its legalization, with the percentage of Americans in favor exceeding 30% by 2000 and 40% by 2009.

Alexis Lewis works for a drug policy institute that focuses on science, health, and human rights. She is analyzing the demographic breakdown of marijuana supporters. Using 2016 results from a Pew Research Center survey, she has found that support for marijuana legalization varies considerably depending on a person's age group. Alexis compiles information on support based on age group as shown in Table 4.8.

TABLE 4.8 Percentage Support for Legalizing Marijuana by Age Group

Age Group	Support
Millennial (18–35)	71%
Generation X (36–51)	57%
Baby Boomer (52–70)	56%
Silent (71 and older)	33%

Source: Pew Research Center, survey conducted August 23 – September 2, 2016.

Alexis finds that another important factor determining the fate of marijuana legalization concerns each age group's ability to sway the vote. For adults eligible to vote as of 2016, she breaks down each age group's voting power. The Millennial, Generation X, Baby Boomer, and Silent generations account for 31%, 25%, 31%, and 13% of the voting population, respectively.

Alexis wants to use this information to

1. Calculate and interpret relevant conditional, unconditional, and joint probabilities.

2. Calculate and interpret the probability of all Americans who support the legalization of marijuana.

Sample
Report—
Linking
Support for
Legalizing
Marijuana
with Age
Group

Driven by growing public support, the legalization of marijuana in America has been moving at a breakneck speed in recent years. As of 2016, marijuana is now legal in some form in 28 states and in Washington, DC. Even recreational marijuana is gaining support, becoming legal in Alaska, California, Colorado, Maine, Massachusetts, Nevada, Oregon, Washington, and Washington, DC. Changing demographics can help explain how the tide has turned in marijuana's favor, especially with Millennials (those between the ages of 18 and 35), who are on the verge of becoming the nation's largest living generation.

A 2016 Pew Research Study provides interesting data regarding support for marijuana legalization. Two factors seem to drive support for the issue: generation (or age group) and the relative size of a generation's voting bloc. For ease of interpretation, let M, G, B, and S denote "Millennial," "Generation X," "Baby Boomer," and "Silent" generations, respectively. Based on data from the study, the following probability statements can be formulated with respect to the relative size of each generation's voting bloc: $P(M) = 0.31$, $P(G) = 0.25$, $P(B) = 0.31$, $P(S) = 0.13$. In other words, Millennials and Baby Boomers have the most voting power, each comprising 31% of the voting population; the Generation X and Silent generations represent 25% and 13% of the voting population, respectively.

Now let L denote "support for legalizing marijuana." Again, based on data from the study, conditional probabilities can be specified as $P(L|M) = 0.71$, $P(L|G) = 0.57$, $P(L|B) = 0.56$, and $P(L|S) = 0.33$. Therefore, the probability that a randomly selected adult supports legal marijuana and is in the Millennial generation is determined as $P(L \cap M) = 0.71 \times 0.31 = 0.2201$. Similarly, $P(L \cap G) = 0.1425$, $P(L \cap B) = 0.1736$, and $P(L \cap S) = 0.0429$. By combining all generations, we deduce the total probability of support for legalizing marijuana as $P(L) = 0.2201 + 0.1425 + 0.1736 + 0.0429 = 0.5791$; in 2016, a staggering 58% of Americans support the legalization of marijuana. Table 4.A is the joint probability table that summarizes unconditional and joint probabilities.

TABLE 4.A Joint Probability Table for the Support for Legalizing Marijuana by Age Group

Age Group	Legalizing Marijuana		Total
	Support	Do not Support	
Millennial (18–35)	0.2201	0.0899	0.31
Generation X (36–51)	0.1425	0.1075	0.25
Baby Boomer (52–70)	0.1736	0.1364	0.31
Silent (71 and older)	0.0429	0.0871	0.13
Total	0.5791	0.4209	1.00

To put it in perspective, suppose that there are 1,000 randomly selected adult attendees at a conference. The results imply that there would be about 310 Millennial, 250 Generation X, 310 Baby Boomer, and 130 Silent attendees. Further, the supporters of marijuana legalization would include about 220 Millennial, 143 Generation X, 174 Baby Boomer, and 43 Silent attendees.

Millennials, with roughly 31% of the overall electorate, are now as large a political force as Baby Boomers. In general, Millennials tend to be liberal on social issues such as gay rights, immigration, and marijuana. This shift in population has not gone unnoticed by political parties, which all hope to court the more than 75 million of these eligible young voters.

CONCEPTUAL REVIEW

LO 4.1 **Describe fundamental probability concepts.**

In order to assign the appropriate probability to an uncertain event, it is useful to establish some terminology. An **experiment** is a process that leads to one of several possible outcomes. A **sample space**, denoted S, of an experiment contains all possible outcomes of the experiment. An **event** is any subset of outcomes of an experiment, and is called a simple event if it contains a single outcome. Events are **exhaustive** if all possible outcomes of an experiment belong to the events. Events are **mutually exclusive** if they do not share any common outcome of an experiment.

A **probability** is a numerical value that measures the likelihood that an event occurs. It assumes a value between zero and one, where a value zero indicates an impossible event and a value one indicates a definite event. The two defining properties of a probability are (1) the probability of any event A is a value between 0 and 1, $0 \leq P(A) \leq 1$, and (2) the sum of the probabilities of any list of mutually exclusive and exhaustive events equals 1.

A **subjective** probability is calculated by drawing on personal and subjective judgment. An **empirical probability** is calculated as a relative frequency of occurrence. A **classical probability** is based on logical analysis rather than on observation or personal judgment.

LO 4.2 Apply the rules of probability.

Rules of probability allow us to calculate the probabilities of more complex events. The **complement rule** states that the probability of the complement of an event can be found by subtracting the probability of the event from one: $P(A^c) = 1 - P(A)$.

The probability that at least one of two events occurs is calculated by using the **addition rule**: $P(A \cup B) = P(A) + P(B) - P(A \cap B)$. Since $P(A \cap B) = 0$ for mutually exclusive events, the addition rule then simplifies in these instances to $P(A \cup B) = P(A) + P(B)$.

The probability of event A, denoted $P(A)$, is an **unconditional probability**. It is the probability that A occurs without any additional information. The probability that A occurs given that B has already occurred, denoted $P(A|B)$, is a **conditional probability**. A conditional probability is computed as $P(A|B) = \frac{P(A \cap B)}{P(B)}$. We rearrange the conditional probability formula to arrive at the **multiplication rule**. When using this rule, we find the probability that two events, A and B, both occur; that is, $P(A \cap B) = P(A|B)P(B) = P(B|A)P(A)$.

LO 4.3 Distinguish between independent and dependent events.

Two events, A and B, are **independent** if $P(A|B) = P(A)$, or if $P(B|A) = P(B)$. Otherwise, the events are **dependent**. For independent events, the multiplication rule simplifies to $P(A \cap B) = P(A)P(B)$.

LO 4.4 Calculate and interpret probabilities from a contingency table.

A **contingency table** generally shows frequencies for two qualitative (categorical) variables, x and y, where each cell represents a mutually exclusive combination of x-y values. Empirical probabilities are easily calculated as the relative frequency of the occurrence of the event.

LO 4.5 Apply the total probability rule.

The **total probability rule** expresses the probability of an event A in terms of probabilities of the intersection of A with two mutually exclusive and exhaustive events, B and B^c:

$$P(A) = P(A \cap B) + P(A \cap B^c), \text{ or equivalently,}$$
$$P(A) = P(A|B)P(B) + P(A|B^c)P(B^c)$$

We can extend this rule where the sample space is partitioned into n mutually exclusive and exhaustive events, $B_1, B_2, \ldots, B_n$. The total probability rule is

$$P(A) = P(A \cap B_1) + P(A \cap B_2) + \cdots + P(A \cap B_n), \text{ or equivalently,}$$
$$P(A) = P(A|B_1)P(B_1) + P(A|B_2)P(B_2) + \cdots + P(A|B_n)P(B_n).$$

Apply Bayes' theorem.

Bayes' theorem provides a procedure for updating probabilities based on new information. Let $P(B)$ be the prior probability and $P(B|A)$ be the posterior probability based on new information provided by A. Then,

$$P(B|A) = \frac{P(A \cap B)}{P(A \cap B) + P(A \cap B^c)} = \frac{P(A|B)P(B)}{P(A|B)P(B) + P(A|B^c)P(B^c)}.$$

For the extended case, Bayes' theorem, for any $i = 1, 2, \ldots, n$, is

$$P(B_i|A) = \frac{P(A \cap B_i)}{P(A \cap B_1) + P(A \cap B_2) + \cdots + P(A \cap B_n)}, \text{ or}$$

equivalently, $P(B_i|A) = \dfrac{P(A|B_i)P(B_i)}{P(A|B_1)P(B_1) + P(A|B_2)P(B_2) + \cdots + P(A|B_n)P(B_n)}.$

LO 4.7 **Use a counting rule to calculate the probability of an event.**

Shortcut rules for counting include the **factorial**, the **combination**, and the **permutation** formulas. When we are interested in arranging a given set of n items, we calculate n factorial as $n! = n \times (n - 1) \times \cdots \times 1$. The combination and permutation formulas apply to two groups of predetermined size. We apply the combination formula when the order of the arrangement does not matter: $_nC_x = \binom{n}{x} = \frac{n!}{(n-x)!x!}$. We use the permutation formula when the order of the arrangement matters: $_nP_x = \frac{n!}{(n-x)!}$. In certain circumstances, counting rules can aid in calculating the probability of an event.

ADDITIONAL EXERCISES AND CASE STUDIES

Exercises

72. According to a global survey of 4,400 parents of children between the ages of 14 to 17, 44% of parents spy on their teen's Facebook account (www.msnbc.com, April 25, 2012). Assume that American parents account for 10% of all parents of teens with Facebook accounts, of which 60% spy on their teen's Facebook account. Suppose a parent is randomly selected, and the following events are defined: A = selecting an American parent and B = selecting a spying parent.
    a. Based on the above information, what are the probabilities that can be established?
    b. Are the events A and B mutually exclusive and/or exhaustive? Explain.
    c. Are the events A and B independent? Explain.
    d. What is the probability of selecting an American parent given that she/he is a spying parent?

73. AccuScore calculated an 84% chance that there would be a fight during the game between the Anaheim Ducks and the Chicago Blackhawks,

two of the National Hockey League's most pugnacious teams (*The Wall Street Journal*, March 3, 2009). What are the odds for a fight occurring?

74. According to eMarketer estimates, 88.3% of 12- to 17-year-olds had a mobile phone in 2016. Among those with mobile phones, 84.0% had smartphones. Calculate the proportion of 12- to 17-year-olds who had smartphones.

75. Henry Chow is a stockbroker working for Merrill Lynch. He knows from past experience that there is a 70% chance that his new client will want to include U.S. equity in her portfolio and a 50% chance that she will want to include foreign equity. There is also a 40% chance that she will want to include both U.S. equity and foreign equity in her portfolio.
    a. What is the probability that the client will want to include U.S. equity if she already has foreign equity in her portfolio?
    b. What is the probability that the client decides to include neither U.S. equity nor foreign equity in her portfolio?

76. The Easy Credit Company reports the following table representing a breakdown of customers according to the amount they owe and whether a cash advance has been made. An auditor randomly selects one of the accounts.

Amounts owed by customers	Cash Advance?	
	Yes	No
$0 – 199.99	245	2,890
$200 – 399.99	380	1,700
$400 – 599.99	500	1,425
$600 – 799.99	415	940
$800 – 999.99	260	480
$1,000 or more	290	475
Total Customers	2,090	7,910

a. What is the probability that a customer received a cash advance?

b. What is the probability that a customer owed less than $200 and received a cash advance?

c. What is the probability that a customer owed less than $200 or received a cash advance?

d. Given that a customer received a cash advance, what is the probability that the customer owed $1,000 or more?

e. Given that a customer owed $1,000 or more, what is the probability that the customer received a cash advance?

f. Are the events "receiving a cash advance" and "owing $1,000 or more" mutually exclusive? Explain using probabilities.

g. Are the events "receiving a cash advance" and "owing $1,000 or more" independent? Explain using probabilities.

77. The following frequency distribution shows the ages of India's 40 richest individuals. One of these individuals is selected at random.

Ages	Frequency
30 up to 40	3
40 up to 50	8
50 up to 60	15
60 up to 70	9
70 up to 80	5

Source: www.forbes.com.

a. What is the probability that the individual is between 50 and 60 years of age?

b. What is the probability that the individual is younger than 50 years of age?

c. What is the probability that the individual is at least 60 years of age?

78. How much you smile in your younger days can predict your later success in marriage (www.msnbc.com, April 16, 2009). The analysis is based on the success rate in marriage of people over age 65 and their smiles when they were only 10 years old. Researchers found that only 11% of the biggest smilers had been divorced, while 31% of the biggest frowners had experienced a broken marriage.

a. Suppose it is known that 2% of the people are the biggest smilers at age 10 and divorced in later years. What percent of people are the biggest smilers?

b. If 25% of people are considered to be the biggest frowners, calculate the probability that a person is a biggest frowner at age 10 and divorced later in life.

79. Anthony Papantonis, owner of Nauset Construction, is bidding on two projects, A and B. The probability that he wins project A is 0.40 and the probability that he wins project B is 0.25. Winning Project A and winning Project B are independent events.

a. What is the probability that he wins project A or project B?

b. What is the probability that he does not win either project?

80. Wooden boxes are commonly used for the packaging and transportation of mangoes. A convenience store in Morganville, New Jersey, regularly buys mangoes from a wholesale dealer. For every shipment, the manager randomly inspects two mangoes from a box containing 20 mangoes for damages due to transportation. Suppose the chosen box contains exactly 3 damaged mangoes.

a. Find the probability that the first mango is not damaged.

b. Find the probability that neither of the mangoes is damaged.

c. Find the probability that both mangoes are damaged.

81. A study shows that unemployment does not impact males and females in the same way (*Newsweek*, April 20, 2009). According to a Bureau of Labor Statistics report, 8.5% of those who are eligible to work are unemployed. The unemployment rate is 8.8% for eligible men and only 7.0% for eligible women. Suppose 52% of the eligible workforce in the U.S. consists of men.

a. You have just heard that another worker in a large firm has been laid off. What is the probability that this worker is a man?

b. You have just heard that another worker in a large firm has been laid off. What is the probability that this worker is a woman?

82. According to the CGMA Economic Index, which measures executive sentiment across the world, 18% of all respondents expressed optimism about the global economy (www.aicpa.org, March 29, 2012). Moreover, 22% of the respondents from the United States and 9% from Asia felt optimistic about the global economy.
    a. What is the probability that an Asian respondent is not optimistic about the global economy?
    b. If 28% of all respondents are from the United States, what is the probability that a respondent is from the United States and is optimistic about the global economy?
    c. Suppose 22% of all respondents are from Asia. If a respondent feels optimistic about the global economy, what is the probability that the respondent is from Asia?

83. A professor of management has heard that eight students in his class of 40 have landed an internship for the summer. Suppose he runs into two of his students in the corridor.
    a. Find the probability that neither of these students has landed an internship.
    b. Find the probability that both of these students have landed an internship.

84. It has generally been believed that it is not feasible for men and women to be just friends (*The New York Times*, April 12, 2012). Others argue that this belief may not be true anymore since gone are the days when men worked and women stayed at home and the only way they could get together was for romance. In a survey, 186 heterosexual college students were asked if it was feasible for men and women to be just friends. Thirty-two percent of females and 57% of males reported that it was not feasible for men and women to be just friends. Suppose the study consisted of 100 female and 86 male students.
    a. Construct a contingency table that shows frequencies for the qualitative variables Gender (men or women) and Feasible (yes or no).
    b. Find the probability that a student believes that men and women can be friends.
    c. If a student believes that men and women can be friends, what is the probability that this student is a male? Find the corresponding probability that this student is a female.

85. At a local bar in a small Midwestern town, beer and wine are the only two alcoholic options. The manager noted that of all male customers who visited over the weekend, 150 ordered beer, 40 ordered wine, and 20 asked for soft drinks. Of female customers, 38 ordered beer, 20 ordered wine, and 12 asked for soft drinks.
    a. Construct a contingency table that shows frequencies for the qualitative variables Gender (male or female) and Drink Choice (beer, wine, or soft drink).
    b. Find the probability that a customer orders wine.
    c. What is the probability that a male customer orders wine?
    d. Are the events "Wine" and "Male" independent? Explain using probabilities.

86. A study in the *Journal of the American Medical Association* (February 20, 2008) found that patients who go into cardiac arrest while in the hospital are more likely to die if it happens after 11 pm. The study investigated 58,593 cardiac arrests that occurred during the day or evening. Of those, 11,604 survived to leave the hospital. There were 28,155 cardiac arrests during the shift that began at 11 pm, commonly referred to as the graveyard shift. Of those, 4,139 survived for discharge. The following contingency table summarizes the results of the study.

	Survived for Discharge	Did not Survive for Discharge	Total
Day or Evening Shift	11,604	46,989	58,593
Graveyard Shift	4,139	24,016	28,155
Total	15,743	71,005	86,748

    a. What is the probability that a randomly selected patient experienced cardiac arrest during the graveyard shift?
    b. What is the probability that a randomly selected patient survived for discharge?
    c. Given that a randomly selected patient experienced cardiac arrest during the graveyard shift, what is the probability the patient survived for discharge?
    d. Given that a randomly selected patient survived for discharge, what is the probability the patient experienced cardiac arrest during the graveyard shift?
    e. Are the events "Survived for Discharge" and "Graveyard Shift" independent? Explain using probabilities. Given your answer, what type of recommendations might you give to hospitals?

87. It has been reported that women end up unhappier than men later in life, even though they start out happier (*Yahoo News,* August 1, 2008). Early in life, women are more likely to fulfill their family life and financial aspirations, leading to greater overall happiness. However, men report a higher satisfaction with their financial situation and family life, and are thus happier than women, in later life. Suppose the results of the survey of 300 men and 300 women are presented in the following table.

Response to the question "Are you satisfied with your financial and family life?"

	Age		
Response by Women	20 to 35	35 to 50	Over 50
Yes	73	36	32
No	67	54	38

	Age		
Response by Men	20 to 35	35 to 50	Over 50
Yes	58	34	38
No	92	46	32

    a. What is the probability that a randomly selected woman is satisfied with her financial and family life?

    b. What is the probability that a randomly selected man is satisfied with his financial and family life?

    c. For women, are the events "Yes" and "20 to 35" independent? Explain using probabilities.

    d. For men, are the events "Yes" and "20 to 35" independent? Explain using probabilities.

88. An analyst predicts that there is a 40% chance that the U.S. economy will perform well. If the U.S. economy performs well, then there is an 80% chance that Asian countries will also perform well. On the other hand, if the U.S. economy performs poorly, the probability of Asian countries performing well goes down to 0.30.

    a. What is the probability that both the U.S. economy and the Asian countries will perform well?

    b. What is the probability that the Asian countries will perform well?

    c. What is the probability that the U.S. economy will perform well, given that the Asian countries perform well?

89. Apparently, depression significantly increases the risk of developing dementia later in life (*BBC News,* July 6, 2010). In a study, it was reported that 22% of those who had depression went on to develop dementia, compared to only 17% of those who did not have depression. Suppose 10% of all people suffer from depression.

    a. What is the probability of a person developing dementia?

    b. If a person has developed dementia, what is the probability that the person suffered from depression earlier in life?

90. According to data from the *National Health and Nutrition Examination Survey*, 36.5% of adult women and 26.6% of adult men are at a healthy weight. Suppose 50.52% of the adult population consists of women.

    a. What proportion of adults is at a healthy weight?

    b. If an adult is at a healthy weight, what is the probability that the adult is a woman?

    c. If an adult is at a healthy weight, what is the probability that the adult is a man?

91. Suppose that 60% of the students do homework regularly. It is also known that 80% of students who had been doing homework regularly end up doing well in the course (get a grade of A or B). Only 20% of students who had not been doing homework regularly end up doing well in the course.

    a. What is the probability that a student does well in the course?

    b. Given that the student did well in the course, what is the probability that the student had been doing homework regularly?

92. There is a growing public support for marijuana law reform, with polls showing more than half the country is in favor of some form of marijuana legalization. However, opinions on marijuana are divided starkly along political party lines. The results of the Pew Research Center survey conducted in 2016 are shown in the following table. In addition, assume that 27% of Americans identify as Republicans, 30% as Democrats, and 43% as independents.

Political Party	Support
Republican	41%
Democrat	66%
Independent	63%

    a. Calculate the probability that a randomly selected American adult supports marijuana legalization and is a Republican.

    b. Calculate the probability that a randomly selected American adult supports marijuana legalization and is a Democrat.

c. Calculate the probability that a randomly selected American adult supports marijuana legalization and is an Independent.

d. What percentage of American adults support marijuana legalization?

e. If a randomly selected American adult supports marijuana legalization, what is the probability that this adult is a Republican?

93. A 2015 national survey by the Washington Post-Kaiser Family Foundation finds that there is a big gender divide between Americans when identifying as feminist or strong feminist. The results of the survey are shown in the following table. In addition, per the 2010 U.S. Census Current Population Survey, 50.8% of the American population is female and 49.2% is male.

Gender	Feminist or Strong Feminist
Female	66%
Male	41%

a. Calculate the probability that a randomly selected American adult is a female who also identifies as feminist or strong feminist.

b. Calculate the probability that a randomly selected American adult is a male who also identifies as feminist or strong feminist.

c. What percentage of American adults identify as feminist or strong feminist?

d. If a randomly selected American adult identifies as feminist or strong feminist, what is the probability that this adult is a female?

94. According to the Census's Population Survey, the percentage of children with two parents at home is the highest for Asians and lowest for blacks (*USA Today*, February 26, 2009). It is reported that 85% of Asian children have two parents at home versus 78% of white, 70% of Hispanic, and 38% of black. Suppose there are 500 students in a representative school of which 280 are white, 50 are Asian, 100 are Hispanic, and 70 are black.

a. What is the probability that a child has both parents at home?

b. If both parents are at home, what is the probability the child is Asian?

c. If both parents are at home, what is the probability the child is black?

95. Prior to the start of the season, a sports analyst is attempting to predict the end-of-season rankings of the 10 teams in a conference.

a. How many different ways can the teams be ranked if ties are not considered?

b. How many different outcomes are possible if only the first three places are considered and ranking (first, second, and third) is important?

c. If each of the outcomes in part b is equally likely, what is the probability that the sports analyst selects the correct end-of-season outcome?

d. How many different outcomes are possible if only the first three places are considered and ranking (first, second, and third) is not important?

e. If each of the outcomes in part d is equally likely, what is the probability that the sports analyst selects the correct end-of-season outcome?

96. Assume high school coach Emily Williams has seven possible swimmers for a four-person relay team.

a. If the order for the freestyle relay is unimportant, how many different relay teams are possible?

b. Assume for the medley relay team that order is important; how many different teams are possible?

c. Swimmer Michael P. is one of the seven swimmers. If the assignment of swimmers is random, how many of the teams in part a will include Michael P.?

CASE STUDIES

CASE STUDY 4.1   Ever since the introduction of New Coke failed miserably in the 1980s, most food and beverage companies have been cautious about changing the taste or formula of their signature offerings. In an attempt to attract more business, Starbucks recently introduced a new milder brew, Pike Place Roast, as its main drip coffee at the majority of its locations nationwide. The idea was to offer a more approachable cup of coffee with a smoother finish. However, the strategy also downplayed the company's more established robust roasts; initially, the milder brew was the only option for customers after noon. Suppose on a recent afternoon, 100 customers were asked whether or not they would return in the near future for another cup of Pike Place Roast. The following contingency table (cross-classified by type of customer and whether or not the customer will return) lists the results:

Data for Case Study 4.1

Return in Near Future?	Customer Type	
	First-time Customer	Established Customer
Yes	35	10
No	5	50

In a report, use the sample information to

1. Calculate and interpret unconditional probabilities.
2. Calculate the probability that a customer will return given that the customer is an established customer.
3. Determine whether the events "Return in Near Future" and "Customer Type" are independent. Shortly after the introduction of Pike Place Roast, Starbucks decided to offer its bolder brew again in the afternoon at many of its locations. Do your results support Starbucks' decision? Explain.

CASE STUDY 4.2 It is common to ignore the thyroid gland of women during pregnancy (*The New York Times,* April 13, 2009). This gland makes hormones that govern metabolism, helping to regulate body weight, heart rate, and a host of other factors. If the thyroid malfunctions, it can produce too little or too much of these hormones. Hypothyroidism, caused by an untreated underactive thyroid in pregnant women, carries the risk of impaired intelligence in the child. According to one research study, 62 out of 25,216 pregnant women were identified with hypothyroidism. Nineteen percent of the children born to women with an untreated underactive thyroid had an I.Q. of 85 or lower, compared with only 5% of those whose mothers had a healthy thyroid. It was also reported that if mothers have their hypothyroidism treated, their children's intelligence would not be impaired.

In a report, use the sample information to

1. Find the likelihood that a woman suffers from hypothyroidism during pregnancy and later has a child with an I.Q. of 85 or lower.
2. Determine the number of children in a sample of 100,000 that are likely to have an I.Q. of 85 or lower if the thyroid gland of pregnant women is ignored.
3. Compare and comment on your answer to part b with the corresponding number if all pregnant women are tested and treated for hypothyroidism.

CASE STUDY 4.3 Enacted in 1998, the Children's Online Privacy Protection Act requires firms to obtain parental consent before tracking the information and the online movement of children; however, the act applies to those children ages 12 and under. Teenagers are often oblivious to the consequences of sharing their lives online. Data reapers create huge libraries of digital profiles and sell these profiles to advertisers, who use it to detect trends and micro-target their ads back to teens. For example, a teen searching online for ways to lose weight could become enticed by an ad for dietary supplements, fed into his/her network by tracking cookies. As a preliminary step in gauging the magnitude of teen usage of social networking sites, an economist surveys 200 teen girls and 200 teen boys. Of teen girls, 166 use social networking sites; of teen boys, 156 use social networking sites.

In a report, use the sample information to

1. Construct a contingency table that shows frequencies for the qualitative variables Gender (male or female) and Use of Social Networking Sites (Yes or No).

2. Determine the probability that a teen uses social networking sites.

3. Determine the probability that a teen girl uses a social networking site.

4. A bill before Congress would like to extend the Children's Online Privacy Protection Act to apply to 15-year-olds. In addition, the bill would also ban Internet companies from sending targeted advertising to children under 16 and give these children and their parents the ability to delete their digital footprint and profile with an "eraser button" (*The Boston Globe*, May 20, 2012). Given the probabilities that you calculated with respect to teen usage of social networking sites, do you think that this legislation is necessary? Explain.

CASE STUDY 4.4   In 2008, it appeared that rising gas prices had made Californians less resistant to offshore drilling. A Field Poll survey showed that a higher proportion of Californians supported the idea of drilling for oil or natural gas along the state's coast than in 2005 (*The Wall Street Journal*, July 17, 2008). Assume that random drilling for oil only succeeds 5% of the time.

An oil company has just announced that it has discovered new technology for detecting oil. The technology is 80% reliable. That is, if there is oil, the technology will signal "oil" 80% of the time. Let there also be a 1% chance that the technology erroneously detects oil, when in fact no oil exists.

In a report, use the above information to

1. Prepare a table that shows the relevant probabilities.

2. Find the probability that, on a recent expedition, oil actually existed but the technology detected "no oil" in the area.

5 Discrete Probability Distributions

LEARNING OBJECTIVES

After reading this chapter you should be able to:

LO **5.1** Describe a discrete random variable and its probability distribution.

LO **5.2** Calculate and interpret summary measures for a discrete random variable.

LO **5.3** Calculate and interpret summary measures to evaluate portfolio returns.

LO **5.4** Calculate and interpret probabilities for a binomial random variable.

LO **5.5** Calculate and interpret probabilities for a Poisson random variable.

LO **5.6** Calculate and interpret probabilities for a hypergeometric random variable.

In this chapter, we extend our discussion about probability by introducing the concept of a random variable. A random variable summarizes the results of an experiment in terms of numerical values. It can be classified as discrete or continuous depending on the range of values that it assumes. A discrete random variable assumes a countable number of distinct values, whereas a continuous random variable is characterized by uncountable values. In this chapter, we focus on a discrete random variable and its associated probability distribution. Examples of discrete random variables include the number of credit cards carried by consumers, the number of fore-closures in a sample of 100 households, and the number of cars lined up at a toll booth. We calculate summary measures for a discrete random variable, including its mean, variance, and standard deviation. Using properties of random variables, we are able to apply these summary measures to describe portfolio returns. Finally, we discuss three widely used discrete probability distributions: the binomial, the Poisson, and the hypergeometric distributions.

©Jewel Samad/AFP/Getty Images

INTRODUCTORY CASE

Available Staff for Probable Customers

In addition to its previous plan to shut 100 stores, Starbucks announced plans in 2008 to close 500 more U.S. locations (*The Wall Street Journal*, July 9, 2008). Executives claimed that a weak economy and higher gas and food prices led to a drop in domestic store traffic. Others speculate that Starbucks' rapid expansion produced a saturated market. The locations that will close are not profitable, are not expected to be profitable, or are located near an existing company-operated Starbucks.

Anne Jones, a manager at a local Starbucks, has been reassured by headquarters that her store will remain open. She is concerned about how other nearby closings might affect business at her store. Anne knows that a typical Starbucks customer visits the chain between 15 and 18 times a month, making it among the nation's most frequented retailers. She believes that her loyal Starbucks customers, along with displaced customers, will average 18 visits to the store over a 30-day month. To decide staffing needs, Anne knows that she needs a solid understanding about the probability distribution of customer arrivals. If too many employees are ready to serve customers, some employees will be idle, which is costly to the store. However, if not enough employees are available to meet demand, this could result in losing angry customers who choose not to wait for service.

Anne wants to use the above information to

1. Calculate the expected number of visits from a typical Starbucks customer in a specified time period.

2. Calculate the probability that a typical Starbucks customer visits the chain a certain number of times in a specified time period.

A synopsis of this case is provided in Section 5.5.

5.1 RANDOM VARIABLES AND DISCRETE PROBABILITY DISTRIBUTIONS

We often have to make important decisions in the face of uncertainty. For example, a car dealership has to determine the number of cars to hold on its lot when the actual demand for cars is unknown. Similarly, an investor has to select a portfolio when the actual outcomes of investment returns are not known. This uncertainty is captured by what we call a **random variable**. A random variable summarizes outcomes of an experiment with numerical values.

We generally use the letter X to denote a random variable. A **discrete random variable** assumes a countable number of distinct values such as x_1, x_2, x_3, and so on. A **continuous random variable**, on the other hand, is characterized by uncountable values. In other words, a continuous random variable can take on any value within an interval or collection of intervals.

> ### DISCRETE VERSUS CONTINUOUS RANDOM VARIABLES
>
> A random variable is a function that assigns numerical values to the outcomes of an experiment. A discrete random variable assumes a countable number of distinct values. A continuous random variable, on the other hand, is characterized by uncountable values in an interval.

Recall from Chapter 4, the sample space S is a set of all outcomes of an experiment. Whenever some numerical values are assigned to these outcomes, a random variable X can be defined. Consider the following experiments, and some examples of discrete random variables (with their possible values shown) that are associated with the experiments:

Experiment 1. Rolling a six-sided die; $S = \{1, 2, 3, 4, 5, 6\}$.

Let X = Win \$10 if odd number, lose \$10 if even number; possible values of $X = \{-10, 10\}$

Let X = Win \$10 if number less than 3, lose \$10 if number more than 4; possible values of $X = \{-10, 0, 10\}$

Experiment 2. Two shirts are selected from the production line and each is either defective (D) or nondefective (N); $S = \{(D, D), (D, N), (N, D), (N, N)\}$.

Let X = the number of defective shirts; possible values of $X = \{0, 1, 2\}$

Let X = the proportion of defective shirts; possible values of $X = \{0, 1/2, 1\}$

Experiment 3. Reviewing a single mortgage application and deciding whether the client gets approved (A) or denied (D); $S = \{A, D\}$.

Let X = 1 for A and 0 for D; possible values of $X = \{0, 1\}$

Let X = 1 for A and −1 for D; possible values of $X = \{-1, 1\}$

Experiment 4. Reviewing multiple mortgage applications and, for each client, deciding whether the client gets approved (A) or denied (D); S = the set of all possible infinite sequences whose elements are A or D.

Let X = the number of approvals; possible values of $X = \{0, 1, 2, 3, \ldots\}$

Let X = the squared number of approvals; possible values of $X = \{0, 1, 4, 9, \ldots\}$

The random variables defined for Experiments 1, 2, and 3 have finite and countable numbers, while the two random variables defined for Experiment 4 have infinite but countable numbers.

Sometimes, we can define a random variable *directly* by identifying its values with some numerical outcomes. For example, we may be interested in the number of students who get financial aid out of the 100 students who applied. Then the set of possible values of the random variable, equivalent to the sample space, is {0, 1, . . . , 100}. In a similar way, we can define a discrete random variable by the infinite number of values that it may take. For example, consider the number of cars that cross the Brooklyn Bridge between 9:00 am and 10:00 am on a Monday morning. Here the discrete random variable takes an infinite but countable number of values from {0, 1, 2, . . .}. Note that we cannot specify an upper bound on the observed number of cars.

Although, we explore discrete random variables in this chapter, random variables can also be continuous. For example, the time taken by a student to complete a 60-minute exam may assume any value between 0 and 60 minutes. Thus, the set of such values is uncountable; that is, it is impossible to put all real numbers from the interval [0, 60] in a sequence. Here, the random variable is continuous because the outcomes are uncountable. Some students may think that time in the earlier example is countable in seconds; however, this is not the case once we consider fractions of a second. We will discuss the details of continuous random variables in the next chapter.

The Discrete Probability Distribution

Every random variable is associated with a **probability distribution** that describes it completely. It is common to define discrete random variables in terms of their **probability mass function** and continuous random variables in terms of their **probability density function**. Discrete and continuous random variables can also be defined in terms of their **cumulative distribution function**, or equivalently, $P(X \leq x)$.

> The probability mass function for a discrete random variable X is a list of the values of X with the associated probabilities; that is, the list of all possible pairs $(x, P(X = x))$. The cumulative distribution function of X is defined as $P(X \leq x)$.

For convenience, we will use terms like "probability distribution" and "distribution" for the probability mass function. Similarly, we will use "cumulative probability distribution" for the cumulative distribution function.

We can view a discrete probability distribution in several ways, including tabular, algebraic, and graphical forms. Example 5.1 shows one of two tabular forms. In general, we can construct a table in two different ways. The first approach directly specifies the probability that the random variable assumes a specific value.

EXAMPLE 5.1

Refer back to Experiment 1 of rolling a fair six-sided die, with the random variable defined as the number rolled. Present the probability distribution in a tabular form.

SOLUTION: A probability distribution for rolling a six-sided die is shown in Table 5.1.

TABLE 5.1 Probability Distribution for Example 5.1

x	1	2	3	4	5	6
P(X = x)	1/6	1/6	1/6	1/6	1/6	1/6

From Table 5.1, we can deduce, for instance, that $P(X = 5)$ equals 1/6. For that matter, the probability that X assumes any of the six possible values is 1/6.

The probability distribution defined in Example 5.1 illustrates two components of all discrete probability distributions.

The second tabular view of a probability distribution is based on the cumulative probability distribution. The cumulative probability distribution is convenient when we are interested in finding the probability that the random variable assumes a range of values rather than a specific value. For the random variable defined in Example 5.1, the cumulative probability distribution is shown in Table 5.2.

TABLE 5.2 Cumulative Probability Distribution for Example 5.1

x	1	2	3	4	5	6
$P(X \le x)$	1/6	2/6	3/6	4/6	5/6	6/6

If we are interested in finding the probability of rolling a four or less, $P(X \le 4)$, we see from the cumulative probability distribution that this probability is 4/6. With the earlier probability representation, we would add up the probabilities to compute $P(X \le 4)$ as

$$P(X = 1) + P(X = 2) + P(X = 3) + P(X = 4) = 1/6 + 1/6 + 1/6 + 1/6 = 4/6.$$

At the same time, we can use the cumulative probability distribution to find the probability that the random variable assumes a specific value. For example, $P(X = 3)$ can be found as $P(X \le 3) - P(X \le 2) = 3/6 - 2/6 = 1/6$.

In many instances, we can express a probability distribution by applying an algebraic formula. A formula representation of the probability distribution for the random variable defined in Example 5.1 is

$$P(X = x) = \begin{cases} 1/6 & \text{if } x = 1, 2, 3, 4, 5, 6 \\ 0 & \text{otherwise.} \end{cases}$$

Thus, from the formula we can ascertain that $P(X = 5) = 1/6$ and $P(X = 7) = 0$.

In order to graphically depict a probability distribution, we place all values x of X on the horizontal axis and the associated probabilities $P(X = x)$ on the vertical axis. We then draw a line segment that emerges from each x and ends where its height equals $P(X = x)$. Figure 5.1 graphically illustrates the probability distribution for the random variable defined in Example 5.1.

FIGURE 5.1
Probability distribution
when rolling a six-
sided die

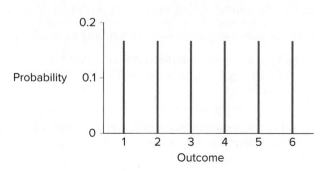

The probability distribution in Figure 5.1 is an example of a **discrete uniform distribution**, which has the following characteristics:

- The distribution has a finite number of specified values.
- Each value is equally likely.
- The distribution is symmetric.

EXAMPLE 5.2

The number of homes that a realtor sells over a one-month period has the probability distribution shown in Table 5.3.

TABLE 5.3 Probability Distribution for the Number of Houses Sold

Number of Houses Sold	Probability
0	0.30
1	0.50
2	0.15
3	0.05

a. Is this a valid probability distribution?
b. What is the probability that the realtor does not sell any houses in a one-month period?
c. What is the probability that the realtor sells at most one house in a one-month period?
d. What is the probability that the realtor sells at least two houses in a one-month period?
e. Graphically depict the probability distribution and comment on its symmetry/skewness.

SOLUTION:

a. We first note that the random variable X denotes the number of houses that the realtor sells over a one-month period, and the possible values of X are 0, 1, 2, or 3. The probability distribution is valid because it satisfies the following two conditions: (1) all probabilities fall between 0 and 1, and (2) the probabilities sum to 1 ($0.30 + 0.50 + 0.15 + 0.05 = 1$).

b. In order to find the probability that the realtor does not sell any houses in a one-month period, we find $P(X = 0) = 0.30$.

c. We find the probability that a realtor sells at most one house as $P(X \le 1) = P(X = 0) + P(X = 1) = 0.30 + 0.50 = 0.80$.

d. We find the probability that the realtor sells at least two houses as $P(X \ge 2) = P(X = 2) + P(X = 3) = 0.15 + 0.05 = 0.20$.

Note that since the sum of the probabilities over all values of X equals 1, we can also find the above probability as $P(X \ge 2) = 1 - P(X \le 1) = 1 - 0.80 = 0.20$.

e. The graph in Figure 5.2 shows that the distribution is not symmetric; rather, it is positively skewed. There are small chances of selling two or three houses in a one-month period. The most likely outcome by far is selling one house over a one-month period, with a probability of 0.50.

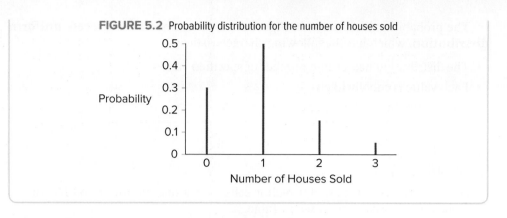

FIGURE 5.2 Probability distribution for the number of houses sold

EXERCISES 5.1

Mechanics

1. Consider the following discrete probability distribution.

x	15	22	34	40
P(X = x)	0.14	0.40	0.26	0.20

a. Is this a valid probability distribution? Explain.
b. Graphically depict this probability distribution.
c. What is the probability that the random variable X is less than 40?
d. What is the probability that the random variable X is between 10 and 30?
e. What is the probability that the random variable X is greater than 20?

2. Consider the following discrete probability distribution.

x	−25	−15	10	20
P(X = x)	0.35	0.10		0.10

a. Complete the probability distribution.
b. Graphically depict the probability distribution and comment on the symmetry of the distribution.
c. What is the probability that the random variable X is negative?
d. What is the probability that the random variable X is greater than −20?
e. What is the probability that the random variable X is less than 20?

3. Consider the following cumulative probability distribution.

x	0	1	2	3	4	5
P(X ≤ x)	0.15	0.35	0.52	0.78	0.84	1

a. Calculate P(X ≤ 3).
b. Calculate P(X = 3).
c. Calculate P(2 ≤ X ≤ 4).

4. Consider the following cumulative probability distribution.

x	−25	0	25	50
P(X ≤ x)	0.25	0.50	0.75	1

a. Calculate P(X ≤ 0).
b. Calculate P(X = 50).
c. Is this a discrete uniform distribution? Explain.

Applications

5. Identify the possible values of the following random variables. Which of the random variables are discrete?
   a. The numerical grade a student receives in a course.
   b. The grade point average of a student.
   c. The salary of an employee, defined in figures (four-figure, five-figure, etc.).
   d. The salary of an employee defined in dollars.

6. Identify the possible values of the following random variables. Which of the random variables are discrete?
   a. The advertised size of a round Domino's pizza.
   b. The actual size of a round Domino's pizza.
   c. The number of daily visitors to Yosemite National Park.
   d. The age of a visitor to Yosemite National Park.

7. India is the second most populous country in the world, with a population of over 1 billion people. Although the government has offered various incentives for population control, some argue that the birth rate, especially in rural India, is still too high to be sustainable. A demographer assumes the following probability distribution for the household size in India.

Household Size	Probability
1	0.05
2	0.09
3	0.12
4	0.24
5	0.25
6	0.12
7	0.07
8	0.06

a. What is the probability that there are less than 5 members in a household in India?

b. What is the probability that there are 5 or more members in a household in India?

c. What is the probability that the number of members in a household in India is strictly between 3 and 6?

d. Graphically depict this probability distribution and comment on its symmetry.

8. A financial analyst creates the following probability distribution for the performance of an equity income mutual fund.

Performance	Numerical Score	Probability
Very poor	1	0.14
Poor	2	0.43
Neutral	3	0.22
Good	4	0.16
Very good	5	0.05

a. Comment on the optimism or pessimism depicted in the analyst's estimates.

b. Convert the above probability distribution to a cumulative probability distribution.

c. What is the probability that this mutual fund will do at least Good?

9. A basketball player is fouled while attempting to make a basket and receives two free throws. The opposing coach believes there is a 55% chance that the player will miss both shots, a 25% chance that he will make one of the shots, and a 20% chance that he will make both shots.

a. Construct the appropriate probability distribution.

b. What is the probability that he makes no more than one of the shots?

c. What is the probability that he makes at least one of the shots?

10. After Donald Trump won the election, the consumer confidence index rose to 93.8, a six-month high (www.bloomberg.com, November 23, 2016). Given new economic data, an analyst believes that there is a 75% chance that the index will fall below 90 and only a 5% chance that it will rise above 95. The analyst defines the confidence score as 1 if the index is below 90, 2 if it is between 90 and 95, and 3 if it is above 95.

a. According to the analyst, what is the probability that the confidence score is 2?

b. According to the analyst, what is the probability that the confidence score is not 1?

11. Professor Sanchez has been teaching Principles of Economics for over 25 years. He uses the following scale for grading.

Grade	Numerical Score	Probability
A	4	0.10
B	3	0.30
C	2	0.40
D	1	0.10
F	0	0.10

a. Depict the above probability distribution graphically. Comment on whether or not the probability distribution is symmetric.

b. Convert the above probability distribution to a cumulative probability distribution.

c. What is the probability of earning at least a B in Professor Sanchez's course?

d. What is the probability of passing Professor Sanchez's course?

12. Jane Wormley is a professor of management at a university. She expects to be able to use her grant money to fund up to two students for research assistance. While she realizes that there is a 5% chance that she may not be able to fund any student, there is an 80% chance that she will be able to fund two students.

a. What is the probability that Jane will fund one student?

b. Construct a cumulative probability distribution of the random variable defined as the number of students that Jane will be able to fund.

13. Fifty percent of the customers who go to Sears Auto Center for tires buy four tires and 30% buy two tires. Moreover, 18% buy fewer than two tires, with 5% buying none.

a. What is the probability that a customer buys three tires?

b. Construct a cumulative probability distribution for the number of tires bought.

5.2 EXPECTED VALUE, VARIANCE, AND STANDARD DEVIATION

LO 5.2

The analysis of probability distributions is useful because it allows us to calculate various probabilities associated with the different values that the random variable assumes. In addition, it helps us calculate summary measures for a random variable. These summary measures include the mean, the variance, and the standard deviation.

Calculate and interpret summary measures for a discrete random variable.

Expected Value

One of the most important probabilistic concepts in statistics is that of the **expected value**, also referred to as the population mean. The expected value of the discrete random variable X, denoted by $E(X)$ or simply, μ, is a weighted average of all possible values of X. Before we present its formula, we would like to point out that the expected value of a random variable should not be confused with its most probable value. As we will see later, the expected value is, in general, not even one of the possible values of the random variable. We can think of the expected value as the long-run average value of the random variable over infinitely many independent repetitions of an experiment. Consider a simple experiment with a fair coin, where you win $10 if it is heads and lose $10 if it is tails. If you flip the coin many times, the expected gain is $0, which is neither of the two possible values, namely $10 or −$10.

> **EXPECTED VALUE OF A DISCRETE RANDOM VARIABLE**
>
> For a discrete random variable X with values $x_1, x_2, x_3, \ldots$, which occur with probabilities $P(X = x_i)$, the expected value of X is calculated as
> $$E(X) = \mu = \Sigma x_i P(X = x_i).$$

Variance and Standard Deviation

The mean μ of the random variable X provides us with a measure of the central location of the distribution of X, but it does not give us information on how the various values are dispersed from μ. We again use the measures of variance and standard deviation to indicate whether the values of X are clustered about μ or widely scattered from μ.

> **VARIANCE AND STANDARD DEVIATION OF A DISCRETE RANDOM VARIABLE**
>
> For a discrete random variable X with values $x_1, x_2, x_3, \ldots$, which occur with probabilities $P(X = x_i)$, the variance of X, denoted as $Var(X)$ or σ^2, is calculated as
> $$Var(X) = \sigma^2 = \Sigma(x_i - \mu)^2 \, P(X = x_i).$$
> The standard deviation of X, denoted as $SD(X)$ or σ, is the positive square root of the variance of X or, equivalently, $SD(X) = \sigma = \sqrt{\sigma^2}$.

EXAMPLE 5.3

Brad Williams is the owner of a large car dealership in Chicago. Brad decides to construct an incentive compensation program that equitably and consistently compensates employees on the basis of their performance. He offers an annual bonus of $10,000 for superior performance, $6,000 for good performance, $3,000 for fair performance, and $0 for poor performance. Based on prior records, he expects an employee to perform at superior, good, fair, and poor performance levels with probabilities 0.15, 0.25, 0.40, and 0.20, respectively. Table 5.4 lists the bonus amount, performance type, and the corresponding probabilities.

TABLE 5.4 Probability Distribution for Compensation Program

Bonus (in $1,000s)	Performance Type	Probability
10	Superior	0.15
6	Good	0.25
3	Fair	0.40
0	Poor	0.20

a. Calculate the expected value of the annual bonus amount.

b. Calculate the variance and the standard deviation of the annual bonus amount.

c. What is the total annual amount that Brad can expect to pay in bonuses if he has 25 employees?

SOLUTION:

a. Let the random variable X denote the bonus amount (in $1,000s) for an employee. The first and second columns of Table 5.5 represent the probability distribution of X. The calculations for the mean are provided in the third column. We weigh each outcome by its respective probability, $x_i P(X = x_i)$, and then sum these weighted values. Thus, as shown at the bottom of the third column, $E(X) = \mu = \Sigma x_i P(X = x_i) = 4.2$, or $4,200. Note that the expected value is not one of the possible values of X; that is, none of the employees will earn a bonus of $4,200. This outcome reinforces the interpretation of expected value as a long-run average.

TABLE 5.5 Calculations for Example 5.3

Value, x_i	Probability, $P(X = x_i)$	Weighted Value, $x_i P(X = x_i)$	Weighted Squared Deviation, $(x_i - \mu)^2 P(X = x_i)$
10	0.15	$10 \times 0.15 = 1.5$	$(10 - 4.2)^2 \times 0.15 = 5.05$
6	0.25	$6 \times 0.25 = 1.5$	$(6 - 4.2)^2 \times 0.25 = 0.81$
3	0.40	$3 \times 0.40 = 1.2$	$(3 - 4.2)^2 \times 0.40 = 0.58$
0	0.20	$0 \times 0.20 = 0$	$(0 - 4.2)^2 \times 0.20 = 3.53$
		Total = 4.2	Total = 9.97

b. The last column of Table 5.5 shows the calculation for the variance. We first calculate each x_i's squared difference from the mean $(x_i - \mu)^2$, weigh each value by the appropriate probability, $(x_i - \mu)^2 P(X = x_i)$, and then sum these weighted squared differences. Thus, as shown at the bottom of the last column, $Var(X) = \sigma^2 = \Sigma(x_i - \mu)^2 P(X = x_i) = 9.97$, or 9.97 (in ($1,000s)^2$). The standard deviation is the positive square root of the variance, $SD(X) = \sigma = \sqrt{9.97} = 3.158$, or $3,158.

c. In part a we found that the expected bonus of an employee is $4,200. Since Brad has 25 employees, he can expect to pay $4,200 \times 25 = $105,000 in bonuses.

Risk Neutrality and Risk Aversion

An important concept in economics, finance, and psychology relates to the behavior of consumers under uncertainty. Consumers are said to be **risk neutral** if they are indifferent to risk and care only about their expected gains. They are said to be **risk-averse** if they care about risk and, if confronted with two choices with the same expected gains, they prefer the one with lower risk. In other words, a risk-averse consumer will take a risk only if it entails a suitable compensation. Consider a seemingly fair gamble where you flip a coin and get $10 if it is heads and lose $10 if it is tails, resulting in an expected gain of zero ($10 \times 0.5 - 10 \times 0.5 = 0$). A risk-neutral consumer is indifferent about participating in this gamble. For a risk-averse consumer, the pain associated with losing $10 is more than the pleasure of winning $10. Therefore, the consumer will not want to participate in this seemingly fair gamble because there is no reward to compensate for the risk. Example 5.4 expands on this type of consumer behavior.

A risk-neutral consumer completely ignores risk and makes his/her decisions solely on the basis of expected gains. A risk-averse consumer demands a positive expected gain as compensation for taking risk. This compensation increases with the level of risk taken and the degree of risk aversion. Finally, a risk-loving consumer may be willing to take a risk even if the expected gain is negative.

EXAMPLE 5.4

You have a choice of receiving $1,000 in cash or receiving a beautiful painting from your grandmother. The actual value of the painting is uncertain. You are told that the painting has a 20% chance of being worth $2,000, a 50% chance of being worth $1,000, and a 30% chance of being worth $500. What should you do?

SOLUTION: Let the random variable X represent the worth of the painting. Given the above information, we define the probability distribution as shown in Table 5.6.

TABLE 5.6 Probability Distribution for the Value of the Painting

x	$P(X = x)$
2,000	0.20
1,000	0.50
500	0.30

We calculate the expected value as

$$E(X) = \Sigma x_i P(X = x_i) = 2{,}000 \times 0.20 + 1{,}000 \times 0.50 + 500 \times 0.30$$
$$= \$1{,}050.$$

Since the expected value of the painting is more than $1,000, it may appear that the right choice is to pick the painting over $1,000 in cash. This choice, however, is based entirely on the expected value of the painting, paying no attention to risk. While the expected value of $1,050 is more than $1,000, the painting entails some risk. For instance, there is a 30% chance that it may be worth only $500. Therefore, a risk-neutral consumer will take the painting because its expected value exceeds the risk-free cash value of $1,000. This consumer is not concerned with risk. A risk lover will be thrilled to take the painting. For a risk-averse consumer, however, the decision is not clear-cut. It depends on the risk involved in picking the painting and how much he/she wants to be compensated for this risk. One way to resolve this issue is to define the utility function of the consumer, which in essence conveys the degree of risk aversion. A risk-averse consumer will pick the risky prospect if the expected utility (not the expected money) of the risky prospect exceeds the utility of a risk-free alternative. Further details are beyond the scope of this text.

EXERCISES 5.2

Mechanics

14. Calculate the mean, the variance, and the standard deviation of the following discrete probability distribution.

x	5	10	15	20
$P(X = x)$	0.35	0.30	0.20	0.15

15. Calculate the mean, the variance, and the standard deviation of the following discrete probability distribution.

x	−23	−17	−9	−3
$P(X = x)$	0.50	0.25	0.15	0.10

Applications

16. The number of homes that a realtor sells over a one-month period has the following probability distribution.

Number of Houses Sold	Probability
0	0.30
1	0.50
2	0.15
3	0.05

a. On average, how many houses is the realtor expected to sell over a one-month period?

b. What is the standard deviation of this probability distribution?

17. A marketing firm is considering making up to three new hires. Given its specific needs, the management feels that there is a 60% chance of hiring at least two candidates. There is only a 5% chance that it will not make any hires and a 10% chance that it will make all three hires.

a. What is the probability that the firm will make at least one hire?

b. Find the expected value and the standard deviation of the number of hires.

18. An analyst has developed the following probability distribution for the rate of return for a common stock.

Scenario	Probability	Rate of Return (in %)
1	0.30	−5
2	0.45	0
3	0.25	10

a. Calculate the expected rate of return.

b. Calculate the variance and the standard deviation of this probability distribution.

19. Organizers of an outdoor summer concert in Toronto are concerned about the weather conditions on the day of the concert. They will make a profit of $25,000 on a clear day and $10,000 on a cloudy day. They will take a loss of $5,000 if it rains. The weather channel has predicted a 60% chance of rain on the day of the concert. Calculate the expected profit from the concert if the likelihood is 10% that it will be sunny and 30% that it will be cloudy.

20. Mark Underwood is a professor of economics at Indiana University. He has been teaching Principles of Economics for over 25 years. Professor Underwood uses the following scale for grading.

Grade	Probability
A	0.10
B	0.30
C	0.40
D	0.10
F	0.10

Calculate the expected numerical grade in Professor Underwood's class using 4.0 for A, 3.0 for B, etc.

21. The manager of a publishing company plans to give a $20,000 bonus to the top 15%, $10,000 to the next 30%, and $5,000 to the next 10% of sales representatives. If the publishing company has a total of 200 sales representatives, what is the expected bonus that the company will pay?

22. An appliance store sells additional warranties on its refrigerators. Twenty percent of the buyers buy the limited warranty for $100 and 5% buy the extended warranty for $200. What is the expected revenue for the store from the warranty if it sells 120 refrigerators?

23. You are considering buying insurance for your new laptop computer, which you have recently bought for $1,500. The insurance premium for three years is $80. Over the three-year period there is an 8% chance that your laptop computer will require work worth $400, a 3% chance that it will require work worth $800, and a 2% chance that it will completely break down with a scrap value of $100. Should you buy the insurance? (Assume risk neutrality.)

24. Four years ago, Victor purchased a very reliable automobile. His warranty has just expired, but the manufacturer has just offered him a 5-year, bumper-to-bumper warranty extension. The warranty costs $3,400. Victor constructs the following probability distribution with respect to anticipated costs if he chooses not to purchase the extended warranty.

Cost (in $)	Probability
1,000	0.25
2,000	0.45
5,000	0.20
10,000	0.10

a. Calculate Victor's expected cost.

b. Given your answer in part a, should Victor purchase the extended warranty? (Assume risk neutrality.) Explain.

25. An investor considers investing $10,000 in the stock market. He believes that the probability is 0.30 that the economy will improve, 0.40 that it will stay the same, and 0.30 that it will deteriorate. Further, if the economy improves, he expects his investment to grow to $15,000, but it can also go down to $8,000 if the economy deteriorates. If the economy stays the same, his investment will stay at $10,000.

a. What is the expected value of his investment?

b. Should he invest the $10,000 in the stock market if he is risk neutral?

c. Is the decision clear-cut if he is risk averse? Explain.

26. You are considering two mutual funds as an investment. The possible returns for the funds are dependent on the state of the economy and are given in the accompanying table.

State of the Economy	Fund 1 (in %)	Fund 2 (in %)
Good	20	40
Fair	10	20
Poor	−10	−40

You believe that the likelihood is 20% that the economy will be good, 50% that it will be fair, and 30% that it will be poor.

a. Find the expected value and the standard deviation of returns for Fund 1.

b. Find the expected value and the standard deviation of returns for Fund 2.

c. Which fund will you pick if you are risk averse? Explain.

27. Investment advisors recommend risk reduction through international diversification. International investing allows you to take advantage of the potential for growth in foreign economies, particularly in emerging markets. Janice Wong is considering investment in either Europe or Asia. She has studied these markets and believes that both markets will be influenced by the U.S. economy, which has a 20% chance for being good, a 50% chance for being fair, and a 30% chance for being poor. Probability distributions of the returns for these markets are given in the accompanying table.

State of the U.S. Economy	Returns in Europe (in %)	Returns in Asia (in %)
Good	10	18
Fair	6	10
Poor	−6	−12

a. Find the expected value and the standard deviation of returns in Europe and Asia.

b. What will Janice pick as an investment if she is risk neutral?

c. Discuss Janice's decision if she is risk averse.

5.3 PORTFOLIO RETURNS

Calculate and interpret summary measures to evaluate portfolio returns.

As discussed in Chapter 3, we often evaluate investment opportunities using expected return as a measure of reward and variance or standard deviation as a measure of risk. Consider two assets where Asset A is expected to have a return of 12% and Asset B is expected to have a return of 8% for the year. While Asset A is attractive in terms of its reward, an investor may still choose Asset B over Asset A if the risk associated with Asset A is too high. In other words, both reward as well as risk are relevant for evaluating the investment.

So far we have considered assets separately. However, most investors hold a **portfolio** of assets, where a portfolio is defined as a collection of assets such as stocks and bonds. As in the case of an individual asset, an investor is concerned about the reward as well as the risk of a portfolio. The derivations of the expected return and the variance of a portfolio depend on some important results regarding the joint distribution of random variables.

Let X and Y represent two random variables of interest, denoting, say, the returns of two assets. Since an investor may have invested in both assets, we would like to evaluate the portfolio return formed by a linear combination of X and Y. The following properties for random variables are useful in evaluating portfolio returns.

Properties of Random Variables

Given two random variables X and Y, the expected value of their sum, $E(X + Y)$, is equal to the sum of their individual expected values, $E(X)$ and $E(Y)$, or

$$E(X + Y) = E(X) + E(Y).$$

Using algebra, it can be shown that the variance of the sum for two random variables, $Var(X + Y)$, yields

$$Var(X + Y) = Var(X) + Var(Y) + 2Cov(X, Y),$$

where Cov is the covariance between the random variables X and Y.

For given constants a and b, the above results are extended as

$$E(aX + bY) = aE(X) + bE(Y), \text{ and}$$
$$Var(aX + bY) = a^2 Var(X) + b^2 Var(Y) + 2abCov(X, Y).$$

Expected Return, Variance, and Standard Deviation for a Portfolio

We are now in a position to derive the expected return and the variance for a portfolio based on these properties. For the sake of simplicity, consider a portfolio consisting of only two assets, Asset A and Asset B. These assets, for instance, may represent stocks and bonds. Following popular notation in finance, let R_A and R_B be the random variables of interest, representing the returns for assets A and B, respectively. It is important to note that a portfolio is described not only by its assets but also by its portfolio weights. Consider a portfolio with a total value of $5,000, with $1,000 invested in Asset A and $4,000 in Asset B. The portfolio weights are derived as

$$w_A = \frac{1,000}{5,000} = 0.20 \quad \text{and} \quad w_B = \frac{4,000}{5,000} = 0.80.$$

Note that the portfolio weights add up to one; that is, $w_A + w_B = 0.20 + 0.80 = 1$. We then define the portfolio return R_p as a linear combination of the individual returns,

$$R_p = w_A R_A + w_B R_B.$$

PORTFOLIO EXPECTED RETURN

Given a portfolio with two assets, Asset A and Asset B, the expected return for the portfolio $E(R_p)$ is computed as

$$E(R_p) = w_A E(R_A) + w_B E(R_B),$$

where w_A and w_B are the portfolio weights ($w_A + w_B = 1$) and $E(R_A)$ and $E(R_B)$ are the expected returns on assets A and B, respectively.

EXAMPLE 5.5

Consider an investment portfolio of $40,000 in Stock A and $60,000 in Stock B. Calculate the expected return for this portfolio based on the information in Table 5.7.

TABLE 5.7 Data for Example 5.5

Stock A	Stock B
$E(R_A) = \mu_A = 9.5$	$E(R_B) = \mu_B = 7.6$
$SD(R_A) = \sigma_A = 12.93$	$SD(R_B) = \sigma_B = 8.20$
$Cov(R_A, R_B) = \sigma_{AB} = 18.60$	

SOLUTION: First we compute the portfolio weights. Since $40,000 is invested in Stock A and $60,000 in Stock B, we compute

$$w_A = \frac{40,000}{100,000} = 0.40 \quad \text{and} \quad w_B = \frac{60,000}{100,000} = 0.60.$$

Thus, using the formula for portfolio expected return, we compute

$$E(R_p) = (0.40 \times 9.5\%) + (0.60 \times 7.6\%) = 3.80\% + 4.56\% = 8.36\%.$$

Note that the portfolio expected return of 8.36% is lower than the expected return of investing entirely in Stock A with an expected return of 9.5%, yet higher than the expected return of investing entirely in Stock B with an expected return of 7.6%.

The risk of the portfolio depends not only on the individual risks of the assets but also on the interplay between the asset returns. For example, if one asset does poorly, the second asset may serve as an offsetting factor to stabilize the risk of the overall portfolio. This result will work as long as the return of the second asset is not perfectly correlated with the return of the first asset. Similar to the covariance $Cov(x, y) = \sigma_{xy}$ introduced in Chapter 3, the covariance $Cov(R_A, R_B) = \sigma_{AB}$ helps determine whether the linear relationship between the asset returns is positive, negative, or zero. Recall that an easier measure to interpret is the correlation coefficient ρ, which describes both the direction and the strength of the linear relationship between two random variables. The value of the correlation coefficient falls between -1 and 1. The closer the value is to 1, the stronger is the positive relationship between the variables. Similarly, the closer the value is to -1, the stronger is the negative relationship between the variables. Let $\rho_{AB} = \frac{\sigma_{AB}}{\sigma_A \sigma_B}$ denote the correlation coefficient between the returns R_A and R_B.

With information on either the covariance or the correlation coefficient for the two returns, we can now determine the portfolio variance.

PORTFOLIO VARIANCE

The portfolio variance, $Var(R_p) = Var(w_A R_A + w_B R_B)$, is computed as
$$Var(R_p) = w_A^2 \sigma_A^2 + w_B^2 \sigma_B^2 + 2w_A w_B \sigma_{AB}$$
or, equivalently,
$$Var(R_p) = w_A^2 \sigma_A^2 + w_B^2 \sigma_B^2 + 2w_A w_B \rho_{AB} \sigma_A \sigma_B$$

where σ_A^2 and σ_B^2 are the variances for Asset A and Asset B, respectively, σ_{AB} is the covariance between Asset A and Asset B, and ρ_{AB} is the correlation coefficient between Asset A and Asset B.

The standard deviation $SD(R_p)$ is then calculated as the positive square root of the portfolio variance.

EXAMPLE 5.6

Using the information in Example 5.5, solve the following:
a. Calculate and interpret the correlation coefficient between the returns for Stock A and Stock B.
b. Calculate the portfolio variance using both formulas.
c. Calculate the portfolio standard deviation.
d. Comment on the findings.

SOLUTION:

a. We calculate the correlation coefficient as $\rho_{AB} = \frac{\sigma_{AB}}{\sigma_A \sigma_B} = \frac{18.60}{12.93 \times 8.20} = 0.1754$. This value implies that the returns have a positive linear relationship, though the magnitude of the relationship is weak (ρ_{AB} is well below 1).

b. Using the first formula for portfolio variance, we calculate
$$Var(R_p) = w_A^2 \sigma_A^2 + w_B^2 \sigma_B^2 + 2w_A w_B \sigma_{AB}$$
$$= (0.40)^2 (12.93)^2 + (0.60)^2 (8.20)^2 + 2(0.40)(0.60)(18.60)$$
$$= 26.75 + 24.21 + 8.93$$
$$= 59.89.$$

Using the alternative formula for portfolio variance, we calculate

$$Var(R_p) = w_A^2\sigma_A^2 + w_B^2\sigma_B^2 + 2w_Aw_B\rho_{AB}\sigma_A\sigma_B$$
$$= (0.40)^2(12.93)^2 + (0.60)^2(8.20)^2$$
$$+ 2(0.40)(0.60)(0.1754)(12.93)(8.20)$$
$$= 26.75 + 24.21 + 8.93$$
$$= 59.89.$$

Using either formula, the portfolio variance is 59.89 $(\%)^2$.

c. The portfolio standard deviation is $SD(R_p) = \sqrt{59.89} = 7.74$, or 7.74%.

d. We note how the portfolio standard deviation (risk) of 7.74% is lower than the risk of 12.93% of investing entirely in Stock A, as well as the risk of 8.20% of investing entirely in Stock B. This occurs because the returns of Stock A and Stock B have a correlation of only 0.1754. This example highlights the benefits of properly diversifying your portfolio in order to reduce risk. In general, the benefits of diversification depend on the correlation between the assets: the lower the correlation, the larger the benefit.

EXERCISES 5.3

28. What are the portfolio weights for a portfolio that has 100 shares of Stock X that sell for $20 per share and 200 shares of Stock Y that sell for $12 per share?

29. You own a portfolio that has $4,400 invested in stocks and $5,600 invested in bonds. What is the expected return of the portfolio if stocks and bonds are expected to yield a return of 9% and 5%, respectively?

30. A portfolio has $200,000 invested in Asset X and $300,000 in Asset Y. Consider the summary measures in the following table.

Measures	Asset X	Asset Y
Expected return (%)	8	12
Standard deviation (%)	12	20
Correlation coefficient	0.40	

a. Calculate the portfolio weights for assets X and Y.
b. Calculate the expected return for the portfolio.
c. Calculate the standard deviation for the portfolio.

31. An analyst has predicted the following returns for Stock A and Stock B in three possible states of the economy.

State	Probability	A	B
Boom	0.3	0.15	0.25
Normal	0.5	0.10	0.20
Recession	?	0.02	0.01

a. What is the probability of a recession?
b. Calculate the expected return for Stock A and Stock B.
c. Calculate the expected return for a portfolio that is invested 55% in A and 45% in B.

32. A pension fund manager is considering three mutual funds for investment. The first one is a stock fund, the second is a bond fund, and the third is a money market fund. The money market fund yields a risk-free return of 4%. The inputs for the risky funds are given in the following table.

Fund	Expected Return (in %)	Standard Deviation (in %)
Stock fund	14	26
Bond fund	8	14

The correlation coefficient between the stock and the bond funds is 0.20.

a. What is the expected return and the variance for a portfolio that invests 60% in the stock fund and 40% in the bond fund?
b. What is the expected return and the variance for a portfolio that invests 60% in the stock fund and 40% in the money market fund? [Hint: Note that the correlation coefficient between the portfolio and the money market fund is zero.]
c. Compare the portfolios in parts a and b with a portfolio that is invested entirely in the bond fund.

33. You have $400,000 invested in a well-diversified portfolio. You inherit a house that is presently worth $200,000. Consider the summary measures in the following table:

Investment	Expected Return (in %)	Standard Deviation (in %)
Old portfolio	6	16
House	8	20

The correlation coefficient between your portfolio and the house is 0.38.

a. What is the expected return and the standard deviation for your portfolio comprising your old portfolio and the house?
b. Suppose you decide to sell the house and use the proceeds of $200,000 to buy risk-free T-bills that promise a 3% rate of return. Calculate the expected return and the standard deviation for the resulting portfolio. [Hint: Note that the correlation coefficient between any asset and the risk-free T-bills is zero.]

5.4 THE BINOMIAL DISTRIBUTION

Calculate and interpret
probabilities for a binomial
random variable.

Different types of experiments generate different probability distributions. In the next three sections, we discuss three special cases: the binomial, the Poisson, and the hypergeometric probability distributions. Here we focus on the binomial distribution. Before we can discuss the binomial distribution, we first must ensure that the experiment satisfies the conditions of a **Bernoulli process**, which is a particular type of experiment named after the person who first described it, the Swiss mathematician James Bernoulli (1654–1705).

> **A BERNOULLI PROCESS**
>
> A Bernoulli process consists of a series of n independent and identical trials of an experiment such that on each trial:
> - There are only two possible outcomes, conventionally labeled success and failure; and
> - The probabilities of success and failure remain the same from trial to trial.

We use p to denote the probability of success, and therefore, $1 - p$ is the probability of failure.

A **binomial random variable** is defined as the number of successes achieved in the n trials of a Bernoulli process. The possible values of a binomial random variable include $0, 1, \ldots, n$. Many experiments fit the conditions of a Bernoulli process. For instance:

- A bank grants or denies a loan to a mortgage applicant.
- A consumer either uses or does not use a credit card.
- An employee travels or does not travel by public transportation.
- A life insurance policy holder dies or does not die.
- A drug is either effective or ineffective.
- A college graduate applies or does not apply to graduate school.

Our goal is to attach probabilities to various outcomes of a Bernoulli process. The result is a **binomial probability distribution**, or simply, a **binomial distribution**.

> A binomial random variable X is defined as the number of successes achieved in the n trials of a Bernoulli process. The binomial distribution for X shows the probabilities associated with the possible values of X.

We will eventually arrive at a general formula that helps us derive a binomial distribution. First, however, we will use a specific example and construct a **probability tree** in order to illustrate the possible outcomes and their associated probabilities.

> **EXAMPLE 5.7**
>
> From past experience, a manager of an upscale shoe store knows that 85% of her customers will use a credit card when making purchases. Suppose three customers are in line to make a purchase.
>
> a. Does this example satisfy the conditions of a Bernoulli process?
> b. Construct a probability tree.
> c. Using the probability tree, derive the binomial probability distribution.

SOLUTION:

a. This example satisfies the conditions of a Bernoulli process because a customer either uses a credit card (labeled success), with an 85% likelihood, or does not use a credit card (labeled failure), with a 15% likelihood. Moreover, given a large number of customers, these probabilities of success and failure do not change from customer to customer.

b. Recall from Chapter 4 that we can use a probability tree whenever an experiment can be broken down into stages. Here we can view each stage as a trial. The probability tree for Example 5.7 is shown in Figure 5.3. We let S denote the outcome that a customer uses a credit card and F denote the outcome that a customer does not use a credit card. Starting from the unlabeled node on the left, customer 1 has an 85% chance of using a credit card and a 15% chance of not using one. The branches emanating from customer 1 denote conditional probabilities of customer 2 using a credit card, given whether or not customer 1 used a credit card. However, since we assume that the trials of a Bernoulli process are independent, the conditional probability is the same as the unconditional probability. In other words, customer 2 has the same 85% chance of using a credit card and a 15% chance of not using one regardless of what customer 1 uses. The same holds for the probabilities for customer 3. The fourth column shows that there are eight possible events at the end of the probability tree. We are able to obtain relevant probabilities by using the multiplication rule for independent events. For instance, following the top branches throughout the probability tree, we calculate the probability that all three customers use a credit card as $(0.85)(0.85)(0.85) = 0.6141$. The probabilities for the remaining events are found in a similar manner.

c. Since we are not interested in identifying the particular customer who uses a credit card, but rather the number of customers who use a credit card,

FIGURE 5.3 Probability tree for Example 5.7

Customer 1	Customer 2	Customer 3	Events	Customers using credit card, x	Probabilities
		S	SSS	3	$(0.85)(0.85)(0.85)$ $= 0.6141$
	S	F	SSF	2	$(0.85)(0.85)(0.15)$ $= 0.1084$
	F	S	SFS	2	$(0.85)(0.15)(0.85)$ $= 0.1084$
S		F	SFF	1	$(0.85)(0.15)(0.15)$ $= 0.0191$
		S	FSS	2	$(0.15)(0.85)(0.85)$ $= 0.1084$
F	S	F	FSF	1	$(0.15)(0.85)(0.15)$ $= 0.0191$
	F	S	FFS	1	$(0.15)(0.15)(0.85)$ $= 0.0191$
		F	FFF	0	$(0.15)(0.15)(0.15)$ $= 0.0034$

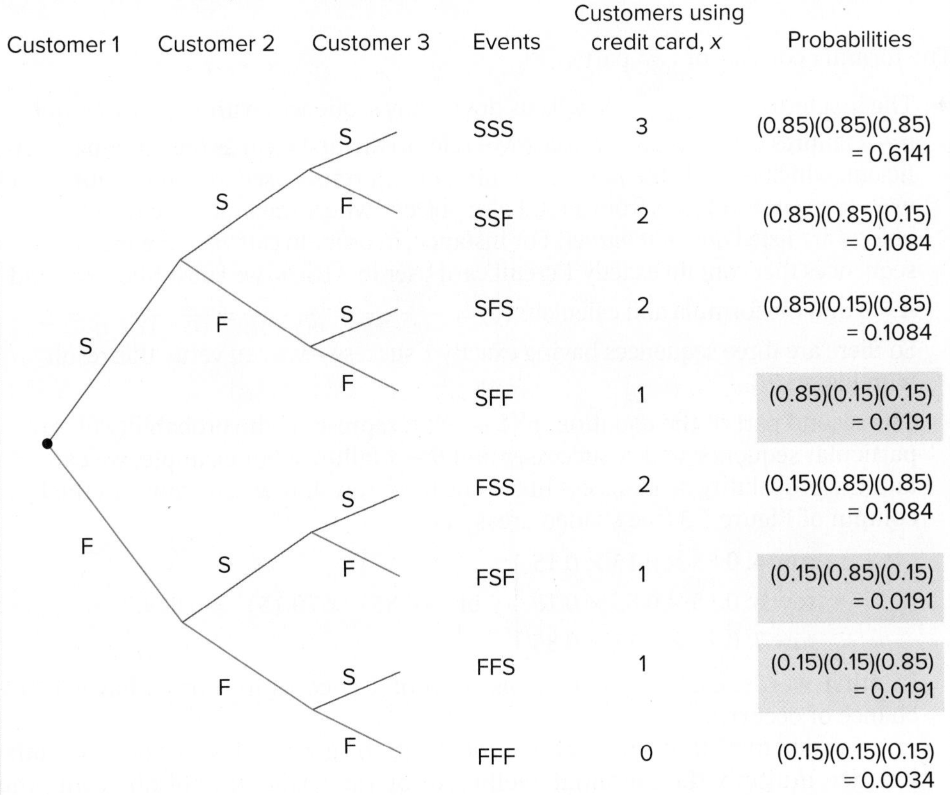

we can combine events with the same number of successes, using the addition rule for mutually exclusive events. For instance, in order to find the probability that one customer uses a credit card, we add the probabilities that correspond to the outcome $x = 1$ (see shaded areas in Figure 5.3): $0.0191 + 0.0191 + 0.0191 = 0.0573$. Similarly, we calculate the remaining probabilities corresponding to the other values of X and construct the probability distribution shown in Table 5.8.

TABLE 5.8 Binomial Probabilities for Example 5.7

x	P(X = x)
0	0.0034
1	0.0573
2	0.3252
3	0.6141
	Total = 1

Fortunately, we do not have to construct a probability tree each time we want to construct a binomial distribution. We can use the following formula for calculating probabilities associated with a binomial random variable.

THE BINOMIAL DISTRIBUTION

For a binomial random variable X, the probability of x successes in n Bernoulli trials is

$$P(X = x) = \binom{n}{x} p^x (1 - p)^{n-x} = \frac{n!}{x!(n - x)!} p^x (1 - p)^{n-x}$$

for $x = 0, 1, 2, \ldots, n$. By definition, $0! = 1$.

The formula consists of two parts:

- The first term, $\binom{n}{x} = \frac{n!}{x!(n - x)!}$, tells us how many sequences with x successes and $n - x$ failures are possible in n trials. We refer to the first term as the binomial coefficient, which is really the familiar combination formula used to find the number of ways to choose x objects from a total of n objects, where the order in which the x objects are listed *does not matter*. For instance, in order to calculate the number of sequences that contain exactly 1 credit card user in 3 trials, we substitute $x = 1$ and $n = 3$ into the formula and calculate $\binom{n}{x} = \frac{n!}{x!(n - x)!} = \frac{3!}{1!(3 - 1)!} = \frac{3 \times 2 \times 1}{(1) \times (2 \times 1)} = 3$. So there are three sequences having exactly 1 success—we can verify this result with Figure 5.3.

- The second part of the equation, $p^x (1 - p)^{n-x}$, represents the probability of any particular sequence with x successes and $n - x$ failures. For example, we can obtain the probability of 1 success in 3 trials from row 4, row 6, or row 7 in the last column of Figure 5.3 (see shaded areas) as

$$\left.\begin{array}{l} \text{row 4: } 0.85 \times 0.15 \times 0.15 \\ \text{row 6: } 0.15 \times 0.85 \times 0.15 \\ \text{row 7: } 0.15 \times 0.15 \times 0.85 \end{array}\right\} \text{ or } (0.85)^1 \times (0.15)^2 = 0.019.$$

In other words, each sequence consisting of 1 success in 3 trials has a 1.91% chance of occurring.

In order to obtain the overall probability of getting 1 success in 3 trials, we then multiply the binomial coefficient by the probability of obtaining the particular sequence, or here, $3 \times 0.0191 = 0.0573$. This is precisely the probability that we found for $P(X = 1)$ using the probability tree.

Moreover, we could use the formulas shown in Section 5.2 to calculate the expected value, the variance, and the standard deviation for any binomial random variable. Fortunately, for the binomial distribution, these formulas simplify to $E(X) = np$, $Var(X) = np(1 - p)$, and $SD(X) = \sqrt{np(1 - p)}$. The simplified formula for the expected value is rather intuitive in that if we know the probability of success p of an experiment and we repeat the experiment n times, then on average, we expect np successes.

EXPECTED VALUE, VARIANCE, AND STANDARD DEVIATION
OF A BINOMIAL RANDOM VARIABLE

If X is a binomial random variable, then

$$E(X) = \mu = np,$$
$$Var(X) = \sigma^2 = np(1 - p), \text{ and}$$
$$SD(X) = \sigma = \sqrt{np(1 - p)}.$$

For instance, for the binomial probability distribution assumed in Example 5.7, we can derive the expected value with the earlier general formula as

$$E(X) = \Sigma x_i P(X = x_i) = (0 \times 0.0034) + (1 \times 0.0573) + (2 \times 0.3252) + (3 \times 0.6141) = 2.55.$$

However, an easier way is to use $E(X) = np$ and thus calculate the expected value as $3 \times 0.85 = 2.55$. Similarly, the variance and the standard deviation can be easily calculated as

$$Var(X) = \sigma^2 = np(1 - p) = 3 \times 0.85 \times 0.15 = 0.38 \text{ and}$$
$$SD(X) = \sigma = \sqrt{np(1 - p)} = \sqrt{0.38} = 0.62.$$

EXAMPLE 5.8

In the United States, about 30% of adults have four-year college degrees (*The Wall Street Journal*, April 26, 2012). Suppose five adults are randomly selected.

a. What is the probability that none of the adults has a college degree?

b. What is the probability that no more than two of the adults have a college degree?

c. What is the probability that at least two of the adults have a college degree?

d. Calculate the expected value, the variance, and the standard deviation of this binomial distribution.

e. Graphically depict the probability distribution and comment on its symmetry/skewness.

SOLUTION: First, this problem satisfies the conditions for a Bernoulli process with a random selection of five adults, $n = 5$. Here, an adult either has a college degree, with probability $p = 0.30$, or does not have a college degree, with probability $1 - p = 1 - 0.30 = 0.70$. Given a large number of adults, it fulfills the requirement that the probability that an adult has a college degree stays the same from adult to adult.

a. In order to find the probability that none of the adults has a college degree, we let $x = 0$ and find

$$P(X = 0) = \frac{5!}{0!(5-0)!} \times (0.30)^0 \times (0.70)^{5-0}$$

$$= \frac{5 \times 4 \times \cdots \times 1}{(1) \times (5 \times 4 \times \cdots \times 1)} \times 1 \times (0.70)^5 = 1 \times 1 \times 0.1681$$

$$= 0.1681.$$

In other words, from a random sample of five adults, there is a 16.81% chance that none of the adults has a college degree.

b. We find the probability that no more than two adults have a college degree as

$$P(X \leq 2) = P(X = 0) + P(X = 1) + P(X = 2).$$

We have already found $P(X = 0)$ from part a. So we now compute $P(X = 1)$ and $P(X = 2)$:

$$P(X = 1) = \frac{5!}{1!(5-1)!} \times (0.30)^1 \times (0.70)^{5-1} = 0.3602$$

$$P(X = 2) = \frac{5!}{2!(5-2)!} \times (0.30)^2 \times (0.70)^{5-2} = 0.3087$$

Next we sum the three relevant probabilities and obtain $P(X \leq 2) = 0.1681 + 0.3602 + 0.3087 = 0.8370$. From a random sample of five adults, there is an 83.7% likelihood that no more than two of them will have a college degree.

c. We find the probability that at least two adults have a college degree as

$$P(X \geq 2) = P(X = 2) + P(X = 3) + P(X = 4) + P(X = 5).$$

We can solve this problem by calculating and then summing each of the four probabilities, from $P(X = 2)$ to $P(X = 5)$. A simpler method uses one of the key properties of a probability distribution, which states that the sum of the probabilities over all values of X equals 1. Therefore, $P(X \geq 2)$ can be written as $1 - [P(X = 0) + P(X = 1)]$. We have already calculated $P(X = 0)$ and $P(X = 1)$ from parts a and b, so

$$P(X \geq 2) = 1 - [P(X = 0) + P(X = 1)] = 1 - (0.1681 + 0.3602) = 0.4717.$$

From a random sample of five adults, there is a 47.17% likelihood that at least two adults will have a college degree.

d. We use the simplified formulas to calculate the mean, the variance, and the standard deviation as

$$E(X) = np = 5 \times 0.30 = 1.5 \text{ adults,}$$

$$Var(X) = \sigma^2 = np(1-p) = 5 \times 0.30 \times 0.70 = 1.05 \text{ (adults)}^2, \text{ and}$$

$$SD(X) = \sigma = \sqrt{np(1-p)} = \sqrt{1.05} = 1.02 = 1.02 \text{ adults.}$$

e. Before we graph this distribution, we first show the complete binomial distribution for Example 5.8 in Table 5.9.

TABLE 5.9 Binomial Distribution
with $n = 5$ and $p = 0.30$

x	P(X = x)
0	0.1681
1	0.3602
2	0.3087
3	0.1323
4	0.0284
5	0.0024

This binomial distribution is graphically depicted in Figure 5.4. When randomly selecting five adults, the most likely outcome is that exactly one adult will have a college degree. The distribution is not symmetric; rather, it is positively skewed. In later chapters, we will learn that the binomial distribution is approximately symmetric when the sample size n is large.

FIGURE 5.4 Binomial distribution with $n = 5$ and $p = 0.30$

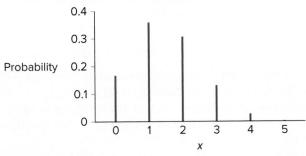

Using Excel and R to Obtain Binomial Probabilities

As you may have noticed, at times it is somewhat tedious and cumbersome to solve binomial distribution problems using the formulas. This issue becomes even more pronounced when we encounter large values for n and we wish to determine probabilities where X assumes a wide range of values. Table 5.10 shows Excel and R functions that we can use to solve problems associated with discrete probability distributions. Example 5.9 illustrates the use of these functions with respect to the binomial distribution. We will refer back to Table 5.10 in later sections of this chapter when we discuss the Poisson and hypergeometric distributions.

TABLE 5.10 Discrete Probability Distributions and Function Names in Excel and R

Distribution	Excel	R
Binomial		
$P(X = x)$:	=BINOM.DIST(x, n, p, 0)	dbinom(x, n, p)
$P(X \leq x)$:	=BINOM.DIST(x, n, p, 1)	pbinom(x, n, p)
Poisson		
$P(X = x)$:	=POISSON.DIST(x, μ, 0)	dpois (x, μ)
$P(X \leq x)$:	=POISSON.DIST(x, μ, 1)	ppois (x, μ)
Hypergeometric		
$P(X = x)$:	=HYPGEOM.DIST(x, n, S, N, 0)	dhyper(x, S, N − S, n)
$P(X \leq x)$:	=HYPGEOM.DIST(x, n, S, N, 1)	phyper(x, S, N − S, n)

EXAMPLE 5.9

In the past decade, the use of technology has skyrocketed, with social media blooming into one of the most valuable methods of communication. People are turning to social media to stay in touch with friends and family members, connect with old friends, catch the news, look for employment, and be entertained. According to a 2016 Pew Research survey, 68% of all U.S. adults are Facebook users. Consider a sample of 100 randomly selected American adults.

a. What is the probability that exactly 70 American adults are Facebook users?

b. What is the probability that no more than 70 American adults are Facebook users?

c. What is the probability that at least 70 American adults are Facebook users?

SOLUTION: We let X denote the number of American adults who are Facebook users. We also know that $p = 0.68$ and $n = 100$.

Using Excel

We use Excel's **BINOM.DIST** function to calculate binomial probabilities. In order to find $P(X = x)$, we enter "=BINOM.DIST(x, n, p, 0)" where x is the number of successes, n is the number of trials, and p is the probability of success. If we enter a "1" for the last argument in the function, then Excel returns $P(X \leq x)$.

a. In order to find the probability that exactly 70 American adults are Facebook users, $P(X = 70)$, we enter "=BINOM.DIST(70, 100, 0.68, 0)" and Excel returns 0.0791.

b. In order to find the probability that no more than 70 American adults are Facebook users, $P(X \leq 70)$, we enter "=BINOM.DIST(70, 100, 0.68, 1)" and Excel returns 0.7007.

c. In order to find the probability that at least 70 American adults are Facebook users, $P(X \geq 70) = 1 - P(X \leq 69)$, we enter "=1−BINOM.DIST(69, 100, 0.68, 1)" and Excel returns 0.3784.

Using R

We use R's **dbinom** and **pbinom** functions to calculate binomial probabilities. In order to calculate $P(X = x)$, we enter "dbinom(x, n, p)" where x is the number of successes, n is the number of trials, and p is the probability of success. In order to calculate $P(X \leq x)$, we enter "pbinom(x, n, p)".

a. In order to find $P(X = 70)$, we enter:

```
> dbinom(70, 100, 0.68)
```

And R returns: 0.07907911.

b. In order to find $P(X \leq 70)$, we enter:

```
> pbinom(70, 100, 0.68)
```

And R returns: 0.7006736.

c. In order to find $P(X \geq 70) = 1 - P(X \leq 69)$, we enter:

```
> 1 − pbinom(69, 100, 0.68)
```

And R returns: 0.3784055.

EXERCISES 5.4

Mechanics

34. Assume that X is a binomial random variable with $n = 5$ and $p = 0.35$. Calculate the following probabilities.

  a. $P(X = 0)$

  b. $P(X = 1)$

  c. $P(X \leq 1)$

35. Assume that X is a binomial random variable with $n = 6$ and $p = 0.68$. Calculate the following probabilities.

  a. $P(X = 5)$

  b. $P(X = 4)$

  c. $P(X \geq 4)$

36. Assume that X is a binomial random variable with $n = 8$ and $p = 0.32$. Calculate the following probabilities.

  a. $P(3 < X < 5)$

  b. $P(3 < X \leq 5)$

  c. $P(3 \leq X \leq 5)$

37. Let the probability of success on a Bernoulli trial be 0.30. In five Bernoulli trials, what is the probability that there will be (a) four failures, and (b) more than the expected number of failures?

38. Let X represent a binomial random variable with $n = 150$ and $p = 0.36$. Find the following probabilities.

  a. $P(X \leq 50)$

  b. $P(X = 40)$

  c. $P(X > 60)$

  d. $P(X \geq 55)$

39. Let X represent a binomial random variable with $n = 200$ and $p = 0.77$. Find the following probabilities.

  a. $P(X \leq 150)$

  b. $P(X > 160)$

  c. $P(155 \leq X \leq 165)$

  d. $P(X = 160)$

Applications

40. According to a survey by Transamerica Center for Health Studies, 15% of Americans still have no health insurance even after passage of the Affordable Care Act, better known as Obamacare (www.cbsnews.com, September 24, 2014). Suppose five individuals are randomly selected.

  a. What is the probability that all five have health insurance?

  b. What is the probability that no more than two have health insurance?

  c. What is the probability that at least four have health insurance?

  d. What is the expected number of individuals who have health insurance?

  e. Calculate the variance and the standard deviation for this probability distribution.

41. At a local community college, 40% of students who enter the college as freshmen go on to graduate. Ten freshmen are randomly selected.

  a. What is the probability that none of them graduates from the local community college?

  b. What is the probability that at most nine will graduate from the local community college?

  c. What is the expected number that will graduate?

42. In 2013, only 26% of Americans had confidence in U.S. banks, which is still far below the pre-recession level of 41% reported in June 2007 (www.gallup.com, June 26, 2014).

  a. What is the probability that fewer than half of four Americans in 2013 have confidence in U.S. banks?

  b. What would have been the corresponding probability in 2007?

43. Approximately 45% of Baby Boomers—those born between 1946 and 1964—are still in the workforce (www.pewresearch.org, May 11, 2015). Six Baby Boomers are selected at random.

  a. What is the probability that exactly one of the Baby Boomers is still in the workforce?

  b. What is the probability that at least five of the Baby Boomers are still in the workforce?

  c. What is the probability that less than two of the Baby Boomers are still in the workforce?

  d. What is the probability that more than the expected number of the Baby Boomers are still in the workforce?

44. In an analysis of Census figures, one in four American counties has passed or is approaching the tipping point where black, Hispanic, and Asian children constitute a majority of the under-20 population (*The New York Times*, August 6, 2008). Racial and ethnic minorities now account for 43% of Americans under 20.

  a. What is the expected number of whites in a random sample of 5,000 under-20 Americans? What is the corresponding standard deviation?

  b. What is the expected number of racial and ethnic minorities in a random sample of 5,000 under-20 Americans? What is the corresponding standard deviation?

  c. If you randomly sample six American counties, what is the probability that for the under-20 population, whites have a majority in all of the counties?

45. Sikhism, a religion founded in the 15th century in India, is going through turmoil due to a rapid decline in the number of Sikh youths who wear turbans (*The Washington Post*, March 29, 2009). The tedious task of combing and tying up long hair and a desire to assimilate has led to approximately 25% of Sikh youths giving up the turban.

  a. What is the probability that exactly two in a random sample of five Sikh youths wear a turban?

  b. What is the probability that two or more in a random sample of five Sikh youths wear a turban?

c. What is the probability that more than the expected number of Sikh youths wear a turban in a random sample of five Sikh youths?

d. What is the probability that more than the expected number of Sikh youths wear a turban in a random sample of 10 Sikh youths?

46. According to the U.S. Census, roughly half of all marriages in the United States end in divorce. Researchers from leading universities have shown that the emotions aroused by one person's divorce can transfer like a virus, making divorce contagious (*CNN,* June 10, 2010). A split-up between immediate friends increases a person's own chances of getting divorced from 36% to 63%, an increase of 75%.

a. Compute the probability that more than half of four randomly selected marriages will end in divorce.

b. Redo part a if it is known that the couple's immediate friends have split up.

c. Redo part a if it is known that none of the couple's immediate friends has split up.

47. Sixty percent of a firm's employees are men. Suppose four of the firm's employees are randomly selected.

a. What is more likely, finding three men and one woman or two men and two women?

b. Do you obtain the same answer as in part a if 70% of the firm's employees had been men?

48. The principal of an architecture firm tells her client that there is at least a 50% chance of having an acceptable design by the end of the week. She knows that there is only a 25% chance that any one designer would be able to do so by the end of the week.

a. Would she be correct in her statement to the client if she asks two of her designers to work on the design, independently?

b. If not, what if she asks three of her designers to work on the design, independently?

49. Suppose 40% of recent college graduates plan on pursuing a graduate degree. Fifteen recent college graduates are randomly selected.

a. What is the probability that no more than four of the college graduates plan to pursue a graduate degree?

b. What is the probability that exactly seven of the college graduates plan to pursue a graduate degree?

c. What is the probability that at least six but no more than nine of the college graduates plan to pursue a graduate degree?

50. At the University of Notre Dame Mendoza College of Business, 40% of the students seeking a master's degree specialize in finance (*Kiplinger's Personal Finance*, March 2009). Twenty master's degree students are randomly selected.

a. What is the probability that exactly 10 of the students specialize in finance?

b. What is the probability that no more than 10 of the students specialize in finance?

c. What is the probability that at least 15 of the students specialize in finance?

51. The Washington, DC, region has one of the fastest-growing foreclosure rates in the nation, as 15,613 homes went into foreclosure during the one-year period ending in February 2008 (*The Washington Post*, June 19, 2008). Over the past year, the number of foreclosures per 10,000 homes is 131 for the Washington area, while it is 87 nationally. In other words, the foreclosure rate is 1.31% for the Washington, DC, area and 0.87% for the nation. Assume that the foreclosure rates remain stable.

a. What is the probability that in a given year, fewer than 2 out of 100 houses in the Washington, DC, area will go up for foreclosure?

b. What is the probability that in a given year, fewer than 2 out of 100 houses in the nation will go up for foreclosure?

c. Comment on the above findings.

5.5 THE POISSON DISTRIBUTION

Calculate and interpret probabilities for a Poisson random variable.

Another important discrete probability distribution is the **Poisson distribution**, named after the French mathematician Simeon Poisson (1781−1849). It is particularly useful in problems that deal with finding the number of occurrences of a certain event over time or space, where space refers to area or region. For simplicity, we call these occurrences "successes." Before we can discuss the Poisson distribution, we first must ensure that our experiment satisfies the conditions of a **Poisson process**.

A POISSON PROCESS

An experiment satisfies a Poisson process if
- The number of successes within a specified time or space interval equals any integer between zero and infinity.
- The number of successes counted in nonoverlapping intervals are independent.
- The probability of success in any interval is the same for all intervals of equal size and is proportional to the size of the interval.

For a Poisson process, we define the number of successes achieved in a specified time or space interval as a **Poisson random variable**.

> A Poisson random variable counts the number of occurrences (successes) of a certain event over a given interval of time or space.

Like the Bernoulli process, many experiments fit the conditions of a Poisson process. Consider the following examples of Poisson random variables categorized by those relating to time and those relating to space.

Examples of Poisson Random Variables with Respect to Time

- The number of cars that cross the Brooklyn Bridge between 9:00 am and 10:00 am on a Monday morning.
- The number of customers that use a McDonald's drive-thru in a day.
- The number of bankruptcies that are filed in a month.
- The number of homicides that occur in a year.

Examples of Poisson Random Variables with Respect to Space

- The number of defects in a 50-yard roll of fabric.
- The number of schools of fish in 100 square miles.
- The number of leaks in a specified stretch of a pipeline.
- The number of bacteria in a specified culture.

We use the following formula for calculating probabilities associated with a Poisson random variable.

> ### THE POISSON DISTRIBUTION
>
> For a Poisson random variable X, the probability of x successes over a given interval of time or space is
>
> $$P(X = x) = \frac{e^{-\mu}\mu^x}{x!},$$
>
> for $x = 0, 1, 2, \ldots$, where μ is the mean number of successes and $e \approx 2.718$ is the base of the natural logarithm.

As with the binomial random variable, we have simplified formulas to calculate the variance and the standard deviation of a Poisson random variable. An interesting fact is that the mean of the Poisson random variable is equal to the variance.

> ### EXPECTED VALUE, VARIANCE, AND STANDARD DEVIATION OF A POISSON RANDOM VARIABLE
>
> If X is a Poisson random variable, then
>
> $$E(X) = \mu,$$
> $$Var(X) = \sigma^2 = \mu, \quad \text{and}$$
> $$SD(X) = \sigma = \sqrt{\mu}.$$

EXAMPLE 5.10

We can now address questions first posed by Anne Jones in the introductory case of this chapter. Recall that Anne is concerned about staffing needs at the Starbucks that she manages. She has specific questions about the probability distribution of customer arrivals at her store. Anne believes that the typical Starbucks customer averages 18 visits to the store over a 30-day month. She has the following questions:

a. How many visits should Anne expect in a 5-day period from a typical Starbucks customer?

b. What is the probability that a customer visits the chain five times in a 5-day period?

c. What is the probability that a customer visits the chain no more than two times in a 5-day period?

d. What is the probability that a customer visits the chain at least three times in a 5-day period?

SOLUTION: In applications of the Poisson distribution, we first determine the mean number of successes in the relevant time or space interval. We use the Poisson process condition that the probability that success occurs in any interval is the same for all intervals of equal size and is proportional to the size of the interval. Here, the relevant mean will be based on the rate of 18 visits over a 30-day month.

a. Given the rate of 18 visits over a 30-day month, we can write the mean for the 30-day period as $\mu_{30} = 18$. For this problem, we compute the proportional mean for a 5-day period as $\mu_5 = 3$ because $\frac{18 \text{ visits}}{30 \text{ days}} = \frac{3 \text{ visits}}{5 \text{ days}}$.
   In other words, on average, a typical Starbucks customer visits the store three times over a 5-day period.

b. In order to find the probability that a customer visits the chain five times in a 5-day period, we calculate

$$P(X = 5) = \frac{e^{-3}3^5}{5!} = \frac{(0.0498)(243)}{120} = 0.1008.$$

c. For the probability that a customer visits the chain no more than two times in a 5-day period, we find $P(X \leq 2) = P(X = 0) + P(X = 1) + P(X = 2)$. We calculate the individual probabilities, and then find the sum:

$$P(X = 0) = \frac{e^{-3}3^0}{0!} = \frac{(0.0498)(1)}{1} = 0.0498,$$

$$P(X = 1) = \frac{e^{-3}3^1}{1!} = \frac{(0.0498)(3)}{1} = 0.1494, \quad \text{and}$$

$$P(X = 2) = \frac{e^{-3}3^2}{2!} = \frac{(0.0498)(9)}{2} = 0.2241.$$

Thus, $P(X \leq 2) = 0.0498 + 0.1494 + 0.2241 = 0.4233$. There is approximately a 42% chance that a customer visits the chain no more than two times in a 5-day period.

d. We write the probability that a customer visits the chain at least three times in a 5-day period as $P(X \geq 3)$. Initially, we might attempt to solve this problem by evaluating $P(X \geq 3) = P(X = 3) + P(X = 4) + P(X = 5) + \cdots$. However, given the infinite number of possible values, we cannot solve a Poisson problem this way. Here, we find $P(X \geq 3)$ as $1 - [P(X = 0) + P(X = 1) + P(X = 2)]$. Based on the probabilities in part c, we have $P(X \geq 3) = 1 - [0.0498 + 0.1494 + 0.2241] = 1 - 0.4233 = 0.5767$. Thus, there is about a 58% chance that a customer will frequent the chain at least three times in a 5-day period.

Figure 5.5 graphs the Poisson distribution $P(X = x)$ with $\mu = 3$, for x ranging from 0 to 8. The most likely outcomes are when x equals 2 and x equals 3, and the distribution is positively skewed. Remember that, theoretically, the values that the Poisson random variable assumes are infinitely countable, but the probabilities approach zero beyond those shown here.

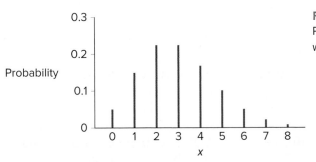

FIGURE 5.5
Poisson distribution with $\mu = 3$

SYNOPSIS OF INTRODUCTORY CASE

Anne Jones, the manager of a Starbucks store, is concerned about how other nearby store closings might affect foot traffic at her store. A solid understanding of the likelihood of customer arrivals is necessary before she can make further statistical inference. Historical data allow her to assume that a typical Starbucks customer averages 18 visits to a Starbucks store over a 30-day month. With this information and the knowledge that she can model customer arrivals using the Poisson distribution, she deduces that a typical customer averages three visits in a 5-day period. The likelihood that a typical customer frequents her store five times in a 5-day period is approximately 10%. Moreover, there is approximately a 42% chance that a typical customer goes to Starbucks no more than two times in a 5-day period, while the chances that this customer visits the chain at least three times is approximately 58%. These preliminary probabilities will prove vital as Anne plans her future staffing needs.

©Monkey Business Images/Shutterstock RF

Using Excel and R to Obtain Poisson Probabilities

Like the binomial formula, the manual use of the Poisson formula can become quite cumbersome, especially when the values of x and μ become large. Excel and R again prove useful when calculating Poisson probabilities. Table 5.10 shows Excel and R functions that we can use to find Poisson probabilities. Example 5.11 illustrates the use of these functions.

EXAMPLE 5.11

Craft breweries that make beer in small batches are experiencing a spectacular growth in bars and liquor stores across the nation. The craft beer industry now boasts of 4,269 breweries, representing a 12% market share of the total beer market in the United States (*Fortune*, March 22, 2016). It has been estimated that 1.5 craft breweries open every day. Assume this number represents an average that remains constant over time.

a. What is the probability that no more than 10 craft breweries open every week?

b. What is the probability that exactly 10 craft breweries open every week?

SOLUTION: We let X denote the number of craft breweries that open every week and compute the weekly mean, $\mu = 1.5 \times 7 = 10.5$.

Using Excel

We use Excel's **POISSON.DIST** function to calculate Poisson probabilities. In order to find $P(X = x)$, we enter "=POISSON.DIST(x, μ, 0)" where x is the number of successes over some interval and μ is the mean over this interval. If we enter a "1" for the last argument in the function, then Excel returns $P(X \leq x)$.

a. In order to find the probability that no more than 10 craft breweries open every week, $P(X \leq 10)$, we enter "=POISSON.DIST(10, 10.5, 1)" and Excel returns 0.5207. There is a 52.07% chance that no more than 10 craft breweries open every week.

b. In order to find the probability that exactly 10 craft breweries open every week, $P(X = 10)$, we enter "=POISSON.DIST(10, 10.5, 0)" and Excel returns 0.1236. There is a 12.36% chance that 10 craft breweries open every week.

Using R

We use R's **dpois** and **ppois** functions to calculate Poisson probabilities. In order to calculate $P(X = x)$, we enter "dpois(x, μ)" where x is the number of successes over some interval and μ is the mean over this interval. In order to calculate $P(X \leq x)$, we enter "ppois(x, μ)".

a. In order to find $P(X \leq 10)$, we enter:
```
> ppois(10, 10.5)
```
And R returns: 0.5207381.

b. In order to find $P(X = 10)$, we enter:
```
> dpois(10, 10.5)
```
And R returns: 0.1236055.

EXERCISES 5.5

Mechanics

52. Assume that X is a Poisson random variable with $\mu = 1.5$. Calculate the following probabilities.
    a. $P(X = 1)$
    b. $P(X = 2)$
    c. $P(X \geq 2)$

53. Assume that X is a Poisson random variable with $\mu = 4$. Calculate the following probabilities.
    a. $P(X = 4)$
    b. $P(X = 2)$
    c. $P(X \leq 1)$

54. Let the mean success rate of a Poisson process be 8 successes per hour.
    a. Find the expected number of successes in a half-hour period.
    b. Find the probability of at least two successes in a given half-hour period.
    c. Find the expected number of successes in a two-hour period.
    d. Find the probability of 10 successes in a given two-hour period.

55. Assume that X is a Poisson random variable with $\mu = 15$. Calculate the following probabilities.
    a. $P(X \leq 10)$
    b. $P(X = 13)$
    c. $P(X > 15)$
    d. $P(12 \leq X \leq 18)$

56. Assume that X is a Poisson random variable with $\mu = 20$. Calculate the following probabilities.
   a. $P(X < 14)$
   b. $P(X \geq 20)$
   c. $P(X = 25)$
   d. $P(18 \leq X \leq 23)$

Applications

57. Which of the following probabilities are likely to be found using a Poisson distribution?
   a. The probability that there will be six leaks in a specified stretch of a pipeline.
   b. The probability that at least 10 students in a class of 40 will land a job right after graduation.
   c. The probability that at least 50 families will visit Acadia National Park over the weekend.
   d. The probability that no customer will show up in the next five minutes.

58. Which of the following scenarios are likely to represent Poisson random variables?
   a. The number of violent crimes in New York over a six-week period.
   b. The number of customers of a bank manager who will default.
   c. The number of scratches on a 2-by-1-foot portion of a large wooden table.
   d. The number of patients of a doctor for whom the drug will be effective.

59. On average, there are 12 potholes per mile on a particular stretch of the state highway. Suppose the potholes are distributed evenly on the highway.
   a. Find the probability of finding fewer than two potholes in a quarter-mile stretch of the highway.
   b. Find the probability of finding more than one pothole in a quarter-mile stretch of the highway.

60. A tollbooth operator has observed that cars arrive randomly at an average rate of 360 cars per hour.
   a. Find the probability that two cars arrive during a specified one-minute period.
   b. Find the probability that at least two cars arrive during a specified one-minute period.
   c. Find the probability that 40 cars arrive between 10:00 am and 10:10 am.

61. A textile manufacturing process finds that on average, two flaws occur per every 50 yards of material produced.
   a. What is the probability of exactly two flaws in a 50-yard piece of material?
   b. What is the probability of no more than two flaws in a 50-yard piece of material?
   c. What is the probability of no flaws in a 25-yard piece of material?

62. Motorists arrive at a Gulf gas station at the rate of two per minute during morning hours.
   a. What is the probability that more than two motorists will arrive at the Gulf gas station during a one-minute interval in the morning?
   b. What is the probability that exactly six motorists will arrive at the Gulf gas station during a five-minute interval in the morning?
   c. How many motorists can an employee expect in her three-hour morning shift?

63. Airline travelers should be ready to be more flexible as airlines once again cancel thousands of flights this summer. The Coalition for Airline Passengers Rights, Health, and Safety averages 400 calls a day to help stranded travelers deal with airlines (seattlepi.com, July 10, 2008). Suppose the hotline is staffed for 16 hours a day.
   a. Calculate the average number of calls in a one-hour interval, 30-minute interval, and 15-minute interval.
   b. What is the probability of exactly six calls in a 15-minute interval?
   c. What is the probability of no calls in a 15-minute interval?
   d. What is the probability of at least two calls in a 15-minute interval?

64. On average, 400 people are struck by lightning in the United States each year (*The Boston Globe*, July 21, 2008).
   a. What is the probability that at most 425 people are struck by lightning in a year?
   b. What is the probability that at least 375 people are struck by lightning in a year?

65. According to a government report, the aging of the U.S. population is translating into many more visits to doctors' offices and hospitals (*USA Today,* August 7, 2008). It is estimated that an average person makes four visits a year to doctors' offices and hospitals.
   a. What are the mean and the standard deviation of an average person's number of monthly visits to doctors' offices and hospitals?
   b. What is the probability that an average person does not make any monthly visits to doctors' offices and hospitals?
   c. What is the probability that an average person makes at least one monthly visit to doctors' offices and hospitals?

66. Due to the advent of tablets, American adults are watching significantly less television than they did in previous decades. In 2016, Nielsen reported that American adults are watching an average of five hours and four minutes, or 304 minutes, of television per day.
   a. Find the probability that an average American adult watches more than 320 minutes of television per day.
   b. Find the probability that an average American adult watches more than 2,200 minutes of television per week.

67. In the fiscal year that ended September 30, 2008, there were 24,584 age-discrimination claims filed with the Equal Employment Opportunity Commission, an increase of 29% from the previous year (*The Wall Street Journal*, March 7–8, 2009). Assume there were 260 working days in the fiscal year for which a worker could file a claim.

   a. Calculate the average number of claims filed on a working day.
   b. What is the probability that exactly 100 claims were filed on a working day?
   c. What is the probability that no more than 100 claims were filed on a working day?

5.6 THE HYPERGEOMETRIC DISTRIBUTION

Calculate and interpret probabilities for a hypergeometric random variable.

In Section 5.4, we defined a binomial random variable X as the number of successes in the n trials of a Bernoulli process. The trials, according to a Bernoulli process, are independent and the probability of success does not change from trial to trial. The **hypergeometric distribution** is appropriate in applications where we cannot assume that the trials are independent.

Consider a box full of production items, of which 10% are known to be defective. Let success be labeled as the draw of a defective item. The probability of success may not be the same from trial to trial; it will depend on the size of the population and whether the sampling was done with or without replacement. Suppose the box consists of 20 items of which 10%, or 2, are defective. The probability of success in the first draw is 0.10 (= 2/20). However, the probability of success in subsequent draws will depend on the outcome of the first draw. For example, if the first item was defective, the probability of success in the second draw will be 0.0526 (= 1/19), while if the first item was not defective, the probability of success in the second draw will be 0.1053 (= 2/19). Therefore, the binomial distribution is not appropriate because the trials are not independent and the probability of success changes from trial to trial.

In the preceding example, we assumed sampling without replacement; in other words, after an item is drawn, it is not put back in the box for subsequent draws. The binomial distribution would be appropriate if we sample with replacement since, in that case, for each draw there will be 20 items, of which 2 are defective, resulting in an unchanging probability of success. Moreover, the dependence of the trials can be ignored if the population size is very large relative to the sample size. For instance, if the box consists of 10,000, items, of which 10%, or 1,000, are defective, then the probability of success in the second draw will be either 999/9,999 or 1,000/9,999, which are both approximately equal to 0.10.

We use the hypergeometric distribution in place of the binomial distribution when we are sampling without replacement from a population whose size N is not significantly larger than the sample size n. The **hypergeometric random variable** is the number of successes achieved in the n trials of a two-outcome experiment, where the trials are not assumed to be independent.

> ### THE HYPERGEOMETRIC DISTRIBUTION
> For a hypergeometric random variable X, the probability of x successes in a random selection of n items is
> $$P(X = x) = \frac{\binom{S}{x}\binom{N-S}{n-x}}{\binom{N}{n}},$$
> for $x = 0, 1, 2, \ldots, n$ if $n \leq S$ or $x = 0, 1, 2, \ldots, S$ if $n > S$, where N denotes the number of items in the population of which S are successes.

The formula consists of three parts:

- The first term in the numerator, $\binom{S}{x} = \frac{S!}{x!(S-x)!}$, represents the number of ways x successes can be selected from S successes in the population.
- The second term in the numerator, $\binom{N-S}{n-x} = \frac{(N-S)!}{(n-x)!(N-S-n+x)!}$, represents the number of ways $(n-x)$ failures can be selected from $(N-S)$ failures in the population.
- The denominator, $\binom{N}{n} = \frac{N!}{n!(N-n)!}$, represents the number of ways a sample of size n can be selected from the population of size N.

As with the binomial and Poisson distributions, simplified formulas can be used to calculate the mean, the variance, and the standard deviation of a hypergeometric random variable.

EXPECTED VALUE, VARIANCE, AND STANDARD DEVIATION
OF A HYPERGEOMETRIC RANDOM VARIABLE

If X is a hypergeometric random variable, then

$$E(X) = \mu = n\left(\frac{S}{N}\right),$$

$$Var(X) = \sigma^2 = n\left(\frac{S}{N}\right)\left(1 - \frac{S}{N}\right)\left(\frac{N-n}{N-1}\right), \quad \text{and}$$

$$SD(X) = \sigma = \sqrt{n\left(\frac{S}{N}\right)\left(1 - \frac{S}{N}\right)\left(\frac{N-n}{N-1}\right)}.$$

EXAMPLE 5.12

Wooden boxes are commonly used for the packaging and transportation of mangoes. A convenience store in Morganville, New Jersey, regularly buys mangoes from a wholesale dealer. For every shipment, the manager randomly inspects five mangoes from a box containing 20 mangoes for damages due to transportation. Suppose the chosen box contains exactly two damaged mangoes.

a. What is the probability that one out of five mangoes used in the inspection is damaged?

b. If the manager decides to reject the shipment if one or more mangoes are damaged, what is the probability that the shipment will be rejected?

c. Calculate the expected value, the variance, and the standard deviation of the number of damaged mangoes used in the inspection.

SOLUTION: The hypergeometric distribution is appropriate because the probability of finding a damaged mango changes from draw to draw (sampling is without replacement and the population size N is not significantly more than the sample size n). We use the following values to solve the problems: $N = 20$, $n = 5$, $S = 2$.

a. The probability that one out of five mangoes is damaged is $P(X = 1)$. We calculate

$$P(X = 1) = \frac{\binom{2}{1}\binom{20-2}{5-1}}{\binom{20}{5}} = \frac{\left(\frac{2!}{1!1!}\right)\left(\frac{18!}{4!14!}\right)}{\left(\frac{20!}{5!15!}\right)} = \frac{(2)(3,060)}{15,504} = 0.3947.$$

Therefore, the likelihood that exactly one out of five mangoes is damaged is 39.47%.

b. In order to find the probability that one or more mangoes are damaged, we need to calculate $P(X \geq 1)$. We note that $P(X \geq 1) = 1 - P(X = 0)$ where

$$P(X = 0) = \frac{\binom{2}{0}\binom{20-2}{5-0}}{\binom{20}{5}} = \frac{\left(\frac{2!}{0!2!}\right)\left(\frac{18!}{5!13!}\right)}{\left(\frac{20!}{5!15!}\right)} = \frac{(1)(8{,}568)}{15{,}504} = 0.5526.$$

Therefore, the probability that the shipment will be rejected equals $P(X \geq 1) = 1 - P(X = 0) = 1 - 0.5526 = 0.4474$.

c. We use the simplified formulas to obtain the mean, the variance, and the standard deviation as

$$E(X) = n\left(\frac{S}{N}\right) = 5\left(\frac{2}{20}\right) = 0.50,$$

$$Var(X) = n\left(\frac{S}{N}\right)\left(1 - \frac{S}{N}\right)\left(\frac{N-n}{N-1}\right) = 5\left(\frac{2}{20}\right)\left(1 - \frac{2}{20}\right)\left(\frac{20-5}{20-1}\right) = 0.3553,$$

$$SD(X) = \sqrt{0.3553} = 0.5960.$$

Using Excel and R to Obtain Hypergeometric Probabilities

Since it is tedious to solve for hypergeometric probabilities by hand, we typically use the computer to aid in the calculations. Table 5.10 shows Excel and R functions that we can use to find hypergeometric probabilities. Example 5.13 illustrates the use of these functions.

EXAMPLE 5.13

Employment for management occupations is projected to grow 6% from 2014 to 2024, resulting in about 505,400 new jobs (*Bureau of Labor Statistics, December 2015*). Among 25 applicants for a management position, 15 have college degrees in business. Suppose four applicants are randomly chosen for interviews.

a. What is the probability that none of the applicants has a college degree in business?

b. What is the probability that no more than two of the applicants have college degrees in business?

SOLUTION: We let X denote the number of applicants with a college degree in business. We know that $n = 4$, $S = 15$, and $N = 25$.

Using Excel

We use Excel's **HYPGEOM.DIST** function to calculate hypergeometric probabilities. In order to find $P(X = x)$, we enter "=HYPGEOM.DIST($x, n, S, N, 0$)" where x is the number of successes in the sample, n is the sample size, S is the number of successes in the population, and N is the population size. If we enter a "1" for the last argument in the function, then Excel returns $P(X \leq x)$.

a. In order to find the probability that none of the applicants has a college degree in business, $P(X = 0)$, we enter "=HYPGEOM.DIST(0, 4, 15, 25, 0)" and Excel returns 0.0166.

b. In order to find the probability that no more than two of the applicants have a college degree in business, $P(X \le 2)$, we enter "=HYPGEOM. DIST(2, 4, 15, 25, 1)" and Excel returns 0.5324.

Using R

We use R's **dhyper** and **phyper** functions to calculate hypergeometric probabilities. In order to calculate $P(X = x)$, we enter "dhyper($x, S, N - S, n$)" where x is the number of successes in the sample, S is the number of successes in the population, $N - S$ is the number of failures in the population, and n is the sample size. In order to calculate $P(X \le x)$, we enter "phyper($x, S, N - S, n$)".

a. In order to find $P(X = 0)$, we enter:

```
> dhyper(0, 15, 10, 4)
```

And R returns: 0.01660079.

b. In order to find $P(X \le 2)$, we enter:

```
> phyper(2, 15, 10, 4)
```

And R returns: 0.5324111.

EXERCISES 5.6

Mechanics

68. Assume that X is a hypergeometric random variable with $N = 25$, $S = 3$, and $n = 4$. Calculate the following probabilities.
   a. $P(X = 0)$
   b. $P(X = 1)$
   c. $P(X \le 1)$

69. Assume that X is a hypergeometric random variable with $N = 15$, $S = 4$, and $n = 3$. Calculate the following probabilities.
   a. $P(X = 1)$
   b. $P(X = 2)$
   c. $P(X \ge 2)$

70. Compute the probability of no successes in a random sample of three items obtained from a population of 12 items that contains two successes. What are the expected number and the standard deviation of the number of successes from the sample?

71. Assume that X is a hypergeometric random variable with $N = 50$, $S = 20$, and $n = 5$. Calculate the following probabilities.
   a. $P(X = 2)$
   b. $P(X \ge 2)$
   c. $P(X \le 3)$

72. Compute the probability of at least eight successes in a random sample of 20 items obtained from a population of 100 items that contains 25 successes. What are the expected number and the standard deviation of the number of successes?

Applications

73. Suppose you have an urn of ten marbles, of which five are red and five are green. If you draw two marbles from this urn, what is the probability that both marbles are red? What is the probability that at least one of the marbles is red?

74. A professor of management has heard that eight students in his class of 40 have landed an internship for the summer. Suppose he runs into three of his students in the corridor.
   a. Find the probability that none of these students has landed an internship.
   b. Find the probability that at least one of these students has landed an internship.

75. Despite the repeated effort by the government to reform how Wall Street pays its executives, some of the nation's biggest banks are continuing to pay out bonuses nearly as large as those in the best years before the crisis (*The Washington Post,* January 15, 2010). It is known that 10 out of 15 members of the board of directors of a company were in favor of a bonus. Suppose three members were randomly selected by the media.
   a. What is the probability that all of them were in favor of a bonus?
   b. What is the probability that at least two members were in favor of a bonus?

76. Many programming teams work independently at a large software company. The management has been putting pressure on these teams to finish a project on time. The company currently has 18 large programming projects, of which only 12 are likely to finish on time. Suppose the manager decides to randomly supervise three such projects.

a. What is the probability that all three projects finish on time?

b. What is the probability that at least two projects finish on time?

77. David Barnes and his fiancée Valerie Shah are visiting Hawaii. There are 20 guests registered for orientation. It is announced that 12 randomly selected registered guests will receive a free lesson of Tahitian dance.

   a. What is the probability that both David and Valerie get picked for the Tahitian dance lesson?

   b. What is the probability that neither of them gets picked for the Tahitian dance lesson?

78. The National Science Foundation is fielding applications for grants to study climate change. Twenty universities apply for a grant, and only four of them will be awarded. If Syracuse University and Auburn University are among the 20 applicants, what is the probability that these two universities will receive a grant? Assume that the selection is made randomly.

79. A committee of 40 members consists of 24 men and 16 women. A subcommittee consisting of 10 randomly selected members will be formed.

   a. What are the expected number of men and women on the subcommittee?

   b. What is the probability that at least half of the members on the subcommittee will be women?

80. Powerball is a jackpot game with a grand prize starting at $20 million and often rolling over into the hundreds of millions. In 2006, the jackpot was $365 million. The winner may choose to receive the jackpot prize paid over 29 years or as a lump-sum payment. For $1 the player selects six numbers for the base game of Powerball. There are two independent stages of the game. Five balls are randomly drawn from 59 consecutively numbered white balls. Moreover, one ball, called the Powerball, is randomly drawn from 39 consecutively numbered red balls. To be a winner, the numbers selected by the player must match the numbers on the randomly drawn white balls as well as the Powerball.

   a. What is the probability that the player is able to match the numbers of two out of five randomly drawn white balls?

   b. What is the probability that the player is able to match the numbers of all five randomly drawn white balls?

   c. What is the probability that the player is able to match the Powerball for a randomly drawn red ball?

   d. What is the probability of winning the jackpot? [*Hint: Remember that the two stages of drawing white and red balls are independent.*]

WRITING WITH STATISTICS

©Image Source/Getty Images RF

Senior executives at Skyhigh Construction, Inc., participate in a pick-your-salary plan. They choose salaries in a range between $125,000 and $150,000. By choosing a lower salary, an executive has an opportunity to make a larger bonus. If Skyhigh does not generate an operating profit during the year, then no bonuses are paid. Skyhigh has just hired two new senior executives, Allen Grossman and Felicia Arroyo. Each must decide whether to choose *Option* 1: a base pay of $125,000 with a possibility of a large bonus or *Option* 2: a base pay of $150,000 with a possibility of a bonus, but the bonus would be one-half of the bonus under Option 1.

Grossman, 44 years old, is married with two young children. He bought his home at the height of the market and has a rather large monthly mortgage payment. Arroyo, 32 years old, just completed her MBA at a prestigious Ivy League university. She is single and has no student loans due to a timely inheritance upon entering graduate school. Arroyo just moved to the area so she has decided to rent an apartment for at least one year. Given their personal profiles, inherent perceptions of risk, and subjective views of the economy, Grossman and Arroyo construct their individual probability distributions with respect to bonus outcomes shown in Table 5.11.

TABLE 5.11 Grossman's and Arroyo's Probability Distributions

Bonus (in $)	Probability	
	Grossman	Arroyo
0	0.35	0.20
50,000	0.45	0.25
100,000	0.10	0.35
150,000	0.10	0.20

Jordan Lake, an independent human resources specialist, is asked to summarize the payment plans with respect to each executive's probability distribution.

Jordan would like to use the above probability distributions to

1. Compute expected values to evaluate payment plans for Grossman and Arroyo.

2. Help Grossman and Arroyo decide whether to choose Option 1 or Option 2 for his/her compensation package.

Skyhigh Construction, Inc., has just hired two new senior executives, Allen Grossman and Felicia Arroyo, to oversee planned expansion of operations. As senior executives, they participate in a pick-your-salary plan. Each executive is given two options for compensation:

Option 1: A base pay of $125,000 with a possibility of a large bonus.
Option 2: A base pay of $150,000 with a possibility of a bonus, but the bonus would be one-half of the bonus under Option 1.

Grossman and Arroyo understand that if the firm does not generate an operating profit in the fiscal year, then no bonuses are paid. Each executive has constructed a probability distribution given his/her personal background, underlying risk preferences, and subjective view of the economy.

Given the probability distributions and with the aid of expected values, the following analysis will attempt to choose the best option for each executive. Grossman, a married father with two young children, believes that Table 5.A best reflects his bonus payment expectations.

TABLE 5.A Calculating Grossman's Expected Bonus

Bonus (in $), x_i	Probability, $P(x_i)$	Weighted Value, $x_i P(x_i)$
0	0.35	$0 \times 0.35 = 0$
50,000	0.45	$50{,}000 \times 0.45 = 22{,}500$
100,000	0.10	$100{,}000 \times 0.10 = 10{,}000$
150,000	0.10	$150{,}000 \times 0.10 = 15{,}000$
		Total = 47,500

Expected bonus, $E(X)$, is calculated as a weighted average of all possible bonus values and is shown at the bottom of the third column of Table 5.A. Grossman's expected bonus is $47,500. Using this value for his bonus, his salary options are

Option 1: $125,000 + $47,500 = $172,500
Option 2: $150,000 + (1/2 × $47,500) = $173,750

Grossman should choose *Option 2* as his salary plan.

Arroyo is single with few financial constraints. Table 5.B shows the expected value of her bonus given her probability distribution.

TABLE 5.B Calculating Arroyo's Expected Bonus

Bonus (in $), x_i	Probability, $P(x_i)$	Weighted Value, $x_i P(x_i)$
0	0.20	$0 \times 0.20 = 0$
50,000	0.25	$50{,}000 \times 0.25 = 12{,}500$
100,000	0.35	$100{,}000 \times 0.35 = 35{,}000$
150,000	0.20	$150{,}000 \times 0.20 = 30{,}000$
		Total = 77,500

Arroyo's expected bonus amounts to $77,500. Thus, her salary options are

Option 1: $125,000 + $77,500 = $202,500
Option 2: $150,000 + (1/2 × $77,500) = $188,750

Arroyo should choose *Option 1* as her salary plan.

CONCEPTUAL REVIEW

LO 5.1 **Describe a discrete random variable and its probability distribution.**

A **random variable** summarizes outcomes of an experiment with numerical values. A **discrete random variable** assumes a countable number of distinct values, whereas a **continuous random variable** is characterized by uncountable values in an interval.

The **probability mass function** for a discrete random variable X is a list of the values of X with the associated probabilities; that is, the list of all possible pairs $(x, P(X = x))$. The **cumulative distribution function** of X is defined as $P(X \leq x)$.

LO 5.2 **Calculate and interpret summary measures for a discrete random variable.**

For a discrete random variable X with values $x_1, x_2, x_3, \ldots$, which occur with probabilities $P(X = x_i)$, the **expected value** of X is calculated as $E(X) = \mu = \Sigma x_i P(X = x_i)$. We interpret the expected value as the long-run average value of the random variable over infinitely many independent repetitions of an experiment. Measures of dispersion indicate whether the values of X are clustered about μ or widely scattered from μ. The variance of X is calculated as $Var(X) = \sigma^2 = \Sigma(x_i - \mu)^2 P(X = x_i)$. The standard deviation of X is $SD(X) = \sigma = \sqrt{\sigma^2}$.

In general, a **risk-averse consumer** expects a reward for taking risk. A risk-averse consumer may decline a risky prospect even if it offers a positive expected gain. A **risk-neutral consumer** completely ignores risk and always accepts a prospect that offers a positive expected gain. Finally, **a risk-loving consumer** may accept a risky prospect even if the expected gain is negative.

LO 5.3 **Calculate and interpret summary measures to evaluate portfolio returns.**

Portfolio return R_p is represented as a linear combination of the individual returns. The **expected return** for a portfolio with two assets is $E(R_p) = w_A E(R_A) + w_B E(R_B)$, where R_A and R_B represent asset returns and w_A and w_B are the corresponding portfolio weights. The **variance** for the portfolio is $Var(R_p) = w_A^2 \sigma_A^2 + w_B^2 \sigma_B^2 + 2w_A w_B \sigma_{AB}$, or equivalently, $Var(R_p) = w_A^2 \sigma_A^2 + w_B^2 \sigma_B^2 + 2w_A w_B \rho_{AB} \sigma_A \sigma_B$.

LO 5.4 **Calculate and interpret probabilities for a binomial random variable.**

A **Bernoulli process** is a series of n independent and identical trials of an experiment such that on each trial there are only two possible outcomes, conventionally labeled "success" and "failure." The probabilities of success and failure, denoted p and $1 - p$, remain the same from trial to trial.

For a **binomial random variable** X, the probability of x successes in n Bernoulli trials is $P(X = x) = \binom{n}{x} p^x (1 - p)^{n-x} = \frac{n!}{x!(n-x)!} p^x (1 - p)^{n-x}$ for $x = 0, 1, 2, \ldots, n$.

The expected value, the variance, and the standard deviation of a binomial random variable are $E(X) = np$, $Var(X) = \sigma^2 = np(1 - p)$, and $SD(X) = \sigma = \sqrt{np(1 - p)}$, respectively.

Calculate and interpret probabilities for a Poisson random variable.

A **Poisson random variable** counts the number of occurrences of a certain event over a given interval of time or space. For simplicity, we call these occurrences "successes." For a Poisson random variable X, the probability of x successes over a given interval of time or space is $P(X = x) = \frac{e^{-\mu}\mu^x}{x!}$ for $x = 0, 1, 2, \ldots$, where μ is the mean number of successes and $e \approx 2.718$ is the base of the natural logarithm. The expected value, the variance, and the standard deviation of a Poisson distribution are $E(X) = \mu$, $Var(X) = \sigma^2 = \mu$, and $SD(X) = \sigma = \sqrt{\mu}$, respectively.

Calculate and interpret probabilities for a hypergeometric random variable.

The hypergeometric distribution is appropriate in applications where the trials are not independent and the probability of success changes from trial to trial. We use it in place of the binomial distribution when we are sampling without replacement from a population whose size N is not significantly larger than the sample size n. For a **hypergeometric random variable** X, the probability of x successes in a random selection of n items is $P(X = x) = \frac{\binom{S}{x}\binom{N-S}{n-x}}{\binom{N}{n}}$ for $x = 0, 1, 2, \ldots, n$ if $n \leq S$ or $x = 0, 1, 2, \ldots, S$ if $n > S$, where N denotes the number of items in the population of which S are successes. The expected value, the variance, and the standard deviation of a hypergeometric distribution are $E(X) = n\left(\frac{S}{N}\right)$, $Var(X) = \sigma^2 = n\left(\frac{S}{N}\right)\left(1 - \frac{S}{N}\right)\left(\frac{N-n}{N-1}\right)$, and $SD(X) = \sigma = \sqrt{n\left(\frac{S}{N}\right)\left(1 - \frac{S}{N}\right)\left(\frac{N-n}{N-1}\right)}$, respectively.

ADDITIONAL EXERCISES AND CASE STUDIES

Exercises

81. An analyst developed the following probability distribution for the rate of return for a common stock.

Scenario	Probability	Rate of Return (in %)
1	0.25	−15
2	0.35	5
3	0.40	10

   a. Calculate the expected rate of return.
   b. Calculate the variance and the standard deviation of this probability distribution.

82. Facing the worst economic climate since the dot-com bust in the early 2000s, high-tech companies in the United States search for investment opportunities with cautious optimism (*USA TODAY*, February 17, 2009). Suppose the investment team at Microsoft is considering an innovative start-up project. According to its estimates, Microsoft can make a profit of $5 million if the project is very successful and $2 million if it is somewhat successful. It also stands to lose $4 million if the project fails. Calculate the expected profit or loss for Microsoft if the probabilities that the project is very successful and somewhat successful are 0.10 and 0.40, respectively, with the remaining amount being the failure probability.

83. Consider the following information on the expected return for companies X and Y.

Economy	Probability	X (in %)	Y (in %)
Boom	0.20	30	10
Neutral	0.50	10	20
Poor	0.30	−30	5

   a. Calculate the expected value and the standard deviation of returns for companies X and Y.
   b. Calculate the correlation coefficient if the covariance between X and Y is 88.

84. A professor uses a relative scale for grading. She announces that 60% of the students will get at

least a B, with 15% getting A's. Also, 5% will get a D and another 5% will get an F. Assume that no incompletes are given in the course. Let Score be defined by 4 for A, 3 for B, 2 for C, 1 for D, and 0 for F.

a. Find the probability that a student gets a B.
b. Find the probability that a student gets at least a C.
c. Compute the expected value and the standard deviation of Score.

85. An investor owns a portfolio consisting of two mutual funds, A and B, with 35% invested in A. The following table lists the inputs for these funds.

Measures	Fund A	Fund B
Expected Value	10	5
Variance	98	26
Covariance	22	

a. Calculate the expected value for the portfolio return.
b. Calculate the standard deviation for the portfolio return.

86. Fifty percent of the customers who go to Sears Auto Center for tires buy four tires and 30% buy two tires. Moreover, 18% buy fewer than two tires, with 5% buying none.

a. Find the expected value and the standard deviation of the number of tires a customer buys.
b. If Sears Auto Center makes a $15 profit on every tire it sells, what is its expected profit if it services 120 customers?

87. Forty-four percent of consumers with credit cards carry balances from month to month (bankrate.com, February 20, 2007). Four consumers with credit cards are randomly selected.

a. What is the probability that all four consumers carry a credit card balance?
b. What is the probability that fewer than two consumers carry a credit card balance?
c. Calculate the expected value, the variance, and the standard deviation for this distribution.

88. Rent-to-own (RTO) stores allow consumers immediate access to merchandise in exchange for a series of weekly or monthly payments. The agreement is for a fixed time period. At the same time, the customer has the flexibility to terminate the contract by returning the merchandise. Suppose an RTO store makes a $200 profit on appliances when the customer ends up owning the merchandise by making all payments. It makes a $20 profit when the customer returns the product and a loss of $600 when the customer defaults. Let the return and default probabilities be 0.60 and 0.05, respectively.

a. Construct a probability distribution for the profit per appliance.
b. What is the expected profit for a store that sells 200 rent-to-own contracts?

89. According to the Department of Transportation, 27% of domestic flights were delayed in 2007 (*Money*, May 2008). At New York's John F. Kennedy Airport, five flights are randomly selected.

a. What is the probability that all five flights are delayed?
b. What is the probability that all five are on time?

90. Apple products have become a household name in America, with 51% of all households owning at least one Apple product (*CNN*, March 19, 2012).

a. What is the probability that two in a random sample of four households own an Apple product?
b. What is the probability that all four in a random sample of four households own an Apple product?
c. In a random sample of 100 households, find the expected value and the standard deviation for the number of households that own an Apple product.

91. Twenty percent of U.S. mortgages are "underwater" (*The Boston Globe*, March 5, 2009). A mortgage is considered underwater if the value of the home is less than what is owed on the mortgage. Suppose 100 mortgage holders are randomly selected.

a. What is the probability that exactly 15 of the mortgages are underwater?
b. What is the probability that more than 20 of the mortgages are underwater?
c. What is the probability that at least 25 of the mortgages are underwater?

92. According to a survey by consulting firm Watson Wyatt, approximately 19% of employers have eliminated perks or plan to do so in the next year (*Kiplinger's Personal Finance*,

February 2009). Suppose 30 employers are randomly selected.

a. What is the probability that exactly ten of the employers have eliminated or plan to eliminate perks?

b. What is the probability that at least ten employers, but no more than 20 employers, have eliminated or plan to eliminate perks?

c. What is the probability that at most eight employers have eliminated or plan to eliminate perks?

93. Studies have shown that bats can consume an average of ten mosquitoes per minute (berkshiremuseum.org).

a. Calculate the average number of mosquitoes that a bat consumes in a 30-second interval.

b. What is the probability that a bat consumes four mosquitoes in a 30-second interval?

c. What is the probability that a bat does not consume any mosquitoes in a 30-second interval?

d. What is the probability that a bat consumes at least one mosquito in a 30-second interval?

94. Despite the fact that home prices seem affordable and mortgage rates are at historic lows, real estate agents say they are showing more homes, but not selling more (*The Boston Globe*, March 7, 2009). A real estate company estimates that an average of five people show up at an open house to view a property. There is going to be an open house on Sunday.

a. What is the probability that at least five people will show up to view the property?

b. What is the probability that fewer than five people will show up to view the property?

95. The police have estimated that there are 12 major accidents per day on a particular 10-mile stretch of a national highway. Suppose the incidence of accidents is evenly distributed on this 10-mile stretch of the highway.

a. Find the probability that there will be fewer than eight major accidents per day on this 10-mile stretch of the highway.

b. Find the probability that there will be more than two accidents per day on a 1-mile stretch of this highway.

96. Suppose you draw three cards, without replacement, from a deck of well-shuffled cards. Remember that each deck consists of 52 cards, with 13 each of spades, hearts, clubs, and diamonds.

a. What is the probability that you draw all spades?

b. What is the probability that you draw two or fewer spades?

c. What is the probability that you draw all spades or hearts?

97. A professor has learned that three students in her class of 20 will cheat on the exam. She decides to focus her attention on four randomly chosen students during the exam.

a. What is the probability that she finds at least one of the students cheating?

b. What is the probability that she finds at least one of the students cheating if she focuses on six randomly chosen students?

98. Find the probability that an Internal Revenue Service (IRS) auditor will catch only 4 income tax returns with illegitimate deductions if he randomly selects 5 returns from among 20 returns, of which 10 contain illegitimate deductions.

99. A committee of 10 is to be chosen from 50 people, 25 of whom are Republicans and 25 Democrats. The committee is chosen at random.

a. What is the probability that there will be five Republicans and five Democrats?

b. What is the probability that a majority of the committee will be Republicans?

100. Many U.S. households still do not have Internet access. Suppose 20 out of 80 households in a small southern town do not have Internet access. A company that provides high-speed Internet has recently entered the market. As part of the marketing campaign, the company decides to randomly select ten households and offer them free laptops along with a brochure that describes their services. The aim is to build goodwill and, with a free laptop, tempt nonusers into getting Internet access.

a. What is the probability that six laptop recipients do not have Internet access?

b. What is the probability that at least five laptop recipients do not have Internet access?

c. What is the probability that two or fewer laptop recipients do not have Internet access?

d. What is the expected number of laptop recipients who do not have Internet access?

CASE STUDIES

CASE STUDY 5.1 An extended warranty is a prolonged warranty offered to consumers by the warranty administrator, the retailer, or the manufacturer. A report in *The New York Times* (November 23, 2009) suggests that 20.4% of laptops fail over three years. Roberto D'Angelo is interested in an extended warranty for his laptop. A good extended warranty is being offered at Compuvest.com for $74. It will cover any repair job that his laptop may need in the next three years. Based on his research, he determines that the likelihood of a repair job in the next three years is 13% for a minor repair, 8% for a major repair, and 3% for a catastrophic repair. The extended warranty will save him $80 for a minor repair, $320 for a major repair, and $500 for a catastrophic repair. These results are summarized in the following probability distribution.

Data for Case Study 5.1 Probability Distribution for Repair Cost

Type of Repair	Probability	Repair Cost (in $)
None	0.76	0
Minor	0.13	80
Major	0.08	320
Catastrophic	0.03	500

In a report, use the above information to

1. Calculate and interpret the expected value of the repair cost.
2. Analyze the expected gain or loss for a consumer who buys the extended warranty.
3. Determine what kind of a consumer (risk neutral, risk averse, or both) will buy this extended warranty.

CASE STUDY 5.2 According to figures released by the New York City government, smoking among New York City teenagers is on a decline, continuing a trend that began more than a decade ago (*The New York Times*, January 2, 2008). According to the New York City Youth Risk Behavior Survey, the teenage smoking rate dropped to 8.5% in 2007 from about 17.6% in 2001 and 23% in 1997. City officials attribute the lower smoking rate to factors including a cigarette tax increase, a ban on workplace smoking, and television and subway ads that graphically depict tobacco-related illnesses.

In a report, use the above information to

1. Calculate the probability that at least one in a group of 10 New York City teenagers smoked in 2007.
2. Calculate the probability that at least one in a group of 10 New York City teenagers smoked in 2001.
3. Calculate the probability that at least one in a group of 10 New York City teenagers smoked in 1997.
4. Comment on the smoking trend between 1997 and 2007.

CASE STUDY 5.3 Disturbing news regarding Scottish police concerns the number of crashes involving vehicles on operational duties (*BBC News*, March 10, 2008). Statistics showed that Scottish forces' vehicles had been involved in traffic accidents at the rate of 1,000 per year. The statistics included vehicles involved in 999 calls (the equivalent of 911 in the United States) and pursuits. Fire service and ambulance vehicles were not included in the figures.

In a report, use the above information to

1. Calculate and interpret the expected number of traffic accidents per day involving vehicles on operational duties.
2. Use this expected value to construct the probability distribution table that lists the probability of 0, 1, 2, . . . , 10 traffic accidents per day. Graph this distribution and summarize your findings.

APPENDIX 5.1 Guidelines for Other Software Packages

The following section provides brief commands for Minitab, SPSS, and JMP.

Minitab

The Binomial Distribution

A. (Replicating Example 5.9a) From the menu, choose **Calc > Probability Distributions > Binomial**.
B. Select **Probability** since we are finding $P(X = 70)$. (For cumulative probabilities, select **Cumulative probability**.) Enter 100 as the **Number of trials** and 0.68 as the **Event probability**. Select **Input constant** and enter the value 70.

The Poisson Distribution

A. (Replicating Example 5.11a) From the menu, choose **Calc > Probability Distributions > Poisson**.
B. Select **Cumulative probability** since we are finding $P(X \leq 10)$. (For calculating $P(X = x)$, select **Probability**.) Enter 10.5 for the **Mean**. Select **Input constant** and enter the value 10.

The Hypergeometric Distribution

A. (Replicating Example 5.13a) From the menu, choose **Calc > Probability Distributions > Hypergeometric**.
B. Select **Probability** since we are finding $P(X = 0)$. (For cumulative probabilities, select **Cumulative probability**.) Enter 25 for the **Population size (N)**, 15 for **Event count in population (M)**, and 4 for the **Sample size (n)**. Select **Input constant** and enter 0.

SPSS

Note: In order for the calculated probability to be seen on the spreadsheet, SPSS must first "view" data on the spreadsheet. For this purpose, enter a value of zero in the first cell of the first column.

The Binomial Distribution

A. (Replicating Example 5.9a) From the menu, choose **Transform > Compute Variable**.

B. Under **Target Variable**, type pdfbinomial. Under **Function group**, select **PDF & Noncentral PDF**, and under **Functions and Special Variables**, double-click on **Pdf.Binom**. (For cumulative probabilities, under **Function group** select **CDF & Noncentral CDF**, and under **Functions and Special Variables** double-click on **Cdf.Binom**.) In the **Numeric Expression** box, enter 70 for **quant**, 100 for **n**, and 0.68 for **prob**.

The Poisson Distribution

A. (Replicating Example 5.11a) From the menu, choose **Transform > Compute Variable**.

B. Under **Target Variable**, type cdfpoisson. Under **Function group**, select **CDF & Noncentral CDF**, and under **Functions and Special Variables**, double-click on **Pdf.Poisson**. (For calculating $P(X = x)$, under **Function group** select **PDF & Noncentral PDF**, and under **Functions and Special Variables**, double-click on **Pdf.Poisson**.) In the **Numeric Expression** box, enter 10 for **quant** and 10.5 for **Mean**.

The Hypergeometric Distribution

A. (Replicating Example 5.13a) From the menu, choose **Transform > Compute Variable**.

B. Under **Target Variable**, type pdfhyper. Under **Function group**, select **PDF & Noncentral PDF**, and under **Functions and Special Variables**, double-click on **Pdf.Hyper**. (For cumulative probabilities, under **Function group** select **CDF & Noncentral CDF**, and under **Functions and Special Variables** double-click on **Cdf.Hyper**.) In the **Numeric Expression** box, enter 0 for **quant**, 25 for **total**, 4 for **sample**, and 15 for **hits**.

JMP

Note: In order for the calculated probability to be seen on the spreadsheet, JMP must first "view" data on the spreadsheet. For this purpose, enter a value of zero in the first cell of the first column.

The Binomial Distribution

A. (Replicating Example 5.9a) Right-click at the top of the column in the spreadsheet view and select **Formula**. Under **Functions (grouped)**, choose **Discrete Probability > Binomial Probability**. (For cumulative probabilities, select **Binomial Distribution**.)

B. Enter 0.68 for **p**, 100 for **n**, and 70 for **k**.

The Poisson Distribution

A. (Replicating Example 5.11a) Right-click at the top of the column in the spread-sheet view and select **Formula**. Under **Functions (grouped)**, choose **Discrete Probability > Poisson Distribution**. (For calculating $P(X = x)$, select **Poisson Probability**.)

B. Enter 10.5 for **lambda** and 10 for **k**.

The Hypergeometric Distribution

A. (Replicating Example 5.13a) Right-click at the top of the column in the spread-sheet view and select **Formula**. Under **Functions (grouped)**, choose **Discrete Probability > Hypergeometric Probability**. (For cumulative probabilities, select **Hypergeometric Distribution**.)

B. Enter 25 for **N**, 15 for **K**, 4 for **n**, and 0 for **x**.

6 Continuous Probability Distributions

n Chapter 5, we classified a random variable as either discrete or continuous. A discrete random variable assumes a countable number of distinct values, such as the number of houses that a realtor sells in a month, the number of defective pieces in a sample of 20 machine parts, and the number of cars lined up at a toll booth. A continuous random variable, on the other hand, is characterized by uncountable values because it can take on any value within an interval. Examples of a continuous random variable include the investment return on a mutual fund, the waiting time at a toll booth, and the amount of soda in a cup. In all of these examples, it is impossible to list all possible values of the random variable. In this chapter, we focus on continuous random variables. Most of this chapter is devoted to the normal distribution, which is the most extensively used continuous probability distribution and is the cornerstone of statistical inference. Other important continuous distributions discussed are the continuous uniform, the exponential, and the lognormal distributions.

©Vision SRL/Photodisc/Getty Images RF

INTRODUCTORY CASE

Demand for Salmon

Akiko Hamaguchi is the manager of a small sushi restaurant called Little Ginza in Phoenix, Arizona. As part of her job, Akiko has to purchase salmon every day for the restaurant. For the sake of freshness, it is important that she buys the right amount of salmon daily. Buying too much may result in wastage, and buying too little may disappoint some customers on high-demand days.

Akiko has estimated that the daily consumption of salmon is normally distributed with a mean of 12 pounds and a standard deviation of 3.2 pounds. She has always bought 20 pounds of salmon every day. Lately, she has been criticized by the owners because this amount of salmon was too often resulting in wastage. As part of cost cutting, Akiko is considering a new strategy. She will buy salmon that is sufficient to meet the daily demand of customers on 90% of the days.

Akiko wants to use the above information to

1. Calculate the probability that the demand for salmon at Little Ginza is above 20 pounds.

2. Calculate the probability that the demand for salmon at Little Ginza is below 15 pounds.

3. Determine the amount of salmon that should be bought daily so that the restaurant meets demand on 90% of the days.

A synopsis of this case is provided in Section 6.2.

6.1 CONTINUOUS RANDOM VARIABLES AND THE UNIFORM DISTRIBUTION

As discussed in Chapter 5, a discrete random variable X assumes a countable number of distinct values such as x_1, x_2, x_3, and so on. A continuous random variable, on the other hand, is characterized by uncountable values because it can take on any value within an interval. Unlike the case of a discrete random variable, we cannot describe the possible values of a continuous random variable X with a list x_1, x_2, ... because the value $(x_1 + x_2)/2$, not in the list, might also be possible. Consider, for example, a continuous random variable defined by the amount of time a student takes to finish the exam. Here, it is impossible to put in a sequence all possible values of the random variable. Some students may think that time is countable in seconds; however, this may not be the case once we consider fractions of a second. Similarly, other continuous random variables, such as the investment return on a mutual fund and the amount of soda in a cup, are characterized by uncountable values.

For a discrete random variable, we can compute the probability that it assumes a particular value x, or written as a probability statement, $P(X = x)$. For instance, for a binomial random variable, we can calculate the probability of exactly one success in n trials; that is, $P(X = 1)$. We cannot make this calculation with a continuous random variable. The probability that a continuous random variable assumes a particular value x is zero; that is, $P(X = x) = 0$. This occurs because we cannot assign a nonzero probability to each of the uncountable values and still have the probabilities sum to one. Thus, for a continuous random variable, it is only meaningful to calculate the probability that the value of the random variable falls within some specified interval. Therefore, for a continuous random variable, $P(a \le X \le b) = P(a < X < b) = P(a \le X < b) = P(a < X \le b)$, since $P(X = a)$ and $P(X = b)$ are both zero.

In Chapter 5, we learned that a probability mass function for a discrete random variable X is a list of the values of X with the associated probabilities. For a continuous random variable, the counterpart to the probability mass function is called the probability density function, denoted by $f(x)$. As mentioned in Chapter 5, in this text we often use the term "probability distribution" to refer to both functions. The graph of $f(x)$ approximates the relative frequency polygon for the population. Unlike the probability mass function, $f(x)$ does not provide probabilities directly. The probability that the variable assumes a value within an interval, say $P(a \le X \le b)$, is defined as the area under $f(x)$ between points a and b. Moreover, the entire area under $f(x)$ over all values of x must equal one; this is equivalent to the fact that, for discrete random variables, the probabilities add up to one.

THE PROBABILITY DENSITY FUNCTION

The probability density function $f(x)$ for a continuous random variable X has the following properties:

- $f(x) \ge 0$ for all possible values x of X, and
- the area under $f(x)$ over all values x of X equals one.

As in the case for a discrete random variable, we can use the cumulative distribution function, denoted by $F(x)$, to compute probabilities for a continuous random variable. For a value x of the random variable X, $F(x) = P(X \le x)$ is simply the area under the probability density function up to the value x.

If you are familiar with calculus, then you will recognize that this cumulative probability is the integral of $f(u)$ for values less than or equal to x. Similarly, $P(a \le X \le b) = F(b) - F(a)$ is the integral of $f(u)$ between points a and b. Fortunately, we do not necessarily need the knowledge of integral calculus to compute probabilities for the continuous random variables discussed in this text.

The Continuous Uniform Distribution

LO 6.2

Calculate and interpret probabilities for a random variable that follows the continuous uniform distribution.

One of the simplest continuous probability distributions is called the **continuous uniform distribution**. This distribution is appropriate when the underlying random variable has an equally likely chance of assuming a value within a specified range. Examples of uniformly distributed random variables include the delivery time of an appliance, the scheduled flight time between cities, and the waiting time for a campus bus. Any specified range for each of the above random variables can be assumed to be equally probable.

Suppose you are informed that your new refrigerator will be delivered between 2:00 pm and 3:00 pm. Let the random variable X denote the delivery time of your refrigerator. This variable is bounded below by 2:00 pm and above by 3:00 pm for a total range of 60 minutes. It is reasonable to infer that the probability of delivery between 2:00 pm and 2:30 pm equals 0.50 (=30/60), as does the probability of delivery between 2:30 pm and 3:00 pm. Similarly, the probability of delivery in any 15-minute interval equals 0.25 (=15/60), and so on.

Figure 6.1 depicts the probability density function for a continuous uniform random variable. The values a and b on the horizontal axis represent its lower and upper limits, respectively. The continuous uniform distribution is symmetric around its mean μ, computed as $\frac{a+b}{2}$. In the refrigerator delivery example, the mean is $\mu = \frac{2+3}{2} = 2.5$, implying that you expect the delivery at 2:30 pm. The standard deviation σ of a continuous uniform variable equals $\sqrt{(b-a)^2/12}$.

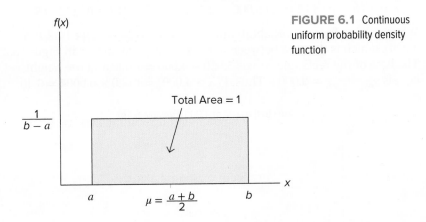

FIGURE 6.1 Continuous uniform probability density function

It is important to emphasize that the height of the probability density function does not directly represent a probability. As mentioned earlier, for all continuous random variables, it is the area under $f(x)$ that corresponds to probability. For the continuous uniform distribution, the probability is essentially the area of a rectangle, which is the base times the height. Therefore, the probability is easily computed by multiplying the length of a specified interval (base) with $f(x) = \frac{1}{b-a}$ (height).

THE CONTINUOUS UNIFORM DISTRIBUTION

A random variable X follows the continuous uniform distribution if its probability density function is

$$f(x) = \begin{cases} \dfrac{1}{b-a} & \text{for } a \leq x \leq b, \text{ and} \\ 0 & \text{for } x < a \text{ or } x > b, \end{cases}$$

where a and b represent the lower and upper limits of values, respectively, that the random variable assumes.

The expected value and the standard deviation of X are computed as

$$E(X) = \mu = \frac{a+b}{2} \quad \text{and} \quad SD(X) = \sigma = \sqrt{(b-a)^2/12}.$$

EXAMPLE 6.1

A manager of a local drugstore is projecting next month's sales for a particular cosmetic line. She knows from historical data that sales follow a continuous uniform distribution with a lower limit of $2,500 and an upper limit of $5,000.

a. What are the mean and the standard deviation for this continuous uniform distribution?

b. What is the probability that sales exceed $4,000?

c. What is the probability that sales are between $3,200 and $3,800?

SOLUTION:

a. With a value for the lower limit of $a = 2,500$ and a value for the upper limit of $b = 5,000$, we calculate the mean and the standard deviation for this continuous uniform distribution as

$$\mu = \frac{a+b}{2} = \frac{2,500 + 5,000}{2} = 3,750, \text{ or } \$3,750, \text{ and}$$

$$\sigma = \sqrt{(b-a)^2/12} = \sqrt{(5,000 - 2,500)^2/12} = 721.69, \text{ or } \$721.69.$$

b. When solving for the probability that sales exceed $4,000, we find $P(X > 4,000)$, which is the area between 4,000 and 5,000, as shown in Figure 6.2. The base of the rectangle equals $5,000 - 4,000 = 1,000$ and the height equals $\frac{1}{5,000 - 2,500} = 0.0004$. Thus, $P(X > 4,000) = 1,000 \times 0.0004 = 0.40$.

FIGURE 6.2 Area to the right of 4,000 (Example 6.1b)

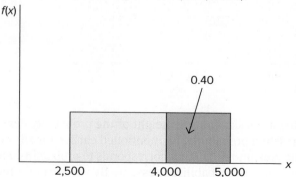

---

c. When solving for the probability that sales are between $3,200 and $3,800, we find $P(3,200 \le X \le 3,800)$. Using the same methodology as in part b, we multiply the base times the height of the rectangle, as shown in Figure 6.3. Therefore, we obtain the probability as $(3,800 - 3,200) \times 0.0004 = 0.24$.

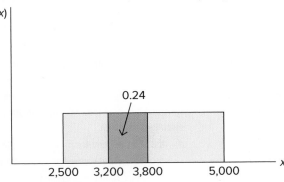

FIGURE 6.3 Area between 3,200 and 3,800 (Example 6.1c)

EXERCISES 6.1

Mechanics

1. The cumulative probabilities for a continuous random variable X are $P(X \le 10) = 0.42$ and $P(X \le 20) = 0.66$. Calculate the following probabilities.
   a. $P(X > 10)$
   b. $P(X > 20)$
   c. $P(10 < X < 20)$

2. For a continuous random variable X with an upper bound of 4, $P(0 \le X \le 2.5) = 0.54$ and $P(2.5 \le X \le 4) = 0.16$. Calculate the following probabilities.
   a. $P(X < 0)$
   b. $P(X > 2.5)$
   c. $P(0 \le X \le 4)$

3. For a continuous random variable X, $P(20 \le X \le 40) = 0.15$ and $P(X > 40) = 0.16$. Calculate the following probabilities.
   a. $P(X < 40)$
   b. $P(X < 20)$
   c. $P(X = 40)$

4. A random variable X follows the continuous uniform distribution with a lower bound of 5 and an upper bound of 35.
   a. What is the height of the density function $f(x)$?
   b. What are the mean and the standard deviation for the distribution?
   c. Calculate $P(X > 10)$.

5. A random variable X follows the continuous uniform distribution with a lower bound of −2 and an upper bound of 4.
   a. What is the height of the density function $f(x)$?
   b. What are the mean and the standard deviation for the distribution?
   c. Calculate $P(X \le -1)$.

6. A random variable X follows the continuous uniform distribution with a lower limit of 10 and an upper limit of 30.
   a. Calculate the mean and the standard deviation for the distribution.
   b. What is the probability that X is greater than 22?
   c. What is the probability that X is between 15 and 23?

7. A random variable X follows the continuous uniform distribution with a lower limit of 750 and an upper limit of 800.
   a. Calculate the mean and the standard deviation for the distribution.
   b. What is the probability that X is less than 770?

Applications

8. Suppose the average price of electricity for a New England customer follows the continuous uniform distribution with a lower bound of 12 cents per kilowatt-hour and an upper bound of 20 cents per kilowatt-hour.
   a. Calculate the average price of electricity for a New England customer.
   b. What is the probability that a New England customer pays less than 15.5 cents per kilowatt-hour?
   c. A local carnival is not able to operate its rides if the average price of electricity is more than 14 cents per kilowatt-hour. What is the probability that the carnival will need to close?

9. The arrival time of an elevator in a 12-story dormitory is equally likely at any time range during the next 4 minutes.
   a. Calculate the expected arrival time.
   b. What is the probability that an elevator arrives in less than 1½ minutes?

c. What is the probability that the wait for an elevator is more than 1½ minutes?

10. The Netherlands is one of the world leaders in the production and sale of tulips. Suppose the heights of the tulips in the greenhouse of Rotterdam's Fantastic Flora follow a continuous uniform distribution with a lower bound of 7 inches and an upper bound of 16 inches. You have come to the greenhouse to select a bouquet of tulips, but only tulips with a height greater than 10 inches may be selected. What is the probability that a randomly selected tulip is tall enough to pick?

11. The scheduled arrival time for a daily flight from Boston to New York is 9:25 am. Historical data show that the arrival time follows the continuous uniform distribution with an early arrival time of 9:15 am and a late arrival time of 9:55 am.
    a. Calculate the mean and the standard deviation of the distribution.
    b. What is the probability that a flight arrives late (later than 9:25 am)?

12. You were informed at the nursery that your peach tree will definitely bloom sometime between March 18 and March 30. Assume that the bloom times follow a continuous uniform distribution between these specified dates.
    a. What is the probability that the tree does not bloom until March 25?
    b. What is the probability that the tree will bloom by March 20?

13. You have been informed that the assessor will visit your home sometime between 10:00 am and 12:00 pm. It is reasonable to assume that his visitation time is uniformly distributed over the specified two-hour interval. Suppose you have to run a quick errand at 10:00 am.
    a. If it takes 15 minutes to run the errand, what is the probability that you will be back before the assessor visits?
    b. If it takes 30 minutes to run the errand, what is the probability that you will be back before the assessor visits?

6.2 THE NORMAL DISTRIBUTION

The **normal probability distribution**, or simply the **normal distribution**, is the familiar **bell-shaped distribution**. It is also referred to as the Gaussian distribution.[1] The normal distribution is the most extensively used probability distribution in statistical work. One reason for this common use is that the normal distribution closely approximates the probability distribution for a wide range of random variables of interest. Examples of random variables that closely follow a normal distribution include:

- Heights and weights of newborn babies
- Scores on the SAT
- Cumulative debt of college graduates
- Advertising expenditure of firms
- Rate of return on an investment

Whenever possible, it is instructive to analyze the underlying data to determine if the normal distribution is appropriate for a given application. There are various ways to do this, including inspecting histograms (Chapter 2) and boxplots (Chapter 3) for symmetry and bell shape. In this chapter, we simply assume that the random variable in question is normally distributed and focus on finding probabilities associated with this type of random variable. The computation of these probabilities is easy and direct.

Another important function of the normal distribution is that it serves as the cornerstone of statistical inference. Recall from Chapter 1 that the study of statistics is divided into two branches: descriptive statistics and inferential statistics. Statistical inference is generally based on the assumption of the normal distribution and serves as the major topic in the remainder of this text.

[1]The discovery of the normal (Gaussian) distribution is often credited to Carl Friedrich Gauss (1777–1855), even though some attribute the credit to De Moivre (1667–1754), who had earlier discovered it in the context of simplifying the binomial distribution calculations.

Characteristics of the Normal Distribution

- The normal distribution is **bell-shaped** and **symmetric** around its mean; that is, one side of the mean is just the mirror image of the other side. The mean, the median, and the mode are all equal for a normally distributed random variable.
- The normal distribution is **completely described by two parameters**—the population mean μ and the population variance σ^2. The population mean describes the central location and the population variance describes the dispersion of the distribution.
- The normal distribution is **asymptotic** in the sense that the tails get closer and closer to the horizontal axis but never touch it. Thus, theoretically, a normal random variable can assume any value between minus infinity and plus infinity.

The probability density function for the normal distribution is defined as follows.

THE NORMAL DISTRIBUTION

A random variable X with mean μ and variance σ^2 follows the normal distribution if its probability density function is

$$f(x) = \frac{1}{\sigma\sqrt{2\pi}} \exp\left(-\frac{(x-\mu)^2}{2\sigma^2}\right),$$

where π equals approximately 3.14159 and $\exp(w) = e^w$ is the exponential function, where $e \approx 2.718$ is the base of the natural logarithm.

A graph depicting the normal probability density function is often referred to as the normal curve or the bell curve. The following example relates the normal curve to the location and the dispersion of the normally distributed random variable.

EXAMPLE 6.2

Suppose we know that the ages of employees in Industries A, B, and C are normally distributed. We are given the following information on the relevant parameters:

Industry A	Industry B	Industry C
$\mu = 42$ years	$\mu = 36$ years	$\mu = 42$ years
$\sigma = 5$ years	$\sigma = 5$ years	$\sigma = 8$ years

Graphically compare the ages of employees in Industry A with Industry B. Repeat the comparison for Industry A with Industry C.

SOLUTION: Since the mean age of employees in Industry A is greater than that in Industry B, the normal curve for Industry A is located to the right of Industry B as shown in Figure 6.4. Both curves show equal dispersion from the mean, given that the standard deviations are the same.

FIGURE 6.4 Normal probability density function for two values of μ along with $\sigma = 5$

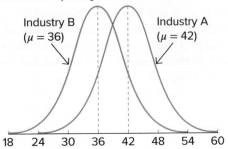

Since the mean age of employees in Industry A and Industry C is the same, the normal curves for each industry have the same center as shown in Figure 6.5. However, since the standard deviation for Industry A is less than that of Industry C, the normal curve for Industry A is less dispersed. Its peak is higher than that of Industry C, reflecting the fact that an employee's age is likelier to be closer to the mean age in Industry A. Figures 6.4 and 6.5 show that we can capture the entire distribution of any normally distributed random variable based on its mean and variance (or standard deviation).

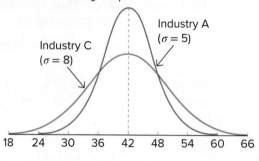

FIGURE 6.5 Normal probability density function for two values of σ along with $\mu = 42$

Industry C ($\sigma = 8$)

Industry A ($\sigma = 5$)

18 24 30 36 42 48 54 60 66

We generally use the cumulative distribution function $F(x)$ to compute probabilities for a normally distributed random variable, where $F(x) = P(X \leq x)$ is simply the area under $f(x)$ up to the value x. As mentioned earlier, we do not necessarily need the knowledge of integral calculus to compute probabilities for the normal distribution. Instead, we rely on a table to find probabilities. We can also compute probabilities with certain calculators, Excel, R, and other statistical packages. The specifics of how to use the table are delineated next.

The Standard Normal Distribution

The **standard normal distribution** is a special case of the normal distribution with a mean equal to zero and a standard deviation (or variance) equal to one. Using the letter Z to denote a random variable with the standard normal distribution, we have $\mu = E(Z) = 0$ and $\sigma = SD(Z) = 1$. As usual, we use the lowercase letter z to denote the value that the standard normal variable Z may assume.

The value z is actually the z-score that we discussed in Chapter 3. It measures the number of standard deviations a given value is away from the mean. For example, a z-score of 2 implies that the given value is 2 standard deviations above the mean. Similarly, a z-score of -1.5 implies that the given value is 1.5 standard deviations below the mean. As mentioned in Chapter 3, converting values into z-scores is called standardizing the data.

We will first show how to compute probabilities related to the standard normal distribution. Later, we will show that any normal distribution is equivalent to the standard normal distribution when the unit of measurement is changed to measure standard deviations from the mean. Therefore, while most real-world normally distributed variables are not standard normal, we can always transform (standardize) them into standard normal to compute the relevant probabilities.

Virtually all introductory statistics texts include a **standard normal table**, also referred to as the **z table**, that provides areas (probabilities) under the z curve. However, the format of these tables is sometimes different. In this text, the z table provides cumulative probabilities $P(Z \leq z)$; this table appears on two pages in Appendix B and is labeled Table 1. The left-hand page provides cumulative probabilities for z values less than or equal to zero. The right-hand page shows cumulative probabilities for z values greater than or equal to zero. Given the symmetry of the normal distribution and the fact that the area under the entire curve is one, other probabilities can be easily computed.

Figure 6.6 represents the standard normal probability density function (z distribution). Since the random variable Z is symmetric around its mean of zero, $P(Z < 0) = P(Z > 0) = 0.5$. As is the case with all continuous random variables, we can also write the probabilities as $P(Z \leq 0) = P(Z \geq 0) = 0.5$.

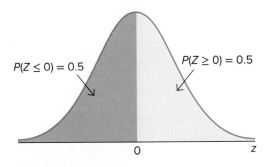

FIGURE 6.6
Standard normal probability density function

Finding a Probability for a Given *z* Value

As mentioned earlier, the z table provides cumulative probabilities $P(Z \leq z)$ for a given z. Consider, for example, a cumulative probability $P(Z \leq 1.52)$. Since $z = 1.52$ is positive, we can look up this probability from the right-hand page of the z table in Appendix B; Table 6.1 shows a portion of the table.

TABLE 6.1 Portion of the Right-Hand Page of the z Table

z	0.00	0.01	0.02
0.0	0.5000	0.5040	↓
0.1	0.5398	0.5438	↓
⋮	⋮	⋮	⋮
1.5	→	→	0.9357

The first column of the table, denoted as the z column, shows values of z up to the tenth decimal point, while the first row of the table, denoted as the z row, shows hundredths values. Thus, for $z = 1.52$, we match 1.5 on the z column with 0.02 on the z row to find a corresponding probability of 0.9357. The arrows in Table 6.1 indicate that $P(Z \leq 1.52) = 0.9357$.

In Figure 6.7, the cumulative probability corresponding to $z = 1.52$ is highlighted. Note that $P(Z \leq 1.52) = 0.9357$ represents the area under the z curve to the left of 1.52. Therefore, the area to the right of 1.52 can be computed as $P(Z > 1.52) = 1 - P(Z \leq 1.52) = 1 - 0.9357 = 0.0643$.

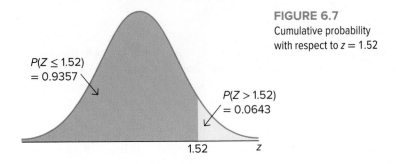

FIGURE 6.7
Cumulative probability with respect to $z = 1.52$

Suppose we want to find $P(Z \leq -1.96)$. Since z is a negative value, we can look up this probability from the left-hand page of the z table; Table 6.2 shows a portion of the table with arrows indicating that $P(Z \leq -1.96) = 0.0250$. Figure 6.8 highlights the corresponding probability. As before, the area to the right of -1.96 can be computed as $P(Z > -1.96) = 1 - P(Z \leq -1.96) = 1 - 0.0250 = 0.9750$.

TABLE 6.2 Portion of the Left-Hand Page of the z Table

z	0.00	0.01	0.02	0.03	0.04	0.05	0.06
−3.9	0.0000	0.0000	0.0000	0.0000	0.0000	0.0000	↓
−3.8	0.0001	0.0001	0.0001	0.0001	0.0001	0.0001	↓
⋮	⋮	⋮	⋮	⋮	⋮	⋮	⋮
−1.9	→	→	→	→	→	→	0.0250

FIGURE 6.8 Cumulative probability with respect to $z = -1.96$

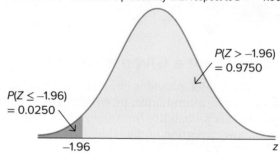

$P(Z > -1.96)$
$= 0.9750$

$P(Z \leq -1.96)$
$= 0.0250$

−1.96

z

EXAMPLE 6.3

Find the following probabilities for the standard normal random variable Z.
a. $P(0 \leq Z \leq 1.96)$ c. $P(-1.52 \leq Z \leq 1.96)$
b. $P(1.52 \leq Z \leq 1.96)$ d. $P(Z > 4)$

SOLUTION: It always helps to start by highlighting the relevant probability in the z graph.

a. As shown in Figure 6.9, the area between 0 and 1.96 is equivalent to the area to the left of 1.96 minus the area to the left of 0. Therefore, $P(0 \leq Z \leq 1.96) = P(Z \leq 1.96) - P(Z < 0) = 0.9750 - 0.50 = 0.4750$.

FIGURE 6.9 Finding the probability between 0 and 1.96

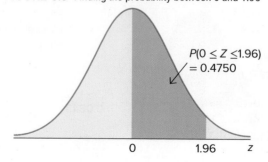

$P(0 \leq Z \leq 1.96)$
$= 0.4750$

0   1.96 z

b. As in part a and shown in Figure 6.10, $P(1.52 \leq Z \leq 1.96) = P(Z \leq 1.96) - P(Z < 1.52) = 0.9750 - 0.9357 = 0.0393$.

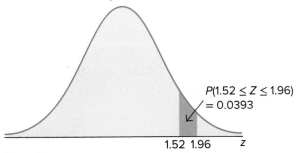

FIGURE 6.10 Finding the probability between 1.52 and 1.96

$P(1.52 \leq Z \leq 1.96) = 0.0393$

1.52 1.96 z

c. From Figure 6.11, $P(-1.52 \leq Z \leq 1.96) = P(Z \leq 1.96) - P(Z < -1.52) = 0.9750 - 0.0643 = 0.9107$.

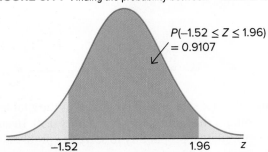

FIGURE 6.11 Finding the probability between −1.52 and 1.96

$P(-1.52 \leq Z \leq 1.96) = 0.9107$

−1.52   1.96 z

d. $P(Z > 4) = 1 - P(Z \leq 4)$. However, the z table only goes up to 3.99 with $P(Z \leq 3.99) = 1.0$ (approximately). In fact, for any z value greater than 3.99, it is acceptable to treat $P(Z \leq z) = 1.0$. Therefore, $P(Z > 4) = 1 - P(Z \leq 4) = 1 - 1 = 0$.

Finding a z Value for a Given Probability

So far we have computed probabilities for given z values. Now we will evaluate z values for given probabilities.

EXAMPLE 6.4

For the standard normal variable Z, find the z values that satisfy the following probability statements.

a. $P(Z \leq z) = 0.6808$ d. $P(Z > z) = 0.0212$

b. $P(Z \leq z) = 0.90$ e. $P(-z \leq Z \leq z) = 0.95$

c. $P(Z \leq z) = 0.0643$

SOLUTION: As mentioned earlier, it helps to first highlight the relevant probability in the z graph. Recall, too, that the z table lists z values along with the corresponding cumulative probabilities. Noncumulative probabilities can be evaluated using symmetry.

a. Since the probability is already in a cumulative format—that is, $P(Z \le z) = 0.6808$—we simply look up 0.6808 from the body of the table (right-hand side) to find the corresponding z value from the row/column of z. Table 6.3 shows the relevant portion of the z table, and Figure 6.12 depicts the corresponding area. Therefore, $z = 0.47$.

TABLE 6.3 Portion of the z Table for Example 6.4a

z	0.00	0.01	0.02	0.03	0.04	0.05	0.06	0.07
0.0	0.5000	0.5040	0.5080	0.5120	0.5160	0.5199	0.5239	↑
0.1	0.5398	0.5438	0.5478	0.5517	0.5557	0.5596	0.5636	↑
⋮	⋮	⋮	⋮	⋮	⋮	⋮	⋮	⋮
0.4	←	←	←	←	←	←	←	0.6808

FIGURE 6.12 Finding z given $P(Z \le z) = 0.6808$

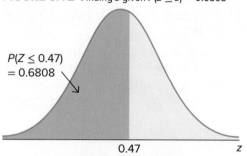

$P(Z \le 0.47)$
$= 0.6808$

0.47　　　　z

b. When deriving z for $P(Z \le z) = 0.90$, we find that the z table (right-hand side) does not contain the cumulative probability 0.90. In such cases, we use the closest cumulative probability to solve the problem. Therefore, z is approximately equal to 1.28, which corresponds to a cumulative probability of 0.8997. Figure 6.13 shows this result graphically.

FIGURE 6.13 Finding z given $P(Z \le z) = 0.90$

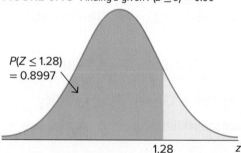

$P(Z \le 1.28)$
$= 0.8997$

1.28　　　　z

c. As shown in Figure 6.14, the z value that solves $P(Z \le z) = 0.0643$ must be negative because the probability to its left is less than 0.50. We look up the cumulative probability 0.0643 in the table (left-hand side) to get $z = -1.52$.

FIGURE 6.14 Finding z given $P(Z \le z) = 0.0643$

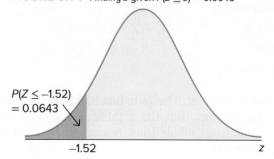

$P(Z \le -1.52)$
$= 0.0643$

−1.52　　　　z

d. When deriving z for $P(Z > z) = 0.0212$, we have to find a z value such that the probability to the right of this value is 0.0212. Since the table states cumulative probabilities, we look up $P(Z \leq z) = 1 - 0.0212 = 0.9788$ in the table (right-hand side) to get $z = 2.03$. Figure 6.15 shows the results.

FIGURE 6.15 Finding z given $P(Z > z) = 0.0212$

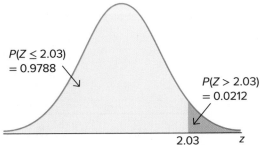

$P(Z \leq 2.03)$
$= 0.9788$

$P(Z > 2.03)$
$= 0.0212$

2.03 z

e. Since we know that the total area under the curve equals one, and we want to find $-z$ and z such that the area between the two values equals 0.95, we can conclude that the area in either tail is 0.025; that is, $P(Z < -z) = 0.025$ and $P(Z > z) = 0.025$. Figure 6.16 shows these results. We then use the cumulative probability, $P(Z \leq z) = 0.95 + 0.025 = 0.975$, to find $z = 1.96$.

FIGURE 6.16 Finding z given $P(-z \leq Z \leq z) = 0.95$

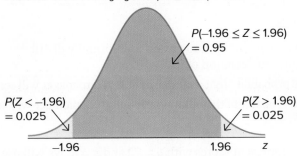

$P(-1.96 \leq Z \leq 1.96)$
$= 0.95$

$P(Z < -1.96)$
$= 0.025$

$P(Z > 1.96)$
$= 0.025$

−1.96   1.96 z

The Transformation of Normal Random Variables

LO 6.4

The importance of the standard normal distribution arises from the fact that any normal random variable can be transformed into the standard normal random variable to derive the relevant probabilities. In other words, any normally distributed random variable X with mean μ and standard deviation σ can be transformed (standardized) into the standard normal variable Z with mean zero and standard deviation one. We transform X into Z by subtracting from X its mean and dividing by its standard deviation; this is referred to as the **standard transformation**.

Calculate and interpret probabilities for a random variable that follows the normal distribution.

> **THE STANDARD TRANSFORMATION: CONVERTING X INTO Z**
>
> Any normally distributed random variable X with mean μ and standard deviation σ can be transformed into the standard normal random variable Z as
>
> $$Z = \frac{X - \mu}{\sigma}.$$
>
> Therefore, any value x has a corresponding value z given by
>
> $$z = \frac{x - \mu}{\sigma}.$$

As illustrated in Figure 6.17, if the x value is at the mean—that is, $x = \mu$—then the corresponding z value is $z = \frac{\mu - \mu}{\sigma} = 0$. Similarly, if the x value is at one standard deviation above the mean—that is, $x = \mu + \sigma$—then the corresponding z value is $z = \frac{\mu + \sigma - \mu}{\sigma} = 1$. Therefore, by construction, $E(Z) = 0$ and $SD(Z) = 1$.

FIGURE 6.17
Transforming X with mean μ and standard deviation σ to Z

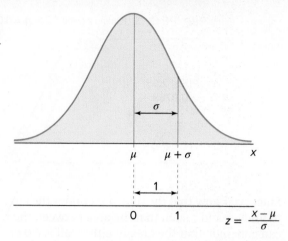

We are now in a position to solve any normal distribution problem by first transforming it to the z distribution.

EXAMPLE 6.5

Scores on a management aptitude exam are normally distributed with a mean of 72 and a standard deviation of 8.

a. What is the probability that a randomly selected manager will score above 60?

b. What is the probability that a randomly selected manager will score between 68 and 84?

SOLUTION: Let X represent scores with $\mu = 72$ and $\sigma = 8$. We will use the standard transformation $z = \frac{x - \mu}{\sigma}$ to solve these problems.

a. The probability that a manager scores above 60 is $P(X > 60)$. Figure 6.18 shows the probability as the shaded area to the right of 60. We derive $P(X > 60) = P\left(Z > \frac{60 - 72}{8}\right) = P(Z > -1.5)$. Since $P(Z > -1.5) = 1 - P(Z \leq -1.5)$, we look up -1.50 in the z table (left-hand side) to get this probability as $1 - 0.0668 = 0.9332$.

FIGURE 6.18 Finding $P(X > 60)$

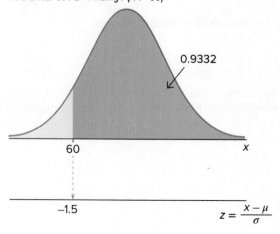

b. When solving for the probability that a manager scores between 68 and 84, we find $P(68 \leq X \leq 84)$. The shaded area in Figure 6.19 shows this probability. We derive $P(68 \leq X \leq 84) = P\left(\frac{68 - 72}{8} \leq Z \leq \frac{84 - 72}{8}\right) = P(-0.5 \leq Z \leq 1.5)$. We compute this probability using the z table as $P(Z \leq 1.5) - P(Z < -0.5) = 0.9332 - 0.3085 = 0.6247$.

FIGURE 6.19 Finding $P(68 \leq X \leq 84)$

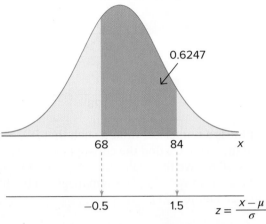

So far we have used the standard transformation to compute probabilities for given x values. We can use the **inverse transformation**, $x = \mu + z\sigma$, to compute x values for given probabilities.

THE INVERSE TRANSFORMATION: CONVERTING Z INTO X

The standard normal variable Z can be transformed to the normally distributed random variable X with mean μ and standard deviation σ as $X = \mu + Z\sigma$.

Therefore, any value z has a corresponding value x given by $x = \mu + z\sigma$.

EXAMPLE 6.6

Scores on a management aptitude examination are normally distributed with a mean of 72 and a standard deviation of 8.

a. What is the lowest score that will place a manager in the top 10% (90th percentile) of the distribution?

b. What is the highest score that will place a manager in the bottom 25% (25th percentile) of the distribution?

SOLUTION: Let X represent scores on a management aptitude examination with $\mu = 72$ and $\sigma = 8$. We will use the inverse transformation $x = \mu + z\sigma$ to solve these problems.

a. The 90th percentile is a numerical value x such that $P(X < x) = 0.90$. We look up 0.90 (or the closest value to 0.90) in the z table (right-hand side) to get $z = 1.28$ and use the inverse transformation to find $x = 72 + 1.28(8) = 82.24$. Therefore, a score of 82.24 or higher will place a manager in the top 10% of the distribution (see Figure 6.20).

FIGURE 6.20 Finding x given $P(X < x) = 0.90$

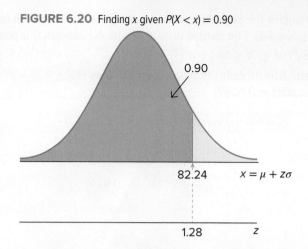

b. The 25th percentile is a numerical value x such that $P(X < x) = 0.25$. Using the z table (left-hand side), we find the corresponding z value that satisfies $P(Z < z) = 0.25$ as -0.67. We then solve $x = 72 - 0.67(8) = 66.64$. Therefore, a score of 66.64 or lower will place a manager in the bottom 25% of the distribution (see Figure 6.21).

FIGURE 6.21 Finding x given $P(X < x) = 0.25$

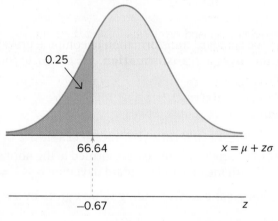

EXAMPLE 6.7

We can now answer the questions first posed by Akiko Hamaguchi in the introductory case of this chapter. Recall that Akiko would like to buy the right amount of salmon for daily consumption at Little Ginza. Akiko has estimated that the daily consumption of salmon is normally distributed with a mean of 12 pounds and a standard deviation of 3.2 pounds. She wants to answer the following questions:

a. What is the probability that the demand for salmon at Little Ginza is above 20 pounds?

b. What is the probability that the demand for salmon at Little Ginza is below 15 pounds?

c. How much salmon should be bought so that it meets customer demand on 90% of the days?

SOLUTION: Let X denote customer demand for salmon at the restaurant. We know that X is normally distributed with $\mu = 12$ and $\sigma = 3.2$.

a. When solving for the probability that the demand for salmon is more than 20 pounds, we find $P(X > 20) = P\left(Z > \frac{20 - 12}{3.2}\right) = P(Z > 2.50) = 1 - 0.9938 = 0.0062$.

b. When solving for the probability that the demand for salmon is less than 15 pounds, we find $P(X < 15) = P\left(Z < \frac{15 - 12}{3.2}\right) = P(Z < 0.94) = 0.8264$.

c. In order to compute the required amount of salmon that should be purchased to meet demand on 90% of the days, we solve for x in $P(X \le x) = 0.90$. Since $P(X \le x) = 0.90$ is equivalent to $P(Z \le z) = 0.90$, we first derive $z = 1.28$. Given $x = \mu + z\sigma$, we find $x = 12 + 1.28(3.2) = 16.10$. Therefore, Akiko should buy 16.10 pounds of salmon daily to ensure that customer demand is met on 90% of the days.

SYNOPSIS OF INTRODUCTORY CASE

Akiko Hamaguchi is a manager at a small sushi restaurant called Little Ginza in Phoenix, Arizona. She is aware of the importance of purchasing the right amount of salmon daily. While purchasing too much salmon results in wastage, purchasing too little can disappoint customers who may choose not to frequent the restaurant in the future. In the past, she has always bought 20 pounds of salmon daily. A careful analysis of her purchasing habits and customer demand reveals that Akiko is buying too much salmon. The probability that the demand for salmon would exceed 20 pounds is very small at 0.0062. Even a purchase of 15 pounds satisfies customer demand on 82.64% of the days. In order to execute her new strategy of meeting daily demand of customers on 90% of the days, Akiko should purchase approximately 16 pounds of salmon daily.

©gkrphoto/Getty Images

A Note on the Normal Approximation of the Binomial Distribution

Recall from Chapter 5 that it is tedious to compute binomial probabilities with the formula when we encounter large values for n. As it turns out, with large values for n, the binomial distribution can be approximated by the normal distribution. Based on this normal distribution approximation, with mean $\mu = np$ and standard deviation $\sigma = \sqrt{npq}$, we can use the z table to compute relevant binomial probabilities. Some researchers believe that the discovery of the normal distribution in the 18th century was due to the need to simplify the binomial probability calculations. The popularity of this method, however, has been greatly reduced by the advent of computers. As we learned in Chapter 5, it is easy to compute exact binomial probabilities with Excel and R; thus, there is no reason to approximate. The normal distribution approximation, however, is extremely important when making an inference for the population proportion p, which is a key parameter of the binomial distribution. In later chapters, we will study the details of this approximation and how it is used for making inferences.

Using Excel and R for the Normal Distribution

Table 6.4 shows Excel and R functions that we can use to solve problems associated with continuous probability distributions. Example 6.8 illustrates the use of these functions with respect to the normal distribution. We will refer back to Table 6.4 with respect to the exponential and the lognormal distributions discussed in the next section.

TABLE 6.4 Continuous Probability Distributions and Function Names in Excel and R

Distribution	Excel	R
Normal		
$P(X \leq x)$:	=NORM.DIST(x, μ, σ, 1)	pnorm(x, μ, σ, lower.tail = TRUE)
Finding x:	=NORM.INV($cumulprob$, μ, σ)	qnorm($cumulprob$, μ, σ)
Exponential		
$P(X \leq x)$:	=EXPON.DIST(x, λ, 1)	pexp(x, λ, lower.tail = TRUE)
Finding x:	NA*	qexp($cumulprob$, λ)
Lognormal		
$P(Y \leq y)$:	=LOGNORM.DIST(y, μ, σ, 1)	plnorm(y, μ, σ, lower.tail = TRUE)
Finding y:	=LOGNORM.INV($cumulprob$, μ, σ)	qlnorm($cumulprob$, μ, σ)

*NA denotes that this function is not readily available in Excel.

EXAMPLE 6.8

The Vanguard Balanced Index Fund seeks to maintain an allocation of 60% to stocks and 40% to bonds. With low fees and a consistent investment approach, this fund ranks fourth out of 792 funds that allocate 50% to 70% to stocks (*US News*, March 2017). Based on historical data, the expected return and standard deviation of this fund is estimated as 7.49% and 6.41%, respectively. Assume that the fund returns are stable and are normally distributed.

a. What is the probability that the fund will generate a return between 5% and 10%?

b. What is the lowest return of the fund that will place it in the top 10% (90th percentile) of the distribution?

SOLUTION: We let X denote the return on the Vanguard Balanced fund. We know that X is normally distributed with $\mu = 7.49$ and $\sigma = 6.41$.

Using Excel

We use Excel's **NORM.DIST** and **NORM.INV** functions to solve problems pertaining to the normal distribution. In order to find $P(X \leq x)$, we enter "=NORM.DIST(x, μ, σ, 1)" where x is the value for which we want to evaluate the cumulative probability, μ is the mean of the distribution, and σ is the standard deviation of the distribution. (If we enter "0" for the last argument in the function, then Excel returns the height of the normal distribution at the point x. This feature is useful if we want to plot the normal distribution.) If we want to find a particular x value for a given cumulative probability (*cumulprob*), then we enter "=NORM.INV(*cumulprob*, μ, σ)".

a. In order to find the probability of a return between 5% and 10%, $P(5 \leq X \leq 10)$, we enter "=NORM.DIST(10, 7.49, 6.41, 1) − NORM.DIST (5, 7.49, 6.41, 1)". Excel returns 0.3035.

b. In order to find the lowest return that will place it in the top 10% (90th percentile) of the distribution, $P(X > x) = 0.10$, we enter "=NORM. INV(0.90, 7.49, 6.41)". Excel returns 15.70.

Using R

We use R's **pnorm** and **qnorm** functions to solve problems associated with the normal distribution. In order to find $P(X \leq x)$, we enter "pnorm(x, μ, σ, lower.tail = TRUE)" where x is the value for which we want to evaluate the cumulative probability, μ is the mean of the distribution, and σ is the standard deviation of the distribution. If we enter "lower.tail=FALSE" for the last argument in the function, then R returns $P(X > x)$. If we want to find a particular x value for a given cumulative probability (*cumulprob*), then we enter "qnorm(*cumulprob*, μ, σ)".

a. In order to find $P(5 \leq X \leq 10)$, we enter:

```
> pnorm(10, 7.49, 6.41, lower.tail=TRUE) - pnorm(5, 7.49,
  6.41, lower.tail=TRUE)
```

And R returns: 0.3034746.

b. In order to solve for x to satisfy $P(X > x) = 0.10$, we enter:

```
> qnorm(0.90, 7.49, 6.41)
```

And R returns: 15.70475.

EXERCISES 6.2

Mechanics

14. Find the following probabilities based on the standard normal variable Z.
    a. $P(Z > 1.32)$
    b. $P(Z \leq -1.32)$
    c. $P(1.32 \leq Z \leq 2.37)$
    d. $P(-1.32 \leq Z \leq 2.37)$

15. Find the following probabilities based on the standard normal variable Z.
    a. $P(Z > 0.74)$
    b. $P(Z \leq -1.92)$
    c. $P(0 \leq Z \leq 1.62)$
    d. $P(-0.90 \leq Z \leq 2.94)$

16. Find the following probabilities based on the standard normal variable Z.
    a. $P(-0.67 \leq Z \leq -0.23)$
    b. $P(0 \leq Z \leq 1.96)$
    c. $P(-1.28 \leq Z \leq 0)$
    d. $P(Z > 4.2)$

17. Find the following z values for the standard normal variable Z.
    a. $P(Z \leq z) = 0.9744$
    b. $P(Z > z) = 0.8389$
    c. $P(-z \leq Z \leq z) = 0.95$
    d. $P(0 \leq Z \leq z) = 0.3315$

18. Find the following z values for the standard normal variable Z.
    a. $P(Z \leq z) = 0.1020$
    b. $P(z \leq Z \leq 0) = 0.1772$
    c. $P(Z > z) = 0.9929$
    d. $P(0.40 \leq Z \leq z) = 0.3368$

19. Let X be normally distributed with mean $\mu = 10$ and standard deviation $\sigma = 6$.
    a. Find $P(X \leq 0)$.
    b. Find $P(X > 2)$.
    c. Find $P(4 \leq X \leq 10)$.
    d. Find $P(6 \leq X \leq 14)$.

20. Let X be normally distributed with mean $\mu = 10$ and standard deviation $\sigma = 4$.
    a. Find $P(X \leq 0)$.
    b. Find $P(X > 2)$.
    c. Find $P(4 \leq X \leq 10)$.
    d. Find $P(6 \leq X \leq 14)$.

21. Let X be normally distributed with mean $\mu = 120$ and standard deviation $\sigma = 20$.
    a. Find $P(X \leq 86)$.
    b. Find $P(80 \leq X \leq 100)$.
    c. Find x such that $P(X \leq x) = 0.40$.
    d. Find x such that $P(X > x) = 0.90$.

22. Let X be normally distributed with mean $\mu = 2.5$ and standard deviation $\sigma = 2$.
    a. Find $P(X > 7.6)$.
    b. Find $P(7.4 \leq X \leq 10.6)$.
    c. Find x such that $P(X > x) = 0.025$.
    d. Find x such that $P(x \leq X \leq 2.5) = 0.4943$.

23. Let X be normally distributed with mean $\mu = 2,500$ and standard deviation $\sigma = 800$.
    a. Find x such that $P(X \leq x) = 0.9382$.
    b. Find x such that $P(X > x) = 0.025$.
    c. Find x such that $P(2500 \leq X \leq x) = 0.1217$.
    d. Find x such that $P(X \leq x) = 0.4840$.

24. The random variable X is normally distributed. Also, it is known that $P(X > 150) = 0.10$.
    a. Find the population mean μ if the population standard deviation $\sigma = 15$.
    b. Find the population mean μ if the population standard deviation $\sigma = 25$.
    c. Find the population standard deviation σ if the population mean $\mu = 136$.
    d. Find the population standard deviation σ if the population mean $\mu = 128$.

25. Let X be normally distributed with $\mu = 254$ and $\sigma = 11$.
    a. Find $P(X \leq 266)$.
    b. Find $P(250 < X < 270)$.
    c. Find x such that $P(X \leq x) = 0.33$.
    d. Find x such that $P(X > x) = 0.33$.

26. Let X be normally distributed with $\mu = -15$ and $\sigma = 9$.
    a. Find $P(X > -12)$.
    b. Find $P(0 \leq X \leq 5)$.
    c. Find x such that $P(X \leq x) = 0.25$.
    d. Find x such that $P(X > x) = 0.25$.

Applications

27. The historical returns on a balanced portfolio have had an average return of 8% and a standard deviation of 12%. Assume that returns on this portfolio follow a normal distribution.
    a. What percentage of returns were greater than 20%?
    b. What percentage of returns were below −16%?

28. Assume that IQ scores follow a normal distribution with a mean of 100 and a standard deviation of 16.
    a. What is the probability that an individual scores between 84 and 116?
    b. What is the probability that an individual scores less than 68?
    c. What is the lowest score that will place an individual in the top 1% of IQ scores?

29. The average rent in a city is $1,500 per month with a standard deviation of $250. Assume rent follows the normal distribution.
    a. What percentage of rents are between $1,250 and $1,750?
    b. What percentage of rents are less than $1,250?
    c. What percentage of rents are greater than $2,000?

30. A professional basketball team averages 80 points per game with a standard deviation of 10 points. Assume points per game follow the normal distribution.
    a. What is the probability that a game's score is between 60 and 100 points?
    b. What is the probability that a game's score is more than 100 points? If there are 82 games in a regular season, in how many games will the team score more than 100 points?

31. The average high school teacher annual salary is $43,000 (Payscale.com, August 20, 2010). Let teacher salary be normally distributed with a standard deviation of $18,000.
    a. What percentage of high school teachers make between $40,000 and $50,000?
    b. What percentage of high school teachers make more than $80,000?

32. Americans are increasingly skimping on their sleep (*National Geographic News,* February 24, 2005). A health expert believes that American adults sleep an average of 6.2 hours on weekdays, with a standard deviation of 1.2 hours. Assume that sleep time on weekdays is normally distributed.
    a. What percentage of American adults sleep more than 8 hours on weekdays?
    b. What percentage of American adults sleep less than 6 hours on weekdays?
    c. What percentage of American adults sleep between 6 and 8 hours on weekdays?

33. The weight of turkeys is normally distributed with a mean of 22 pounds and a standard deviation of 5 pounds.
    a. Find the probability that a randomly selected turkey weighs between 20 and 26 pounds.
    b. Find the probability that a randomly selected turkey weighs less than 12 pounds.

34. Suppose that the miles-per-gallon (mpg) rating of passenger cars is a normally distributed random variable with a mean and a standard deviation of 33.8 mpg and 3.5 mpg, respectively.
    a. What is the probability that a randomly selected passenger car gets at least 40 mpg?
    b. What is the probability that a randomly selected passenger car gets between 30 and 35 mpg?
    c. An automobile manufacturer wants to build a new passenger car with an mpg rating that improves upon 99% of existing cars. What is the minimum mpg that would achieve this goal?

35. According to a company's website, the top 25% of the candidates who take the entrance test will be called for an interview. You have just been called for an interview. The reported mean and standard deviation of the test scores are 68 and 8, respectively. What is the possible range for your test score if you assume that the scores are normally distributed?

36. A financial advisor informs a client that the expected return on a portfolio is 8% with a standard deviation of 12%. There is a 15% chance that the return would be above 16%. If the advisor is right about her assessment, is it reasonable to assume that the underlying return distribution is normal?

37. A packaging system fills boxes to an average weight of 18 ounces with a standard deviation of 0.2 ounce. It is reasonable to assume that the weights are normally distributed. Calculate the 1st, 2nd, and 3rd quartiles of the box weight.

38. According to the Bureau of Labor Statistics, it takes an average of 22 weeks for someone over 55 to find a new job, compared with 16 weeks for younger workers (*The Wall Street Journal*, September 2, 2008). Assume that the probability distributions are normal and that the standard deviation is 2 weeks for both distributions.

a. What is the probability that it takes a worker over the age of 55 more than 19 weeks to find a job?

b. What is the probability that it takes a younger worker more than 19 weeks to find a job?

c. What is the probability that it takes a worker over the age of 55 between 23 and 25 weeks to find a job?

d. What is the probability that it takes a younger worker between 23 and 25 weeks to find a job?

39. Loans that are 60 days or more past due are considered seriously delinquent. The Mortgage Bankers Association reported that the rate of seriously delinquent loans has an average of 9.1% (*The Wall Street Journal,* August 26, 2010). Let the rate of seriously delinquent loans follow a normal distribution with a standard deviation of 0.80%.

a. What is the probability that the rate of seriously delinquent loans is above 8%?

b. What is the probability that the rate of seriously delinquent loans is between 9.5% and 10.5%?

40. The time required to assemble an electronic component is normally distributed with a mean and a standard deviation of 16 minutes and 4 minutes, respectively.

a. Find the probability that a randomly picked assembly takes between 10 and 20 minutes.

b. It is unusual for the assembly time to be above 24 minutes or below 6 minutes. What proportion of assembly times fall in these unusual categories?

41. Research suggests that Americans make an average of 10 phone calls per day (*CNN*, August 26, 2010). Let the number of calls be normally distributed with a standard deviation of 3 calls.

a. What is the probability that an average American makes between 4 and 12 calls per day?

b. What is the probability that an average American makes more than 6 calls per day?

c. What is the probability that an average American makes more than 16 calls per day?

42. The manager of a night club in Boston stated that 95% of the customers are between the ages of 22 and 28 years. If the age of customers is normally distributed with a mean of 25 years, calculate its standard deviation.

43. An estimated 1.8 million students take on student loans to pay ever-rising tuition and room and board (*The New York Times*, April 17, 2009). It is also known that the average cumulative debt of recent college graduates is about $22,500. Let the cumulative debt among recent college graduates be normally distributed with a standard deviation of $7,000. Approximately how many recent college graduates have accumulated student loans of more than $30,000?

44. Scores on a marketing exam are known to be normally distributed with a mean and a standard deviation of 60 and 20, respectively.

a. Find the probability that a randomly selected student scores between 50 and 80.

b. Find the probability that a randomly selected student scores between 20 and 40.

c. The syllabus suggests that the top 15% of the students will get an A in the course. What is the minimum score required to get an A?

d. What is the passing score if 10% of the students will fail the course?

45. On average, an American professional football game lasts about three hours, even though the ball is actually in play only 11 minutes (www.sportsgrid.com, January 14, 2014). Assume that game times are normally distributed with a standard deviation of 0.4 hour.

a. Find the probability that a game lasts less than 2.5 hours.

b. Find the probability that a game lasts either less than 2.5 hours or more than 3.5 hours.

c. Find the maximum value for the game time that will place it in the bottom 1% of the distribution.

46. A young investment manager tells his client that the probability of making a positive return with his suggested portfolio is 90%. If it is known that returns are normally distributed with a mean of 5.6%, what is the risk, measured by standard deviation, that this investment manager assumes in his calculation?

47. A construction company in Naples, Florida, is struggling to sell condominiums. In order to attract buyers, the company has made numerous price reductions and better financing offers. Although condominiums were once listed for $300,000, the company believes that it will be able to get an average sale price of $210,000. Let the price of these condominiums in the next quarter be normally distributed with a standard deviation of $15,000.

a. What is the probability that the condominium will sell at a price (i) below $200,000? (ii) Above $240,000?

b. The company is also trying to sell an artist's condo. Potential buyers will find the unusual features of this condo either pleasing or objectionable. The manager expects the average sale price of this condo to be the same as others at $210,000, but with a higher standard deviation of $20,000. What is the probability that this condo will sell at a price (i) below $200,000? (ii) Above $240,000?

48. You are considering the risk-return profile of two mutual funds for investment. The relatively risky fund promises an expected return of 8% with a standard deviation of 14%. The relatively less risky fund promises an expected return and standard deviation of 4% and 5%, respectively. Assume that the returns are approximately normally distributed.

a. Which mutual fund will you pick if your objective is to minimize the probability of earning a negative return?

b. Which mutual fund will you pick if your objective is to maximize the probability of earning a return above 8%?

49. First introduced in Los Angeles, the concept of Korean-style tacos sold from a catering truck has been gaining popularity nationally (*The New York Times,* July 27, 2010). This taco is an interesting mix of corn tortillas with Korean-style beef, garnished with onion, cilantro, and a hash of chili-soy-dressed lettuce. Suppose one such taco truck operates in the Detroit area. The owners have estimated that the daily consumption of beef is normally distributed with a mean of 24 pounds and a standard deviation of 6 pounds. While purchasing too much beef results in wastage, purchasing too little can disappoint customers.

    a. Determine the amount of beef the owners should buy so that it meets demand on 80% of the days.

    b. How much should the owners buy if they want to meet demand on 95% of the days?

50. While Massachusetts is no California when it comes to sun, the solar energy industry is flourishing in this state (*The Boston Globe,* May 27, 2012). The state's capital, Boston, averages 211.7 sunny days per year. Assume that the number of sunny days follows a normal distribution with a standard deviation of 20 days.

    a. What is the probability that Boston has less than 200 sunny days in a given year?

    b. Los Angeles averages 266.5 sunny days per year. What is the probability that Boston has at least as many sunny days as Los Angeles?

    c. Suppose a dismal year in Boston is one where the number of sunny days is in the bottom 10% for that year. At most, how many sunny days must occur annually for it to be a dismal year in Boston?

    d. In 2012, Boston experienced unusually warm, dry, and sunny weather. Suppose this occurs only 1% of the time. What is the minimum number of sunny days that would satisfy the criteria for being an unusually warm, dry, and sunny year in Boston?

51. A new car battery is sold with a two-year warranty whereby the owner gets the battery replaced free of cost if it breaks down during the warranty period. Suppose an auto store makes a net profit of $20 on batteries that stay trouble-free during the warranty period; it makes a net loss of $10 on batteries that break down. The life of batteries is known to be normally distributed with a mean and a standard deviation of 40 and 16 months, respectively.

    a. What is the probability that a battery will break down during the warranty period?

    b. What is the expected profit of the auto store on a battery?

    c. What is the expected monthly profit on batteries if the auto store sells an average of 500 batteries a month?

52. A certain brand of refrigerators has a length of life that is normally distributed with a mean and a standard deviation of 15 years and 2 years, respectively.

    a. What is the probability a refrigerator will last less than 6.5 years?

    b. What is the probability that a refrigerator will last more than 23 years?

    c. What length of life should the retailer advertise for these refrigerators so that only 3% of the refrigerators fail before the advertised length of life?

6.3 OTHER CONTINUOUS PROBABILITY DISTRIBUTIONS

As discussed earlier, the normal distribution is the most extensively used probability distribution in statistical work. One reason that this occurs is because the normal distribution accurately describes numerous random variables of interest. However, there are applications where other continuous distributions are more appropriate.

The Exponential Distribution

LO 6.5

Calculate and interpret probabilities for a random variable that follows the exponential distribution.

A useful nonsymmetric continuous probability distribution is the **exponential distribution**. The exponential distribution is related to the Poisson distribution, even though the Poisson distribution deals with discrete random variables. Recall from Chapter 5 that the Poisson random variable counts the number of occurrences of an event over a given interval of time or space. For instance, the Poisson distribution is used to calculate the likelihood of a specified number of cars arriving at a McDonald's drive-thru over a particular time period or the likelihood of a specified number of defects in a 50-yard roll of fabric. Sometimes we are less interested in the *number* of occurrences over a given interval of time or space, but rather in the time that has elapsed or space encountered *between* such occurrences. For instance, we might be interested in the length of time that elapses between car arrivals at the McDonald's drive-thru or the distance between defects in a 50-yard roll of fabric. We use the exponential distribution for describing these times or distances. The exponential random variable is nonnegative; that is, the underlying variable X is defined for $x \geq 0$.

In order to better understand the connection between the Poisson and the exponential distributions, consider the introductory case of Chapter 5 where Anne was concerned about staffing needs at the Starbucks that she managed. Recall that Anne believed that the typical Starbucks customer averaged 18 visits to the store over a 30-day period. The Poisson random variable appropriately captures the number of visits, with the expected value (mean), over a 30-day period, as

$$\mu_{\text{Poisson}} = 18.$$

Since the number of visits follows the Poisson distribution, the time between visits has an exponential distribution. In addition, given the expected number of 18 visits over a 30-day month, the expected time between visits is derived as

$$\mu_{\text{Exponential}} = \frac{30}{18} = 1.67.$$

It is common to define the exponential probability distribution in terms of its *rate parameter* λ (the Greek letter lambda), which is the inverse of its mean. In the above example,

$$\lambda = \frac{1}{\mu} = \frac{1}{1.67} = 0.60.$$

We can think of the mean of the exponential distribution as the average time between arrivals, whereas the rate parameter measures the average number of arrivals per unit of time. Note that the rate parameter is the same as the mean of the Poisson distribution, when defined per unit of time. For a Poisson process, the mean of 18 visits over a 30-day period is equivalent to a mean of $18/30 = 0.60$ per day, which is the same as the rate parameter λ.

The probability density function for the exponential distribution is defined as follows.

THE EXPONENTIAL DISTRIBUTION

A random variable X follows the exponential distribution if its probability density function is

$$f(x) = \lambda e^{-\lambda x} \quad \text{for } x \geq 0,$$

where λ is a rate parameter and $e \approx 2.718$ is the base of the natural logarithm.

The mean and the standard deviation of X are equal: $E(X) = SD(X) = \frac{1}{\lambda}$. For $x \geq 0$, the cumulative distribution function of X is

$$P(X \leq x) = 1 - e^{-\lambda x}.$$

Therefore, $P(X > x) = 1 - P(X \leq x) = e^{-\lambda x}.$

The graphs in Figure 6.22 show the shapes of the exponential probability density function based on various values of the rate parameter λ.

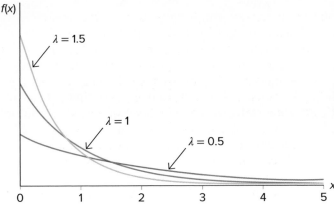

FIGURE 6.22
Exponential probability density function for various values of λ

EXAMPLE 6.9

Let the time between e-mail messages during work hours be exponentially distributed with a mean of 25 minutes.

a. Calculate the rate parameter λ.

b. What is the probability that you do not get an e-mail for more than one hour?

c. What is the probability that you get an e-mail within 10 minutes?

SOLUTION:

a. Since the mean $E(X)$ equals $\frac{1}{\lambda}$, we compute $\lambda = \frac{1}{E(X)} = \frac{1}{25} = 0.04$.

b. The probability that you do not get an e-mail for more than an hour is $P(X > 60)$. We use $P(X > x) = e^{-\lambda x}$ to compute $P(X > 60) = e^{-0.04(60)} = 0.0907$. The probability of not getting an e-mail for more than one hour is 0.0907. Figure 6.23 highlights this probability.

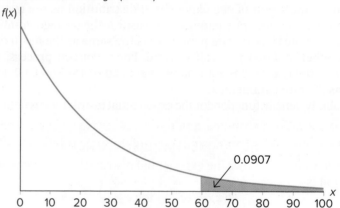

FIGURE 6.23 Finding $P(X > 60)$

c. The probability that you get an e-mail within 10 minutes is $P(X \le 10) = 1 - e^{-0.04(10)} = 1 - 0.6703 = 0.3297$. Figure 6.24 highlights this probability.

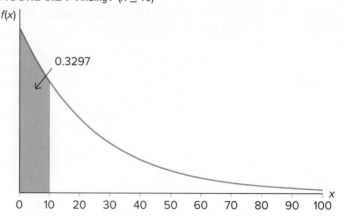

FIGURE 6.24 Finding $P(X \le 10)$

The exponential distribution is also used in modeling lifetimes or failure times. For example, an electric bulb with a rated life of 1,000 hours is expected to fail after about 1,000 hours of use. However, the bulb may burn out either before or after 1,000 hours. Thus, the lifetime of an electric bulb is a random variable with an expected value of 1,000. A noted feature of the exponential distribution is that it is "memoryless," thus implying a constant failure rate. In the electric bulb example, it implies that the probability that the bulb will burn out on a given day is independent of whether the bulb has already been used for 10, 100, or 1,000 hours.

The Lognormal Distribution

LO 6.6

Calculate and interpret probabilities for a random variable that follows the lognormal distribution.

The **lognormal distribution** is defined with reference to the normal distribution. It is positively skewed, and it is relevant for a positive random variable. Thus, it is useful for describing variables such as income, real estate values, and asset prices. Unlike the exponential distribution whose failure rate is constant, the failure rate of the lognormal distribution may increase or decrease over time. This flexibility has led to broad applications of the lognormal distribution, ranging from modeling the failure time of new equipment to the lifetime of cancer patients. For instance, in the break-in period of new equipment, the failure rate is high. However, if it survives this initial period, the subsequent failure rate is greatly reduced. The same is true for cancer survivors.

A random variable Y is lognormal if its natural logarithm $X = \ln(Y)$ is normally distributed. Alternatively, if X is a normal random variable, the lognormal variable is defined as $Y = e^X$. The probability density function for the lognormal distribution is defined as follows.

THE LOGNORMAL DISTRIBUTION

Let X be a normally distributed random variable with mean μ and standard deviation σ. The random variable $Y = e^X$ follows the lognormal distribution with a probability density function defined as

$$f(y) = \frac{1}{y\sigma\sqrt{2\pi}} \exp\left(-\frac{(\ln(y) - \mu)^2}{2\sigma^2}\right) \quad \text{for } y > 0,$$

where π equals approximately 3.14159, $\exp(x) = e^x$ is the exponential function, and $e \approx 2.718$ is the base of the natural logarithm.

The graphs in Figure 6.25 show the shapes of the lognormal density function based on various values of σ. The lognormal distribution is clearly positively skewed for $\sigma > 1$. For $\sigma < 1$, the lognormal distribution somewhat resembles the normal distribution.

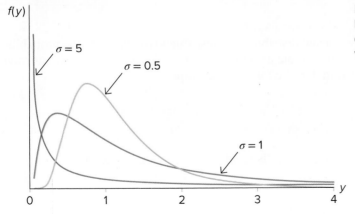

FIGURE 6.25
Lognormal probability density function for various values of σ along with $\mu = 0$

The mean and the variance of the lognormal random variable Y are related to the mean and the standard deviation of the corresponding normal random variable X.

EXPECTED VALUES AND STANDARD DEVIATIONS OF THE LOGNORMAL AND NORMAL DISTRIBUTIONS

Let X be a normal random variable with mean μ and standard deviation σ, and let $Y = e^X$ be the corresponding lognormal variable. The mean μ_Y and the standard deviation σ_Y of Y are derived as

$$\mu_Y = \exp\left(\frac{2\mu + \sigma^2}{2}\right) \quad \text{and} \quad \sigma_Y = \sqrt{(\exp(\sigma^2) - 1)\exp(2\mu + \sigma^2)}.$$

Equivalently, the mean and the standard deviation of the normal variable $X = \ln(Y)$ are derived as

$$\mu = \ln\left(\frac{\mu_Y^2}{\sqrt{\mu_Y^2 + \sigma_Y^2}}\right) \quad \text{and} \quad \sigma = \sqrt{\ln\left(1 + \frac{\sigma_Y^2}{\mu_Y^2}\right)}.$$

EXAMPLE 6.10

Compute the mean and the standard deviation of a lognormal random variable if the mean and the standard deviation of the underlying normal random variable are as follows:

a. $\mu = 0, \sigma = 1$

b. $\mu = 2, \sigma = 1$

c. $\mu = 2, \sigma = 1.5$

SOLUTION: Since X is normal, $Y = e^X$ is lognormal with mean $\mu_Y = \exp\left(\frac{2\mu + \sigma^2}{2}\right)$ and standard deviation $\sigma_Y = \sqrt{(\exp(\sigma^2) - 1)\exp(2\mu + \sigma^2)}$.

a. Given $\mu = 0$ and $\sigma = 1$, we compute $\mu_Y = \exp\left(\frac{0 + 1^2}{2}\right) = 1.65$ and $\sigma_Y = \sqrt{(\exp(1^2) - 1)\exp(0 + 1^2)} = 2.16$.

b. Given $\mu = 2$ and $\sigma = 1$, we compute $\mu_Y = \exp\left(\frac{4 + 1^2}{2}\right) = 12.18$ and $\sigma_Y = \sqrt{(\exp(1^2) - 1)\exp(4 + 1^2)} = 15.97$.

c. Given $\mu = 2$ and $\sigma = 1.5$, we compute $\mu_Y = \exp\left(\frac{4 + 1.5^2}{2}\right) = 22.76$ and $\sigma_Y = \sqrt{(\exp(1.5^2) - 1)\exp(4 + 1.5^2)} = 66.31$.

The popularity of the lognormal distribution is also due to the fact that the probabilities of a lognormal random variable are easily evaluated by reference to the normal distribution. This is illustrated in the following example.

EXAMPLE 6.11

Let $Y = e^X$ where X is normally distributed with mean $\mu = 5$ and standard deviation $\sigma = 1.2$.

a. Find $P(Y \leq 200)$.

b. Find the 90th percentile of Y.

SOLUTION: We solve these problems by first converting them into the corresponding normal distribution problems.

a. Note that $P(Y \leq 200) = P(\ln(Y) \leq \ln(200)) = P(X \leq 5.30)$. We transform $x = 5.30$ in the usual way to get $z = \frac{5.30 - 5}{1.2} = 0.25$. From the z table, we get $P(Z \leq 0.25) = 0.5987$. Thus, $P(Y \leq 200) = P(X \leq 5.30) = P(Z \leq 0.25) = 0.5987$.

b. The 90th percentile is a value y such that $P(Y < y) = 0.90$. We first note that $P(Y < y) = 0.90$ is equivalent to $P(\ln(Y) < \ln(y)) = P(X < x) = 0.90$, where $x = \ln(y)$. We look up the cumulative probability of 0.90 in the z table to get $z = 1.28$. We use the inverse transformation to derive $x = \mu + z\sigma = 5 + 1.28(1.2) = 6.536$. Finally, we compute $y = e^x = e^{6.536} = 689.52$. Therefore, the 90th percentile of the distribution is 689.52.

Using Excel and R for the Exponential and Lognormal Distributions

Table 6.4 from the last section shows Excel and R functions that we can use to solve problems associated with the exponential and lognormal distributions. Examples 6.12 and 6.13 illustrate the use of these functions with respect these functions.

EXAMPLE 6.12

A barbershop has an average of 12 customers between 8:00 am and 9:00 am every Saturday. Customers arrive according to the Poisson distribution. What is the probability that the time between consecutive arrivals (customers) will fall between 3 and 6 minutes?

SOLUTION: Since the number of arrivals follows the Poisson distribution, the time between arrivals has an exponential distribution. Also, if $\mu_{Poisson} = 12$ (12 arrivals over a 60-minute interval), then $\mu_{Exponential} = \frac{60}{12} = 5$ and $\lambda = \frac{12}{60} = \frac{1}{5} = 0.20$ (per minute). Let X represent the time between arrivals.

Using Excel

We use Excel's **EXPON.DIST** function to solve for probabilities associated with the exponential distribution. In order to find $P(X \leq x)$, we enter "=EXPON.DIST(x, λ, 1)", where x is the value for which we want to evaluate the cumulative probability and λ is the rate parameter. (If we enter "0" for the last argument in the function, then Excel returns the height of the exponential distribution at the point x.) With respect to the exponential distribution, Excel does not provide a function if we want to find a particular x value for a given cumulative probability.

In order to find the probability that the time between consecutive arrivals (customers) will fall between 3 and 6 minutes, $P(3 \leq X \leq 6)$, we enter "=EXPON.DIST(6, 0.20, 1) − EXPON.DIST(3, 0.20, 1)". Excel returns 0.2476.

Using R

We use R's **pexp** and **qexp** functions to solve problems associated with the exponential distribution. In order to find $P(X \leq x)$, we enter "pexp(x, λ, lower.tail = TRUE)" where x is the value for which we want to evaluate the cumulative probability and λ is the rate parameter. If we enter "lower.tail = FALSE" for the last argument in the function, then R returns $P(X > x)$. If we want to find a particular x value for a given cumulative probability (*cumulprob*), then we enter "qexp(*cumulprob*, λ)".

In order to find, $P(3 \le X \le 6)$, we enter:

```
> pexp(6, 0.2, lower.tail=TRUE) - pexp(3, 0.2,
   lower.tail=TRUE)
```

And R returns: 0.2476174.

EXAMPLE 6.13

After years of drought, reservoirs in California are at capacity or overflowing from record-setting rain and snow in 2017. This has made Los Angeles feel more like London than Southern California (*Los Angeles Times*, January 12, 2017). Assume that the amount of annual rainfall in Los Angeles can be represented by a lognormal variable, $Y = e^X$, where X is normally distributed. The mean and the standard deviation of X are known to be 2.6054 and 0.4487, respectively.

a. What is the probability that the annual rainfall in Los Angeles is more than 20 inches?

b. Find the 25th percentile for the annual rainfall in Los Angeles.

SOLUTION: We let Y denote the annual rainfall in Los Angeles. We know that X is normally distributed with $\mu = 2.6054$ and $\sigma = 0.4487$.

Using Excel

We use Excel's **LOGNORM.DIST** and **LOGNORM.INV** functions to solve problems associated with the lognormal distribution. In order to find $P(Y \le y)$, we enter "=LOGNORM.DIST(y, μ, σ, 1)" where y is the nonnegative value for which we want to evaluate the cumulative probability, μ is the mean of the underlying normal distribution, and σ is the standard deviation of the underlying normal distribution. (If we enter "0" for the last argument in the function, then Excel returns the height of the lognormal distribution at the point x.) If we want to find a particular y value for a given cumulative probability (*cumulprob*), then we enter "=LOGNORM.INV(*cumulprob*, μ, σ)".

a. In order to find the probability that the annual rainfall in Los Angeles is more than 20 inches, $P(Y > 20)$, we enter "=1−LOGNORM.DIST(20, 2.6054, 0.4487, 1)". Excel returns 0.1922.

b. In order to find the 25th percentile for the annual rainfall in Los Angeles, or y that satisfies $P(Y < y) = 0.25$, we enter "=LOGNORM.INV(0.25, 2.6054, 0.4487)". Excel returns 10.00, or 10 inches.

Using R

We use R's **plnorm** and **qlnorm** functions to solve problems associated with the lognormal distribution. In order to find $P(Y \le y)$, we enter "plnorm(y, μ, σ, lower.tail = TRUE)" where y is the nonnegative value for which we want to evaluate the cumulative probability, μ is the mean of the underlying normal distribution, and σ is the standard deviation of the underlying normal distribution. If we enter "lower.tail=FALSE" for the last argument in the function, then

R returns $P(Y > y)$. If we want to find a particular y value for a given cumulative probability (*cumulprob*), then we enter "qlnorm(*cumulprob*, μ, σ)".

a. In order to find $P(Y > 20)$, we enter:

```
> plnorm(20, 2.6054, 0.4487, lower.tail=FALSE)
```

And R returns: 0.1921726.

b. In order to find y that satisfies $P(Y < y) = 0.25$, we enter:

```
> qlnorm(0.25, 2.6054, 0.4487)
```

And R returns: 10.00171.

EXERCISES 6.3

Mechanics

53. Assume a Poisson random variable has a mean of 6 successes over a 120-minute period.

   a. Find the mean of the random variable, defined by the time between successes.

   b. What is the rate parameter of the appropriate exponential distribution?

   c. Find the probability that the time to success will be more than 60 minutes.

54. Assume a Poisson random variable has a mean of four arrivals over a 10-minute interval.

   a. What is the mean of the random variable, defined by the time between arrivals?

   b. Find the probability that the next arrival would be within the mean time.

   c. Find the probability that the next arrival would be between one and two minutes.

55. A random variable X is exponentially distributed with a mean of 0.1.

   a. What is the rate parameter λ? What is the standard deviation of X?

   b. Compute $P(X > 0.20)$.

   c. Compute $P(0.10 \leq X \leq 0.20)$.

56. A random variable X is exponentially distributed with a probability density function of $f(x) = 5e^{-5x}$. Calculate the mean and the standard deviation of X.

57. A random variable X is exponentially distributed with an expected value of 25.

   a. What is the rate parameter λ? What is the standard deviation of X?

   b. Compute $P(20 \leq X \leq 30)$.

   c. Compute $P(15 \leq X \leq 35)$.

58. Let X be exponentially distributed with $\lambda = 0.5$. Compute the following values.

   a. $P(X \leq 1)$

   b. $P(2 < X < 4)$

   c. $P(X > 10)$

59. Let X be exponentially distributed with $\mu = 1.25$. Compute the following values.

   a. $P(X < 2.3)$

   b. $P(1.5 \leq X \leq 5.5)$

   c. $P(X > 7)$

60. Compute the mean and the variance of a lognormal variable $Y = e^X$ where X is normally distributed with the following mean and variance:

   a. $\mu = 3, \sigma^2 = 2$

   b. $\mu = 5, \sigma^2 = 2$

   c. $\mu = 5, \sigma^2 = 3$

61. Let $Y = e^X$ where X is normally distributed with $\mu = 1.8$ and $\sigma = 0.80$. Compute the following values.

   a. $P(Y \leq 7.5)$

   b. $P(8 < Y < 9)$

   c. The 90th percentile of Y

62. Let $Y = e^X$, where X is normally distributed. Compute the mean and the variance of X given the following information.

   a. $\mu_Y = 14, \sigma_Y^2 = 22$

   b. $\mu_Y = 20, \sigma_Y^2 = 22$

   c. $\mu_Y = 20, \sigma_Y^2 = 120$

63. Let Y have the lognormal distribution with mean 82.8 and variance 156.25. Compute the following probabilities.

   a. $P(Y > 100)$

   b. $P(80 < Y < 100)$

Applications

64. Studies have shown that bats can consume an average of 10 mosquitoes per minute (berkshiremuseum.org). Assume that the number of mosquitoes consumed per minute follows a Poison distribution.

   a. What is the mean time between eating mosquitoes?

   b. Find the probability that the time between eating mosquitoes is more than 15 seconds.

   c. Find the probability that the time between eating mosquitoes is between 15 and 20 seconds.

65. According to the *Daily Mail* (February 28, 2012), there was an average of one complaint every 12 seconds against Britain's biggest banks in 2011. It is reasonable to assume that the time between complaints is exponentially distributed.
    a. What is the mean time between complaints?
    b. What is the probability that the next complaint will take less than the mean time?
    c. What is the probability that the next complaint will take between 5 and 10 seconds?

66. A tollbooth operator has observed that cars arrive randomly at an average rate of 360 cars per hour.
    a. What is the mean time between car arrivals at this tollbooth?
    b. What is the probability that the next car will arrive within ten seconds?

67. Customers make purchases at a convenience store, on average, every six minutes. It is fair to assume that the time between customer purchases is exponentially distributed. Jack operates the cash register at this store.
    a. What is the rate parameter λ? What is the standard deviation of this distribution?
    b. Jack wants to take a five-minute break. He believes that if he goes right after he has serviced a customer, he will lower the probability of someone showing up during his five-minute break. Is he right in this belief?
    c. What is the probability that a customer will show up in less than five minutes?
    d. What is the probability that nobody shows up for over half an hour?

68. A hospital administrator worries about the possible loss of electric power as a result of a power blackout. The hospital, of course, has a standby generator, but it, too, is subject to failure, having a mean time between failures of 500 hours. It is reasonable to assume that the time between failures is exponentially distributed.
    a. What is the probability that the standby generator fails during the next 24-hour blackout?
    b. Suppose the hospital owns two standby generators that work independently of one another. What is the probability that both generators fail during the next 24-hour blackout?

69. When crossing the Golden Gate Bridge traveling into San Francisco, all drivers must pay a toll. Suppose the amount of time (in minutes) drivers wait in line to pay the toll follows an exponential distribution with a probability density function of $f(x) = 0.2e^{-0.2x}$.
    a. What is the mean waiting time that drivers face when entering San Francisco via the Golden Gate Bridge?
    b. What is the probability that a driver spends more than the average time to pay the toll?
    c. What is the probability that a driver spends more than 10 minutes to pay the toll?
    d. What is the probability that a driver spends between 4 and 6 minutes to pay the toll?

70. On average, the state police catch eight speeders per hour at a certain location on Interstate 90. Assume that the number of speeders per hour follows the Poisson distribution.
    a. What is the probability that the state police wait less than 10 minutes for the next speeder?
    b. What is the probability that the state police wait between 15 and 20 minutes for the next speeder?
    c. What is the probability that the state police wait more than 25 minutes for the next speeder?

71. The Bahamas is a tropical paradise made up of 700 islands sprinkled over 100,000 square miles of the Atlantic Ocean. According to the figures released by the government of the Bahamas, the mean household income in the Bahamas is $39,626 and the median income is $33,600. A demographer decides to use the lognormal random variable to model this nonsymmetric income distribution. Let Y represent household income, where for a normally distributed X, $Y = e^X$. In addition, suppose the standard deviation of household income is $10,000.
    a. Compute the mean and the standard deviation of X.
    b. What proportion of the people in the Bahamas have household income above the mean?
    c. What proportion of the people in the Bahamas have household income below $20,000?
    d. Compute the 75th percentile of the income distribution in the Bahamas.

72. Motorists arrive at a Gulf station at the rate of two per minute during morning hours. Assume that the arrival of motorists at the station follows a Poisson distribution.
    a. What is the probability that the next car's arrival is in less than one minute?
    b. What is the probability that the next car's arrival is in more than five minutes?

73. It is well documented that a typical washing machine can last anywhere between 5 to 12 years. Let the life of a washing machine be represented by a lognormal variable, $Y = e^X$, where X is normally distributed. In addition, let the mean and standard deviation of the life of a washing machine be 8 years and 4 years, respectively.
    a. Compute the mean and the standard deviation of X.
    b. What proportion of the washing machines will last for more than 10 years?
    c. What proportion of the washing machines will last for less than 6 years?
    d. Compute the 90th percentile of the life of the washing machines.

WRITING WITH STATISTICS

Professor Lang is a professor of economics at Salem State University. She has been teaching a course in Principles of Economics for over 25 years. Professor Lang has never graded on a curve since she believes that relative grading may unduly penalize (benefit) a good (poor) student in an unusually strong (weak) class. She always uses an absolute scale for making grades, as shown in the two left columns of Table 6.5.

TABLE 6.5 Grading Scales with Absolute Grading versus Relative Grading

Absolute Grading		Relative Grading	
Grade	Score	Grade	Probability
A	92 and above	A	0.10
B	78 up to 92	B	0.35
C	64 up to 78	C	0.40
D	58 up to 64	D	0.10
F	Below 58	F	0.05

©Image Source, all rights reserved. RF

A colleague of Professor Lang's has convinced her to move to relative grading, since it corrects for unanticipated problems. Professor Lang decides to experiment with grading based on the relative scale as shown in the two right columns of Table 6.5. Using this relative grading scheme, the top 10% of students will get A's, the next 35% B's, and so on. Based on her years of teaching experience, Professor Lang believes that the scores in her course follow a normal distribution with a mean of 78.6 and a standard deviation of 12.4.

Professor Lang wants to use the above information to

1. Calculate probabilities based on the absolute scale. Compare these probabilities to the relative scale.

2. Calculate the range of scores for various grades based on the relative scale. Compare these ranges to the absolute scale.

3. Determine which grading scale makes it harder to get higher grades.

Many teachers would confess that grading is one of the most difficult tasks of their profession. Two common grading systems used in higher education are relative and absolute. Relative grading systems are norm-referenced or curve-based, in which a grade is based on the student's relative position in class. Absolute grading systems, on the other hand, are criterion-referenced, in which a grade is related to the student's absolute performance in class. In short, with absolute grading, the student's score is compared to a predetermined scale, whereas with relative grading, the score is compared to the scores of other students in the class.

Let X represent a grade in Professor Lang's class, which is normally distributed with a mean of 78.6 and a standard deviation of 12.4. This information is used to derive the grade probabilities based on the absolute scale. For instance, the probability of receiving an A is derived as $P(X \geq 92) = P(Z \geq 1.08) = 0.14$. Other probabilities, derived similarly, are presented in Table 6.A.

Sample Report— Absolute Grading versus Relative Grading

TABLE 6.A Probabilities Based on Absolute Scale and Relative Scale

Grade	Probability Based on Absolute Scale	Probability Based on Relative Scale
A	0.14	0.10
B	0.38	0.35
C	0.36	0.40
D	0.07	0.10
F	0.05	0.05

The second column of Table 6.A shows that 14% of students are expected to receive A's, 38% B's, and so on. Although these numbers are generally consistent with the relative scale restated in the third column of Table 6.A, it appears that the relative scale makes it harder for students to get higher grades. For instance, 14% get A's with the absolute scale compared to only 10% with the relative scale.

Alternatively, we can compare the two grading methods on the basis of the range of scores for various grades. The second column of Table 6.B restates the range of scores based on absolute grading. In order to obtain the range of scores based on relative grading, it is once again necessary to apply concepts from the normal distribution. For instance, the minimum score required to earn an A with relative grading is derived by solving for x in $P(X \geq x) = 0.10$. Since $P(X \geq x) = 0.10$ is equivalent to $P(Z \geq z) = 0.10$, it follows that $z = 1.28$. Inserting the proper values of the mean, the standard deviation, and z into $x = \mu + z\sigma$ yields a value of x equal to 94.47. Ranges for other grades, derived similarly, are presented in the third column of Table 6.B.

TABLE 6.B Range of Scores with Absolute Grading versus Relative Grading

Grade	Range of Scores Based on Absolute Grading	Range of Scores Based on Relative Grading
A	92 and above	94.47 and above
B	78 up to 92	80.21 up to 94.47
C	64 up to 78	65.70 up to 80.21
D	58 up to 64	58.20 up to 65.70
F	Below 58	Below 58.20

Once again comparing the results in Table 6.B, the use of the relative scale makes it harder for students to get higher grades in Professor Lang's courses. For instance, in order to receive an A with relative grading, a student must have a score of at least 94.47 versus a score of at least 92 with absolute grading. Both absolute and relative grading methods have their merits and teachers often make the decision on the basis of their teaching philosophy. However, if Professor Lang wants to keep the grades consistent with her earlier absolute scale, she should base her relative scale on the probabilities computed in the second column of Table 6.A.

CONCEPTUAL REVIEW

LO 6.1 **Describe a continuous random variable.**

A **continuous random variable** is characterized by uncountable values because it can take on any value within an interval. The probability that a continuous random variable X assumes a particular value x is zero; that is, $P(X = x) = 0$. Thus, for a continuous random variable, we calculate the probability within a specified interval. Moreover, the following equalities hold: $P(a \leq X \leq b) = P(a < X < b) = P(a \leq X < b) = P(a < X \leq b)$.

The **probability density function** $f(x)$ of a continuous random variable X is nonnegative and the entire area under this function equals one. The probability $P(a \leq X \leq b)$ is the area under $f(x)$ between points a and b.

For any value x of the random variable X, the **cumulative distribution function** $F(x)$ is defined as $F(x) = P(X \leq x)$.

LO 6.2 **Calculate and interpret probabilities for a random variable that follows the continuous uniform distribution.**

The **continuous uniform distribution** describes a random variable that has an equally likely chance of assuming a value within a specified range. The probability is essentially the area of a rectangle, which is the base times the height; that is, the length of a specified interval times the probability density function $f(x) = \frac{1}{b-a}$, where a and b are the lower and upper bounds of the interval, respectively.

LO 6.3 Explain the characteristics of the normal distribution.

The **normal distribution** is the most extensively used continuous probability distribution and is the cornerstone of statistical inference. It is the familiar bell-shaped distribution, which is symmetric around the mean. The normal distribution is completely described by two parameters: the population mean μ and the population variance σ^2.

The **standard normal distribution**, also referred to as the z **distribution**, is a special case of the normal distribution, with mean equal to zero and standard deviation (or variance) equal to one. The **standard normal table**, also called the z **table**, provides **cumulative probabilities** $P(Z \leq z)$; this table appears on two pages in Table 1 of Appendix B. The left-hand page provides cumulative probabilities for z values less than or equal to zero. The right-hand page shows cumulative probabilities for z values greater than or equal to zero. We also use the table to compute z values for given cumulative probabilities.

LO 6.4 Calculate and interpret probabilities for a random variable that follows the normal distribution.

Any normally distributed random variable X with mean μ and standard deviation σ can be transformed into the standard normal random variable Z as $Z = \frac{X - \mu}{\sigma}$. This standard transformation implies that any value x has a corresponding value z given by $z = \frac{x - \mu}{\sigma}$.

The standard normal variable Z can be transformed to the normally distributed random variable X with mean μ and standard deviation σ as $X = \mu + Z\sigma$. This inverse transformation implies that any value z has a corresponding value x given by $x = \mu + z\sigma$.

LO 6.5 Calculate and interpret probabilities for a random variable that follows the exponential distribution.

A useful nonsymmetric continuous probability distribution is the **exponential distribution**. A random variable X follows the exponential distribution if its probability density function is $f(x) = \lambda e^{-\lambda x}$ for $x \geq 0$, where λ is a rate parameter and $e \approx 2.718$ is the base of the natural logarithm. The mean and the standard deviation of the distribution are both equal to $1/\lambda$. For $x \geq 0$, the **cumulative probability** is computed as $P(X \leq x) = 1 - e^{-\lambda x}$.

LO 6.6 Calculate and interpret probabilities for a random variable that follows the lognormal distribution.

The **lognormal distribution** is another useful positively skewed distribution. Let X be a normal random variable with mean μ and variance σ^2 and let $Y = e^X$ be the corresponding lognormal variable. The mean μ_Y and standard deviation σ_Y of Y are derived as $\mu_Y = \exp\left(\frac{2\mu + \sigma^2}{2}\right)$ and $\sigma_Y = \sqrt{(\exp(\sigma^2) - 1)\exp(2\mu + \sigma^2)}$, respectively. Equivalently, the mean and standard deviation of the normal variable $X = \ln(Y)$ are derived as $\mu = \ln\left(\frac{\mu_Y^2}{\sqrt{\mu_Y^2 + \sigma_Y^2}}\right)$ and $\sigma = \sqrt{\ln\left(1 + \frac{\sigma_Y^2}{\mu_Y^2}\right)}$, respectively. Probabilities for a lognormal random variable are easily evaluated by reference to the normal distribution.

ADDITIONAL EXERCISES AND CASE STUDIES

Exercises

74. A florist makes deliveries between 1:00 pm and 5:00 pm daily. Assume delivery times follow the continuous uniform distribution.
    a. Calculate the mean and the variance of this distribution.
    b. Determine the percentage of deliveries that are made after 4:00 pm.
    c. Determine the percentage of deliveries that are made prior to 2:30 pm.

75. A worker at a landscape design center uses a machine to fill bags with potting soil. Assume that the quantity put in each bag follows the continuous uniform distribution with low and high filling weights of 10 pounds and 12 pounds, respectively.
    a. Calculate the expected value and the standard deviation of this distribution.
    b. Find the probability that the weight of a randomly selected bag is no more than 11 pounds.
    c. Find the probability that the weight of a randomly selected bag is at least 10.5 pounds.

76. The revised guidelines from the National High Blood Pressure Education Program define normal blood pressure as readings below 120/80 millimeters of mercury (*The New York Times*, May 14, 2003). Prehypertension is suspected when the top number (systolic) is between 120 and 139 or when the bottom number (diastolic) is between 80 and 90. A recent survey reported that the mean systolic reading of Canadians is 125 with a standard deviation of 17 and the mean diastolic reading is 79 with a standard deviation of 10. Assume that diastolic as well as systolic readings are normally distributed.
    a. What proportion of Canadians are suffering from prehypertension caused by high diastolic readings?
    b. What proportion of Canadians are suffering from prehypertension caused by high systolic readings?

77. U.S. consumers are increasingly viewing debit cards as a convenient substitute for cash and checks. The average amount spent annually on a debit card is $7,790 (*Kiplinger's*, August 2007). Assume that the average amount spent on a debit card is normally distributed with a standard deviation of $500.

    a. A consumer advocate comments that the majority of consumers spend over $8,000 on a debit card. Find a flaw in this statement.
    b. Compute the 25th percentile of the amount spent on a debit card.
    c. Compute the 75th percentile of the amount spent on a debit card.
    d. What is the interquartile range of this distribution?

78. On St. Patrick's Day, men spend an average of $43.87 while women spend an average of $29.54 (*USA TODAY*, March 17, 2009). Assume the standard deviations of spending for men and women are $3 and $11, respectively, and that both distributions are normally distributed.
    a. What is the probability that men spend over $50 on St. Patrick's Day?
    b. What is the probability that women spend over $50 on St. Patrick's Day?
    c. Are men or women more likely to spend over $50 on St. Patrick's Day?

79. Lisa Mendes and Brad Lee work in the sales department of an AT&T Wireless store. Lisa has been signing up an average of 48 new cell phone customers every month with a standard deviation of 22, while Brad signs up an average of 56 new customers with a standard deviation of 17. The store manager offers both Lisa and Brad a $100 incentive bonus if they can sign up more than 100 new customers in a month. Assume a normal distribution to answer the following questions.
    a. What is the probability that Lisa will earn the $100 incentive bonus?
    b. What is the probability that Brad will earn the $100 incentive bonus?
    c. Are you surprised by the results? Explain.

80. The car speeds on a certain stretch of the interstate highway I-95 are known to be normally distributed with a mean of 72 and a standard deviation of 15. You have just heard a policeman comment that about 3% of the drivers drive at extremely dangerous speeds. What is the minimum speed that the policeman considers extremely dangerous?

81. The average household income in a community is known to be $80,000. Also, 20% of the households have an income below $60,000 and another 20% have an income above $90,000. Is it reasonable to use the normal distribution to model the household income in this community?

82. The length of components produced by a company is normally distributed with a mean of 6 cm and a standard deviation of 0.02 cm. Calculate the first, second, and third quartiles of the component length.

83. Entrance to a prestigious MBA program in India is determined by a national test where only the top 10% of the examinees are admitted to the program. Suppose it is known that the scores on this test are normally distributed with a mean of 420 and a standard deviation of 80. Parul Monga is trying desperately to get into this program. What is the minimum score that she must earn to get admitted?

84. A new water filtration system is sold with a 10-year warranty that includes all parts and repairs. Suppose the life of this water filtration system is normally distributed with mean and standard deviation of 16 and 5 years, respectively.
   a. What is the probability that the water filtration system will require a repair during the warranty period?
   b. Suppose the water filtration firm makes a $300 profit for every new system it installs. This profit, however, is reduced to $50 if the system requires repair during the warranty period. Find the expected profit of the firm if it installs 1,000 new water filtration systems.

85. Suppose that the average IQ score is normally distributed with a mean of 100 and a standard deviation of 16.
   a. What is the probability a randomly selected person will have an IQ score of less than 80?
   b. What is the probability that a randomly selected person will have an IQ score greater than 125?
   c. What minimum IQ score does a person have to achieve to be in the top 2.5% of IQ scores?

86. Suppose that the annual household income in a small Midwestern community is normally distributed with a mean of $55,000 and a standard deviation of $4,500.
   a. What is the probability that a randomly selected household will have an income between $50,000 and $65,000?
   b. What is the probability that a randomly selected household will have an income of more than $70,000?
   c. What minimum income does a household need to earn to be in the top 5% of incomes?
   d. What maximum income does a household need to earn to be in the bottom 40% of incomes?

87. On a particularly busy section of the Garden State Parkway in New Jersey, police use radar guns to detect speeders. Assume the time that elapses between successive speeders is exponentially distributed with a mean of 15 minutes.
   a. Calculate the rate parameter λ.
   b. What is the probability of a waiting time less than 10 minutes between successive speeders?
   c. What is the probability of a waiting time in excess of 25 minutes between successive speeders?

88. In a local law office, jobs to a printer are sent at a rate of 8 jobs per hour. Suppose that the number of jobs sent to a printer follows the Poisson distribution.
   a. What is the expected time between successive jobs?
   b. What is the probability that the next job will be sent within five minutes?

89. According to the Federal Bureau of Investigation, there is a violent crime in the United States every 22 seconds (*ABC News,* September 25, 2007). Assume that the time between successive violent crimes is exponentially distributed.
   a. What is the probability that there is a violent crime in the United States in the next one minute?
   b. If there has not been a violent crime in the previous minute, what is the probability that there will be a violent crime in the subsequent minute?

90. Disturbing news regarding Scottish police concerns the number of crashes involving vehicles on operational duties (*BBC News,* March 10, 2008). Statistics showed that Scottish forces' vehicles had been involved in traffic accidents at the rate of 1,000 per year. Suppose the number of crashes involving vehicles on operational duties follows a Poisson distribution.
   a. What is the average number of days between successive crashes?
   b. What is the rate parameter of the appropriate exponential distribution?
   c. What is the probability that the next vehicle will crash within a day?

91. The mileage (in 1,000s of miles) that car owners get with a certain kind of radial tire is a random variable having an exponential distribution with a mean of 50.
   a. What is the probability that a tire will last at most 40,000 miles?

b. What is the probability that a tire will last at least 65,000 miles?

c. What is the probability that a tire will last between 70,000 and 80,000 miles?

92. A large technology firm receives an average of 12 new job applications every 10 days for positions that are not even advertised. Suppose the number of job applications received follows a Poisson distribution.

a. What is the average number of days between successive job applications?

b. What is the probability that the next job application is received within a day?

c. What is the probability that the next job application is received between the next 1 and 2 days?

93. The relief time provided by a standard dose of a popular children's allergy medicine averages six hours with a standard deviation of two hours.

a. Determine the percentage of children who experience relief for less than four hours if the relief time follows a normal distribution.

b. Determine the percentage of children who experience relief for less than four hours if the relief time follows a lognormal distribution.

c. Compare the results based on these two distributions.

94. On average, a certain kind of kitchen appliance requires repairs once every four years. Assume that the times between repairs are exponentially distributed.

a. What is the probability that the appliance will work no more than three years without requiring repairs?

b. What is the probability that the appliance will work at least six years without requiring repairs?

95. The mileage (in 1,000s of miles) that car owners get with a certain kind of radial tire is a random variable Y having a lognormal distribution such that $Y = e^X$, where X is normally distributed. Let the mean and the standard deviation of the life of a radial tire be 40,000 miles and 5,000 miles, respectively.

a. Compute the mean and standard deviation of X.

b. What proportion of the tires will last for more than 50,000 miles?

c. What proportion of the tires will last for no more than 35,000 miles?

d. Compute the 95th percentile of the life expectancy of the tire.

96. In 2015, the U.S. Census Bureau reported that the median income for American households was $52,353, whereas the mean income was $71,932 (www.census.gov, data retrieved March 26, 2017). Suppose income can be represented by a lognormal variable, $Y = e^X$, where X is normally distributed. The mean and the standard deviation of X are 11.1 and 0.4, respectively.

a. What is the probability that a household's income is less than $50,000?

b. What is the probability that a household's income is greater than $60,000?

c. What is the lowest income that places a household in the 99th percentile?

d. What is the highest income that places a household in the 10th percentile?

CASE STUDIES

CASE STUDY 6.1   Body mass index (BMI) is a reliable indicator of body fat for most children and teens. BMI is calculated from a child's weight and height and is used as an easy-to-perform method of screening for weight categories that may lead to health problems. For children and teens, BMI is age- and sex-specific and is often referred to as BMI-for-age.

The Centers for Disease Control and Prevention (CDC) reports BMI-for-age growth charts for girls as well as boys to obtain a percentile ranking. Percentiles are the most commonly used indicator to assess the size and growth patterns of individual children in the United States.

The following table provides weight status categories and the corresponding percentiles and BMI ranges for 10-year-old boys in the United States.

Weight Status Category	Percentile Range	BMI Range
Underweight	Less than 5th	Less than 14.2
Healthy Weight	Between 5th and 85th	Between 14.2 and 19.4
Overweight	Between 85th and 95th	Between 19.4 and 22.2
Obese	More than 95th	More than 22.2

Health officials of a Midwestern town are concerned about the weight of children in their town. They believe that the BMI of their 10-year-old boys is normally distributed with mean 19.2 and standard deviation 2.6.

In a report, use the sample information to

1. Compute the proportion of 10-year-old boys in this town that are in the various weight status categories given the BMI ranges.
2. Discuss whether the concern of health officials is justified.

CASE STUDY 6.2   Vanguard's Precious Metals and Mining fund (Metals) and Fidelity's Strategic Income fund (Income) were two top-performing mutual funds for the years 2000 through 2009. An analysis of annual return data for these two funds provided important information for any type of investor. Over the past 10 years, the Metals fund posted a mean return of 24.65% with a standard deviation of 37.13%. On the other hand, the mean and the standard deviation of return for the Income fund were 8.51% and 11.07%, respectively. It is reasonable to assume that the returns of the Metals and the Income funds are both normally distributed, where the means and the standard deviations are derived from the 10-year sample period.

In a report, use the sample information to compare and contrast the Metals and Income funds from the perspective of an investor whose objective is to

1. Minimize the probability of earning a negative return.
2. Maximize the probability of earning a return between 0% and 10%.
3. Maximize the probability of earning a return greater than 10%.

CASE STUDY 6.3   A variety of packaging solutions exist for products that must be kept within a specific temperature range. A cold chain distribution is a temperature-controlled supply chain. An unbroken cold chain is an uninterrupted series of storage and distribution activities that maintain a given temperature range. Cold chains are particularly useful in the food and pharmaceutical industries. A common suggested temperature range for a cold chain distribution in pharmaceutical industries is between 2 and 8 degrees Celsius.

Gopal Vasudeva works in the packaging branch of Merck & Co. He is in charge of analyzing a new package that the company has developed. With repeated trials, Gopal has determined that the mean temperature that this package is able to maintain during its use is 5.6°C with a standard deviation of 1.2°C. He is not sure if the distribution of temperature is symmetric or skewed to the right.

In a report, use the sample information to

1. Calculate and interpret the probability that temperature goes (a) below 2°C and (b) above 8°C using a normal distribution approximation.
2. Calculate the probability that temperature goes (a) below 2°C and (b) above 8°C using a lognormal distribution approximation.
3. Compare the results from the two distributions used in the analysis.

APPENDIX 6.1   Guidelines for Other Software Packages

The following section provides brief commands for Minitab, SPSS, and JMP.

Minitab

The Uniform Distribution

A. (Replicating Example 6.1b) From the menu, choose **Calc > Probability Distributions > Uniform**.

B. Select **Cumulative probability**. Enter 2,500 as the **Lower endpoint** and 5,000 as the **Upper endpoint**. Select **Input constant** and enter 4,000. Minitab returns $P(X \leq 4,000)$.

The Normal Distribution
The Standard Transformation

A. (Replicating Example 6.8a) From the menu, choose **Calc > Probability Distributions > Normal**.

B. Select **Cumulative probability**. Enter 7.49 for the **Mean** and 6.41 for the **Standard deviation**. Select **Input constant** and enter 10. Minitab returns $P(X \leq 10)$. Perform similar steps to find $P(X \leq 5)$, and then find the difference between the probabilities.

The Inverse Transformation

A. (Replicating Example 6.8b) From the menu, choose **Calc > Probability Distributions > Normal**.

B. Select **Inverse cumulative probability**. Enter 7.49 for the **Mean** and 6.41 for the **Standard deviation**. Select **Input constant** and enter 0.90.

The Exponential Distribution

A. (Replicating Example 6.12) Choose **Calc > Probability Distributions > Exponential**.

B. Select **Cumulative probability**. Enter 5 for **Scale** (since Scale $= E(X) = 5$) and 0.0 for **Threshold**. Select **Input constant** and enter 6. Minitab returns $P(X \leq 6)$. Perform similar steps to find $P(X \leq 3)$, and then find the difference between the probabilities.

The Lognormal Distribution
The Lognormal Transformation

A. (Replicating Example 6.13a) From the menu, choose **Calc > Probability Distributions > Lognormal**.

B. Select **Cumulative probability**. Enter 2.6054 for the **Location** and 0.4487 for the **Scale**. Select **Input constant** and enter 20. Minitab returns $P(Y \leq 20)$.

The Inverse Transformation

A. (Replicating Example 6.13b) From the menu, choose **Calc > Probability Distributions > Lognormal**.

B. Select **Inverse cumulative probability**. Enter 2.6054 for the **Location** and 0.4487 for the **Scale**. Select **Input constant** and enter 0.25.

SPSS

Note: In order for the calculated probability to be seen on the spreadsheet, SPSS must first "view" data on the spreadsheet. For this purpose, enter a value of zero in the first cell of the first column.

The Uniform Distribution

A. (Replicating Example 6.1b) From the menu, choose **Transform** > **Compute Variable**.

B. Under **Target Variable**, type cdfuniform. Under **Function group**, select **CDF & Noncentral CDF** and under **Functions and Special Variables**, double-click on **Cdf.Uniform**. In the Numeric Expression box, enter 4,000 for **quant**, 2,500 for **min**, and 5,000 for **max**. SPSS returns $P(X \le 4,000)$.

The Normal Distribution

The Standard Transformation

A. (Replicating Example 6.8a) From the menu, choose **Transform** > **Compute Variable**.

B. Under **Target Variable**, type cdfnorm. Under **Function group**, select **CDF & Noncentral CDF,** and under **Functions and Special Variables**, double-click on **Cdf.Normal**. In the **Numeric Expression** box, enter 10 for **quant**, 7.49 for **mean**, and 6.41 for **stddev**. SPSS returns $P(X \le 10)$. Perform similar steps to find $P(X \le 5)$, and then find the difference between the probabilities.

The Inverse Transformation

A. (Replicating Example 6.8b) From the menu, choose **Transform** > **Compute Variable**.

B. Under **Target Variable**, type invnorm. Under **Function group**, select **Inverse DF**, and under **Functions and Special Variables**, double-click on **Idf.Normal**. In the **Numeric Expression** box, enter 0.9 for **prob**, 7.49 for **mean**, and 6.41 for **stddev**.

The Exponential Distribution

A. (Replicating Example 6.12) From the menu, choose **Transform** > **Compute Variable**.

B. Under **Target Variable**, type cdfexp. Under **Function group**, select **CDF & Noncentral CDF,** and under **Functions and Special Variables**, double-click on **Cdf.Exp**. In the **Numeric Expression** box, enter 6 for **quant** and 0.2 for **scale**. SPSS returns $P(X \le 6)$. Perform similar steps to find $P(X \le 3)$, and then find the difference between the probabilities.

The Lognormal Distribution

The Lognormal Transformation

A. (Replicating Example 6.13a) The easiest way to solve lognormal distribution problems in SPSS is to modify the normal distribution instructions. So, from the menu, choose **Transform** > **Compute Variable**.

B. Under **Target Variable**, type cdflognorm. Under **Function group**, select **CDF & Noncentral CDF,** and under **Function and Special Variables**, double-click on **CDF.Normal**. In the **Numeric Expression** box, enter ln(20) for **quant**, 2.6054 for **mean**, and 0.4487 for **stddev**. SPSS returns $P(Y \le 20)$.

The Inverse Transformation

A. (Replicating Example 6.13b) From the menu, choose **Transform > Compute Variable**.

B. Under **Target Variable**, type invlognorm. In the **Numeric Expression** box, type exp(IDF.NORMAL(0.25, 2.6054, 0.4487)).

JMP

Note: In order for the calculated probability to be seen on the spreadsheet, JMP must first "view" data on the spreadsheet. For this purpose, enter a value of zero in the first cell of the first column.

The Normal Distribution

The Standard Transformation

A. (Replicating Example 6.8a) Right-click on the header at the top of the column in the spreadsheet view and select **Formula**. Under **Functions (grouped)**, choose **Probability > Normal Distribution**.

B. Put the insertion marker on the box for **x** and click the insert button (shown as a caret ^ with the mathematical operations) until you see **mean** and **std dev** next to **x**. Enter 10 for **x**, 7.49 for **mean**, and 6.41 for **std dev**. JMP returns $P(X \leq 10)$. Perform similar steps to find $P(X \leq 5)$, and then find the difference between the probabilities.

The Inverse Transformation

A. (Replicating Example 6.8b) Right-click on the header at the top of the column in the spreadsheet view and select **Formula**. Under **Functions (grouped)**, choose **Probability > Normal Quantile**.

B. Put the insertion marker on the box for **p** and click the insert button (shown as a caret ^ with the mathematical operations) until you see **mean** and **std dev** next to **p**. Enter 0.90 for **p**, 7.49 for **mean**, and 6.41 for **std dev**.

The Exponential Distribution

A. (Replicating Example 6.12) Right-click on the header at the top of the column in the spreadsheet view and select **Formula**. Under **Functions (grouped)**, choose **Probability > Weibull Distribution**. (The exponential distribution is a special case of the Weibull distribution, when the shape parameter, see next step, equals 1.)

B. Put the insertion marker on the box for **x** and click the insert button (shown as a caret ^ with the mathematical operations) until you see **shape** and **scale** next to **x**. Enter 6 for **x**, 1 for **shape**, and 5 for **scale**. JMP returns $P(X \leq 6)$. Perform similar steps to find $P(X \leq 3)$, and then find the difference between the probabilities.

The Lognormal Distribution

The Lognormal Transformation

A. (Replicating Example 6.13a) Right-click on the header at the top of the column in the spreadsheet view and select **Formula.** Under **Function (grouped)**, choose **Probability > GLog Distribution**.

B. Put the insertion marker on the box for **x** and click the insert button (shown as a caret ^ with the mathematical operations) until you see **mu**, **sigma**, and **lambda** next to **x**. Enter 20 for **x**, 2.6054 for **mu**, 0.4487 for **sigma**, and 0 for **lambda**. JMP returns $P(Y \leq 20)$.

The Inverse Transformation

A. (Replicating Example 6.13b) Right-click on the header at the top of the column in the spreadsheet view and select **Formula.** Under **Function (grouped)**, choose **Probability > GLog Quantile**.

B. Put the insertion marker on the box for **p** and click the insert button (shown as a caret ^ with the mathematical operations) until you see **mu**, **sigma**, and **lambda** next to **p**. Enter 0.25 for **p**, 2.6054 for **mu**, 0.4487 for **sigma**, and 0 for **lambda**.

7

Sampling and Sampling Distributions

In the last few chapters, we had information on the population parameters, such as the population proportion and the population mean, for the analysis of discrete and continuous random variables. In many instances, we do not have information on the parameters, so we make statistical inferences on the basis of sample statistics. The credibility of any statistical inference depends on the quality of the sample on which it is based. In this chapter, we discuss various ways to draw a good sample and also highlight cases in which the sample misrepresents the population. It is important to note that any given statistical problem involves only one population, but many possible samples, from which a statistic can be derived. Therefore, while the population parameter is a constant, the sample statistic is a random variable whose value depends on the choice of the random sample. We will discuss how to evaluate the properties of sample statistics. In particular, we will study the probability distributions of the sample mean and the sample proportion based on simple random sampling. Finally, we will use these distributions to construct control charts, which are popular statistical tools for monitoring and improving quality.

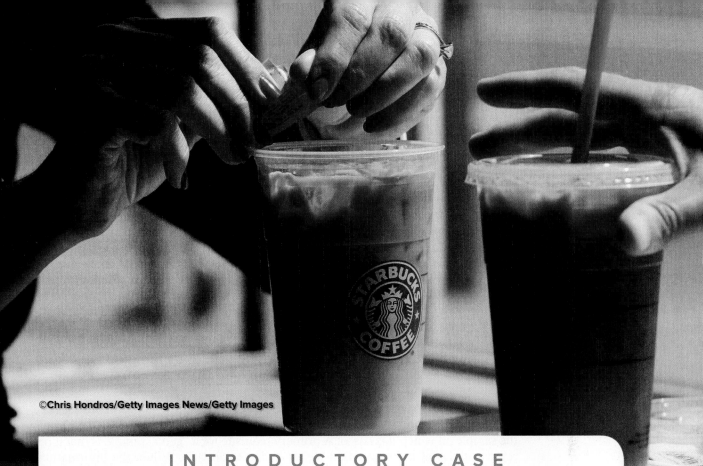

©Chris Hondros/Getty Images News/Getty Images

INTRODUCTORY CASE

Marketing Iced Coffee

Although hot coffee is still Americans' drink of choice, the market share of iced coffee is growing steadily. Thirty percent of coffee drinkers had at least one iced, frozen, or blended coffee drink in 2009, up from 28% in 2008 (*The Boston Globe*, April 6, 2010). In response to this growing change in taste, the coffee chains have ramped up their offerings: Starbucks recently introduced an upgraded Frappuccino; Dunkin' Donuts launched a new iced dark roast; and McDonald's unveiled new blended coffee iced drinks and smoothies.

In order to capitalize on this trend, Starbucks advertised a Happy Hour from May 7 through May 16 when customers enjoyed a half-price Frappuccino beverage between 3 pm and 5 pm (www.starbucks.com). Anne Jones, a manager at a local Starbucks (see the Chapter 5 introductory case), wonders how this marketing campaign has affected her business. She knows that women and teenage girls comprise the majority of the iced-coffee market, since they are willing to spend more on indulgences. In fact, Anne reviews her records prior to the promotion and finds that 43% of iced-coffee customers were women and 21% were teenage girls. She also finds that customers spent an average of $4.18 on iced coffee with a standard deviation of $0.84.

One month after the marketing period ends, Anne surveys 50 of her iced-coffee customers and finds that they had spent an average of $4.26. In addition, 23 (46%) of the customers were women and 17 (34%) were teenage girls. Anne wants to determine if the marketing campaign has had a lingering effect on the amount of money customers spend on iced coffee and on the proportion of customers who are women and teenage girls. Anne wonders if Starbucks would have gotten such business if it had chosen not to pursue the marketing campaign.

Anne wants to use the above survey information to

1. Calculate the probability that customers spend an average of $4.26 or more on iced coffee.

2. Calculate the probability that 46% or more of iced-coffee customers are women.

3. Calculate the probability that 34% or more of iced-coffee customers are teenage girls.

A synopsis of this case is provided at the end of Section 7.3.

Explain common
sample biases.

A major portion of statistics is concerned with statistical inference, where we examine the problem of estimating population parameters or testing hypotheses about such parameters. Recall that a population consists of all items of interest in the statistical problem. If we had access to data that encompass the entire population, then the values of the parameters would be known and no statistical inference would be needed. Since it is generally not feasible to gather data on an entire population, we use a subset of the population, or a sample, and use this information to make statistical inference. We can think of a census and survey data as representative of population and sample data, respectively. While a census captures almost everyone in the country, a survey captures a small number of people who fit a particular category. We regularly use survey data to analyze government and business activities.

POPULATION VERSUS SAMPLE

A population consists of all items of interest in a statistical problem, whereas a sample is a subset of the population. We use a sample statistic, or simply statistic, to make inferences about the unknown population parameter.

In later chapters, we explore estimation and hypothesis testing, which are based on sample information. It is important to note that no matter how sophisticated the statistical methods are, the credibility of statistical inference depends on the quality of the sample on which it is based. A primary requisite for a "good" sample is that it be representative of the population we are trying to describe. When the information from a sample is not typical of information in the population in a systematic way, we say that **bias** has occurred.

Bias refers to the tendency of a sample statistic to systematically overestimate or underestimate a population parameter. It is often caused by samples that are not representative of the population.

Classic Case of a "Bad" Sample: The *Literary Digest* Debacle of 1936

In theory, drawing conclusions about a population based on a good sample sounds logical; however, in practice, what constitutes a "good" sample? Unfortunately, there are many ways to collect a "bad" sample. One way is to inadvertently pick a sample that represents only a portion of the population. The *Literary Digest*'s attempt to predict the 1936 presidential election is a classic example of an embarrassingly inaccurate poll.

In 1932 and amid the Great Depression, Herbert Hoover was voted out of the White House and Franklin Delano Roosevelt (FDR) was elected the 32nd president of the United States. Although FDR's attempts to end the Great Depression within four years were largely unsuccessful, he retained the general public's faith. In 1936, FDR ran for reelection against Alf Landon, the governor of Kansas and the Republican nominee. The *Literary Digest,* an influential, general-interest weekly magazine, wanted to predict the next U.S. president, as it had done successfully five times before.

After conducting the largest poll in history, the *Literary Digest* predicted a landslide victory for Alf Landon: 57% of the vote to FDR's 43%. Moreover, the *Literary Digest* claimed that its prediction would be within a fraction of 1% of the actual vote. Instead, FDR won in a landslide: 62% to 38%. So what went wrong?

The *Literary Digest* sent postcards to 10 million people (one-quarter of the voting population at the time) and received responses from 2.4 million people. The response rate of 24% (2.4 million/10 million) might seem low to some, but in reality it is a reasonable response rate given this type of polling. What was atypical of the poll is the manner in which the *Literary Digest* obtained the respondents' names. The *Literary Digest* randomly sampled its own subscriber list, club membership rosters, telephone directories, and automobile registration rolls. This sample reflected predominantly middle- and upper-class people; that is, the vast majority of those polled were wealthier people, who were more inclined to vote for the Republican candidate. Back in the 1930s, owning a phone, for instance, was far from universal. Only 11 million residential phones were in service in 1936, and these homes were disproportionately well-to-do and in favor of Landon. The sampling methodology employed by the *Literary Digest* suffered from **selection bias**. Selection bias occurs when portions of the population are underrepresented in the sample. FDR's support came from lower-income classes whose opinion was not reflected in the poll. The sample, unfortunately, misrepresented the general electorate.

> Selection bias refers to a systematic underrepresentation of certain groups from consideration for the sample.

What should the *Literary Digest* have done differently? At a minimum, most would agree that names should have been obtained from voter registration lists rather than telephone directory lists and car registrations.

In addition to selection bias, the *Literary Digest* survey also had a great deal of **nonresponse bias**. This occurs when those responding to a survey or poll differ systematically from the nonrespondents. In the survey, a larger percentage of educated people mailed back the questionnaires. During that time period, the more educated tended to come from affluent families that again favored the Republican candidate.

> Nonresponse bias refers to a systematic difference in preferences between respondents and nonrespondents to a survey or a poll.

The most effective way to deal with nonresponse bias is to reduce nonresponse rates. Paying attention to survey design, wording, and ordering of the questions can increase the response rate. Sometimes, rather than sending out a very large number of surveys, it may be preferable to use a smaller representative sample for which the response rate is likely to be high.

It turns out that someone did accurately predict the 1936 presidential election. From a sample of 50,000 with a response rate of 10% (5,000 respondents), a young pollster named George Gallup predicted that FDR would win 56% of the vote to Landon's 44%. Despite using a far smaller sample with a lower response rate, it was far more *representative* of the true voting population. Gallup later founded the Gallup Organization, one of the leading polling companies of all time.

Trump's Stunning Victory in 2016

The results of the U.S. presidential election in 2016 came as a surprise to nearly everyone who had been following the national and state election polling, which consistently projected Hillary Clinton as defeating Donald Trump (www.pewresearch.org, November 9, 2016). It appears that problems with selection bias and nonresponse bias persist today. Many pollsters and strategists believe that rural white voters, who were a key demographic for Trump on Election Day, eluded polling altogether. It is also believed that the frustration and anti-institutional feelings that drove the campaign may also have aligned these same voters with an unwillingness to respond to surveys (www.politico.com, March 27, 2017).

Another theory that has gained some traction in explaining the polling missteps in the 2016 election was the presence of **social-desirability bias**. This bias occurs when voters provide incorrect answers to a survey or poll because they think that others will look unfavorably on their ultimate choices.

> Social-desirability bias refers to a systematic difference between a group's "socially acceptable" responses to a survey or poll and this group's ultimate choice.

Due to Trump's inflammatory comments, many voters did not want to be associated with him by their peers. This was perfectly exemplified by the fact that Trump consistently performed better in online polling. For example, in one aggregation of telephone polls, Clinton led Trump by nine percentage points; however, in a similar aggregation of online polls, Clinton's lead was only four percentage points (*The New York Times*, May 11, 2016). This seems to suggest that one way to battle social-desirability bias is to use online surveys. Despite their flaws, online surveys resemble an anonymous voting booth and remove the human factor of the pollsters.

LO 7.2

Describe various sampling methods.

Sampling Methods

As mentioned earlier, a primary requisite for a "good" sample is that it be representative of the population you are trying to describe. The basic type of sample that can be used to draw statistically sound conclusions about a population is a **simple random sample**.

> ### SIMPLE RANDOM SAMPLE
> A simple random sample is a sample of n observations that has the same probability of being selected from the population as any other sample of n observations. Most statistical methods presume simple random samples.

While a simple random sample is the most commonly used sampling method, in some situations, other sampling methods have an advantage over simple random samples. Two alternative methods for forming a sample are stratified random sampling and cluster sampling.

Political pollsters often employ **stratified random sampling** in an attempt to ensure that each area of the country, each ethnic group, each religious group, and so forth, is appropriately represented in the sample. With stratified random sampling, the population is divided into groups (strata) based on one or more classification criteria. Simple random samples are then drawn from each stratum in sizes proportional to the relative size of each stratum in the population. These samples are then pooled.

> ### STRATIFIED RANDOM SAMPLING
> In stratified random sampling, the population is first divided up into mutually exclusive and collectively exhaustive groups, called *strata*. A stratified sample includes randomly selected observations from each stratum. The number of observations per stratum is proportional to the stratum's size in the population. The data for each stratum are eventually pooled.

Stratified random sampling has two advantages. First, it guarantees that the population subdivisions of interest are represented in the sample. Second, the estimates of parameters produced from stratified random sampling have greater precision than estimates obtained from simple random sampling.

Even stratified random sampling, however, can fall short with its predictive ability. One of the nagging mysteries of the 2008 Democratic presidential primaries was: why were the polls so wrong in New Hampshire? All nine major polling groups predicted that Barack Obama would beat Hillary Clinton in the New Hampshire primary, by an average of 8.3 percentage points. When the votes were counted, Clinton won by 2.6%. Several factors contributed to the wrong prediction by the polling industry. First, pollsters overestimated the turnout of young voters, who overwhelmingly favored Obama in exit polls but did not surge to vote as they had in the Iowa caucus. Second, Clinton's campaign made a decision to target female Democrats, especially single women. This focus did not pay off in Iowa, but it did in New Hampshire. Finally, on the eve of the primary, a woman in Portsmouth asked Clinton: "How do you do it?" Clinton's teary response was powerful and warm. Voters, who rarely saw Clinton in such an emotional moment, found her response humanizing and appealing. Most polls had stopped phoning voters over the weekend, too soon to catch the likely voter shift.

Cluster sampling is another method for forming a representative sample. A cluster sample is formed by dividing the population into groups (clusters), such as geographic areas, and then selecting a sample of the groups for the analysis. The technique works best when most of the variation in the population is within the groups and not between the groups. In such instances, a cluster is a miniversion of the population.

CLUSTER SAMPLING

In cluster sampling, the population is first divided up into mutually exclusive and collectively exhaustive groups, called *clusters*. A cluster sample includes observations from randomly selected clusters.

In general, cluster sampling is cheaper as compared to other sampling methods. However, for a given sample size, it provides less precision than either simple random sampling or stratified sampling. Cluster sampling is useful in applications where the population is concentrated in natural clusters such as city blocks, schools, and other geographic areas. It is especially attractive when constructing a complete list of the population members is difficult and/or costly. For example, since it may not be possible to create a full list of customers who go to Walmart, we can form a sample that includes customers only from selected stores.

STRATIFIED VERSUS CLUSTER SAMPLING

In stratified sampling, the sample consists of observations from each group, whereas in cluster sampling, the sample consists of observations from the selected groups. Stratified sampling is preferred when the objective is to increase precision, and cluster sampling is preferred when the objective is to reduce costs.

In practice, it is extremely difficult to obtain a truly random sample that is representative of the underlying population. As researchers, we need to be aware of the population from which the sample was selected and then limit our conclusions to that population. For the remainder of the text, we assume that the sample data are void of "human error." That is, we have sampled from the correct population (no selection bias); we have no nonresponse or social-desirability biases; and we have collected, analyzed, and reported the data properly.

Using Excel and R to Generate a Simple Random Sample

Excel and R provide functions that we can use to draw simple random samples. Example 7.1 illustrates the use of some of these functions.

EXAMPLE 7.1

There has been an increase in students working their way through college to offset rising tuition costs (*US News*, January 11, 2017). Work helps them to lower student loans and learn crucial time management skills. A dean at the Orfalea College of Business (OCOB) wants to analyze performance of her students who work while they are enrolled. For the analysis, use Excel or R to generate a random sample of 100 students drawn from 2,750 OCOB students.

SOLUTION: Since each student has a unique student identification number, we start by creating an ordered list using 1 and 2,750 as the smallest and largest student identification numbers, respectively. We then generate 100 random integers (numbers) between these values and use them to identify students based on their order on the list.

Using Excel

We use Excel's **RANDBETWEEN** function to generate random integers within some interval. In general, we enter "=RANDBETWEEN(lower, upper)" where lower and upper refer to the smallest and largest integers in the interval, respectively. In this example, we enter "=RANDBETWEEN(1, 2750)." Suppose Excel returns 983. The student whose order on the list is 983 is then selected for the sample. To generate the remaining 99 numbers, we select the cell with the value 983, drag it down 99 additional cells, and from the menu, choose **Home > Fill > Down**.

Using R

We use R's **sample** function to generate random integers within some interval. In general, we enter "sample(lower:upper, n)" where lower and upper refer to the smallest and largest integers in the interval, respectively, and n denotes the sample size. We label the random sample as Sample_draw, and we also use the **list** function to show the integers. We enter:

```
> Sample_draw <- sample(1:2750, 100)
> list(Sample_draw)
```

The first five values that R returns (answers will vary greatly) are as follows: 1,546 1,984 303 984 702.

EXERCISES 7.1

1. In 2010, Apple introduced the iPad, a tablet-style computer that its former CEO Steve Jobs called a "a truly magical and revolutionary product" (*CNN*, January 28, 2010). Suppose you are put in charge of determining the age profile of people who purchased the iPad in the United States. Explain in detail the following sampling strategies that you could use to select a representative sample.
   a. Simple random sampling
   b. Stratified random sampling
   c. Cluster sampling

2. A marketing firm opens a small booth at a local mall over the weekend, where shoppers are asked how much money they spent at the food court. The objective is to determine the average monthly expenditure of shoppers at the food court. Has the marketing firm committed any sampling bias? Discuss.

3. Natalie Min is an undergraduate in the Haas School of Business at Berkeley. She wishes to pursue an MBA from Berkeley and wants to know the profile of other students who are likely to apply to the Berkeley MBA program. In particular, she wants to know the GPA of students with whom she might be competing. She randomly surveys 40 students from her accounting class for the analysis. Discuss in detail whether or not Natalie's analysis is based on a representative sample.

4. Vons, a large supermarket in Grover Beach, California, is considering extending its store hours from 7:00 am to midnight, seven days a week, to 6:00 am to midnight. Discuss the sampling bias in the following sampling strategies:

   a. Mail a prepaid envelope to randomly selected residents in the Grover Beach area, asking for their preference for the store hours.

   b. Ask the customers who frequent the store in the morning if they would prefer an earlier opening time.

   c. Place an ad in the local newspaper, requesting people to submit their preference for store hours on the store's website.

5. In the previous question regarding Vons' store hours, explain how you can obtain a representative sample based on the following sampling strategies:

   a. Simple random sampling.

   b. Stratified random sampling.

   c. Cluster sampling.

7.2 THE SAMPLING DISTRIBUTION OF THE SAMPLE MEAN

As mentioned earlier, we are generally interested in the characteristics of a population. For instance, a student is interested in the average starting salary (population mean) of business graduates. Similarly, a banker is interested in the default probability (population proportion) of mortgage holders. Recall that the population mean and the population proportion are parameters that describe quantitative and qualitative data, respectively. Since it is cumbersome, if not impossible, to analyze the entire population, we generally make inferences about the characteristics of the population on the basis of a random sample drawn from the population.

It is important to note that there is only one population, but many possible samples of a given size can be drawn from the population. Therefore, a population parameter is a constant, even though its value may be unknown. On the other hand, a statistic, such as the sample mean or the sample proportion, is a random variable whose value depends on the particular sample that is randomly drawn from the population.

> A parameter is a constant, although its value may be unknown. A statistic is a random variable whose value depends on the chosen random sample.

Consider the starting salary of business graduates as the variable of interest. If you decide to make inferences about the population mean salary on the basis of a random draw of 38 recent business graduates, then the sample mean $\overline{X}$ is the relevant statistic. Note that the value of $\overline{X}$ will change if you choose a different random sample of 38 business graduates. In other words, $\overline{X}$ is a random variable whose value depends on the chosen random sample. The sample mean is commonly referred to as the **estimator**, or the **point estimator**, of the population mean.

In the starting salary example, the sample mean $\overline{X}$ is the estimator of the mean starting salary of business graduates. If the average derived from a specific sample is $54,000, then $\bar{x} = 54,000$ is the **estimate** of the population mean. Similarly, if the variable of interest is the default probability of mortgage holders, then the sample proportion of defaults, denoted by $\overline{P}$, from a random sample of 80 mortgage holders is the estimator of the population proportion. If 10 out of 80 mortgage holders in a given sample default, then $\bar{p} = 10/80 = 0.125$ is the estimate of the population proportion.

ESTIMATOR AND ESTIMATE

When a statistic is used to estimate a parameter, it is referred to as an estimator. A particular value of the estimator is called an estimate.

In this section, we will focus on the probability distribution of the sample mean $\bar{X}$, which is also referred to as the **sampling distribution** of $\bar{X}$. Since $\bar{X}$ is a random variable, its sampling distribution is simply the probability distribution derived from all possible samples of a given size from the population. Consider, for example, a mean derived from a sample of n observations. Another mean can similarly be derived from a different sample of n observations. If we repeat this process a very large number of times, then the frequency distribution of the sample means can be thought of as its sampling distribution. In particular, we will discuss the expected value and the standard deviation of the sample mean. We will also study the conditions under which the sampling distribution of the sample mean is normally distributed.

The Expected Value and the Standard Error of the Sample Mean

LO 7.3

Describe the sampling distribution of the sample mean.

Let the random variable X represent a certain characteristic of a population under study, with an expected value, $E(X) = \mu$, and a variance, $Var(X) = \sigma^2$. For example, X could represent the salary of business graduates or the return on investment. We can think of μ and σ^2 as the mean and the variance of an individual observation drawn randomly from the population of interest, or simply as the population mean and the population variance. Let the sample mean $\bar{X}$ be based on a random sample of n observations from this population. It is easy to derive the expected value and the variance of $\bar{X}$; see Appendix 7.1 for the derivations.

The expected value of $\bar{X}$ is the same as the expected value of the individual observation—that is, $E(\bar{X}) = E(X) = \mu$. In other words, if we were to sample repeatedly from a given population, the average value of the sample means will equal the average value of all individual observations in the population, or simply, the population mean. This is an important property of an estimator, called unbiasedness, that holds irrespective of whether the sample mean is based on a small or a large sample. An estimator is **unbiased** if its expected value equals the population parameter. Other desirable properties of an estimator are described in Appendix 7.2.

THE EXPECTED VALUE OF THE SAMPLE MEAN

The expected value of the sample mean $\bar{X}$ equals the population mean, or $E(\bar{X}) = \mu$. In other words, the sample mean is an unbiased estimator of the population mean.

It is important to note that we estimate the population mean on the basis of just one sample. The above result shows that we are not systematically underestimating- or overestimating the population parameter.

The variance of $\bar{X}$ is equal to $Var(\bar{X}) = \frac{\sigma^2}{n}$. In other words, if we were to sample repeatedly from a given population, the variance of the sample mean will equal the variance of all individual observations in the population, divided by the sample size, n. Note that $Var(\bar{X})$ is smaller than the variance of X, which is equal to $Var(X) = \sigma^2$. This is an intuitive result, suggesting that the variability between sample means is less than the variability between observations. Since each sample is likely to contain both high and low observations, the highs and lows cancel one another, making the variance of $\bar{X}$ smaller than the variance of X. As usual, the standard deviation of $\bar{X}$ is calculated as the positive square root of the variance. However, in order to distinguish the variability between samples from the variability between individual observations, we refer to the standard deviation of $\bar{X}$ as the **standard error** of the sample mean, computed as $se(\bar{X}) = \frac{\sigma}{\sqrt{n}}$.

THE STANDARD ERROR OF THE SAMPLE MEAN

The standard deviation of the sample mean $\bar{X}$ is referred to as the standard error of the sample mean. It equals the population standard deviation divided by the square root of the sample size; that is, $se(\bar{X}) = \frac{\sigma}{\sqrt{n}}$.

In Chapter 8, we will discuss that the exact standard error of an estimator is often not known and, therefore, must be estimated from the given sample data. For convenience, we use "*se*" to denote both the exact and the estimated standard errors of an estimator.

EXAMPLE 7.2

The chefs at a local pizza chain in Cambria, California, strive to maintain the suggested size of their 16-inch pizzas. Despite their best efforts, they are unable to make every pizza exactly 16 inches in diameter. The manager has determined that the size of the pizzas is normally distributed with a mean of 16 inches and a standard deviation of 0.8 inch.

a. What are the expected value and the standard error of the sample mean derived from a random sample of 2 pizzas?

b. What are the expected value and the standard error of the sample mean derived from a random sample of 4 pizzas?

c. Compare the expected value and the standard error of the sample mean with those of an individual pizza.

SOLUTION: We know that the population mean $\mu = 16$ and the population standard deviation $\sigma = 0.8$. We use $E(\bar{X}) = \mu$ and $se(\bar{X}) = \frac{\sigma}{\sqrt{n}}$ to calculate the following results.

a. With the sample size $n = 2$, $E(\bar{X}) = 16$ and $se(\bar{X}) = \frac{0.8}{\sqrt{2}} = 0.57$.

b. With the sample size $n = 4$, $E(\bar{X}) = 16$ and $se(\bar{X}) = \frac{0.8}{\sqrt{4}} = 0.40$.

c. The expected value of the sample mean for both sample sizes is identical to the expected value of the individual pizza. However, the standard error of the sample mean with $n = 4$ is lower than the one with $n = 2$. For both sample sizes, the standard error of the sample mean is lower than the standard deviation of the individual pizza. This result confirms that averaging reduces variability.

Sampling from a Normal Population

An important feature of the sampling distribution of the sample mean $\bar{X}$ is that, irrespective of the sample size n, $\bar{X}$ is normally distributed if the population X from which the sample is drawn is normal. In other words, if X is normal with expected value μ and standard deviation σ, then $\bar{X}$ is also normal with expected value μ and standard error $\sigma/\sqrt{n}$.

For any sample size n, the sampling distribution of $\overline{X}$ is normal if the population X from which the sample is drawn is normally distributed.

If $\overline{X}$ is normally distributed, then it can be transformed into a standard normal random variable as

$$Z = \frac{\overline{X} - E(\overline{X})}{se(\overline{X})} = \frac{\overline{X} - \mu}{\sigma/\sqrt{n}}.$$

Therefore, any value $\bar{x}$ has a corresponding value z given by $z = \frac{\bar{x} - \mu}{\sigma/\sqrt{n}}$.

EXAMPLE 7.3

Use the information in Example 7.2 to answer the following questions:

a. What is the probability that a randomly selected pizza is less than 15.5 inches?

b. What is the probability that 2 randomly selected pizzas average less than 15.5 inches?

c. What is the probability that 4 randomly selected pizzas average less than 15.5 inches?

d. Comment on the computed probabilities.

SOLUTION: Since the population is normally distributed, the sampling distribution of the sample mean is also normal. Figure 7.1 depicts the shapes of the three distributions based on the population mean $\mu = 16$ and the population standard deviation $\sigma = 0.8$.

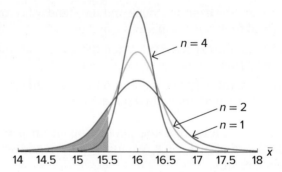

FIGURE 7.1
Normal distribution of the sample mean

Note that when the sample size $n = 1$, the sample mean $\bar{x}$ is the same as the individual observation x.

a. We use the standard transformation to derive $P(X < 15.5) = P\left(Z < \frac{15.5 - 16}{0.8}\right) = P(Z < -0.63) = 0.2643$. There is a 26.43% chance that an individual pizza is less than 15.5 inches.

b. Here we use the standard transformation to derive $P(\overline{X} < 15.5) = P\left(Z < \frac{15.5 - 16}{0.8/\sqrt{2}}\right) = P(Z < -0.88) = 0.1894$. In a random sample of 2 pizzas, there is an 18.94% chance that the average size is less than 15.5 inches.

c. Again we find $P(\overline{X} < 15.5)$, but now $n = 4$. Therefore, $P(\overline{X} < 15.5) = P\left(Z < \frac{15.5 - 16}{0.8/\sqrt{4}}\right) = P(Z < -1.25) = 0.1056$. In a random sample of 4 pizzas, there is a 10.56% chance that the average size is less than 15.5 inches.

d. The probability that the average size is under 15.5 inches, for 4 randomly selected pizzas, is less than half of that for an individual pizza. This is due to the fact that while X and $\overline{X}$ have the same expected value of 16, the variance of $\overline{X}$ is less than that of X.

The Central Limit Theorem

LO 7.4

Explain the importance of the central limit theorem.

For making statistical inferences, it is essential that the sampling distribution of $\overline{X}$ is normally distributed. So far we have only considered the case where $\overline{X}$ is normally distributed because the population X from which the sample is drawn is normal. What if the underlying population is not normal? Here we present the **central limit theorem (CLT)**, which perhaps is the most remarkable result of probability theory. The CLT states that the sum or the average of a large number of independent observations from the same underlying distribution has an approximate normal distribution. The approximation steadily improves as the number of observations increases. In other words, irrespective of whether or not the population X is normal, the sample mean $\overline{X}$ computed from a random sample of size n will be approximately normally distributed as long as n is sufficiently large.

THE CENTRAL LIMIT THEOREM FOR THE SAMPLE MEAN

For any population X with expected value μ and standard deviation σ, the sampling distribution of $\overline{X}$ will be approximately normal if the sample size n is sufficiently large. As a general guideline, the normal distribution approximation is justified when $n \geq 30$.

As before, if $\overline{X}$ is approximately normally distributed, then any value $\bar{x}$ can be transformed to its corresponding value z given by $z = \frac{\bar{x} - \mu}{\sigma/\sqrt{n}}$.

Figure 7.1, discussed in Example 7.3, is not representative of the CLT principle because, for a normal population, the sampling distribution of $\overline{X}$ is normal irrespective of the sample size. Figures 7.2 and 7.3, however, illustrate the CLT by using random samples of various sizes drawn from nonnormal populations. The relative frequency polygon of $\overline{X}$, which essentially represents its distribution, is generated from repeated draws (computer simulations) from the continuous uniform distribution (Figure 7.2) and the exponential distribution (Figure 7.3). Both of these nonnormal distributions were discussed in Chapter 6.

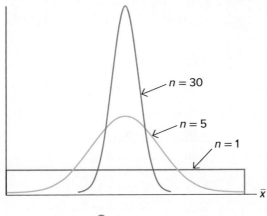

FIGURE 7.2
Sampling distribution of $\overline{X}$ when the population has a uniform distribution

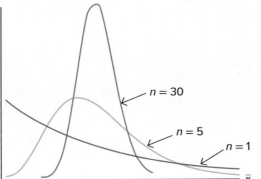

FIGURE 7.3
Sampling distribution of $\overline{X}$ when the population has an exponential distribution

Note that when the sample size $n = 1$, the sample mean is the same as the individual observation (population) with the familiar uniform and exponential shapes. With $n = 5$, the sampling distribution of $\overline{X}$ is already approximately normal when the population has the uniform distribution. With $n = 30$, the shape of the sampling distribution of $\overline{X}$ is approximately normal when the population has the exponential distribution. The CLT can similarly be illustrated with other distributions of the population. How large a sample is necessary for normal convergence depends on the magnitude of the departure of the population from normality. As mentioned earlier, practitioners often use the normal distribution approximation when $n \geq 30$.

EXAMPLE 7.4

Consider the information presented in the introductory case of this chapter. Recall that Anne wants to determine if the marketing campaign has had a lingering effect on the amount of money customers spend on iced coffee. Before the campaign, customers spent an average of $4.18 on iced coffee with a standard deviation of $0.84. Anne reports that the average amount, based on 50 customers sampled after the campaign, is $4.26. If Starbucks chose not to pursue the marketing campaign, how likely is it that customers will spend an average of $4.26 or more on iced coffee?

SOLUTION: If Starbucks did not pursue the marketing campaign, spending on iced coffee would still have mean $\mu = 4.18$ and standard deviation $\sigma = 0.84$. Anne needs to calculate the probability that the sample mean is at least 4.26, or, $P(\overline{X} \geq 4.26)$. The population from which the sample is drawn is not known to be normally distributed. However, since $n \geq 30$, from the central limit theorem we know that $\overline{X}$ is approximately normally distributed. Therefore, as shown in Figure 7.4, $P(\overline{X} \geq 4.26) = P\left(Z \geq \frac{4.26 - 4.18}{0.84/\sqrt{50}}\right) = P(Z \geq 0.67) = 1 - 0.7486 = 0.2514$. It is quite plausible (probability $= 0.2514$) that in a sample of 50 customers, the sample mean is $4.26 or more even if Starbucks did not pursue the marketing campaign.

FIGURE 7.4 Finding $P(\overline{X} \geq 4.26)$

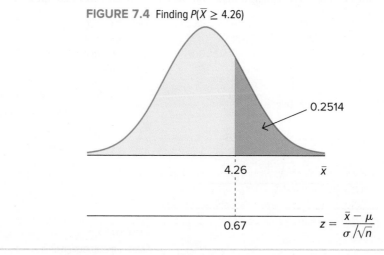

EXERCISES 7.2

Mechanics

6. A random sample is drawn from a normally distributed population with mean $\mu = 12$ and standard deviation $\sigma = 1.5$.
   a. Comment on the sampling distribution of the sample mean with $n = 20$ and $n = 40$.

   b. Can you use the standard normal distribution to calculate the probability that the sample mean is less than 12.5 for both sample sizes?

   c. Report the probability if you answered yes to the previous question for either sample size.

7. A random sample is drawn from a population with mean $\mu = 66$ and standard deviation $\sigma = 5.5$.
   a. Comment on the sampling distribution of the sample mean with $n = 16$ and $n = 36$.
   b. Can you use the standard normal distribution to calculate the probability that the sample mean falls between 66 and 68 for both sample sizes?
   c. Report the probability if you answered yes to the previous question for either sample size.

8. A random sample of size $n = 100$ is taken from a population with mean $\mu = 80$ and standard deviation $\sigma = 14$.
   a. Calculate the expected value and the standard error for the sampling distribution of the sample mean.
   b. What is the probability that the sample mean falls between 77 and 85?
   c. What is the probability that the sample mean is greater than 84?

9. A random sample of size $n = 50$ is taken from a population with mean $\mu = -9.5$ and standard deviation $\sigma = 2$.
   a. Calculate the expected value and the standard error for the sampling distribution of the sample mean.
   b. What is the probability that the sample mean is less than -10?
   c. What is the probability that the sample mean falls between -10 and -9?

Applications

10. According to a survey, high school girls average 100 text messages daily (*The Boston Globe*, April 21, 2010). Assume the population standard deviation is 20 text messages. Suppose a random sample of 50 high school girls is taken.
    a. What is the probability that the sample mean is more than 105?
    b. What is the probability that the sample mean is less than 95?
    c. What is the probability that the sample mean is between 95 and 105?

11. Beer bottles are filled so that they contain an average of 330 ml of beer in each bottle. Suppose that the amount of beer in a bottle is normally distributed with a standard deviation of 4 ml.
    a. What is the probability that a randomly selected bottle will have less than 325 ml of beer?
    b. What is the probability that a randomly selected 6-pack of beer will have a mean amount less than 325 ml?
    c. What is the probability that a randomly selected 12-pack of beer will have a mean amount less than 325 ml?
    d. Comment on the sample size and the corresponding probabilities.

12. Despite its nutritional value, seafood is only a tiny part of the American diet, with the average American eating just 16 pounds of seafood per year. Janice and Nina both work in the seafood industry and they decide to create their own random samples and document the average seafood diet in their sample. Let the standard deviation of the American seafood diet be 7 pounds.
    a. Janice samples 42 Americans and finds an average seafood consumption of 18 pounds. How likely is it to get an average of 18 pounds or more if she had a representative sample?
    b. Nina samples 90 Americans and finds an average seafood consumption of 17.5 pounds. How likely is it to get an average of 17.5 pounds or more if she had a representative sample?
    c. Which of the two women is likely to have used a more representative sample? Explain.

13. The weight of people in a small town in Missouri is known to be normally distributed with a mean of 180 pounds and a standard deviation of 28 pounds. On a raft that takes people across the river, a sign states, "Maximum capacity 3,200 pounds or 16 persons." What is the probability that a random sample of 16 persons will exceed the weight limit of 3,200 pounds?

14. The weight of turkeys is known to be normally distributed with a mean of 22 pounds and a standard deviation of 5 pounds.
    a. Discuss the sampling distribution of the sample mean based on a random draw of 16 turkeys.
    b. Find the probability that the mean weight of 16 randomly selected turkeys is more than 25 pounds.
    c. Find the probability that the mean weight of 16 randomly selected turkeys is between 18 and 24 pounds.

15. A small hair salon in Denver, Colorado, averages about 30 customers on weekdays with a standard deviation of 6. It is safe to assume that the underlying distribution is normal. In an attempt to increase the number of weekday customers, the manager offers a $2 discount on 5 consecutive weekdays. She reports that her strategy has worked since the sample mean of customers during this 5 weekday period jumps to 35.
    a. How unusual would it be to get a sample average of 35 or more customers if the manager had not offered the discount?
    b. Do you feel confident that the manager's discount strategy has worked? Explain.

16. The typical college student graduates with $27,200 in debt (*The Boston Globe*, May 27, 2012). Let debt among recent college graduates be normally distributed with a standard deviation of $7,000.
    a. What is the probability that the average debt of four recent college graduates is more than $25,000?
    b. What is the probability that the average debt of four recent college graduates is more than $30,000?

17. Forty families gathered for a fund-raising event. Suppose the individual contribution for each family is normally distributed with a mean and a standard deviation of $115 and $35,

respectively. The organizers would call this event a success if the total contributions exceed $5,000. What is the probability that this fund-raising event is a success?

18. A doctor is getting sued for malpractice by four of her former patients. It is believed that the amount that each patient will sue her for is normally distributed with a mean of $800,000 and a standard deviation of $250,000.

    a. What is the probability that a given patient sues the doctor for more than $1,000,000?

    b. If the four patients sue the doctor independently, what is the probability that the total amount they sue for is over $4,000,000?

19. Suppose that the miles-per-gallon (mpg) rating of passenger cars is normally distributed with a mean and a standard deviation of 33.8 and 3.5 mpg, respectively.

    a. What is the probability that a randomly selected passenger car gets more than 35 mpg?

    b. What is the probability that the average mpg of four randomly selected passenger cars is more than 35 mpg?

    c. If four passenger cars are randomly selected, what is the probability that all of the passenger cars get more than 35 mpg?

20. Suppose that IQ scores are normally distributed with a mean of 100 and a standard deviation of 16.

    a. What is the probability that a randomly selected person will have an IQ score of less than 90?

    b. What is the probability that the average IQ score of four randomly selected people is less than 90?

    c. If four people are randomly selected, what is the probability that all of them have an IQ score of less than 90?

7.3 THE SAMPLING DISTRIBUTION OF THE SAMPLE PROPORTION

LO 7.5

Describe the sampling distribution of the sample proportion.

Our discussion thus far has focused on the population mean, but many business, socioeconomic, and political matters are concerned with the population proportion. For instance, a banker is interested in the default probability of mortgage holders; a superintendent may note the proportion of students suffering from the flu when determining whether to keep school open; an incumbent seeking reelection cares about the proportion of constituents that will ultimately cast a vote for him/her. In all of these examples, the parameter of interest is the population proportion p. As in the case of the population mean, we almost always make inferences about the population proportion on the basis of sample data. Here, the relevant statistic (estimator) is the sample proportion, $\bar{P}$; a particular value (estimate) is denoted by $\bar{p}$. Since $\bar{P}$ is a random variable, we need to discuss its sampling distribution.

The Expected Value and the Standard Error of the Sample Proportion

We first introduced the population proportion p in Chapter 5, when we discussed the binomial distribution. It turns out that the sampling distribution of $\bar{P}$ is closely related to the binomial distribution. Recall that the binomial distribution describes the number of successes X in n trials of a Bernoulli process where p is the probability of success; thus, $\bar{P} = \frac{X}{n}$ is the number of successes X divided by the sample size n. We can derive the expected value and the variance of the sampling distribution of $\bar{P}$ as $E(\bar{P}) = p$ and $Var(\bar{P}) = \frac{p(1-p)}{n}$, respectively. (See Appendix 7.1 for the derivations.) Note that since $E(\bar{P}) = p$, it implies that $\bar{P}$ is an unbiased estimator of p.

> ### THE EXPECTED VALUE OF THE SAMPLE PROPORTION
>
> The expected value of the sample proportion $\bar{P}$ is equal to the population proportion, or, $E(\bar{P}) = p$. In other words, the sample proportion is an unbiased estimator of the population proportion.

Analogous to our discussion in the last section, we refer to the standard deviation of the sample proportion as the standard error of the sample proportion; that is, $se(\bar{P}) = \sqrt{\frac{p(1-p)}{n}}$.

THE STANDARD ERROR OF THE SAMPLE PROPORTION

The standard deviation of the sample proportion $\bar{P}$ is referred to as the standard error of the sample proportion. It equals $se(\bar{P}) = \sqrt{\frac{p(1-p)}{n}}$.

EXAMPLE 7.5

Many people apply for jobs to serve as paramedics or firefighters, yet they cannot complete basic physical fitness standards. A study found that 77% of all candidates for paramedic and firefighter positions were overweight or obese (*Obesity*, March 19, 2009).

a. What are the expected value and the standard error of the sample proportion derived from a random sample of 100 candidates for paramedic or firefighter positions?

b. What are the expected value and the standard error of the sample proportion derived from a random sample of 200 candidates for paramedic or firefighter positions?

c. Comment on the value of the standard error as the sample size gets larger.

SOLUTION: Given that $p = 0.77$, we can derive the expected value and the standard error of $\bar{P}$ as follows.

a. With $n = 100$, $E(\bar{P}) = 0.77$ and $se(\bar{P}) = \sqrt{\frac{0.77(1 - 0.77)}{100}} = 0.042$.

b. With $n = 200$, $E(\bar{P}) = 0.77$ and $se(\bar{P}) = \sqrt{\frac{0.77(1 - 0.77)}{200}} = 0.030$.

c. As in the case of the sample mean, while the expected value of the sample proportion is unaffected by the sample size, the standard error of the sample proportion is reduced as the sample size increases.

In this text, we make statistical inferences about the population proportion only when the sampling distribution of $\bar{P}$ is approximately normal. From the discussion of the central limit theorem (CLT) in Section 7.2, we can conclude that $\bar{P}$ is approximately normally distributed when the sample size is sufficiently large.

THE CENTRAL LIMIT THEOREM FOR THE SAMPLE PROPORTION

For any population proportion p, the sampling distribution of $\bar{P}$ is approximately normal if the sample size n is sufficiently large. As a general guideline, the normal distribution approximation is justified when $np \geq 5$ and $n(1 - p) \geq 5$.

If $\bar{P}$ is normally distributed, we can transform it into the standard normal random variable as

$$Z = \frac{\bar{P} - E(\bar{P})}{se(\bar{P})} = \frac{\bar{P} - p}{\sqrt{\frac{p(1-p)}{n}}}.$$

Therefore, any value $\bar{p}$ has a corresponding value z given by

$$z = \frac{\bar{p} - p}{\sqrt{\dfrac{p(1-p)}{n}}}.$$

According to the CLT, the sampling distribution of $\bar{P}$ approaches the normal distribution as the sample size increases. However, as the population proportion deviates from $p = 0.50$, we need a larger sample size for the approximation. We illustrate these results by generating the sampling distribution of $\bar{P}$ from repeated draws from a population with various values of the population proportion and sample sizes. As in the case of $\bar{X}$, we use the relative frequency polygon to represent the distribution of $\bar{P}$. The simulated sampling distribution of $\bar{P}$ is based on the population proportion $p = 0.10$ (Figure 7.5) and $p = 0.30$ (Figure 7.6).

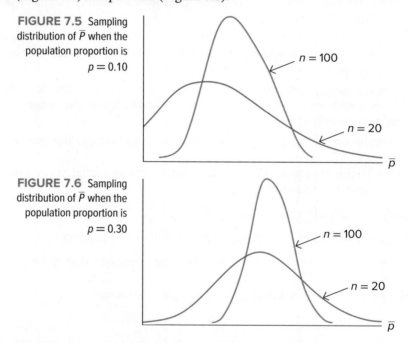

FIGURE 7.5 Sampling distribution of $\bar{P}$ when the population proportion is $p = 0.10$

FIGURE 7.6 Sampling distribution of $\bar{P}$ when the population proportion is $p = 0.30$

When $p = 0.10$, the sampling distribution of $\bar{P}$ does not resemble the bell shape of the normal distribution with $n = 20$ since the approximation condition $np \geq 5$ and $n(1-p) \geq 5$ is not satisfied. However, the graph becomes somewhat bell-shaped with $n = 100$. When $p = 0.30$, the shape of the sampling distribution of $\bar{P}$ is approximately normal since the approximation condition is satisfied with both sample sizes. In empirical work, it is common to work with large survey data, and, as a result, the normal distribution approximation is justified.

EXAMPLE 7.6

Consider the information presented in the introductory case of this chapter. Recall that Anne Jones wants to determine if the marketing campaign has had a lingering effect on the proportion of customers who are women and teenage girls. Prior to the campaign, 43% of the customers were women and 21% were teenage girls. Based on a random sample of 50 customers after the campaign, these proportions increase to 46% for women and 34% for teenage girls. Anne has the following questions.

a. If Starbucks chose not to pursue the marketing campaign, how likely is it that 46% or more of iced-coffee customers are women?

b. If Starbucks chose not to pursue the marketing campaign, how likely is it that 34% or more of iced-coffee customers are teenage girls?

SOLUTION: If Starbucks had not pursued the marketing campaign, the proportion of customers would still be $p = 0.43$ for women and $p = 0.21$ for teenage girls. With $n = 50$, the normal approximation for the sample proportion is justified for both population proportions.

a. As shown in Figure 7.7, we find that $P(\bar{P} \geq 0.46) = P\left(Z \geq \dfrac{0.46 - 0.43}{\sqrt{\frac{0.43(1 - 0.43)}{50}}}\right) =$ $P(Z \geq 0.43) = 1 - 0.6664 = 0.3336.$

FIGURE 7.7 Finding $P(\bar{P} \geq 0.46)$

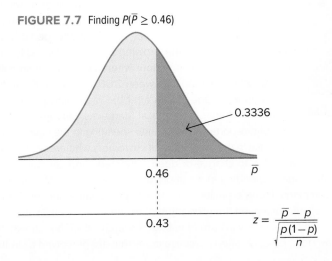

With a chance of 33.36%, it is quite plausible that the proportion of iced coffee purchased by women is at least 0.46 even if Starbucks did not pursue the marketing campaign.

b. As shown in Figure 7.8, we find $P(\bar{P} \geq 0.34) = P\left(Z \geq \dfrac{0.34 - 0.21}{\sqrt{\frac{0.21(1 - 0.21)}{50}}}\right) =$ $P(Z \geq 2.26) = 1 - 0.9881 = 0.0119.$

FIGURE 7.8 Finding $P(\bar{P} \geq 0.34)$

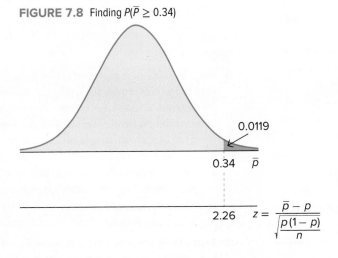

With only a 1.19% chance, it is unlikely that the proportion of iced coffee purchased by teenage girls is at least 0.34 if Starbucks did not pursue the marketing campaign.

Therefore, Anne can use this sample information to infer that the increase in the proportion of iced-coffee sales to women may not necessarily be due to the marketing campaign. However, the marketing campaign may have been successful in increasing the proportion of iced-coffee sales to teenage girls.

SYNOPSIS OF INTRODUCTORY CASE

©Joe Raedle/Getty Images News/Getty Images

Iced coffee, traditionally a warm-weather and warm-region drink, has broadened its appeal over the years. According to a May 13, 2010, report in *Bloomberg Businessweek*, the number of servings of iced coffee surged from 300 million in 2001 to 1.2 billion in 2009. Large corporations have taken notice and have engaged in various strategies to capitalize on the growing trend. Starbucks, for instance, recently promoted a happy hour where customers paid half-price for a Frappuccino beverage between 3:00 pm and 5:00 pm for a 10-day period in May. One month after the marketing period ended, Anne Jones, the manager at a local Starbucks, surveys 50 of her customers. She reports an increase in spending in the sample, as well as an increase in the proportion of customers who are women and teenage

girls. Anne wants to determine if the increase is due to chance or due to the marketing campaign. Based on an analysis with probabilities, Anne finds that higher spending in a sample of 50 customers is plausible even if Starbucks had not pursued the marketing campaign. Using a similar analysis with proportions, she infers that while the marketing campaign may not have necessarily increased the proportion of women customers, it seems to have attracted more teenage girls. The findings are consistent with current market research, which has shown that teenage girls have substantial income of their own to spend and often purchase items that are perceived as indulgences.

EXERCISES 7.3

Mechanics

21. Consider a population proportion $p = 0.68$.
    a. Calculate the expected value and the standard error of $\bar{P}$ with $n = 20$. Is it appropriate to use the normal distribution approximation for $\bar{P}$? Explain.
    b. Calculate the expected value and the standard error of $\bar{P}$ with $n = 50$. Is it appropriate to use the normal distribution approximation for $\bar{P}$? Explain.

22. Consider a population proportion $p = 0.12$.
    a. Discuss the sampling distribution of the sample proportion with $n = 20$ and $n = 50$.
    b. Can you use the normal approximation to calculate the probability that the sample proportion is between 0.10 and 0.12 for both sample sizes?
    c. Report the probabilities if you answered yes to the previous question.

23. A random sample of size $n = 200$ is taken from a population with a population proportion $p = 0.75$.
    a. Calculate the expected value and the standard error for the sampling distribution of the sample proportion.

    b. What is the probability that the sample proportion is between 0.70 and 0.80?
    c. What is the probability that the sample proportion is less than 0.70?

Applications

24. Europeans are increasingly upset at their leaders for making deep budget cuts to many social programs that are becoming too expensive to sustain. For example, the popularity of then-President Nicolas Sarkozy of France plummeted in 2010, giving him an approval rating of just 26% (*The Wall Street Journal*, July 2, 2010).
    a. What is the probability that fewer than 60 of 200 French people gave President Sarkozy a favorable rating?
    b. What is the probability that more than 150 of 200 French people gave President Sarkozy an *unfavorable* rating?

25. A study by Allstate Insurance Co. finds that 82% of teenagers have used cell phones while driving (*The Wall Street Journal*, May 5, 2010). Suppose a random sample of 100 teen drivers is taken.

a. Discuss the sampling distribution of the sample proportion.

b. What is the probability that the sample proportion is less than 0.80?

c. What is the probability that the sample proportion is within ±0.02 of the population proportion?

26. According to a FCC survey, one in six cell phone users has experienced "bill shock" from unexpectedly high cell phone bills (*Tech Daily Dose,* May 26, 2010).

a. Discuss the sampling distribution of the sample proportion based on a sample of 200 cell phone users. Is it appropriate to use the normal distribution approximation for the sample proportion?

b. What is the probability that more than 20% of cell phone users in the sample have experienced "bill shock"?

27. A car manufacturer is concerned about poor customer satisfaction at one of its dealerships. The management decides to evaluate the satisfaction surveys of its next 40 customers. The dealer will be fined if the number of customers who report favorably is between 22 and 26. The dealership will be dissolved if fewer than 22 customers report favorably. It is known that 70% of the dealer's customers report favorably on satisfaction surveys.

a. What is the probability that the dealer will be fined?

b. What is the probability that the dealership will be dissolved?

28. At a new exhibit in the Museum of Science, people are asked to choose between 50 or 100 random draws from a machine. The machine is known to have 60 green balls and 40 red balls. After each draw, the color of the ball is noted and the ball is put back for the next draw. You win a prize if more than 70% of the draws result in a green ball. Would you choose 50 or 100 draws for the game? Explain.

29. After years of rapid growth, illegal immigration into the United States has declined, perhaps owing to the recession and increased border enforcement by the United States (*Los Angeles Times*, September 1, 2010). While its share has declined, California still accounts for 23% of the nation's estimated 11.1 million undocumented immigrants.

a. In a sample of 50 illegal immigrants, what is the probability that more than 20% live in California?

b. In a sample of 200 illegal immigrants, what is the probability that more than 20% live in California?

c. Comment on the reason for the difference between the computed probabilities in parts a and b.

7.4 THE FINITE POPULATION CORRECTION FACTOR

LO 7.6

One of the implicit assumptions we have made thus far is that the sample size n is much smaller than the population size N. In many applications, the size of the population is not even known. For instance, we do not have information on the total number of pizzas made at a local pizza chain in Cambria (Examples 7.2 and 7.3) or the total number of customers at the local Starbucks store (Examples 7.4 and 7.6). If the sample size is large relative to the population size, then the standard errors of the estimators must be multiplied by a correction factor. This correction factor, called the **finite population correction factor**, accounts for the added precision gained by sampling a larger percentage of the population. As a general guideline, we use the finite population correction factor $\sqrt{\frac{N-n}{N-1}}$ when the sample constitutes at least 5% of the population—that is, $n \geq 0.05N$.

Use a finite population correction factor.

> ### THE FINITE POPULATION CORRECTION FACTOR FOR THE SAMPLE MEAN
>
> When the sample size is large relative to the population size ($n \geq 0.05N$), the finite population correction factor is used to reduce the sampling variation of the sample mean $\overline{X}$. The resulting standard error of $\overline{X}$ is $se(\overline{X}) = \frac{\sigma}{\sqrt{n}}\left(\sqrt{\frac{N-n}{N-1}}\right)$. The transformation for any value $\overline{x}$ to its corresponding z value is made accordingly.

Note that the correction factor is always less than one; when N is large relative to n, the correction factor is close to one and the difference between the formulas with and without the correction is negligible.

EXAMPLE 7.7

A large introductory marketing class has 340 students. The class is divided up into groups for the final course project. Connie is in a group of 34 students. These students had averaged 72 on the midterm, when the class as a whole had an average score of 73 with a standard deviation of 10.

a. Calculate the expected value and the standard error of the sample mean based on a random sample of 34 students.

b. How likely is it that a random sample of 34 students will average 72 or lower?

SOLUTION: The population mean is $\mu = 73$ and the population standard deviation is $\sigma = 10$.

a. The expected value of the sample mean is $E(\overline{X}) = \mu = 73$. We use the finite population correction factor because the sample size $n = 34$ is more than 5% of the population size $N = 340$. Therefore, the standard error of the sample mean is $se(\overline{X}) = \frac{\sigma}{\sqrt{n}}\left(\sqrt{\frac{N-n}{N-1}}\right) = \frac{10}{\sqrt{34}}\left(\sqrt{\frac{340-34}{340-1}}\right) = 1.6294$. Note that without the correction factor, the standard error would be higher at $se(\overline{X}) = \frac{\sigma}{\sqrt{n}} = \frac{10}{\sqrt{34}} = 1.7150$.

b. We find $P(\overline{X} \le 72) = P\left(Z \le \frac{72-73}{1.6294}\right) = P(Z \le -0.61) = 0.2709$. That is, the likelihood of 34 students averaging 72 or lower is 27.09%.

We use a similar finite population correction factor for the sample proportion when the sample size is at least 5% of the population size.

THE FINITE POPULATION CORRECTION FACTOR FOR THE SAMPLE PROPORTION

When the sample size is large relative to the population size ($n \ge 0.05N$), the finite population correction factor is used to reduce the sampling variation of the sample proportion $\overline{P}$. The resulting standard error of $\overline{P}$ is $se(\overline{P}) = \sqrt{\frac{p(1-p)}{n}}\left(\sqrt{\frac{N-n}{N-1}}\right)$. The transformation for any value $\overline{p}$ to its corresponding z value is made accordingly.

EXAMPLE 7.8

The home ownership rate during 2009 declined to approximately 67%, becoming comparable to the rate in early 2000 (*U.S. Census Bureau News*, February 2, 2010). A random sample of 80 households is taken from a small island community with 1,000 households. The home ownership rate on the island is equivalent to the national home ownership rate of 67%.

a. Calculate the expected value and the standard error for the sampling distribution of the sample proportion. Is it necessary to apply the finite population correction factor? Explain.

b. What is the probability that the sample proportion is within 0.02 of the population proportion?

SOLUTION:

a. We must apply the finite population correction factor because the sample size $n = 80$ is at least 5% of the population size $N = 1,000$. Therefore, $E(\bar{P}) = p = 0.67$ and

$$se(\bar{P}) = \sqrt{\frac{p(1-p)}{n}} \left(\sqrt{\frac{N-n}{N-1}} \right) = \sqrt{\frac{0.67(1-0.67)}{80}} \left(\sqrt{\frac{1,000-80}{1,000-1}} \right) = 0.0505.$$

b. The probability that the sample proportion is within 0.02 of the population proportion is $P(0.65 \leq \bar{P} \leq 0.69)$. We find that $P(0.65 \leq \bar{P} \leq 0.69) = P\left(\frac{0.65 - 0.67}{0.0505} \leq Z \leq \frac{0.69 - 0.67}{0.0505} \right) = P(-0.40 \leq Z \leq 0.40) = 0.6554 - 0.3446 = 0.3108$. The likelihood that the home ownership rate is within 0.02 of the population proportion is 31.08%.

EXERCISES 7.4

Mechanics

30. A random sample of size $n = 100$ is taken from a population of size $N = 2,500$ with mean $\mu = -45$ and variance $\sigma^2 = 81$.
    a. Is it necessary to apply the finite population correction factor? Explain. Calculate the expected value and the standard error of the sample mean.
    b. What is the probability that the sample mean is between -47 and -43?
    c. What is the probability that the sample mean is greater than -44?

31. A random sample of size $n = 70$ is taken from a finite population of size $N = 500$ with mean $\mu = 220$ and variance $\sigma^2 = 324$.
    a. Is it necessary to apply the finite population correction factor? Explain. Calculate the expected value and the standard error of the sample mean.
    b. What is the probability that the sample mean is less than 210?
    c. What is the probability that the sample mean lies between 215 and 230?

32. A random sample of size $n = 100$ is taken from a population of size $N = 3,000$ with a population proportion of $p = 0.34$.
    a. Is it necessary to apply the finite population correction factor? Explain. Calculate the expected value and the standard error of the sample proportion.
    b. What is the probability that the sample proportion is greater than 0.37?

33. A random sample of size $n = 80$ is taken from a population of size $N = 600$ with a population proportion $p = 0.46$.
    a. Is it necessary to apply the finite population correction factor? Explain. Calculate the expected value and the standard error of the sample proportion.
    b. What is the probability that the sample mean is less than 0.40?

Applications

34. A study finds that companies are setting aside a large chunk of their IT spending for green technology projects (*BusinessWeek*, March 5, 2009). Two out of three of the large companies surveyed by Deloitte said they have at least 5% of their IT budget earmarked for green IT projects. Suppose that the survey was based on 1,000 large companies. What is the probability that more than 75 of 120 large companies will have at least 5% of their IT expenditure earmarked for green IT projects?

35. The issues surrounding the levels and structure of executive compensation have gained added prominence in the wake of the financial crisis that erupted in the fall of 2008. Based on the 2006 compensation data obtained from the Securities and Exchange Commission (SEC) website, it was determined that the mean and the standard deviation of compensation for the 500 highest paid CEOs in publicly traded U.S. companies are $10.32 million and $9.78 million, respectively. An analyst randomly chooses 32 CEO compensations for 2006.
    a. Is it necessary to apply the finite population correction factor? Explain.
    b. Is the sampling distribution of the sample mean approximately normally distributed? Explain.
    c. Calculate the expected value and the standard error of the sample mean.
    d. What is the probability that the sample mean is more than $12 million?

36. Suppose in the previous question that the analyst had randomly chosen 12 CEO compensations for 2006.
    a. Is it necessary to apply the finite population correction factor? Explain.
    b. Is the sampling distribution of the sample mean approximately normally distributed? Explain.

c. Calculate the expected value and the standard error of the sample mean.

d. Can you use the normal approximation to calculate the probability that the sample mean is more than $12 million? Explain.

37. It is expected that only 60% in a graduating class of 250 will find employment in the first round of a job search. You have 20 friends who have recently graduated.

a. Discuss the sampling distribution of the sample proportion of your friends who will find employment in the first round of a job search.

b. What is the probability that less than 50% of your friends will find employment in the first round of a job search?

7.5 STATISTICAL QUALITY CONTROL

Construct and interpret control charts for quantitative and qualitative data.

Now more than ever, a successful firm must focus on the quality of the products and services it offers. Global competition, technological advances, and consumer expectations are all factors contributing to the quest for quality. In order to ensure the production of high-quality goods and services, a successful firm implements some form of quality control. In this section, we give a brief overview of the field of **statistical quality control**.

> Statistical quality control involves statistical techniques used to develop and maintain a firm's ability to produce high-quality goods and services.

In general, two approaches are used for statistical quality control. A firm uses **acceptance sampling** if it produces a product (or offers a service) and at the completion of the production process, the firm then inspects a portion of the products. If a particular product does not conform to certain specifications, then it is either discarded or repaired. There are several problems with this approach to quality control. First, it is costly to discard or repair a product. Second, the detection of all defective products is not guaranteed. Defective products may be delivered to customers, thus damaging the firm's reputation.

A preferred approach to quality control is the **detection approach**. A firm using the detection approach inspects the production process and determines at which point the production process does not conform to specifications. The goal is to determine whether the production process should be continued or adjusted before a large number of defects are produced. In this section, we focus on the detection approach to quality control.

In general, no two products or services are identical. In any production process, variation in the quality of the end product is inevitable. Two types of variation occur. **Chance variation** is caused by a number of randomly occurring events that are part of the production process. This type of variation is not generally considered to be under the control of the individual worker or machine. For example, suppose a machine fills one-gallon jugs of milk. It is unlikely that the filling weight of each jug is exactly 128 ounces. Very slight differences in the production process lead to minor differences in the weights of one jug to the next. Chance variation is expected and is not a source of alarm in the production process so long as its magnitude is tolerable and the end product meets acceptable specifications.

The other source of variation is referred to as **assignable variation**. This type of variation in the production process is caused by specific events or factors that can usually be identified and eliminated. Suppose in the milk example that the machine is "drifting" out of alignment. This causes the machine to overfill each jug—a costly expense for the firm. Similarly, it is bad for the firm in terms of its reputation if the machine begins to underfill each jug. The firm wants to identify and correct these types of variations in the production process.

Control Charts

Walter A. Shewhart, a researcher at Bell Telephone Laboratories during the 1920s, is often credited as being the first to apply statistics to improve the quality of output. He developed the **control chart**—a tool used to monitor the behavior of a production process.

THE CONTROL CHART

The most commonly used statistical tool in quality control is the control chart, a plot of calculated statistics of the production process over time. If the calculated statistics fall in an expected range, then the production process is in control. If the calculated statistics reveal an undesirable trend, then adjustment of the production process is likely necessary.

We can construct a number of different control charts where each differs by either the variable of interest and/or the type of data that are available. For quantitative data, examples of control charts include

- The $\bar{x}$ **chart**, which monitors the *central tendency* of a production process, and
- The R **chart** and the s **chart**, which monitor the *variability* of a production process.

For qualitative data, examples of control charts include

- The $\bar{p}$ **chart**, which monitors the *proportion* of defectives (or some other characteristic) in a production process, and
- The c **chart**, which monitors the *count* of defects per item, such as the number of blemishes on a sampled piece of furniture.

In general, all of these control charts (and others that we have not mentioned) have the following characteristics:

1. A control chart plots the sample estimates, such as $\bar{x}$ or $\bar{p}$. So as more and more samples are taken, the resulting control chart provides one type of safeguard when assessing if the production process is operating within predetermined guidelines.
2. All sample estimates are plotted with reference to a **centerline**. The centerline represents the variable's expected value when the production process is in control.
3. In addition to the centerline, all control charts include an **upper control limit (UCL)** and a **lower control limit (LCL)**. These limits indicate excessive deviation above (UCL) or below (LCL) the expected value of the variable of interest. A control chart is valid only if the sampling distribution of the relevant estimator is (approximately) normal. Under this assumption, the control limits are generally set at three standard deviations from the centerline. The area under the normal curve that corresponds to ± 3 standard deviations from the expected value is 0.9973. Thus, there is only a $1 - 0.9973 = 0.0027$ chance that the sample

estimates will fall outside the limit boundaries. In general, we define the upper and lower control limits as follows:

$$\text{UCL: Expected Value} + (3 \times \text{Standard Error})$$

$$\text{LCL: Expected Value} - (3 \times \text{Standard Error})$$

If the sample estimates fall randomly within the upper and lower control limits, then the production process is deemed in control. Any sample estimate that falls above the upper control limit or below the lower control limit is considered evidence that the production process is out of control and should be adjusted. In addition, any type of patterns within the control limits may suggest possible problems with the process. One indication of a process that is potentially heading out of control is unusually long runs above or below the centerline. Another possible problem is any evidence of a trend within the control limits.

In the next example, we focus on quantitative data and illustrate the $\bar{x}$ chart. We then turn to qualitative data and construct the $\bar{p}$ chart.

EXAMPLE 7.9

A firm that produces one-gallon jugs of milk wants to ensure that the machine is operating properly. Every two hours, the company samples 25 jugs and calculates the following sample mean filling weights (in ounces):

$\bar{x}_1 = 128.7$	$\bar{x}_2 = 128.4$	$\bar{x}_3 = 128.0$	$\bar{x}_4 = 127.8$	$\bar{x}_5 = 127.5$	$\bar{x}_6 = 126.9$

Assume that when the machine is operating properly, $\mu = 128$ and $\sigma = 2$, and that filling weights follow the normal distribution. Can the firm conclude that the machine is operating properly? Should the firm have any concerns with respect to this machine?

SOLUTION: Here the firm is interested in monitoring the population mean. To answer these questions, we construct an $\bar{x}$ chart. As mentioned earlier, this chart relies on the normal distribution for the sampling distribution of the estimator $\bar{X}$. Recall that if we are sampling from a normal population, then $\bar{X}$ is normally distributed even for small sample sizes. In this example, we are told that filling weights follow the normal distribution, a common assumption in the literature on quality control.

For the $\bar{x}$ chart, the centerline is the mean when the process is in control. Here, we are given that $\mu = 128$. We then calculate the UCL as three standard deviations above the mean and the LCL as three standard deviations below the mean:

$$\text{UCL: } \mu + 3\frac{\sigma}{\sqrt{n}} = 128 + 3\frac{2}{\sqrt{25}} = 129.2$$

$$\text{LCL: } \mu - 3\frac{\sigma}{\sqrt{n}} = 128 - 3\frac{2}{\sqrt{25}} = 126.8$$

Figure 7.9 shows the centerline and the control limits as well as the sample means.

All of the sample means fall within the upper control and the lower control limits, which indicates, at least initially, that the production process is in control. However, the sample means should be randomly spread between these limits; there should be no pattern. In this example, there is clearly a downward trend in the sample means. It appears as though the machine is beginning to underfill the one-gallon jugs. So even though none of the sample means lies beyond the control limits, the production process is likely veering out of control and the firm would be wise to inspect the machine sooner rather than later.

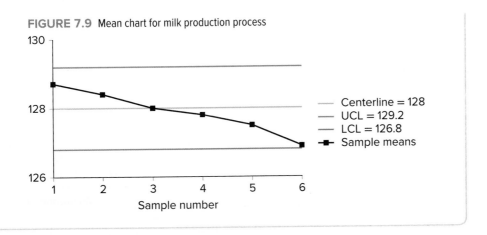

FIGURE 7.9 Mean chart for milk production process

Centerline = 128
UCL = 129.2
LCL = 126.8
Sample means

A firm may be interested in the stability of the proportion of its goods or services possessing a certain attribute or characteristic. For example, most firms strive to produce high-quality goods (or services) and thus hope to keep the proportion of defects at a minimum. When a production process is to be assessed based on sample proportions—here, the proportion of defects—then a $\bar{p}$ chart proves quite useful. Since the primary purpose of the $\bar{p}$ chart is to track the proportion of defects in a production process, it is also referred to as a fraction defective chart or a percent defective chart. Consider the next example.

EXAMPLE 7.10

A production process has a 5% defective rate. A quality inspector takes 6 samples of $n = 500$. The following sample proportions are obtained:

| $\bar{p}_1 = 0.065$ | $\bar{p}_2 = 0.075$ | $\bar{p}_3 = 0.082$ | $\bar{p}_4 = 0.086$ | $\bar{p}_5 = 0.090$ | $\bar{p}_6 = 0.092$ |

a. Construct a $\bar{p}$ chart. Plot the sample proportions on the $\bar{p}$ chart.
b. Is the production process in control? Explain.

SOLUTION:

a. The $\bar{p}$ chart relies on the central limit theorem for the normal approximation for the sampling distribution of the estimator $\bar{P}$. Recall that so long as np and $n(1 - p)$ are greater than or equal to five, then the sampling distribution of $\bar{P}$ is approximately normal. This condition is satisfied in this example. Since the expected proportion of defects is equal to 0.05, we set the centerline at $p = 0.05$. We then calculate the UCL and the LCL as follows.

$$\text{UCL: } p + 3\sqrt{\frac{p(1 - p)}{n}} = 0.05 + 3\sqrt{\frac{0.05(1 - 0.05)}{500}} = 0.079$$

$$\text{LCL: } p - 3\sqrt{\frac{p(1 - p)}{n}} = 0.05 - 3\sqrt{\frac{0.05(1 - 0.05)}{500}} = 0.021$$

We note that if the UCL is a value greater than one, then we reset the UCL to one in the control chart. Similarly, if the LCL is a negative value, we reset the LCL to zero in the control chart.

Plotting the values for the centerline, the UCL, the LCL, as well as the sample proportions, yields Figure 7.10.

b. Four of the most recent sample proportions fall above the upper control limit. This provides evidence that the process is out of control and needs adjustment.

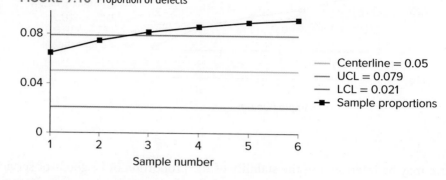

FIGURE 7.10 Proportion of defects

Using Excel and R to Create a Control Chart

Even though Excel does not have a built-in function to create a control chart, it is still relatively easy to construct one. If we are not given values for the centerline, the UCL, the LCL, and the sample means, then we first must provide these values in an Excel spreadsheet. Other software packages, including R, do these calculations for us. We will illustrate the construction of an $\bar{x}$ chart using Example 7.11.

EXAMPLE 7.11

JK Paints manufactures various kinds of paints in 4-liter cans. The cans are filled on an assembly line with an automatic valve regulating the amount of paint. To ensure that the correct amount of paint goes into each can, the quality control manager draws a random sample of four cans each hour and measures their amounts of paint. Since past experience has produced a standard deviation of $\sigma = 0.25$, the quality control manager has been able to calculate lower and upper control limits of $3.625 (= 4 - 3 \times 0.25/\sqrt{4})$ and $4.375 (= 4 + 3 \times 0.25/\sqrt{4})$, respectively. Table 7.1 shows a portion of the results from the last 25 hours. The table also includes the sample mean of the four randomly selected cans, the LCL, the centerline, and the UCL. Create an $\bar{x}$ chart to determine whether the cans are being filled properly.

FILE
Paint

TABLE 7.1 Data for Example 7.11

Sample	Obs. 1	Obs. 2	Obs. 3	Obs. 4	$\bar{x}$	LCL	Centerline	UCL
1	4.175	3.574	3.795	4.211	3.939	3.625	4	4.375
2	4.254	4.012	4.119	3.866	4.063	3.625	4	4.375
⋮	⋮	⋮	⋮	⋮	⋮	⋮	⋮	⋮
25	4.104	4.107	4.236	3.505	3.988	3.625	4	4.375

SOLUTION: As mentioned earlier, if only the first five columns of Table 7.1 were provided, we would have had to first populate the rest of the table by finding values for $\bar{x}$, LCL, Centerline, and UCL to make the $\bar{x}$ chart in Excel; R creates the $\bar{x}$ chart directly from the information given in columns 2 through 5.

Using Excel

a. Open the data file **Paint**.

b. Simultaneously select the headings and values in the $\bar{x}$, LCL, Centerline, and UCL columns and choose **Insert > Line Chart > 2-D Line**. Then, choose the option on the top left.

c. Formatting (regarding axis titles, colors, etc.) can be done by selecting **Format > Add Chart Element** from the menu.

Figure 7.11 shows the control chart that Excel produces. All sample means fall within the lower and upper limits, and they also fall randomly above and below the centerline. This indicates that the cans are being filled properly.

FIGURE 7.11 Using Excel to create a control chart

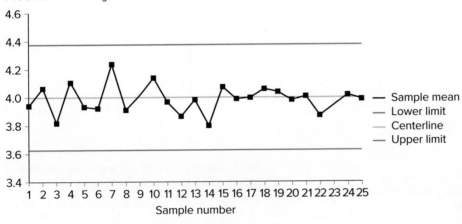

Using R

a. Import the **Paint** data into a data frame (table) in R.

b. Install and load the *qcc* package (where *qcc* stands for Quality Control Charts). Enter:

```
> install.packages("qcc")
> library(qcc)
```

c. We then create an $\bar{x}$ chart using the **qcc** function from the *qcc* package. Within the function, we first need to extract the data in columns 2 through 5 from the **Paint** data frame. This is easily done with the use of square brackets. Then, for options, we use *type* to designate the type of control chart, *center* to denote the centerline, *std.dev* to denote the standard deviation, *nsigmas* to denote the number of standard deviations from the centerline, and *title* to specify a main title for the chart. We enter:

```
> qcc(Paint[, 2:5], type="xbar", center=4,
    st.dev.=0.25, nsigmas=3, title="Control Chart
    for Paint")
```

Figure 7.12 shows the control chart that R produces. We arrive at the same conclusion, that is, the cans are being filled properly.

FIGURE 7.12 Using R to create a control chart

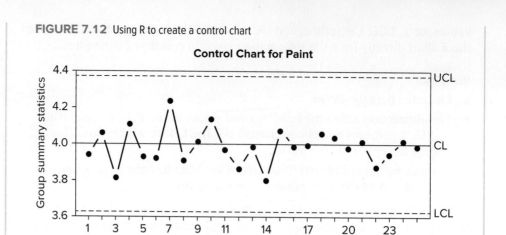

Control Chart for Paint

Number of groups = 25
Center = 4
StdDev = 0.25

LCL = 3.625
UCL = 4.375

Number beyond limits = 0
Number violating runs = 0

EXERCISES 7.5

Mechanics

38. Consider a normally distributed population with mean $\mu = 80$ and standard deviation $\sigma = 14$.
    a. Construct the centerline and the upper and lower control limits for the $\bar{x}$ chart if samples of size 5 are used.
    b. Repeat the analysis with samples of size 10.
    c. Discuss the effect of the sample size on the control limits.

39. Random samples of size $n = 250$ are taken from a population with $p = 0.04$.
    a. Construct the centerline and the upper and lower control limits for the $\bar{p}$ chart.
    b. Repeat the analysis with $n = 150$.
    c. Discuss the effect of the sample size on the control limits.

40. Random samples of size $n = 25$ are taken from a normally distributed population with mean $\mu = 20$ and standard deviation $\sigma = 10$.
    a. Construct the centerline and the upper and lower control limits for the $\bar{x}$ chart.
    b. Suppose six samples of size 25 produced the following sample means: 18, 16, 19, 24, 28, and 30. Plot these values on the $\bar{x}$ chart.
    c. Are any points outside the control limits? Does it appear that the process is under control? Explain.

41. Random samples of size $n = 36$ are taken from a population with mean $\mu = 150$ and standard deviation $\sigma = 42$.
    a. Construct the centerline and the upper and lower control limits for the $\bar{x}$ chart.
    b. Suppose five samples of size 36 produced the following sample means: 133, 142, 150, 165, and 169. Plot these values on the $\bar{x}$ chart.
    c. Are any points outside the control limits? Does it appear that the process is under control? Explain.

42. Random samples of size $n = 500$ are taken from a population with $p = 0.34$.
    a. Construct the centerline and the upper and lower control limits for the $\bar{p}$ chart.
    b. Suppose six samples of size 500 produced the following sample proportions: 0.28, 0.30, 0.33, 0.34, 0.37, and 0.39. Plot these values on the $\bar{p}$ chart.
    c. Are any points outside the control limits? Does it appear that the process is under control? Explain.

43. Random samples of size $n = 400$ are taken from a population with $p = 0.10$.
    a. Construct the centerline and the upper and lower control limits for the $\bar{p}$ chart.
    b. Suppose six samples of size 400 produced the following sample proportions: 0.06, 0.11, 0.09, 0.08, 0.14, and 0.16. Plot these values on the $\bar{p}$ chart.
    c. Is the production process under control? Explain.

Applications

44. Major League Baseball Rule 1.09 states that "the baseball shall weigh not less than 5 or more than 5¼ ounces" (www.mlb.com). Use these values as the lower and the upper control limits, respectively. Assume the centerline equals 5.125 ounces. Periodic samples of 50 baseballs produce the following sample means:

$\bar{x}_1 = 5.05$	$\bar{x}_2 = 5.10$	$\bar{x}_3 = 5.15$	$\bar{x}_4 = 5.20$	$\bar{x}_5 = 5.22$	$\bar{x}_6 = 5.24$

   a. Construct an $\bar{x}$ chart. Plot the sample means on the $\bar{x}$ chart.
   b. Are any points outside the control limits? Does it appear that the process is under control? Explain.

45. A production process is designed to fill boxes with an average of 14 ounces of cereal. The population of filling weights is normally distributed with a standard deviation of 2 ounces. Inspectors take periodic samples of 10 boxes. The following sample means are obtained.

$\bar{x}_1 = 13.7$	$\bar{x}_2 = 14.2$	$\bar{x}_3 = 13.9$	$\bar{x}_4 = 14.1$	$\bar{x}_5 = 14.3$	$\bar{x}_6 = 13.9$

   a. Construct an $\bar{x}$ chart. Plot the sample means on the $\bar{x}$ chart.
   b. Can the firm conclude that the production process is operating properly? Explain.

46. **FILE** *Cricket.* Fast bowling, also known as pace bowling, is an important component of the bowling attack in the sport of cricket. The objective is to bowl at a high speed and make the ball turn in the air and off the ground so that it becomes difficult for the batsman to hit it cleanly. Kalwant Singh is a budding Indian cricketer in a special bowling camp. While his coach is happy with Kalwant's average bowling speed, he feels that Kalwant lacks consistency. He records his bowling speed on the next four overs, where each over consists of six balls.

Over 1	Over 2	Over 3	Over 4
96.8	99.2	88.4	98.4
99.5	100.2	97.8	91.4
88.8	90.1	82.8	85.5
81.9	98.7	91.2	87.6
100.1	96.4	94.2	90.3
96.8	98.8	89.8	85.9

It is fair to assume that Kalwant's bowling speed is normally distributed with a mean and a standard deviation of 94 miles per hour and 2.8 miles per hour, respectively.
   a. Construct the centerline and the upper and lower control limits for the $\bar{x}$ chart. Plot the average speed of Kalwant's four overs on the $\bar{x}$ chart.
   b. Is there any pattern in Kalwant's bowling that justifies his coach's concerns that he is not consistent in bowling? Explain.

47. A manufacturing process produces steel rods in batches of 1,000. The firm believes that the percent of defective items generated by this process is 5%.
   a. Construct the centerline and the upper and lower control limits for the $\bar{p}$ chart.
   b. An engineer inspects the next batch of 1,000 steel rods and finds that 6.2% are defective. Is the manufacturing process under control? Explain.

48. A firm produces computer chips for personal computers. From past experience, the firm knows that 4% of the chips are defective. The firm collects a sample of the first 500 chips manufactured at 1:00 pm for the past two weeks. The following sample proportions are obtained:

$\bar{p}_1 = 0.044$	$\bar{p}_2 = 0.052$	$\bar{p}_3 = 0.060$	$\bar{p}_4 = 0.036$	$\bar{p}_5 = 0.028$
$\bar{p}_6 = 0.042$	$\bar{p}_7 = 0.034$	$\bar{p}_8 = 0.054$	$\bar{p}_9 = 0.048$	$\bar{p}_{10} = 0.025$

   a. Construct a $\bar{p}$ chart. Plot the sample proportions on the $\bar{p}$ chart.
   b. Can the firm conclude that the process is operating properly?

49. The college admissions office at a local university usually admits 750 students and knows from previous experience that 25% of these students choose not to enroll at the university.
   a. Construct the centerline and the upper and lower control limits for the $\bar{p}$ chart.
   b. Assume that this year the university admits 750 students and 240 choose not to enroll at the university. Should the university be concerned? Explain.

50. Following customer complaints about the quality of service, Dell stopped routing corporate customers to a technical support call center in Bangalore, India (*USA TODAY*, November 24, 2003). Suppose Dell's decision to direct customers to call centers outside of India was based on consumer complaints in the last six months. Let the number of complaints per month for 80 randomly selected customers be given below.

Month	Number of Complaints
1	20
2	12
3	24
4	14
5	25
6	22

   a. Construct the centerline and the upper and lower control limits for the $\bar{p}$ chart if management allows a 15% complaint rate.
   b. Can you justify Dell's decision to direct customers to call centers outside of India?

©Ryan McVay/Photodisc/Getty Images RF

Barbara Dwyer, the manager at Lux Hotel, makes every effort to ensure that customers attempting to make phone reservations wait an average of only 60 seconds to speak with a reservations specialist. She knows that this is likely to be the customer's first impression of the hotel and she wants the initial interaction to be a positive one. Since the hotel accepts phone reservations 24 hours a day, Barbara wonders if the quality of service is consistently maintained throughout the day. She takes six samples of $n = 4$ calls during each of four shifts over one 24-hour period and records the wait time of each call. A portion of the data, in seconds, is presented in Table 7.2.

Barbara assumes that wait times are normally distributed with a mean and standard deviation of 60 seconds and 30 seconds, respectively. She wants to use the sample information to

1. Prepare a control chart for wait times.

2. Determine, using the control chart, whether the quality of service is consistently maintained throughout the day.

FILE

Lux_Hotel

TABLE 7.2 Wait times for phone reservations

Shift	Sample	Wait Time (in seconds)				Sample Mean, $\bar{x}$
Shift 1: 12:00 am–6:00 am	1	67	48	52	71	60
	2	57	68	60	66	63
	3	37	41	60	41	45
	4	83	59	49	66	64
	5	82	63	64	83	73
	6	87	53	66	69	69
⋮	⋮	⋮	⋮	⋮	⋮	⋮
Shift 4: 6:00 pm–12:00 am	19	6	11	8	9	9
	20	10	8	10	9	9
	21	11	7	14	7	10
	22	8	9	9	12	10
	23	9	12	9	14	11
	24	5	8	15	11	10

Sample Report— Customer Wait Time

When a potential customer phones Lux Hotel, it is imperative for the reservations specialist to set a tone that relays the high standard of service that the customer will receive if he/she chooses to stay at the Lux. For this reason, management at the Lux strives to minimize the time that elapses before a potential customer speaks with a reservations specialist; however, management also recognizes the need to use its resources wisely. If too many reservations specialists are on duty, then resources are wasted due to idle time; yet if too few reservations specialists are on duty, the result might mean angry first-time customers or, worse, lost customers. In order to ensure customer satisfaction as well as an efficient use of resources, a study is conducted to determine whether a typical customer waits an average of 60 seconds to speak with a reservations specialist. Before data are collected, a control chart is constructed. The upper control limit (UCL) and the lower control limit (LCL) are set three standard deviations from the desired average of 60 seconds. In Figure 7.A, the desired average of 60 seconds is denoted as the centerline and the upper and lower control limits amount to 105 seconds and 15 seconds $\left(\mu \pm 3\frac{\sigma}{\sqrt{n}} = 60 \pm 3\frac{30}{\sqrt{4}} = 60 \pm 45 \right)$, respectively. The reservation process is deemed under control if the sample means fall randomly within the upper and lower control limits; otherwise the process is out of control and adjustments should be made.

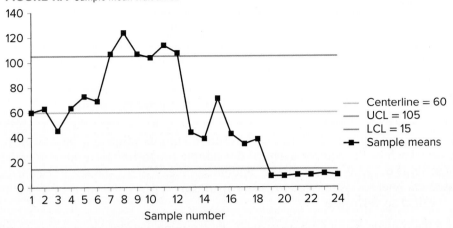

FIGURE 7.A Sample mean wait times

During each of four shifts, six samples of $n = 4$ calls are randomly selected over one 24-hour period and the average wait time of each sample is recorded. All six sample means from the first shift (1st shift: 12:00 am–6:00 am, sample numbers 1 through 6) fall within the control limits, indicating that the reservation process is in control. However, five sample means from the second shift (2nd shift: 6:00 am–12:00 pm, sample numbers 7 through 12) lie above the upper control limit. Customers calling during the second shift are waiting too long before they speak with a specialist. In terms of quality standards, this is unacceptable from the hotel's perspective. All six sample means from the third shift fall within the control limits (3rd shift: 12:00 pm–6:00 pm, sample numbers 13 through 18), yet all sample means for the fourth shift fall below the lower control limit (4th shift: 6:00 pm–12:00 am, sample numbers 19 through 24). Customers are waiting for very short periods of time to speak with a reservations specialist, but reservations specialists may have too much idle time. Perhaps one solution is to shift some reservations specialists from shift four to shift two.

CONCEPTUAL REVIEW

LO 7.1 **Explain common sample biases.**

A sampling **bias** occurs when the information from a sample is not typical of that in the population in a systematic way. It is often caused by samples that are not representative of the population. **Selection bias** refers to a systematic underrepresentation of certain groups from consideration for the sample. **Nonresponse bias** refers to a systematic difference in preferences between respondents and nonrespondents to a survey or a poll. **Social-desirability bias** refers to a systematic difference between a group's "socially acceptable" responses to a survey or poll and this group's ultimate choice.

LO 7.2 **Describe various sampling methods.**

A **simple random sample** is a sample of n observations that has the same probability of being selected from the population as any other sample of n observations. Most statistical methods presume simple random samples.

A **stratified random sample** is formed when the population is divided into groups (strata) based on one or more classification criteria. A stratified random sample includes randomly selected observations from each stratum. The number of observations per stratum is proportional to the stratum's size in the population. The data for each stratum are eventually pooled. A **cluster sample** is formed when the population is divided into groups (clusters) based on geographic areas. Whereas a stratified random sample consists of elements from each group, a cluster sample includes observations from randomly selected clusters. Stratified random sampling is preferred when the objective is to increase precision and cluster sampling is preferred when the objective is to reduce costs.

LO 7.3 Describe the sampling distribution of the sample mean.

A particular characteristic of a population, such as the mean or the proportion, is called a parameter, which is a constant even though its value may be unknown. A statistic, such as the sample mean or the sample proportion, is a random variable whose value depends on the chosen random sample. When a statistic is used to estimate a parameter, it is referred to as an **estimator**. A particular value of the estimator is called an **estimate**.

Since the statistic $\overline{X}$ is a random variable, its sampling distribution is the probability distribution of sample means derived from all possible samples of a given size from the population. The expected value of the sample mean $\overline{X}$ equals $E(\overline{X}) = \mu$, and the standard deviation, commonly referred to as the standard error of the sample mean, equals $se(\overline{X}) = \frac{\sigma}{\sqrt{n}}$. For any sample size, the sampling distribution of $\overline{X}$ is normal if the population is normally distributed.

If $\overline{X}$ is normally distributed, then any value $\overline{x}$ can be transformed to its corresponding z value as $z = \frac{\overline{x} - \mu}{\sigma/\sqrt{n}}$.

LO 7.4 Explain the importance of the central limit theorem.

The **central limit theorem** (**CLT**) is used when the random sample is drawn from an unknown or a nonnormal population. It states that for any population X with expected value μ and standard deviation σ, the sampling distribution of $\overline{X}$ is approximately normal if the sample size n is sufficiently large. As a general guideline, the normal distribution approximation is justified when $n \geq 30$.

LO 7.5 Describe the sampling distribution of the sample proportion.

The expected value of the sample proportion $\overline{P}$ equals $E(\overline{P}) = p$ and its standard error equals $se(\overline{P}) = \sqrt{\frac{p(1-p)}{n}}$. From the CLT, we can conclude that for any population proportion p, the sampling distribution of $\overline{P}$ is approximately normal if the sample size n is sufficiently large. As a general guideline, the normal distribution approximation is justified when $np \geq 5$ and $n(1-p) \geq 5$. If $\overline{P}$ is normally distributed, then any value $\overline{p}$ can be transformed to its corresponding z value as

$$z = \frac{\overline{p} - p}{\sqrt{\frac{p(1-p)}{n}}}.$$

LO 7.6 Use a finite population correction factor.

If the sample size is large relative to the population size, then the standard errors of the estimators must be multiplied by a correction factor. This correction factor, called the **finite population correction factor**, is used when the sample constitutes at least 5% of the population—that is, $n \geq 0.05N$. With the correction factor, $se(\overline{X}) = \frac{\sigma}{\sqrt{n}}\left(\sqrt{\frac{N-n}{N-1}}\right)$ and $se(\overline{P}) = \sqrt{\frac{p(1-p)}{n}}\left(\sqrt{\frac{N-n}{N-1}}\right)$. The transformation to the corresponding z value is made accordingly.

LO 7.7 Construct and interpret control charts for quantitative and qualitative data.

Statistical quality control involves statistical techniques used to develop and maintain a firm's ability to produce high-quality goods and services. The most commonly used statistical tool in quality control is the **control chart**. A control chart specifies a center-line as well as an upper control limit (UCL) and a lower control limit (LCL). In general, the UCL and the LCL are set within three standard deviations of the centerline.

The UCL and the LCL for the $\bar{x}$ **chart** are defined as $\mu + 3\frac{\sigma}{\sqrt{n}}$ and $\mu - 3\frac{\sigma}{\sqrt{n}}$, respectively. For the $\bar{p}$ **chart**, these limits are defined as $p + 3\sqrt{\frac{p(1-p)}{n}}$ and $p - 3\sqrt{\frac{p(1-p)}{n}}$, respectively. In general, if the sample means or the sample proportions fall within the control limits, then the process is under control; otherwise it is out of control and adjustment is necessary. However, even if these sample estimates fall within the control limits, they must be randomly spread between the limits. If there is a trend or unusually long runs above or below the centerline, then the process may be veering out of control.

ADDITIONAL EXERCISES AND CASE STUDIES

Exercises

51. A seminal study conducted by scientists at the University of Illinois found evidence of improved memory and reasoning for those who took three vigorous 40-minute walks a week over six months (*Newsweek*, June 28–July 5, 2010). As an assistant manager working for a public health institute based in Florida, you would like to estimate the proportion of adults in Miami, Florida, who follow such a walking regimen. Discuss the sampling bias in the following strategies where people are asked if they walk regularly:
    a. Randomly selected adult beachgoers in Miami.
    b. Randomly selected Miami residents who are requested to disclose the information in prepaid envelopes.
    c. Randomly selected Miami residents who are requested to disclose the information on the firm's website.
    d. Randomly selected adult patients at all hospitals in Miami.

52. In the previous question regarding walking regimens of the residents of Miami, explain how you can obtain a representative sample based on the following sampling strategies:
    a. Simple random sampling.
    b. Stratified random sampling.
    c. Cluster sampling.

53. According to the Bureau of Labor Statistics, it takes an average of 22 weeks for someone over 55 to find a new job, compared with 16 weeks

for younger workers (*The Wall Street Journal*, September 2, 2008). Assume that the probability distributions are normal and that the standard deviation is 2 weeks for both distributions.
    a. What is the probability that 8 workers over the age of 55 take an average of more than 20 weeks to find a job?
    b. What is the probability that 20 younger workers average less than 15 weeks to find a job?

54. Presidential job approval is the most-watched statistic in American politics. According to the June 2010 NBC/*Wall Street Journal* public opinion poll, President Barack Obama had reached his lowest approval rating since taking office in January of 2009. The poll showed that 48% of people disapproved of the job Obama was doing as president of the United States, while only 45% approved. Experts attributed the drop in approval ratings to a poor economy and the government's reaction to the massive oil spill in the Gulf of Mexico. Use the June 2010 approval and disapproval ratings to answer the following questions.
    a. What is the probability that President Obama gets a majority support in a random sample of 50 Americans?
    b. What is the probability that President Obama gets a majority disapproval in a random sample of 50 Americans?

55. While starting salaries have fallen for college graduates in many of the top hiring fields, there is some good news for business

undergraduates with concentrations in accounting and finance (*Bloomberg Businessweek,* July 1, 2010). According to the National Association of Colleges and Employers' Summer 2010 Salary Survey, accounting graduates commanded the second highest salary at $50,402, followed by finance graduates at $49,703. Let the standard deviation for accounting and finance graduates be $6,000 and $10,000, respectively.

   a. What is the probability that 100 randomly selected accounting graduates will average more than $52,000 in salary?

   b. What is the probability that 100 randomly selected finance graduates will average more than $52,000 in salary?

   c. Comment on the above probabilities.

56. An automatic machine in a manufacturing process is operating properly if the length of an important subcomponent is normally distributed with a mean $\mu = 80$ cm and a standard deviation $\sigma = 2$ cm.

   a. Find the probability that the length of one randomly selected unit is less than 79 cm.

   b. Find the probability that the average length of 10 randomly selected units is less than 79 cm.

   c. Find the probability that the average length of 30 randomly selected units is less than 79 cm.

57. Trader Joe's is a privately held chain of specialty grocery stores in the United States. Starting out as a small chain of convenience stores, it has expanded to over 340 stores as of June 2010 (www.traderjoes.com). It has developed a reputation as a unique grocery store selling products such as gourmet foods, beer and wine, bread, nuts, cereal, and coffee. One of their best-selling nuts is Raw California Almonds, which are priced at $4.49 for 16 ounces. Since it is impossible to pack exactly 16 ounces in each packet, a researcher has determined that the weight of almonds in each packet is normally distributed with a mean and a standard deviation equal to 16.01 ounces and 0.08 ounces, respectively.

   a. Discuss the sampling distribution of the sample mean based on any given sample size.

   b. Find the probability that a random sample of 20 bags of almonds will average less than 16 ounces.

   c. Suppose your cereal recipe calls for no less than 48 ounces of almonds. What is the probability that three packets of almonds will meet your requirement?

58. Georgia residents spent an average of $470.73 on the lottery in 2010, or 1% of their personal income (www.msn.com, May 23, 2012). Suppose the amount spent on the lottery follows a normal distribution with a standard deviation of $50.

   a. What is the probability that a randomly selected Georgian spent more than $500 on the lottery?

   b. If four Georgians are randomly selected, what is the probability that the average amount spent on the lottery was more than $500?

   c. If four Georgians are randomly selected, what is the probability that all of them spent more than $500 on the lottery?

59. Data from the Bureau of Labor Statistics' Consumer Expenditure Survey show that annual expenditures for cellular phone services per consumer unit increased from $210 in 2001 to $608 in 2007. Let the standard deviation of annual cellular expenditure be $48 in 2001 and $132 in 2007.

   a. What is the probability that the average annual expenditure of 100 cellular customers in 2001 exceeded $200?

   b. What is the probability that the average annual expenditure of 100 cellular customers in 2007 exceeded $600?

60. According to a report, scientists in New England say they have identified a set of genetic variants that predicts extreme longevity with 77% accuracy (*The New York Times,* July 1, 2010). Assume 150 patients decide to get their genomes sequenced.

   a. If the claim by scientists is accurate, what is the probability that more than 120 patients will get a correct diagnosis for extreme longevity?

   b. If the claim by scientists is accurate, what is the probability that fewer than 70% of the patients will get a correct diagnosis for extreme longevity?

61. American workers are increasingly planning to delay retirement (*U.S. News & World Report,* June 30, 2010). According to a Pew Research Center comprehensive survey, 35% of employed adults of age 62 and older say they have pushed back their retirement date.
    a. What is the probability that in a sample of 100 employed adults of age 62 and older, more than 40% have pushed back their retirement date?
    b. What is the probability that in a sample of 200 employed adults of age 62 and older, more than 40% have pushed back their retirement date?
    c. Comment on the difference between the two estimated probabilities.

62. **FILE** *Packaging.* A variety of packaging solutions exist for products that must be kept within a specific temperature range. Cold chain distribution is particularly useful in the food and pharmaceutical industries. A packaging company strives to maintain a constant temperature for its packages. It is believed that the temperature of its packages follows a normal distribution with a mean of 5 degrees Celsius and a standard deviation of 0.3 degree Celsius. Inspectors take weekly samples for 5 weeks of eight randomly selected boxes and report the temperatures in degrees Celsius. A portion of the data is given below.

Week 1	Week 2	Week 3	Week 4	Week 5
3.98	5.52	5.79	3.98	5.14
4.99	5.52	6.42	5.79	6.25
⋮	⋮	⋮	⋮	⋮
4.95	4.95	5.44	5.95	4.28

   a. Construct an $\bar{x}$ chart for quality control. Plot the five weekly sample means on the $\bar{x}$ chart.
   b. Are any points outside the control limits? Does it appear that the process is in control? Explain.

63. The producer of a particular brand of soup claims that its sodium content is 50% less than that of its competitor. The food label states that the sodium content measures 410 milligrams per serving. Assume the population of sodium content is normally distributed with a standard deviation of 25 milligrams. Inspectors take periodic samples of 25 cans and measure the sodium content. The following sample means are obtained.

$\bar{x}_1 = 405$	$\bar{x}_2 = 412$	$\bar{x}_3 = 399$
$\bar{x}_4 = 420$	$\bar{x}_5 = 430$	$\bar{x}_6 = 428$

   a. Construct an $\bar{x}$ chart. Plot the sample means on the $\bar{x}$ chart.
   b. Can the inspectors conclude that the producer is advertising the sodium content accurately? Explain.

64. Acceptance sampling is an important quality control technique, where a batch of data is tested to determine if the proportion of units having a particular attribute exceeds a given percentage. Suppose that 10% of produced items are known to be nonconforming. Every week a batch of items is evaluated and the production machines are adjusted if the proportion of nonconforming items exceeds 15%.
    a. What is the probability that the production machines will be adjusted if the batch consists of 50 items?
    b. What is the probability that the production machines will be adjusted if the batch consists of 100 items?

65. In the previous question, suppose that the management decides to use a $\bar{p}$ chart for the analysis. As noted earlier, 10% of produced items are known to be nonconforming. The firm analyzes a batch of production items for 6 weeks and computes the following percentages of nonconforming items.

Week	Nonconforming Percentage
1	5.5
2	13.1
3	16.8
4	13.6
5	19.8
6	2.0

   a. Suppose weekly batches consisted of 50 items. Construct a $\bar{p}$ chart and determine if the machine needs adjustment in any of the weeks.
   b. Suppose weekly batches consisted of 100 items. Construct a $\bar{p}$ chart and determine if the machine needs adjustment in any of the weeks.

CASE STUDIES

CASE STUDY 7.1   The significant decline of savings in the United States from the 1970s and 1980s to the 1990s and 2000s has been widely discussed by economists (www.money.cnn.com, June 30, 2010). According to the Bureau of Economic Analysis, the savings rate of American households, defined as a percentage of the disposable personal income, was 4.20% in 2009. The reported savings rate is not uniform across the country. A public policy institute conducts two of its own surveys to compute the savings rate in the Midwest. In the first survey, a sample of 160 households is taken and the average savings rate is found to be 4.48%. Another sample of 40 households finds an average savings rate of 4.60%. Assume that the population standard deviation is 1.4%.

In a report, use the above information to

1. Compute the probability of obtaining a sample mean that is at least as high as the one computed in each of the two surveys.

2. Use these probabilities to decide which of the two samples is likely to be more representative of the United States as a whole.

CASE STUDY 7.2   According to a report, college graduates in 2010 were likely to face better job prospects than 2009 graduates (*The New York Times,* May 24, 2010). Many employers who might have been pessimistic at the start of the 2009–2010 academic year were making more offers than expected. Despite the improvement in job prospects, the Bureau of Labor Statistics reported that the current jobless rate for college graduates under age 25 was still 8%. For high school graduates under age 25 who did not enroll in college, the current jobless rate was 24.5%. Cindy Chan works in the sales department of a trendy apparel company and has recently been relocated to a small town in Iowa. She finds that there are a total of 220 college graduates and 140 high school graduates under age 25 who live in this town. Cindy wants to gauge the demand for her products by the number of youths in this town who are employed.

In a report, use the above information to

1. Compute the expected number of college and high school graduates who are employed.

2. Report the probabilities that at least 200 college graduates and at least 100 high school graduates under age 25 are employed.

CASE STUDY 7.3   Hockey pucks used by the National Hockey League (NHL) and other professional leagues weigh an average of 163 grams (5.75 ounces). A quality inspector monitors the manufacturing process for hockey pucks. She takes eight samples of $n = 10$. It is believed that puck weights are normally distributed, and when the production process is in control, $\mu = 163$ and $\sigma = 7.5$. A portion of the data, measured in grams, is shown in the accompanying table.

FILE
Hockey_Puck

Data for Case Study 7.3 Hockey Puck Weights (in grams)

#1	#2	#3	#4	#5	#6	#7	#8
162.2	165.8	156.4	165.3	168.6	167.0	186.8	178.3
159.8	166.2	156.4	173.3	175.8	171.4	160.4	163.0
⋮	⋮	⋮	⋮	⋮	⋮	⋮	⋮
160.3	160.6	152.2	166.4	168.2	168.4	176.8	171.3

In a report, use the above information to

1. Prepare a control chart that specifies a centerline as well as an upper control limit (UCL) and a lower control limit (LCL).
2. Determine, using the control chart, whether the process is in control.

APPENDIX 7.1   Derivation of the Mean and the Variance for $\overline{X}$ and $\overline{P}$

Sample Mean, $\overline{X}$

Let the expected value and the variance of the population X be denoted by $E(X) = \mu$ and $Var(X) = \sigma^2$, respectively. The sample mean $\overline{X}$ based on a random draw of n observations, $X_1, X_2, \ldots, X_n$, from the population is computed as $\overline{X} = \frac{X_1 + X_2 + \cdots + X_n}{n}$.

We use the properties of the sum of random variables to derive

$$E(\overline{X}) = E\left(\frac{X_1 + X_2 + \cdots + X_n}{n}\right) = \frac{E(X_1) + E(X_2) + \cdots + E(X_n)}{n}$$

$$= \frac{\mu + \mu + \cdots + \mu}{n} = \frac{n\mu}{n} = \mu.$$

Since the sample mean is based on n independent draws from the population, the covariance terms drop out and the variance of the sample mean is thus derived as

$$Var(\overline{X}) = Var\left(\frac{X_1 + X_2 + \cdots + X_n}{n}\right) = \frac{1}{n^2}Var(X_1 + X_2 + \cdots + X_n)$$

$$= \frac{1}{n^2}(Var(X_1) + Var(X_2) + \cdots + Var(X_n))$$

$$= \frac{\sigma^2 + \sigma^2 + \cdots + \sigma^2}{n^2} = \frac{n\sigma^2}{n^2} = \frac{\sigma^2}{n}.$$

Sample Proportion, $\overline{P}$

Let X be a binomial random variable representing the number of successes in n trials. Recall from Chapter 5 that $E(X) = np$ and $Var(X) = np(1-p)$ where p is the probability of success. For the sample proportion $\overline{P} = \frac{X}{n}$,

$$E(\overline{P}) = E\left(\frac{X}{n}\right) = \frac{E(X)}{n} = \frac{np}{n} = p, \quad \text{and}$$

$$Var(\overline{P}) = Var\left(\frac{X}{n}\right) = \frac{Var(X)}{n^2} = \frac{np(1-p)}{n^2} = \frac{p(1-p)}{n}.$$

APPENDIX 7.2   Properties of Point Estimators

We generally discuss the performance of an estimator in terms of its statistical properties. Some of the desirable properties of a point estimator include unbiasedness, consistency, and efficiency. An estimator is **unbiased** if, based on repeated sampling from the population, the average value of the estimator equals the population parameter. In other words, for an unbiased estimator, the expected value of the point estimator equals the population parameter.

Figure A7.1 shows the sampling distributions for two estimators U_1 and U_2, which are assumed to be normally distributed. Let θ (the Greek letter read as theta) be the true parameter value of the population. Estimator U_1 is unbiased because its expected value $E(U_1)$ equals θ. Estimator U_2 is biased because $E(U_2) \neq \theta$; the degree of bias is given by the difference between $E(U_2)$ and θ.

FIGURE A7.1 The distributions of unbiased (U_1) and biased (U_2) estimators

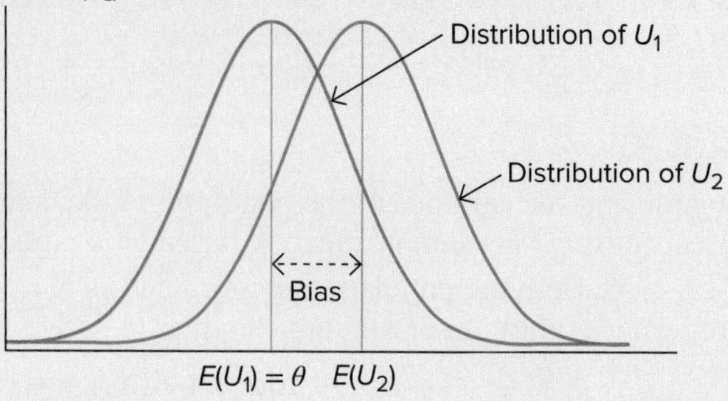

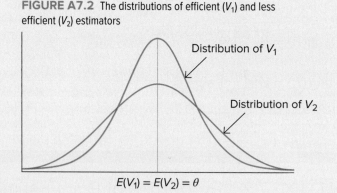

Since $E(\overline{X}) = \mu$ and $E(\overline{P}) = p$, $\overline{X}$ and $\overline{P}$ are the unbiased estimators of μ and p, respectively. This property is independent of the sample size. For instance, the expected value of the sample mean is equal to the population mean irrespective of the sample size.

We often compare the performance of the unbiased estimators in terms of their relative **efficiency**. An estimator is deemed efficient if its variability between samples is smaller than that of other unbiased estimators. Recall that the variability is often measured by the standard error of the estimator. For an unbiased estimator to be efficient, its standard error must be lower than that of other unbiased estimators. It is well documented that the estimators $\overline{X}$ and $\overline{P}$ are not only unbiased, but also efficient.

Figure A7.2 shows the sampling distributions for two unbiased estimators, V_1 and V_2, for the true population parameter θ. Again, for illustration, V_1 and V_2 follow the normal distribution. While both V_1 and V_2 are unbiased ($E(V_1) = E(V_2) = \theta$), V_1 is more efficient because it has less variability.

FIGURE A7.2 The distributions of efficient (V_1) and less efficient (V_2) estimators

Another desirable property, which is often considered a minimum requirement for an estimator, is **consistency**. An estimator is consistent if it approaches the population parameter of interest as the sample size increases. Consistency implies that we will get the inference right if we take a large enough sample. The estimators $\overline{X}$

and $\bar{P}$ are not only unbiased, but also consistent. For instance, the sample mean collapses to the population mean $(\bar{X} \rightarrow \mu)$ as the sample size approaches infinity $(n \rightarrow \infty)$. An unbiased estimator is consistent if its standard error collapses to zero as the sample size increases.

The consistency of $\bar{X}$ is illustrated in Figure A7.3.

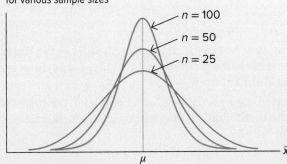

FIGURE A7.3 The distribution of a consistent estimator $\bar{X}$ for various sample sizes

As the sample size n increases, the variability of $\bar{X}$ decreases. In particular as $n \rightarrow \infty$, $SD(\bar{X}) = \sigma/\sqrt{n} \rightarrow 0$, thus implying that $\bar{X}$ is a consistent estimator of μ.

APPENDIX 7.3 Guidelines for Other Software Packages

The following section provides brief commands for Minitab, SPSS, and JMP.

Minitab

Generating a Random Sample

A. (Replicating Example 7.1) From the menu, choose **Calc > Random Data > Integer**.

B. Enter 100 as the **Number of rows of data to generate**; enter C1 for **Store in column**; enter 1 for **Minimum value** and 2,750 as **Maximum value**.

Constructing an $\bar{x}$ Chart

A. (Replicating Figure 7.11). Stack all the observations (columns 2–5) into one column, and label it "observations."

B. From the menu, choose **Stat > Control Charts > Variables Charts for Subgroups > Xbar**.

C. Choose **All observations for a chart are in one column**, and in the box directly under this one, select observations. For **Subgroup sizes**, enter the number 4. Choose **Xbar Options** and enter 4 for **Mean** and 0.25 for **Standard deviation**.

SPSS

Constructing an $\bar{x}$ Chart

A. (Replicating Figure 7.11). Stack the observations (columns 2–5) into one column, and label it "observations." In an adjacent column, indicate how the data are grouped and label this column "group." For instance, the first four observations are given the value 1; the next four observations are given the value 2, and so on.

B. From the menu, select **Analyze > Quality Control > Control Charts > X-bar, R, s**.

C. Under **Process Measurement**, select observations, and under **Subgroups Defined by** select group. Under **Charts**, select **X-bar using standard deviation**. Choose **Options**. After **Number of Sigmas**, enter 3, and after **Minimum subgroup size**, enter 4. Choose **Statistics**. Under **Specification Limits**, enter 4.375 for **Upper**, 3.625 for **Lower**, and 4 for **Target**.

JMP

Generating a Random Sample

A. (Replicating Example 7.1) Right-click on the header at the top of the column in the spreadsheet view and select **Formula**. Under **Functions (grouped)**, choose **Random > Random Integer**.

B. Put the insertion marker on the box for **n1** and click the insert button (shown as a caret ^ with the mathematical operations) until you see **n2** next to **n1**. Enter 1 for **n1** and 2,750 for **n2**.

Paint

Constructing the $\bar{x}$ Chart

A. (Replicating Figure 7.11). Stack all the observations (columns 2–5) into one column, and label it "observations."

B. From the menu, choose **Analyze > Quality and Process > Control Chart > X-bar**.

C. Under **Select Columns**, select observations, and under **Cast Columns into Roles**, select Process. Under **Parameters**, select **KSigma** and enter 3. Under **Sample Size**, select **Sample Size Constant** and enter 4. Select **Specify Stats**. Enter 0.25 for **Sigma** and 4 for **Mean(measure)**.

8 Interval Estimation

In earlier chapters, we made a distinction between the population parameters, such as the population mean and the population proportion, and the corresponding sample statistics. The sample statistics are used to make statistical inferences regarding the unknown values of the population parameters. In general, two basic methodologies emerge from the inferential branch of statistics: estimation and hypothesis testing. As discussed in Chapter 7, a point estimator uses sample data to produce a single value as an estimate for the unknown population parameter of interest. A confidence interval, on the other hand, produces a range of values that estimate the unknown population parameter. In this chapter, we develop and interpret confidence intervals for the population mean and the population proportion. Since obtaining a sample is one of the first steps in making statistical inferences, we also learn how an appropriate sample size is determined in order to achieve a certain level of precision in the estimates.

©1000 Words/Shutterstock RF

INTRODUCTORY CASE

Fuel Usage of "Ultra-Green" Cars

A car manufacturer advertises that its new "ultra-green" car obtains an average of 100 miles per gallon (mpg) and, based on its fuel emissions, is one of the few cars that earns an A+ rating from the Environmental Protection Agency. Jared Beane, an analyst at Pinnacle Research, records the mpg for a sample of 25 "ultra-green" cars after the cars were driven equal distances under identical conditions. Table 8.1 shows each car's mpg.

TABLE 8.1 MPG for a Sample of 25 "Ultra-Green" Cars

FILE MPG

97	117	93	79	97
87	78	83	94	96
102	98	82	96	113
113	111	90	101	99
112	89	92	96	98

Jared has already used tabular and graphical methods to summarize the data in his report. He would like to make statistical inferences regarding key population parameters. In particular, he wants to use the above sample information to

1. Estimate the mean mpg of all ultra-green cars with 90% confidence.

2. Estimate the proportion of all ultra-green cars that obtain over 100 mpg with 90% confidence.

3. Determine the sample size that will enable him to achieve a specified level of precision in his mean and proportion estimates.

A synopsis of this case is provided at the end of Section 8.4.

8.1 CONFIDENCE INTERVAL FOR THE POPULATION MEAN WHEN σ IS KNOWN

Recall that a population consists of all items of interest in a statistical problem, whereas a sample is a subset of the population. Given sample data, we use the sample statistics to make inferences about the unknown population parameters, such as the population mean and the population proportion. Two basic methodologies emerge from the inferential branch of statistics: estimation and hypothesis testing. Although the sample statistics are based on a portion of the population, they contain useful information to estimate the population parameters and to conduct tests regarding the population parameters. In this chapter, we focus on estimation.

As discussed in Chapter 7, when a statistic is used to estimate a parameter, it is referred to as a point estimator, or simply an estimator. A particular value of the estimator is called a point estimate or an estimate. Recall that the sample mean $\overline{X}$ is the estimator of the population mean μ, and the sample proportion $\overline{P}$ is the estimator of the population proportion p. Let us consider the introductory case where Jared Beane records the mpg for a sample of 25 ultra-green cars. We use the sample information in Table 8.1 to compute the mean mpg of the cars as $\bar{x} = 96.52$ mpg. Similarly, since Jared is also interested in the proportion of these cars that get an mpg greater than 100, and seven of the cars in the sample satisfied this criterion, we compute the relevant sample proportion as $\bar{p} = 7/25 = 0.28$. Therefore, our estimate for the mean mpg of all ultra-green cars is 96.52 mpg, and our estimate for the proportion of all ultra-green cars with mpg greater than 100 is 0.28.

It is important to note that the above estimates are based on a sample of 25 cars and, therefore, are likely to vary between samples. For instance, the values will change if another sample of 25 cars is used. What Jared really wishes to estimate are the mean and the proportion (parameters) of all ultra-green cars (population), not just those comprising the sample. We now examine how we can extract useful information from a single sample to make inferences about these population parameters.

So far we have only discussed point estimators. Often it is more informative to provide a range of values—an interval—rather than a single point estimate for the unknown population parameter. This range of values is called a **confidence interval**, also referred to as an **interval estimate**, for the population parameter.

CONFIDENCE INTERVAL

A confidence interval, or interval estimate, provides a range of values that, with a certain level of confidence, contains the population parameter of interest.

In order to construct a confidence interval for the population mean μ or the population proportion p, it is essential that the sampling distributions of $\overline{X}$ and $\overline{P}$ follow, or approximately follow, a normal distribution. Other methods that do not require the normality condition are not discussed in this text. Recall from Chapter 7 that $\overline{X}$ follows a normal distribution when the underlying population is normally distributed; this result holds irrespective of the sample size n. If the underlying population is not normally distributed, then by the central limit theorem, the sampling distribution of $\overline{X}$ will be approximately normal if the sample size is sufficiently large—that is, when $n \geq 30$. Similarly, the sampling distribution of $\overline{P}$ is approximately normal if the sample size is sufficiently large—that is, when $np \geq 5$ and $n(1 - p) \geq 5$.

The main ingredient for developing a confidence interval is the sampling distribution of the underlying statistic. The sampling distribution of $\overline{X}$, for example, describes how the sample mean varies between samples. Recall that the variability between samples is measured by the standard error of $\overline{X}$. If the standard error is small, it implies that the sample means are not only close to one another, they are also close to the unknown population mean μ.

A confidence interval is generally associated with a **margin of error** that accounts for the standard error of the estimator and the desired confidence level of the interval. As we have just stressed, the sampling distributions of the estimators for the population mean and the population proportion must be approximately normal. The symmetry implied by the normal distribution allows us to construct a confidence interval by adding and subtracting the same margin of error to the point estimate.

An analogy to a simple weather example is instructive. If you feel that the outside temperature is about 50 degrees, then perhaps you can, with a certain level of confidence, suggest that the actual temperature is between 40 and 60 degrees. In this example, 50 degrees is analogous to a point estimate of the actual temperature, and 10 degrees is the margin of error that is added to and subtracted from this point estimate.

We know from the introductory case study that the point estimate for the population mean mpg of all ultra-green cars is 96.52 mpg; that is, $\bar{x} = 96.52$. We can construct a confidence interval by using the point estimate as a base to which we add and subtract the margin of error.

Constructing a Confidence Interval for μ When σ Is Known

LO 8.2

Calculate a confidence interval for the population mean when the population standard deviation is known.

Let us construct the 95% confidence interval for μ when the sampling distribution of $\overline{X}$ is normal. Consider the standard normal random variable Z. Using the symmetry of Z, we can compute $P(Z > 1.96) = P(Z < -1.96) = 0.025$; see Figure 8.1. Remember that $z = 1.96$ is easily determined from the z table given the probability of 0.025 in the upper tail of the distribution. Therefore, we formulate the probability statement $P(-1.96 \leq Z \leq 1.96) = 0.95$.

FIGURE 8.1 Graphical depiction of $P(Z < -1.96) = 0.025$ and $P(Z > 1.96) = 0.025$

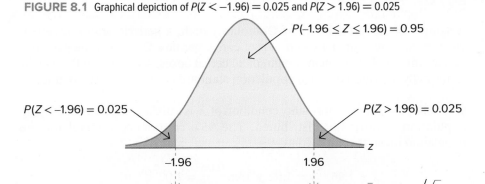

Since $Z = \frac{X - \mu}{\sigma/\sqrt{n}}$, for a normally distributed $\overline{X}$ with mean μ and standard error $\sigma/\sqrt{n}$, we get
$$P\left(-1.96 \leq \frac{\overline{X} - \mu}{\sigma/\sqrt{n}} \leq 1.96\right) = 0.95.$$

We multiply by $\sigma/\sqrt{n}$ and add μ to obtain
$$P(\mu - 1.96\sigma/\sqrt{n} \leq \overline{X} \leq \mu + 1.96\sigma/\sqrt{n}) = 0.95.$$

This equation (see also the lower portion of Figure 8.1) implies that there is a 0.95 probability that the sample mean $\overline{X}$ will fall between $\mu - 1.96\sigma/\sqrt{n}$ and $\mu + 1.96\sigma/\sqrt{n}$, that is, within the interval $\mu \pm 1.96\sigma/\sqrt{n}$. If samples of size n are drawn repeatedly from a given population, 95% of the computed sample means, $\bar{x}$'s, will fall within the interval and the remaining 5% will fall outside the interval.

We do not know the population mean μ and, therefore, cannot determine if a particular $\bar{x}$ falls within the interval or not. However, we do know that $\bar{x}$ will fall within the interval $\mu \pm 1.96\sigma/\sqrt{n}$ if, and only if, μ falls within the interval $\bar{x} \pm 1.96\sigma/\sqrt{n}$. This will happen 95% of the time given how the interval is constructed. Therefore, we call the interval $\bar{x} \pm 1.96\sigma/\sqrt{n}$ the 95% confidence interval for the population mean, where $1.96\sigma/\sqrt{n}$ is its margin of error.

Confidence intervals are often misinterpreted; we need to exercise care in characterizing them. For instance, the above 95% confidence interval does *not* imply that the probability that μ falls in the confidence interval is 0.95. Remember that μ is a constant, although its value is not known. It either falls in the interval (probability equals one) or does not fall in the interval (probability equals zero). The randomness comes from $\overline{X}$, not μ, since many possible sample means can be derived from a population. Therefore, it is incorrect to say that the probability that μ falls in the $\bar{x} \pm 1.96\sigma/\sqrt{n}$ interval is 0.95. The 95% confidence interval simply implies that if numerous samples of size n are drawn from a given population, then 95% of the intervals formed by the preceding procedure (formula) will contain μ. Keep in mind that we only use a single sample to derive the estimates. Since there are many possible samples, we will be right 95% of the time, thus giving us 95% confidence.

INTERPRETING THE 95% CONFIDENCE INTERVAL

Technically, the 95% confidence interval for the population mean μ implies that for 95% of the samples, the procedure (formula) produces an interval that contains μ. Informally, we can report with 95% confidence that μ lies in the given interval. It is not correct to say that there is a 95% chance that μ lies in the given interval.

EXAMPLE 8.1

A sample of 25 cereal boxes of Granola Crunch, a generic brand of cereal, yields a mean weight of 1.02 pounds of cereal per box. Construct the 95% confidence interval for the mean weight of all cereal boxes. Assume that the weight is normally distributed with a population standard deviation of 0.03 pound.

SOLUTION: Note that the normality condition of $\overline{X}$ is satisfied since the underlying population is normally distributed. The 95% confidence interval for the population mean is computed as

$$\bar{x} \pm 1.96 \frac{\sigma}{\sqrt{n}} = 1.02 \pm 1.96 \frac{0.03}{\sqrt{25}} = 1.02 \pm 0.012.$$

With 95% confidence, we can report that the mean weight of all cereal boxes falls between 1.008 and 1.032 pounds.

While it is common to report the 95% confidence interval, in theory we can construct an interval of any level of confidence ranging from 0 to 100%. Let's now extend the analysis to include intervals of any confidence level. Let the Greek letter α (alpha) denote the allowed probability of error; in Chapter 9 this is referred to as the significance level. This is the probability that the estimation procedure will generate an interval that does not contain μ. The **confidence coefficient** $(1 - \alpha)$ is interpreted as the probability that the estimation procedure will generate an interval that contains μ. Thus, the probability of error α is related to the confidence coefficient and the confidence level as follows:

- Confidence coefficient $= 1 - \alpha$, and
- Confidence level $= 100(1 - \alpha)\%$.

For example, the confidence coefficient of 0.95 implies that the probability of error α equals $1 - 0.95 = 0.05$ and the confidence level equals $100(1 - 0.05)\% = 95\%$. Similarly, for the 90% confidence interval, the confidence coefficient equals 0.90 and $\alpha = 1 - 0.90 = 0.10$. The following statement generalizes the construction of a confidence interval for μ when σ is known.

CONFIDENCE INTERVAL FOR μ WHEN σ IS KNOWN

A $100(1 - \alpha)\%$ confidence interval for the population mean μ when the population standard deviation σ is known is computed as

$$\bar{x} \pm z_{\alpha/2}\frac{\sigma}{\sqrt{n}} \quad \text{or} \quad \left[\bar{x} - z_{\alpha/2}\frac{\sigma}{\sqrt{n}}, \bar{x} + z_{\alpha/2}\frac{\sigma}{\sqrt{n}}\right].$$

This formula is valid only if $\overline{X}$ (approximately) follows a normal distribution.

The notation $z_{\alpha/2}$ is the z value associated with the probability of $\alpha/2$ in the upper tail of the standard normal probability distribution. In other words, if Z is a standard normal random variable and α is any probability, then $z_{\alpha/2}$ represents the z value such that the area under the z curve to the right of $z_{\alpha/2}$ is $\alpha/2$, that is, $P(Z \geq z_{\alpha/2}) = \alpha/2$. Figure 8.2 depicts the notation $z_{\alpha/2}$.

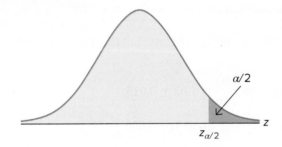

FIGURE 8.2 Graphical depiction of the notation $z_{\alpha/2}$

As discussed earlier, for the 95% confidence interval, $\alpha = 0.05$ and $\alpha/2 = 0.025$. Therefore, $z_{\alpha/2} = z_{0.025} = 1.96$. Similarly, using the z table, we can derive the following:

- For the 90% confidence interval, $\alpha = 0.10$, $\alpha/2 = 0.05$, and $z_{\alpha/2} = z_{0.05} = 1.645$.
- For the 99% confidence interval, $\alpha = 0.01$, $\alpha/2 = 0.005$, and $z_{\alpha/2} = z_{0.005} = 2.576$.

These values can also be obtained using Excel's **norm.inv** function with $\mu = 0$ and $\sigma = 1$ or R's **qnorm** function. Both of these functions were discussed in Chapter 6.

The Width of a Confidence Interval

LO 8.3

The margin of error used in the computation of the confidence interval for the population mean, when the population standard deviation is known, is $z_{\alpha/2}\frac{\sigma}{\sqrt{n}}$. Since we are basically adding and subtracting this quantity from $\bar{x}$, the width of the confidence interval is two times the margin of error. In Example 8.1, the margin of error for the 95% confidence interval is 0.012 and the width of the interval is $1.032 - 1.008 = 2(0.012) = 0.024$. Now let's examine how the width of a confidence interval is influenced by various factors.

Describe the factors that influence the width of a confidence interval.

I. For a given confidence level $100(1 - \alpha)\%$ and sample size n, the larger the population standard deviation σ, the wider the confidence interval.

EXAMPLE 8.1b

Let the standard deviation of the population in Example 8.1 be 0.05 instead of 0.03. Compute the 95% confidence interval based on the same sample information.

SOLUTION: We use the same formula as before, but we substitute 0.05 for the standard deviation instead of 0.03:

$$1.02 \pm 1.96 \frac{0.05}{\sqrt{25}} = 1.02 \pm 0.020.$$

The width has increased from 0.024 to $2(0.020) = 0.040$.

II. For a given confidence level $100(1 - \alpha)\%$ and population standard deviation σ, the smaller the sample size n, the wider the confidence interval.

EXAMPLE 8.1c

Instead of 25 observations, let the sample in Example 8.1 be based on 16 observations. Compute the 95% confidence interval using the same sample mean of 1.02 pounds and the same population standard deviation of 0.03.

SOLUTION: Again, we use the same formula as before, but this time we substitute 16 for n instead of 25:

$$1.02 \pm 1.96 \frac{0.03}{\sqrt{16}} = 1.02 \pm 0.015.$$

The width has increased from 0.024 to $2(0.015) = 0.030$.

III. For a given sample size n and population standard deviation σ, the greater the confidence level $100(1 - \alpha)\%$, the wider the confidence interval.

EXAMPLE 8.1d

Compute the 99%, instead of the 95%, confidence interval based on the information in Example 8.1.

SOLUTION: Now we use the same formula and substitute the value 2.576 for $z_{\alpha/2}$ instead of 1.96:

$$1.02 \pm 2.576 \frac{0.03}{\sqrt{25}} = 1.02 \pm 0.015.$$

The width has increased from 0.024 to $2(0.015) = 0.030$.

The precision is directly linked with the width of the confidence interval—the wider the interval, the lower its precision. Continuing with the weather analogy, a temperature estimate of 40 to 80 degrees is imprecise because the interval is too wide to be of value. We lose precision when the sample does not reveal a great deal about the population, resulting in a wide confidence interval. Examples 8.1b and 8.1c suggest that the estimate will be less precise if the variability of the underlying population is high (σ is high) or a small segment of the population is sampled (n is small). Example 8.1d relates the width with the confidence level. For given sample information, the only way we can gain confidence is by making the interval wider. If you are 95% confident that the outside temperature is between 40 and 60, then you can increase your confidence level to 99% only by using a wider range, say between 35 and 65. This result also helps us understand the difference between precision (width of the interval) and the confidence level. There is a trade-off between the amount of confidence we have in an interval and its width.

EXAMPLE 8.2

IQ tests are designed to yield scores that are approximately normally distributed. A reporter is interested in estimating the average IQ of employees in a large high-tech firm in California. She gathers the IQ scores from 22 employees of this firm and records the sample mean IQ as 106. She assumes that the population standard deviation is 15.

a. Compute 90% and 99% confidence intervals for the average IQ in this firm.
b. Use these results to infer if the mean IQ in this firm is significantly different from the national average of 100.

SOLUTION:

a. For the 90% confidence interval, $z_{\alpha/2} = z_{0.05} = 1.645$. Similarly, for the 99% confidence interval, $z_{\alpha/2} = z_{0.005} = 2.576$.

The 90% confidence interval is $106 \pm 1.645 \frac{15}{\sqrt{22}} = 106 \pm 5.26$.

The 99% confidence interval is $106 \pm 2.576 \frac{15}{\sqrt{22}} = 106 \pm 8.24$.

Note that the 99% interval is wider than the 90% interval.

b. With 90% confidence, the reporter can infer that the average IQ of this firm's employees differs from the national average, since the value 100 falls outside the 90% confidence interval, [100.74, 111.26]. However, she cannot infer the same result with 99% confidence, since the wider range of the interval, [97.76, 114.24], includes the value 100. We will study the link between estimation and testing in more detail in the next chapter.

Using Excel and R to Construct a Confidence Interval for μ When σ Is Known

We can use functions in Excel and R to construct confidence intervals. These functions are particularly useful with large data sets. Consider the following example.

EXAMPLE 8.3

Table 8.2 lists a portion of the weights (in grams) for a sample of 80 hockey pucks. Construct the 90% confidence interval for the population mean weight assuming that the population standard deviation is 7.5 grams.

TABLE 8.2 Hockey Puck
Weights, $n = 80$

Weight
162.2
159.8
⋮
171.3

FILE
Hockey_Pucks

SOLUTION: We compute $\bar{x} \pm z_{\alpha/2}\frac{\sigma}{\sqrt{n}}$, or, equivalently, we find the lower and upper limits of the confidence interval: $\left[\bar{x} - z_{\alpha/2}\frac{\sigma}{\sqrt{n}}, \bar{x} + z_{\alpha/2}\frac{\sigma}{\sqrt{n}}\right]$. We are given $\sigma = 7.5$ and $n = 80$.

Using Excel

a. Open the *Hockey_Pucks* data file. Note that the values for weights are in cells A2 through A81.

b. Recall from Chapter 6 that Excel's **NORM.INV** function finds a particular z value for a given cumulative probability. For the 90% confidence interval, $\alpha = 0.10$ and $z_{\alpha/2} = z_{0.05}$. To find the z value such that the area under the z curve to the right of $z_{0.05}$ is 0.05 (and area to the left of $z_{0.05}$ is 0.95), we use "NORM.INV(0.95, 0, 1)". In order to find the lower limit of the confidence level we enter:

"=AVERAGE(A2:A81)–NORM.INV (0.95, 0, 1) * 7.5/SQRT(80)", and Excel returns 165.33. For the upper limit, we enter "=AVERAGE(A2:A81) + NORM.INV (0.95, 0, 1) * 7.5/SQRT(80)", and Excel returns 168.09. With 90% confidence, we conclude that the mean weight of all hockey pucks falls between 165.33 and 168.09 grams.

Using R

a. Import the *Hockey_Pucks* data into a data frame (table) in R.

b. We first find the margin of error. Recall from Chapter 6 that R's **qnorm** function finds a particular z value for a given cumulative probability. For the 90% confidence interval, $\alpha = 0.10$ and $z_{\alpha/2} = z_{0.05}$. To find the z value such that the area under the z curve to the right of $z_{0.05}$ is 0.05 (and area to the left of $z_{0.05}$ is 0.95), we use "qnorm(0.95, 0, 1)." Thus, for the margin of error, labeled Error, we enter:

```
> Error <- qnorm(0.95, 0, 1)*7.5/sqrt(80)
```

c. We find the lower and upper limits of the confidence interval and then list them. For the lower limit, we enter

```
> Lower <- mean(Hockey_Pucks$'Weight') – Error
> list(Lower)
```

And R returns: 165.332.

For the upper limit, we enter

```
> Upper <- mean(Hockey_Pucks$'Weight') + Error
> list(Upper)
```

And R returns: 168.0905.

EXERCISES 8.1

Mechanics

1. Find $z_{\alpha/2}$ for each of the following confidence levels used in estimating the population mean.
   a. 90%
   b. 98%
   c. 88%

2. Find $z_{\alpha/2}$ for each of the following confidence levels used in estimating the population mean.
   a. 89%
   b. 92%
   c. 96%

3. A simple random sample of 25 observations is derived from a normally distributed population with a known standard deviation of 8.2.
   a. Is the condition that $\overline{X}$ is normally distributed satisfied? Explain.
   b. Compute the margin of error with 80% confidence.
   c. Compute the margin of error with 90% confidence.
   d. Which of the two margins of error will lead to a wider interval?

4. Consider a population with a known standard deviation of 26.8. In order to compute an interval estimate for the population mean, a sample of 64 observations is drawn.
   a. Is the condition that $\overline{X}$ is normally distributed satisfied? Explain.
   b. Compute the margin of error at the 95% confidence level.
   c. Compute the margin of error at the 95% confidence level based on a larger sample of 225 observations.
   d. Which of the two margins of error will lead to a wider confidence interval?

5. Discuss the factors that influence the margin of error for the confidence interval for the population mean. What can a practitioner do to reduce the margin of error?

Applications

6. The average life expectancy for Bostonians is 78.1 years (*The Boston Globe*, August 16, 2010). Assume that this average was based on a sample of 50 Bostonians and that the population standard deviation is 4.5 years.
   a. What is the point estimate of the population mean?
   b. At 90% confidence, what is the margin of error?
   c. Construct the 90% confidence interval for the population average life expectancy of Bostonians.

7. In order to estimate the mean 30-year fixed mortgage rate for a home loan in the United States, a random sample of 28 recent loans is taken. The average calculated from this sample is 5.25%. It can be assumed that 30-year fixed mortgage rates are normally distributed with a standard deviation of 0.50%. Compute 90% and 99% confidence intervals for the population mean 30-year fixed mortgage rate.

8. An article in the *National Geographic News* ("U.S. Racking Up Huge Sleep Debt," February 24, 2005) argues that Americans are increasingly skimping on their sleep. A researcher in a small Midwestern town wants to estimate the mean weekday sleep time of its adult residents. He takes a random sample of 80 adult residents and records their weekday mean sleep time as 6.4 hours. Assume that the population standard deviation is fairly stable at 1.8 hours.
   a. Calculate the 95% confidence interval for the population mean weekday sleep time of all adult residents of this Midwestern town.
   b. Can we conclude with 95% confidence that the mean sleep time of all adult residents in this Midwestern town is not 7 hours?

9. A family is relocating from St. Louis, Missouri, to California. Due to an increasing inventory of houses in St. Louis, it is taking longer than before to sell a house. The wife is concerned and wants to know when it is optimal to put their house on the market. Her realtor friend informs them that the last 26 houses that sold in their neighborhood took an average time of 218 days to sell. The realtor also tells them that based on her prior experience, the population standard deviation is 72 days.
   a. What assumption regarding the population is necessary for making an interval estimate for the population mean?
   b. Construct the 90% confidence interval for the mean sale time for all homes in the neighborhood.

10. U.S. consumers are increasingly viewing debit cards as a convenient substitute for cash and checks. The average amount spent annually on a debit card is $7,790 (*Kiplinger's*, August 2007). Assume that this average was based on a sample of 100 consumers and that the population standard deviation is $500.
    a. At 99% confidence, what is the margin of error?
    b. Construct the 99% confidence interval for the population mean amount spent annually on a debit card.

11. Suppose the 95% confidence interval for the mean salary of college graduates in a town in Mississippi is given by [$36,080, $43,920]. The population standard deviation used for the analysis is known to be $12,000.
    a. What is the point estimate of the mean salary for all college graduates in this town?
    b. Determine the sample size used for the analysis.

12. A manager is interested in estimating the mean time (in minutes) required to complete a job. His assistant uses a sample of 100 observations to report the confidence interval as [14.355, 17.645]. The population standard deviation is known to be equal to 10 minutes.
    a. Find the sample mean time used to compute the confidence interval.
    b. Determine the confidence level used for the analysis.

13. **FILE** *CT_Undergrad_Debt.* A study reports that recent college graduates from New Hampshire face the highest average debt of $31,048 (*The Boston Globe*, May 27, 2012). A researcher from Connecticut wants to determine how recent undergraduates from that state fare. He collects data on debt from 40 recent undergraduates. A portion of the data is shown in the accompanying table. Assume that the population standard deviation is $5,000.

Debt
24040
19153
⋮
29329

a. Construct the 95% confidence interval for the mean debt of all undergraduates from Connecticut.

b. Use the 95% confidence interval to determine if the debt of Connecticut undergraduates differs from that of New Hampshire undergraduates.

14. **FILE** *Hourly_Wage.* An economist wants to estimate the mean hourly wage (in $) of all workers. She collects data on 50 hourly wage earners. A portion of the data is shown in the accompanying table. Assume that the population standard deviation is $6. Construct and interpret 90% and 99% confidence intervals for the mean hourly wage of all workers.

Hourly Wage
37.85
21.72
⋮
24.18

15. **FILE** *Highway_Speeds.* A safety officer is concerned about speeds on a certain section of the New Jersey Turnpike. He records the speeds of 40 cars on a Saturday afternoon. The accompanying table shows a portion of the results. Assume that the population standard deviation is 5 mph. Construct the 95% confidence interval for the mean speed of all cars on that section of the turnpike. Are the safety officer's concerns valid if the speed limit is 55 mph? Explain.

Highway Speeds
70
60
⋮
65

8.2 CONFIDENCE INTERVAL FOR THE POPULATION MEAN WHEN σ IS UNKNOWN

So far we have considered confidence intervals for the population mean when the population standard deviation σ is known. In reality, σ is rarely known. Recall from Chapter 3 that the population variance and the population standard deviation are calculated as $\sigma^2 = \frac{\Sigma(x_i - \mu)^2}{N}$ and $\sigma = \sqrt{\sigma^2}$, respectively. It is highly unlikely that σ is known when μ is not. However, there are instances when the population standard deviation is considered fairly stable and, therefore, can be determined from prior experience. In these cases, the population standard deviation is treated as known.

Recall that the margin of error in a confidence interval depends on the standard error of the estimator and the desired confidence level. With σ unknown, the standard error of $\overline{X}$, given by $\sigma/\sqrt{n}$, can be conveniently estimated by $s/\sqrt{n}$, where s denotes the sample standard deviation. For convenience, we denote this estimate of the standard error of $\overline{X}$ also by $se(\overline{X}) = s/\sqrt{n}$.

LO 8.4

Discuss features of the *t* distribution.

The *t* Distribution

As discussed earlier, in order to derive a confidence interval for μ, it is essential that $\overline{X}$ be normally distributed. A normally distributed $\overline{X}$ is standardized as $Z = \frac{\overline{X} - \mu}{\sigma/\sqrt{n}}$ where Z follows the z distribution. Another standardized statistic, which uses the estimator S in place of σ, is computed as $T = \frac{\bar{X} - \mu}{S/\sqrt{n}}$. The random variable T follows the **Student's t distribution**, more commonly known as the ***t* distribution**.[1]

> ### THE t DISTRIBUTION
>
> If a random sample of size n is taken from a normal population with a finite variance, then the statistic $T = \frac{\bar{X} - \mu}{S/\sqrt{n}}$ follows the t distribution with $(n-1)$ degrees of freedom, *df*.

The t distribution is actually a family of distributions, which are similar to the z distribution in that they are all bell-shaped and symmetric around zero. However, all t distributions have slightly broader tails than the z distribution. Each t distribution is identified by the **degrees of freedom**, or simply, *df*. The degrees of freedom determine the extent of the broadness of the tails of the distribution; the fewer the degrees of freedom, the broader the tails. Since the t distribution is defined by the degrees of freedom, it is common to refer to it as the t_{df} distribution.

Specifically, the degrees of freedom refer to the number of independent pieces of information that go into the calculation of a given statistic and, in this sense, can be "freely chosen." Consider the number of independent observations that enter into the calculation of the sample mean. If it is known that $\bar{x} = 20$, $n = 4$, and three of the observations have values of $x_1 = 16$, $x_2 = 24$, and $x_3 = 18$, then there is no choice but for the fourth observation to have a value of 22. In other words, three degrees of freedom are involved in computing $\bar{x} = 20$ if $n = 4$; in effect, one degree of freedom is lost.

Summary of the t_{df} Distribution

- Like the z distribution, the t_{df} distribution is bell-shaped and symmetric around 0 with asymptotic tails (the tails get closer and closer to the horizontal axis but never touch it).
- The t_{df} distribution has slightly broader tails than the z distribution.
- The t_{df} distribution consists of a family of distributions where the actual shape of each one depends on the degrees of freedom *df*. As *df* increases, the t_{df} distribution becomes similar to the z distribution; it is identical to the z distribution when *df* approaches infinity.

From Figure 8.3 we note that the tails of the t_2 and t_5 distributions are broader than the tails of the t_{50} distribution. For instance, for t_2 and t_5, the area exceeding a value of 3, or $P(T_{df} > 3)$, is greater than that for t_{50}. In addition, the t_{50} resembles the z distribution.

FIGURE 8.3

The t_{df} distribution with various degrees of freedom

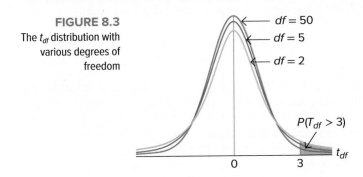

[1]William S. Gossett (1876–1937) published his research concerning the t distribution under the pen name "Student" because his employer, the Guinness Brewery, did not allow employees to publish their research results.

Locating t_{df} Values and Probabilities

Table 8.3 lists t_{df} values for selected upper-tail probabilities and degrees of freedom df. Table 2 of Appendix B provides a more complete table. Since the t_{df} distribution is a family of distributions identified by the df parameter, the t table is not as comprehensive as the z table. It only lists probabilities corresponding to a limited number of values. Also, unlike the cumulative probabilities in the z table, the t table provides the probabilities in the upper tail of the distribution.

TABLE 8.3 Portion of the t Table

df	Area in Upper Tail, α					
	0.20	0.10	0.05	0.025	0.01	0.005
1	1.376	3.078	6.314	12.706	31.821	63.657
⋮	⋮	⋮	⋮	⋮	⋮	⋮
10	0.879	1.372	**1.812**	2.228	2.764	3.169
⋮	⋮	⋮	⋮	⋮	⋮	⋮
∞	0.842	1.282	1.645	1.960	2.326	2.576

We use the notation $t_{\alpha,df}$ to denote a value such that the area in the upper tail equals α for a given df. In other words, for a random variable T_{df}, the notation $t_{\alpha,df}$ represents a value such that $P(T_{df} \geq t_{\alpha,df}) = \alpha$. Similarly, $t_{\alpha/2,df}$ represents a value such that $P(T_{df} \geq t_{\alpha/2,df}) = \alpha/2$. Figure 8.4 illustrates the notation.

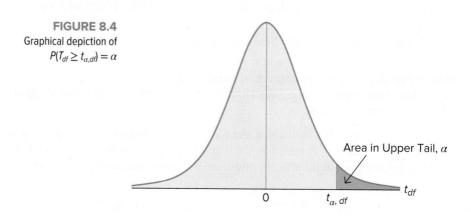

FIGURE 8.4
Graphical depiction of
$P(T_{df} \geq t_{\alpha,df}) = \alpha$

When determining the value $t_{\alpha,df}$, we need two pieces of information: (a) the sample size n or, analogously, $df = n - 1$, and (b) α. For instance, suppose we want to find the value $t_{\alpha,df}$ with $\alpha = 0.05$ and $df = 10$; that is, $t_{0.05,10}$. Using Table 8.3, we look at the first column labeled df and find the row 10. We then continue along this row until we reach the column $\alpha = 0.05$. The value 1.812 suggests that $P(T_{10} \geq 1.812) = 0.05$. Due to the symmetry of the t distribution, we also get $P(T_{10} \leq -1.812) = 0.05$. Figure 8.5 shows these results graphically. Also, since the area under the entire t_{df} distribution sums to one, we deduce that $P(T_{10} < 1.812) = 1 - 0.05 = 0.95$, which also equals $P(T_{10} > -1.812)$.

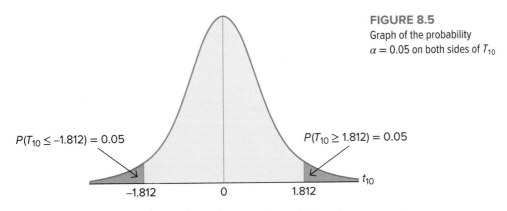

FIGURE 8.5
Graph of the probability
$\alpha = 0.05$ on both sides of T_{10}

$P(T_{10} \le -1.812) = 0.05$

$P(T_{10} \ge 1.812) = 0.05$

t_{10}

-1.812 0 1.812

Sometimes the exact probability cannot be determined from the t table. For example, given $df = 10$, the exact probability $P(T_{10} \ge 1.562)$ is not included in the table. However, this probability is between 0.05 and 0.10 because the value 1.562 falls between 1.372 and 1.812. Similarly, $P(T_{10} < 1.562)$ is between 0.90 and 0.95. We can use Excel, R, and other statistical packages to find exact probabilities.

EXAMPLE 8.4

Compute $t_{\alpha,df}$ for $\alpha = 0.025$ using 2, 5, and 50 degrees of freedom.

SOLUTION:

- For $df = 2$, $t_{0.025,2} = 4.303$.
- For $df = 5$, $t_{0.025,5} = 2.571$.
- For $df = 50$, $t_{0.025,50} = 2.009$.

Note that the t_{df} values change with the degrees of freedom. Moreover, as df increases, the t_{df} distribution begins to resemble the z distribution. In fact, with $df = \infty$, $t_{0.025,\infty} = 1.96$, which is identical to the corresponding z value; recall that $P(Z \ge 1.96) = 0.025$.

Constructing a Confidence Interval for μ When σ Is Unknown

LO 8.5

Calculate a confidence interval for the population mean when the population standard deviation is not known.

We can never stress enough the importance of the requirement that $\overline{X}$ follows a normal distribution in estimating the population mean. Recall that $\overline{X}$ follows the normal distribution when the underlying population is normally distributed or when the sample size is sufficiently large ($n \ge 30$). We still construct the confidence interval for μ as point estimate ± margin of error. However, when the population standard deviation is unknown, we now use the t_{df} distribution to calculate the margin of error.

CONFIDENCE INTERVAL FOR μ WHEN σ IS NOT KNOWN

A $100(1 - \alpha)\%$ confidence interval for the population mean μ when the population standard deviation σ is not known is computed as

$$\overline{x} \pm t_{\alpha/2,df}\frac{s}{\sqrt{n}} \quad \text{or} \quad \left[\overline{x} - t_{\alpha/2,df}\frac{s}{\sqrt{n}}, \overline{x} + t_{\alpha/2,df}\frac{s}{\sqrt{n}}\right],$$

where s is the sample standard deviation. This formula is valid only if $\overline{X}$ (approximately) follows a normal distribution.

As before, $100(1 - \alpha)\%$ is the confidence level and $t_{\alpha/2,df}$ is the t_{df} value associated with the probability $\alpha/2$ in the upper tail of the distribution with $df = n - 1$. In other words, $P(T_{df} > t_{\alpha/2,df}) = \alpha/2$. It is important to note that uncertainty is increased when we estimate the population standard deviation with the sample standard deviation, making the confidence interval wider, especially for smaller samples. This is appropriately captured by the wider tail of the $t_{\alpha/2}$ distribution.

EXAMPLE 8.5

In the introductory case of this chapter, Jared Beane wants to estimate the mean mpg for all ultra-green cars. Table 8.1 lists the mpg of a sample of 25 cars. Use this information to construct the 90% confidence interval for the population mean. Assume that mpg follows a normal distribution.

SOLUTION: The condition that $\overline{X}$ follows a normal distribution is satisfied since we assumed that mpg is normally distributed. Thus, we construct the confidence interval as $\overline{x} \pm t_{\alpha/2,df} \frac{s}{\sqrt{n}}$. This is a classic example where a statistician has access only to sample data. Since the population standard deviation is not known, the sample standard deviation has to be computed from the sample. From the sample data in Table 8.1, we find that $\overline{x} = \frac{\Sigma x_i}{n} = \frac{2,413}{25} = 96.52$ mpg and $s = \sqrt{\frac{\Sigma(x_i - \overline{x})^2}{n - 1}} = \sqrt{\frac{2,746.24}{25 - 1}} = 10.70$. For the 90% confidence interval, $\alpha = 0.10$, $\alpha/2 = 0.05$, and, given $n = 25$, $df = 25 - 1 = 24$. Thus, $t_{0.05,24} = 1.711$.

The 90% confidence interval for μ is computed as

$$\overline{x} \pm t_{\alpha/2,df} \frac{s}{\sqrt{n}} = 96.52 \pm 1.711 \frac{10.70}{\sqrt{25}} = 96.52 \pm 3.66.$$

Thus, Jared concludes with 90% confidence that the average mpg of all ultra-green cars is between 92.86 mpg and 100.18 mpg. Note that the manufacturer's claim that the ultra-green car will average 100 mpg cannot be rejected by the sample data since the value 100 falls within the 90% confidence interval.

Using Excel and R to Construct a Confidence Interval for μ When σ Is Unknown

Again we find that functions in Excel and R are quite useful when constructing confidence intervals. Consider the following example.

EXAMPLE 8.6

A recent article found that Massachusetts residents spent an average of $860.70 on the lottery in 2010 (www.businessweek.com, March 14, 2012). In order to verify the results, a researcher at a Boston think tank surveys 100 Massachusetts residents and asks them about their annual lottery expenditures (in $). Table 8.4 shows a portion of the results. Construct the 95% confidence interval for the average annual expenditures on the lottery for all Massachusetts residents. Do the results dispute the article's claim? Explain.

TABLE 8.4 Massachusetts Residents' Annual Lottery Expenditures, $n = 100$

Expenditures
790
594
⋮
759

SOLUTION: We compute $\bar{x} + t_{\alpha/2,df} \frac{s}{\sqrt{n}}$, or, equivalently, we find the lower and upper limits of the confidence interval: $\left[\bar{x} - t_{\alpha/2,df} \frac{s}{\sqrt{n}}, \bar{x} + t_{\alpha/2,df} \frac{s}{\sqrt{n}}\right]$. We are given $n = 100$.

Using Excel

a. Open the *Lottery* data file. Note that the values are in cells A2 through A101.

b. We apply a procedure analogous to the one used in Section 8.1, except we use Excel's **T.INV** function instead of the **NORM.INV** function. The **T.INV** function finds a particular t_{df} value for a given cumulative probability (*cumulprob*). If we want to find t_{df} to satisfy $P(T_{df} < t_{df}) = cumulprob$, we use "T.INV(*cumulprob*, *df*)". For the 95% confidence interval, $\alpha/2 = 0.025$ and $df = n - 1 = 99$. Since we want to find $t_{\alpha/2,df}$ such that the area under the t_{df} curve to the right of this value is $\alpha/2$ (and the area to the left of this value is $1 - \alpha/2$), we use "T.INV(0.975,99)". In order to find the lower limit of the confidence level we enter "=AVERAGE(A2:A101) − T.INV(0.975,99) * STDEV.S(A2:A101)/SQRT(100)", and Excel returns 798.85. For the upper limit, we enter "=AVERAGE(A2:A101) + T.INV(0.975,99) * STDEV.S(A2:A101)/SQRT(100)", and Excel returns 885.03. With 95% confidence, we conclude that the average annual expenditures on the lottery for all Massachusetts residents fall between $798.85 and $885.03. The results do not dispute the article's claim since the interval includes the reported mean value of $860.70.

Using R

a. Import the *Lottery* data into a data frame (table) in R.

b. When finding the margin of error, we apply a procedure analogous to the one used in Section 8.1, except we use R's **qt** function instead of the **qnorm** function. The **qt** function finds a particular t_{df} value for a given cumulative probability (*cumulprob*). If we want to find t_{df} to satisfy $P(T_{df} < t_{df}) = cumulprob$, we enter "qt(*cumulprob*, *df*, lower.tail = TRUE)". For the 95% confidence interval, $\alpha/2 = 0.025$ and $df = n - 1 = 99$. Since we want to find $t_{\alpha/2,df}$ such that the area under the t_{df} curve to the right of this value is $\alpha/2$ (and the area to the left of this value is $1 - \alpha/2$), we use "qt(0.975, 99, lower.tail = TRUE)." Thus, for the margin of error, labeled Error, we enter:

```
> Error <- qt(0.975, 99, lower.tail = TRUE)*sd(Lottery$
  'Expenditures')/sqrt(100)
```

c. We find the lower and upper limits of the confidence interval and then list them. For the lower limit, we enter

```
> Lower <- mean(Lottery$'Expenditures') - Error
> list(Lower)
```
And R returns: 798.8522.

For the upper limit, we enter

```
> Upper <- mean(Lottery$'Expenditures') + Error
> list(Upper)
```
And R returns: 885.0278.

EXERCISES 8.2

Mechanics

16. Find $t_{\alpha,df}$ from the following information.
   a. $\alpha = 0.025$ and $df = 12$
   b. $\alpha = 0.10$ and $df = 12$
   c. $\alpha = 0.025$ and $df = 25$
   d. $\alpha = 0.10$ and $df = 25$

17. We use the t distribution to construct a confidence interval for the population mean when the underlying population standard deviation is not known. Under the assumption that the population is normally distributed, find $t_{\alpha/2,df}$ for the following scenarios.
   a. A 90% confidence level and a sample of 28 observations.
   b. A 95% confidence level and a sample of 28 observations.
   c. A 90% confidence level and a sample of 15 observations.
   d. A 95% confidence level and a sample of 15 observations.

18. A random sample of 24 observations is used to estimate the population mean. The sample mean and the sample standard deviation are calculated as 104.6 and 28.8, respectively. Assume that the population is normally distributed.
   a. Construct the 90% confidence interval for the population mean.
   b. Construct the 99% confidence interval for the population mean.
   c. Use your answers to discuss the impact of the confidence level on the width of the interval.

19. Consider a normal population with an unknown population standard deviation. A random sample results in $\bar{x} = 48.68$ and $s^2 = 33.64$.
   a. Compute the 95% confidence interval for μ if $\bar{x}$ and s^2 were obtained from a sample of 16 observations.
   b. Compute the 95% confidence interval for μ if $\bar{x}$ and s^2 were obtained from a sample of 25 observations.
   c. Use your answers to discuss the impact of the sample size on the width of the interval.

20. Let the following sample of 8 observations be drawn from a normal population with unknown mean and standard deviation: 22, 18, 14, 25, 17, 28, 15, 21.
   a. Calculate the sample mean and the sample standard deviation.
   b. Construct the 80% confidence interval for the population mean.
   c. Construct the 90% confidence interval for the population mean.
   d. What happens to the margin of error as the confidence level increases from 80% to 90%?

Applications

21. A random sample of eight drugstores shows the following prices (in $) of a popular pain reliever:

3.50	4.00	2.00	3.00	2.50	3.50	2.50	3.00

   Assume the normal distribution for the underlying population to construct the 90% confidence interval for the population mean.

22. A popular weight loss program claims that with its recommended healthy diet regimen, users lose significant weight within a month. In order to estimate the mean weight loss of all customers, a nutritionist takes a sample of 18 dieters and records their weight loss one month after joining the program. He computes the sample mean and the standard deviation of weight loss as 12.5 pounds and 9.2 pounds, respectively. He believes that weight loss is likely to be normally distributed.
   a. Calculate the margin of error with 95% confidence.
   b. Calculate the 95% confidence interval for the population mean.

23. The manager of The Cheesecake Factory in Boston reports that on six randomly selected weekdays, the number of customers served was 120, 130, 100, 205, 185, and 220. She believes that the number of customers served on weekdays follows a normal distribution. Construct the 90% confidence interval for the average number of customers served on weekdays.

24. According to a recent survey, high school girls average 100 text messages daily (*The Boston Globe*, April 21, 2010). Assume that the survey was based on a random sample of 36 high school girls. The sample standard deviation is computed as 10 text messages daily.

    a. Calculate the margin of error with 99% confidence.

    b. What is the 99% confidence interval for the population mean texts that all high school girls send daily?

25. The Chartered Financial Analyst (CFA) designation is fast becoming a requirement for serious investment professionals. Although it requires a successful completion of three levels of grueling exams, it also entails promising careers with lucrative salaries. A student of finance is curious about the average salary of a CFA charterholder. He takes a random sample of 36 recent charterholders and computes a mean salary of $158,000 with a standard deviation of $36,000. Use this sample information to determine the 95% confidence interval for the average salary of a CFA charterholder.

26. The sudoku puzzle has become very popular all over the world. It is based on a 9 × 9 grid and the challenge is to fill in the grid so that every row, every column, and every 3 × 3 box contains the digits 1 through 9. A researcher is interested in estimating the average time taken by a college student to solve the puzzle. He takes a random sample of 8 college students and records their solving times (in minutes) as 14, 7, 17, 20, 18, 15, 19, 28.

    a. Construct the 99% confidence interval for the average time taken by a college student to solve a sudoku puzzle.

    b. What assumption is necessary to make this inference?

27. Executive compensation has risen dramatically compared to the rising levels of an average worker's wage over the years. Sarah is an MBA student who decides to use her statistical skills to estimate the mean CEO compensation in 2010 for all large companies in the United States. She takes a random sample of six CEO compensations (in $ millions).

Firm	Compensation
Intel	8.20
Coca-Cola	2.76
Wells Fargo	6.57
Caterpillar	3.88
McDonald's	6.56
U.S. Bancorp	4.10

Source: www.finance.yahoo.com.

    a. Help Sarah use the above information to construct the 90% confidence interval for the mean CEO compensation for all large companies in the United States.

    b. What assumption is necessary for deriving the interval estimate?

    c. How can the margin of error reported in part a be reduced?

28. As reported by tradingeconomics.com on September 2, 2012, the unemployment rates (in %) in major economies around the world were as follows:

Country	Unemployment Rate
Australia	5.2
China	4.1
France	10.0
Germany	6.8
India	3.8
United Kingdom	8.0
United States	8.3

    a. Calculate the margin of error used in the 95% confidence level for the population mean unemployment rate. Explain the assumption made for the analysis.

    b. How can we reduce the margin of error for the 95% confidence interval?

29. A price-earnings ratio, or P/E ratio, is calculated as a firm's share price compared to the income or profit earned by the firm per share. Generally, a high P/E ratio suggests that investors are expecting higher earnings growth in the future compared to companies with a lower P/E ratio. The following table shows the P/E ratios for a sample of firms in the footwear industry:

Firm	P/E Ratio
Brown Shoe Co., Inc.	26
CROCS, Inc.	13
DSW, Inc.	21
Foot Locker, Inc.	16
Nike, Inc.	21

Source: www.finance.yahoo.com, data retrieved September 2, 2012.

Let these ratios represent a random sample drawn from a normally distributed population. Construct the 90% confidence interval for the mean P/E ratio for the entire footwear industry.

30. The following table shows the annual returns (in percent) for Fidelity's Electronics and Utilities funds.

Year	Electronics	Utilities
2010	17	11
2011	−8	13
2012	4	7
2013	39	21
2014	38	22

Source: www.finance.yahoo.com, data retrieved April 3, 2015.

    a. Derive the 99% confidence intervals for the mean returns for Fidelity's Electronics and Utilities funds.

    b. What did you have to assume to make the above inferences?

31. The monthly closing stock prices (rounded to the nearest dollar) for Panera Bread Co. for the first six months of 2010 are reported in the following table.

Month	Closing Stock Price
January	71
February	73
March	76
April	78
May	81
June	75

Source: www.finance.yahoo.com.

a. Calculate the sample mean and the sample standard deviation.
b. Calculate the 90% confidence interval for the mean stock price of Panera Bread Co., assuming that the stock price is normally distributed.
c. What happens to the margin of error if a higher confidence level is used for the interval estimate?

32. Suppose the 90% confidence interval for the mean SAT scores of applicants at a business college is given by [1690, 1810]. This confidence interval uses the sample mean and the sample standard deviation based on 25 observations. What are the sample mean and the sample standard deviation used when computing the interval?

33. A teacher wants to estimate the mean time (in minutes) that students take to go from one classroom to the next. His research assistant uses the sample time of 36 students to report the confidence interval as [8.20, 9.80].
a. Find the sample mean time used to compute the confidence interval.
b. Determine the confidence level if the sample standard deviation used for the interval is 2.365.

34. In order to lure female customers, a new clothing store offers free gourmet coffee and pastry to its customers. The average daily revenue over the past five-week period has been $1,080 with a standard deviation of $260. Use this sample information to construct the 95% confidence interval for the average daily revenue. The store manager believes that the coffee and pastry strategy would lead to an average daily revenue of $1,200. Use the 95% interval to determine if the manager is wrong.

35. **FILE** *Debt_Payments.* A study found that consumers are making average monthly debt payments of $983 (Experian. com, November 11, 2010). The accompanying table shows a portion of average monthly debt payments (Debt in $) for 26 metropolitan areas. Construct 90% and 95% confidence intervals for the population mean. Comment on the width of the interval.

City	Debt
Washington, D.C.	1285
Seattle	1135
⋮	⋮
Pittsburgh	763

Source: www.Experian.com, November 11, 2010.

36. **FILE** *Economics.* An associate dean of a university wishes to compare the means on the standardized final exams in microeconomics and macroeconomics. He has access to a random sample of 40 scores from each of these two courses. A portion of the data is shown in the accompanying table.

Micro	Macro
85	48
78	79
⋮	⋮
75	74

a. Construct 95% confidence intervals for the mean score in microeconomics and the mean score in macroeconomics.
b. Explain why the widths of the two intervals are different.

37. **FILE** *Math_Scores.* For decades, people have believed that boys are innately more capable than girls in math. In other words, due to the intrinsic differences in brains, boys are better suited for doing math than girls. Recent research challenges this stereotype, arguing that gender differences in math performance have more to do with culture than innate aptitude. Others argue, however, that while the average may be the same, there is more variability in math ability for boys than girls, resulting in some boys with soaring math skills. A portion of the data on math scores of boys and girls is shown in the accompanying table.

Boys	Girls
74	83
89	76
⋮	⋮
66	74

a. Construct 95% confidence intervals for the mean scores of boys and the mean scores of girls. Explain your assumptions.
b. Explain why the widths of the two intervals are different.

38. **FILE** *Startups.* Many of today's leading companies, including Google, Microsoft, and Facebook, are based on technologies developed within universities. Lisa Fisher is a business school professor who believes that a university's research expenditure (Research in $ millions) and the age of its technology transfer office (Duration in years) are major factors that enhance innovation. She wants to know what the average values are for the Research and the Duration variables. She collects data from 143 universities on these variables for the academic year 2008. A portion of the data is shown in the accompanying table.

Research	Duration
145.52	23
237.52	23
⋮	⋮
154.38	9

Source: Association of University Managers and National Science Foundation.

a. Construct and interpret the 95% confidence interval for the mean research expenditure of all universities.

b. Construct and interpret the 95% confidence interval for the mean duration of all universities.

8.3 CONFIDENCE INTERVAL FOR THE POPULATION PROPORTION

LO 8.6

Sometimes the parameter of interest describes a population that is qualitative rather than quantitative. Recall that while the population mean μ and the population variance σ^2 describe quantitative data, the population proportion p is the essential descriptive measure when the data type is qualitative. The parameter p represents the proportion of successes in the population, where success is defined by a particular outcome. Examples of population proportions include the proportion of women students at a university, the proportion of defective items in a manufacturing process, and the default probability on a mortgage loan.

Calculate a confidence interval for the population proportion.

As in the case of the population mean, we estimate the population proportion on the basis of its sample counterpart. In particular, we use the sample proportion $\bar{P}$ as the point estimator of the population proportion p. Also, although the sampling distribution of $\bar{P}$ is based on a binomial distribution, we can approximate it by a normal distribution for large samples, according to the central limit theorem. This approximation is valid when the sample size n is such that $np \geq 5$ and $n(1 - p) \geq 5$.

Using the normal approximation for $\bar{P}$ with $E(\bar{P}) = p$ and $se(\bar{P}) = \sqrt{p(1-p)/n}$, and analogous to the derivation of the confidence interval for the population mean, a $100(1 - \alpha)\%$ confidence interval for the population proportion is

$$\bar{p} \pm z_{\alpha/2}\sqrt{\frac{p(1-p)}{n}} \quad \text{or} \quad \left[\bar{p} - z_{\alpha/2}\sqrt{\frac{p(1-p)}{n}}, \bar{p} + z_{\alpha/2}\sqrt{\frac{p(1-p)}{n}}\right].$$

This confidence interval is theoretically sound; however, it cannot be implemented because it uses p in the derivation, which is unknown. Since we always use large samples for the normal distribution approximation, we can also conveniently replace p with its estimate $\bar{p}$ in the construction of the interval. Therefore, for $\sqrt{\frac{p(1-p)}{n}}$, we substitute $\sqrt{\frac{\bar{p}(1-\bar{p})}{n}}$. This substitution yields a feasible confidence interval for the population proportion.

CONFIDENCE INTERVAL FOR p

A $100(1 - \alpha)\%$ confidence interval for the population proportion p is computed as

$$\bar{p} \pm z_{\alpha/2}\sqrt{\frac{\bar{p}(1-\bar{p})}{n}} \quad \text{or} \quad \left[\bar{p} - z_{\alpha/2}\sqrt{\frac{\bar{p}(1-\bar{p})}{n}}, \bar{p} + z_{\alpha/2}\sqrt{\frac{\bar{p}(1-\bar{p})}{n}}\right].$$

This formula is valid only if $\bar{P}$ (approximately) follows a normal distribution.

The normality condition is evaluated at the sample proportion $\bar{p}$. In other words, for constructing a confidence interval for the population proportion p, we require that $n\bar{p} \geq 5$ and $n(1 - \bar{p}) \geq 5$.

EXAMPLE 8.7

In the introductory case of this chapter, Jared Beane wants to estimate the proportion of all ultra-green cars that obtain over 100 mpg. Use the information in Table 8.1 to construct 90% and 99% confidence intervals for the population proportion.

SOLUTION: As shown in Table 8.1, 7 of the 25 cars obtain over 100 mpg; thus, the point estimate of the population proportion is $\bar{p} = 7/25 = 0.28$. Note that the normality condition is satisfied, since $np \geq 5$ and $n(1 - p) \geq 5$, where p is evaluated at $\bar{p} = 0.28$. With the 90% confidence level, $\alpha/2 = 0.10/2 = 0.05$; thus, we find $z_{\alpha/2} = z_{0.05} = 1.645$. Substituting the appropriate values into $\bar{p} \pm z_{\alpha/2}\sqrt{\frac{\bar{p}(1-\bar{p})}{n}}$ yields

$$0.28 \pm 1.645\sqrt{\frac{0.28(1 - 0.28)}{25}} = 0.28 \pm 0.148.$$

With 90% confidence, Jared reports that the percentage of cars that obtain over 100 mpg is between 13.2% and 42.8%.

If Jared had wanted the 99% confidence level, we would use $\alpha/2 = 0.01/2 = 0.005$ and $z_{\alpha/2} = z_{0.005} = 2.576$ to obtain

$$0.28 \pm 2.576\sqrt{\frac{0.28(1 - 0.28)}{25}} = 0.28 \pm 0.231.$$

At a higher confidence level of 99%, the interval for the percentage of cars that obtain over 100 mpg becomes 4.9% to 51.1%. Given the current sample size of 25 cars, Jared can gain confidence (from 90% to 99%) at the expense of precision, as the corresponding margin of error increases from 0.148 to 0.231.

EXERCISES 8.3

Mechanics

39. A random sample of 80 observations results in 50 successes.
    a. Construct the 95% confidence interval for the population proportion of successes.
    b. Construct the 95% confidence interval for the population proportion of failures.

40. Assume $\bar{p} = 0.6$ in a sample of size $n = 50$.
    a. Construct the 95% confidence interval for the population proportion.
    b. What happens to the margin of error if the above sample proportion is based on $n = 200$ instead of $n = 50$?

41. A sample of 80 results in 30 successes.
    a. Calculate the point estimate for the population proportion of successes.
    b. Construct 90% and 99% confidence intervals for the population proportion.

c. Can we conclude at 90% confidence that the population proportion differs from 0.5?
d. Can we conclude at 99% confidence that the population proportion differs from 0.5?

42. A random sample of 100 observations results in 40 successes.
    a. What is the point estimate for the population proportion of successes?
    b. Construct 90% and 99% confidence intervals for the population proportion.
    c. Can we conclude at 90% confidence that the population proportion differs from 0.5?
    d. Can we conclude at 99% confidence that the population proportion differs from 0.5?

43. In a sample of 30 observations, the number of successes equals 18.
    a. Construct the 88% confidence interval for the population proportion of successes.

b. Construct the 98% confidence interval for the population proportion of successes.

c. What happens to the margin of error as you move from the 88% confidence interval to the 98% confidence interval?

Applications

44. A poll of 1,079 adults found that 51% of Americans support Arizona's stringent new immigration enforcement law, even though it may lead to racial profiling (*The New York Times*/CBS News, April 28–May 2, 2010). Use the sample information to compute the 95% confidence interval for the population parameter of interest.

45. A survey of 1,026 people asked: "What would you do with an unexpected tax refund?" Forty-seven percent responded that they would pay off debts (*Vanity Fair*, June 2010).
    a. At 95% confidence, what is the margin of error?
    b. Construct the 95% confidence interval for the population proportion of people who would pay off debts with an unexpected tax refund.

46. In a CNNMoney.com poll conducted on July 13, 2010, a sample of 5,324 Americans were asked about what matters most to them in a place to live. Thirty-seven percent of the respondents felt job opportunities matter most.
    a. Construct the 90% confidence interval for the proportion of Americans who feel that good job opportunities matter most in a place to live.
    b. Construct the 99% confidence interval for the proportion of Americans who feel that good job opportunities matter most in a place to live.
    c. Which of the above two intervals has a higher margin of error? Explain why.

47. An economist reports that 560 out of a sample of 1,200 middle-income American households actively participate in the stock market.
    a. Construct the 90% confidence interval for the proportion of middle-income Americans who actively participate in the stock market.
    b. Can we conclude that the percentage of middle-income Americans who actively participate in the stock market is not 50%?

48. In an NBC News/*Wall Street Journal* poll of 1,000 American adults conducted August 5–9, 2010, 44% of respondents approved of the job that Barack Obama was doing in handling the economy.
    a. Compute the 90% confidence interval for the proportion of Americans who approved of Barack Obama's handling of the economy.
    b. What is the resulting margin of error?
    c. Compute the margin of error associated with the 99% confidence level.

49. In a recent poll of 760 homeowners in the United States, one in five homeowners reports having a home equity loan that he or she is currently paying off. Using a confidence coefficient of 0.90, derive the interval estimate for the proportion of all homeowners in the United States that hold a home equity loan.

50. Obesity is generally defined as 30 or more pounds over a healthy weight. A recent study of obesity reports 27.5% of a random sample of 400 adults in the United States to be obese.
    a. Use this sample information to compute the 90% confidence interval for the adult obesity rate in the United States.
    b. Is it reasonable to conclude with 90% confidence that the adult obesity rate in the United States differs from 30%?

51. An accounting professor is notorious for being stingy in giving out good letter grades. In a large section of 140 students in the fall semester, she gave out only 5% A's, 23% B's, 42% C's, and 30% D's and F's. Assuming that this was a representative class, compute the 95% confidence interval of the probability of getting at least a B from this professor.

52. A survey conducted by CBS News asked 1,026 respondents: "What would you do with an unexpected tax refund?" The responses are summarized in the following table.

Response	Frequency
Pay off debts	482
Put it in the bank	308
Spend it	112
I never get a refund	103
Other	21

Source: *Vanity Fair*, June 2010.

   a. Construct the 90% confidence interval for the population proportion of those who would put the tax refund in the bank.
   b. Construct the 90% confidence interval for the population proportion of those who never get a refund.

53. A recent survey asked 5,324 individuals: What's most important to you when choosing where to live? The responses are shown by the following frequency distribution.

Response	Frequency
Good jobs	1,969
Affordable homes	799
Top schools	586
Low crime	1,225
Things to do	745

Source: CNNMoney.com, July 13, 2010.

   a. Calculate the margin of error used in the 95% confidence level for the population proportion of those who believe that low crime is most important.
   b. Calculate the margin of error used in the 95% confidence level for the population proportion of those who believe that good jobs or affordable homes are most important.

c. Explain why the margins of error in parts a and b are different.

54. One in five 18-year-old Americans has not graduated from high school (*The Wall Street Journal*, April 19, 2007). A mayor of a Northeastern city comments that its residents do not have the same graduation rate as the rest of the country. An analyst from the Department of Education decides to test the mayor's claim. In particular, she draws a random sample of 80 18-year-olds in the city and finds that 20 of them have not graduated from high school.

a. Compute the point estimate for the proportion of 18-year-olds who have not graduated from high school in this city.

b. Use this point estimate to derive the 95% confidence interval for the population proportion.

c. Can the mayor's comment be justified at 95% confidence?

8.4 SELECTING THE REQUIRED SAMPLE SIZE

Select a sample size to estimate the population mean and the population proportion.

So far we have discussed how a confidence interval provides useful information on an unknown population parameter. We compute the confidence interval by adding and subtracting the margin of error to/from the point estimate. If the margin of error is very large, the confidence interval becomes too wide to be of much value. For instance, little useful information can be gained from a confidence interval that suggests that the average annual starting salary of a business graduate is between $16,000 and $64,000. Similarly, an interval estimate that 10% to 60% of business students pursue an MBA is not very informative.

Statisticians like precision in their interval estimates, which is implied by a low margin of error. If we are able to increase the size of the sample, the larger n reduces the margin of error for the interval estimates. Although a larger sample size improves precision, it also entails the added cost in terms of time and money. Before getting into data collection, it is important that we first decide on the sample size that is adequate for what we wish to accomplish. In this section, we examine the required sample size, for a desired margin of error, in the confidence intervals for the population mean μ and the population proportion p. In order to be conservative, we always round up noninteger values for the required sample size.

Selecting n to Estimate μ

Consider a confidence interval for μ with a known population standard deviation σ. In addition, let E denote the desired margin of error. In other words, you do not want the sample mean to deviate from the population mean by more than E for a given level of confidence. Since $E = z_{\alpha/2}\frac{\sigma}{\sqrt{n}}$, we rearrange this equation to derive the formula for the required sample size as $n = \left(\frac{z_{\alpha/2}\sigma}{E}\right)^2$. The sample size can be computed if we specify the population standard deviation σ, the value of $z_{\alpha/2}$ based on the confidence level $100(1 - \alpha)\%$, and the desired margin of error E.

This formula is based on a knowledge of σ. However, in most cases σ is not known and, therefore, has to be estimated. Note that the sample standard deviation s cannot be used as an estimate for σ because s can be computed only after a sample of size n has been selected. In such cases, we replace σ with its reasonable estimate $\hat{\sigma}$.

> ### THE REQUIRED SAMPLE SIZE WHEN ESTIMATING THE POPULATION MEAN
>
> For a desired margin of error E, the minimum sample size n required to estimate a $100(1 - \alpha)\%$ confidence interval for the population mean μ is
>
> $$n = \left(\frac{z_{\alpha/2}\,\hat{\sigma}}{E}\right)^2,$$
>
> where $\hat{\sigma}$ is a reasonable estimate of σ in the planning stage.

If σ is known, we replace $\hat{\sigma}$ with σ. Sometimes we use the sample standard deviation from a preselected sample as $\hat{\sigma}$ in the planning stage. Another choice for $\hat{\sigma}$ is to use an estimate of the population standard deviation from prior studies. Finally, if the minimum and maximum values of the population are available, a rough approximation for the population standard deviation is given by $\hat{\sigma} = \text{range}/4$.

EXAMPLE 8.8

Let us revisit Example 8.5, where Jared Beane wants to construct the 90% confidence interval for the mean mpg of all ultra-green cars. Suppose Jared would like to constrain the margin of error to within 2 mpg. Further, Jared knows that the minimum mpg in the population is 76 mpg, whereas the maximum is 118 mpg. How large a sample does Jared need to compute the 90% confidence interval for the population mean?

SOLUTION: For the 90% confidence level, Jared computes $z_{\alpha/2} = z_{0.05} = 1.645$. He estimates the population standard deviation as $\hat{\sigma} = \text{range}/4 = (118 - 76)/4 = 10.50$. Given $E = 2$, the required sample size is

$$n = \left(\frac{z_{\alpha/2}\,\hat{\sigma}}{E}\right)^2 = \left(\frac{1.645 \times 10.50}{2}\right)^2 = 74.58,$$

which is rounded up to 75. Therefore, Jared needs a random sample of at least 75 ultra-green cars to provide a more precise interval estimate of the mean mpg.

Selecting n to Estimate p

The margin of error E for the confidence interval for the population proportion p is $E = z_{\alpha/2}\sqrt{\frac{\bar{p}(1-\bar{p})}{n}}$, where $\bar{p}$ represents the sample proportion. By rearranging, we derive the formula for the required sample size as $n = \left(\frac{z_{\alpha/2}}{E}\right)^2 \bar{p}(1-\bar{p})$. Analogous to the case of the population mean, this formula is not feasible because it uses $\bar{p}$, which cannot be computed unless a sample of size n has already been selected. We replace $\bar{p}$ with a reasonable estimate $\hat{p}$ of the population proportion p.

THE REQUIRED SAMPLE SIZE WHEN ESTIMATING THE POPULATION PROPORTION

For a desired margin of error E, the minimum sample size n required to estimate a $100(1 - \alpha)\%$ confidence interval for the population proportion p is

$$n = \left(\frac{z_{\alpha/2}}{E}\right)^2 \hat{p}(1 - \hat{p}),$$

where $\hat{p}$ is a reasonable estimate of p in the planning stage.

Sometimes we use the sample proportion from a preselected sample as $\hat{p}$ in the planning stage. Another choice for $\hat{p}$ is to use an estimate of the population proportion from prior studies. If no other reasonable estimate of the population proportion is available, we can use $\hat{p} = 0.5$ as a conservative estimate to derive the optimal sample size; note that the required sample is the largest when $\hat{p} = 0.5$.

EXAMPLE 8.9

Let us revisit Example 8.7, where Jared Beane wants to construct the 90% confidence interval for the proportion of all ultra-green cars that obtain over 100 mpg. Jared does not want the margin of error to be more than 0.10. How large a sample does Jared need for his analysis of the population proportion?

SOLUTION: For the 90% confidence level, Jared computes $z_{\alpha/2} = z_{0.05} = 1.645$. Since no estimate for the population proportion is readily available, Jared uses a conservative estimate of $\hat{p} = 0.50$. Given $E = 0.10$, the required sample size is

$$n = \left(\frac{z_{\alpha/2}}{E}\right)^2 \hat{p}(1-\hat{p}) = \left(\frac{1.645}{0.10}\right)^2 0.50(1-0.50) = 67.65,$$

which is rounded up to 68. Therefore, Jared needs to find another random sample of at least 68 ultra-green cars to provide a more precise interval estimate for the proportion of all ultra-green cars that obtain over 100 mpg.

SYNOPSIS OF INTRODUCTORY CASE

©McGraw-Hill Education/Mark Dierker, photographer

Jared Beane, an analyst at a research firm, prepares to write a report on the new ultra-green car that boasts an average of 100 mpg. Based on a sample of 25 cars, Jared reports with 90% confidence that the average mpg of all ultra-green cars is between 92.86 mpg and 100.18 mpg. Jared also constructs the 90% confidence interval for the proportion of cars that obtain more than 100 mpg and reports the interval between 0.132 and 0.428. Jared wishes to increase the precision of his confidence intervals by reducing the margin of error. If his desired margin of error is 2 mpg for the population mean, he must use a sample of at least 75 cars for the analysis. Jared also wants to reduce the margin of error to 0.10 for the proportion of cars that obtain more than 100 mpg. Using a conservative estimate, he calculates that a sample of at least 68 cars is needed to achieve this goal. Thus, in order to gain precision in the interval estimate for both the mean and the proportion with 90% confidence, Jared's sample must contain at least 75 cars.

EXERCISES 8.4

Mechanics

55. The minimum and maximum observations in a population are 20 and 80, respectively. What is the minimum sample size n required to estimate μ with 80% confidence if the desired margin of error is $E = 2.6$? What happens to n if you decide to estimate μ with 95% confidence?

56. Find the required sample size for estimating the population mean in order to be 95% confident that the sample mean is within 10 units of the population mean. Assume that the population standard deviation is 40.

57. You need to compute the 99% confidence interval for the population mean. How large a sample should you draw to ensure that the sample mean does not deviate from the population mean by more than 1.2? (Use 6.0 as an estimate of the population standard deviation from prior studies.)

58. What is the minimum sample size n required to estimate μ with 90% confidence if the desired margin of error is $E = 1.2$? The population standard deviation is estimated as $\hat{\sigma} = 3.5$. What happens to n if the desired margin of error decreases to $E = 0.7$?

59. In the planning stage, a sample proportion is estimated as $\hat{p} = 40/50 = 0.80$. Use this information to compute the minimum sample size n required to estimate p with 99% confidence if the desired margin of error $E = 0.12$. What happens to n if you decide to estimate p with 90% confidence?

60. What is the minimum sample size n required to estimate p with 95% confidence if the desired margin of error $E = 0.08$? The population proportion is estimated as $\hat{p} = 0.36$ from prior studies. What happens to n if the desired margin of error increases to $E = 0.12$?

61. You wish to compute the 95% confidence interval for the population proportion. How large a sample should you draw to ensure that the sample proportion does not deviate from the population proportion by more than 0.06? No prior estimate for the population proportion is available.

Applications

62. Mortgage lenders often use FICO scores to check the credit worthiness of consumers applying for real estate loans. In general, FICO scores range from 300 to 850 with higher scores representing a better credit profile. A lender in a Midwestern town would like to estimate the mean credit score of its residents. What is the required number of sample FICO scores needed if the lender does not want the margin of error to exceed 20, with 95% confidence?

63. An analyst from an energy research institute in California wishes to estimate the 99% confidence interval for the average price of unleaded gasoline in the state. In particular, she does not want the sample mean to deviate from the population mean by more than $0.06. What is the minimum number of gas stations that she should include in her sample if she uses the standard deviation estimate of $0.32, as reported in the popular press?

64. An analyst would like to construct 95% confidence intervals for the mean stock returns in two industries. Industry A is a high-risk industry with a known population standard deviation of 20.6%, whereas Industry B is a low-risk industry with a known population standard deviation of 12.8%.
    a. What is the minimum sample size required by the analyst if she wants to restrict the margin of error to 4% for Industry A?
    b. What is the minimum sample size required by the analyst if she wants to restrict the margin of error to 4% for Industry B?
    c. Why do the results differ if they use the same margin of error?

65. The manager of a pizza chain in Albuquerque, New Mexico, wants to determine the average size of their advertised 16-inch pizzas. She takes a random sample of 25 pizzas and records their mean and standard deviation as 16.10 inches and 1.8 inches, respectively. She subsequently computes the 95% confidence interval of the mean size of all pizzas as [15.36, 16.84]. However, she finds this interval to be too broad to implement quality control

and decides to reestimate the mean based on a bigger sample. Using the standard deviation estimate of 1.8 from her earlier analysis, how large a sample must she take if she wants the margin of error to be under 0.5 inch?

66. The manager of a newly opened Target store wants to estimate the average expenditure of his customers. From a preselected sample, the standard deviation was determined to be $18. The manager would like to construct the 95% confidence interval for the mean customer expenditure.
    a. Find the appropriate sample size necessary to achieve a margin of error of $5.
    b. Find the appropriate sample size necessary to achieve a margin of error of $3.

67. A budget airline wants to estimate what proportion of customers would consider paying $12 for in-flight wireless access. Given that the airline has no prior knowledge of the proportion, how many customers would it have to sample to ensure a margin of error of no more than 0.05 for the 90% confidence interval?

68. Newscasters wish to estimate the proportion of registered voters who support the incumbent candidate in the mayoral election. In an earlier poll of 240 registered voters, 110 had supported the incumbent candidate. Find the sample size required to construct the 90% confidence interval if newscasters do not want the margin of error to exceed 0.02.

69. A survey by AARP (*Money*, June 2007) reported that approximately 70% of people in the 50 to 64 age bracket have tried some type of alternative therapy (for instance, acupuncture or the use of nutrition supplements). Assume this survey was based on a sample of 400 people.
    a. Identify the relevant parameter of interest for these qualitative data and compute its point estimate as well as the margin of error with 90% confidence.
    b. You decide to redo the analysis with the margin of error reduced to 2%. How large a sample do you need to draw? State your assumptions in computing the required sample size.

70. Subprime lending was big business in the United States in the mid-2000s, when lenders provided mortgages to people with poor credit. However, subsequent increases in interest rates coupled with a drop in home values necessitated many borrowers to default. Suppose a recent report finds that two in five subprime mortgages are likely to default nationally. A research economist is interested in estimating default rates in Illinois with 95% confidence. How large a sample is needed to restrict the margin of error to within 0.06, using the reported national default rate?

71. A business student is interested in estimating the 99% confidence interval for the proportion of students who bring laptops to campus. He wishes a precise estimate and is willing to draw a large sample that will keep the sample proportion within five percentage points of the population proportion. What is the minimum sample size required by this student, given that no prior estimate of the population proportion is available?

WRITING WITH STATISTICS

©McGraw-Hill Education/Andrew Resek,
photographer

©Todd A. Merport/Shutterstock RF

Callie Fitzpatrick, a research analyst with an investment firm, has been asked to write a report summarizing the weekly stock performance of Home Depot and Lowe's. Her manager is trying to decide whether or not to include one of these stocks in a client's portfolio and the average stock performance is one of the factors influencing this decision. Callie decides to use descriptive measures to summarize stock returns in her report, as well as provide confidence intervals for the average return for Home Depot and Lowe's. She collects weekly returns for each firm for the first eight months of 2010. A portion of the return data is shown in Table 8.5.

FILE
Weekly_Returns

TABLE 8.5 Weekly Returns (in percent) for Home Depot and Lowe's

Date	Home Depot	Lowe's
1/11/2010	−1.44	−1.59
1/19/2010	−2.98	−3.53
⋮	⋮	⋮
8/30/2010	−2.61	−3.89

Source: www.finance.yahoo.com.

Callie would like to use the sample information to

1. Summarize weekly returns for Home Depot and Lowe's.
2. Provide confidence intervals for the average weekly returns.
3. Make recommendations for further analysis.

Sample Report— Weekly Stock Performance: Home Depot vs. Lowe's

Grim news continues to distress the housing sector. On August 24, 2010, Reuters reported that the sales of previously owned U.S. homes took a record plunge in July to the slowest pace in 15 years. Combine this fact with the continued fallout from the subprime mortgage debacle, a sluggish economy, and high unemployment, and the housing sector appears quite unstable. Have these unfavorable events managed to trickle down and harm the financial performance of Home Depot and Lowe's, the two largest home improvement retailers in the United States?

One way to analyze their financial stability is to observe their stock performance during this period. In order to make valid statements concerning the reward of holding these stocks, weekly return data for each firm were gathered from January through August of 2010. Table 8.A summarizes the important descriptive statistics.

TABLE 8.A Descriptive Statistics for Weekly Returns of Home Depot and Lowe's ($n = 34$)

	Home Depot (in %)	Lowe's (in %)
Mean	0.00	−0.33
Median	0.76	−0.49
Minimum	−8.08	−7.17
Maximum	5.30	7.71
Standard deviation	3.59	3.83
Margin of error with 95% confidence	1.25	1.34

Over the past 34 weeks, Home Depot posted both a higher average return and median return of 0.00% and 0.76%, respectively. Lowe's return over the same period was negative, whether the central tendency was measured by its mean (−0.33%) or its median (−0.49%). In terms of dispersion, Lowe's return data had the higher standard deviation (3.83% > 3.59%). In terms of descriptive measures, the investment in Home Depot's stock not only provided higher returns, but also was less risky than the investment in Lowe's stock.

Table 8.A also shows the margins of error for 95% confidence intervals for the mean returns. With 95% confidence, the mean return for Home Depot fell in the range [−1.25%, 1.25%], while that for Lowe's fell in the range [−1.67%, 1.01%]. Given that these two intervals overlap, one cannot conclude that Home Depot delivered the higher reward over this period—a conclusion one may have arrived at had only the point estimates been evaluated. It is not possible to recommend one stock over the other for inclusion in a client's portfolio based solely on the mean return performance. Other factors, such as the correlation between the stock and the existing portfolio, must be analyzed before this decision can be made.

CONCEPTUAL REVIEW

LO 8.1 Explain a confidence interval.

The sample mean $\overline{X}$ is the point estimator for the population mean μ, and the sample proportion $\overline{P}$ is the point estimator for the population proportion p. Sample values of the point estimators represent the point estimates for the population parameter of interest; $\overline{x}$ and $\overline{p}$ are the point estimates for μ and p, respectively. While a point estimator provides a single value that approximates the unknown parameter, a **confidence interval**, or an **interval estimate**, provides a range of values that, with a certain level of confidence, will contain the population parameter of interest.

Often, we construct a confidence interval as point estimate ± margin of error. The **margin of error** accounts for the variability of the estimator and the desired confidence level of the interval.

LO 8.2 Calculate a confidence interval for the population mean when the population standard deviation is known.

A $100(1 - \alpha)\%$ confidence interval for the population mean μ when the population standard deviation σ is known is computed as $\overline{x} \pm z_{\alpha/2}\frac{\sigma}{\sqrt{n}}$, where $z_{\alpha/2}\frac{\sigma}{\sqrt{n}}$ is the margin of error. This formula is valid only if $\overline{X}$ (approximately) follows a normal distribution.

LO 8.3 Describe the factors that influence the width of a confidence interval.

The precision of a confidence interval is directly linked with the width of the interval: the wider the interval, the lower its precision. A confidence interval is wider (a) the greater the population standard deviation σ, (b) the smaller the sample size n, and (c) the greater the confidence level.

LO 8.4 Discuss features of the t distribution.

The **t distribution** is a family of distributions that are similar to the z distribution, in that they are all symmetric and bell-shaped around zero with asymptotic tails. However, the t distribution has broader tails than does the z distribution. Each t distribution is identified by a parameter known as the **degrees of freedom df**. The df determine the extent of broadness—the smaller the df, the broader the tails. Since the t distribution is defined by the degrees of freedom, it is common to refer to it as the t_{df} distribution.

Calculate a confidence interval for the population mean when the population standard deviation is not known.

A $100(1 - \alpha)\%$ confidence interval for the population mean μ when the population standard deviation σ is not known is computed as $\bar{x} \pm t_{\alpha/2, df} \frac{s}{\sqrt{n}}$, where s is the sample standard deviation. This formula is valid only if $\bar{X}$ (approximately) follows a normal distribution.

LO 8.6 **Calculate a confidence interval for the population proportion.**

A $100(1 - \alpha)\%$ confidence interval for the population proportion p is computed as $\bar{p} \pm z_{\alpha/2}\sqrt{\frac{\bar{p}(1 - \bar{p})}{n}}$, where $\bar{p}$ is the sample proportion. This formula is valid only if $\bar{P}$ (approximately) follows a normal distribution.

LO 8.7 **Select a sample size to estimate the population mean and the population proportion.**

For a desired margin of error E, the minimum n required to estimate μ with $100(1 - \alpha)\%$ confidence is $n = \left(\frac{z_{\alpha/2}\hat{\sigma}}{E}\right)^2$, where $\hat{\sigma}$ is a reasonable estimate of σ in the planning stage. If σ is known, we replace $\hat{\sigma}$ with σ. Other choices for $\hat{\sigma}$ include an estimate from a preselected sample, prior studies, or $\hat{\sigma} = \text{range}/4$.

For a desired margin of error E, the minimum n required to estimate p with $100(1 - \alpha)\%$ confidence is $n = \left(\frac{z_{\alpha/2}}{E}\right)^2 \hat{p}(1 - \hat{p})$, where $\hat{p}$ is a reasonable estimate of p in the planning stage. Choices for $\hat{p}$ include an estimate from a preselected sample or prior studies; a conservative estimate of $\hat{p} = 0.5$ is used when no other reasonable estimate is available.

ADDITIONAL EXERCISES AND CASE STUDIES

Exercises

72. Over a 10-year sample period, the mean and the standard deviation of annual returns on a portfolio you are analyzing were 10% and 15%, respectively. You assume that returns are normally distributed. Construct the 95% confidence interval for the population mean.

73. A hair salon in Cambridge, Massachusetts, reports that on seven randomly selected weekdays, the number of customers who visited the salon were 40, 30, 28, 22, 36, 16, and 50. It can be assumed that weekday customer visits follow a normal distribution.
    a. Construct the 90% confidence interval for the average number of customers who visit the salon on weekdays.
    b. Construct the 99% confidence interval for the average number of customers who visit the salon on weekdays.
    c. What happens to the width of the interval as the confidence level increases?

74. According to data from the Organization for Economic Cooperation and Development, the average U.S. worker takes 16 days of vacation each year (*The Wall Street Journal*, June 20,

2007). Assume that these data were based on a sample of 225 workers and that the sample standard deviation is 12 days.
    a. Construct the 95% confidence interval for the population mean.
    b. At the 95% confidence level, can we conclude that the average U.S. worker does not take 14 days of vacation each year?

75. Recently, six single-family homes in San Luis Obispo County in California sold at the following prices (in $1,000s): 549, 449, 705, 529, 639, and 609.
    a. Construct the 95% confidence interval for the mean sale price in San Luis Obispo County.
    b. What assumption have you made when constructing this confidence interval?

76. Students who graduated from college in 2010 owed an average of $25,250 in student loans (*The New York Times*, November 2, 2011). An economist wants to determine if average debt has changed. She takes a sample of 40 recent graduates and finds that their average debt was $27,500 with a standard deviation of $9,120. Use the 90% confidence interval to determine if average debt has changed.

77. A machine that is programmed to package 1.20 pounds of cereal is being tested for its accuracy. In a sample of 36 cereal boxes, the sample mean filling weight is calculated as 1.22 pounds. The population standard deviation is known to be 0.06 pound.
   a. Identify the relevant parameter of interest for these quantitative data and compute its point estimate as well as the margin of error with 95% confidence.
   b. Can we conclude that the packaging machine is operating improperly?
   c. How large a sample must we take if we want the margin of error to be at most 0.01 pound with 95% confidence?

78. The SAT is the most widely used test in the undergraduate admissions process. Scores on the math portion of the SAT are believed to be normally distributed and range from 200 to 800. A researcher from the admissions department at the University of New Hampshire is interested in estimating the mean math SAT scores of the incoming class with 90% confidence. How large a sample should she take to ensure that the margin of error is below 15?

79. A study by Allstate Insurance Co. finds that 82% of teenagers have used cell phones while driving (*The Wall Street Journal*, May 5, 2010). Suppose this study was based on a random sample of 50 teen drivers.
   a. Construct the 99% confidence interval for the proportion of all teenagers that have used cell phones while driving.
   b. What is the margin of error with 99% confidence?

80. The following table shows the annual returns (in percent) for the Vanguard Energy Fund.

Year	Return
2010	13
2011	−2
2012	3
2013	18
2014	−14

Source: www.finance.yahoo.com, data retrieved April 4, 2015.

   a. Calculate the point estimate for μ.
   b. Construct the 95% confidence interval for μ.
   c. What assumption did you make when constructing the interval?

81. **FILE** *MV_Houses.* A realtor wants to estimate the mean price of houses in Mission Viejo, California. She collects a sample of 36 recent house sales (in $1,000s), a portion of which is shown in the accompanying table. Assume that the population standard deviation is 100 (in $1,000s). Construct and interpret 95% and 98% confidence intervals for the mean price of all houses in Mission Viejo, CA.

Prices
430
520
⋮
430

82. **FILE** *MI_Life_Expectancy.* Residents of Hawaii have the longest life expectancies, averaging 81.48 years (www.worldlifeexpectancy.com, data retrieved June 4, 2012). A sociologist collects data on the age at death for 50 recently deceased Michigan residents. A portion of the data is shown in the accompanying table. Assume that the population standard deviation is 5 years.

Age at Death
76.4
76.0
⋮
73.6

   a. Construct the 95% confidence interval for the mean life expectancy of all residents of Michigan.
   b. Use the 95% confidence interval to determine if the mean life expectancy of Michigan residents differs from that for Hawaii residents.

83. **FILE** *Fastballs.* The manager of a minor league baseball team wants to estimate the average fastball speed of two pitchers. He clocks 50 fastballs, in miles per hour, for each pitcher. A portion of the data is shown in the accompanying table.

Pitcher 1	Pitcher 2
87	82
86	92
⋮	⋮
86	93

   a. Construct 95% confidence intervals for the mean speed for each pitcher.
   b. Explain why the widths of the two intervals are different.

84. **FILE** *Theater.* The new manager of a theater would like to offer discounts to increase the number of tickets sold for shows on Monday and Tuesday evenings. She uses a sample of 30 weeks to record the number of tickets sold on these two days. A portion of the data is shown in the accompanying table.

Monday	Tuesday
221	208
187	199
⋮	⋮
194	180

Response	Relative Frequency
A few days	0.21
A few long weekends	0.18
One week	0.36
Two weeks	0.22

Source: *The Boston Globe*, June 12, 2007.

a. Compare the margin of error for the 95% confidence intervals for the mean number of tickets sold for shows on Monday and Tuesday evenings.

b. Construct the 95% confidence intervals for the mean number of tickets sold for shows on Monday and Tuesday evenings.

c. Determine if the population mean differs from 200 for shows on Monday and Tuesday evenings.

85. **FILE** *AnnArbor_Rental.* Real estate investment in college towns continues to promise good returns (*The Wall Street Journal*, September 24, 2010). Marcela Treisman works for an investment firm in Michigan. Her assignment is to analyze the rental market in Ann Arbor, which is home to the University of Michigan. She gathers data on monthly rents for 2011 along with the square footage of 40 homes. A portion of the data is shown in the accompanying table.

Monthly Rent	Square Footage
645	500
675	648
⋮	⋮
2400	2700

Source: www.zillow.com.

a. Construct 90% and 95% confidence intervals for the mean rent for all rental homes in Ann Arbor, Michigan.

b. Construct 90% and 95% confidence intervals for the mean square footage for all rental homes in Ann Arbor, Michigan.

86. According to a survey of 1,235 businesses by IDC, a market-research concern in Framingham, Massachusetts, 12.1% of sole proprietors are engaging in e-commerce (*The Wall Street Journal*, July 26, 2007).

a. With 95% confidence, what is the margin of error when estimating the proportion of sole proprietors that engage in e-commerce?

b. Construct the 95% confidence interval for the population proportion.

87. A Monster.com poll of 3,057 individuals asked: "What's the longest vacation you plan to take this summer?" The following relative frequency distribution summarizes the results.

a. Construct the 95% confidence interval for the proportion of people who plan to take a one-week vacation this summer.

b. Construct the 99% confidence interval for the proportion of people who plan to take a one-week vacation this summer.

c. Which of the two confidence intervals is wider?

88. Linda Barnes has learned from prior studies that one out of five applicants gets admitted to top MBA programs in the country. She wishes to construct her own 90% confidence interval for the acceptance rate in top MBA programs. How large a sample should she take if she does not want the acceptance rate of the sample to deviate from that of the population by more than five percentage points? State your assumptions in computing the required sample size.

89. **FILE** *Field_Choice.* There is a declining interest among teenagers to pursue a career in science and health care (*U.S. News & World Report*, May 23, 2011). Thirty college-bound students in Portland, Oregon, are asked about the field they would like to pursue in college. The choices offered in the questionnaire are science, business, and other. The gender information also is included in the questionnaire. A portion of the data is shown.

Field Choice	Gender
Business	Male
Other	Female
⋮	⋮
Science	Female

a. Compare the 95% confidence interval for the proportion of students who would like to pursue science with the proportion who would like to pursue business.

b. Construct and interpret the 90% confidence interval for the proportion of female students who are college bound.

90. **FILE** *Pedestrians.* A study examined "sidewalk rage" in an attempt to find insight into anger's origins and offer suggestions for anger-management treatments (*The Wall Street Journal*, February 15, 2011). "Sidewalk ragers" tend to believe that pedestrians should behave in a certain way. One possible strategy for sidewalk

ragers is to avoid walkers who are distracted by other activities such as smoking and tourism. Sample data were obtained from 50 pedestrians in Lower Manhattan. It was noted if the pedestrian was smoking (equaled 1 if smoking, 0 otherwise) or was a tourist (equaled 1 if tourist, 0 otherwise). The accompanying table shows a portion of the data.

Smoking	Tourist
0	1
0	1
⋮	⋮
0	0

a. Construct and interpret the 95% confidence interval for the proportion of pedestrians in Lower Manhattan who smoke while walking.

b. Construct and interpret the 95% confidence interval for the proportion of pedestrians in Lower Manhattan who are tourists.

91. An economist would like to estimate the 95% confidence interval for the average real estate taxes collected by a small town in California. In a prior analysis, the standard deviation of real estate taxes was reported as $1,580. What is the minimum sample size required by the economist if he wants to restrict the margin of error to $500?

92. An employee of the Bureau of Transportation Statistics has been given the task of estimating the proportion of on-time arrivals of a budget airline. A prior study had estimated this on-time arrival rate as 78.5%. What is the minimum number of arrivals this employee must include in the sample to ensure that the margin of error for the 95% confidence interval is no more than 0.05?

93. According to a report by the PEW Research Center, 85% of adults under 30 feel optimistic about the economy, but the optimism is shared by only 45% of those who are over 50 (*Newsweek*, September 13, 2010). A research analyst would like to construct 95% confidence intervals for the proportion patterns in various regions of the country. She uses the reported rates by the PEW Research Center to determine the sample size that would restrict the margin of error to within 0.05.

a. How large a sample is required to estimate the proportion of adults under 30 who feel optimistic about the economy?

b. How large a sample is required to estimate the proportion of adults over 50 who feel optimistic about the economy?

CASE STUDIES

CASE STUDY 8.1 Texas is home to more than one million undocumented immigrants, and most of them are stuck in low-paying jobs. Meanwhile, the state also suffers from a lack of skilled workers. The Texas Workforce Commission estimates that 133,000 jobs are currently unfilled, many because employers cannot find qualified applicants (*The Boston Globe*, September 29, 2011). Texas was the first state to pass a law that allows children of undocumented immigrants to pay in-state college tuition rates if they have lived in Texas for three years and plan to become permanent residents. The law passed easily back in 2001 because most legislators believed that producing college graduates and keeping them in Texas benefits the business community. In addition, since college graduates earn more money, they also provide the state with more revenue. Carol Capaldo wishes to estimate the mean hourly wage of workers with various levels of education. She collects a sample of the hourly wages (in $) of 30 workers with a bachelor's degree or higher, 30 workers with only a high school diploma, and 30 workers who did not finish high school. A portion of the data is shown in the accompanying table.

Data for Case Study 8.1 Hourly Wages of Texas Workers by Education Level (in $)

Bachelor's Degree or Higher	High School Diploma	No High School Diploma
22.50	12.68	11.21
19.57	11.23	8.54
⋮	⋮	⋮
21.44	7.47	10.27

FILE

Texas_Wages

In a report, use the information to

1. Calculate descriptive statistics to compare the hourly wages for the three education levels.

2. Construct and interpret 95% confidence intervals for the mean hourly wage at each education level.

CASE STUDY 8.2   The following table presents a portion of the annual returns for two mutual funds offered by the investment giant Fidelity. The *Fidelity Select Automotive Fund* invests primarily in companies engaged in the manufacturing, marketing, or sales of automobiles, trucks, specialty vehicles, parts, tires, and related services. The *Fidelity Gold Fund* invests primarily in companies engaged in exploration, mining, processing, or dealing in gold and, to a lesser degree, in other precious metals and minerals.

Data for Case Study 8.2   Annual Total Return (%) History

Year	Annual Total Return History (in %)	
	Automotive	Gold
2001	22.82	24.99
2002	−6.48	64.28
⋮	⋮	⋮
2016	−5.83	47.28

Source: www.finance.yahoo.com, data retrieved April 2, 2017.

In a report, use the above information to

1. Calculate descriptive statistics to compare the returns of the mutual funds.

2. Assess reward by constructing and interpreting 95% confidence intervals for the population mean return. What assumption did you make for the interval estimates?

CASE STUDY 8.3   The information gathered from opinion polls and political surveys is becoming so increasingly important for candidates on the campaign trail that it is hard to imagine an election that lacks extensive polling. An NBC News/*Wall Street Journal* survey (August 5–9, 2010) of 1,000 adults asked people's preferences on candidates and issues prior to the midterm 2010 elections. Some of the responses to the survey are shown below, as well as responses from prior surveys. (Copyright © 2010 Dow Jones & Co., Inc.)

Question: In general, do you approve or disapprove of the way Barack Obama is handling the aftermath of the Gulf Coast oil spill in August 2010 (and George W. Bush's handling of Katrina in March 2006)?

	August 2010 (%)	March 2006 (%)
Approve	50	36
Disapprove	38	53
Not sure	12	11

Question: Which are more important to you in your vote for Congress this November: domestic issues such as the economy, health care, and immigration; or international issues such as Afghanistan, Iran, and terrorism?

	August 2010 (%)	September 2006 (%)
Domestic issues	73	43
International issues	12	28
Both equally important	15	28

In a report, construct 95% confidence intervals for the relevant population proportions to

1. Compare the approval rates of President Obama's handling of the Gulf Coast oil spill and President George W. Bush's handling of the Hurricane Katrina crisis.

2. Compare the importance of domestic issues in August 2010 and in September 2006.

APPENDIX 8.1 Guidelines for Other Software Packages

The following section provides brief commands for Minitab, SPSS, and JMP. Copy and paste the specified data file into the relevant software spreadsheet prior to following the commands.

Minitab

Estimating μ, σ Known

A. (Replicating Example 8.3) From the menu, choose **Stat > Basic Statistics > 1-Sample Z**.

B. Select **One or more samples, each in a column**, and then select Weight. After **Known standard deviation**, enter 7.5. Choose **Options**. Enter 90.0 for **Confidence Level**.

FILE
Hockey_Pucks

Estimating μ, σ Unknown

A. (Replicating Example 8.6) From the menu, choose **Stat > Basic Statistics > 1-Sample t**.

B. Select **One or more samples, each in a column**, and then select Expenditures. Choose **Options**. Enter 95.0 for **Confidence Level**.

FILE
Lottery

Estimating p

A. (Replicating Example 8.7) From the menu, choose **Stat > Basic Statistics > 1 Proportion**.

B. Select **Summarized data**. Enter 7 for **Number of events** and 25 for **Number of trials**. Choose **Options**. Enter 90.0 for **Confidence Level** and check **Use test and interval based on normal distribution**.

SPSS

Estimating μ, σ Unknown

(Replicating Example 8.6) From the menu, choose **Analyze > Compare Means > One-Sample T Test**. Under **Test Variable(s)**, select Expenditures. Choose **Options**. After **Confidence Interval Percentage** enter 95.

FILE
Lottery

JMP

Estimating μ, σ Known

A. (Replicating Example 8.3) From the menu, choose **Analyze > Distribution**.

B. Under **Select Columns**, select Weight, and then under **Cast Selected Columns into Roles**, select **Y, Columns**.

C. Click on the red triangle in the output window beside Weight. Choose **Confidence Interval > Other**, and after **Enter (1-alpha for Confidence level)**, enter 0.90. Select **Use known sigma** and enter 7.5.

FILE
Hockey_Pucks

Estimating μ, σ Unknown

A. (Replicating Example 8.6) From the menu, choose **Analyze > Distribution**.

B. Under **Select Columns**, select Expenditures, and then under **Cast Selected Columns into Roles**, select **Y, Columns**.

C. Click on the red triangle in the output window beside Expenditures. Choose **Confidence Interval > 0.95**.

FILE
Lottery

9 Hypothesis Testing

LEARNING OBJECTIVES

After reading this chapter you should be able to:

LO **9.1** Define the null hypothesis and the alternative hypothesis.

LO **9.2** Distinguish between Type I and Type II errors.

LO **9.3** Conduct a hypothesis test for the population mean when σ is known.

LO **9.4** Conduct a hypothesis test for the population mean when σ is unknown.

LO **9.5** Conduct a hypothesis test for the population proportion.

In Chapter 8, we used confidence intervals to estimate an unknown population parameter of interest. In this chapter, we will focus on the second major area of statistical inference: hypothesis testing. We use a hypothesis test to challenge the status quo, or some belief about an underlying population parameter, based on sample data. In particular, we develop hypothesis tests for the population mean and the population proportion. For instance, we may wish to test whether the average age of MBA students in the United States is less than 30 years or whether the percentage of defective items in a production process differs from 5%. In either case, since we do not have access to the entire population, we have to perform statistical inference on the basis of limited sample information. If the sample information is not consistent with the status quo, we use the hypothesis testing framework to determine if the inconsistency is real (that is, we contradict the status quo) or due to chance (that is, we do not contradict the status quo).

INTRODUCTORY CASE

Undergraduate Study Habits

©Ken Seet/Corbis Images/SuperStock RF

Are today's college students studying hard or hardly studying? A study asserts that, over the past five decades, the number of hours that the average college student studies each week has been steadily dropping (*The Boston Globe*, July 4, 2010). In 1961, students invested 24 hours per week in their academic pursuits, whereas today's students study an average of 14 hours per week.

Susan Knight is a dean at a large university in California. She wonders if the study trend is reflective of the students at her university. She randomly selects 35 students and asks their average study time per week (in hours). The responses are shown in Table 9.1.

FILE
Study_Hours

TABLE 9.1 Average Hours Studied per Week for a Sample of 35 College Students

25	17	8	14	17	7	11
19	16	9	15	12	17	19
26	14	22	17	14	35	24
11	21	6	20	27	17	6
29	10	10	4	25	13	16

Summary measures: $\bar{x} = 16.3714$ hours and $s = 7.2155$ hours.

Susan wants to use the sample information to

1. Determine if the mean study time of students at her university is below the 1961 national average of 24 hours per week.

2. Determine if the mean study time of students at her university differs from today's national average of 14 hours per week.

A synopsis of this case is provided at the end of Section 9.3.

9.1 INTRODUCTION TO HYPOTHESIS TESTING

Every day people make decisions based on their beliefs about the true state of the world. They hold certain things to be true and others to be false, and then act accordingly. For example, an engineer believes that a certain steel cable has a breaking strength of 5,000 pounds or more, and then permits its use at a construction site; a manufacturer believes that a certain process yields capsules that contain precisely 100 milligrams of a drug, and then ships the capsules to a pharmacy; a manager believes that an incoming shipment contains 2%, or fewer, of defects, and then accepts the shipment. In these cases, and many more, the formation of these beliefs may have started as a mere conjecture, an informed guess, or a proposition tentatively advanced as true. When people formulate a belief in this way, we refer to it as a hypothesis. Sooner or later, however, every hypothesis eventually confronts evidence that either substantiates or refutes it. Determining the validity of an assumption of this nature is called hypothesis testing.

We use hypothesis testing to resolve conflicts between two competing hypotheses on a particular population parameter of interest. We refer to one hypothesis as the **null hypothesis**, denoted H_0, and the other as the **alternative hypothesis**, denoted H_A. We think of the null hypothesis as corresponding to a presumed default state of nature or status quo. The alternative hypothesis, on the other hand, contradicts the default state or status quo.

NULL HYPOTHESIS VERSUS ALTERNATIVE HYPOTHESIS

When constructing a hypothesis test, we define a null hypothesis, denoted H_0, and an alternative hypothesis, denoted H_A. We conduct a hypothesis test to determine whether or not sample evidence contradicts H_0.

In statistics, we use sample information to make inferences regarding the unknown population parameters of interest. In this chapter, our goal is to determine if the null hypothesis can be rejected in favor of the alternative hypothesis. An analogy can be drawn with applications in the medical and legal fields, where we can define the null hypothesis as "an individual is free of a particular disease" or "an accused is innocent." In both cases, the verdict is based on limited evidence, which in statistics translates into making a decision based on limited sample information.

The Decision to "Reject" or "Not Reject" the Null Hypothesis

The hypothesis testing procedure enables us to make one of two decisions. If sample evidence is inconsistent with the null hypothesis, we reject the null hypothesis. Conversely, if sample evidence is not inconsistent with the null hypothesis, then we do not reject the null hypothesis. It is not correct to conclude that "we accept the null hypothesis" because while the sample information may not be inconsistent with the null hypothesis, it does not necessarily prove that the null hypothesis is true.

On the basis of sample information, we either "reject the null hypothesis" or "do not reject the null hypothesis."

Consider the example just referenced where the null is defined as "an individual is free of a particular disease." Suppose a medical procedure does not detect this disease. On the basis of this limited information, we can only conclude that we are unable to detect the disease (do not reject the null hypothesis). It does not necessarily prove that the person does not have the disease (accept the null hypothesis). Similarly, in the court example where the null hypothesis is defined as "an accused is innocent," we can conclude that the person is guilty (reject the null hypothesis) or that there is not enough evidence to convict (do not reject the null hypothesis).

Defining the Null and the Alternative Hypotheses

As mentioned earlier, we use a hypothesis test to contest the status quo, or some belief about an underlying population parameter, based on sample data. A very crucial step concerns the formulation of the two competing hypotheses, since the conclusion of the test depends on how the hypotheses are stated. As a general guideline, whatever we wish to establish is placed in the alternative hypothesis, whereas the null hypothesis includes the status quo. If we are unable to reject the null hypothesis, then we maintain the status quo or "business as usual." However, if we reject the null hypothesis, this establishes that the evidence supports the alternative hypothesis, which may require that we take some kind of action. For instance, if we reject the null hypothesis that an individual is free of a particular disease, then we conclude that the person is sick, for which treatment is prescribed. Similarly, if we reject the null hypothesis that an accused is innocent, we conclude that the person is guilty and is suitably punished.

In most applications, we require some form of the equality sign in the null hypothesis. (The justification for the equality sign will be provided later.) In general, any statement including one of the three signs "=", "≤", or "≥" is valid for the null hypothesis. Given that the alternative hypothesis states the opposite of the null hypothesis, the alternative hypothesis is then specified with a "≠", ">", or "<" sign.

> As a general guideline, we use the alternative hypothesis as a vehicle to establish something new—that is, contest the status quo. In most applications, the null hypothesis regarding a particular population parameter of interest is specified with one of the following signs: =, ≤, or ≥; the alternative hypothesis is then specified with the corresponding opposite sign: ≠, >, or <.

A hypothesis test can be **one-tailed** or **two-tailed**. A two-tailed test is defined when the alternative hypothesis includes the sign "≠". For example, $H_0: \mu = \mu_0$ versus $H_A: \mu \neq \mu_0$ and $H_0: p = p_0$ versus $H_A: p \neq p_0$ are examples of two-tailed tests, where μ_0 and p_0 represent hypothesized values of the population mean and the population proportion, respectively. If the null hypothesis is rejected, it suggests that the true parameter does not equal the hypothesized value.

A one-tailed test, on the other hand, involves a null hypothesis that can only be rejected on one side of the hypothesized value. For example, consider $H_0: \mu \leq \mu_0$ versus $H_A: \mu > \mu_0$. Here we can reject the null hypothesis only when there is substantial evidence that the population mean is greater than μ_0. It is also referred to as a right-tailed test since rejection of the null hypothesis occurs on the right side of the hypothesized mean. Another example is a left-tailed test, $H_0: \mu \geq \mu_0$ versus $H_A: \mu < \mu_0$, where the null hypothesis can only be rejected on the left side of the hypothesized mean. One-tailed tests for the population proportion are defined similarly.

> ### ONE-TAILED VERSUS TWO-TAILED HYPOTHESIS TESTS
>
> Hypothesis tests can be one-tailed or two-tailed. In a one-tailed test, we can reject the null hypothesis only on one side of the hypothesized value of the population parameter. In a two-tailed test, we can reject the null hypothesis on either side of the hypothesized value of the population parameter.

In general, we follow three steps when formulating the competing hypotheses:

1. Identify the relevant population parameter of interest.
2. Determine whether it is a one- or two-tailed test.
3. Include some form of the equality sign in the null hypothesis and use the alternative hypothesis to establish a claim.

The following examples highlight one- and two-tailed tests for the population mean and the population proportion. In each example, we want to state the appropriate competing hypotheses.

EXAMPLE 9.1

A trade group predicts that back-to-school spending will average $606.40 per family this year. A different economic model is needed if the prediction is wrong. Specify the null and the alternative hypotheses to determine if a different economic model is needed.

SOLUTION: Given that we are examining average back-to-school spending, the parameter of interest is the population mean μ. Since we want to be able to determine if the population mean differs from $606.40 ($\mu \neq 606.40$), we need a two-tailed test and formulate the null and alternative hypotheses as

$$H_0: \mu = 606.40$$

$$H_A: \mu \neq 606.40$$

The trade group is advised to use a different economic model if the null hypothesis is rejected.

EXAMPLE 9.2

An advertisement for a popular weight-loss clinic suggests that participants in its new diet program experience an average weight loss of more than 10 pounds. A consumer activist wants to determine if the advertisement's claim is valid. Specify the null and the alternative hypotheses to validate the advertisement's claim.

SOLUTION: The advertisement's claim concerns average weight loss; thus, the parameter of interest is again the population mean μ. This is an example of a one-tailed test because we want to determine if the mean weight loss is more than 10 pounds ($\mu > 10$). We specify the competing hypotheses as

$$H_0: \mu \leq 10 \text{ pounds}$$

$$H_A: \mu > 10 \text{ pounds}$$

The underlying claim that the mean weight loss is more than 10 pounds is true if our decision is to reject the null hypothesis. Conversely, if we do not reject the null hypothesis, we cannot support the claim.

EXAMPLE 9.3

A television research analyst wishes to test a claim that more than 50% of the households will tune in for a TV episode. Specify the null and the alternative hypotheses to test the claim.

SOLUTION: This is an example of a one-tailed test regarding the population proportion p. Given that the analyst wants to determine whether $p > 0.50$, this claim is placed in the alternative hypothesis, whereas the null hypothesis is just its opposite.

$$H_0: p \leq 0.50$$

$$H_A: p > 0.50$$

The claim that more than 50% of the households will tune in for a TV episode is valid only if the null hypothesis is rejected.

EXAMPLE 9.4

It is generally believed that at least 60% of the residents in a small town in Texas are happy with their lives. A sociologist wonders whether recent economic woes have adversely affected the happiness level in this town. Specify the null and the alternative hypotheses to determine if the sociologist's concern is valid.

SOLUTION: This is also a one-tailed test regarding the population proportion p. While the population proportion has been at least 0.60 ($p \geq 0.60$), the sociologist wants to establish that the current population proportion is below 0.60 ($p < 0.60$). Therefore, the hypotheses are formulated as

$$H_0: p \geq 0.60$$

$$H_A: p < 0.60$$

In this case, the sociologist's concern is valid if the null hypothesis is rejected. Nothing new is established if the null hypothesis is not rejected.

Type I and Type II Errors

LO 9.2

Distinguish between Type I and Type II errors.

Since the decision of a hypothesis test is based on limited sample information, we are bound to make errors. Ideally, we would like to be able to reject the null hypothesis when the null hypothesis is false and not reject the null hypothesis when the null hypothesis is true. However, we may end up rejecting or not rejecting the null hypothesis erroneously. In other words, sometimes we reject the null hypothesis when we should not, or not reject the null hypothesis when we should.

We consider two types of errors in the context of hypothesis testing: a **Type I error** and a **Type II error**. A Type I error is committed when we reject the null hypothesis when the null hypothesis is actually true. On the other hand, a Type II error is made when we do not reject the null hypothesis when the null hypothesis is actually false.

Table 9.2 summarizes the circumstances surrounding Type I and Type II errors. Two correct decisions are possible: not rejecting the null hypothesis when the null hypothesis is true and rejecting the null hypothesis when the null hypothesis is false. Conversely, two incorrect decisions (errors) are also possible: rejecting the null hypothesis when the null hypothesis is true (Type I error) and not rejecting the null hypothesis when the null hypothesis is false (Type II error).

TABLE 9.2 Type I and Type II Errors

Decision	Null hypothesis is true	Null hypothesis is false
Reject the null hypothesis	Type I error	Correct decision
Do not reject the null hypothesis	Correct decision	Type II error

EXAMPLE 9.5

Consider the following hypotheses that relate to the medical example mentioned earlier.

$$H_0: \text{A person is free of a particular disease}$$

$$H_A: \text{A person has a particular disease}$$

Suppose the person takes a medical test that attempts to detect this disease. Discuss the consequences of a Type I error and a Type II error.

SOLUTION: A Type I error occurs when the medical test indicates that the person has the disease (reject H_0), but, in reality, the person is free of the disease. We often refer to this type of result as a false positive. If the medical test shows that the person is free of the disease (do not reject H_0), when the person actually has the disease, then a Type II error occurs. We often call this type of result a false negative. Arguably, the consequences of a Type II error in this example are more serious than those of a Type I error.

EXAMPLE 9.6

Consider the following competing hypotheses that relate to the court of law.

$$H_0: \text{An accused person is innocent}$$

$$H_A: \text{An accused person is guilty}$$

Suppose the accused person is judged by a jury of her peers. Discuss the consequences of a Type I error and a Type II error.

SOLUTION: A Type I error is a verdict that finds that the accused is guilty (reject H_0) when she is actually innocent. A Type II error is a verdict that finds that the accused is innocent (do not reject H_0) when she is actually guilty. In this example, it is not clear which of the two errors is more costly to society.

As noted in Example 9.6, it is not always easy to determine which of the two errors has more serious consequences. For given evidence, there is a trade-off between these errors; by reducing the likelihood of a Type I error, we implicitly increase the likelihood of a Type II error, and vice versa. The only way we can reduce both errors is by collecting more evidence. Let us denote the probability of a Type I error by α, the probability of a Type II error by β, and the strength of the evidence by the sample size n. Therefore, we can conclude that the only way we can lower both α and β is by increasing n. For a given n, however, we can reduce α only at the expense of a higher β and reduce β only at the expense of a higher α. The optimal choice of α and β depends on the relative cost of these two types of errors, and determining these costs is not always easy. Typically, the decision regarding the optimal level of Type I and Type II errors is made by the management of a firm where the job of a statistician is to conduct the hypothesis test for a chosen value of α.

EXERCISES 9.1

1. Explain why the following hypotheses are not constructed correctly.
   a. $H_0: \mu \leq 10; H_A: \mu \geq 10$
   b. $H_0: \mu \neq 500; H_A: \mu = 500$
   c. $H_0: p \leq 0.40; H_A: p > 0.42$
   d. $H_0: \bar{X} \leq 128; H_A: \bar{X} > 128$

2. Which of the following statements are valid null and alternative hypotheses? If they are invalid hypotheses, explain why.
   a. $H_0: \bar{X} \leq 210; H_A: \bar{X} > 210$
   b. $H_0: \mu = 120; H_A: \mu \neq 120$
   c. $H_0: p \leq 0.24; H_A: p > 0.24$
   d. $H_0: \mu < 252; H_A: \mu > 252$

3. Explain why the following statements are not correct.
   a. "With my methodological approach, I can reduce the Type I error with the given sample information without changing the Type II error."
   b. "I have already decided how much of the Type I error I am going to allow. A bigger sample will not change either the Type I or Type II error."
   c. "I can reduce the Type II error by making it difficult to reject the null hypothesis."
   d. "By making it easy to reject the null hypothesis, I am reducing the Type I error."

4. Which of the following statements are correct? Explain if incorrect.
   a. "I accept the null hypothesis since sample evidence is not inconsistent with the null hypothesis."
   b. "Since sample evidence cannot be supported by the null hypothesis, I reject the null hypothesis."
   c. "I can establish a given claim if sample evidence is consistent with the null hypothesis."
   d. "I cannot establish a given claim if the null hypothesis is not rejected."

5. Construct the null and the alternative hypotheses for the following tests:
   a. Test if the mean weight of cereal in a cereal box differs from 18 ounces.
   b. Test if the stock price increases on more than 60% of the trading days.
   c. Test if Americans get an average of less than seven hours of sleep.

6. Define the consequences of Type I and Type II errors for each of the tests considered in the preceding question.

7. Construct the null and the alternative hypotheses for the following claims:
   a. "I am going to get the majority of the votes to win this election."
   b. "I suspect that your 10-inch pizzas are, on average, less than 10 inches in size."

c. "I will have to fine the company since its tablets do not contain an average of 250 mg of ibuprofen as advertised."

8. Discuss the consequences of Type I and Type II errors for each of the claims considered in the preceding question.

9. A polygraph (lie detector) is an instrument used to determine if an individual is telling the truth. These tests are considered to be 95% reliable. In other words, if an individual lies, there is a 0.95 probability that the test will detect a lie. Let there also be a 0.005 probability that the test erroneously detects a lie even when the individual is actually telling the truth. Consider the null hypothesis, "the individual is telling the truth," to answer the following questions.
   a. What is the probability of a Type I error?
   b. What is the probability of a Type II error?
   c. What are the consequences of Type I and Type II errors?
   d. What is wrong with the statement, "I can prove that the individual is telling the truth on the basis of the polygraph result"?

10. The manager of a large manufacturing firm is considering switching to new and expensive software that promises to reduce its assembly costs. Before purchasing the software, the manager wants to conduct a hypothesis test to determine if the new software does reduce its assembly costs.
    a. Would the manager of the manufacturing firm be more concerned about a Type I error or a Type II error? Explain.
    b. Would the software company be more concerned about a Type I error or a Type II error? Explain.

11. The screening process for detecting a rare disease is not perfect. Researchers have developed a blood test that is considered fairly reliable. It gives a positive reaction in 98% of the people who have that disease. However, it erroneously gives a positive reaction in 3% of the people who do not have the disease. Consider the null hypothesis "the individual does not have the disease" to answer the following questions.
    a. What is the probability of a Type I error?
    b. What is the probability of a Type II error?
    c. What are the consequences of Type I and Type II errors?
    d. What is wrong with the nurse's analysis, "The blood test result has proved that the individual is free of disease"?

12. A consumer group has accused a restaurant of using higher fat content than what is reported on its menu. The group has been asked to conduct a hypothesis test to substantiate its claims.
    a. Is the manager of the restaurant more concerned about a Type I error or a Type II error? Explain.
    b. Is the consumer group more concerned about a Type I error or a Type II error? Explain.

9.2 HYPOTHESIS TEST FOR THE POPULATION MEAN WHEN σ IS KNOWN

In order to introduce the basic methodology for hypothesis testing, we first conduct a hypothesis test regarding the population mean μ under the assumption that the population standard deviation σ is known. While it is true that σ is rarely known, there are instances when σ is considered fairly stable and, therefore, can be determined from prior experience. In such cases, σ is treated as known. Fortunately, this assumption has no bearing on the overall procedure of conducting a hypothesis test, a procedure we use throughout the remainder of the text.

A hypothesis test regarding the population mean μ is based on the sampling distribution of the sample mean $\overline{X}$. In particular, it uses the fact that $E(\overline{X}) = \mu$ and $se(\overline{X}) = \sigma/\sqrt{n}$. Also, in order to implement the test, it is essential that $\overline{X}$ is normally distributed. Recall that $\overline{X}$ is normally distributed when the underlying population is normally distributed. If the underlying population is not normally distributed, then, by the central limit theorem, $\overline{X}$ is approximately normally distributed if the sample size is sufficiently large—that is, $n \geq 30$.

The basic principle of hypothesis testing is to first assume that the null hypothesis is true and then determine if sample evidence contradicts this assumption. This principle is analogous to the scenario in the court of law where the null hypothesis is defined as "the individual is innocent" and the decision rule is best described by "innocent until proven guilty."

There are two approaches to implementing a hypothesis test—the p-value approach and the critical value approach. The critical value approach is attractive when a computer is unavailable and all calculations must be done by hand. We discuss this approach in the appendix to this chapter. Most researchers and practitioners, however, favor the p-value approach since virtually every statistical software package reports p-values. In this text, we too will focus on the p-value approach. We implement a four-step procedure that is valid for one- and two-tailed tests regarding the population mean, the population proportion, or any other population parameter of interest.

LO 9.3

Conduct a hypothesis test for the population mean when σ is known.

The p-Value Approach

Suppose a sociologist wants to establish that the mean retirement age is greater than 67 ($\mu > 67$). It is assumed that retirement age is normally distributed with a known population standard deviation of 9 years ($\sigma = 9$). We can investigate the sociologist's belief by specifying the competing hypotheses as

$$H_0: \mu \leq 67$$
$$H_A: \mu > 67$$

Let a random sample of 25 retirees produce an average retirement age of 71—that is, $\bar{x} = 71$. This sample evidence casts doubt on the validity of the null hypothesis, since the sample mean is greater than the hypothesized value, $\mu_0 = 67$. However, the discrepancy between $\bar{x}$ and μ_0 does not necessarily imply that the null hypothesis is false. Perhaps the discrepancy can be explained by pure chance. It is common to evaluate this discrepancy in terms of the appropriate **test statistic**.

> ### TEST STATISTIC FOR μ WHEN σ IS KNOWN
>
> The value of the test statistic for the hypothesis test of the population mean μ when the population standard deviation σ is known is computed as
>
> $$z = \frac{\bar{x} - \mu_0}{\sigma/\sqrt{n}},$$
>
> where μ_0 is the hypothesized value of the population mean. This formula is valid only if $\overline{X}$ (approximately) follows a normal distribution.

Note that the value of the test statistic z is evaluated at $\mu = \mu_0$, which explains why we need some form of the equality sign in the null hypothesis. Given that the population is normally distributed with a known standard deviation, $\sigma = 9$, we compute the value of the test statistic as $z = \frac{\bar{x} - \mu_0}{\sigma/\sqrt{n}} = \frac{71 - 67}{9/\sqrt{25}} = 2.22$. Therefore, comparing $\bar{x} = 71$ with 67 is identical to comparing $z = 2.22$ with 0, where 67 and 0 are the means of $\bar{X}$ and Z, respectively.

We now find the **p-value**, which is the likelihood of obtaining a sample mean that is at least as extreme as the one derived from the given sample, under the assumption that the null hypothesis is true as an equality—that is, $\mu_0 = 67$. Since in this example $\bar{x} = 71$, we define the extreme value as a sample mean of 71 or higher and use the z table to find the p-value as $P(\bar{X} \geq 71) = P(Z \geq 2.22) = 1 - 0.9868 = 0.0132$. Figure 9.1 shows the computed p-value.

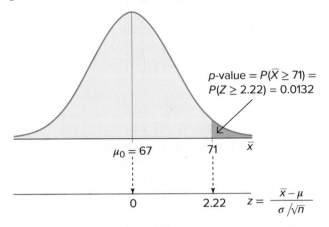

FIGURE 9.1 The p-value for a right-tailed test with $z = 2.22$

$$\text{p-value} = P(\bar{X} \geq 71) = P(Z \geq 2.22) = 0.0132$$

Note that when the null hypothesis is true, there is only a 1.32% chance that the sample mean will be 71 or more. This seems like a very small chance, but is it small enough to allow us to reject the null hypothesis in favor of the alternative hypothesis? Let's see how we define "small enough."

Remember that a Type I error occurs when we reject the null hypothesis when it is actually true. We define the *allowed* probability of making a Type I error as α; we refer to $100\alpha\%$ as the **significance level**. The p-value, on the other hand, is referred to as the *observed* probability of making a Type I error. When using the p-value approach, **the decision rule is to reject the null hypothesis if the p-value $< \alpha$ and not reject the null hypothesis if the p-value $\geq \alpha$.**

We generally choose a value for α *before* implementing a hypothesis test; that is, we set the rules of the game before playing. Care must be exercised in choosing α because important decisions are often based on the results of a hypothesis test, which in turn depend on α. Most hypothesis tests are conducted using a significance level of 1%, 5%, or 10%, using $\alpha = 0.01$, 0.05, or 0.10, respectively. For example, $\alpha = 0.05$ means that we allow a 5% chance of rejecting a true null hypothesis. We can also interpret these conventional significance levels as follows:

- If we reject a null hypothesis at the 10% significance level ($\alpha = 0.10$), then we have *some evidence* that the null hypothesis is false;
- If we reject a null hypothesis at the 5% significance level ($\alpha = 0.05$), then we have *strong evidence* that the null hypothesis is false; and
- If we reject a null hypothesis at the 1% significance level ($\alpha = 0.01$), then we have *very strong evidence* that the null hypothesis is false.

In our example, given the p-value of 0.0132, if we decide to reject the null hypothesis, then there is a 1.32% chance that our decision will be erroneous.

Suppose we had chosen $\alpha = 0.05$ to conduct the above test. At this significance level, we reject the null hypothesis because $0.0132 < 0.05$. This means that the sample data support the sociologist's claim that the average retirement age is greater than 67 years old. Individuals may be working past the normal retirement age of 67 because of poor savings and/or because this generation is expected to outlive any previous generation and needs jobs to pay the bills. We should note that if α had been set at 0.01, then the findings would have been different. At this smaller significance level, the evidence does not allow us to reject the null hypothesis (0.0132 > 0.01). At the 1% significance level, we cannot conclude that the mean retirement age is greater than 67.

In the retirement age example of a right-tailed test, we calculated the p-value as $P(Z \geq z)$. Analogously, for a left-tailed test, the p-value is given by $P(Z \leq z)$. For a two-tailed test, the extreme values exist on both sides of the distribution of the test statistic. Given the symmetry of the z distribution, the p-value for a two-tailed test is twice that of the p-value for a one-tailed test. It is calculated as $2P(Z \geq z)$ if $z > 0$ or as $2P(Z \leq z)$ if $z < 0$.

THE p-VALUE APPROACH

Under the assumption that $\mu = \mu_0$, the p-value is the likelihood of observing a sample mean that is at least as extreme as the one derived from the given sample. Its calculation depends on the specification of the alternative hypothesis.

Alternative Hypothesis	p-value
$H_A: \mu > \mu_0$	Right-tail probability: $P(Z \geq z)$
$H_A: \mu < \mu_0$	Left-tail probability: $P(Z \leq z)$
$H_A: \mu \neq \mu_0$	Two-tail probability: $2P(Z \geq z)$ if $z > 0$ or $2P(Z \leq z)$ if $z < 0$

The decision rule is:

* Reject H_0 if the p-value $< \alpha$, or
* Do not reject H_0 if p-value $\geq \alpha$.

Figure 9.2 shows the three different scenarios of determining the p-value depending on the specification of the competing hypotheses.

FIGURE 9.2 The p-values for one- and two-tailed tests

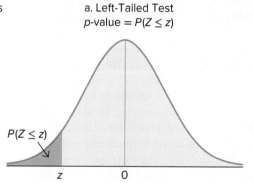

a. Left-Tailed Test
p-value $= P(Z \leq z)$

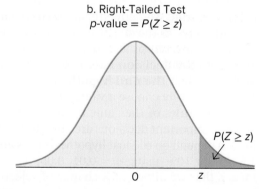

b. Right-Tailed Test
p-value $= P(Z \geq z)$

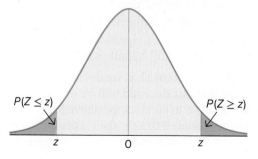

c. Two-Tailed Test
If $z < 0$, then p-value $= 2P(Z \leq z)$
If $z > 0$, then p-value $= 2P(Z \geq z)$

Figure 9.2a shows the p-value for a left-tailed test. Since the appropriate test statistic follows the standard normal distribution, we compute the p-value as $P(Z \leq z)$. When calculating the p-value for a right-tailed test (see Figure 9.2b), we find the area to the right of the value of the test statistic z or, equivalently, $P(Z \geq z)$. Figure 9.2c shows the p-value for a two-tailed test, calculated as $2P(Z \leq z)$ when $z < 0$ or as $2P(Z \geq z)$ when $z > 0$.

It is important to note that we *cannot* reject H_0 for a right-tailed test if $\bar{x} \leq \mu_0$ or, equivalently, $z \leq 0$. Consider, for example, a right-tailed test with the hypotheses specified as $H_0: \mu \leq 67$ versus $H_A: \mu > 67$. Here, if $\bar{x} = 65$, there is no need for formal testing since we have no discrepancy between the sample mean and the hypothesized value of the population mean. Similarly, we *cannot* reject H_0 for a left-tailed test if $\bar{x} \geq \mu_0$ or, equivalently, $z \geq 0$. We will now summarize the four-step procedure using the p-value approach.

THE FOUR-STEP PROCEDURE USING THE p-VALUE APPROACH

Step 1. Specify the null and the alternative hypotheses. We identify the relevant population parameter of interest, determine whether it is a one- or a two-tailed test and, most importantly, include some form of the equality sign in the null hypothesis and place whatever we wish to establish in the alternative hypothesis.

Step 2. Specify the significance level. Before implementing a hypothesis test, we first specify α, which is the *allowed* probability of making a Type I error.

Step 3. Calculate the value of the test statistic and the p-value. When the population standard deviation σ is known, the value of the test statistic is $z = \frac{\bar{x} - \mu}{\sigma/\sqrt{n}}$, where μ_0 is the hypothesized value of the population mean. For a right-tailed test, the p-value is $P(Z \geq z)$, and for a left-tailed test, the p-value is $P(Z \leq z)$. For a two-tailed test, the p-value is $2P(Z \geq z)$ if $z > 0$, or $2P(Z \leq z)$ if $z < 0$.

Step 4. State the conclusion and interpret results. The decision rule is to reject the null hypothesis when the p-value $< \alpha$ and not reject the null hypothesis when the p-value $\geq \alpha$. Clearly interpret the results in the context of a problem.

EXAMPLE 9.7

A research analyst disputes a trade group's prediction that back-to-school spending will average $606.40 per family this year. She believes that average back-to-school spending will differ from this amount. She decides to conduct a test on the basis of a random sample of 30 households with school-age children. She calculates the sample mean as $622.85. She also believes that back-to-school spending is normally distributed with a population standard deviation of $65. She wants to conduct the test at the 5% significance level.

a. Specify the competing hypotheses in order to test the research analyst's claim.

b. What is the allowed probability of a Type I error?

c. Calculate the value of the test statistic and the p-value.

d. At the 5% significance level, does average back-to-school spending differ from $606.40?

SOLUTION:

a. Since we want to determine if the average is different from the predicted value of $606.40, we specify the hypotheses as

$$H_0: \mu = 606.40$$

$$H_A: \mu \neq 606.40$$

b. The allowed probability of a Type I error is equivalent to the significance level of the test, which in this example is given as $\alpha = 0.05$.

c. Note that $\overline{X}$ is normally distributed since it is computed from a random sample drawn from a normal population. Since σ is known, the test statistic follows the standard normal distribution, and its value is

$$z = \frac{\overline{x} - \mu_0}{\sigma/\sqrt{n}} = \frac{622.85 - 606.40}{65/\sqrt{30}} = 1.39.$$

For a two-tailed test with a positive value for the test statistic, we find the p-value as $2P(Z \geq 1.39)$. From the z table, we first find $P(Z \geq 1.39) = 1 - 0.9177 = 0.0823$; so the p-value $= 2 \times 0.0823 = 0.1646$.

d. The decision rule is to reject the null hypothesis if the p-value is less than α. Since $0.1646 > 0.05$, we do not reject H_0. Therefore, at the 5% significance level, we cannot conclude that average back-to-school spending differs from $606.40 per family this year. The sample data do not support the research analyst's claim.

Confidence Intervals and Two-Tailed Hypothesis Tests

A confidence interval for the population parameter is sometimes used as an alternative method for conducting a two-tailed hypothesis test. Informally, we had used this procedure when discussing confidence intervals in Chapter 8. Given that we conduct the hypothesis test at the α significance level, we can use the sample data to determine a corresponding $100(1 - \alpha)\%$ confidence interval for the population mean μ. If the confidence interval does not contain the hypothesized value of the population mean μ_0, then we reject the null hypothesis. If the confidence interval contains μ_0, then we do not reject the null hypothesis.

IMPLEMENTING A TWO-TAILED TEST USING A CONFIDENCE INTERVAL

The general specification for a $100(1 - \alpha)\%$ confidence interval for the population mean μ when the population standard deviation σ is known is computed as

$$\overline{x} \pm z_{\alpha/2}\frac{\sigma}{\sqrt{n}} \quad \text{or} \quad \left[\overline{x} - z_{\alpha/2}\frac{\sigma}{\sqrt{n}}, \overline{x} + z_{\alpha/2}\frac{\sigma}{\sqrt{n}}\right].$$

Given a hypothesized value of the population mean μ_0, the decision rule is:

- Reject H_0 if μ_0 does not fall within the confidence interval, or
- Do not reject H_0 if μ_0 falls within the confidence interval.

EXAMPLE 9.8

Use the confidence interval approach to conduct the hypothesis test described in Example 9.7.

SOLUTION: We are testing $H_0: \mu = 606.40$ versus $H_A: \mu \neq 606.40$ at the 5% significance level. We use $n = 30$, $\bar{x} = 622.85$, and $\sigma = 65$, along with $\alpha = 0.05$, to determine the 95% confidence interval for μ. We find $z_{\alpha/2} = z_{0.025} = 1.96$ and compute

$$\bar{x} \pm z_{\alpha/2}\frac{\sigma}{\sqrt{n}} = 622.85 \pm 1.96\frac{65}{\sqrt{30}} = 622.85 \pm 23.26,$$

resulting in the interval [599.59, 646.11]. Since the hypothesized value of the population mean $\mu_0 = 606.40$ falls within the 95% confidence interval, we do not reject H_0. Thus, we arrive at the same conclusion as with the p-value approach; that is, the sample data do not support the research analyst's claim that average back-to-school spending differs from $606.40 per family this year.

As shown above, we use the confidence interval as an alternative method for conducting a two-tailed test. It is possible to adjust the confidence interval to accommodate a one-tailed test, but we do not discuss this adjustment in this text.

Using Excel and R to Test μ When σ Is Known

Excel and R provide various functions that simplify the steps of conducting a hypothesis test. We use the following example to demonstrate some of these functions.

EXAMPLE 9.9

A report in *The New York Times* (August 7, 2010) suggests that consumers are spending less due to a realization that excessive spending does not make them happier. A researcher wants to use debit card data to contradict the generally held view that the average amount spent annually on a debit card is at least $8,000. She surveys 20 consumers and asks them how much they spend annually on their debit cards. The results are given below.

7960	7700	7727	7704	8543	7661	7767	8761	7530	8128
7938	7771	7272	8113	7727	7697	7690	8000	8079	7547

FILE
Debit_Spending

It is assumed that the population standard deviation is $500 and that spending on debit cards is normally distributed. Test the claim at the 1% level of significance.

SOLUTION: The researcher would like to establish that average spending on debit cards is less than $8,000 or, equivalently, $\mu < 8,000$. Thus, we formulate the competing hypotheses as

$$H_0: \mu \geq 8,000$$

$$H_A: \mu < 8,000$$

The normality condition of $\overline{X}$ is satisfied since spending on debit cards is assumed to be normally distributed. Also, since the population standard deviation is known, here $\sigma = 500$, the test statistic is assumed to follow the z distribution.

Using Excel

a. Open the ***Debit_Spending*** data file. Note that the values for spending are in cells A2 through A21.

b. We use Excel's **AVERAGE** function to help in the calculation of the value of the test statistic $z = \frac{\bar{x} - \mu}{\sigma/\sqrt{n}}$. We enter "=(AVERAGE(A2:A21) − 8000)/(500/ SQRT(20))," and Excel returns −1.2008, so $z = -1.2008$.

c. We use Excel's **NORM.DIST** function to find the *p*-value. Recall that in order to find $P(X \leq x)$ for a normally distributed random variable, we enter "=NORM.DIST(x, μ, σ, 1)" where x is the value for which we want to evaluate the cumulative probability, μ is the mean of the distribution, and σ is the standard deviation of the distribution. If we enter "=1 − NORM.DIST (x, μ, σ, 1)," then Excel returns $P(X \geq x)$. In order to find $P(Z \leq -1.2008)$, we enter "=NORM.DIST(−1.2008, 0, 1, 1)." Excel returns 0.1149.

d. The hypothesis test is conducted at the 1% significance level. Thus, since the *p*-value of 0.1149 is not less than $\alpha = 0.01$, we do not reject the null hypothesis. In other words, at the 1% significance level, the researcher cannot conclude that annual spending on debit cards is less than $8,000. Perhaps these findings can be reconciled with a report that claims that individuals are shunning their credit cards and using debit cards to avoid incurring more debt (www.businessweek.com, September 8, 2010).

Using R

a. Import the ***Debit_Spending*** data into a data frame (table) in R.

b. We use R's **mean** function to help in the calculation of the value of the test statistic $z = \frac{\bar{x} - \mu}{\sigma / \sqrt{n}}$. We label the test statistic as Teststat and enter

```
> Teststat <- (mean(Debit_Spending$'Spending') -
  8000)/(500/sqrt(20))
> list(Teststat)
```

And R returns: −1.200769.

c. We use R's **pnorm** function to find the *p*-value. Recall that in order to find $P(X \leq x)$ for a normal random variable we enter "pnorm(x, μ, σ, lower.tail = TRUE)" where x is the value for which we want to evaluate the probability, μ is the mean of the distribution, and σ is the standard deviation of the distribution. If we enter "lower.tail = FALSE" for the last argument in the function, then R returns $P(X \geq x)$. In order to find $P(Z \leq -1.2008)$, we enter

```
> pnorm(Teststat, 0, 1, lower.tail=TRUE)
```

And R returns: 0.1149205.

Again, since the *p*-value $= 0.1149 > 0.01 = \alpha$, we cannot reject H_0. At the 1% significance level, we cannot conclude that annual debit spending is less than $8,000.

One Last Remark

An important component of any well-executed statistical analysis is to clearly communicate the results. Thus, it is not sufficient to end the analysis with a conclusion that you reject the null hypothesis or you do not reject the null hypothesis. You must interpret the results, clearly reporting whether or not the claim regarding the population parameter of interest can be justified on the basis of the sample information.

EXERCISES 9.2

Mechanics

13. Consider the following hypotheses:
$$H_0: \mu \leq 12.6$$
$$H_A: \mu > 12.6$$

A sample of 25 observations yields a sample mean of 13.4. Assume that the sample is drawn from a normal population with a population standard deviation of 3.2.

a. Calculate the p-value. What is the conclusion if $\alpha = 0.10$?

b. Calculate the p-value if the above sample mean was based on a sample of 100 observations. What is the conclusion if $\alpha = 0.10$?

14. Consider the following hypotheses:
$$H_0: \mu = 100$$
$$H_A: \mu \neq 100$$

A sample of 16 observations yields a sample mean of 95. Assume that the sample is drawn from a normal population with a population standard deviation of 10.

a. Calculate the value of the test statistic.

b. Find the p-value.

c. At the 10% significance level, what is the conclusion?

15. Consider the following hypotheses:
$$H_0: \mu \geq 150$$
$$H_A: \mu < 150$$

A sample of 80 observations results in a sample mean of 144. The population standard deviation is known to be 28.

a. Calculate the value of the test statistic and the p-value.

b. Does the above sample evidence enable us to reject the null hypothesis at $\alpha = 0.01$?

c. Does the above sample evidence enable us to reject the null hypothesis at $\alpha = 0.05$?

16. A researcher wants to determine if the population mean is greater than 45. A random sample of 36 observations yields a sample mean of 47. Assume that the population standard deviation is 8.

a. Specify the competing hypotheses to test the researcher's claim.

b. Calculate the value of the test statistic.

c. Find the p-value.

d. At the 5% significance level, what is the conclusion?

17. Consider the following hypotheses:
$$H_0: \mu = 1,800$$
$$H_A: \mu \neq 1,800$$

The population is normally distributed with a population standard deviation of 440. Compute the value of the test

statistic and the resulting p-value for each of the following sample results. For each sample, determine if you can reject the null hypothesis at the 10% significance level.

a. $\bar{x} = 1,850; n = 110$

b. $\bar{x} = 1,850; n = 280$

c. $\bar{x} = 1,650; n = 32$

d. $\bar{x} = 1,700; n = 32$

18. Consider the following hypothesis test:
$$H_0: \mu \leq -5$$
$$H_A: \mu > -5$$

A random sample of 50 observations yields a sample mean of -3. The population standard deviation is 10. Calculate the p-value. What is the conclusion to the test if $\alpha = 0.05$?

19. Consider the following hypothesis test:
$$H_0: \mu \leq 75$$
$$H_A: \mu > 75$$

A random sample of 100 observations yields a sample mean of 80. The population standard deviation is 30. Calculate the p-value. What is the conclusion to the test if $\alpha = 0.10$?

20. Consider the following hypothesis test:
$$H_0: \mu = -100$$
$$H_A: \mu \neq -100$$

A random sample of 36 observations yields a sample mean of -125. The population standard deviation is 42. Conduct the test at $\alpha = 0.01$.

21. Consider the following hypotheses:
$$H_0: \mu = 120$$
$$H_A: \mu \neq 120$$

The population is normally distributed with a population standard deviation of 46.

a. If $\bar{x} = 132$ and $n = 50$, what is the conclusion at the 5% significance level?

b. If $\bar{x} = 108$ and $n = 50$, what is the conclusion at the 10% significance level?

Applications

22. It is advertised that the average braking distance for a small car traveling at 65 miles per hour equals 120 feet. A transportation researcher wants to determine if the statement made in the advertisement is false. She randomly test drives 36 small cars at 65 miles per hour and records the braking distance. The sample average braking distance is computed as 114 feet. Assume that the population standard deviation is 22 feet.

a. State the null and the alternative hypotheses for the test.

b. Calculate the value of the test statistic and the p-value.

c. Use $\alpha = 0.01$ to determine if the average breaking distance differs from 120 feet.

23. Customers at Costco spend an average of $130 per trip (*The Wall Street Journal*, October 6, 2010). One of Costco's rivals would like to determine whether its customers spend more per trip. A survey of the receipts of 25 customers found that the sample mean was $135.25. Assume that the population standard deviation is $10.50 and that spending follows a normal distribution.

a. Specify the null and alternative hypotheses to test whether average spending at the rival's store is more than $130.

b. Calculate the value of the test statistic and the p-value.

c. At the 5% significance level, what is the conclusion to the test?

24. In May 2008, CNN reported that sports utility vehicles (SUVs) are plunging toward the "endangered" list. Due to the uncertainty of oil prices and environmental concerns, consumers are replacing gas-guzzling vehicles with fuel-efficient smaller cars. As a result, there has been a big drop in the demand for new as well as used SUVs. A sales manager of a used car dealership for SUVs believes that it takes more than 90 days, on average, to sell an SUV. In order to test his claim, he samples 40 recently sold SUVs and finds that it took an average of 95 days to sell an SUV. He believes that the population standard deviation is fairly stable at 20 days.

a. State the null and the alternative hypotheses for the test.

b. What is the p-value?

c. Is the sales manager's claim justified at $\alpha = 0.01$?

25. According to the *Centers for Disease Control and Prevention* (February 18, 2016), 1 in 3 American adults don't get enough sleep. A researcher wants to determine if Americans are sleeping less than the recommended 7 hours of sleep on weekdays. He takes a random sample of 150 Americans and computes the average sleep time of 6.7 hours on weekdays. Assume that the population is normally distributed with a known standard deviation of 2.1 hours. Test the researcher's claim at $\alpha = 0.01$.

26. A local bottler in Hawaii wishes to ensure that an average of 16 ounces of passion fruit juice is used to fill each bottle. In order to analyze the accuracy of the bottling process, he takes a random sample of 48 bottles. The mean weight of the passion fruit juice in the sample is 15.80 ounces. Assume that the population standard deviation is 0.8 ounce.

a. State the null and the alternative hypotheses to test if the bottling process is inaccurate.

b. What is the value of the test statistic and the p-value?

c. At $\alpha = 0.05$, what is the conclusion to the hypothesis test? Make a recommendation to the bottler.

27. **FILE** *MV_Houses.* A realtor in Mission Viejo, California, believes that the average price of a house is more than $500,000.

a. State the null and the alternative hypotheses for the test.

b. The data accompanying this exercise show house prices. (Data are in $1,000s.) Assume the population standard deviation is $100 (in $1,000s). What is the value of the test statistic and the p-value?

c. At $\alpha = 0.05$, what is the conclusion to the test? Is the realtor's claim supported by the data?

28. **FILE** *Home_Depot.* The data accompanying this exercise show the weekly stock price for Home Depot. Assume that stock prices are normally distributed with a population standard deviation of $3.

a. State the null and the alternative hypotheses in order to test whether or not the average weekly stock price differs from $30.

b. Find the value of the test statistic and the p-value.

c. At $\alpha = 0.05$, can you conclude that the average weekly stock price does not equal $30?

29. **FILE** *Hourly_Wage.* An economist wants to test if the average hourly wage is less than $22. Assume that the population standard deviation is $6.

a. State the null and the alternative hypotheses for the test.

b. The data accompanying this exercise show hourly wages. Find the value of the test statistic and the p-value.

c. At $\alpha = 0.05$, what is the conclusion to the test? Is the average hourly wage less than $22?

30. **FILE** *CT_Undergrad_Debt.* On average, a college student graduates with $27,200 in debt (*The Boston Globe*, May 27, 2012). A researcher collects data on debt from 40 recent undergraduates from Connecticut. Assume that the population standard deviation is $5,000.

a. The researcher believes that recent undergraduates from Connecticut have less debt than the national average. Specify the competing hypotheses to test this belief.

b. Find the value of the test statistic and the p-value.

c. Do the data support the researcher's claim, at $\alpha = 0.10$?

9.3 HYPOTHESIS TEST FOR THE POPULATION MEAN WHEN σ IS UNKNOWN

So far we have considered hypothesis tests for the population mean μ under the assumption that the population standard deviation σ is known. In most business applications, σ is not known and we have to replace σ with the sample standard deviation s to estimate the standard error of $\overline{X}$.

Conduct a hypothesis test for the population mean when σ is unknown.

TEST STATISTIC FOR μ WHEN σ IS UNKNOWN

The value of the test statistic for the hypothesis test of the population mean μ when the population standard deviation σ is unknown is computed as

$$t_{df} = \frac{\overline{x} - \mu_0}{s/\sqrt{n}},$$

where μ_0 is the hypothesized value of the population mean, s is the sample standard deviation, n is the sample size, and the degrees of freedom $df = n - 1$. This formula is valid only if $\overline{X}$ (approximately) follows a normal distribution.

The next two examples show how we use the four-step procedure for hypothesis testing when we are testing the population mean μ and the population standard deviation σ is unknown.

EXAMPLE 9.10

In the introductory case to this chapter, the dean at a large university in California wonders if students at her university study less than the 1961 national average of 24 hours per week. She randomly selects 35 students and asks their average study time per week (in hours). From their responses (see Table 9.1), she calculates a sample mean of 16.3714 hours and a sample standard deviation of 7.2155 hours.

a. Specify the competing hypotheses to test the dean's concern.

b. Calculate the value of the test statistic.

c. Find the p-value.

d. At the 5% significance level, what is the conclusion to the hypothesis test?

SOLUTION:

a. This is an example of a one-tailed test where we would like to determine if the mean hours studied is less than 24; that is, $\mu < 24$. We formulate the competing hypotheses as

$$H_0: \mu \geq 24 \text{ hours}$$

$$H_A: \mu < 24 \text{ hours}$$

b. Recall that for any statistical inference regarding the population mean, it is essential that the sample mean $\overline{X}$ is normally distributed. This condition is satisfied because the sample size is greater than 30, specifically $n = 35$. The

---

degrees of freedom, $df = n - 1 = 34$. Given $\bar{x} = 16.3714$ and $s = 7.2155$, we compute the value of the test statistic as

$$t_{34} = \frac{\bar{x} - \mu_0}{s/\sqrt{n}} = \frac{16.3714 - 24}{7.2155/\sqrt{35}} = -6.255.$$

c. Since this is a left-tailed test, we compute the p-value as $P(T_{34} \leq t_{34})$. Table 9.3 shows a portion of the t table. Referencing Table 9.3 for $df = 34$, we find that the exact probability $P(T_{34} \leq -6.255)$, which is equivalent to $P(T_{34} \geq 6.255)$, cannot be determined. Since 6.255 is larger than any value in this row, it implies that the p-value is less than 0.005. In other words, we approximate the p-value as $P(T_{34} \leq -6.255) < 0.005$. In the next example, we will show how to use Excel and R to obtain exact p-values.

TABLE 9.3 Portion of the t Table

df	Area in Upper Tail					
	0.20	0.10	0.05	0.025	0.01	0.005
1	1.376	3.078	6.341	12.706	31.821	63.657
	⋮	⋮	⋮	⋮	⋮	⋮
34	0.852	1.307	1.691	2.032	2.441	2.728

d. We reject the null hypothesis since the p-value is less than $\alpha = 0.05$. At the 5% significance level, we conclude that the average study time at the university is less than the 1961 average of 24 hours per week.

Using Excel and R to Test μ When σ is Unknown

Again we find that functions in Excel and R are quite useful when calculating the value of the test statistic and the exact p-value. Consider the following example.

EXAMPLE 9.11

FILE
Study_Hours

As the introductory case to this chapter mentions, research finds that today's undergraduates study an average of 14 hours per week. Using the sample data from Table 9.1, the dean would also like to test if the mean study time of students at her university differs from today's national average of 14 hours per week. At the 5% significance level, what is the conclusion to this test?

SOLUTION: Since the dean would like to test if the mean study time of students at her university differs from 14 hours per week, we formulate the competing hypotheses for the test as

$$H_0: \mu = 14 \text{ hours}$$
$$H_A: \mu \neq 14 \text{ hours}$$

Using Excel

a. Open the **Study_Hours** data file. Note that the values for spending are in cells A2 through A36.

b. We use Excel's **AVERAGE** and **STDEV.S** functions to help in the calculation of the value of the test statistic $t_{df} = \frac{\bar{x} - \mu}{s/\sqrt{n}}$. We enter "=(AVERAGE(A2:A36) − 14)/(STDEV.S(A2:A36)/SQRT(35))." Excel returns 1.9444, so $t_{34} = 1.9444$.

c. Even though Excel offers a number of functions that generate p-values, we use the **T.DIST.RT** function. If we enter "=T.DIST.RT(t_{df}, df)," where t_{df} is the value of the test statistic and df is the relevant degrees of freedom, then Excel returns $P(T_{df} \geq t_{df})$; this probability is the p-value for a right-tailed test. If we enter "=1 − T.DIST.RT (t_{df}, df)," then Excel returns $P(T_{df} \leq t_{df})$. Thus, in order to find the exact probability for this two-tailed hypothesis test where $t_{34} = 1.9444$, we enter "=2*T.DIST.RT(1.9444, 34)." Excel returns 0.0602.

d. Since the p-value of 0.0602 is not less than $\alpha = 0.05$, we do not reject the null hypothesis. At the 5% significance level, we cannot conclude that the mean study time of students at the university is different from today's national average of 14 hours per week.

Using R

a. Import the **Study_Hours** data into a data frame (table) in R.

b. We use R's **mean** and **sd** functions to help in the calculation of the value of the test statistic $t_{df} = \frac{\bar{x} - \mu}{s/\sqrt{n}}$. We label the test statistic as Teststat and enter

```
> Teststat <- (mean(Study_Hours$'Hours') - 14)/
  (sd(Study_Hours$'Hours')/sqrt(35))
> list(Teststat)
```

And R returns: 1.944356.

c. We use R's **pt** function to find the p-value. In general, in order to find the probability that satisfies $P(T_{df} \leq t_{df})$, we enter "pt(t_{df}, df, lower.tail=TRUE)," where t_{df} is the value of the test statistic and df are the relevant degrees of freedom. If we enter "pt(t_{df}, df, lower.tail=FALSE)," then R returns $P(T_{df} \geq t_{df})$. Therefore, to find the p-value for this two tailed test—that is, $2P(T_{34} \geq 1.9444)$—we enter

```
> 2*pt(Teststat, 34, lower.tail=FALSE)
```

And R returns: 0.06016369.

Again, since the p-value = 0.0602 > 0.05 = α, we cannot reject H_0. At the 5% significance level, we cannot conclude that average study hours per week differ from 14 hours.

©Asia Images Group/Getty Images RF

A report claims that undergraduates are studying far less today as compared to five decades ago (*The Boston Globe*, July 4, 2010). The report finds that in 1961, students invested 24 hours per week in their academic pursuits, whereas today's students study an average of 14 hours per week. In an attempt to determine whether or not this national trend is present at a large university in California, 35 students are randomly selected and asked their average study time per week (in hours). The sample produces a mean of 16.37 hours with a standard deviation of 7.22 hours. Two hypothesis tests are conducted. The first test examines whether the mean study time of students at this university is below the 1961 national average of 24 hours per week. At the 5% significance level, the sample data suggest that the mean is less than 24 hours per week. The second test investigates whether the mean study time of students at this university differs from today's national average of 14 hours per week. At the 5% significance level, the results suggest that the mean study time is not different from 14 hours per week. Thus, the sample results support the overall findings of the report: undergraduates study, on average, 14 hours per week, far below the 1961 average of 24 hours per week. The present analysis, however, does not explain why that might be the case. For instance, it cannot be determined whether students have just become lazier, or if with the advent of the computer, they can access information in less time.

EXERCISES 9.3

Mechanics

31. Consider the following hypotheses:

$$H_0: \mu \leq 210$$
$$H_A: \mu > 210$$

Find the *p*-value for this test based on the following sample information.

a. $\bar{x} = 216; s = 26; n = 40$
b. $\bar{x} = 216; s = 26; n = 80$
c. $\bar{x} = 216; s = 16; n = 40$
d. $\bar{x} = 214; s = 16; n = 40$

32. Which of the sample information in the preceding question enables us to reject the null hypothesis at $\alpha = 0.01$ and at $\alpha = 0.10$?

33. Consider the following hypotheses:

$$H_0: \mu = 12$$
$$H_A: \mu \neq 12$$

Find the *p*-value for this test based on the following sample information.

a. $\bar{x} = 11; s = 3.2; n = 36$
b. $\bar{x} = 13; s = 3.2; n = 36$
c. $\bar{x} = 11; s = 2.8; n = 36$
d. $\bar{x} = 11; s = 2.8; n = 49$

34. Which of the sample information in the preceding question enables us to reject the null hypothesis at $\alpha = 0.01$ and at $\alpha = 0.10$?

35. Consider the following hypotheses:

$$H_0: \mu = 50$$
$$H_A: \mu \neq 50$$

A sample of 16 observations yields a sample mean of 46. Assume that the sample is drawn from a normal population with a sample standard deviation of 10.

a. Calculate the value of the test statistic.
b. At the 5% significance level, does the population mean differ from 50? Explain.

36. In order to test if the population mean differs from 16, you draw a random sample of 32 observations and compute the sample mean and the sample standard deviation as 15.2 and 0.6, respectively. Conduct the test at the 1% level of significance.

37. In order to conduct a hypothesis test for the population mean, a random sample of 24 observations is drawn from a normally distributed population. The resulting sample mean and sample standard deviation are calculated as 4.8 and 0.8, respectively. Conduct the following tests at $\alpha = 0.05$.

a. $H_0: \mu \leq 4.5$ against $H_A: \mu > 4.5$
b. $H_0: \mu = 4.5$ against $H_A: \mu \neq 4.5$

38. Consider the following hypotheses:

$$H_0: \mu \geq -10$$
$$H_A: \mu < -10$$

A sample of 25 observations yields a sample mean of -12. Assume that the sample is drawn from a normal population with a sample standard deviation of 4.

a. Calculate the value of the test statistic.

b. At the 5% significance level, is the population mean less than -10? Explain.

39. Consider the following hypotheses:

$$H_0: \mu = 8$$
$$H_A: \mu \neq 8$$

The population is normally distributed. A sample produces the following observations:

6	9	8	7	7	11	10

Conduct the test at the 5% level of significance.

40. Consider the following hypotheses:

$$H_0: \mu \geq 100$$
$$H_A: \mu < 100$$

The population is normally distributed. A sample produces the following observations:

95	99	85	80	98	97

Conduct the test at the 1% level of significance.

Applications

41. A machine that is programmed to package 1.20 pounds of cereal in each cereal box is being tested for its accuracy. In a sample of 36 cereal boxes, the mean and the standard deviation are calculated as 1.22 pounds and 0.06 pound, respectively.

a. Set up the null and the alternative hypotheses to determine if the machine is working improperly—that is, it is either underfilling or overfilling the cereal boxes.

b. Calculate the value of the test statistic and the p-value.

c. At the 5% level of significance, can you conclude that the machine is working improperly? Explain.

42. The manager of a small convenience store does not want her customers standing in line for too long prior to a purchase. In particular, she is willing to hire an employee for another cash register if the average wait time of the customers is more than five minutes. She randomly observes the wait time (in minutes) of customers during the day as:

3.5	5.8	7.2	1.9	6.8	8.1	5.4

a. Set up the null and the alternative hypotheses to determine if the manager needs to hire another employee.

b. Calculate the value of the test statistic and the p-value. What assumption regarding the population is necessary to implement this step?

c. Decide whether the manager needs to hire another employee at $\alpha = 0.10$.

43. Small, energy-efficient, Internet-centric, new computers are increasingly gaining popularity (*The New York Times,* July 20, 2008). Some of the biggest companies are wary of the new breed of computers because their low price could threaten PC makers' already thin profit margins. An analyst comments that the larger companies have a cause for concern since the mean price of these small computers has fallen below $350. She examines six popular brands of these small computers and records their retail prices as:

322	269	373	412	299	389

a. What assumption regarding the distribution of the price of small computers is necessary to test the analyst's claim?

b. Specify the null and alternative hypotheses to test the analyst's claim.

c. Calculate the value of the test statistic and the p-value.

d. At the 5% significance level, what is the conclusion to the test? Should the larger computer companies be concerned?

44. A local brewery wishes to ensure that an average of 12 ounces of beer is used to fill each bottle. In order to analyze the accuracy of the bottling process, the bottler takes a random sample of 48 bottles. The sample mean weight and the sample standard deviation of the bottles are 11.80 ounces and 0.8 ounce, respectively.

a. State the null and the alternative hypotheses to test if the accuracy of the bottling process is compromised.

b. Do you need to make any assumption regarding the population for testing?

c. Calculate the value of the test statistic and the p-value.

d. At $\alpha = 0.05$, what is the conclusion to the test? Make a recommendation to the bottler.

45. Based on the average predictions of 47 members of the National Association of Business Economists (NABE), the U.S. gross domestic product (GDP) will expand by 3.2% in 2011 (*The Wall Street Journal,* May 23, 2010). Suppose the sample standard deviation of their predictions was 1%. At the 5% significance level, test if the mean forecast GDP of all NABE members is greater than 3%.

46. In September 2007, U.S. home prices fell at a record pace, and price declines in Los Angeles and Orange counties in California outpaced other major metropolitan areas (*Los Angeles Times,* November 28, 2007). The report was based on the Standard & Poor's/Case-Shiller index that measures the value of single-family homes based on their sales histories. According to this index, the prices in San Diego dropped by an average of 9.6% from a year earlier. Assume that the survey was based on recent sales of 34 houses in San Diego that also resulted in a standard deviation of 5.2%. Can we conclude that the mean drop of all

home prices in San Diego is greater than the 7% drop in Los Angeles? Use a 1% level of significance for the analysis.

47. A car manufacturer is trying to develop a new sports car. Engineers are hoping that the average amount of time that the car takes to go from 0 to 60 miles per hour is below 6 seconds. The manufacturer tested 12 of the cars and clocked their performance times. Three of the cars clocked in at 5.8 seconds, 5 cars at 5.9 seconds, 3 cars at 6.0 seconds, and 1 car at 6.1 seconds. At the 5% level of significance, test if the new sports car is meeting its goal to go from 0 to 60 miles per hour in less than 6 seconds. Assume a normal distribution for the analysis.

48. A mortgage specialist would like to analyze the average mortgage rates for Atlanta, Georgia. He collects data on the annual percentage rates (APR in %) for 30-year fixed loans as shown in the following table. If he is willing to assume that these rates are randomly drawn from a normally distributed population, can he conclude that the mean mortgage rate for the population exceeds 4.2%? Test the hypothesis at the 10% level of significance.

Financial Institution	APR
G Squared Financial	4.125
Best Possible Mortgage	4.250
Hersch Financial Group	4.250
Total Mortgages Services	4.375
Wells Fargo	4.375
Quicken Loans	4.500
Amerisave	4.750

Source: MSN Money.com; data retrieved October 1, 2010.

49. One of the consequences of the Great Recession was a free fall of the stock market's average price/earnings ratio, or P/E ratio (*The Wall Street Journal*, August 30, 2010). Generally, a high P/E ratio suggests that investors are expecting higher earnings growth in the future compared to companies with a lower P/E ratio. An analyst wants to determine if the P/E ratio of firms in the footwear industry is different from the overall average of 14.9. The following table shows the P/E ratios for a sample of seven firms in the footwear industry.

Firm	P/E Ratio
Brown Shoe Co., Inc.	20.54
Collective Brands, Inc.	9.33
Crocs, Inc.	22.63
DSW, Inc.	14.42
Nike, Inc.	18.68
Skechers USA, Inc.	9.35
Timberland Co.	14.93

Source: biz.yahoo.com, data retrieved August 23, 2010.

a. State the null and the alternative hypotheses in order to test whether the P/E ratio of firms in the footwear industry differs from the overall average of 14.9.

b. What assumption regarding the population is necessary?

c. Calculate the value of the test statistic and the *p*-value.

d. At $\alpha = 0.10$, does the P/E ratio of firms in the footwear industry differ from the overall average of 14.9? Explain.

50. **FILE** *MPG.* The data accompanying this exercise show miles per gallon (MPG).

a. State the null and the alternative hypotheses in order to test whether the average MPG differs from 95.

b. Calculate the value of the test statistic and the *p*-value.

c. At $\alpha = 0.05$, can you conclude that the average MPG differs from 95?

51. **FILE** *Debt_Payments.* A study found that consumers are making average monthly debt payments of $983 (Experian.com, November 11, 2010). The data accompanying this exercise show the average debt payments (Debt, in $) for 26 metropolitan areas, a portion of which is shown in the following table.

City	Debt
Washington, D.C.	1285
Seattle	1135
⋮	⋮
Pittsburgh	763

Source: www.Experian.com, November 11, 2010.

a. State the null and the alternative hypotheses in order to test whether average monthly debt payments are greater than $900.

b. What assumption regarding the population is necessary to implement this step?

c. Calculate the value of the test statistic and the *p*-value.

d. At $\alpha = 0.05$, are average monthly debt payments greater than $900? Explain.

52. **FILE** *Highway_Speeds.* A police officer is concerned about speeds on a certain section of Interstate 95. The data accompanying this exercise show the speeds of 40 cars on a Saturday afternoon.

a. The speed limit on this portion of Interstate 95 is 65 mph. Specify the competing hypotheses in order to determine if the average speed is greater than the speed limit.

b. Calculate the value of the test statistic and the *p*-value.

c. At $\alpha = 0.01$, are the officer's concerns warranted? Explain.

53. **FILE** *Lottery.* An article found that Massachusetts residents spent an average of $860.70 on the lottery in 2010, more than three times the U.S. average (www.businessweek.com, March 14, 2012). A researcher at a Boston think tank believes that Massachusetts residents spend less than this amount. He surveys 100 Massachusetts residents and asks them about their annual expenditures on the lottery.

a. Specify the competing hypotheses to test the researcher's claim.

b. Calculate the value of the test statistic and the *p*-value.

c. At the 10% significance level, do the data support the researcher's claim? Explain.

9.4 HYPOTHESIS TEST FOR THE POPULATION PROPORTION

LO 9.5

Conduct a hypothesis test for the population proportion.

As discussed earlier, sometimes the variable of interest is *qualitative* rather than *quantitative*. While the population mean μ and the population standard deviation σ describe quantitative data, the population proportion p is the essential descriptive measure when the data type is qualitative. The parameter p represents the proportion of observations with a particular attribute.

As in the case for the population mean, we estimate the population proportion on the basis of its sample counterpart. In particular, we use the sample proportion $\bar{P}$ to estimate the population proportion p. Recall that although $\bar{P}$ is based on a binomial distribution, it can be approximated by a normal distribution in large samples. This approximation is considered valid when $np \geq 5$ and $n(1 - p) \geq 5$. Since p is not known, we typically test the sample size requirement under the hypothesized value of the population proportion p_0. In most applications, the sample size is large and the normal distribution approximation is justified. However, when the sample size is not deemed large enough, the statistical methods suggested here for inference regarding the population proportion are no longer valid.

Recall from Chapter 7 that the mean and the standard error of the sample proportion $\bar{P}$ are given by $E(\bar{P}) = p$ and $se(\bar{P}) = \sqrt{p(1 - p)/n}$, respectively. The test statistic for p is defined as follows.

TEST STATISTIC FOR p

The value of the test statistic for the hypothesis test of the population proportion p is computed as

$$z = \frac{\bar{p} - p_0}{\sqrt{p_0(1 - p_0)/n}},$$

where p_0 is the hypothesized value of the population proportion. This formula is valid only if $\bar{P}$ (approximately) follows a normal distribution.

The following examples elaborate on the four-step procedure for a hypothesis test for the population proportion.

EXAMPLE 9.12

A popular weekly magazine asserts that fewer than 40% of households in the United States have changed their lifestyles because of environmental concerns. A recent survey of 180 households finds that 67 households have made lifestyle changes due to environmental concerns.

a. Specify the competing hypotheses to test the magazine's claim.
b. Calculate the value of the test statistic and the p-value.
c. At the 5% level of significance, what is the conclusion to the test?

SOLUTION:

a. We wish to establish that the population proportion is less than 0.40—that is, $p < 0.40$. Thus, we construct the competing hypotheses as

$$H_0: p \geq 0.40$$

$$H_A: p < 0.40$$

---

b. We first ensure that the normality condition is satisfied. Since both np_0 and $n(1 - p_0)$ exceed 5, the normal approximation is justified. We use the sample proportion, $\bar{p} = 67/180 = 0.3722$, to compute the value of the test statistic as

$$z = \frac{\bar{p} - p_0}{\sqrt{p_0(1 - p_0)/n}} = \frac{0.3722 - 0.40}{\sqrt{0.40(1 - 0.40)/180}} = -0.76.$$

Since this is a left-tailed test for the population proportion, we find the p-value as $P(Z \le z) = P(Z \le -0.76) = 0.2236$.

c. The p-value of 0.2236 is greater than the chosen $\alpha = 0.05$. Therefore, we do not reject the null hypothesis. This means that the magazine's claim that fewer than 40% of households in the United States have changed their lifestyles because of environmental concerns is not justified by the sample data at the 5% significance level. Such a conclusion may be welcomed by firms that have invested in alternative energy.

EXAMPLE 9.13

Driven by growing public support, the legalization of marijuana in America has been moving at a breakneck speed. Today, 57% of adults say the use of marijuana should be made legal (www.pewresearch.org, October 12, 2016). A health practitioner in Ohio collects data from 200 adults and finds that 102 of them favor marijuana legalization.

a. The health practitioner believes that the proportion of adults who favor marijuana legalization in Ohio is not representative of the national proportion. Specify the competing hypotheses to test her claim.

b. Calculate the value of the test statistic and the p-value.

c. At the 10% significance level, do the sample data support the health practitioner's belief?

SOLUTION:

a. The parameter of interest is again the population proportion p. The health practitioner wants to test if the population proportion of those who favor marijuana legalization in Ohio differs from the national proportion of 0.57. We construct the competing hypotheses as

$$H_0: p = 0.57$$

$$H_A: p \ne 0.57$$

b. When evaluated at $p_0 = 0.57$ with $n = 200$, the normality requirement that $np \ge 5$ and $n(1 - p) \ge 5$ is easily satisfied. We use the sample proportion $\bar{p} = 102/200 = 0.51$ to compute the value of the test statistic as

$$z = \frac{\bar{p} - p_0}{\sqrt{p_0(1 - p_0)/n}} = \frac{0.51 - 0.57}{\sqrt{0.57(1 - 0.57)/200}} = -1.71.$$

Given a two-tailed test and $z < 0$, we compute the p-value as $2P(Z \le z) = 2P(Z \le -1.71) = 0.0872$.

c. Since the p-value of 0.0872 is less than $\alpha = 0.10$, we reject the null hypothesis. Therefore, at the 10% significance level, the proportion of adults who favor marijuana legalization in Ohio differs from the national proportion of 0.57.

EXERCISES 9.4

Mechanics

54. Consider the following hypotheses:
$$H_0: p \geq 0.38$$
$$H_A: p < 0.38$$

Calculate the p-value based on the following sample information.
a. $x = 22; n = 74$
b. $x = 110; n = 300$
c. $\bar{p} = 0.34; n = 50$
d. $\bar{p} = 0.34; n = 400$

55. Which sample information in the preceding question enables us to reject the null hypothesis at $\alpha = 0.01$ and at $\alpha = 0.10$?

56. Consider the following hypotheses:
$$H_0: p = 0.32$$
$$H_A: p \neq 0.32$$

Calculate the p-value based on the following sample information
a. $x = 20; n = 66$
b. $x = 100; n = 264$
c. $\bar{p} = 0.40; n = 40$
d. $\bar{p} = 0.38; n = 180$

57. Which sample information in the preceding question enables us to reject the null hypothesis at $\alpha = 0.05$ and at $\alpha = 0.10$?

58. In order to test if the population proportion differs from 0.40, you draw a random sample of 100 observations and obtain a sample proportion of 0.48.
a. Specify the competing hypotheses.
b. Is the normality condition satisfied? Explain.
c. Calculate the value of the test statistic and the p-value.
d. At the 5% significance level, does the population proportion differ from 0.40? Explain.

59. In order to conduct a hypothesis test for the population proportion, you sample 320 observations that result in 128 successes. Conduct the following tests at $\alpha = 0.05$.
a. $H_0: p \geq 0.45$; $H_A: p < 0.45$
b. $H_0: p = 0.45$; $H_A: p \neq 0.45$

60. In order to test if the population proportion is greater than 0.65, you draw a random sample of 200 observations and obtain a sample proportion of 0.72.
a. Specify the competing hypotheses.
b. Is the normality condition satisfied? Explain.
c. Calculate the value of the test statistic and the p-value.
d. At the 5% significance level, is the population proportion greater than 0.65? Explain.

61. You would like to determine if the population probability of success differs from 0.70. You find 62 successes in 80 binomial trials. Implement the test at the 1% level of significance.

62. You would like to determine if more than 50% of the observations in a population are below 10. At $\alpha = 0.05$, conduct the test on the basis of the following 20 sample observations:

8	12	5	9	14	11	9	3	7	8
12	6	8	9	2	6	11	4	13	10

Applications

63. A study by Allstate Insurance Co. finds that 82% of teenagers have used cell phones while driving (*The Wall Street Journal*, May 5, 2010). In October 2010, Massachusetts enacted a law that forbids cell phone use by drivers under the age of 18. A policy analyst would like to determine whether the law has decreased the proportion of drivers under the age of 18 who use a cell phone.
a. State the null and the alternative hypotheses to test the policy analyst's objective.
b. Suppose a sample of 200 drivers under the age of 18 results in 150 who still use a cell phone while driving. What is the value of the test statistic? What is the p-value?
c. At $\alpha = 0.05$, has the law been effective?

64. In order to endure financial hardships such as unemployment and medical emergencies, Americans have increasingly been raiding their already fragile retirement accounts (*MSN Money*, July 16, 2008). It is reported that between 1998 and 2004, about 12% of families with 401(k) plans borrowed from them. An economist is concerned that this percentage now exceeds 20%. He randomly surveys 190 households with 401(k) plans and finds that 50 are borrowing against them.
a. Set up the null and the alternative hypotheses to test the economist's concern.
b. Calculate the value of the test statistic and the p-value.
c. Determine if the economist's concern is justifiable at $\alpha = 0.05$.

65. The margarita is one of the most common tequila-based cocktails, made with tequila mixed with triple sec and lime or lemon juice, often served with salt on the glass rim. A common ratio for a margarita is 2:1:1, which includes 50% tequila, 25% triple sec, and 25% fresh lime or lemon juice. A manager at a local bar is concerned that the bartender uses incorrect proportions in more than 50% of margaritas. He secretly observes the bartender and finds that he used the correct proportions in only 10 out of 30 margaritas. Test if the manager's suspicion is justified at $\alpha = 0.05$.

66. Research shows that many banks are unwittingly training their online customers to take risks with their passwords and other sensitive account information, leaving them more vulnerable to fraud (Yahoo.com, July 23, 2008). Even

web-savvy surfers could find themselves the victims of identity theft because they have been conditioned to ignore potential signs about whether the banking site they are visiting is real or a bogus site served up by hackers. Researchers at the University of Michigan found design flaws in 78% of the 214 U.S. financial institution websites they studied. Is the sample evidence sufficient to conclude that more than three out of four financial institutions that offer online banking facilities are prone to fraud? Use a 5% significance level for the test.

67. Research commissioned by Vodafone suggests that older workers are the happiest employees (*BBC News,* July 21, 2008). The report documents that 70% of older workers in England feel fulfilled, compared with just 50% of younger workers. A demographer believes that an identical pattern does not exist in Asia. A survey of 120 older workers in Asia finds that 75 feel fulfilled. A similar survey finds that 58% of 210 younger workers feel fulfilled.

    a. At the 5% level of significance, test if older workers in Asia feel less fulfilled than their British counterparts.

    b. At the 5% level of significance, test if younger workers in Asia feel more fulfilled than their British counterparts.

68. A politician claims that he is supported by a clear majority of voters. In a recent survey, 24 out of 40 randomly selected voters indicated that they would vote for the politician. Is the politician's claim justified at the 5% level of significance?

69. A movie production company is releasing a movie with the hopes of many viewers returning to see the movie in the theater for a second time. Their target is to have 30 million viewers, and they want more than 30% of the viewers to want to see the movie again. They show the movie to a test audience of 200 people, and after the movie they asked them if they would see the movie in theaters again. Of the test audience, 68 people said they would see the movie again.

    a. At the 5% level of significance, test if more than 30% of the viewers will return to see the movie again.

    b. Repeat the analysis at the 10% level of significance.

    c. Interpret your results.

70. With increasing out-of-pocket healthcare costs, it is claimed that more than 60% of senior citizens are likely to make serious adjustments to their lifestyle. Test this claim at the 1% level of significance if in a survey of 140 senior citizens, 90 reported that they have made serious adjustments to their lifestyle.

71. **FILE** *Silicon_Valley.* According to a report on workforce diversity, about 60% of the employees in high-tech firms in Silicon Valley are white and about 20% are Asian (www.money.cnn.com, November 9, 2011). Women, along with blacks and Latinos, are highly underrepresented. Just about 30% of all employees are women, with blacks and Latinos accounting for only about 15% of the workforce. Tara Jones is a recent college graduate, working for a large high-tech firm in Silicon Valley. She wants to determine if her firm faces the same diversity as in the report. She collects gender and ethnicity information on 50 employees in her firm. A portion of the data is shown in the accompanying table.

Gender	Ethnicity
Female	White
Male	White
⋮	⋮
Male	Nonwhite

    a. At the 5% level of significance, determine if the proportion of women in Tara's firm is different from 0.30.

    b. At the 5% level of significance, determine if the proportion of whites in Tara's firm is more than 0.50.

WRITING WITH STATISTICS

©Ariel Skelley/Blend Images LLC RF

The Associated Press reports that income inequality is at record levels in the United States (September 28, 2010). Over the years, the rich have become richer while working-class wages have stagnated. A local Latino politician has been vocal regarding his concern about the welfare of Latinos. In various speeches, he has stated that the mean salary of Latino households in his county has fallen below the 2008 mean of $49,000. He has also stated that the proportion of Latino households making less than $30,000 has risen above the 2008 level of 20%. Both of his statements are based on income data for 36 Latino households in the county, as shown in Table 9.4.

TABLE 9.4 Representative Sample of Latino Household Incomes in 2010

22	36	78	103	38	43
62	53	26	28	25	31
62	44	51	38	77	37
29	38	46	52	61	57
20	72	41	73	16	32
52	28	69	27	53	46

Incomes are measured in $1,000s and have been adjusted for inflation.

Trevor Jones is a newspaper reporter who is interested in verifying the concerns of the local politician.

Trevor wants to use the sample information to

1. Determine if the mean income of Latino households has fallen below the 2008 level of $49,000.

2. Determine if the percentage of Latino households making less than $30,000 has risen above 20%.

Sample Report— Income Inequality in the United States

One of the hotly debated topics in the United States is that of growing income inequality. Market forces such as increased trade and technological advances have made highly skilled and well-educated workers more productive, thus increasing their pay. Institutional forces, such as deregulation, the decline of unions, and the stagnation of the minimum wage, have contributed to income inequality. Arguably, this income inequality has been felt by minorities, especially African Americans and Latinos, since a very high proportion of both groups is working class. The condition has been further exacerbated by the Great Recession.

A sample of 36 Latino households resulted in a mean household income of $46,278 with a standard deviation of $19,524. The sample mean is below the 2008 level of $49,000. In addition, nine Latino households, or 25%, make less than $30,000; the corresponding percentage in 2008 was 20%. Based on these results, a politician concludes that current market conditions continue to negatively impact the welfare of Latinos. However, it is essential to provide statistically significant evidence to substantiate these claims. Toward this end, formal tests of hypotheses regarding the population mean and the population proportion are conducted. The results of the tests are summarized in Table 9.A.

TABLE 9.A Test Statistic Values and *p*-Values for Hypothesis Tests

Hypotheses	Test Statistic Value	*p*-value
$H_0: \mu \geq 49{,}000$ $H_A: \mu < 49{,}000$	$t_{35} = \dfrac{46{,}278 - 49{,}000}{19{,}524/\sqrt{36}} = -0.84$	0.2033
$H_0: p \leq 0.20$ $H_A: p > 0.20$	$z = \dfrac{0.25 - 0.20}{\sqrt{\dfrac{(0.20)(0.80)}{36}}} = 0.75$	0.2266

When testing whether the mean income of Latino households has fallen below the 2008 level of $49,000, a test statistic value of −0.84 is obtained. Given a *p*-value of 0.2033, the null hypothesis regarding the population mean, specified in Table 9.A, cannot be rejected at any reasonable level of significance. Similarly, given a *p*-value of 0.2266, the null hypothesis regarding the population proportion cannot be rejected. Therefore, sample evidence does not support the claims that the mean income of Latino households has fallen below $49,000 or that the proportion of Latino households making less than $30,000 has risen above 20%. Perhaps the politician's remarks were based on a cursory look at the sample statistics and not on a thorough statistical analysis.

CONCEPTUAL REVIEW

LO 9.1 **Define the null hypothesis and the alternative hypothesis.**

Every hypothesis test contains two competing hypotheses: the **null hypothesis**, denoted H_0, and the **alternative hypothesis**, denoted H_A. We can think of the null hypothesis as corresponding to a presumed default state of nature or status quo, whereas the alternative hypothesis contradicts the default state or status quo.

On the basis of sample information, we either reject H_0 or do not reject H_0. As a general guideline, whatever we wish to establish is placed in the alternative hypothesis. If we reject the null hypothesis, we are able to conclude that the alternative hypothesis is true.

Hypothesis tests can be **one-tailed** or **two-tailed**. A one-tailed test allows the rejection of the null hypothesis only on one side of the hypothesized value of the population parameter. In a two-tailed test, the null hypothesis can be rejected on both sides of the hypothesized value of the population parameter.

LO 9.2 **Distinguish between Type I and Type II errors.**

Since the statistical conclusion of a hypothesis test relies on sample data, there are two types of errors that may occur: a **Type I error** or a **Type II error**. A Type I error is committed when we reject the null hypothesis when it is actually true. On the other hand, a Type II error is made when we do not reject the null hypothesis when it is actually false. We denote the probability of a Type I error by α and the probability of a Type II error by β. For a given sample size n, a decrease (increase) in α will increase (decrease) β. However, both α and β will decrease if the sample size n increases.

LO 9.3 **Conduct a hypothesis test for the population mean when σ is known.**

Step 1. Specify the null and the alternative hypothesis. We identify the relevant population parameter of interest (in this case, the population mean μ), determine whether it is a one- or a two-tailed test and, include some form of the equality sign in the null hypothesis and place whatever we wish to establish in the alternative hypothesis.

Step 2. Specify the significance level. Before implementing a hypothesis test, we first specify α, which is the significance level or the allowed probability of making a Type I error.

Step 3. Calculate the value of the test statistic and the p-value. When testing the population mean μ when the population standard deviation σ is known, the value of the test statistic is calculated as $z = \frac{\bar{x} - \mu_0}{\sigma/\sqrt{n}}$. The p-value is the probability that this test statistic is as extreme as its value computed from the given sample. The p-value is calculated as

- $P(Z \geq z)$ for a right-tailed test,
- $P(Z \leq z)$ for a left-tailed test, or
- $2P(Z \geq z)$ if $z > 0$ or $2P(Z \leq z)$ if $z < 0$ for a two-tailed test.

Step 4. State the conclusion and interpret the results. The decision rule is to reject the null hypothesis if the p-value $< \alpha$ and not reject the null hypothesis if the p-value $\geq \alpha$. Clearly interpret the results in the context of the problem.

LO 9.4 Conduct a hypothesis test for the population mean when σ is unknown.

Step 1 and Step 2. The first two steps are the same as those in the previous case.

Step 3. Calculate the value of the test statistic and the p-value. When testing the population mean μ when the population standard deviation σ is unknown, the value of the test statistic is calculated as $t_{df} = \frac{\bar{x} - \mu_0}{s/\sqrt{n}}$, where s is the sample standard deviation, n is the sample size, and the degrees of freedom $df = n - 1$. The p-value is calculated as

- $P(T_{df} \geq t_{df})$ for a right-tailed test,
- $P(T_{df} \leq t_{df})$ for a left-tailed test, or
- $2P(T_{df} \geq t_{df})$ if $t_{df} > 0$ or $2P(T_{df} \leq t_{df})$ if $t_{df} < 0$ for a two-tailed test.

Step 4. State the conclusion and interpret the results. The decision rule is to reject the null hypothesis if the p-value $< \alpha$ and not reject the null hypothesis if the p-value $\geq \alpha$. Clearly interpret the results in the context of the problem.

LO 9.5 Conduct a hypothesis test for the population proportion.

Step 1. Specify the null and the alternative hypothesis. We identify the relevant population parameter of interest (in this case, the population proportion p), determine whether it is a one- or a two-tailed test and, include some form of the equality sign in the null hypothesis and place whatever we wish to establish in the alternative hypothesis.

Step 2. Specify the significance level. This step is the same as in the previous two cases.

Step 3. Calculate the value of the test statistic and the p-value. When testing the population proportion p, the value of the test statistic is computed as $z = \frac{\bar{p} - p_0}{\sqrt{p_0(1 - p_0)/n}}$. The p-value is calculated as

- $P(Z \geq z)$ for a right-tailed test,
- $P(Z \leq z)$ for a left-tailed test, or
- $2P(Z \geq z)$ if $z > 0$ or $2P(Z \leq z)$ if $z < 0$ for a two-tailed test.

Step 4. State the conclusion and interpret the results. The decision rule is to reject the null hypothesis if the p-value $< \alpha$ and not reject the null hypothesis if the p-value $\geq \alpha$. Clearly interpret the results in the context of the problem.

ADDITIONAL EXERCISES AND CASE STUDIES

Exercises

72. A pharmaceutical company has developed a new drug for depression. There is a concern, however, that the drug also raises the blood pressure of its users. A researcher wants to conduct a test to validate this claim. Would the manager of the pharmaceutical company be more concerned about a Type I error or a Type II error? Explain.

73. A company has developed a new diet that it claims will lower one's weight by more than 10 pounds. Health officials decide to conduct a test to validate this claim.

a. Would the manager of the company be more concerned about a Type I error or a Type II error? Explain.

b. Would the consumers be more concerned about a Type I error or a Type II error? Explain.

74. An advertisement for a popular weight loss clinic suggests that participants in its new diet program lose, on average, more than 10 pounds. A consumer activist decides to test the authenticity of the claim. She follows the progress of 18 women who recently joined the weight reduction program. She calculates the mean weight loss of these participants as 10.8 pounds with a standard deviation of 2.4 pounds.

a. Set up the competing hypotheses to test the advertisement's claim.

b. Calculate the value of the test statistic and the p-value.

c. At the 5% significance level, what does the consumer activist conclude?

75. A phone manufacturer wants to compete in the touch screen phone market. He understands that the lead product has a battery life of just 5 hours. The manufacturer claims that while the new touch screen phone is more expensive, its battery life is more than twice as long as that of the leading product. In order to test the claim, a researcher samples 45 units of the new phone and finds that the sample battery life averages 10.5 hours with a sample standard deviation of 1.8 hours.

a. Set up the competing hypotheses to test the manufacturer's claim.

b. Calculate the value of the test statistic and the p-value.

c. Test the phone manufacturer's claim at $\alpha = 0.05$.

76. A city council is deciding whether or not to spend additional money to reduce the amount of traffic. The council decides that it will increase the transportation budget if the amount of waiting time for drivers exceeds 20 minutes. A sample of 32 main roads results in a mean waiting time of 22.08 minutes with a standard deviation of 5.42 minutes. Conduct a hypothesis test at the 1% level of significance to determine whether or not the city should increase its transportation budget.

77. Rates on 30-year fixed mortgages continue to be at historic lows (*Chron Business News*, September 23, 2010). According to Freddie Mac, the average rate for 30-year fixed loans for the week was 4.37%.

An economist wants to test if there is any change in the mortgage rates in the following week. She searches the Internet for 30-year fixed loans in the following week and reports the rates offered by seven banks as 4.25%, 4.125%, 4.375%, 4.50%, 4.75%, 4.375%, and 4.875%. Assume that rates are normally distributed.

a. State the hypotheses to test if the average mortgage rate differs from 4.37%.

b. Calculate the value of the test statistic and the p-value.

c. At the 5% significance level, does the average mortgage rate differ from 4.37%? Explain.

78. The Great Recession cost America trillions of dollars in lost wealth and also levied a heavy toll on the national psyche (*The Wall Street Journal*, December 21, 2009). According to a poll, just 33% of those surveyed said America was headed in the right direction. Suppose this poll was based on a sample of 1,000 people. Does the sample evidence suggest that the proportion of Americans who feel that America is headed in the right direction is below 35%? Use a 5% level of significance for the analysis. What if the sample size was 2,000?

79. A retailer is looking to evaluate its customer service. Management has determined that if the retailer wants to stay competitive, then it will have to have at least a 90% satisfaction rate among its customers. Management will take corrective actions if the satisfaction rate falls below 90%. A survey of 1,200 customers showed that 1,068 were satisfied with their customer service.

a. State the hypotheses to test if the retailer needs to improve its services.

b. What is the value of the test statistic?

c. Find the p-value.

d. Interpret the results at $\alpha = 0.05$.

80. A national survey found that 33% of high school students said they texted or e-mailed while driving (*The Boston Globe*, June 8, 2012). These findings came a day after a Massachusetts teenager was convicted for causing a fatal crash while texting. A researcher wonders whether texting or e-mailing while driving is more prevalent among Massachusetts teens. He surveys 100 teens and 42% of them admitted that they texted or e-mailed while behind the wheel. Can he conclude at the 1% significance level that Massachusetts teens engage in this behavior at a rate greater than the national rate?

81. A television network is deciding whether or not to give its newest television show a spot during

prime viewing time at night. For this to happen, it will have to move one of its most viewed shows to another slot. The network conducts a survey asking its viewers which show they would rather watch. The network will keep its current lineup of shows unless the majority of the customers want to watch the new show. The network receives 827 responses, of which 428 indicate that they would like to see the new show in the lineup.

a. Set up the hypotheses to test if the television network should give its newest television show a spot during prime viewing time at night.

b. Calculate the value of the test statistic and the *p*-value.

c. At $\alpha = 0.01$, what should the television network do?

82. A survey finds that 17% of Americans cannot part with their landlines (*The Washington Post*, February 27, 2014). A researcher in the rural South collects data from 200 households and finds that 45 of them still have landlines.

a. The researcher believes that the proportion of households with landlines in the rural South is not representative of the national proportion. Specify the competing hypotheses to test her claim.

b. Calculate the value of the test statistic and the *p*-value.

c. At the 5% significance level, do the sample data support the researcher's belief?

83. **FILE** *Metals.* Using data from the past 25 years, an investor wants to test whether the average return of Vanguard's Precious Metals and Mining Fund is greater than 12%. Assume returns are normally distributed with a population standard deviation of 30%.

a. State the null and the alternative hypotheses for the test.

b. Calculate the value of the test statistic and the *p*-value.

c. At $\alpha = 0.05$, what is the conclusion? Is the return on Vanguard's Precious Metals and Mining Fund greater than 12%?

84. **FILE** *Midwest_Drivers.* On average, Americans drive 13,500 miles per year (*The Boston Globe*, June 7, 2012). An economist gathers data on the driving habits of 50 residents in the Midwest.

a. The economist believes that the average number of miles driven annually by Midwesterners is different from the U.S. average. Specify the competing hypotheses to test the economist's claim.

b. Calculate the value of the test statistic and the *p*-value.

c. At the 10% significance level, do the data support the researcher's claim? Explain.

85. **FILE** *Convenience_Stores.* An entrepreneur examines monthly sales (in $1,000s) for 40 convenience stores in Rhode Island.

a. State the null and the alternative hypotheses in order to test whether average sales differ from $130,000.

b. Calculate the value of the test statistic and the *p*-value.

c. At $\alpha = 0.05$, what is your conclusion to the test? Do average sales differ from $130,000?

86. **FILE** *DJIA_Volume.* The euro-zone crisis has wreaked havoc on U.S. stock markets (*The Wall Street Journal*, June 8, 2012). A portfolio analyst wonders if the average trading volume on the Dow Jones Industrial Average (DJIA) has decreased since the beginning of the year. She gathers data on daily trading volumes for 30 days.

a. The average trading volume in the beginning of the year was about 4,000 shares (in millions). Specify the competing hypotheses to test her claim.

b. Calculate the value of the test statistic and the *p*-value.

c. At the 5% significance level, does it appear that the trading volume has increased since the beginning of the year?

87. **FILE** *Study_Hard.* A report suggests that business majors spend the least amount of time on course work than do all other college students (*The New York Times*, November 17, 2011). A provost of a university conducts a survey of 50 business and 50 nonbusiness students. Students are asked if they study hard, defined as spending at least 20 hours per week on course work. The response shows "yes" if they study hard or "no" otherwise; a portion is shown in the following table.

Business Majors	Nonbusiness Majors
Yes	No
No	Yes
⋮	⋮
Yes	Yes

a. At the 5% level of significance, determine if the percentage of business majors who study hard is less than 20%.

b. At the 5% level of significance, determine if the percentage of nonbusiness majors who study hard is more than 20%.

88. **FILE** *MI_Life.* Residents of Hawaii have the longest life expectancies in the United States, averaging 81.48 years (www.worldlifeexpectancy.com; data retrieved June 4, 2012). A sociologist collects data on the age at death for 50 recently deceased Michigan residents.

a. The sociologist believes that the life expectancies of Michigan residents are less than those of Hawaii residents. Specify the competing hypotheses to test this belief.

b. Calculate the value of the test statistic and the *p*-value.

c. At the 1% significance level, do the data support the sociologist's belief?

89. Thirty-three percent of children and teens in the United States are obese or overweight (*Health*, October 2010). A health practitioner in the Midwest collects data on 200 children and teens and finds that 84 of them are either obese or overweight.

a. The health practitioner believes that the proportion of obese and overweight children in the Midwest is not representative of the national proportion. Specify the competing hypotheses to test her claim.

b. Calculate the value of the test statistic and the *p*-value.

c. At the 1% significance level, do the sample data support the health practitioner's belief?

CASE STUDIES

CASE STUDY 9.1 Harvard University revolutionized its financial aid policies, aimed at easing the financial strain on middle and upper-middle income families (*Newsweek*, August 18–25, 2008). The expected contribution of students who are admitted to Harvard has been greatly reduced. Many other elite private colleges are following suit to compete for top students. The motivation for these policy changes stems from competition from public universities as well as political pressure.

A spokesman from an elite college claims that elite colleges have been very responsive to financial hardships faced by families due to the rising costs of education. Now, he says, families with an income of $40,000 will have to spend less than $6,500 to send their children to prestigious colleges. Similarly, families with incomes of $80,000 and $120,000 will have to spend less than $20,000 and $35,000, respectively, for their children's education.

Although in general the cost of attendance has gone down at each family-income level, it still varies by thousands of dollars among prestigious schools. The accompanying table shows information on the cost of attendance by family income for 10 prestigious schools.

Data for Case Study 9.1 Cost of Attendance to Schools by Family Income

FILE
Family_Income

School	Family Income		
	40000	80000	120000
Amherst College	5302	19731	37558
Bowdoin College	5502	19931	37758
Columbia University	4500	12800	36845
Davidson College	5702	20131	37958
Harvard University	3700	8000	16000
Northwestern University	6311	26120	44146
Pomona College	5516	19655	37283
Princeton University	3887	11055	17792
Univ. of California system	10306	19828	25039
Yale University	4300	6048	13946

Source: *Newsweek*, August 18–25, 2008.

In a report, use the sample information to

1. Determine whether families with incomes of $40,000 will spend less than $6,500 to send their children to prestigious colleges. (Use $\alpha = 0.05$.)

2. Repeat the hypothesis test from part 1 by testing the spokesman's claims concerning college costs for families with incomes of $80,000 and $120,000, respectively. (Use $\alpha = 0.05$.)

3. Assess the validity of the spokesman's claims.

CASE STUDY 9.2 The effort to reward city students for passing Advanced Placement tests is part of a growing trend nationally and internationally. Financial incentives are offered in order to lift attendance and achievement rates. One such program in Dallas, Texas, offers $100 for every Advanced Placement test on which a student gets a score of 3 or higher (Reuters, September 20, 2010). A wealthy entrepreneur decides to experiment with the same idea of rewarding students to enhance performance, but in Chicago. He offers monetary incentives to students at an inner-city high school. Due to this incentive, 122 students take the Advancement Placement tests. Twelve students get a 5, the highest possible score. There are 49 students with scores of 3 and 4, and 61 students with failing scores of 1 and 2. Historically, about 100 of these tests are taken at this school each year, where 8% of students score 5, 38% score 3 and 4, and the remaining get failing scores of 1 and 2.

In a report, use the sample information to

1. Provide a descriptive analysis of student achievement on Advanced Placement before and after the monetary incentive is offered.

2. Conduct a hypothesis test that determines, at the 5% significance level, whether the monetary incentive has resulted in a higher proportion of scores of 5, the highest possible score.

3. Conduct a hypothesis test that determines, at the 5% significance level, whether the monetary incentive has decreased the proportion of failing scores of 1 and 2.

4. Assess the effectiveness of monetary incentives in improving student achievement.

CASE STUDY 9.3 The Gallup-Healthways Well-Being Index (www.well-beingindex.com) provides an assessment measure of health and well-being of U.S. residents. By collecting periodic data on life evaluation, physical health, emotional health, healthy behavior, work environment, and basic access, this assessment measure is of immense value to researchers in diverse fields such as business, medical sciences, and journalism. The overall composite score, as well as a score in each of the above six categories, is calculated on a scale from 0 to 100, where 100 represents fully realized well-being. In 2009, the overall well-being index score of American residents was reported as 65.9. Let the following table represent the overall well-being score of a random sample of 35 residents in Hawaii.

Data for Case Study 9.3 Overall Well-being of Hawaiians, $n = 35$

FILE
Hawaiians

20	40	40	100	60	20	40
90	90	60	60	90	90	90
80	100	90	80	80	80	100
70	90	80	100	20	70	90
80	30	80	90	90	80	30

In a report, use the sample information to

1. Determine whether the well-being score of Hawaiians is more than the national average of 65.9 at the 5% significance level.

2. Determine if fewer than 40% of Hawaiians report a score below 50 at the 5% significance level.

3. Comment on the well-being of Hawaiians given your results.

APPENDIX 9.1   The Critical Value Approach

We always use sample evidence and the chosen significance level α to conduct hypothesis tests. The p-value approach makes the comparison in terms of probabilities. As discussed in Section 9.2, the value of the test statistic is used to compute the p-value, which is then compared with α in order to arrive at a decision. Most statistical software packages report p-values, so the p-value approach to hypothesis testing tends to be favored by most researchers and practitioners. The critical value approach, on the other hand, makes the comparison directly in terms of the value of the test statistic. This approach is particularly useful when a computer is unavailable and all calculations must be done manually. Both approaches, however, always lead to the same conclusion.

In Section 9.2, we used the p-value approach to validate a sociologist's claim that the mean retirement age in the United States is greater than 67 at the 5% significance level. In a random sample of 25 retirees, the average retirement age was 71. It was also assumed that the retirement age is normally distributed with a population standard deviation of 9 years. With the critical value approach, we still specify the competing hypotheses and calculate the value of the test statistic as we did with the p-value approach. In the retirement age example, the competing hypotheses are $H_0: \mu \le 67$ versus $H_A: \mu > 67$ and the value of the test statistic is $z = \frac{\bar{x} - \mu_0}{\sigma/\sqrt{n}} = \frac{71 - 67}{9/\sqrt{25}} = 2.22$.

The critical value approach specifies a region of values, also called the rejection region, such that if the value of the test statistic falls into this region, then we reject the null hypothesis. The critical value is a point that separates the rejection region from the nonrejection region. Once again we need to make distinctions between the three types of competing hypotheses. For a right-tailed test, the critical value is z_α, where $P(Z \ge z_\alpha) = \alpha$. The resulting rejection region includes values greater than z_α.

With α known, we can easily find the corresponding z_α from the z table. In the retirement age example with $\alpha = 0.05$, we evaluate $P(Z \ge z_\alpha) = 0.05$ to derive the critical value as $z_\alpha = z_{0.05} = 1.645$. Figure A9.1 shows the critical value as well as the corresponding rejection region for the test.

FIGURE A9.1
The critical value for a right-tailed test with $\alpha = 0.05$

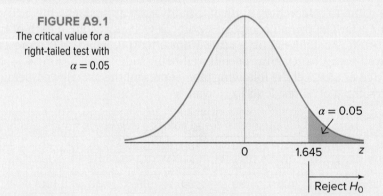

As shown in Figure A9.1, the decision rule is to reject H_0 if $z > 1.645$. Since the value of the test statistic, $z = 2.22$, exceeds the critical value, $z_\alpha = 1.645$, we reject the null hypothesis and conclude that the mean age is greater than 67. Thus, we confirm the conclusion reached with the p-value approach.

We would like to stress that we always arrive at the same conclusion whether we use the p-value approach or the critical value approach. If z falls in the rejection region, then the p-value must be less than α. Similarly, if z does not fall in the rejection region, then the p-value must be greater than α. Figure A9.2 shows the equivalence of the two results in the retirement age example of a right-tailed test.

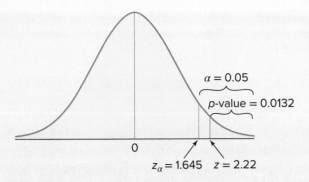

$\alpha = 0.05$

p-value = 0.0132

0

$z_\alpha = 1.645$ $z = 2.22$

We reject the null hypothesis because the *p*-value = 0.0132 is less than $\alpha = 0.05$ or, equivalently, because $z = 2.22$ is greater than $z_\alpha = 1.645$.

The retirement age example uses a right-tailed test to calculate the critical value as z_α. Given the symmetry of the z distribution around zero, the critical value for a left-tailed test is simply $-z_\alpha$. For a two-tailed test, we split the significance level in half to determine *two* critical values, $-z_{\alpha/2}$ and $z_{\alpha/2}$, where $P(Z \geq z_{\alpha/2}) = \alpha/2$.

For a given α, Figure A9.3 shows the three different scenarios of determining the critical value(s) depending on the specification of the competing hypotheses. For the illustration, we assume that the test statistic follows the z distribution.

Figure A9.3a shows a negative critical value for a left-tailed test where we reject the null hypothesis if $z < -z_\alpha$. Similarly, Figure A9.3b shows a positive critical value for a right-tailed test where we reject the null hypothesis if $z > z_\alpha$. There are two critical values for a two-tailed test, where we reject the null hypothesis when $z < -z_{\alpha/2}$ or when $z > z_{\alpha/2}$ (see Figure A9.3c).

FIGURE A9.3 Critical values for one- and two-tailed tests

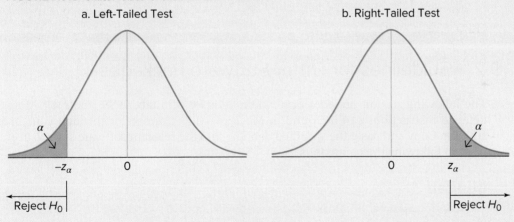

a. Left-Tailed Test

b. Right-Tailed Test

α

$-z_\alpha$ 0

Reject H_0

α

0   z_α

Reject H_0

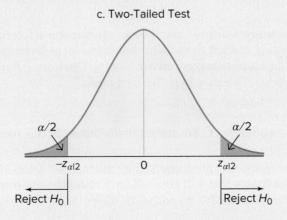

c. Two-Tailed Test

$\alpha/2$

$\alpha/2$

$-z_{\alpha/2}$ 0 $z_{\alpha/2}$

Reject H_0

Reject H_0

We now summarize the general procedure for implementing the critical value approach.

THE FOUR-STEP PROCEDURE USING THE CRITICAL VALUE APPROACH

Step 1. Specify the null and the alternative hypothesis. This step is the same as in the p-value approach.

Step 2. Specify the significance level and find the critical value(s). We first specify α. The critical value(s) is a point that separates the rejection region from the nonrejection region. If the test statistic follows the z distribution, then, for a given α, we find the critical value(s) as

- z_α where $P(Z \geq z_\alpha) = \alpha$ for a right-tailed test,
- $-z_\alpha$ where $P(Z \geq z_\alpha) = \alpha$ for a left-tailed test, or
- $-z_{\alpha/2}$ and $z_{\alpha/2}$ where $P(Z \geq z_{\alpha/2}) = \alpha/2$ for a two-tailed test.

Z and z_α are replaced with T_{df} and t_{df} if the test statistic follows the t_{df} distribution with degrees of freedom, $df = n - 1$.

Step 3. Calculate the value of the test statistic. We calculate the value of the test statistic by converting the estimate of the relevant population parameter into its corresponding standardized value, either z or t_{df}.

Step 4. State the conclusion and interpret the results. The decision rule is to reject the null hypothesis if the test statistic falls in the rejection region. We interpret the results in the context of a problem.

APPENDIX 9.2   Guidelines for Other Software Packages

The following section provides brief commands for Minitab, SPSS, and JMP. More detailed instructions can be found in McGraw-Hill's Connect or through your instructor. Copy and paste the specified data file into the relevant software spreadsheet prior to following the commands.

Minitab

Testing μ, σ Known

FILE
Debit_Spending

A. (Replicating Example 9.9). From the menu, choose **Stat > Basic Statistics > 1-Sample Z**.

B. Select **One or more samples, each in a column** and select Spending. Enter 500 for **Known standard deviation**. Select **Perform hypothesis test** and enter 8000 after **Hypothesized mean**. Choose **Options**. After **Alternative hypothesis**, select "Mean < hypothesized mean."

Testing μ, σ Unknown

FILE
Study_Hours

A. (Replicating Example 9.11) From the menu, choose **Stat > Basic Statistics > 1-Sample t**.

B. Select **One or more samples, each in a column** and select Hours. Select **Perform hypothesis test** and enter 14 after **Hypothesized mean**. Choose **Options**. After **Alternative hypothesis**, select "Mean ≠ hypothesized mean."

Testing p

A. (Replicating Example 9.12) From the menu, choose **Stat > Basic Statistics > 1-Proportion**.

B. Choose **Summarized data** and then enter 67 after **Number of events** and 180 after **Number of trials**. Select **Perform hypothesis test** and enter 0.40 for **Hypothesized proportion**. Choose **Options**. After **Alternative hypothesis**, select "Proportion < hypothesized proportion" and after **Method** select "Normal approximation."

SPSS

Testing μ, σ Unknown

A. (Replicating Example 9.11). From the menu, choose **Analyze > Compare Means > One-Sample T-Test**. Under **Test Variable(s)**, select Hours. After **Test Value**, enter 14.

Study_Hours

JMP

Testing μ, σ Known

A. (Replicating Example 9.9). From the menu, choose **Analyze > Distribution**.

B. Under **Select Columns**, select Spending, and then under **Cast Selected Columns into Roles**, select **Y, Columns**.

C. Click on the red triangle in the output window beside Spending. Choose **Test Mean**. After **Specify Hypothesized Mean**, enter 8000, and after **Enter true standard deviation to do z-test rather than t-test**, enter 500.

Debit_Spending

Testing μ, σ Unknown

A. (Replicating Example 9.11). From the menu, choose **Analyze > Distribution**.

B. Under **Select Columns**, select Hours, and then under **Cast Selected Columns into Roles**, select **Y, Columns**.

C. Click on the red triangle in the output window beside Hours. Choose **Test Mean**. After **Specify Hypothesized Mean**, enter 14.

Study_Hours

10 Statistical Inference Concerning Two Populations

LEARNING OBJECTIVES

After reading this chapter you should be able to:

LO **10.1** Make inferences about the difference between two population means based on independent sampling.

LO **10.2** Make inferences about the mean difference based on matched-pairs sampling.

LO **10.3** Make inferences about the difference between two population proportions based on independent sampling.

In the preceding two chapters, we used estimation and hypothesis testing to analyze a single parameter, such as the population mean and the population proportion. In this chapter, we extend our discussion from the analysis of a single population to the comparison of two populations. We first analyze differences between two population means. For instance, an economist may be interested in analyzing the salary difference between male and female employees. Similarly, a marketing researcher might want to compare the operating lives of two popular brands of batteries. In these examples, we use independent sampling for the analysis. We will also consider the mean difference of two populations based on matched-pairs sampling. An example would be a consumer group activist wanting to analyze the mean weight of customers before and after they enroll in a new diet program. Finally, we look at qualitative data and compare the difference between two population proportions. For instance, marketing executives and advertisers are often interested in the different preferences between males and females when determining where to target advertising dollars. In each of the statistical inferences concerning two populations, we first develop the procedure for estimation and then follow with hypothesis testing.

©John Smock/SIPA/Newscom

INTRODUCTORY CASE

Effectiveness of Mandatory Caloric Postings

The federal health care law enacted in March 2010 requires chain restaurants with 20 locations or more to post caloric information on their menus. The government wants calorie listings posted to make it easier for consumers to select healthier options. New York City pioneered the requirement of caloric information on menus in 2008, but research has shown mixed results on whether this requirement has prompted consumers to select healthier foods (*The Wall Street Journal*, August 31, 2010). Molly Hosler, a nutritionist in San Mateo, California, would like to study the effects of a recent local menu ordinance requiring caloric postings. She obtains transaction data for 40 Starbucks cardholders around the time that San Mateo implemented the ordinance. For each cardholder, drink and food calories were recorded prior to the ordinance and then after the ordinance. Table 10.1 shows a portion of the data.

TABLE 10.1 Average Caloric Intake Before and After Menu-Labeling Ordinance

FILE
Drink_Calories
Food_Calories

Customer	Drink Calories		Food Calories	
	Before	After	Before	After
1	141	142	395	378
2	137	140	404	392
⋮	⋮	⋮	⋮	⋮
40	147	141	406	400

Molly wants to use the sample information to

1. Determine whether the average calories of purchased drinks declined after the passage of the ordinance.

2. Determine whether the average calories of purchased food declined after the passage of the ordinance.

3. Assess the implications of caloric postings for Starbucks and other chains.

A synopsis of this case is provided at the end of Section 10.2.

10.1 INFERENCE CONCERNING THE DIFFERENCE BETWEEN TWO MEANS

In this section, we consider statistical inference about the difference between two population means based on **independent random samples**. Independent random samples are samples that are completely unrelated to one another. Consider the example where we are interested in the difference between male and female salaries. For one sample, we collect data from the male population, while for the other sample we collect data from the female population. The two samples are considered to be independent because the selection of one is in no way influenced by the selection of the other. Similarly, in a comparison of battery lives between Brand A and Brand B, one sample comes from the Brand A population, while the other sample comes from the Brand B population. Again, both samples can be considered to be drawn independently.

> ### INDEPENDENT RANDOM SAMPLES
>
> Two (or more) random samples are considered independent if the process that generates one sample is completely separate from the process that generates the other sample. The samples are clearly delineated.

Confidence Interval for $\mu_1 - \mu_2$

As discussed earlier, we use sample statistics to estimate the population parameter of interest. For example, the sample mean $\overline{X}$ is the point estimator for the population mean μ. In a similar vein, the difference between the two sample means $\overline{X}_1 - \overline{X}_2$ is a point estimator for the difference between two population means $\mu_1 - \mu_2$, where μ_1 is the mean of the first population and μ_2 is the mean of the second population. The estimate is found by taking the difference of the sample means $\overline{x}_1$ and $\overline{x}_2$ computed from two independent random samples with n_1 and n_2 observations, respectively.

Let's first discuss the sampling distribution of $\overline{X}_1 - \overline{X}_2$. As in the case of a single population mean, this estimator is unbiased; that is, $E(\overline{X}_1 - \overline{X}_2) = \mu_1 - \mu_2$. Moreover, recall that the statistical inference regarding the population mean μ is based on the condition that the sample mean $\overline{X}$ is normally distributed. Similarly, for statistical inference regarding $\mu_1 - \mu_2$, it is imperative that the sampling distribution of $\overline{X}_1 - \overline{X}_2$ is normal. Therefore, if we assume that the two sample means are derived from two independent and normally distributed populations, then $\overline{X}_1 - \overline{X}_2$ is also normally distributed. If the underlying populations cannot be assumed to be normally distributed, then by the central limit theorem, the sampling distribution of $\overline{X}_1 - \overline{X}_2$ is approximately normal only if both sample sizes are sufficiently large—that is, $n_1 \geq 30$ and $n_2 \geq 30$.

As in the case of a single population mean, we consider two scenarios. If we know the variances of the two populations σ_1^2 and σ_2^2 (or the standard deviations σ_1 and σ_2), we use the z distribution for the statistical inference. A more common case is to use the t_{df} distribution, where the sample variances s_1^2 and s_2^2 are used in place of the unknown population variances. When σ_1^2 and σ_2^2 are not known, we will examine two cases: (a) they can be assumed equal ($\sigma_1^2 = \sigma_2^2$) or (b) they cannot be assumed equal ($\sigma_1^2 \neq \sigma_2^2$).

The confidence interval for the difference in means is based on the same procedure outlined in Chapter 8. In particular, the formula for the confidence interval will follow the standard format given by point estimate ± margin of error.

We use sample data to calculate the point estimate for $\mu_1 - \mu_2$ as the difference between the two sample means $\overline{x}_1 - \overline{x}_2$. The margin of error equals the standard error $se(\overline{X}_1 - \overline{X}_2)$ multiplied by $z_{\alpha/2}$ or $t_{\alpha/2,df}$, depending on whether or not the population variances are known.

A $100(1 - \alpha)\%$ confidence interval for the difference between two population means $\mu_1 - \mu_2$ is given by

1. $(\bar{x}_1 - \bar{x}_2) \pm z_{\alpha/2}\sqrt{\frac{\sigma_1^2}{n_1} + \frac{\sigma_2^2}{n_2}}$, if the population variances, σ_1^2 and σ_2^2, are known.

2. $(\bar{x}_1 - \bar{x}_2) \pm t_{\alpha/2,df}\sqrt{s_p^2\left(\frac{1}{n_1} + \frac{1}{n_2}\right)}$, if σ_1^2 and σ_2^2 are unknown but assumed equal. A pooled estimate of the common variance is $s_p^2 = \frac{(n_1 - 1)s_1^2 + (n_2 - 1)s_2^2}{n_1 + n_2 - 2}$, where s_1^2 and s_2^2 are the corresponding sample variances and the degrees of freedom $df = n_1 + n_2 - 2$.

3. $(\bar{x}_1 - \bar{x}_2) \pm t_{\alpha/2,df}\sqrt{\frac{s_1^2}{n_1} + \frac{s_2^2}{n_2}}$, if σ_1^2 and σ_2^2 are unknown and cannot be assumed equal. The degrees of freedom $df = \frac{(s_1^2/n_1 + s_2^2/n_2)^2}{(s_1^2/n_1)^2/(n_1 - 1) + (s_2^2/n_2)^2/(n_2 - 1)}$. Since the resultant value for df is rarely an integer, we generally round the value down to obtain the appropriate t value from the t table. Software packages use various rounding rules when reporting the resultant value for df.

These formulas are valid only if $\bar{X}_1 - \bar{X}_2$ (approximately) follows a normal distribution.

Note that in the case when we construct a confidence interval for $\mu_1 - \mu_2$ where σ_1^2 and σ_2^2 are unknown but assumed equal, we calculate a pooled estimate of the common variance s_p^2. In other words, because the two populations are assumed to have the same population variance, the two sample variances s_1^2 and s_2^2 are simply two separate estimates of this population variance. We estimate the population variance by a *weighted* average of s_1^2 and s_2^2, where the weights applied are their respective degrees of freedom relative to the total number of degrees of freedom. In the case when σ_1^2 and σ_2^2 are unknown and cannot be assumed equal, we cannot calculate a pooled estimate of the population variance.

EXAMPLE 10.1

A consumer advocate analyzes the nicotine content in two brands of cigarettes. A sample of 20 cigarettes of Brand A resulted in an average nicotine content of 1.68 milligrams with a standard deviation of 0.22 milligram; 25 cigarettes of Brand B yielded an average nicotine content of 1.95 milligrams with a standard deviation of 0.24 milligram.

Brand A	Brand B
$\bar{x}_1 = 1.68$	$\bar{x}_2 = 1.95$
$s_1 = 0.22$	$s_2 = 0.24$
$n_1 = 20$	$n_2 = 25$

Construct the 95% confidence interval for the difference between the two population means. Nicotine content is assumed to be normally distributed. In addition, the population variances are unknown but assumed equal.

SOLUTION: We wish to construct a confidence interval for $\mu_1 - \mu_2$ where μ_1 is the mean nicotine level for Brand A and μ_2 is the mean nicotine level for Brand B. Since the population variances are unknown but assumed equal, we use the formula

$$(\bar{x}_1 - \bar{x}_2) \pm t_{\alpha/2,df}\sqrt{s_p^2\left(\frac{1}{n_1} + \frac{1}{n_2}\right)}.$$

We calculate the point estimate $\bar{x}_1 - \bar{x}_2 = 1.68 - 1.95 = -0.27$. In order to find $t_{\alpha/2,df}$, we determine $df = n_1 + n_2 - 2 = 20 + 25 - 2 = 43$. For the 95% confidence interval ($\alpha = 0.05$), we reference the t table to find $t_{0.025,43} = 2.017$.

We then calculate the pooled estimate of the population variance as

$$s_p^2 = \frac{(n_1 - 1)s_1^2 + (n_2 - 1)s_2^2}{n_1 + n_2 - 2} = \frac{(20 - 1)(0.22)^2 + (25 - 1)(0.24)^2}{20 + 25 - 2} = 0.0535.$$

Inserting the appropriate values into the formula, we have

$$-0.27 \pm 2.017\sqrt{0.0535\left(\frac{1}{20} + \frac{1}{25}\right)} = -0.27 \pm 0.14.$$

In other words, the 95% confidence interval for the difference between the two means ranges from -0.41 to -0.13. Shortly, we will use this interval to conduct a two-tailed hypothesis test.

Hypothesis Test for $\mu_1 - \mu_2$

As always, when specifying the competing hypotheses, it is important to (1) identify the relevant population parameter, (2) determine whether a one- or a two-tailed test is appropriate, and (3) include some form of the equality sign in the null hypothesis and use the alternative hypothesis to establish a claim. In order to conduct a hypothesis test concerning the parameter $\mu_1 - \mu_2$, the competing hypotheses will take one of the following general forms:

Two-Tailed Test	Right-Tailed Test	Left-Tailed Test
$H_0\colon \mu_1 - \mu_2 = d_0$	$H_0\colon \mu_1 - \mu_2 \leq d_0$	$H_0\colon \mu_1 - \mu_2 \geq d_0$
$H_A\colon \mu_1 - \mu_2 \neq d_0$	$H_A\colon \mu_1 - \mu_2 > d_0$	$H_A\colon \mu_1 - \mu_2 < d_0$

In most applications, the hypothesized difference d_0 between two population means μ_1 and μ_2 is zero. In this scenario, a two-tailed test determines whether the two means differ from one another, a right-tailed test determines whether μ_1 is greater than μ_2, and a left-tailed test determines whether μ_1 is less than μ_2.

We can also construct hypotheses where the hypothesized difference d_0 is a value other than zero. For example, if we wish to determine if the mean return of an emerging market fund is more than two percentage points higher than that of a developed market fund, the resulting hypotheses are $H_0\colon \mu_1 - \mu_2 \leq 2$ versus $H_A\colon \mu_1 - \mu_2 > 2$.

EXAMPLE 10.2

Revisit Example 10.1.

a. Specify the competing hypotheses in order to determine whether the average nicotine levels differ between Brand A and Brand B.

b. Using the 95% confidence interval, what is the conclusion to the test?

SOLUTION:

a. We want to determine if the average nicotine levels differ between the two brands, or $\mu_1 \neq \mu_2$, so we formulate a two-tailed hypothesis test as

$$H_0\colon \mu_1 - \mu_2 = 0$$

$$H_A\colon \mu_1 - \mu_2 \neq 0$$

b. In Example 10.1, we calculated the 95% confidence interval for the difference between the two means as -0.27 ± 0.14 or, equivalently, the confidence interval ranges from -0.41 to -0.13. This interval does not contain zero, the value hypothesized under the null hypothesis. This information allows us to reject H_0; the sample data support the conclusion that average nicotine levels between the two brands differ at the 5% significance level.

While it is true that we can use confidence intervals to conduct two-tailed hypothesis tests, the four-step procedure outlined in Chapter 9 can be implemented to conduct one- or two-tailed hypothesis tests. (It is possible to adjust the confidence interval to accommodate a one-tailed test, but we do not discuss this modification.) The only real change in the process is the specification of the test statistic. We use the point estimate $\bar{x}_1 - \bar{x}_2$ to derive the value of the test statistic z or t_{df} by dividing $(\bar{x}_1 - \bar{x}_2) - d_0$ by the standard error of the estimator $se(\bar{X}_1 - \bar{X}_2)$.

TEST STATISTIC FOR TESTING $\mu_1 - \mu_2$

The value of the test statistic for a hypothesis test concerning the difference between two population means, $\mu_1 - \mu_2$, is computed using one of the following three formulas:

1. If σ_1^2 and σ_2^2 are known, then the value of the test statistic is computed as

$$z = \frac{(\bar{x}_1 - \bar{x}_2) - d_0}{\sqrt{\frac{\sigma_1^2}{n_1} + \frac{\sigma_2^2}{n_2}}}.$$

2. If σ_1^2 and σ_2^2 are unknown but assumed equal, then the value of the test statistic is computed as $t_{df} = \dfrac{(\bar{x}_1 - \bar{x}_2) - d_0}{\sqrt{s_p^2\left(\frac{1}{n_1} + \frac{1}{n_2}\right)}}$, where $s_p^2 = \dfrac{(n_1 - 1)s_1^2 + (n_2 - 1)s_2^2}{n_1 + n_2 - 2}$ and $df = n_1 + n_2 - 2$.

3. If σ_1^2 and σ_2^2 are unknown and cannot be assumed equal, then the value of the test statistic is computed as $t_{df} = \dfrac{(\bar{x}_1 - \bar{x}_2) - d_0}{\sqrt{\frac{s_1^2}{n_1} + \frac{s_2^2}{n_2}}}$, where

$df = \dfrac{(s_1^2/n_1 + s_2^2/n_2)^2}{(s_1^2/n_1)^2/(n_1 - 1) + (s_2^2/n_2)^2/(n_2 - 1)}$. For df, we generally round the value down; software packages use various rounding rules when reporting the resultant value for df.

These formulas are valid only if $\bar{X}_1 - \bar{X}_2$ (approximately) follows a normal distribution.

EXAMPLE 10.3

An economist claims that average weekly food expenditure for households in City 1 is more than the average weekly food expenditure for households in City 2. She surveys 35 households in City 1 and obtains an average weekly food expenditure of $164. A sample of 30 households in City 2 yields an average weekly food expenditure of $159. Prior studies suggest that the population standard deviation for City 1 and City 2 are $12.50 and $9.25, respectively.

City 1	City 2
$\bar{x}_1 = 164$	$\bar{x}_2 = 159$
$\sigma_1 = 12.50$	$\sigma_2 = 9.25$
$n_1 = 35$	$n_2 = 30$

a. Specify the competing hypotheses to test the economist's claim.

b. Calculate the value of the test statistic and the *p*-value.

c. At the 5% significance level, is the economist's claim supported by the data?

SOLUTION:

a. The relevant parameter of interest is $\mu_1 - \mu_2$, where μ_1 is the mean weekly food expenditure for City 1 and μ_2 is the mean weekly food expenditure for City 2. The economist wishes to determine if the mean weekly food expenditure in City 1 is more than that of City 2; that is, $\mu_1 > \mu_2$. This is an example of a right-tailed test where the appropriate hypotheses are

$$H_0: \mu_1 - \mu_2 \leq 0$$
$$H_A: \mu_1 - \mu_2 > 0$$

b. Since the population standard deviations are known, we compute the value of the test statistic as

$$z = \frac{(\bar{x}_1 - \bar{x}_2) - d_0}{\sqrt{\dfrac{\sigma_1^2}{n_1} + \dfrac{\sigma_2^2}{n_2}}} = \frac{(164 - 159) - 0}{\sqrt{\dfrac{(12.50)^2}{35} + \dfrac{(9.25)^2}{30}}} = \frac{5}{2.70} = 1.85.$$

The *p*-value of the right-tailed test is computed as *p*-value $= P(Z \geq 1.85) = 1 - 0.9678 = 0.0322$.

c. We reject the null hypothesis since the *p*-value of 0.0322 is less than the chosen $\alpha = 0.05$. Therefore, at the 5% significance level, the economist concludes that average weekly food expenditure in City 1 is more than that of City 2.

Using Excel and R for Testing Hypotheses about $\mu_1 - \mu_2$

Excel and R provide several options that simplify the steps when conducting a hypothesis test about $\mu_1 - \mu_2$. If we are only provided with summary statistics, then the best way to calculate the value of the test statistic and the *p*-value would be to use methods analogous to those outlined in Chapter 9. However, when given raw sample data, it is possible to use a single function in Excel and R that generates all the necessary information. Consider the following example.

EXAMPLE 10.4

Table 10.2 shows annual return data for 10 firms in the gold industry and 10 firms in the oil industry. Can we conclude at the 5% significance level that the average returns in the two industries differ? Here we assume that the sample data are drawn independently from normally distributed populations. We cannot assume, however, that the population variances are equal. Since the variance is a common measure of risk when analyzing financial returns, the risk from investing in the gold industry is not the same as the risk from investing in the oil industry.

TABLE 10.2 Annual Returns (in percent)

Gold	Oil
6	−3
15	15
19	28
26	18
2	32
16	31
31	15
14	12
15	10
16	15

SOLUTION: We let μ_1 denote the mean return for the gold industry and μ_2 denote the mean return for the oil industry. Since we wish to test whether the mean returns differ, we set up the null and alternative hypotheses as

$$H_0: \mu_1 - \mu_2 = 0$$
$$H_A: \mu_1 - \mu_2 \neq 0$$

Given that we are testing the difference between two means when the population variances are unknown and not equal, we need to calculate $t_{df} = \dfrac{(\bar{x}_1 - \bar{x}_2) - d_0}{\sqrt{\dfrac{s_1^2}{n_1} + \dfrac{s_2^2}{n_2}}}$.

Recall that the calculation for the degrees of freedom for the corresponding test statistic is rather involved. Fortunately, Excel and R provide the degrees of freedom, the value of the test statistic, and the p-value.

Using Excel

a. Open the **Gold_Oil** data file.

b. Choose **Data > Data Analysis > t-Test: Two-Sample Assuming Unequal Variances > OK**. (Note: Excel provides two other options when we want to test the difference between two population means from independent samples and we have access to the raw data. If the population variances are known, we use the option **z-Test: Two-Sample for Means**. If the population variances are unknown but assumed equal, we use the option **t-Test: Two-Sample Assuming Equal Variances**.)

c. See Figure 10.1. In the dialog box, choose *Variable 1 Range* and select the Gold data. Then, choose *Variable 2 Range* and select the Oil data. Enter a *Hypothesized Mean Difference* of 0 since $d_0 = 0$, check the *Labels* box if you include Gold and Oil as headings, and enter an α value of 0.05 since the test is conducted at the 5% significance level. Click **OK**.

FIGURE 10.1 Excel's dialog box for *t*-test with unequal variances

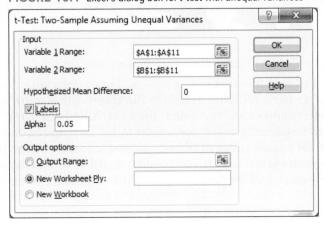

Table 10.3 shows the Excel output.

The value of the test statistic and the p-value for this two-tailed test are -0.3023 and 0.7661, respectively (see these values in boldface in Table 10.3). At the 5% significance level, we cannot reject H_0 since the p-value is greater than 0.05. While average returns in the oil industry seem to slightly outperform average returns in the gold industry ($\bar{x}_2 = 17.3 > 16.0 = \bar{x}_1$), the difference is not statistically significant.

TABLE 10.3 Excel's Output for t-Test concerning $\mu_1 - \mu_2$

	Gold	Oil
Mean	16	17.3
Variance	70.6667	114.2333
Observations	10	10
Hypothesized Mean Difference	0	
Df	17	
t Stat	**−0.3023**	
P(T ≤ t) one-tail	0.3830	
t Critical one-tail	1.7396	
P(T ≤ t) two-tail	**0.7661**	
t Critical two-tail	**2.1098**	

Given the information in Table 10.3, it is also possible to calculate the corresponding 95% confidence interval for $\mu_1 - \mu_2$. Recall that when we estimate the difference between two population means when the population variances are unknown and cannot be assumed equal, we use $t_{\alpha/2,df}$ in its construction. Since we entered 0.05 for the significance level, the value for $t_{\alpha/2,df} = t_{0.025,17} = 2.1098$ (see this value in boldface in Table 10.3). We then calculate:

$$(\bar{x}_1 - \bar{x}_2) \pm t_{\alpha/2,df}\sqrt{\frac{s_1^2}{n_1} + \frac{s_2^2}{n_2}} = (16.0 - 17.3) \pm 2.1098\sqrt{\frac{70.6667}{10} + \frac{114.2333}{10}}$$

$$= -1.3 \pm 9.07.$$

That is, the 95% confidence interval for the difference between the two means ranges from -10.37 to 7.77. We note that this interval contains zero, the value hypothesized under the null hypothesis. Using the 95% confidence interval, we again cannot support the conclusion that the population mean returns differ at the 5% significance level.

Using R

a. Import the ***Gold_Oil*** data into a data frame (table) in R.

b. We use R's **t.test** function to test $\mu_1 - \mu_2$. For options within the **t.test** function we use *alternative* to denote the specification of the alternative hypothesis (denoted as "two.sided" for a two-tailed test, "less" for a left-tailed test, and "greater" for a right-tailed test), *mu* to denote the value of the hypothesized difference, *paired* to indicate if we have a matched-pairs sample, *var.equal* to indicate if the variances are assumed equal, and *conf.level* to specify the confidence level. When testing $\mu_1 - \mu_2$ under the assumption that the variances are unknown and not equal, we enter

```
> t.test(Gold_Oil$'Gold', Gold_Oil$'Oil',
    alternative="two.sided", mu=0, paired=FALSE,
    var.equal = FALSE, conf.level=0.95)
```

Table 10.4 shows the R output. We have put the value of the test statistic, the p-value, and the 95% confidence level in boldface. The results are consistent with the Excel output; that is, since the p-value = 0.7661 > 0.05 = α, we cannot reject the null hypothesis. Equivalently, the 95% confidence interval for $\mu_1 - \mu_2$ is [−10.37, 7.77] which includes 0, the hypothesized value under the null hypothesis. At the 5% significance level, we cannot conclude that average returns between the gold industry and the oil industry differ.

TABLE 10.4 R's Output for t-Test concerning $\mu_1 - \mu_2$

```
Welch Two Sample t-test
data: Gold_Oil$Gold and Gold_Oil$Oil
t = -0.30233, df = 17.053, p-value = 0.7661
alternative hypothesis: true difference in means is not equal to 0
    95 percent confidence interval:
    -10.37005 7.77005
sample estimates:
mean of x mean of y
      16.0      17.3
```

A Note on the Assumption of Normality

In Example 10.4, we may have made a strong assumption that the populations were normally distributed. We could not invoke the central limit theorem, as we had small sample sizes. In Chapter 12, we will explore tests that check for normality. If we wish to draw inferences about $\mu_1 - \mu_2$ from nonnormal populations, we can use the nonparametric Wilcoxon rank-sum test for independent samples, discussed in Chapter 20.

EXERCISES 10.1

Mechanics

1. Consider the following data drawn independently from normally distributed populations:

    $\bar{x}_1 = 25.7$ $\bar{x}_2 = 30.6$
    $\sigma_1^2 = 98.2$ $\sigma_2^2 = 87.4$
    $n_1 = 20$ $n_2 = 25$

    a. Construct the 95% confidence interval for the difference between the population means.

    b. Specify the competing hypotheses in order to determine whether or not the population means differ.

    c. Using the confidence interval from part a, can you reject the null hypothesis? Explain.

2. Consider the following data drawn independently from normally distributed populations:

    $\bar{x}_1 = -10.5$ $\bar{x}_2 = -16.8$
    $s_1^2 = 7.9$ $s_2^2 = 9.3$
    $n_1 = 15$ $n_2 = 20$

    a. Construct the 95% confidence interval for the difference between the population means. Assume that the population variances are equal.

b. Specify the competing hypotheses in order to determine whether or not the population means differ.

c. Using the confidence interval from part a, can you reject the null hypothesis? Explain.

3. Consider the following competing hypotheses and accompanying sample data drawn independently from normally distributed populations.

$$H_0: \mu_1 - \mu_2 = 0$$
$$H_A: \mu_1 - \mu_2 \neq 0$$

$\bar{x}_1 = 57$	$\bar{x}_2 = 63$
$\sigma_1 = 11.5$	$\sigma_2 = 15.2$
$n_1 = 20$	$n_2 = 20$

Test whether the population means differ at the 5% significance level.

4. Consider the following competing hypotheses and accompanying sample data. The two populations are known to be normally distributed.

$$H_0: \mu_1 - \mu_2 \leq 0$$
$$H_A: \mu_1 - \mu_2 > 0$$

$\bar{x}_1 = 20.2$	$\bar{x}_2 = 17.5$
$s_1 = 2.5$	$s_2 = 4.4$
$n_1 = 10$	$n_2 = 12$

a. Implement the test at the 5% significance level under the assumption that the population variances are equal.

b. Repeat the analysis at the 10% significance level.

5. Consider the following competing hypotheses and accompanying sample data drawn independently from normally distributed populations.

$$H_0: \mu_1 - \mu_2 \geq 0$$
$$H_A: \mu_1 - \mu_2 < 0$$

$\bar{x}_1 = 249$	$\bar{x}_2 = 262$
$s_1 = 35$	$s_2 = 23$
$n_1 = 10$	$n_2 = 10$

a. Implement the test at the 5% significance level under the assumption that the population variances are equal.

b. Implement the test at the 5% significance level under the assumption that the population variances are not equal.

6. Consider the following competing hypotheses and accompanying sample data.

$$H_0: \mu_1 - \mu_2 = 5$$
$$H_A: \mu_1 - \mu_2 \neq 5$$

$\bar{x}_1 = 57$	$\bar{x}_2 = 43$
$s_1 = 21.5$	$s_2 = 15.2$
$n_1 = 22$	$n_2 = 18$

Assume that the populations are normally distributed with equal variances.

a. Calculate the value of the test statistic and the p-value.

b. At the 5% significance level, can you conclude that the difference between the two means differs from 5?

7. Consider the following sample data drawn independently from normally distributed populations with equal population variances.

Sample 1	Sample 2
12.1	8.9
9.5	10.9
7.3	11.2
10.2	10.6
8.9	9.8
9.8	9.8
7.2	11.2
10.2	12.1

a. Construct the relevant hypotheses to test if the mean of the second population is greater than the mean of the first population.

b. Implement the test at the 1% significance level.

c. Implement the test at the 10% significance level.

8. Consider the following sample data drawn independently from normally distributed populations with unequal population variances.

Sample 1	Sample 2
88	98
110	114
102	118
96	128
74	102
120	110

a. Construct the relevant hypothesis to test if the means of the two populations differ.

b. What is the value of the test statistic and the p-value?

c. At the 10% significance level, do the two population means differ?

Applications

9. According to a Health of Boston report, female residents in Boston have a higher average life expectancy as compared to male residents (*The Boston Globe*, August 16, 2010). You collect the following sample data to verify the results of the report. You also use the historical (population) standard deviation of 8.2 years for females and 8.6 years for males.

Female	Male
$\bar{x}_1 = 81.1$	$\bar{x}_2 = 74.8$
$n_1 = 32$	$n_2 = 32$

a. Set up the hypotheses to test whether the average life expectancy of female Bostonians is higher than that of male Bostonians.

b. Calculate the value of the test statistic and the p-value.

c. At the 10% significance level, can we conclude that female Bostonians live longer than male Bostonians?

10. A joint project of the U.S. Census Bureau and the National Science Foundation shows that people with a bachelor's degree who transferred from a community college earn less than those who start at a four-year school (*USA TODAY*, March 17, 2009). Previous studies referred to this occurrence as a "community college penalty." Lucille Barnes wonders if a similar pattern applies to her university. The accompanying table shows the average salary of 100 graduates with an associate degree and the average salary of 100 graduates with no associate degree. Lucille believes that the population standard deviation is $4,400 for graduates with an associate degree and $1,500 for graduates with no associate degree.

Bachelor's Degree with Associate Degree	Bachelor's Degree with No Associate Degree
$\bar{x}_1 = 52,000$	$\bar{x}_2 = 54,700$
$n_1 = 100$	$n_2 = 100$

a. Set up the hypotheses to test if the report's conclusion also applies to Lucille's university.

b. Calculate the value of the test statistic and the p-value.

c. At the 5% significance level, can we conclude that there is a "community college penalty" at Lucille's university?

11. The Chartered Financial Analyst (CFA) designation is fast becoming a requirement for serious investment professionals. It is an attractive alternative to getting an MBA for students wanting a career in investment. A student of finance is curious to know if a CFA designation is a more lucrative option than an MBA. He collects data on 38 recent CFAs with a mean salary of $138,000 and a standard deviation of $34,000. A sample of 80 MBAs results in a mean salary of $130,000 with a standard deviation of $46,000.

a. Specify the hypotheses to test whether a CFA designation is more lucrative than an MBA.

b. Calculate the value of the test statistic and the p-value. Do not assume that the population variances are equal.

c. At the 5% significance level, is a CFA designation more lucrative than an MBA?

12. An entrepreneur owns some land that he wishes to develop. He identifies two development options: build condominiums or build apartment buildings. Accordingly, he reviews public records and derives the following summary measures concerning annual profitability based on a random sample of 30 for each such local business venture. For the analysis, he uses a historical (population) standard deviation of $22,500 for condominiums and $20,000 for apartment buildings.

Condominiums	Apartment Buildings
$\bar{x}_1 = 244,200$	$\bar{x}_2 = 235,800$
$n_1 = 30$	$n_2 = 30$

a. Set up the hypotheses to test whether the mean profitability differs between condominiums and apartment buildings.

b. Calculate the value of the test statistic and the p-value.

c. At the 5% significance level, what is the conclusion to the test? What if the significance level is 10%?

13. David Anderson has been working as a lecturer at Michigan State University for the last three years. He teaches two large sections of introductory accounting every semester. While he uses the same lecture notes in both sections, his students in the first section outperform those in the second section. He believes that students in the first section not only tend to get higher scores, they also tend to have lower variability in scores. David decides to carry out a formal test to validate his hunch regarding the difference in average scores. In a random sample of 18 students in the first section, he computes a mean and a standard deviation of 77.4 and 10.8, respectively. In the second section, a random sample of 14 students results in a mean of 74.1 and a standard deviation of 12.2.

a. Construct the null and the alternative hypotheses to test David's hunch.

b. Compute the value of the test statistic. What assumption regarding the populations is necessary to implement this step?

c. Implement the test at $\alpha = 0.01$ and interpret your results.

14. A design engineer at Sperling Manufacturing, a supplier of high-quality ball bearings, claims a new machining process can result in a higher daily output rate. Accordingly, the production group is conducting an experiment to determine if this claim can be substantiated. The mean and the standard deviation of bearings in a sample of 8 days' output using the new process equal 2,613.63 and 90.78, respectively. A similar sample of 10 days' output using the old process yields the mean and the standard deviation of 2,485.10 and 148.22, respectively.

a. Set up the hypotheses to test whether the mean output rate of the new process exceeds that of the old process. Assume normally distributed populations and equal population variances for each process.

b. Compute the value of the test statistic and the p-value.

c. At the 5% significance level, what is the conclusion of the experiment?

d. At the 1% significance level, what is the conclusion of the experiment?

15. A phone manufacturer wants to compete in the touch screen phone market. Management understands that the leading product has a less than desirable battery life. They aim to compete with a new touch screen phone that is guaranteed to have a battery life more than two hours longer than the leading

product. A recent sample of 120 units of the leading product provides a mean battery life of 5 hours and 40 minutes with a standard deviation of 30 minutes. A similar analysis of 100 units of the new product results in a mean battery life of 8 hours and 5 minutes and a standard deviation of 55 minutes. It is not reasonable to assume that the population variances of the two products are equal.

a. Set up the hypotheses to test if the new product has a battery life more than two hours longer than the leading product.

b. Implement the test at the 5% significance level.

16. In May 2008, CNN reported that sports utility vehicles (SUVs) are plunging toward the "endangered" list. Due to soaring oil prices and environmental concerns, consumers are replacing gas-guzzling vehicles with fuel-efficient smaller cars. As a result, there has been a big drop in the demand for new as well as used SUVs. A sales manager of a used car dealership believes that it takes an average of 30 days longer to sell an SUV as compared to a small car. In the last two months, he sold 18 SUVs that took an average of 95 days to sell with a standard deviation of 32 days. He also sold 38 small cars with an average of 48 days to sell and a standard deviation of 24 days.

a. Construct the null and the alternative hypotheses to contradict the manager's claim.

b. Compute the value of the test statistic and the p-value. Assume that the populations are normally distributed and that the variability of selling time for the SUVs and the small cars is the same.

c. Implement the test at $\alpha = 0.10$ and interpret your results.

17. **FILE** *Refrigerator_Longevity.* A consumer advocate researches the length of life between two brands of refrigerators, Brand A and Brand B. He collects data (measured in years) on the longevity of 40 refrigerators for Brand A and repeats the sampling for Brand B.

a. Specify the competing hypotheses to test whether the average length of life differs between the two brands.

b. Calculate the value of the test statistic and the p-value. Assume that $\sigma_A^2 = 4.4$ and $\sigma_B^2 = 5.2$.

c. At the 5% significance level, what is the conclusion?

18. **FILE** *Website_Searches.* The "See Me" marketing agency wants to determine if time of day for a television advertisement influences website searches for a product. They have extracted the number of website searches occurring during a one-hour period after an advertisement was aired for a random sample of 30 day and 30 evening advertisements. A portion of the data is shown in the accompanying table.

Day Searches	Evening Searches
96670	118379
97855	111005
⋮	⋮
95103	114721

a. Set up the hypotheses to test whether the mean number of website searches differs between the day and evening advertisements.

b. Calculate the value of the test statistic and the p-value. Assume that the population variances are equal.

c. At the 5% significance level, what is the conclusion?

19. **FILE** *Different_Diets.* According to a study published in the *New England Journal of Medicine,* overweight people on low-carbohydrate and Mediterranean diets lost more weight and got greater cardiovascular benefits than people on a conventional low-fat diet (*The Boston Globe*, July 17, 2008). A nutritionist wishes to verify these results and documents the weight loss (in pounds) of 30 dieters on the low-carbohydrate and Mediterranean diets and 30 dieters on the low-fat diet.

a. Set up the hypotheses to test the claim that the mean weight loss for those on low-carbohydrate or Mediterranean diets is greater than the mean weight loss for those on a conventional low-fat diet.

b. Calculate the value of the test statistic and the p-value. Assume that the population variances are equal.

c. At the 5% significance level, can the nutritionist conclude that people on low-carbohydrate or Mediterranean diets lost more weight than people on a conventional low-fat diet?

20. **FILE** *Tractor_Times.* The production department at Greenside Corporation, a manufacturer of lawn equipment, has devised a new manual assembly method for its lawn tractors. Now it wishes to determine if it is reasonable to conclude that the mean assembly time of the new method is less than the old method. Accordingly, they have randomly sampled assembly times (in minutes) from 40 tractors using the old method and 32 tractors using the new method. A portion of the data is shown in the accompanying table.

Old Method	New Method
32	30
36	32
⋮	⋮

a. Set up the hypotheses to test the claim that the mean assembly time using the new method is less than the old method.

b. Calculate the value of the test statistic and the p-value. Assume that the population variances are not equal.

c. At the 5% significance level, what is the conclusion? What if the significance level is 10%?

21. **FILE** *Nicknames.* Baseball has always been a favorite pastime in America and is rife with statistics and theories. In a paper, researchers showed that major league players who have nicknames live an average of 2½ years longer than those without them (*The Wall Street Journal*, July 16, 2009). You do not believe in this result and decide to collect data

on the lifespan of 30 baseball players along with a nickname variable that equals 1 if the player had a nickname and 0 otherwise. A portion of the data is shown in the accompanying table.

Years	Nickname
74	1
62	1
⋮	⋮
64	0

a. Create two subsamples consisting of players with and without nicknames. Calculate the average longevity for each subsample.

b. Specify the hypotheses to contradict the claim made by the researchers.

c. Calculate the value of the test statistic and the p-value. Assume that the population variances are equal.

d. What is the conclusion of the test using a 5% level of significance?

22. **FILE** *Starting_Salaries.* Recent evidence suggests that graduating from college during bad economic times can impact the graduate's earning power for a long time (*Financial Times*, June 1, 2012). An associate dean at a prestigious college wants to determine if the starting salary of his college graduates has declined from 2008 to 2010. He expects the variance of the salaries to be different between these two years. A portion of the data is shown in the accompanying table.

Salary 2008	Salary 2010
35000	34000
56000	62000
⋮	⋮
47000	54000

At the 5% significance level, determine if the mean starting salary has decreased from 2008 to 2010.

23. **FILE** *Spending_Gender.* Researchers at the Wharton School of Business have found that men and women shop for different reasons. While women enjoy the shopping experience, men are on a mission to get the job done. Men do not shop as frequently, but when they do, they make big purchases like expensive electronics. The accompanying table shows a portion of the amount spent (in $) over the weekend by 40 men and 60 women at a local mall.

Spending by Men	Spending by Women
85	90
102	79
⋮	⋮

At the 1% significance level, determine if the mean amount spent by men is more than that by women. Assume that the population variances are equal.

10.2 INFERENCE CONCERNING MEAN DIFFERENCES

LO **10.2**

One of the crucial assumptions in Section 10.1 concerning differences between two population means is that the samples are drawn independently. As mentioned earlier, two samples are independent if the selection of one is not influenced by the selection of the other. When we want to conduct tests on two population means based on samples that we believe are not independent, we need to employ a different methodology.

A common case of dependent sampling, commonly referred to as **matched-pairs sampling**, is when the samples are paired or matched in some way. Such samples are useful in evaluating strategies because the comparison is made between "apples" and "apples." For instance, an effective way to assess the benefits of a new medical treatment is by evaluating the same patients before and after the treatment. If, however, one group of people is given the treatment and another group is not, then it is not clear if the observed differences are due to the treatment or due to other important differences between the groups.

For matched-pairs sampling, the parameter of interest is referred to as the mean difference μ_D where $D = X_1 - X_2$, and the random variables X_1 and X_2 are matched in a pair. The statistical inference regarding μ_D is based on the estimator $\bar{D}$, representing the sample mean difference. It requires that $X_1 - X_2$ is normally distributed or that the sample size is sufficiently large ($n \geq 30$).

Make inferences about the mean difference based on matched-pairs sampling.

Recognizing a Matched-Pairs Experiment

It is important to be able to determine whether a particular experiment uses independent or matched-pairs sampling. In general, two types of matched-pairs sampling occur:

1. The first type of matched-pairs sample is characterized by a measurement, an intervention of some type, and then another measurement. We generally refer to these experiments as "before" and "after" studies. For example, an operation manager of a production facility wants to determine whether a new workstation layout improves productivity at her plant. She first measures output of employees before the layout change. Then she measures output of the same employees after the change. Another classic before-and-after example concerns weight loss of clients at a diet center. In these examples, the same individual gets sampled before and after the experiment.

2. The second type of matched-pairs sample is characterized by a pairing of observations, where it is not the same individual who gets sampled twice. Suppose an agronomist wishes to switch to an organic fertilizer but is unsure what the effects might be on his crop yield. It is important to the agronomist that the yields be similar. He matches 20 adjacent plots of land using the nonorganic fertilizer on one half of the plot and the organic fertilizer on the other.

In order to recognize a matched-pairs experiment, we watch for a natural pairing between one observation in the first sample and one observation in the second sample. If a natural pairing exists, then the experiment involves matched samples.

Confidence Interval for μ_D

When constructing a confidence interval for the mean difference μ_D, we follow the same general format of point estimate ± margin of error.

CONFIDENCE INTERVAL FOR μ_D

A $100(1 - \alpha)\%$ confidence interval for the mean difference μ_D is given by
$$\bar{d} \pm t_{\alpha/2,df} s_D/\sqrt{n},$$
where $\bar{d}$ and s_D are the mean and the standard deviation, respectively, of the n sample differences and $df = n - 1$. This formula is valid only if $\bar{D}$ (approximately) follows a normal distribution.

In the next example, the values for $\bar{d}$ and s_D are explicitly given; we will outline the calculations when we discuss hypothesis testing.

EXAMPLE 10.5

A manager is interested in improving productivity at a plant by changing the layout of the workstation. For each of 10 workers, she measures the time it takes to complete a task before the change and again after the change. She calculates the following summary statistics for the sample difference: $\bar{d} = 8.5$, $s_D = 11.38$, and $n = 10$. Construct the 95% confidence interval for the mean difference, assuming that the productivity variable, before minus after, is normally distributed.

SOLUTION: In order to construct the 95% confidence interval for the mean difference, we use $\bar{d} \pm t_{\alpha/2,df} s_D/\sqrt{n}$. With $df = n - 1 = 10 - 1 = 9$ and $\alpha = 0.05$, we find $t_{\alpha/2,df} = t_{0.025,9} = 2.262$. Plugging the relevant values into the formula, we calculate $8.5 \pm 2.262(11.38/\sqrt{10}) = 8.5 \pm 8.14$. That is, the 95% confidence interval for the mean difference ranges from 0.36 to 16.64. This represents a fairly wide interval, caused by the high standard deviation s_D of the 10 sample differences.

Hypothesis Test for μ_D

As before, we generally want to test whether the mean difference μ_D differs from, is greater than, or is less than a given hypothesized mean difference d_0, or:

Two-Tailed Test	Right-Tailed Test	Left-Tailed Test
$H_0: \mu_D = d_0$	$H_0: \mu_D \leq d_0$	$H_0: \mu_D \geq d_0$
$H_A: \mu_D \neq d_0$	$H_A: \mu_D > d_0$	$H_A: \mu_D < d_0$

In practice, the competing hypotheses tend to be based on $d_0 = 0$. For example, when testing if the mean difference differs from zero, we use a two-tailed test with the competing hypotheses defined as $H_0: \mu_D = 0$ versus $H_A: \mu_D \neq 0$. If, on the other hand, we wish to determine whether or not the mean difference differs by some amount, say by 5 units, we set $d_0 = 5$ and define the competing hypotheses as $H_0: \mu_D = 5$ versus $H_A: \mu_D \neq 5$. One-tailed tests are defined similarly.

EXAMPLE 10.6

Using the information from Example 10.5, can the manager conclude at the 5% significance level that there has been a change in productivity since the adoption of the new workstation?

SOLUTION: In order to determine whether or not there has been a change in the mean difference, we formulate the null and the alternative hypotheses as

$$H_0: \mu_D = 0$$

$$H_A: \mu_D \neq 0$$

In Example 10.5, we found that the 95% confidence interval for the mean difference ranges from 0.36 to 16.64. Although the interval is very wide, the entire range is above the hypothesized value of zero. Therefore, at the 5% significance level the sample data suggest that the mean difference differs from zero. In other words, there has been a change in productivity due to the different layout in the workstation.

We now examine the four-step procedure to conduct one- or two-tailed hypothesis tests concerning the mean difference. We again convert the sample mean difference into its corresponding t_{df} statistic by dividing the difference between the sample mean difference and the hypothesized mean difference by the standard error of the estimator $se(\overline{D})$.

TEST STATISTIC FOR TESTING μ_D

The value of the test statistic for a hypothesis test concerning the population mean difference μ_D is computed as $t_{df} = \frac{\bar{d} - d_0}{s_D/\sqrt{n}}$, where $df = n - 1$, $\bar{d}$ and s_D are the mean and the standard deviation, respectively, of the n sample differences and d_0 is the hypothesized mean difference. This formula is valid only if $\overline{D}$ (approximately) follows a normal distribution.

FILE
Drink_Calories

EXAMPLE 10.7

Let's revisit the chapter's introductory case. Recall that a local ordinance requires chain restaurants to post caloric information on their menus. A nutritionist wants to examine whether average drink calories declined at Starbucks after the passage of the ordinance. The nutritionist obtains transaction data for 40 Starbucks cardholders and records each cardholder's drink calories prior to the ordinance and then after the ordinance. A portion of the data is shown in Table 10.5. Can she conclude at the 5% significance level that the ordinance reduced average drink calories?

SOLUTION: We first note that this is a matched-pairs experiment; specifically, it conforms to a "before" and "after" type of study. Moreover, we want to find out whether average drink calories consumed prior to the ordinance are greater than average drink calories consumed after passage of the ordinance. Thus, we want to test if the mean difference μ_D is greater than zero, where $D = X_1 - X_2$, X_1 denotes drink calories before the ordinance, and X_2 denotes drink calories after the ordinance for a randomly selected Starbuck's customer. We specify the competing hypotheses as

$$H_0: \mu_D \leq 0$$

$$H_A: \mu_D > 0$$

The normality condition for the test is satisfied since the sample size $n \geq 30$. The value of the test statistic is calculated as $t_{df} = \frac{\bar{d} - d_0}{s_D/\sqrt{n}}$ where d_0 equals 0. In order to determine $\bar{d}$ and s_D, we first calculate the difference d_i for each i-th customer. For instance, customer 1 consumes 141 calories prior to the ordinance and 142 calories after the ordinance, for a difference of $d_1 = 141 - 142 = -1$. The differences for a portion of the other customers appear in the fourth column of Table 10.5.

Table 10.5 Data and Calculations for Example 10.7, $n = 40$

Customer	Drink Calories Before	Drink Calories After	d_i	$(d_i - \bar{d})^2$
1	141	142	−1	$(-1 - 2.1)^2 = 9.61$
2	137	140	−3	$(-3 - 2.1)^2 = 26.01$
⋮	⋮	⋮	⋮	⋮
40	147	141	6	$(6 - 2.1)^2 = 15.21$
			$\Sigma d_i = 84$	$\Sigma(d_i - \bar{d})^2 = 2593.60$

We obtain the sample mean as

$$\bar{d} = \frac{\Sigma d_i}{n} = \frac{84}{40} = 2.10.$$

Similarly, in the fifth column of Table 10.5, we square the differences between d_i and $\bar{d}$. Summing these squared differences yields the numerator in the formula for the sample variance s_D^2. The denominator is simply $n - 1$, so

$$s_D^2 = \frac{\Sigma(d_i - \bar{d})^2}{n - 1} = \frac{2,593.60}{40 - 1} = 66.5026.$$

As usual, the standard deviation is the positive square root of the sample variance—that is, $s_D = \sqrt{66.5026} = 8.1549$. We compute the value of the t_{df} test statistic with $df = n - 1 = 40 - 1 = 39$ as

$$t_{39} = \frac{\bar{d} - d_0}{s_D/\sqrt{n}} = \frac{2.10 - 0}{8.1549/\sqrt{40}} = 1.629.$$

Given a right-tailed hypothesis test with $df = 39$, we can use the t table to approximate the p-value $= P(T_{39} \geq 1.629)$, as $0.05 < p\text{-value} < 0.10$. Using statistical software, we find that the exact p-value $= 0.0557$. Since the p-value > 0.05, we do not reject H_0. At the 5% significance level, we cannot conclude that the posting of nutritional information decreases average drink calories.

We should note that once we have calculated the mean difference and the standard deviation of the mean difference, the hypothesis test essentially reduces to a one-sample *t*-test for the population mean.

Using Excel and R for Testing Hypotheses about μ_D

Excel and R provide several options that simplify the steps when conducting a hypothesis test about μ_D. If we are only provided with summary statistics, then the best way to calculate the value of the test statistic and the *p*-value would be to use methods analogous to those outlined in Chapter 9. However, when given raw sample data, it is possible to use a single function in Excel and R that generates all the necessary information. Consider the following example.

EXAMPLE 10.8

The nutritionist from Example 10.7 also wants to use the data from the 40 Starbucks cardholders in order to determine if the posting of caloric information has reduced average food calories. This test is also conducted at the 5% significance level.

SOLUTION: We set up the same competing hypotheses as in Example 10.7 since we want to know if average food calories were greater before the ordinance as compared to after the ordinance.

$$H_0: \mu_D \leq 0$$

$$H_A: \mu_D > 0$$

Using Excel

a. Open the **Food_Calories** data file.

b. Choose **Data > Data Analysis > *t*-Test: Paired Two Sample for Means > OK**.

c. See Figure 10.2. In the dialog box, choose *Variable 1 Range* and select the data in the Before column. Choose *Variable 2 Range* and select the data in the After column. Enter a *Hypothesized Mean Difference* of 0 since $d_0 = 0$, check the *Labels* box if you include Before and After as headings, and enter an α value of 0.05 since the test is conducted at the 5% significance level. Click **OK**.

FIGURE 10.2 Excel's dialog box for *t*-test with paired sample

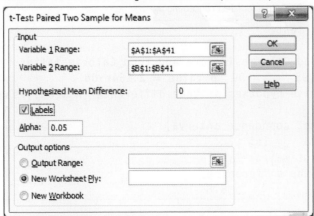

Table 10.6 shows the Excel output. The value of the test statistic and the *p*-value for this one-tailed test are 6.7795 and 2.15E-08, respectively (see these values in boldface in Table 10.6). We can reject H_0 because the *p*-value < 0.05. Thus, at the 5% significance level, we can conclude that average food calories have declined after the passage of the ordinance.

TABLE 10.6 Excel's Output for *t*-Test concerning μ_D

	Before	After
Mean	400.275	391.475
Variance	49.9481	42.3583
Observations	40	40
Pearson Correlation	0.27080	
Hypothesized Mean Difference	0	
Df	39	
t Stat	**6.7795**	
P(T ≤ t) one-tail	**2.15E-08**	
t Critical one-tail	1.6849	
P(T ≤ t) two-tail	4.31E-08	
t Critical two-tail	2.0227	

Note: Although Excel calculates the *p*-value correctly, the expression it uses to denote the *p*-value is not always correct. In this example with a positive value for the test statistic, the expression should be "$P(T \geq t)$ one-tail" rather than "$P(T \leq t)$ one-tail."

Using R

a. Import the **Food_Calories** data into a data frame (table) in R.

b. As discussed in Section 10.1, we use R's **t.test** function to test μ_D. For options within the **t.test** function we use *alternative*, *mu*, and *paired*. We enter

```
> t.test(Food_Calories$'Before',
    Food_Calories$'After', alternative="greater", mu=0,
    paired=TRUE)
```

Table 10.7 shows the R output. We have put the value of the test statistic and the *p*-value in boldface. The results are consistent with the Excel output; that is, since the *p*-value < 0.05, we reject the null hypothesis. At the 5% significance level, we can conclude that average food calories have declined since the passage of the ordinance.

TABLE 10.7 R's Output for *t*-Test concerning μ_D

```
Paired t-test

data: Food_Calories$Before and Food_Calories$After
t = 6.7795, df = 39, p-value = 2.154e-08
alternative hypothesis: true difference in means is greater
than 0
95 percent confidence interval:
 6.612988      Inf
sample estimates:
mean of the differences
             8.8
```

One Last Note on the Matched-Pairs Experiment

Similar to our remarks in the last section, when making inferences concerning μ_D, we require that $\overline{D}$ (approximately) follows a normal distribution. If $\overline{D}$ is not normally distributed, we can use the nonparametric Wilcoxon signed-rank test for matched pairs, discussed in Chapter 20.

SYNOPSIS OF INTRODUCTORY CASE

In an effort to make it easier for consumers to select healthier options, the government wants chain restaurants to post caloric information on their menus. A nutritionist studies the effects of a recent local menu ordinance requiring caloric postings at a Starbucks in San Mateo, California. She obtains transaction data for 40 Starbucks cardholders and records each cardholder's drink and food calories prior to the ordinance and then after the ordinance. Two hypothesis tests are conducted. The first test examines whether average drink calories are less since the passage of the ordinance. After conducting a test on the mean difference at the 5% significance level, the nutritionist infers that the ordinance did not prompt customers to reduce their consumption of drink calories. The second test investigates whether average food calories are less since the passage of the ordinance. At the 5% significance level, the sample data suggest that customers have reduced their consumption of food calories since the passage of the ordinance. In sum, while the government is trying to ensure that customers process the calorie information as they are ordering, the results are consistent with research that has shown mixed results on whether mandatory caloric postings are prompting customers to select healthier foods.

©Chris Hondros/Getty Images News/Getty Images

EXERCISES 10.2

Mechanics

24. A sample of 20 paired observations generates the following data: $\bar{d} = 1.3$ and $s_D^2 = 2.6$. Assume a normal distribution.
    a. Construct the 90% confidence interval for the mean difference μ_D.
    b. Using the confidence interval, test whether the mean difference differs from zero. Explain.

25. The following table contains information on matched sample values whose differences are normally distributed.

Number	Sample 1	Sample 2
1	18	21
2	12	11
3	21	23
4	22	20
5	16	20
6	14	17
7	17	17
8	18	22

    a. Construct the 95% confidence interval for the mean difference μ_D.

    b. Specify the competing hypotheses in order to test whether the mean difference differs from zero.
    c. Using the confidence interval from part a, are you able to reject H_0? Explain.

26. Consider the following competing hypotheses and accompanying results from a matched-pairs sample:

$$H_0: \mu_D \geq 0; H_A: \mu_D < 0$$

$$\bar{d} = -2.8, s_D = 5.7, n = 12$$

    a. Calculate the value of the test statistic and the p-value, assuming that the sample difference is normally distributed.
    b. At the 5% significance level, what is the conclusion to the hypothesis test?

27. Consider the following competing hypotheses and accompanying results from a matched-pairs sample:

$$H_0: \mu_D \leq 2; H_A: \mu_D > 2$$

$$\bar{d} = 5.6, s_D = 6.2, n = 10$$

    a. Calculate the value of the test statistic and the p-value, assuming that the sample difference is normally distributed.
    b. Use the 1% significance level to make a conclusion.

28. A sample of 35 paired observations generates the following results: $\bar{d} = 1.2$ and $s_D = 3.8$.

   a. Specify the appropriate hypotheses to test if the mean difference is greater than zero.

   b. Calculate the value of the test statistic and the p-value.

   c. At the 5% significance level, can you conclude that the mean difference is greater than zero? Explain.

29. Consider the following matched-pairs sample that represents observations before and after an experiment. Assume that the sample differences are normally distributed.

Before	2.5	1.8	1.4	−2.9	1.2	−1.9	−3.1	2.5
After	2.9	3.1	3.9	−1.8	0.2	0.6	−2.5	2.9

   a. Construct the competing hypotheses to determine if the experiment increases the magnitude of the observations.

   b. Implement the test at the 5% significance level.

   c. Do the results change if we implement the test at the 1% significance level?

Applications

30. A manager of an industrial plant asserts that workers on average do not complete a job using Method A in the same amount of time as they would using Method B. Seven workers are randomly selected. Each worker's completion time (in minutes) is recorded by the use of Method A and Method B.

Worker	Method A	Method B
1	15	16
2	21	25
3	16	18
4	18	22
5	19	23
6	22	20
7	20	20

   a. Specify the null and alternative hypotheses to test the manager's assertion.

   b. Assuming that the completion time difference is normally distributed, calculate the value of the test statistic.

   c. Find the p-value.

   d. At the 10% significance level, is the manager's assertion supported by the data?

31. A diet center claims that it has the most effective weight loss program in the region. Its advertisements say, "Participants in our program lose more than 5 pounds within a month." Six clients of this program are weighed on the first day of the diet and then one month later.

Client	Weight on First Day of Diet	Weight One Month Later
1	158	151
2	205	200
3	170	169
4	189	179
5	149	144
6	135	129

   a. Specify the null and alternative hypotheses that test the diet center's claim.

   b. Assuming that weight loss is normally distributed, calculate the value of the test statistic.

   c. Find the p-value.

   d. At the 5% significance level, do the data support the diet center's claim?

32. A bank employs two appraisers. When approving borrowers for mortgages, it is imperative that the appraisers value the same types of properties consistently. To make sure that this is the case, the bank examines six properties (in $1,000s) that the appraisers had valued recently.

Property	Value from Appraiser 1	Value from Appraiser 2
1	235	239
2	195	190
3	264	271
4	315	310
5	435	437
6	515	525

   a. Specify the competing hypotheses that determine whether there is any difference between the values estimated by Appraiser 1 and Appraiser 2.

   b. Assuming that the value difference is normally distributed, calculate the value of the test statistic.

   c. Find the p-value.

   d. At the 5% significance level, is there sufficient evidence to conclude that the appraisers are inconsistent in their estimates? Explain.

33. The quality department at ElectroTech is examining which of two microscope brands (Brand A or Brand B) to purchase. They have hired someone to inspect six circuit boards using both microscopes. Below are the results in terms of the number of defects (e.g., solder voids, misaligned components) found using each microscope.

Circuit Board	Defects with Brand A	Defects with Brand B
1	12	14
2	8	9
3	16	16
4	14	12
5	9	8
6	13	15

a. Specify the null and alternative hypotheses to test for differences in the defects found between the microscope brands.

b. Assuming that the difference in defects is normally distributed, calculate the value of the test statistic and the p-value.

c. At the 5% significance level, is there a difference between the microscope brands?

34. A computer technology firm wishes to check whether the speed of a new processor exceeds that of an existing processor when used in one of its popular laptop computer models. Accordingly, it measures the time required (in seconds) to complete seven common tasks on two otherwise identical computers, one with the new processor and one with the existing processor. The time required is as follows:

Task	New Processor	Existing Processor
1	1.47	1.68
2	2.59	2.99
3	5.21	5.69
4	3.49	3.75
5	3.99	4.25
6	3.10	2.99
7	5.75	6.19

a. Specify the null and alternative hypotheses to test whether the time required for the new processor is less than the existing processor.

b. Assuming that the difference in time is normally distributed, calculate the value of the test statistic and the p-value.

c. At the 5% significance level, is the new processor faster than the old processor?

35. **FILE** *Mock_SAT.* A report criticizes SAT-test-preparation providers for promising big score gains without any hard data to back up such claims (*The Wall Street Journal,* May 20, 2009).

Suppose eight college-bound students take a mock SAT, complete a three-month test-prep course, and then take the real SAT.

Student	Mock SAT	Real SAT
1	1830	1840
2	1760	1800
3	2000	2010
4	2150	2190
5	1630	1620
6	1840	1960
7	1930	1890
8	1710	1780

a. Specify the competing hypotheses that determine whether completion of the test-prep course increases a student's score on the real SAT.

b. Calculate the value of the test statistic and the p-value. Assume that the SAT scores difference is normally distributed.

c. At the 5% significance level, do the sample data support the test-prep providers' claims?

36. **FILE** *Insurance_Premiums.* The marketing department at Insure-Me, a large insurance company, wants to advertise that customers can save, on average, more than $100 on their annual automotive insurance policies (relative to their closest competitor) by switching their policies to Insure-Me. However, to avoid potential litigation for false advertising, they select a random sample of 50 policyholders and compare their premiums to those of their closest competitor. A portion of the data is presented in the following table.

Policyholder	Competitor's Premium	"Insure-Me" Premium
1	958	1086
2	1034	366
⋮	⋮	⋮
50	1161	964

a. Specify the competing hypotheses to determine whether the mean difference between the competitor's premium and *Insure-Me's* premium is over $100.

b. Calculate the value of the test statistic and the p-value.

c. What is the conclusion at the 5% significance level? What is the conclusion at the 10% significance level?

37. **FILE** *Electronic_Utilities.* The following table shows the annual returns (in percent) for Fidelity's Select Electronic and Select Utilities mutual funds for the years 2001 through 2009.

Year	Electronic	Utilities
2001	−14.23	−21.89
2002	−50.54	−30.40
2003	71.89	26.42
2004	−9.81	24.22
2005	15.75	9.36
2006	0.30	30.08
2007	4.67	18.13
2008	−49.87	−36.00
2009	84.99	14.39

Source: www.finance.yahoo.com

a. Set up the hypotheses to test the claim that the mean return for the Electronic mutual fund differs from the mean return for the Utilities mutual fund.
b. Calculate the value of the test statistic and the *p*-value.
c. At the 5% significance level, do the mean returns differ?

38. **FILE** *Labor_Costs.* The labor quotation department at Excabar, a large manufacturing company, wants to verify the accuracy of their labor bidding process (estimated cost per unit versus actual cost per unit). They have randomly chosen 35 product quotations that subsequently were successful (meaning the company won the contract for the product). A portion of the data is shown in the accompanying table.

Product	Estimated	Actual
1	13.90	12.90
2	18.80	15.80
⋮	⋮	⋮
35	17.80	14.80

a. Specify the competing hypotheses to determine whether there is a difference between the estimated cost and the actual cost.
b. Calculate the value of the test statistic and the *p*-value.
c. At the 1% significance level, what is the conclusion?

39. **FILE** *Smoking_Weight.* It is fairly common for people to put on weight when they quit smoking. While a small weight gain is normal, excessive weight gain can create new health concerns that erode the benefits of not smoking. The accompanying table shows a portion of the weight data for 50 women before quitting and six months after quitting.

Weight before Quitting	Weight after Quitting
140	155
144	142
⋮	⋮
135	147

a. Construct and interpret the 95% confidence interval for the mean gain in weight.
b. Use the confidence interval to determine if the mean gain in weight differs from 5 pounds.

40. **FILE** *Shift.* When faced with a power hitter, many baseball teams utilize a defensive shift. A shift usually involves putting three infielders on one side of second base against pull hitters. Many believe that a power hitter's batting average is lower when he faces a shift defense as compared to when he faces a standard defense. Consider the following batting averages of 10 power hitters over the 2010 and 2011 seasons when they faced a shift defense versus when they faced a standard defense.

Player	Shift	Standard
Jack Cust	0.239	0.270
Adam Dunn	0.189	0.230
Prince Fielder	0.150	0.263
Adrian Gonzalez	0.186	0.251
Ryan Howard	0.177	0.317
Brian McCann	0.321	0.250
David Ortiz	0.245	0.232
Carlos Pena	0.243	0.191
Mark Teixeira	0.168	0.182
Jim Thome	0.211	0.205

Source: *The Fielding Bible-Volume III*, March 2012

a. Specify the competing hypotheses to determine whether the use of the defensive shift lowers a power hitter's batting average.
b. Calculate the value of the test statistic and the *p*-value. Assume that the batting average difference is normally distributed.
c. At the 5% significance level, is the defensive shift effective in lowering a power hitter's batting average?

10.3 INFERENCE CONCERNING THE DIFFERENCE BETWEEN TWO PROPORTIONS

LO 10.3

Make inferences about the difference between two population proportions based on independent sampling.

In the preceding two sections, we focused on quantitative data, where we compared means of two populations. Now we turn our attention to qualitative data, where we provide statistical inference concerning the difference between two population proportions. This technique has many practical applications. For instance, an investor may want to determine if the bankruptcy rate is the same in the technology and construction industries. The resulting analysis will help determine the relative risk of investing in these two industries. Or perhaps a marketing executive maintains that the proportion of women who buy a firm's product is greater than the proportion of men who buy the product. If this claim is supported by the data, it provides information as to where the firm should advertise. In another case, a consumer advocacy group may state that the proportion of young adults who carry health insurance is less than the proportion of older adults. Health and government officials might be particularly interested in this type of information. All of these examples deal with comparing two population proportions. Our parameter of interest is $p_1 - p_2$, where p_1 and p_2 denote the proportions in the first and second populations, respectively. The estimator for the difference between two population proportions is $\bar{P}_1 - \bar{P}_2$.

Confidence Interval for $p_1 - p_2$

Since the population proportions p_1 and p_2 are unknown, we estimate them by $\bar{p}_1$ and $\bar{p}_2$, respectively. The first sample proportion is computed as $\bar{p}_1 = x_1/n_1$ where x_1 denotes the number of successes in n_1 observations drawn from population 1. Similarly, $\bar{p}_2 = x_2/n_2$ is the sample proportion derived from population 2 where x_2 is the number of successes in n_2. The difference $\bar{p}_1 - \bar{p}_2$ is a point estimate of $p_1 - p_2$. Recall from Chapter 7 that the standard errors for the estimators $\bar{P}_1$ and $\bar{P}_2$ are $se(\bar{P}_1) = \sqrt{\frac{p_1(1 - p_1)}{n_1}}$ and $se(\bar{P}_2) = \sqrt{\frac{p_2(1 - p_2)}{n_2}}$, respectively. Therefore, for two independently drawn samples, the standard error, $se(\bar{P}_1 - \bar{P}_2) = \sqrt{\frac{p_1(1 - p_1)}{n_1} + \frac{p_2(1 - p_2)}{n_2}}$. Since p_1 and p_2 are unknown, we estimate the standard error by $\sqrt{\frac{\bar{p}_1(1 - \bar{p}_1)}{n_1} + \frac{\bar{p}_2(1 - \bar{p}_2)}{n_2}}$.

Finally, when both n_1 and n_2 are sufficiently large, the sampling distribution of $\bar{P}_1 - \bar{P}_2$ can be approximated by the normal distribution. We construct a confidence interval for the difference between two population proportions using the following formula.

CONFIDENCE INTERVAL FOR $p_1 - p_2$

A $100(1 - \alpha)\%$ confidence interval for the difference between two population proportions $p_1 - p_2$ is given by:

$$(\bar{p}_1 - \bar{p}_2) \pm z_{\alpha/2}\sqrt{\frac{\bar{p}_1(1 - \bar{p}_1)}{n_1} + \frac{\bar{p}_2(1 - \bar{p}_2)}{n_2}}.$$

As noted, the above formula is valid only when the two samples are sufficiently large; the general guideline is that $n_1 p_1$, $n_1(1 - p_1)$, $n_2 p_2$, and $n_2(1 - p_2)$ must all be greater than or equal to 5, where p_1 and p_2 are evaluated at $\bar{p}_1$ and $\bar{p}_2$, respectively.

EXAMPLE 10.9

Despite his inexperience, candidate A appears to have gained support among the electorate. Three months ago, in a survey of 120 registered voters, 55 said that they would vote for Candidate A. Today, 41 registered voters in a sample of 80 said that they would vote for Candidate A. Construct the 95% confidence interval for the difference between the two population proportions.

SOLUTION: Let p_1 and p_2 represent the population proportion of the electorate who support the candidate today and three months ago, respectively. In order to calculate the 95% confidence interval for $p_1 - p_2$, we use the formula $(\bar{p}_1 - \bar{p}_2) \pm z_{\alpha/2}\sqrt{\frac{\bar{p}_1(1 - \bar{p}_1)}{n_1} + \frac{\bar{p}_2(1 - \bar{p}_2)}{n_2}}$. We compute the sample proportions as

$$\bar{p}_1 = x_1/n_1 = 41/80 = 0.5125 \quad \text{and} \quad \bar{p}_2 = x_2/n_2 = 55/120 = 0.4583.$$

Note that the normality condition is satisfied because $n_1\bar{p}_1$, $n_1(1 - \bar{p}_1)$, $n_2\bar{p}_2$, and $n_2(1 - \bar{p}_2)$ all exceed 5. For the 95% confidence interval, we use the z table to find $z_{\alpha/2} = z_{0.05/2} = z_{0.025} = 1.96$. Substituting the values into the formula, we find

$$(0.5125 - 0.4583) \pm 1.96\sqrt{\frac{0.5125(1 - 0.5125)}{80} + \frac{0.4583(1 - 0.4583)}{120}}$$

$$= 0.0542 \pm 0.1412 \text{ or } [-0.0870, 0.1954].$$

With 95% confidence, we can report that the percentage change of support for the candidate is between −8.70% and 19.54%.

Hypothesis Test for $p_1 - p_2$

The null and alternative hypotheses for testing the difference between two population proportions under independent sampling will take one of the following forms:

Two-Tailed Test	Right-Tailed Test	Left-Tailed Test
$H_0: p_1 - p_2 = d_0$	$H_0: p_1 - p_2 \leq d_0$	$H_0: p_1 - p_2 \geq d_0$
$H_A: p_1 - p_2 \neq d_0$	$H_A: p_1 - p_2 > d_0$	$H_A: p_1 - p_2 < d_0$

We use the symbol d_0 to denote a given hypothesized difference between the unknown population proportions p_1 and p_2. In most cases, d_0 is set to zero. For example, when testing if the population proportions differ—that is, if $p_1 \neq p_2$—we use a two-tailed test, with the competing hypotheses defined as $H_0: p_1 - p_2 = 0$ versus $H_A: p_1 - p_2 \neq 0$. If, on the other hand, we wish to determine whether or not the proportions differ by some amount, say 0.20, we set $d_0 = 0.20$ and define the competing hypotheses as $H_0: p_1 - p_2 = 0.20$ versus $H_A: p_1 - p_2 \neq 0.20$. One-tailed tests are defined similarly.

EXAMPLE 10.10

Let's revisit Example 10.9. Specify the competing hypotheses in order to determine whether the proportion of those who favor Candidate A has changed over the three-month period. Using the 95% confidence interval, what is the conclusion to the test? Explain.

SOLUTION: In essence, we would like to determine whether $p_1 \neq p_2$, where p_1 and p_2 represent the population proportion of the electorate who support the candidate today and three months ago, respectively. We formulate the competing hypotheses as

$$H_0: p_1 - p_2 = 0$$

$$H_A: p_1 - p_2 \neq 0$$

In the previous example, we constructed the 95% confidence interval for the difference between the population proportions as $[-0.0870, 0.1954]$. We note that the interval contains zero, the value hypothesized under the null hypothesis. Therefore, we are unable to reject the null hypothesis. In other words, from the given sample data, we cannot conclude at the 5% significance level that the support for candidate A has changed.

We now introduce the standard four-step procedure for conducting one- or two-tailed hypothesis tests concerning the difference between two proportions $p_1 - p_2$. We transform its estimate $\bar{P}_1 - \bar{P}_2$ into a corresponding z statistic by subtracting the hypothesized difference d_0 from this estimate and dividing by the standard error of the estimator $se(\bar{P}_1 - \bar{P}_2)$. When we developed the confidence interval for $p_1 - p_2$, we assumed $se(\bar{P}_1 - \bar{P}_2) = \sqrt{\frac{\bar{p}_1(1 - \bar{p}_1)}{n_1} + \frac{\bar{p}_2(1 - \bar{p}_2)}{n_2}}$. However, if d_0 is zero—that is, $H_0: p_1 = p_2$—both $\bar{p}_1$ and $\bar{p}_2$ are essentially the estimates of the same unknown population proportion. For this reason, the standard error can be improved upon by computing the pooled estimate $\bar{p} = (x_1 + x_2)/(n_1 + n_2)$ for the unknown population proportion, which is now based on a larger sample.

TEST STATISTIC FOR TESTING $p_1 - p_2$

The value of the test statistic for a hypothesis test concerning the difference between two proportions $p_1 - p_2$ is computed using one of the following two formulas:

1. If the hypothesized difference d_0 is zero, then the value of the test statistic is

$$z = \frac{\bar{p}_1 - \bar{p}_2}{\sqrt{\bar{p}(1 - \bar{p})\left(\dfrac{1}{n_1} + \dfrac{1}{n_2}\right)}},$$

where $\bar{p}_1 = \frac{x_1}{n_1}$, $\bar{p}_2 = \frac{x_2}{n_2}$, and $\bar{p} = \frac{x_1 + x_2}{n_1 + n_2}$.

2. If the hypothesized difference d_0 is not zero, then the value of the test statistic is

$$z = \frac{(\bar{p}_1 - \bar{p}_2) - d_0}{\sqrt{\dfrac{\bar{p}_1(1 - \bar{p}_1)}{n_1} + \dfrac{\bar{p}_2(1 - \bar{p}_2)}{n_2}}}.$$

As in the case of the confidence interval, the above formulas are valid only when the two samples are sufficiently large.

EXAMPLE 10.11

Research by analysts and retailers claims gender differences when it comes to online shopping (*The Wall Street Journal*, March 13, 2008). A survey revealed that 5,400 of 6,000 men said they "regularly" or "occasionally" make purchases online, compared with 8,600 of 10,000 women surveyed. At the 5% significance level, test whether the proportion of all men who regularly or occasionally make purchases online is greater than the proportion of all women.

SOLUTION: Let p_1 and p_2 denote the population proportions of men and of women who make online purchases, respectively. We wish to test whether the proportion of men who make purchases online is greater than the proportion of women; that is, $p_1 - p_2 > 0$. Therefore, we construct the competing hypotheses as

$$H_0: p_1 - p_2 \leq 0$$
$$H_A: p_1 - p_2 > 0$$

Since the hypothesized difference is zero, or $d_0 = 0$, we compute the value of the test statistic as $z = \dfrac{\bar{p}_1 - \bar{p}_2}{\sqrt{\bar{p}(1 - \bar{p})\left(\frac{1}{n_1} + \frac{1}{n_2}\right)}}$. We first compute the sample proportions $\bar{p}_1 = x_1/n_1 = 5{,}400/6{,}000 = 0.90$ and $\bar{p}_2 = x_2/n_2 = 8{,}600/10{,}000 = 0.86$. The normality condition is satisfied since $n_1\bar{p}_1$, $n_1(1 - \bar{p}_1)$, $n_2\bar{p}_2$, and $n_2(1 - \bar{p}_2)$ all exceed 5. Next we calculate $\bar{p} = \frac{x_1 + x_2}{n_1 + n_2} = \frac{5{,}400\ +\ 8{,}600}{6{,}000\ +\ 10{,}000} = 0.875$. Thus,

$$z = \frac{(0.90 - 0.86)}{\sqrt{0.875(1 - 0.875)\left(\dfrac{1}{6{,}000} + \dfrac{1}{10{,}000}\right)}} = 7.41.$$

The p-value, computed as $P(Z \geq 7.41)$, is approximately zero. Since the p-value $< \alpha = 0.05$, we reject H_0. At the 5% significance level, we conclude that the proportion of men who shop online either regularly or occasionally is greater than the proportion of women. Our results are consistent with the recent decision by so many retailers to redesign their websites to attract male customers.

EXAMPLE 10.12

While we expect relatively expensive wines to have more desirable characteristics than relatively inexpensive wines, people are often confused in their assessment of the quality of wine in a blind test (*The Telegraph*, April 30, 2015). In a recent experiment at a local winery, the same wine is served to two groups of people but with different price information. In the first group, 60 people are told that they are tasting a $25 wine, of which 48 like the wine. In the second group, only 20 of 50 people like the wine when they are told that it is a $10 wine. The experiment is conducted to determine if the proportion of people who like the wine in the first group is more than 20 percentage points higher than in the second group. Conduct this test at the 5% significance level.

SOLUTION: Let p_1 and p_2 denote the proportions of people who like the wine in groups 1 and 2, respectively. We want to test if the proportion of people who like the wine in the first group is more than 20 percentage points higher than in the second group. Thus, we construct the competing hypotheses as

$$H_0: p_1 - p_2 \leq 0.20$$
$$H_A: p_1 - p_2 > 0.20$$

We first compute the sample proportions as $\bar{p}_1 = x_1/n_1 = 48/60 = 0.80$ and $\bar{p}_2 = x_2/n_2 = 20/50 = 0.40$ and note that the normality condition is satisfied since $n_1\bar{p}_1$, $n_1(1 - \bar{p}_1)$, $n_2\bar{p}_2$, and $n_2(1 - \bar{p}_2)$ all exceed 5.

Since $d_0 = 0.20$, the value of the test statistic is computed as

$$z = \frac{(\bar{p}_1 - \bar{p}_2) - d_0}{\sqrt{\dfrac{\bar{p}_1(1 - \bar{p}_1)}{n_1} + \dfrac{\bar{p}_2(1 - \bar{p}_2)}{n_2}}} = \frac{(0.80 - 0.40) - 0.20}{\sqrt{\dfrac{0.80(1 - 0.80)}{60} + \dfrac{0.40(1 - 0.40)}{50}}} = 2.31.$$

For this right-tailed test, we compute the p-value as $P(Z \geq 2.31) = 0.0104$. Since the p-value $< \alpha = 0.05$, we reject the null hypothesis. At the 5% significance level, we conclude that the proportion of people who like the wine in the first group is more than 20 percentage points higher than in the second group. Overall, this result is consistent with scientific research, which has demonstrated the power of suggestion in wine tasting.

EXERCISES 10.3

Mechanics

41. Given $\bar{p}_1 = 0.85$, $n_1 = 400$, $\bar{p}_2 = 0.90$, $n_2 = 350$, construct the 90% confidence interval for the difference between the population proportions. Is there a difference between the population proportions at the 10% significance level? Explain.

42. Given $x_1 = 50$, $n_1 = 200$, $x_2 = 70$, $n_2 = 250$, construct the 95% confidence interval for the difference between the population proportions. Is there a difference between the population proportions at the 5% significance level? Explain.

43. Consider the following competing hypotheses and accompanying sample data.

$$H_0: p_1 - p_2 \geq 0$$
$$H_A: p_1 - p_2 < 0$$

$x_1 = 250$	$x_2 = 275$
$n_1 = 400$	$n_2 = 400$

a. Calculate the value of the test statistic.
b. Find the p-value.
c. At the 5% significance level, what is the conclusion to the test? Is p_1 less than p_2?

44. Consider the following competing hypotheses and accompanying sample data.

$$H_0: p_1 - p_2 = 0$$
$$H_A: p_1 - p_2 \neq 0$$

$x_1 = 100$	$x_2 = 172$
$n_1 = 250$	$n_2 = 400$

a. Calculate the value of the test statistic.
b. Find the p-value.
c. At the 5% significance level, what is the conclusion to the test? Do the population proportions differ?

45. Consider the following competing hypotheses and accompanying sample data.

$$H_0: p_1 - p_2 = 0$$
$$H_A: p_1 - p_2 \neq 0$$

$x_1 = 300$	$x_2 = 325$
$n_1 = 600$	$n_2 = 500$

a. Calculate the value of the test statistic.
b. Find the p-value.
c. At the 5% significance level, what is the conclusion to the test? Do the population proportions differ?

46. Consider the following competing hypotheses and accompanying sample data.

$$H_0: p_1 - p_2 = 0.20$$
$$H_A: p_1 - p_2 \neq 0.20$$

$x_1 = 150$	$x_2 = 130$
$n_1 = 250$	$n_2 = 400$

a. Calculate the value of the test statistic.

b. Find the p-value.
c. At the 5% significance level, what is the conclusion to the test? Can you conclude that the difference between the population proportions differs from 0.20?

Applications

47. A study claims that girls and boys do not do equally well on math tests taken from the 2nd to 11th grades (*Chicago Tribune*, July 25, 2008). Suppose in a representative sample, 344 of 430 girls and 369 of 450 boys score at proficient or advanced levels on a standardized math test.
    a. Construct the 95% confidence interval for the difference between the population proportions of girls and boys who score at proficient or advanced levels.
    b. Develop the appropriate null and alternative hypotheses to test whether the proportion of girls who score at proficient or advanced levels differs from the proportion of boys.
    c. At the 5% significance level, what is the conclusion to the test? Do the results support the study's claim?

48. Reducing scrap of 4-foot planks of hardwood is an important factor in reducing cost at a wood-flooring manufacturing company. Accordingly, engineers at Lumberworks are investigating a potential new cutting method involving lateral sawing that may reduce the scrap rate. To examine its viability, samples of planks were examined under the old and new methods. Sixty-two of the 500 planks were scrapped under the old method, whereas 36 of the 400 planks were scrapped under the new method.
    a. Construct the 95% confidence interval for the difference between the population scrap rates between the old and new methods.
    b. Specify the null and alternative hypotheses to test for differences in the population scrap rates between the old and new cutting methods.
    c. Using the results from part (a), can we conclude at the 5% significance level that the scrap rate of the new method is different than the old method?

49. According to the Pew report, 14.6% of newly married couples in 2008 reported that their spouse was of another race or ethnicity (*CNNLiving*, June 7, 2010). In a similar survey in 1980, only 6.8% of newlywed couples reported marrying outside their race or ethnicity. Suppose both of these surveys were conducted on 500 newly married couples.
    a. Specify the competing hypotheses to test the claim that there is an increase in the proportion of people who marry outside their race or ethnicity.
    b. Calculate the value of the test statistic and the p-value.
    c. At the 5% level of significance, what is the conclusion to the test?

50. Research by Harvard Medical School experts suggests that boys are more likely than girls to grow out of childhood asthma when they hit their teenage years (*BBC News*, August 15, 2008). Scientists followed over 1,000 children between the ages of 5 and 12, all of whom had mild to moderate asthma. By the age of 18, 27% of the boys and 14% of the girls had grown out of asthma. Suppose the analysis was based on 500 boys and 500 girls.

a. Develop the hypotheses to test whether the proportion of boys who grow out of asthma in their teenage years is more than that of girls.

b. Test the assertion in part (a) at the 5% significance level.

c. A medical researcher has asserted that the proportion of boys who grow out of asthma in their teenage years is more than 0.10 than that of girls. Test this assertion at the 5% significance level.

51. More people are using social media to network, rather than phone calls or e-mails (U.S. *News & World Report,* October 20, 2010). From an employment perspective, jobseekers are no longer calling up friends for help with job placement, as they can now get help online. In a recent survey of 150 jobseekers, 67 said they used LinkedIn to search for jobs. A similar survey of 140 jobseekers, conducted three years ago, had found that 58 jobseekers had used LinkedIn for their job search. Is there sufficient evidence to suggest that more people are now using LinkedIn to search for jobs as compared to three years ago? Use a 5% level of significance for the analysis.

52. The director of housekeeping at *Elegante*, a luxury resort hotel with two locations (*Seaside* and *Oceanfront*), wants to evaluate housekeeping performance at those two locations. Random samples of 100 rooms were inspected at each location for defects (e.g., missing towels, missing soap, dirty floors or showers, dusty tables) after being cleaned. It was found that 21 of the rooms at *Seaside* had some housekeeping defect(s), and 28 rooms at *Oceanfront* had some housekeeping defect(s).

a. Develop the hypotheses to test whether the proportion of housekeeping defects differs between the two hotel locations.

b. Calculate the value of the test statistic and the *p*-value.

c. Do the results suggest that the proportion of housekeeping defects differs between the two hotel locations at the 5% significance level?

d. Construct the 95% confidence interval for the difference between the population housekeeping defect rates at the two hotel locations. How can this confidence interval be used to reach the same conclusion as in part (c)?

53. In an effort to make children's toys safer and more tamperproof, toy packaging has become cumbersome for parents to remove in many cases. Accordingly, the director of marketing at Toys4Tots, a large toy manufacturer, wants to evaluate the effectiveness of a new packaging design that engineers claim will reduce customer complaints by more than 10 percentage points. Customer satisfaction surveys were sent to 250 parents who registered toys packaged under the old design and 250 parents who registered toys packaged under the new design. Of these, 85 parents expressed dissatisfaction with packaging of the old design, and 40 parents expressed dissatisfaction with packaging of the new design.

a. Specify the null and alternative hypotheses to test whether customer complaints have been reduced by more than 10 percentage points under the new packaging design.

b. Calculate the value of the test statistic and the *p*-value.

c. At the 5% significance level, do the results support the engineers' claim?

d. At the 1% significance level, do the results support the engineers' claim?

54. According to a report, 32.2% of American adults are obese (*The New York Times*, August 15, 2008). Among ethnic groups in general, African American women are more overweight than Caucasian women, but African American men are less obese than Caucasian men. Sarah Weber, a recent college graduate, is curious to determine if the same pattern also exists in her hometown on the West Coast. She randomly selects 220 African American adults and 300 Caucasian adults for the analysis. The following table contains the sample information.

Race	Gender	Obese	Not Obese
African Americans	Males	36	94
	Females	35	55
Caucasians	Males	62	118
	Females	31	89

a. Test if the proportion of obese African American men is less than the proportion of obese Caucasian men at $\alpha = 0.05$.

b. Test if the proportion of obese African American women is more than the proportion of obese Caucasian women at $\alpha = 0.05$.

c. Test if the proportion of obese African American adults differs from the proportion of obese Caucasian adults at the 5% significance level.

55. Only 26% of psychology majors are satisfied with their career paths as compared to 50% of accounting majors (*The Wall Street Journal*, October 11, 2010). Suppose these results were obtained from a survey of 300 psychology majors and 350 accounting majors.

a. Develop the null and alternative hypotheses to test whether the proportion of accounting majors satisfied with their career paths is higher than that of psychology majors by more than 20 percentage points.

b. Calculate the value of the test statistic and the *p*-value.

c. At the 5% significance level, what is the conclusion?

56. Due to late delivery problems with an existing supplier, the director of procurement at ElectroTech began to place orders for electrical switches with a new supplier as part of a "dual-source" (two-supplier) strategy. Now she wants to revert to a "single-source" (i.e., one supplier) strategy to simplify purchasing activities. She wishes to conduct a test to infer whether the new supplier will continue to outperform the old supplier. Based on recent sample data, she found that 27 of 150 orders placed with the old supplier arrived late, whereas 6 of 75 orders placed with the new supplier arrived late.

    a. Specify the null and alternative hypotheses to test for whether the proportion of late deliveries with the new supplier is less than that of the old supplier.

    b. Calculate the value of the test statistic and the *p*-value.

    c. At the 5% significance level, what is the conclusion?

57. A report suggests that business majors spend the least amount of time on course work than all other college students (*The New York Times*, November 17, 2011). A provost of a university decides to conduct a survey where students are asked if they study hard, defined as spending at least 20 hours per week on course work. Of 120 business majors included in the survey, 20 said that they studied hard, as compared to 48 out of 150 nonbusiness majors who said that they studied hard. At the 5% significance level, can we conclude that the proportion of business majors who study hard is less than that of nonmajors? Provide the details.

58. It has generally been believed that it is not feasible for men and women to be just friends (*The New York Times*, April 12, 2012). Others argue that this belief may not be true anymore since gone are the days when men worked and women stayed at home and the only way they could get together was for romance. In a recent survey, 200 heterosexual college students were asked if it was feasible for male and female students to be just friends. Thirty-two percent of females and 57% of males reported that it was not feasible for men and women to be just friends. Suppose the study consisted of 100 female and 100 male students. At the 5% significance level, can we conclude that there is a greater than 10 percentage point difference between the proportion of male and female students with this view? Provide the details.

WRITING WITH STATISTICS

The recent phenomenon of online dating has made it as likely for would-be couples to meet via e-mail or other virtual matchmaking services as through friends and family (*CNN*, February 6, 2012). Studies that have looked at gender differences in mate selection have found that women put greater emphasis on the race and financial stability of a partner, while men mostly look for physical attractiveness. Recent survey results reported in *USA Today* (February 2, 2012) showed that 13% of women and 8% of men want their partner to be of the same ethnic background. The same survey also reported that 36% of women and 13% of men would like to meet someone who makes as much money as they do.

©JGI/Blend Images LLC RF

Anka Wilder, working for a small matchmaking service in Cincinnati, Ohio, wants to know if a similar pattern also exists with her customers. She has access to the preferences of 160 women and 120 men customers. In this sample, she finds that 28 women and 12 men customers want their partner to be of the same ethnicity. Also, 50 women and 10 men want their partner to make as much money as they do.

Anka wants to use this sample information to:

1. Determine whether the proportion of women who want their partner to be of the same ethnic background is greater than that of men.

2. Determine whether the proportion of women who want their partner to make as much money as they do is more than 20 percentage points greater than that of men.

©Stock4B-RF/Getty Images RF

With the advent of the Internet, there has been a surge in online dating services that connect individuals with similar interests, religions, and cultural backgrounds for personal relationships. In 1992, when the Internet was still in its infancy, less than 1% of Americans met their partners through online dating services. By 2009, about 22% of heterosexual couples and 61% of same-sex couples reported meeting online (CNN, February 6, 2012). A recent

Sample Report— Online Dating Preferences

survey suggested that a higher proportion of women than men would like to meet someone with a similar ethnic background. Also, the difference between the proportion of women and men who would like to meet someone who makes as much money as they do is greater than 20%.

A couple of hypothesis tests were performed to determine if similar gender differences existed for online dating customers in Cincinnati, Ohio. The sample consisted of responses from 160 women and 120 men. The summary of the test results is presented in Table 10.A.

TABLE 10.A Test Statistics and p-values for Hypothesis Tests

Hypotheses	Test Statistic	p-value
$H_0: p_1 - p_2 \leq 0$ $H_A: p_1 - p_2 > 0$	$z = \dfrac{0.175 - 0.10}{\sqrt{0.1429(1 - 0.1429)\left(\dfrac{1}{160} + \dfrac{1}{120}\right)}} = 1.77$	0.0384
$H_0: p_1 - p_2 \leq 0.20$ $H_A: p_1 - p_2 > 0.20$	$z = \dfrac{0.3125 - 0.0833 - 0.20}{\sqrt{\dfrac{0.3125(1 - 0.3125)}{160} + \dfrac{0.0833(1 - 0.0833)}{120}}} = 0.66$	0.2546

First, it was tested if the proportion of women, denoted p_1, who want their partner to be of the same ethnicity is greater than that of men, denoted p_2. It was found that 28 out of 160 women valued this trait, yielding a sample proportion of $\bar{p}_1 = 28/160 = 0.175$; a similar proportion for men was calculated as $\bar{p}_2 = 12/120 = 0.10$. The first row of Table 10.A shows the competing hypotheses, the value of the test statistic, and the p-value for this test. At the 5% significance level, the proportion of women who want the same ethnicity was greater than that of men. In the second test, p_1 and p_2 denoted the proportion of women and men, respectively, who would like their partner to make as much money as they do; here $\bar{p}_1 = 50/160 = 0.3125$ and $\bar{p}_2 = 10/120 = 0.0833$. The second row of Table 10.A shows the competing hypotheses, the value of the test statistic, and the p-value for this test. At the 5% significance level, the proportion of women who want their partner to make as much income as they do is not more than 20 percentage points greater than that of men. Online dating is a relatively new market and any such information is important for individuals looking for relationships as well as for service providers.

CONCEPTUAL REVIEW

LO 10.1 **Make inferences about the difference between two population means based on independent sampling.**

Independent samples are samples that are completely unrelated to one another. A $100(1 - \alpha)\%$ confidence interval for the difference between two population means $\mu_1 - \mu_2$, based on independent samples, is

- $(\bar{x}_1 - \bar{x}_2) \pm z_{\alpha/2}\sqrt{\dfrac{\sigma_1^2}{n_1} + \dfrac{\sigma_2^2}{n_2}}$, if σ_1^2 and σ_2^2 are known.

- $(\bar{x}_1 - \bar{x}_2) \pm t_{\alpha/2,df}\sqrt{s_p^2\left(\dfrac{1}{n_1} + \dfrac{1}{n_2}\right)}$, if σ_1^2 and σ_2^2 are unknown but assumed equal.

  The pooled sample variance is $s_p^2 = \dfrac{(n_1 - 1)s_1^2 + (n_2 - 1)s_2^2}{n_1 + n_2 - 2}$, and $df = n_1 + n_2 - 2$.

- $(\bar{x}_1 - \bar{x}_2) \pm t_{\alpha/2,df} \sqrt{\left(\frac{s_1^2}{n_1} + \frac{s_2^2}{n_2}\right)}$, if σ_1^2 and σ_2^2 are unknown and cannot be assumed equal. The degrees of freedom is calculated as $df = \frac{(s_1^2/n_1 + s_2^2/n_2)^2}{(s_1^2/n_1)^2/(n_1-1) + (s_2^2/n_2)^2/(n_2-1)}$.

When conducting hypothesis tests about the difference between two means $\mu_1 - \mu_2$, based on independent samples, the value of the test statistic is

- $z = \dfrac{(\bar{x}_1 - \bar{x}_2) - d_0}{\sqrt{\frac{\sigma_1^2}{n_1} + \frac{\sigma_2^2}{n_2}}}$, if σ_1^2 and σ_2^2 are known.

- $t_{df} = \dfrac{(\bar{x}_1 - \bar{x}_2) - d_0}{\sqrt{s_p^2\left(\frac{1}{n_1} + \frac{1}{n_2}\right)}}$, if σ_1^2 and σ_2^2 are unknown but assumed equal.

- $t_{df} = \dfrac{(\bar{x}_1 - \bar{x}_2) - d_0}{\sqrt{\left(\frac{s_1^2}{n_1} + \frac{s_2^2}{n_2}\right)}}$, if σ_1^2 and σ_2^2 are unknown and cannot be assumed equal.

Here, d_0 is the hypothesized difference between μ_1 and μ_2 and the degrees of freedom for the last two tests are the same as the ones defined for the corresponding confidence intervals. The formulas for estimation and testing are valid only if $\bar{X}_1 - \bar{X}_2$ (approximately) follows a normal distribution.

LO 10.2 Make inferences about the mean difference based on matched-pairs sampling.

A common case of dependent sampling, commonly referred to as **matched-pairs sampling**, is when the samples are paired or matched in some way.

For matched-pairs sampling, the population parameter of interest is referred to as the mean difference μ_D where $D = X_1 - X_2$, and the random variables X_1 and X_2 are matched in a pair. A $100(1 - \alpha)\%$ confidence interval for the mean difference μ_D, based on a matched-pairs sample, is given by $\bar{d} \pm t_{\alpha/2,df} s_D/\sqrt{n}$, where $\bar{d}$ and s_D are the mean and the standard deviation, respectively, of D, and $df = n - 1$. When conducting a hypothesis test about μ_D the value of the test statistic is calculated as $t_{df} = \frac{\bar{d} - d_0}{s_D/\sqrt{n}}$, where d_0 is a hypothesized mean difference and $df = n - 1$.

LO 10.3 Make inferences about the difference between two population proportions based on independent sampling.

A $100(1 - \alpha)\%$ confidence interval for the difference between two population proportions $p_1 - p_2$ is given by $(\bar{p}_1 - \bar{p}_2) \pm z_{\alpha/2}\sqrt{\frac{\bar{p}_1(1 - \bar{p}_1)}{n_1} + \frac{\bar{p}_2(1 - \bar{p}_2)}{n_2}}$. When conducting hypothesis tests about the difference between two proportions $p_1 - p_2$, the value of the test statistic is calculated as

- $z = \dfrac{\bar{p}_1 - \bar{p}_2}{\sqrt{\bar{p}(1 - \bar{p})\left(\frac{1}{n_1} + \frac{1}{n_2}\right)}}$, if the hypothesized difference d_0 between p_1 and p_2 is zero. The pooled sample proportion is $\bar{p} = \frac{x_1 + x_2}{n_1 + n_2}$.

- $z = \dfrac{(\bar{p}_1 - \bar{p}_2) - d_0}{\sqrt{\frac{\bar{p}_1(1 - \bar{p}_1)}{n_1} + \frac{\bar{p}_2(1 - \bar{p}_2)}{n_2}}}$, if the hypothesized difference d_0 between p_1 and p_2 is not zero.

ADDITIONAL EXERCISES AND CASE STUDIES

Exercises

59. A study has found that, on average, 6- to 12-year-old children are spending less time on household chores today compared to 1981 levels (*The Wall Street Journal*, August 27, 2008). Suppose two samples representative of the study's results report the following summary statistics for the two periods:

1981 Levels	2008 Levels
$\bar{x}_1 = 30$ minutes	$\bar{x}_2 = 24$ minutes
$s_1 = 4.2$ minutes	$s_1 = 3.9$ minutes
$n_1 = 30$	$n_2 = 30$

   a. Specify the competing hypotheses to test the study's claim that children today spend less time on household chores as compared to children in 1981.
   b. Calculate the value of the test statistic assuming that the unknown population variances are equal.
   c. Find the *p*-value.
   d. At the 5% significance level, do the data support the study's claim? Explain.

60. Do men really spend more money on St. Patrick's Day as compared to women? A survey found that men spend an average of $43.87 while women spend an average of $29.54 (*USA Today*, March 17, 2009). Assume that these data were based on a sample of 100 men and 100 women and the population standard deviations of spending for men and women are $32 and $25, respectively.
   a. Specify the competing hypotheses to determine whether men spend more money on St. Patrick's Day as compared to women.
   b. Calculate the value of the test statistic.
   c. Find the *p*-value.
   d. At the 1% significance level, do men spend more money on St. Patrick's Day as compared to women? Explain.

61. **FILE** *Balanced_European.* The accompanying table shows annual return data from 2001–2009 for Vanguard's Balanced Index and European Stock Index mutual funds.

Year	Balanced	European Stock
2001	−3.02	−20.30
2002	−9.52	−17.95
2003	19.87	38.70
2004	9.33	20.86
2005	4.65	9.26
2006	11.02	33.42
2007	6.16	13.82
2008	−22.21	−44.73
2009	20.05	31.91

Source: www.finance.yahoo.com

   a. Set up the hypotheses to test whether the mean returns of the two funds differ. (*Hint*: This is a matched-pairs comparison.)
   b. Calculate the value of the test statistic and the *p*-value. Assume that the return difference is normally distributed.
   c. At the 5% significance level, what is the conclusion?

62. **FILE** *Cholesterol_Levels.* It is well documented that cholesterol over 200 is a risk factor in developing heart disease for both men and women (www.livestrong.com, January 11, 2011). Younger men are known to have higher cholesterol levels than younger women; however, beyond age 55, women are more likely to have higher cholesterol levels. A recent college graduate working at a local blood lab has access to the cholesterol data of 50 men and 50 women in the 20–40 age group. The accompanying table shows a portion of the data.

Men	Women
181	178
199	193
⋮	⋮
190	182

At the 1% significance level, determine if there are any differences in the mean cholesterol levels for men and women in the age group. It is fair to assume that the population variances for men and women are equal.

63. A farmer is concerned that a change in fertilizer to an organic variant might change his crop yield. He subdivides 6 lots and uses the old fertilizer on one half of each lot and the new fertilizer on the other half. The following table shows the results.

Lot	Crop Yield Using Old Fertilizer	Crop Yield Using New Fertilizer
1	10	12
2	11	10
3	10	13
4	9	9
5	12	11
6	11	12

a. Specify the competing hypotheses that determine whether there is any difference between the average crop yields from the use of the different fertilizers.
b. Assuming that differences in crop yields are normally distributed, calculate the value of the test statistic.
c. Find the p-value.
d. Is there sufficient evidence to conclude that the crop yields are different? Should the farmer be concerned?

64. **FILE** *Pregnancy_Weight.* It is important for women to gain the right amount of weight during pregnancy by eating a healthy, balanced diet. It is recommended that a woman of average weight before pregnancy should gain 25 to 35 pounds during pregnancy (www.babycenter.com, August 2016). The accompanying table shows a portion of the weight data for 40 women before and after pregnancy.

Weight before Pregnancy	Weight after Pregnancy
114	168
107	161
⋮	⋮
136	157

a. At the 5% level of significance, determine if the mean weight gain of women due to pregnancy is more than 30 pounds.
b. At the 5% level of significance, determine if the mean weight gain of women due to pregnancy is more than 35 pounds.

65. A Health of Boston report suggests that 14% of female residents suffer from asthma as opposed to 6% of males (*The Boston Globe*, August 16, 2010). Suppose 250 females and 200 males responded to the study.

a. Develop the appropriate null and alternative hypotheses to test whether the proportion of females suffering from asthma is greater than the proportion of males.
b. Calculate the value of the test statistic and the p-value.
c. At the 5% significance level, what is the conclusion? Do the data suggest that females suffer more from asthma than males?

66. Depression engulfs millions of Americans every day. A federal study reported that 10.9% of adults aged 18–24 identified with some level of depression versus 6.8% of adults aged 65 or older (*The Boston Globe*, October 18, 2010). Suppose 1,000 young adults (18–24 years old) and 1,000 older adults (65 years old and older) responded to the study.

a. Develop the appropriate null and alternative hypotheses to test whether the proportion of young adults suffering from depression is greater than the proportion of older adults suffering from depression.
b. Calculate the value of the test statistic and the p-value.
c. At the 5% significance level, do the sample data suggest that young adults suffer more from depression than older adults?

67. **FILE** *SAT_Writing.* The SAT is required of most students applying for college admission in the United States. This standardized test has gone through many revisions over the years. In 2005, a new writing section was introduced that includes a direct writing measure in the form of an essay. People argue that female students generally do worse on math tests but better on writing tests. Therefore, the new section may help reduce the usual male lead on the overall average SAT score (*The Washington Post,* August 30, 2006). Consider the following scores on the writing component of the test of eight male and eight female students.

Males	620	570	540	580	590	580	480	620
Females	660	590	540	560	610	590	610	650

a. Construct the null and the alternative hypotheses to test if females outscore males on writing tests.

b. Assuming that the difference in scores is normally distributed, calculate the value of the test statistic and the p-value. Do not assume that the population variances are equal.

c. Implement the test at $\alpha = 0.01$ and interpret your results.

68. Fresh numbers from the U.S. Department of Transportation suggest that fewer flights in the United States arrive on time than before. The explanations offered for the lackluster performance are understaffed airlines, a high volume of travelers, and overtaxed air traffic control. A transportation analyst is interested in comparing the performance at two major international airports, namely Kennedy International (JFK) in New York and O'Hare International in Chicago. She finds that 70% of the flights were on time at JFK compared with 63% at O'Hare. Suppose these proportions were based on 200 flights at each of these two airports. The analyst believes that the proportion of on-time flights at JFK is more than 5 percentage points higher than that of O'Hare.

a. Develop the competing hypotheses to test the transportation analyst's belief.

b. Calculate the value of the test statistic and the p-value.

c. At the 5% significance level, do the data support the transportation analyst's belief? Explain.

69. **FILE** *Safety_Program.* An engineer wants to determine the effectiveness of a safety program. He collects annual loss of hours due to accidents in 12 plants before and after the program was put into operation.

Plant	Before	After	Plant	Before	After
1	100	98	7	88	90
2	90	88	8	75	70
3	94	90	9	65	62
4	85	86	10	58	60
5	70	67	11	67	60
6	83	80	12	104	98

a. Specify the competing hypotheses that determine whether the safety program was effective.

b. Calculate the value of the test statistic and the p-value. Assume that the hours difference is normally distributed.

c. At the 5% significance level, is there sufficient evidence to conclude that the safety program was effective? Explain.

CASE STUDIES

CASE STUDY 10.1   Chad Perrone is a financial analyst in Boston studying the annual return data for the health and information technology industries. He randomly samples 20 firms in each industry and notes each firm's annual return. A portion of the data is shown in the accompanying table.

FILE
Health_Info

Data for Case Study 10.1   Annual Returns (in percent) for Firms in Health and Information Technology Industries

Health	Information Technology
10.29	4.77
32.17	1.14
⋮	⋮
13.21	22.61

In a report, use the sample information to

1. Provide descriptive statistics and comment on the reward and risk in each industry.

2. Determine whether the average returns in each industry differ at the 5% significance level. Assume that the population variances are not equal.

CASE STUDY 10.2 The Speedo LZR Racer Suit is a high-end, body-length swimsuit that was launched on February 13, 2008. When 17 world records fell at the December 2008 European Short Course Championships in Croatia, many believed a modification in the rules surrounding swimsuits was necessary. The FINA Congress, the international governing board for swimming, banned the LZR Racer and all other body-length swimsuits from competition, effective January 2010. In a statement to the public, FINA defended its position with the following statement: "FINA wishes to recall the main and core principle that swimming is a sport essentially based on the physical performance of the athlete" (*BBC Sport*, March 14, 2009).

Luke Johnson, a freelance journalist, wonders if the decision made by FINA has statistical backing. He conducts an experiment with the local university's Division I swim team. He times 10 of the swimmers swimming the 50-meter breaststroke in his/her bathing suit and then retests them while wearing the LZR Racer. A portion of the results is shown in the accompanying table.

Data for Case Study 10.2 50-Meter Breaststroke Times (in seconds)

LZR_Racer

Swimmer	Time in Bathing Suit	Time in LZR Racer
1	27.64	27.45
2	27.97	28.06
⋮	⋮	⋮
10	38.08	37.93

In a report, use the sample information to

1. Determine whether the LZR Racer improves swimmers' times at the 5% significance level. Assume that the time difference is normally distributed.

2. Comment on whether the data appear to support FINA's decision.

CASE STUDY 10.3 Paige Thomsen is about to graduate from college at a local university in San Francisco. Her options are to look for a job in San Francisco or go home to Denver and search for work there. Recent data report that average starting salaries for college graduates is $48,900 in San Francisco and $40,900 in Denver (*Forbes*, June 26, 2008). Suppose these data were based on 100 recent graduates in each city where the population standard deviation is $16,000 in San Francisco and $14,500 in Denver. For social reasons, Paige is also interested in the percent of the population who are in their twenties. The same report states that 20% of the population are in their twenties in San Francisco; the corresponding percentage in Denver is 22%.

In a report, use the sample information to

1. Determine whether the average starting salary in San Francisco is greater than Denver's average starting salary at the 5% significance level.

2. Determine whether the proportion of the population in their twenties differs in these two cities at the 5% significance level.

The following section provides brief commands for specific software packages: Minitab, SPSS, and JMP. All three packages have an option to perform a paired-comparisons test. However, it is also possible to conduct this test by finding the differences between the paired items and then using the one-sample *t*-test discussed in Chapter 9.

Copy and paste the specified data file into the relevant software spreadsheet prior to following the commands.

Minitab

Testing $\mu_1 - \mu_2$

Gold_Oil

A. (Replicating Example 10.4) From the menu, choose **Stat > Basic Statistics > 2-Sample t**. Choose **Each sample is in its own column**, and after **Sample 1**, select Gold and after **Sample 2**, select Oil.

B. Choose **Options**. After **Alternative hypothesis**, select "Difference ≠ hypothesized difference."

Testing μ_D

Food_Calories

A. (Replicating Example 10.8) From the menu, choose **Stat > Basic Statistics > Paired t**. **Each sample is in its own column**, and after **Sample 1**, select Before and after **Sample 2**, select After.

B. Choose **Options**. After **Alternative hypothesis**, select "Difference > hypothesized difference."

Testing $p_1 - p_2$

A. (Replicating Example 10.11) From the menu, choose **Stat > Basic Statistics > 2 Proportions**. Choose **Summarized data**. Under **Sample 1**, enter 5,400 for **Number of events** and 6,000 for **Number of trials**. Under **Sample 2**, enter 8,600 for **Number of events** and 10,000 for **Number of trials**.

B. Choose **Options**. After **Alternative hypothesis**, select "Difference > hypothesized difference." After **Test method**, select "Use the pooled estimate for the proportion."

SPSS

Testing $\mu_1 - \mu_2$

Gold_Oil

A. (Replicating Example 10.4) Pool all *Gold_Oil* data in one column and label Pooled. In adjacent column (labeled Group), denote all Gold values with 0 and all Oil values with 1.

B. From the menu, choose **Analyze > Compare Means > Independent-Samples T-Test**.

C. Select Pooled as **Test Variable(s)** and Group as **Grouping Variable**. Select **Define Groups**, and enter 0 for **Group 1** and 1 for **Group 2**.

Testing μ_D

Food_Calories

A. (Replicating Example 10.8) From the menu, choose **Analyze > Compare Means > Paired-Samples T-Test**.

B. Select Before as **Variable1** and After as **Variable2**.

JMP

Testing $\mu_1 - \mu_2$

A. (Replicating Example 10.4) Pool all *Gold_Oil* data in one column and label it Pooled. In adjacent column (labeled Group and read as nominal data), denote all Gold values with 0 and all Oil values with 1.

B. From the menu, choose **Analyze > Fit Y by X**.

C. Select Pooled as **Y, Response** and Group as **X, Factor**.

D. Click on the red triangle next to the header that reads **Oneway Analysis of Column 1 by Column 2** and select **t-test** (to use a pooled variance, select **Means/Anova/Pooled t**).

FILE
Gold_Oil

Testing μ_D

A. (Replicating Example 10.8) From the menu, choose **Analyze > Matched Pairs**.

B. Choose Before and After as **Y, Paired Response**.

FILE
Food_Calories

11 Statistical Inference Concerning Variance

LEARNING OBJECTIVES

After reading this chapter you should be able to:

LO 11.1 Discuss features of the χ^2 distribution.

LO 11.2 Make inferences about the population variance.

LO 11.3 Discuss features of the F distribution.

LO 11.4 Make inferences about the ratio of two population variances.

So far, when conducting statistical inference concerning quantitative data, we have restricted our attention to the population mean. The mean is the primary measure of central location, but in many instances we are also interested in making inferences about measures of variability or dispersion. For instance, quality-control studies use the variance (or the standard deviation) to measure the variability of the weight, size, or volume of a product. Also, within the investment industry, the standard deviation tends to be the most common measure of risk. In this chapter, we study statistical inference with respect to the population variance as well as the ratio of two population variances. In order to construct confidence intervals or conduct hypothesis tests regarding the population variance, we use a new distribution called the χ^2 (chi-square) distribution. We then turn our attention to analyzing the ratio of two population variances. In order to construct confidence intervals or conduct hypothesis tests concerning this ratio, we use another new distribution called the F distribution.

©Hero Images/Getty Images RF

INTRODUCTORY CASE

Assessing the Risk of Mutual Fund Returns

In Chapter 3, investment counselor Jacqueline Brennan examined annual return data for two mutual funds: Vanguard's Growth Index mutual fund (henceforth, Growth) and Vanguard's Value Index mutual fund (henceforth, Value). Table 11.1 shows relevant descriptive statistics for the two funds for the years 2007–2016. Jacqueline measures the reward of investing by its average return and the risk of investing by its standard deviation. A client of Jacqueline's has specific questions related to the risk of investing, measured by the standard deviation of returns. He would like to invest a portion of his money in the Growth fund so long as the risk does not exceed 15%. He also wonders if the risk of investing in the Value fund differs from 10%. Finally, he wonders if the risk from investing in the Growth fund is greater than the risk from investing in the Value fund.

TABLE 11.1 Summary Statistics (in percent) for the Growth and the Value funds, $n = 10$

	Growth	Value
Mean	10.09	7.56
Standard Deviation	20.45	18.46

Jacqueline will use the above sample information to

1. Determine whether the standard deviation of the Growth fund exceeds 15%.
2. Determine whether the standard deviation of the Value fund differs from 10%.
3. Determine whether the risk from investing in the Growth fund is greater than the risk from investing in the Value fund.

A synopsis of this case is provided at the end of Section 11.2.

11.1 INFERENCE CONCERNING THE POPULATION VARIANCE

The population variance (or the population standard deviation) is used in quality-control studies to measure the variability of the weight, size, or volume of a product. Consider, for example, a bottler who wishes its production line to fill a certain amount of beverage in each bottle. It is important not only to get the desired average amount filled in the bottles, but also to keep the variability of the amount filled below some tolerance limit. Similarly, an investor may want to evaluate the risk of a particular investment, where the standard deviation typically corresponds to risk. Other examples for the relevance of making inference regarding the population variance include evaluating the variability of an athlete's performance, the speeds on a highway, and the repair costs of a certain automobile.

Recall that we use the sample mean $\overline{X}$ as the estimator of the population mean μ. Similarly, we use the sample variance S^2 as an estimator of the population variance σ^2. Using a random sample of n observations drawn from the population, we compute $s^2 = \frac{\Sigma(x_i - \bar{x})^2}{n-1}$ as an estimate of σ^2. In order to examine the techniques for statistical inferences regarding σ^2, we first need to analyze the sampling distribution of S^2.

LO 11.1

Discuss features of the χ^2 distribution.

Sampling Distribution of S^2

Statistical inferences regarding σ^2 are based on the χ^2 or **chi-square distribution.** Like the t distribution, the χ^2 distribution is characterized by a family of distributions, where each distribution depends on its particular degrees of freedom df. It is common, therefore, to refer to it as the χ^2_{df} distribution.

In general, the χ^2_{df} distribution is the probability distribution of the sum of several independent, squared standard normal random variables. Here df is defined as the number of squared standard normal random variables included in the summation. Recall that the estimator S^2 of the population variance is based on the squared differences between the sample values and the sample mean. If S^2 is computed from a random sample of n observations drawn from an underlying normal population, then we can define the χ^2_{df} variable as $\frac{(n-1)S^2}{\sigma^2}$.

THE SAMPLING DISTRIBUTION OF $\dfrac{(n-1)S^2}{\sigma^2}$

If a sample of size n is taken from a normal population with a finite variance, then the statistic $\chi^2_{df} = \frac{(n-1)S^2}{\sigma^2}$ follows the χ^2_{df} distribution with $df = n - 1$.

In earlier chapters, we denoted the random variables by uppercase letters and particular values of the random variables by the corresponding lowercase letters. For instance, the statistics Z and T_{df} are random variables, and their values are given by z and t_{df}, respectively. It is cumbersome to continue with the distinction between the random variable and its value in this chapter. Here, we use the notation χ^2_{df} to represent a random variable as well as its value. Similarly, for the $F_{(df_1,df_2)}$ distribution introduced in Section 11.2, we will use $F_{(df_1,df_2)}$ to represent both a random variable and its value.

From Figure 11.1, we note that the χ^2_{df} distributions are positively skewed, where the extent of skewness depends on the degrees of freedom. As the df grow larger, the χ^2_{df} distribution tends to the normal distribution. For instance, as shown in Figure 11.1, the χ^2_{20} distribution resembles the shape of the normal distribution.

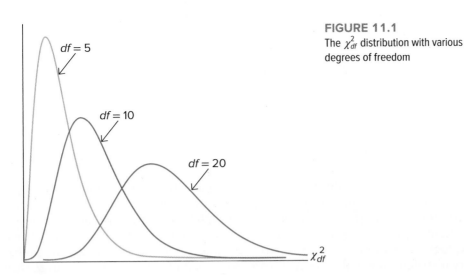

$df = 5$

$df = 10$

$df = 20$

χ^2_{df}

SUMMARY OF THE χ^2_{df} DISTRIBUTION

- The χ^2_{df} distribution is characterized by a family of distributions, where each distribution depends on its particular degrees of freedom df.
- The values of the χ^2_{df} distribution range from zero to infinity.
- The χ^2_{df} distribution is positively skewed, and the extent of skewness depends on the df. As the df grow larger, the χ^2_{df} distribution approaches the normal distribution.

Finding χ^2_{df} Values and Probabilities

For a χ^2_{df} distributed random variable, we use the notation $\chi^2_{\alpha,df}$ to represent a value such that the area in the upper (right) tail of the distribution is α. In other words, $P(\chi^2_{df} \ge \chi^2_{\alpha,df}) = \alpha$. Figure 11.2 illustrates the notation $\chi^2_{\alpha,df}$, which we use to locate χ^2_{df} values and probabilities from the χ^2 table.

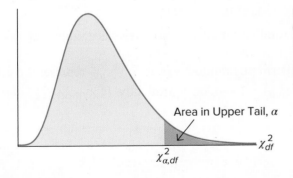

FIGURE 11.2
Graphical depiction of
$P(\chi^2_{df} \ge \chi^2_{\alpha,df}) = \alpha$

Area in Upper Tail, α

$\chi^2_{\alpha,df}$

χ^2_{df}

A portion of the upper tail areas and the corresponding values for the χ^2_{df} distributions are given in Table 11.2. Table 3 of Appendix B provides a more complete table.

Suppose we want to find the $\chi^2_{\alpha,df}$ with $\alpha = 0.05$ and $df = 10$; that is, $\chi^2_{0.05,10}$. Using Table 11.2, we look at the first column labeled df and find the value 10. We then continue along this row until we reach the column 0.050. Here we see the value $\chi^2_{0.05,10} = 18.307$ such that $P(\chi^2_{10} \ge 18.307) = 0.05$.

TABLE 11.2 Portion of the χ^2 table

df	\multicolumn{10}{c}{Area in Upper Tail, α}
	0.995	0.990	0.975	0.950	0.900	0.100	0.050	0.025	0.010	0.005
1	0.000	0.000	0.001	0.004	0.016	2.706	3.841	5.024	6.635	7.879
⋮	⋮	⋮	⋮	⋮	⋮	⋮	⋮	⋮	⋮	⋮
10	2.156	2.558	3.247	**3.940**	4.865	15.987	**18.307**	20.483	23.209	25.188
⋮	⋮	⋮	⋮	⋮	⋮	⋮	⋮	⋮	⋮	⋮
100	67.328	70.065	74.222	77.929	82.358	118.342	124.342	129.561	135.807	140.170

Sometimes we need to derive values in the lower (left) tail of the distribution. Unlike z and t_{df} distributions that are symmetric around a zero mean, the value on the lower tail of the χ^2_{df} distribution does not equal the negative of the value on the upper tail. As mentioned earlier, the χ^2_{df} distribution is not only positively skewed, its values range from 0 to infinity. However, given that the area under any probability distribution equals one, if the area to the left of a given value equals α, then the area to the right must equal $1 - \alpha$. In other words, the relevant value on the lower tail of the distribution is $\chi^2_{1-\alpha,df}$ where $P(\chi^2_{df} \geq \chi^2_{1-\alpha,df}) = 1 - \alpha$.

Suppose that we want to find the value such that the area to the left of the χ^2_{10} variable equals 0.05. Given that the area to the left of this value is 0.05, we know that the area to its right is $1 - 0.05 = 0.95$; thus, we need to find $\chi^2_{1-0.05,10} = \chi^2_{0.95,10}$. Again, we find $df = 10$ in the first column and follow this row until we intersect the column 0.95 and find the value 3.940. This is the value such that $P(\chi^2_{10} \geq 3.940) = 0.95$ or $P(\chi^2_{10} < 3.940) = 0.05$. Figure 11.3 graphically depicts the probability $\alpha = 0.05$ on both sides of the χ^2_{10} distribution and the corresponding χ^2_{10} values.

FIGURE 11.3
Graph of the probability $\alpha = 0.05$ on both sides of χ^2_{10}

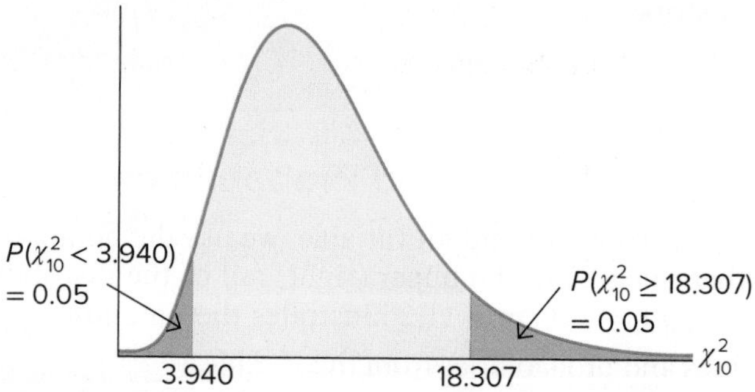

$P(\chi^2_{10} < 3.940)$
$= 0.05$

$P(\chi^2_{10} \geq 18.307)$
$= 0.05$

3.940   18.307 χ^2_{10}

FINDING χ^2_{df} VALUES

- For a χ^2_{df} distributed random variable, $\chi^2_{\alpha,df}$ represents a value such that $P(\chi^2_{df} \geq \chi^2_{\alpha,df}) = \alpha$.
- Similarly, for a χ^2_{df} distributed random variable, $\chi^2_{1-\alpha,df}$ represents a value such that $P(\chi^2_{df} \geq \chi^2_{1-\alpha,df}) = 1 - \alpha$, or, equivalently, $P(\chi^2_{df} < \chi^2_{1-\alpha,df}) = \alpha$.

EXAMPLE 11.1

Find the value x for which:
a. $P(\chi^2_5 \geq x) = 0.025$
b. $P(\chi^2_8 < x) = 0.025$

SOLUTION

a. We find the value x such that the area in the upper tail of the distribution equals 0.025. Referencing Table 3 in Appendix B, we find $df = 5$ in the first column, follow this row until we intersect the column 0.025, and find the value 12.833; therefore, $x = 12.833$.

b. We find the value x such that the area in the lower tail of the distribution equals 0.025. We solve this problem as $P(\chi_8^2 \geq x) = 1 - 0.025 = 0.975$. Again referencing Table 3 in Appendix B, we find $df = 8$ in the first column, follow this row until we intersect the column 0.975, and find $x = 2.180$. This is equivalent to $P(\chi_8^2 < 2.180) = 0.025$.

We will now make inferences about the population variance and, subsequently, the population standard deviation, starting with confidence intervals.

LO 11.2

Make inferences about the population variance.

Confidence Interval for the Population Variance

Consider a χ_{df}^2 distributed random variable. We can use the notation that we just introduced to make the following probability statement concerning this random variable:

$$P(\chi_{1-\alpha/2,df}^2 \leq \chi_{df}^2 \leq \chi_{\alpha/2,df}^2) = 1 - \alpha.$$

This indicates that the probability that χ_{df}^2 falls between $\chi_{1-\alpha/2,df}^2$ and $\chi_{\alpha/2,df}^2$ is equal to $1 - \alpha$, where $1 - \alpha$ can be thought of as the familiar confidence coefficient. Substituting $\chi_{df}^2 = \frac{(n-1)S^2}{\sigma^2}$ into the probability statement yields

$$P\left(\chi_{1-\alpha/2,df}^2 \leq \frac{(n-1)S^2}{\sigma^2} \leq \chi_{\alpha/2,df}^2\right) = 1 - \alpha.$$

After manipulating this equation algebraically, we arrive at the formula for the confidence interval for σ^2.

CONFIDENCE INTERVAL FOR σ^2

A $100(1 - \alpha)\%$ confidence interval for the population variance σ^2 is computed as

$$\left[\frac{(n-1)s^2}{\chi_{\alpha/2,df}^2}, \frac{(n-1)s^2}{\chi_{1-\alpha/2,df}^2}\right],$$

where $df = n - 1$. This formula is valid only when the random sample is drawn from a normally distributed population.

Note that the confidence interval is not in the usual format of point estimate ± margin of error. Since the confidence intervals for the population mean and the population proportion are based on the z or the t_{df} distributions, the symmetry of these distributions around a zero mean leads to the same margin of error that is added to and subtracted from the point estimate. However, for a nonsymmetric χ_{df}^2 distribution, what is added to and subtracted from the point estimate of the population variance is not the same. Finally, since the standard deviation is just the positive square root of the variance, a $100(1 - \alpha)\%$ confidence interval for the population standard deviation is computed as

$$\left[\sqrt{\frac{(n-1)s^2}{\chi_{\alpha/2,df}^2}}, \sqrt{\frac{(n-1)s^2}{\chi_{1-\alpha/2,df}^2}}\right].$$

EXAMPLE 11.2

Compute 95% confidence intervals for the population standard deviation for the Growth fund and the Value fund using the data from Table 11.1 in the introductory case. Assume that returns are normally distributed.

SOLUTION: For the years 2007–2016 ($n = 10$), the sample standard deviation for the Growth fund is $s = 20.45$, while the sample standard deviation for the Value fund is $s = 18.46$.

We first determine the 95% confidence interval for the population variance for the Growth fund. Given $n = 10$, $df = 10 - 1 = 9$. For the 95% confidence interval, $\alpha = 0.05$ and $\alpha/2 = 0.025$. Thus, we find $\chi^2_{\alpha/2,df} = \chi^2_{0.025,9} = 19.023$ and $\chi^2_{1-\alpha/2,df} = \chi^2_{0.975,9} = 2.700$. The 95% confidence interval for the population variance is

$$\left[\frac{(n-1)s^2}{\chi^2_{\alpha/2,df}}, \frac{(n-1)s^2}{\chi^2_{1-\alpha/2,df}}\right] = \left[\frac{(10-1)(20.45)^2}{19.023}, \frac{(10-1)(20.45)^2}{2.700}\right]$$

$$= [197.86, 1{,}394.01].$$

Taking the positive square root of the limits of this interval, we find the corresponding 95% confidence interval for the population standard deviation as [14.07, 37.34]. With 95% confidence, we report that the standard deviation of the return for the Growth fund is between 14.07% and 37.34%. Similarly, for the Value fund, the 95% confidence interval for the population standard deviation is between 12.70% and 33.70%.

Hypothesis Test for the Population Variance

Let's now develop the four-step procedure for conducting a hypothesis test concerning the population variance. Following the methodology used in the last two chapters, the null and the alternative hypotheses will take one of the following forms:

Two-Tailed Test	Right-Tailed Test	Left-Tailed Test
H_0: $\sigma^2 = \sigma_0^2$	H_0: $\sigma^2 \leq \sigma_0^2$	H_0: $\sigma^2 \geq \sigma_0^2$
H_A: $\sigma^2 \neq \sigma_0^2$	H_A: $\sigma^2 > \sigma_0^2$	H_A: $\sigma^2 < \sigma_0^2$

Here, σ_0^2 is the hypothesized value of the population variance σ^2. As before, we can use confidence intervals to implement two-tailed hypothesis tests; however, for one-tailed tests concerning the population variance, we implement the four-step procedure.

TEST STATISTIC FOR σ^2

The value of the test statistic for the hypothesis test for the population variance σ^2 is computed as

$$\chi^2_{df} = \frac{(n-1)s^2}{\sigma_0^2},$$

where $df = n - 1$, s^2 is the sample variance, and σ_0^2 is the hypothesized value of the population variance. This formula is valid only if the underlying population is normally distributed.

EXAMPLE 11.3

Recall the introductory case. Jacqueline Brennan's client asks if the standard deviation of returns for the Growth fund exceeds 15%. This is equivalent to testing if the variance exceeds $225(\%)^2$. Based on the sample information provided in Table 11.1, conduct this test at the 5% significance level. (Assume that returns are normally distributed.)

SOLUTION: In this example, the relevant parameter of interest is the population variance σ^2. Since we wish to determine whether the variance is greater than $225(\%)^2$, we specify the competing hypotheses as

$$H_0: \sigma^2 \leq 225$$
$$H_A: \sigma^2 > 225$$

The χ^2 test is valid because the underlying population is assumed to be normally distributed. Given that $n = 10$ and $s = 20.45$, we compute the value of the test statistic as

$$\chi^2_{df} = \frac{(n-1)s^2}{\sigma^2_0} = \frac{(10-1)(20.45)^2}{225} = 16.728.$$

Since this is a right-tailed test, we compute the p-value as $P(\chi^2_9 \geq 16.728)$. Referencing the χ^2 table for $df = 9$, we see that 16.728 lies between the values 14.684 and 16.919, implying that the p-value is between 0.05 and 0.10. We use statistical software (as explained in Example 11.4) to find the exact p-value as 0.053. Since the p-value is greater than 0.05, we do not reject H_0. At the 5% significance level, the variance of the Growth fund is not greater than $225(\%)^2$. Equivalently, the standard deviation does not exceed 15%, implying that the risk associated with this investment is not more than what the client wants to accept.

Note on Calculating the p-Value for a Two-Tailed Test Concerning σ^2

Recall that the p-value is the probability of obtaining a value of the test statistic that is at least as extreme as the one that we actually observed, given that the null hypothesis is true as an equality. For a two-tailed test, we double the probability that is considered extreme. For example, for a two-tailed test for the population mean μ with a z statistic, the p-value is computed as $2P(Z \geq z)$ if $z > 0$ or $2P(Z \leq z)$ if $z < 0$. Note that $z > 0$ if $\bar{x} > \mu_0$ and $z < 0$ if $\bar{x} < \mu_0$. Similarly, for a two-tailed test for the population variance σ^2, the p-value is computed as two times the area in the right-tail of the distribution if $s^2 > \sigma^2_0$ or two times the area in the left-tail of the distribution if $s^2 < \sigma^2_0$.

Using Excel and R to Test σ^2

EXAMPLE 11.4

FILE
Growth_Value

Jacqueline Brennan's client from the introductory case also wonders if the standard deviation of returns for the Value fund differs from 10%. This is equivalent to testing if the variance differs from $100(\%)^2$. Conduct this test at the 5% significance level. (Assume that returns are normally distributed.)

SOLUTION: This is an example of a two-tailed test for the population variance σ^2. We specify the competing hypotheses for the test as

$$H_0: \sigma^2 = 100$$
$$H_A: \sigma^2 \neq 100$$

Given $n = 10$ and $s = 18.46$, it is easy to simply plug these values into the formula, $\chi^2_{df} = \frac{(n-1)s^2}{\sigma_0^2}$, and obtain the value of the test statistic. We include the steps for obtaining the value of the test statistic in Excel and R for continuity; these commands are also useful if you only have access to the raw data. Note that the values obtained with Excel and R may be slightly different from those calculated manually, due to rounding.

Using Excel

a. Open the ***Growth_Value*** data file. Note that the values for the variable Value are in cells C2 through C11.

b. We use Excel's **VAR.S** function to help in the calculation of the value of the test statistic $\chi^2_{df} = \frac{(n-1)s^2}{\sigma_0^2}$. We enter "=(10 − 1)*VAR.S(C2:C11)/100" and Excel returns 30.667, so $\chi^2_9 = 30.667$.

c. We use Excel's **CHISQ.DIST.RT** function to find the p-value. If we enter "=CHISQ.DIST.RT(χ^2_{df}, df)," where χ^2_{df} is the value of the test statistic and df is the relevant degrees of freedom, then Excel returns the probability in the right-tail of the distribution or, equivalently, the p-value for a right-tailed test. Since we have a two-tailed test and $s^2 > \sigma_0^2$ ($18.46^2 > 10^2$), we compute the p-value as two times the area in the right-tail of the distribution. We enter "=2*CHISQ.DIST.RT(30.667, 9)." Excel returns 0.001.

d. Since the p-value is less than 0.05, we reject the null hypothesis. Therefore, we can conclude that the risk, measured by the variance of the return, differs from $100(\%)^2$ or, equivalently, that the standard deviation differs from 10%.

Using R

a. Import the ***Growth_Value*** data into a data frame (table) in R.

b. We use R's **var** function to help in the calculation of the value of the test statistic $\chi^2_{df} = \frac{(n-1)s^2}{\sigma_0^2}$. We label the test statistic as Teststat and enter

```
> Teststat <- (10 − 1)*var(Growth_Value$'Value')/100
```

And R returns: 30.667.

c. We use R's **pchisq** function to find the p-value. If we enter "pchisq (χ^2_{df}, df, lower.tail = FALSE)," where χ^2_{df} is the value of the test statistic and df is the relevant degrees of freedom, then R returns the probability in the right-tail of the distribution or, equivalently, the p-value for a right-tailed test. Since we have a two-tailed test and $s^2 > \sigma_0^2$ ($18.46^2 > 10^2$), we compute the p-value as two times the area in the right-tail of the distribution. We enter

```
> 2*pchisq(Teststat,9,lower.tail = FALSE)
```

And R returns: 0.001.

Again, at the 5% significance level, we conclude that the variance differs from $100\,(\%)^2$ or, equivalently, that the standard deviation differs from 10%.

EXERCISES 11.1

Concepts

1. Find the value x for which:
   a. $P(\chi_8^2 \geq x) = 0.025$
   b. $P(\chi_8^2 \geq x) = 0.05$
   c. $P(\chi_8^2 < x) = 0.025$
   d. $P(\chi_8^2 < x) = 0.05$

2. Find the value x for which:
   a. $P(\chi_{20}^2 \geq x) = 0.005$
   b. $P(\chi_{20}^2 \geq x) = 0.01$
   c. $P(\chi_{20}^2 < x) = 0.005$
   d. $P(\chi_{20}^2 < x) = 0.01$

3. In order to construct a confidence interval for the population variance, a random sample of n observations is drawn from a normal population. Use this information to find $\chi_{\alpha/2,df}^2$ and $\chi_{1-\alpha/2,df}^2$ under the following scenarios.
   a. A 95% confidence level with $n = 18$
   b. A 95% confidence level with $n = 30$
   c. A 99% confidence level with $n = 18$
   d. A 99% confidence level with $n = 30$

4. A random sample of 25 observations is used to estimate the population variance. The sample mean and sample standard deviation are calculated as 52.5 and 3.8, respectively. Assume that the population is normally distributed.
   a. Construct the 90% interval estimate for the population variance.
   b. Construct the 99% interval estimate for the population variance.
   c. Use your answers to discuss the impact of the confidence level on the width of the interval.

5. The following values are drawn from a normal population.

20	29	32	27	34	25	30	31

   a. Calculate the point estimates for the population variance and the population standard deviation.
   b. Construct the 95% confidence interval for the population variance and the population standard deviation.

6. In order to conduct a hypothesis test for the population variance, you compute $s^2 = 75$ from a sample of 21 observations drawn from a normally distributed population. Conduct the following tests at $\alpha = 0.10$.
   a. $H_0: \sigma^2 \leq 50$; $H_A: \sigma^2 > 50$
   b. $H_0: \sigma^2 = 50$; $H_A: \sigma^2 \neq 50$

7. Consider the following hypotheses:
   $$H_0: \sigma^2 = 200$$
   $$H_A: \sigma^2 \neq 200$$

   Find the p-value based on the following sample information, where the sample is drawn from a normally distributed population.

   a. $s^2 = 300$; $n = 25$
   b. $s^2 = 100$; $n = 25$
   c. Which of the above sample information enables us to reject the null hypothesis at $\alpha = 0.05$?

8. You would like to test the claim that the variance of a normally distributed population is more than 2 squared units. You draw a random sample of 10 observations as 2, 4, 1, 3, 2, 5, 2, 6, 1, 4. At $\alpha = 0.10$, test the claim.

Applications

9. A research analyst is examining a stock for possible inclusion in his client's portfolio. Over a 10-year period, the sample mean and the sample standard deviation of annual returns on the stock were 20% and 15%, respectively. The client wants to know if the risk, as measured by the standard deviation, differs from 18%.
   a. Construct the 95% confidence intervals for the population variance and the population standard deviation.
   b. What assumption did you make in constructing the confidence intervals?
   c. Based on the results in part (a), does the risk differ from 18%?

10. A replacement part for a machine must be produced within close specifications in order for it to be acceptable to customers. A random sample of 20 parts drawn from a normally distributed population yields a sample variance of $s^2 = 0.03$.
    a. Construct the 95% confidence interval for the population variance.
    b. Production specifications call for the variance in the lengths of the parts to be exactly 0.05. Comment on whether or not the specifications are being violated.

11. A consumer advocacy group is concerned about the variability in the cost of prescription medication. The group surveys eight local pharmacies and obtains the following prices (in $) for a particular brand of medication:

25.50	32.00	33.50	28.75	29.50	35.00	27.00	29.00

    a. Calculate the point estimate for the population variance.
    b. The group assumes that the prices represent a random sample drawn from a normally distributed population. Construct the 90% interval estimate for the population variance.
    c. The group decides to begin a lobbying effort on its members' behalf if the variance in the price does not equal 4. What should the group do?

12. The following table shows the annual returns (in percent) for the Vanguard Energy Fund from 2005 through 2009.

Year	Energy
2005	44.60
2006	19.68
2007	37.00
2008	−42.87
2009	38.36

Source: www.finance.yahoo.com.

Construct the 95% confidence interval for the standard deviation of returns. Assume that returns are normally distributed.

13. The manager of a supermarket would like the variance of the waiting times of the customers not to exceed 3 minutes-squared. She would add a new cash register if the variance exceeds this threshold. She regularly checks the waiting times of the customers to ensure that the variance does not rise above the allowed level. In a recent random sample of 28 customer waiting times, she computes the sample variance as 4.2 minutes-squared. She believes that the waiting times are normally distributed.

    a. State the null and the alternative hypotheses to test if the threshold has been crossed.
    b. Conduct the test at $\alpha = 0.05$.
    c. What should the manager do?

14. A restaurant owner is concerned about the consistency of business. He wants to determine if the standard deviation of the profits for each week is less than $300. The profits from last week are listed below (in dollars). Assume that profits are normally distributed.

1,825	1,642	1,675	1,553	1,925	2,037	1,902

    a. State the null and alternative hypotheses for the test.
    b. Calculate the value of the test statistic and the p-value.
    c. Conduct the test at the 1% significance level.
    d. Repeat the test at $\alpha = 0.10$.

15. The India Fund, Inc. (IFN) is a close-ended equity mutual fund launched by the Blackstone Group's Asset Management arm. Although it promises impressive returns, it does so at the cost of greater risk. An analyst would like to test if the variance of the returns for IFN is greater than 1,000 (%)^2. He uses the following annual return data (in percent) to test his claim at the 5% level of significance.

2001	2002	2003	2004	2005	2006	2007
−28.33	7.87	140.63	30.91	63.35	−2.78	58.30

    a. State the competing hypotheses for the analyst's test.

    b. Calculate the value of the test statistic and the p-value. What assumption regarding the IFN returns did you make?
    c. At the 5% significance level, is the variance of returns greater than 1,000(%)^2?

16. Metalworks, a supplier of machine parts, fabricates bearings in which the standard deviation of the bearing diameter must be within 0.002 inch maximum. Otherwise, problems with fit will occur. The engineering department is conducting an experiment to investigate adherence to this requirement. A sample of 25 bearings has revealed a sample standard deviation of 0.0025 inch.

    a. State the null and alternative hypotheses to test if the requirement has been violated.
    b. Compute the value of the test statistic. What assumption did you make regarding the bearing diameters?
    c. Conduct the test at $\alpha = 0.05$. What is your conclusion?
    d. Would your conclusion change at the 10% significance level?

17. Some transportation experts claim that it is the variability of speeds, rather than the level of speeds, that is a critical factor in determining the likelihood of an accident occurring (*Update*, Virginia Department of Transportation, Winter 2000). One of the experts claims that driving conditions are dangerous if the variance of speeds exceeds 80 (mph)^2. On a heavily traveled highway, a random sample of 61 cars revealed a mean and a variance of speeds of 57.5 mph and 88.7 (mph)^2, respectively.

    a. Set up the competing hypotheses to test if the variance of speeds exceeds 80 (mph)^2.
    b. At the 5% significance level, can you conclude that driving conditions are dangerous on this highway? Explain.

18. **FILE** *Sewing.* To maintain high consistency in its manual sewing operations, a custom manufacturer of high-quality fashion clothing has a goal in which all sewing employees should score within a standard deviation of 9 on a sewing dexterity test. To test adherence to this goal, a random sample of 30 employees was subjected to a needle-board dexterity test.

    a. State the hypotheses to test whether the standard deviation of the dexterity test scores exceeds 9.
    b. Calculate the value of the test statistic. Assume that dexterity scores are normally distributed.
    c. Find the p-value.
    d. Make a conclusion at each of the following significance levels: 1%, 5%, and 10%.

19. **FILE** *Wage.* An economist is interested in the variability of hourly wages at a production plant. She collects data on 50 hourly wage earners.

    a. Set up the competing hypotheses to test whether the variance of hourly wages exceeds 35 ($\$^2$).
    b. Calculate the value of the test statistic.
    c. Find the p-value.
    d. At the 5% significance level, does the variance of hourly wages exceed 35 ($\$^2$)? Explain.

20. **FILE** *MV_Houses.* A realtor in Mission Viejo, California, believes that the standard deviation of house prices is more than 100 units, where each unit equals $1,000. Assume house prices are normally distributed.

   a. State the null and the alternative hypotheses for the test.

   b. Calculate the value of the test statistic.

   c. Find the p-value.

   d. At $\alpha = 0.05$, what is the conclusion? Is the realtor's claim supported by the data?

21. **FILE** *MPG.* The data accompanying this exercise show miles per gallon (mpg) for 25 cars.

   a. State the null and the alternative hypotheses in order to test whether the variance differs from 62 mpg^2.

   b. Assuming that mpg is normally distributed, calculate the value of the test statistic.

   c. Find the p-value.

   d. Make a conclusion at $\alpha = 0.01$.

22. **FILE** *Rentals.* Real estate investment in college towns continues to promise good returns (*The Wall Street Journal*, September 24, 2010). With rents holding up, this is good news for investors but the same cannot be said for students. There also tends to be significant variability in rents. Consider monthly rents (in $) of two bedroom apartments in two campus towns: Ann Arbor, Michigan, and Davis, California. A portion of the data is shown in the accompanying table.

Ann Arbor Rent	Davis Rent
850	744
929	850
⋮	⋮
1450	1810

Source: www.zillow.com.

   a. Calculate the standard deviation of rent for Ann Arbor, Michigan, and Davis, California.

   b. Construct and interpret the 95% confidence intervals for the standard deviation of rent for both Ann Arbor, Michigan, and Davis, California.

   c. For each campus town, use the 95% confidence intervals to determine if the standard deviation of rent differs from $200; use $\alpha = 0.05$.

11.2 INFERENCE CONCERNING THE RATIO OF TWO POPULATION VARIANCES

In this section, we turn our attention to comparing two population variances, σ_1^2 and σ_2^2. It is common to compare products on the basis of the relative variability of their weight, size, or volume. For example, a bottler may want to compare two production facilities based on the relative variability of the amount of beverage filled at each facility. Similarly, an investor may want to compare the relative risk of two investment strategies, where variance is used as a measure of risk. Other examples for the relevance of comparing two population variances include comparing the relative variability of athletes' performances, the speeds on highways, and the repair costs of different makes of automobiles.

We specify the parameter of interest as the ratio of the population variances σ_1^2/σ_2^2 rather than their difference $\sigma_1^2 - \sigma_2^2$. Note that the condition $\sigma_1^2 = \sigma_2^2$ is equivalent to $\sigma_1^2 - \sigma_2^2 = 0$ as well as $\sigma_1^2/\sigma_2^2 = 1$. We use the ratio of the sample variances S_1^2/S_2^2 as an estimator of σ_1^2/σ_2^2, where the sample variances are computed from independent random samples drawn from two normally distributed populations. In order to examine the methodologies for statistical inference, we first need to analyze the sampling distribution of S_1^2/S_2^2.

Sampling Distribution of S_1^2/S_2^2

We use the sampling distribution of S_1^2/S_2^2 to define a new distribution, called the **F distribution**.[1] Like the t_{df} and χ_{df}^2 distributions, the F distribution is characterized by a family of distributions; however, each distribution depends on *two* degrees of freedom: the numerator degrees of freedom df_1 and the denominator degrees of

Discuss features of the F distribution.

[1]The F distribution is named in honor of Sir Ronald Fisher, who discovered the distribution in 1922.

freedom df_2. It is common to refer to it as the $F_{(df_1,df_2)}$ distribution. As mentioned earlier, we will use the notation $F_{(df_1,df_2)}$ to represent both a random variable and its value.

In general, the $F_{(df_1,df_2)}$ distribution is the probability distribution of the ratio of two independent chi-square variables, where each variable is divided by its own degrees of freedom; that is, $F_{(df_1,df_2)} = \dfrac{\chi^2_{df_1}/df_1}{\chi^2_{df_2}/df_2}$.

THE SAMPLING DISTRIBUTION OF S_1^2/S_2^2 WHEN $\sigma_1^2 = \sigma_2^2$

If independent samples of size n_1 and n_2 are drawn from normal populations with equal variances, then the statistic $F_{(df_1,df_2)} = S_1^2/S_2^2$ follows the $F_{(df_1,df_2)}$ distribution with $df_1 = n_1 - 1$ and $df_2 = n_2 - 1$.

Like the χ^2_{df} distribution, the $F_{(df_1,df_2)}$ distribution is positively skewed, with values ranging from zero to infinity, but becomes increasingly symmetric as df_1 and df_2 increase. Figure 11.4 shows the $F_{(df_1,df_2)}$ distribution with various degrees of freedom. Note that each $F_{(df_1,df_2)}$ distribution is positively skewed; however, as df_1 and df_2 grow larger, the $F_{(df_1,df_2)}$ distribution becomes less skewed and approaches the normal distribution. For instance, $F_{(20,20)}$ is relatively less skewed as compared to $F_{(2,8)}$ or $F_{(6,8)}$.

FIGURE 11.4

The $F_{(df_1,df_2)}$ distribution with various degrees of freedom

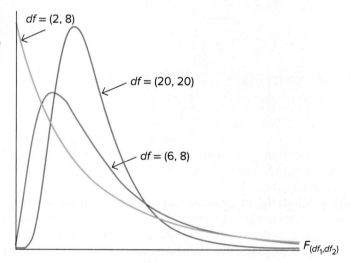

SUMMARY OF THE $F_{(df_1,df_2)}$ DISTRIBUTION

- The $F_{(df_1,df_2)}$ distribution is characterized by a family of distributions, where each distribution depends on two degrees of freedom, df_1 and df_2.
- The values of the $F_{(df_1,df_2)}$ distribution range from zero to infinity.
- The $F_{(df_1,df_2)}$ distribution is positively skewed, where the extent of skewness depends on df_1 and df_2. As df_1 and df_2 grow larger, the $F_{(df_1,df_2)}$ distribution approaches the normal distribution.

Finding $F_{(df_1,df_2)}$ Values and Probabilities

As with other distributions, we use the notation $F_{\alpha,(df_1,df_2)}$ to represent a value such that the area in the upper (right) tail of the distribution is α. In other words, $P(F_{(df_1,df_2)} \geq F_{\alpha,(df_1,df_2)}) = \alpha$. Figure 11.5 illustrates this notation.

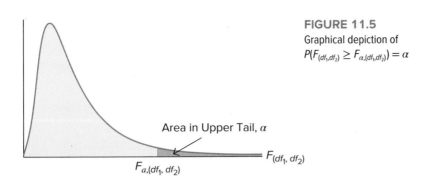

FIGURE 11.5

Graphical depiction of
$$P(F_{(df_1,df_2)} \geq F_{\alpha,(df_1,df_2)}) = \alpha$$

A portion of the upper tail areas and the corresponding values for the $F_{(df_1,df_2)}$ distribution are given in Table 11.3. Table 4 of Appendix B provides a more complete table.

TABLE 11.3 Portion of the F Table

df_2	Area in Upper Tail, α	df_1		
		6	7	8
6	0.10	3.05	3.01	2.98
	0.05	4.28	4.21	4.15
	0.025	5.82	5.70	5.60
	0.01	8.47	8.26	8.10
7	0.10	2.83	2.78	2.75
	0.05	3.87	3.79	3.73
	0.025	5.12	4.99	4.90
	0.01	7.19	6.99	6.84
8	0.10	2.67	2.62	2.59
	0.05	**3.58**	3.50	3.44
	0.025	4.65	4.53	4.43
	0.01	**6.37**	6.18	6.03

Consider the degrees of freedom given by $df_1 = 6$ and $df_2 = 8$. With $df_1 = 6$ (read from the top row) and $df_2 = 8$ (read from the first column), we can easily determine the area in the upper tail as $P(F_{(6,8)} \geq 3.58) = 0.05$ and $P(F_{(6,8)} \geq 6.37) = 0.01$. The F table lists probabilities corresponding to a limited number of values in the upper tail of the distribution. For instance, the exact probability $P(F_{(6,8)} \geq 3.92)$ cannot be determined from the table, and we have to rely on approximate values. All we can say is the area to the right of 3.92 is between 0.025 and 0.05. Shortly, we will use Excel and R to find exact probabilities.

Sometimes we need to derive values such that the area to the left of a given value is equal to α. Given that the area under any distribution equals one, the area to the right of the given value must equal $1 - \alpha$. As in the case of the χ^2_{df} distribution, we let $F_{1-\alpha,(df_1,df_2)}$ denote the value such that the area to its right equals $1 - \alpha$ and, thus, the area to its left equals α. It is convenient, however, to find $F_{1-\alpha,(df_1,df_2)}$ using a simple rule that $F_{1-\alpha,(df_1,df_2)} = \frac{1}{F_{\alpha,(df_2,df_1)}}$. Note that the rule reverses the order of the numerator and the denominator degrees of freedom.

Suppose we need to find $F_{1-\alpha,(df_1,df_2)}$ where $\alpha = 0.05$, $df_1 = 6$, and $df_2 = 8$. We find $F_{0.95,(6,8)} = \frac{1}{F_{0.05,(8,6)}} = \frac{1}{4.15} = 0.24$. In other words, the lower (left) tail area is $P(F_{(6,8)} < 0.24) = 0.05$. Figure 11.6 graphically depicts $P(F_{(6,8)} \geq 3.58) = 0.05$ and $P(F_{(6,8)} < 0.24) = 0.05$.

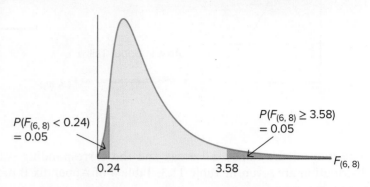

FIGURE 11.6
Graph of the probability $\alpha = 0.05$ on both sides of $F_{(6,8)}$

FINDING $F_{(df_1,df_2)}$ VALUES

- For a $F_{(df_1,df_2)}$ distributed random variable, $F_{\alpha,(df_1,df_2)}$ represents a value such that $P(F_{(df_1,df_2)} \geq F_{\alpha,(df_1,df_2)}) = \alpha$.

- Similarly, for a $F_{(df_1,df_2)}$ distributed random variable, $F_{1-\alpha,(df_1,df_2)}$ represents a value such that $P(F_{(df_1,df_2)} \geq F_{1-\alpha,(df_1,df_2)}) = 1 - \alpha$; equivalently, $P(F_{(df_1,df_2)} < F_{1-\alpha,(df_1,df_2)}) = \alpha$. It is convenient to reverse the order of degrees of freedom and find $F_{1-\alpha,(df_1,df_2)}$ as $\frac{1}{F_{\alpha,(df_2,df_1)}}$.

EXAMPLE 11.5

Find the value x for which:

a. $P(F_{(7,10)} \geq x) = 0.025$
b. $P(F_{(7,10)} < x) = 0.05$

SOLUTION:

a. We find the value x such that the area in the upper tail of the distribution equals 0.025. Referencing Table 4 in Appendix B, we follow the column corresponding to $df_1 = 7$ until it intersects with the row corresponding to $df_2 = 10$ and $\alpha = 0.025$; we find the value 3.95. Therefore, $P(F_{(7,10)} \geq 3.95) = 0.025$.

b. We find the value x such that the area in the lower tail of the distribution equals 0.05, or, equivalently, the area in the upper tail of the distribution equals 0.95. We have $F_{0.95,(7,10)} = \frac{1}{F_{0.05,(10,7)}} = \frac{1}{3.64} = 0.27$. In other words, $P(F_{(7,10)} < 0.27) = 0.05$.

LO 11.4

Make inferences about the ratio of two population variances.

We will now make statistical inferences about the ratio of two population variances, starting with confidence intervals.

Confidence Interval for the Ratio of Two Population Variances

The formula for a confidence interval for the ratio of the population variances σ_1^2/σ_2^2 is derived in a manner analogous to previous confidence intervals. Here, we simply show the end result.

A $100(1 - \alpha)\%$ confidence interval for the ratio of the population variances σ_1^2/σ_2^2 is computed as

$$\left[\left(\frac{s_1^2}{s_2^2}\right)\frac{1}{F_{\alpha/2,(df_1,df_2)}}, \left(\frac{s_1^2}{s_2^2}\right)F_{\alpha/2,(df_2,df_1)} \right],$$

where for samples of size n_1 and n_2, $df_1 = n_1 - 1$ and $df_2 = n_2 - 1$. Note that the order of the degrees of freedom for the right part of the interval is reversed.

This formula is valid if the sample variances are computed from independently drawn samples from two normally distributed populations.

EXAMPLE 11.6

Students of two sections of a statistics course took a common final examination. A professor examines the variability in scores between the two sections. Random samples of $n_1 = 11$ and $n_2 = 16$ yield sample variances of $s_1^2 = 182.25$ and $s_2^2 = 457.96$. Construct the 95% confidence interval for the ratio of the population variances. Assume that the samples are independently drawn from two normally distributed populations.

SOLUTION: In order to construct the 95% confidence interval for the ratio of the population variances, we determine $\left[\left(\frac{s_1^2}{s_2^2}\right)\frac{1}{F_{\alpha/2,(df_1,df_2)}}, \left(\frac{s_1^2}{s_2^2}\right)F_{\alpha/2,(df_2,df_1)} \right]$. We find the degrees of freedom as $df_1 = n_1 - 1 = 11 - 1 = 10$ and $df_2 = n_2 - 1 = 16 - 1 = 15$. From the F table and given $\alpha = .05$, we find

$$F_{\alpha/2,(df_1,df_2)} = F_{0.025,(10,15)} = 3.06 \quad \text{and} \quad F_{\alpha/2,(df_2,df_1)} = F_{0.025,(15,10)} = 3.52.$$

The confidence interval is

$$\left[\left(\frac{182.25}{457.96}\right)\frac{1}{3.06}, \left(\frac{182.25}{457.96}\right)3.52 \right] = [0.13, 1.40].$$

Therefore, the 95% confidence interval for the ratio of the population variances ranges from 0.13 to 1.40. In other words, the variance of scores in the first section is between 13% and 140% of the variance of scores in the second section.

As we have done in earlier chapters, we will be able to use this confidence interval to conduct a two-tailed hypothesis test.

Hypothesis Test for the Ratio of Two Population Variances

When comparing two population variances σ_1^2 and σ_2^2, the competing hypotheses will take one of the following forms:

Two-Tailed Test	Right-Tailed Test	Left-Tailed Test
$H_0: \sigma_1^2/\sigma_2^2 = 1$	$H_0: \sigma_1^2/\sigma_2^2 \leq 1$	$H_0: \sigma_1^2/\sigma_2^2 \geq 1$
$H_A: \sigma_1^2/\sigma_2^2 \neq 1$	$H_A: \sigma_1^2/\sigma_2^2 > 1$	$H_A: \sigma_1^2/\sigma_2^2 < 1$

A two-tailed test determines whether the two population variances differ. As noted earlier, the condition $\sigma_1^2 = \sigma_2^2$ is equivalent to $\sigma_1^2/\sigma_2^2 = 1$. A right-tailed test examines whether σ_1^2 is greater than σ_2^2, whereas a left-tailed test examines whether σ_1^2 is less than σ_2^2.

EXAMPLE 11.7

Let's revisit Example 11.6.

a. Specify the competing hypotheses in order to determine whether or not the variances in the two statistics sections differ.

b. Using the 95% confidence interval, what is the conclusion to the test?

SOLUTION:

a. Since we want to determine if the variances differ between the two sections, we formulate a two-tailed hypothesis test as

$$H_0: \sigma_1^2/\sigma_2^2 = 1$$
$$H_A: \sigma_1^2/\sigma_2^2 \neq 1$$

b. We calculated the 95% confidence interval for the ratio of the two variances that ranged from 0.13 to 1.40. We note that this interval contains the value 1; thus, we do not reject H_0. The sample data do not suggest that the variances between the two statistics sections differ at the 5% significance level.

Now we use the four-step procedure to implement one- or two-tailed hypothesis tests. We use the ratio of the values of the sample variances s_1^2/s_2^2 to conduct hypothesis tests regarding the ratio of the population variances σ_1^2/σ_2^2.

TEST STATISTIC FOR σ_1^2/σ_2^2

The value of the test statistic for the hypothesis test for the ratio of two population variances σ_1^2/σ_2^2 is computed as

$$F_{(df_1, df_2)} = s_1^2/s_2^2,$$

where for samples of size n_1 and n_2, $df_1 = n_1 - 1$ and $df_2 = n_2 - 1$. The $F_{(df_1, df_2)}$ test statistic is valid if the sample variances are computed from independently drawn samples from normally distributed populations.

Note that a left-tailed test can easily be converted into a right-tailed test by interchanging the variances of the two populations. For instance, we can convert $H_0: \sigma_1^2/\sigma_2^2 \geq 1$ versus $H_A: \sigma_1^2/\sigma_2^2 < 1$ into $H_0: \sigma_2^2/\sigma_1^2 \leq 1$ versus $H_A: \sigma_2^2/\sigma_1^2 > 1$.

PLACING THE LARGER SAMPLE VARIANCE IN THE NUMERATOR

It is preferable to place the larger sample variance in the numerator of the $F_{(df_1, df_2)}$ statistic. The resulting value allows us to focus only on the upper (right) tail of the distribution.

In other words, we define the hypotheses such that the resulting test statistic is computed as s_1^2/s_2^2 when $s_1^2 > s_2^2$ and as s_2^2/s_1^2 when $s_2^2 > s_1^2$; the degrees of freedom is adjusted accordingly. This saves us the additional work required to find the area in the lower (left) tail of the $F_{(df_1, df_2)}$ distribution.

Using Excel and R to Test σ_1^2/σ_2^2

EXAMPLE 11.8

Let's again revisit the introductory case. Jacqueline Brennan's client wonders if the Growth fund is riskier than the Value fund. For reference, we repeat the sample summary measures for the two funds.

Growth fund: $\bar{x}_1 = 10.09$, $\quad s_1 = 20.45$, $\quad n_1 = 10$

Value fund: $\bar{x}_2 = 7.56$, $\quad s_2 = 18.46$, $\quad n_2 = 10$

Assume that returns are normally distributed to implement the test at the 5% significance level.

SOLUTION: We define the population variance as the measure of risk, which is equivalent to defining risk in terms of the standard deviation. Let σ_1^2 and σ_2^2 denote the population variances of the Growth and the Value funds, respectively. Since we wish to determine whether the variance of the Growth fund is greater than that of the Value fund, we specify the competing hypotheses as

$$H_0: \sigma_1^2/\sigma_2^2 \leq 1$$
$$H_A: \sigma_1^2/\sigma_2^2 > 1$$

Note that this specification is appropriate since $s_1 > s_2$. If it were the case that $s_2 > s_1$, then would have specified the hypotheses in terms of σ_2^2/σ_1^2 instead of σ_1^2/σ_2^2.

As in Section 11.1, even though we could easily calculate $F_{(df_1, df_2)} = s_1^2/s_2^2$ given the summary statistics, we include the steps for obtaining this statistic in Excel and R for continuity. Note that the values obtained with Excel and R may be slightly different from those calculated manually, due to rounding.

Using Excel

a. Open the **_Growth_Value_** data file. Note that the values for the variables Growth and Value are in cells B2 through C11.

b. We use Excel's **VAR.S** function to calculate the value of the test statistic $F_{(df_1, df_2)} = s_1^2/s_2^2$. We enter "=VAR.S(B2:B11)/VAR.S(C2:C11)" and Excel returns 1.227; so, $F_{(9,9)} = 1.227$.

c. We use Excel's **F.DIST.RT** function to find the p-value. If we enter "=F.DIST.RT$(F_{(df_1, df_2)}, df_1, df_2)$," where $F_{(df_1, df_2)}$ is the value of the test statistic, df_1 is degrees of freedom in the numerator, and df_2 is degrees of freedom in the denominator, then Excel returns the probability in the right-tail of the distribution, or equivalently, the p-value for a right-tailed test. Since we have a right-tailed test, we enter "=F.DIST.RT(1.227, 9, 9)." Excel returns 0.383.

d. Since the p-value of 0.383 is greater than 0.05, we do not reject the null hypothesis. At the 5% significance level, we cannot conclude that the Growth fund is riskier than the Value fund.

Using R

a. Import the **_Growth_Value_** data into a data frame (table) in R.

b. We use R's **var** function to calculate the value of the test statistic $F_{(df_1, df_2)}$. We label the test statistic as Teststat and enter

```
> Teststat<-var(Growth_Value$'Growth')/
  var(Growth_Value$'Value')
```

And R returns: 1.227.

c. We use R's **pf** function to find the *p*-value. If we enter "pf($F_{(df_1, df_2)}$, df_1, df_2, lower.tail=FALSE)," where $F_{(df_1, df_2)}$ is the value of the test statistic, df_1 is degrees of freedom in the numerator, and df_2 is degrees of freedom in the denominator, then Excel returns the probability in the right-tail of the distribution, or equivalently, the *p*-value for a right-tailed test. For this right-tailed test, we enter

```
> pf(Teststat,9,9,lower.tail=FALSE)
```

And R returns: 0.383.

Again, at the 5% significance level, we cannot conclude that the population variance for the Growth fund is greater than the population variance for the Value fund.

SYNOPSIS OF INTRODUCTORY CASE

The annual return data for Vanguard's Growth Index mutual fund (Growth) and Vanguard's Value Index mutual fund (Value) were examined for the years 2007 through 2016. Over this time period, the average annual return for the Growth and the Value mutual funds were 10.09% and 7.56%, respectively. This may seem to imply that the Growth mutual fund had the higher reward due to its higher average return. It turns out, however, that the mean difference of the annual returns does not significantly differ from zero at the 5% significance level. The average return gauges the reward of investing, but it says nothing about the risk of investing when both reward and risk are important. Can we conclude that an investment in one fund may be riskier than an investment in the other?

©dani3315/Shutterstock RF

Variance and standard deviation tend to be the most common measures of risk with financial data, so a number of tests were conducted to assess the risk of investing in either of these mutual funds. Over this time period, the standard deviations of return for the Growth and the Value mutual funds were 20.45% and 18.46%, respectively. The first test examined if the standard deviation of the Growth fund was greater than 15%—a level of risk that a client did not want to exceed. At the 5% significance level, it was found that the standard deviation was not greater than 15%. The second test investigated if the standard deviation of the Value fund differed from 10%. At the 5% significance level, the results suggested that the standard deviation differed from 10%. Finally, it was found that the standard deviation of the Growth mutual fund was not greater than the standard deviation of the Value mutual fund at the 5% significance level.

A cursory glance of the summary statistics for the Growth and the Value mutual funds may lead an investor to incorrectly conclude that the Growth mutual fund has higher reward and higher risk than the Value fund. Formal testing found that neither the reward nor the risk of investing in these two funds was different between the two. Based on this analysis, and assuming similar performance into the future, it appears that the investor should not favor one mutual fund over the other. Since the two investment styles of growth and value investing often complement each other, it might be advisable for the investor to add diversity to his portfolio by using the funds together.

EXERCISES 11.2

Concepts

23. Use the *F* table to find the value *x* for which:
    a. $P(F_{(4,8)} \geq x) = 0.025$
    b. $P(F_{(4,8)} \geq x) = 0.05$
    c. $P(F_{(4,8)} < x) = 0.025$
    d. $P(F_{(4,8)} < x) = 0.05$

24. Use the *F* table to find the following probabilities.
    a. $P(F_{(10,8)} \geq 3.35)$
    b. $P(F_{(10,8)} < 0.42)$
    c. $P(F_{(10,8)} \geq 4.30)$
    d. $P(F_{(10,8)} < 0.26)$

25. Construct the 90% interval estimate for the ratio of the population variances using the following results from two independently drawn samples from normally distributed populations.

Sample 1: $\bar{x}_1 = 157$, $s_1^2 = 23.2$, and $n_1 = 9$
Sample 2: $\bar{x}_2 = 148$, $s_2^2 = 19.9$, and $n_2 = 8$

26. Consider the following measures based on independently drawn samples from normally distributed populations:

Sample 1: $s_1^2 = 220$, and $n_1 = 20$
Sample 2: $s_2^2 = 196$, and $n_2 = 15$

a. Construct the 95% interval estimate for the ratio of the population variances.

b. Using the confidence interval from part (a), test if the ratio of the population variances differs from 1 at the 5% significance level. Explain.

27. Consider the following competing hypotheses and relevant summary statistics:

$$H_0: \sigma_1^2/\sigma_2^2 = 1$$
$$H_A: \sigma_1^2/\sigma_2^2 \neq 1$$

Sample 1: $\bar{x}_1 = 48.5$, $s_1^2 = 18.7$, and $n_1 = 10$
Sample 2: $\bar{x}_2 = 50.2$, $s_2^2 = 12.9$, and $n_2 = 8$

Assume that the two populations are normally distributed. Conduct this test at the 5% significance level.

28. Consider the following competing hypotheses and relevant summary statistics:

$$H_0: \sigma_1^2/\sigma_2^2 \leq 1$$
$$H_A: \sigma_1^2/\sigma_2^2 > 1$$

Sample 1: $s_1^2 = 935$ and $n_1 = 14$
Sample 2: $s_2^2 = 812$ and $n_2 = 11$

Conduct this test at the 5% significance level. State your assumptions.

29. Consider the following competing hypotheses and relevant summary statistics:

$$H_0: \sigma_1^2/\sigma_2^2 \geq 1$$
$$H_A: \sigma_1^2/\sigma_2^2 < 1$$

Sample 1: $s_1^2 = 1{,}315$ and $n_1 = 17$
Sample 2: $s_2^2 = 1{,}523$ and $n_2 = 19$

Conduct this hypothesis test at the 5% significance level. State your assumptions. (*Hint*: You may want to first convert the above left-tailed test into a right-tailed test by switching the two variances.)

Applications

30. A firm has just developed a new cost-reducing technology for producing a certain replacement part for automobiles. Since a replacement part must be produced within close specifications in order for it to be acceptable to customers, the new technology's specifications must not deviate

drastically from the older version. Suppose the sample variance for 26 parts produced using the older version is $s_1^2 = 0.28$, while the sample variance for 26 parts produced using the new technology is $s_2^2 = 0.48$. Assume that the two samples are drawn independently from normally distributed populations.

a. Develop the hypotheses to test whether the population variances differ.

b. Calculate the value of the test statistic and the *p*-value.

c. Can you conclude that the variances are different at the 5% significance level? Given that all other criteria are satisfied, should the company adopt the new technology?

31. Two basketball players on a school team are working hard on consistency of their performance. In particular, they are hoping to bring down the variance of their scores. The coach believes that the players are not equally consistent in their games. Over a 10-game period, the scores of these two players are shown in the accompanying table. Assume that the two samples are drawn independently from normally distributed populations.

Player 1	13	15	12	18	14	15	11	13	11	16
Player 2	11	21	18	9	20	11	13	11	19	8

a. Develop the hypotheses to test whether the players differ in consistency.

b. Test the coach's claim at $\alpha = 0.05$.

32. The following table shows the annual returns (in percent) for Fidelity's Electronic and Utilities funds.

Year	Electronic	Utilities
2010	17	11
2011	−8	13
2012	4	7
2013	39	21
2014	38	22

Source: www.finance.yahoo.com; data retrieved April 3, 2015.

Test if the population variances differ at the 5% significance level. State your assumptions.

33. Nike's total revenues (in millions of $) for the Asian and Latin American regions for the years 2005 through 2009 are as follows:

	2005	2006	2007	2008	2009
Asia	1,897	2,054	2,296	2,888	3,322
Latin America	696	905	967	1,165	1,285

Source: *Nike Online Annual Reports.*

a. Specify the competing hypotheses in order to test whether the variance in revenues is greater in Asia than in Latin America.

b. Calculate the value of the test statistic. Assume that revenues are normally distributed.

c. Find the p-value.

d. At $\alpha = 0.01$, what is your conclusion?

34. The quality manager at a battery manufacturing company wants to determine if lithium-ion batteries have less variability in discharge time than nickel-cadmium batteries. Using products with similar power draws, he has measured the time until discharge (in hours) for random samples of 16 lithium-ion batteries and 26 nickel-cadmium batteries. The sample variance of the discharge times is 0.44 hours^2 for the lithium-ion batteries and 0.89 hours^2 for the nickel-cadmium batteries.

a. State the hypotheses to test whether the variance in discharge time for the lithium-ion batteries is less than the variance for the nickel-cadmium batteries.

b. Compute the value of the test statistic. What assumption did you make?

c. Find the p-value.

d. Make a conclusion at the 5% significance level.

e. Would your conclusion change at the 10% significance level?

35. **FILE** *Purchase_Amounts.* A marketing analyst is studying the variability in customer purchase amounts between shopping mall stores and "big box" discount stores. She suspects the variability is different between those stores due to the nature of the customers involved. To investigate this issue in detail, she compiled two random samples, each consisting of 26 purchase amounts at shopping mall stores and discount stores.

a. State the hypotheses to test whether the variance of the purchase amounts differs between the two types of stores.

b. Construct the 95% confidence interval for the ratio of the population variances. Assume that purchase amounts are normally distributed.

c. Use the confidence interval to test whether the variance of the purchase amounts differs between the two stores at the 5% significance level.

d. Confirm your conclusion using the p-value approach.

36. **FILE** *Monthly_Stock_Prices.* A portion of the monthly stock prices (rounded to the nearest dollar) for Starbucks Corp. and Panera Bread Co. from 2010 to 2013 are reported in the following table.

Date	Starbucks Corp.	Panera Bread Co.
January 2010	20	71
February 2010	21	73
⋮	⋮	⋮
December 2013	78	177

Source: www.finance.yahoo.com.

a. State the null and the alternative hypotheses in order to determine if the variance of price differs for the two firms.

b. What assumption regarding the population is necessary to implement this step?

c. Compute the value of the test statistic and the p-value.

d. At $\alpha = 0.05$, what is your conclusion?

37. **FILE** *Packaging.* A variety of packaging solutions exist for products that must be kept within a specific temperature range. Cold chain distribution is particularly useful in the food and pharmaceutical industries. A packaging company is trying out a new packaging material that might reduce the variation of temperatures in the box. It is believed that the temperature in the box follows a normal distribution with both packaging materials. Inspectors randomly select 16 boxes of new and old packages, and report the temperatures in degrees Celsius 24 hours after they are sealed for shipment. A portion of the data is shown in the accompanying table. Assume that the two samples are drawn independently from normally distributed populations.

New Package	Old Package
3.98	5.79
4.99	6.42
⋮	⋮
4.95	5.95

a. State the hypotheses to test whether the new packaging material reduces the variation of temperatures in the box.

b. Compute the value of the test statistic and the p-value.

c. Make a conclusion at the 5% significance level.

38. **FILE** *Rentals.* The data accompanying this exercise include monthly rents for a two-bedroom apartment in two campus towns: Ann Arbor, Michigan, and Davis, California. Davis, California, is known to have higher rents than Ann Arbor, Michigan; however, it is not clear if it also has higher variability in rents. At the 5% significance level, determine if the variance of rent in Davis, California is more than that of Ann Arbor, Michigan. State your assumptions clearly.

WRITING WITH STATISTICS

Many environmental groups and politicians are suggesting a return to the federal 55-mile-per-hour speed limit on America's highways. They argue that a lower national speed limit will improve traffic safety, save fuel, and reduce greenhouse emissions. Elizabeth Connolly believes that more focus should be put on the variability of speed limits as opposed to average speed limits. She points to recent research that suggests that increases in speed variability decrease overall safety. Specifically, Elizabeth feels that traffic accidents are more likely to occur when the standard deviation of speeds exceeds 5 mph. She records the speeds of 40 cars from a highway with a speed limit of 55 mph (Highway 1) and the speeds of 40 cars from a highway with a speed limit of 65 mph (Highway 2). A portion of the data is shown in Table 11.4.

©Dmitry Kalinovsky/Shutterstock RF

TABLE 11.4 Speeds of Cars from Highway 1 and Highway 2

Highway 1 (55-mph limit)	Highway 2 (65-mph limit)
60	70
55	65
⋮	⋮
52	65

FILE
Highway_Speeds

Elizabeth would like to use this sample information to

1. Determine, at the 5% significance level, whether the standard deviation on the 55-mph highway exceeds 5 mph.

2. Determine, at the 5% significance level, whether the variability on the 55-mph highway is more than the variability on the 65-mph highway.

Sample Report—Traffic Safety and the Variation in Speed

Increasing greenhouse emissions are prompting conservationists to lobby for a return to the federal 55-mile-per-hour (mph) speed limit on America's highways. In addition, advocates point to potential money and fuel savings, noting that fuel efficiency worsens at speeds above 60 mph. It is not clear, however, if the return to 55 mph will increase traffic safety. Many believe that traffic safety is based on the variability of the speed rather than the average speed that people are driving—the more variation in speed, the more dangerous the roads.

In this report, the variability of speeds on two highways is compared. The sample consists of the speeds of 40 cars recorded on a highway with a 55-mph speed limit (Highway 1) and the speeds of 40 cars recorded on a highway with a 65-mph speed limit (Highway 2). Table 11.A shows the most relevant descriptive measures for the analysis.

TABLE 11.A Summary Measures for Highway 1 and Highway 2

	Highway 1 (55-mph speed limit)	Highway 2 (65-mph speed limit)
Mean	56.60	66.00
Standard deviation	6.98	3.00
Number of cars	40	40

While it is true that cars travel at a slower speed, on average, on Highway 1 (56.60 mph < 66.00 mph), the variability of speeds is greater on Highway 1, as measured by the standard deviation (6.98 mph > 3.00 mph).

Two hypothesis tests are conducted. The first test examines whether or not the standard deviation on Highway 1 is greater than 5 mph at the 5% significance level or, alternatively, $\sigma^2 > 25$. The second test analyzes whether the standard deviation on Highway 1 is greater than the standard deviation on Highway 2 or, alternatively, $\sigma_1^2/\sigma_2^2 > 1$. The results of the tests are summarized in Table 11.B.

TABLE 11.B Competing Hypotheses, Test Statistics, and p-values

Hypotheses	Test Statistic	p-value
$H_0: \sigma^2 \leq 25$ $H_A: \sigma^2 > 25$	$\chi_{39}^2 = \dfrac{(n-1)s^2}{\sigma^2} = \dfrac{(40-1)(6.98)^2}{25} = 76.00$	≈ 0.00
$H_0: \sigma_1^2/\sigma_2^2 \leq 1$ $H_A: \sigma_1^2/\sigma_2^2 > 1$	$F_{(39,39)} = \dfrac{s_1^2}{s_2^2} = \dfrac{(6.98)^2}{(3.00)^2} = 5.41$	≈ 0.00

When testing whether or not the standard deviation is greater than 5 mph on Highway 1, a test statistic of 76.00 is obtained with a corresponding p-value that is approximately equal to zero. The null hypothesis regarding the population variance is rejected at any reasonable level of significance. In other words, the sample data suggest that the standard deviation is greater than 5 mph on Highway 1. The second hypothesis test reveals that the variance for Highway 1 is greater than the variance for Highway 2 given a test statistic of 5.41 and a corresponding p-value that is approximately equal to zero.

American drivers love to drive fast, which explains why safety advocates and conservationists are losing the long-running debate over lowering highway speed limits. While a 55-mph speed limit will save fuel and reduce greenhouse emissions, it is still an open question as to whether it will also enhance safety. If traffic safety is based on the variability of the speeds that people are driving rather than the average speed, then the data suggest that a return to a federal 55-mph speed limit may not necessarily enhance safety.

CONCEPTUAL REVIEW

LO 11.1 Discuss features of the χ^2 distribution.

The χ^2 **distribution** is characterized by a family of distributions, where each distribution depends on its particular degrees of freedom df. It is common, therefore, to refer to it as the χ_{df}^2 distribution. It is positively skewed with values ranging from zero to infinity. As the df grows larger, the χ_{df}^2 distribution tends to the normal distribution.

LO 11.2 Make inferences about the population variance.

Statistical inferences regarding σ^2 are based on the χ_{df}^2 distribution. A $100(1-\alpha)\%$ confidence interval for σ^2 is computed as $\left[\dfrac{(n-1)s^2}{\chi_{\alpha/2,df}^2}, \dfrac{(n-1)s^2}{\chi_{1-\alpha/2,df}^2}\right]$. The value of the test statistic for the hypothesis test for σ^2 is computed as $\chi_{df}^2 = \dfrac{(n-1)s^2}{\sigma_0^2}$, where σ_0^2 is the hypothesized value of the population variance. These formulas are valid when s^2 is computed using a random sample drawn from a normally distributed population.

LO 11.3 Discuss features of the F distribution.

The F **distribution** is also characterized by a family of distributions; however, each distribution depends on *two* degrees of freedom: the numerator degrees of freedom

df_1 and the denominator degrees of freedom df_2. It is common to refer to it as the $F_{(df_1, df_2)}$ distribution. The $F_{(df_1, df_2)}$ distribution is positively skewed with values ranging from zero to infinity, but becomes increasingly symmetric as df_1 and df_2 increase.

LO 11.4 **Make inferences about the ratio of two population variances.**

Statistical inferences regarding σ_1^2/σ_2^2 are based on the $F_{(df_1, df_2)}$ distribution. A $100(1 - \alpha)\%$ confidence interval for σ_1^2/σ_2^2 is computed as $\left[\left(\frac{s_1^2}{s_2^2}\right)\frac{1}{F_{\alpha/2,(df_1,df_2)}}, \left(\frac{s_1^2}{s_2^2}\right)F_{\alpha/2,(df_2,df_1)}\right]$.

The value of the test statistic for the hypothesis test of σ_1^2/σ_2^2 is computed as $F_{(df_1, df_2)} = s_1^2/s_2^2$, with $df_1 = n_1 - 1$ and $df_2 = n_2 - 1$. These formulas are valid when s_1^2 and s_2^2 are computed using independently drawn samples from two normally distributed populations.

ADDITIONAL EXERCISES AND CASE STUDIES

Exercises

39. A replacement part for a machine must be produced within close specifications in order for it to be acceptable to customers. A production process is considered to be working properly as long as the variance in the lengths of the parts does not exceed 0.05 squared-units. Suppose the sample variance computed from 30 parts turns out to be $s^2 = 0.07$. Use this sample evidence to test if the production specification is not being met at the 5% level of significance.

40. A consumer advocacy group is concerned about the variability in the cost of a generic drug. There is cause for concern if the variance of the cost exceeds 5 $(\$)^2$. The group surveys seven local pharmacies and obtains the following prices (in $) for a particular generic drug: 32, 36, 38, 32, 40, 31, 34.
    a. Test if there is a cause for concern for the consumer group at the 1% significance level.
    b. What assumption regarding the generic drug prices was made in this analysis?

41. A financial analyst maintains that the risk, measured by the variance, of investing in emerging markets is more than 280$(\%)^2$. Data on 20 stocks from emerging markets revealed the following sample results: $\bar{x} = 12.1(\%)$ and $s^2 = 361(\%)^2$. Assume that the returns are normally distributed.
    a. Specify the competing hypotheses to test the analyst's claim.
    b. What is the value of the test statistic and the p-value?

c. Is the financial analyst's claim supported by the data at the 1% significance level?

42. Fizzco, a beverage manufacturing company, is interested in determining whether the standard deviation of their dispensing process has changed from a required level of 5 milliliters. They have taken a random sample of 12 bottles and have measured the amount of beverage dispensed into each bottle (in milliliters) as shown below:

352	345	347	357	341	356
349	343	346	351	348	361

a. Construct the 95% confidence interval for the population standard deviation. Assume the amount of beverage dispensed follows a normal distribution.
b. At the 5% significance level, can we conclude that the standard deviation of the amount of beverage dispensed differs from the required level of 5 milliliters?

43. **FILE** *Checkout_Arrivals.* For staffing purposes, a retail store manager would like to standardize the number of checkout lanes to keep open on a particular shift. She believes that if the standard deviation of the hourly customer arrival rates is 8 customers or less, then a fixed number of checkout lanes can be staffed without excessive customer waiting time or excessive clerk idle time. However, before determining how many checkout lanes (and thus clerks) to use, she must

verify that the standard deviation of the arrival rates does not exceed 8. Accordingly, a sample of 25 hourly customer arrival rates was compiled for that shift over the past week.

a. State the hypotheses to test whether the standard deviation of the customer arrival rates exceeds 8.

b. Calculate the value of the test statistic. Assume that customer arrival rates are normally distributed.

c. Find the p-value.

d. At $\alpha = 0.05$, what is your conclusion? Would your conclusion change at the 1% significance level?

44. **FILE** *Automotive.* The following table presents a portion of the annual returns for Fidelity's Select Automotive Fund (in percent). This mutual fund invests primarily in companies engaged in the manufacturing, the marketing, or the sales of automobiles, trucks, specialty vehicles, parts, tires, and related services.

Year	Automotive Fund
1987	6.54
1988	20.06
⋮	⋮
2013	46.67

Source: www.biz.yahoo.com.

a. State the null and the alternative hypotheses in order to test whether the standard deviation is greater than 35%.

b. What assumption regarding the population is necessary to implement this step?

c. Calculate the value of the test statistic.

d. Find the p-value.

e. At $\alpha = 0.05$, what is your conclusion?

45. John Daum and Chris Yin are star swimmers at a local college. They are preparing to compete at the NCAA Division II national championship meet, where they both have a good shot at earning a medal in the men's 100-meter freestyle event. The coach feels that Chris is not as consistent as John, even though they clock about the same average time. In order to determine if the coach's concern is valid, you clock their time in the last 20 runs and compute a standard deviation of 0.85 seconds for John and 1.20 seconds for Chris. It is fair to assume that clock time is normally distributed for both John and Chris.

a. Specify the hypotheses to test if the variance of time for John is smaller than that of Chris.

b. Carry out the test at the 10% level of significance.

c. Who has a better likelihood of breaking the record at the meet? Explain.

46. Annual growth rates for individual firms in the toy industry tend to fluctuate dramatically, depending on consumers' tastes and current fads. Consider the following growth rates (in percent) for two companies in this industry, Hasbro and Mattel.

Year	2005	2006	2007	2008	2009
Hasbro	3.0	2.1	21.8	4.8	1.2
Mattel	1.5	9.1	5.7	−0.1	−8.2

Source: Annual Reports for Hasbro, Inc. and Mattel, Inc.

a. State the null and the alternative hypotheses in order to determine if the variance of growth rates differs for the two firms.

b. What assumption regarding the population is necessary to implement this step?

c. What is your conclusion at the 5% significance level?

47. At BurgerJoint, consistency in product and service is the new motto. Accordingly, management has invested in an automated French-fry dispenser to replace the manual dispensing method. The goal is to standardize the number of fries provided. The accompanying table shows the number of fries dispensed in a large-sized container based on samples of 10 orders before and after the process change. Assume these samples were drawn randomly and independently from normally distributed populations.

Manual	27	39	29	31	30	37	41	29	38	31
Automated	30	35	37	38	34	35	35	32	35	32

a. State the hypotheses to test whether the variance of the new automated dispensing method is lower than the previous manual method.

b. Calculate the value of the test statistic and the p-value.

c. What is the conclusion at the 1% significance level?

48. **FILE** *Safety_Stock.* An automotive parts distributor wants to standardize its safety stock level for two parts, A and B. ("Safety stock" is the excess inventory carried above the expected demand level to provide protection against demand variability.) Consequently, the distributor has randomly sampled daily demand for each part over the past 30 days.

a. State the null and alternative hypotheses to test if the variances of the daily demand values for the two parts are different.
b. Calculate the value of the test statistic and the p-value. Assume demand is normally distributed.
c. Make a conclusion at the 5% significance level.

49. **FILE** *Wait_Times.* Barbara Dwyer, the manager at Lux Hotel, makes every effort to ensure that customers attempting to make phone reservations do not have to wait too long to speak with a reservation specialist. Since the hotel accepts phone reservations 24 hours a day, Barbara is especially interested in maintaining consistency in service. Barbara wants to determine if the variance of wait time in the early morning shift (12:00 am – 6:00 am) differs from that in the late morning shift (6:00 am – 12:00 pm). She uses independently drawn samples of wait time for phone reservations for both shifts for the analysis; a portion of the data is shown in the accompanying table. Assume that wait times are normally distributed.

Early	Late
67	98
48	100
⋮	⋮
69	106

a. Specify the hypotheses to test if the variance of wait time in the early morning shift differs from that in the late morning shift.
b. At the 1% significance level, what is your conclusion?

50. **FILE** *Adidas_Revenues.* Adidas revenues (in millions of €) in the Greater China and Western Europe regions for the years 2011 through 2015 are shown in the accompanying table. Assume revenues are normally distributed.

	2011	2012	2013	2014	2015
Greater China	1229	1562	1655	1776	2449
Western Europe	3922	4076	3800	3793	4539

Source: *Adidas Online Annual Reports.*

a. Specify the competing hypotheses in order to test whether the variance in revenues is greater in the Greater China region than in the Western Europe region.
b. Calculate the value of the test statistic.
c. Find the p-value.
d. At $\alpha = 0.05$, what is your conclusion?

CASE STUDIES

CASE STUDY 11.1   Due to environmental concerns and the never-ending volatility of gas prices, drivers are becoming more concerned with their cars' gasoline consumption. Cameron White, a research analyst at a nonprofit organization, shares these concerns and wonders whether his car's gas consumption is as efficient as it was when he first bought the new car five years ago. Despite his best intentions, he has been a bit lax in his upkeep of the car and feels that this may adversely influence its performance. At the time he purchased the car, he was told that his car would average 29 miles per gallon (mpg) on highways, with a standard deviation of 1 mpg. He records his car's mpg from the last 20 fill-ups and obtains the following values.

Data for Case Study 11.1   Gasoline Consumption: Miles per Gallon

26	28	25	29	27	28	30	27	29	28
26	28	29	27	26	27	28	25	28	27

FILE
Gasoline_Consumption

In a report, use the above information to

1. Construct the 95% confidence interval for the population standard deviation. Discuss any assumptions you made for the analysis.
2. Determine whether the variability has increased from the original standard deviation of 1 mpg at the 5% level of significance.

CASE STUDY 11.2 Nicholas Grammas is an investment analyst examining the performance of two mutual funds with Janus Capital Group: the Janus Balanced Fund and the Janus Overseas Fund.

- The Janus Balanced Fund (JANBX): This "core" fund consists of stocks and bonds and its goal is diversification. It has historically produced solid long-term returns through different market cycles.
- The Janus Overseas Fund (JAOSX): This fund invests in overseas companies based on their individual merits instead of their geography or industry sector.

The following table reports a portion of the annual returns (in percent) for these two funds from 2000–2016.

Data for Case Study 11.2 Returns (in percent) for Janus Funds

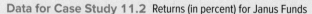

Year	Balanced	Overseas
2000	−2.16	−18.57
2001	−5.04	−23.11
⋮	⋮	⋮
2016	4.51	−6.91

Source: www.finance.yahoo.com, data retrieved March 1, 2017.

In a report, use the above information to

1. Describe the similarities and differences in these two funds' returns.
2. Examine whether the risk of one fund is different from the risk of the other fund at the 5% significance level. Discuss the assumptions made for the analysis.

CASE STUDY 11.3 For decades, people have believed that boys are innately more capable than girls in math. In other words, due to the intrinsic differences in brains, boys are better suited for doing math than girls. Recent research challenges this stereotype, arguing that gender differences in math performance have more to do with culture than innate aptitude. In the United States, for example, girls perform just as well on standardized math tests as boys. Others argue, however, that while the average may be the same, there is more variability in math ability for boys than girls, resulting in some boys with soaring math skills. A portion of representative data on math scores for boys and girls is shown in the accompanying table.

Data for Case Study 11.3 Math Scores for Boys and Girls

Boys	Girls
74	83
89	76
⋮	⋮
66	74

In a report, use the above information to

1. Construct and interpret the 95% confidence interval for the ratio of the variance of math scores for boys and for girls. Discuss the assumptions made for the analysis.
2. Determine at the 5% significance level if boys have more variability in math scores than girls.

APPENDIX 11.1   Guidelines for Other Software Packages

The following section provides brief commands for Minitab and JMP; SPSS does not provide applications suitable to this chapter. Copy and paste the specified data file into the relevant software spreadsheet prior to following the commands.

Minitab

Confidence Interval for σ^2

FILE
Growth_Value

A. (Replicating Example 11.2) From the menu, choose **Stat > Basic Statistics > 1 Variance**.

B. Choose **One or more samples, each in a column.** Select Growth and Value. Choose **Options**. Enter 95.0 for **Confidence Interval**.

Testing σ^2

A. (Replicating Example 11.4) From the menu, choose **Stat > Basic Statistics > 1 Variance**. Select **Perform hypothesis test**, select **Hypothesized variance**, and enter the value 100.

B. Choose **One or more samples, each in a column.** Select Value. Choose **Options**. Select "Variance $\neq$ hypothesized variance."

Confidence Interval for σ_2^1/σ_2^2

A. (Replicating Example 11.6) From the menu, choose **Stat > Basic Statistics > 2 Variances**.

B. Choose **Sample variances,** and under **Sample 1,** enter 11 for **Sample size** and 182.25 for **Variance**. Under **Sample 2**, enter 16 for **Sample size** and 457.96 for **Variance**. Choose **Options**. Enter 95.0 for **Confidence Interval**.

Testing σ_1^2/σ_2^2

A. (Replicating Example 11.8) From the menu, choose **Stat > Basic Statistics > 2 Variances**.

B. Choose **Sample standard deviations,** and under **Sample 1,** enter 10 for **Sample size** and 20.45 for **Standard deviation**. Under **Sample 2**, enter 10 for **Sample size** and 18.46 for **Standard deviation**.

C. Choose **Options**. Select "Ratio > hypothesized ratio."

JMP

Confidence Interval for σ^2

FILE
Growth_Value

A. (Replicating Example 11.2) From the menu, choose **Analyze > Distribution**.

B. Under **Select Columns**, select Growth and Value, and then under **Cast Selected Columns into Roles**, select **Y, Columns**.

C. Click the red triangle in the output window next to Growth and Value, and hover over **Confidence Interval** and select 0.95. Note that JMP only provides confidence interval for σ.

Testing σ^2

A. (Replicating Example 11.4) From the menu, choose **Analyze > Distribution**.

B. Under **Select Columns**, select Value, then under **Cast Selected Columns into Roles**, select **Y, Columns**.

C. Click the red triangle in the output window next to Value, and select **Test Std Dev**. After **Specify Hypothesized Standard Deviation**, enter 10.

12

Chi-Square Tests

LEARNING OBJECTIVES

After reading this chapter you should be able to:

LO **12.1** Conduct a goodness-of-fit test for a multinomial experiment.

LO **12.2** Conduct a test for independence.

LO **12.3** Conduct a goodness-of-fit test for normality.

LO **12.4** Conduct the Jarque-Bera test.

In this chapter, we focus on the χ^2 (chi-square) distribution to develop statistical tests that compare observed data with what we would expect from a population with a specific distribution. Generally, the chi-square tests are used to assess two types of comparison. First, a *goodness-of-fit test* is commonly used with a frequency distribution representing sample data of a qualitative variable. For instance, we may want to substantiate a claim that market shares in the automotive industry have changed dramatically over the past 10 years. Whereas a goodness-of-fit test focuses on a single qualitative variable, a *test for independence* is used to compare two qualitative variables. For example, we may want to determine whether a person's sex influences his/her purchase of a product. We can also extend the goodness-of-fit test to contest the assumption that sample data are drawn from a normal population. Since we use the normal distribution with quantitative data, we first convert the raw data into a frequency distribution. Finally, we introduce the Jarque-Bera test, which allows us to test for normality using the data in their raw form.

©Hongqi Zhang/iStock/Getty Images Plus/Getty Images RF

INTRODUCTORY CASE

Sportswear Brands

In the introductory case to Chapter 4, Annabel Gonzalez, chief retail analyst at a marketing firm, studies the relationship between the brand name of compression garments in the sport-apparel industry and the age of the consumer. Specifically, she wants to know whether the age of the consumer influences the brand name purchased.

Her initial feeling is that the Under Armour brand attracts a younger customer, whereas the more established companies, Nike and Adidas, draw an older clientele. She believes this information is relevant to advertisers and retailers in the sporting goods industry, as well as to some in the financial community. Suppose she collects data on 600 recent purchases in the compression-gear market. Table 12.1 summarizes the results of the sample using a contingency table, cross-classified by age and brand name.

TABLE 12.1 Purchases of Compression Garments Based on Age and Brand Name

Age Group	Brand Name		
	Under Armour	Nike	Adidas
Under 35 years	174	132	90
35 years or older	54	72	78

Annabel wants to use the above sample information to

1. Determine whether the two variables (Age Group and Brand Name) are related at the 5% significance level.

2. Discuss how the findings from the test for independence can be used.

A synopsis of this case will be provided in Section 12.2.

12.1 GOODNESS-OF-FIT TEST FOR A MULTINOMIAL EXPERIMENT

LO 12.1

Conduct a goodness-of-fit test for a multinomial experiment.

In Chapter 10, we compared the difference between two population proportions. Here we extend the analysis to test if two or more population proportions differ from each other or any predetermined (hypothesized) set of values. There are many instances where we may want to make inferences of this type. For instance, in a heavily concentrated industry consisting of four firms, we may want to determine whether market shares differ between the firms. Or, in a political contest, we may want to contest the prediction that Candidates A, B, and C will receive 70%, 20%, and 10% of the vote, respectively. Before conducting a test of this type, we must first ensure that the random experiment satisfies the conditions of a **multinomial experiment**, which is simply a generalization of the Bernoulli process first introduced in Chapter 5.

Recall that a Bernoulli process, also referred to as a binomial experiment, is a series of n independent and identical trials of an experiment, where each trial has only two possible outcomes, conventionally labeled "success" and "failure." For the binomial experiment, we generally denote the probability of success as p and the probability of failure as $1 - p$. Alternatively, we could let p_1 and p_2 represent these probabilities, where $p_1 + p_2 = 1$. Now let us assume that the number of outcomes per trial is k where $k \geq 2$.

A MULTINOMIAL EXPERIMENT

A multinomial experiment consists of a series of n independent and identical trials, such that for each trial:

- There are k possible outcomes called categories.
- The probability p_i associated with the ith category remains the same.
- The sum of the probabilities is one; that is, $p_1 + p_2 + \cdots + p_k = 1$.

Note that when $k = 2$, the multinomial experiment specializes to a binomial experiment.

Numerous experiments fit the conditions of a multinomial experiment. For instance,

- As compared to the previous day, a stockbroker records whether the price of a stock rises, falls, or stays the same. This example has three possible categories ($k = 3$).
- A consumer rates service at a restaurant as excellent, good, fair, or poor ($k = 4$).
- The admissions office records which of the six business concentrations a student picks ($k = 6$).

When setting up the competing hypotheses for a multinomial experiment, we have essentially two choices. We can set all population proportions equal to the same specific value or, equivalently, equal to one another. For instance, if we want to judge on the basis of sample data whether the proportion of voters who favor four different candidates is not the same, the competing hypotheses would take the following form:

$$H_0: p_1 = p_2 = p_3 = p_4 = 0.25$$

$$H_A: \text{Not all population proportions are equal to 0.25.}$$

Note that the hypothesized value under the null hypothesis is 0.25 because the population proportions must sum to one. We can also set each population proportion equal to a different predetermined (hypothesized) value. Suppose we want to contest the prediction that 40% of the voters favor Candidate 1, 30% favor Candidate 2, 20% favor Candidate 3, and 10% favor Candidate 4. The competing hypotheses are formulated as

H_0: $p_1 = 0.40$, $p_2 = 0.30$, $p_3 = 0.20$, and $p_4 = 0.10$

H_A: Not all population proportions equal their hypothesized values.

When conducting a test, we take a random sample and determine whether the sample proportions are close enough to the hypothesized population proportions. For this reason, this type of test is called a **goodness-of-fit test**. Under the usual assumption that the null hypothesis is true, we derive the expected frequencies of the categories in a multinomial experiment and compare them with observed frequencies. The objective is to determine whether we can reject the null hypothesis in favor of the alternative hypothesis. To see how to conduct a goodness-of-fit test, consider the following example.

One year ago, the management at a restaurant chain surveyed its patrons to determine whether changes should be made to the menu. One question on the survey asked patrons to rate the quality of the restaurant's entrées. The percentages of the patrons responding Excellent, Good, Fair, or Poor are listed in the following table:

Excellent	Good	Fair	Poor
15%	30%	45%	10%

Based on responses to the overall survey, management decided to revamp the menu. Recently, the same question concerning the quality of entrées was asked of a random sample of 250 patrons. Their responses are shown below:

Excellent	Good	Fair	Poor
46	83	105	16

At the 5% significance level, we want to determine whether there has been any change in the population proportions calculated one year ago.

Since we want to determine whether the responses of the 250 patrons are inconsistent with the earlier proportions, we let the earlier population proportions denote the hypothesized proportions for the test. Thus, we use p_1, p_2, p_3, and p_4 to denote the population proportions of those that responded Excellent, Good, Fair, or Poor, respectively, and construct the following competing hypotheses.

H_0: $p_1 = 0.15$, $p_2 = 0.30$, $p_3 = 0.45$, and $p_4 = 0.10$

H_A: Not all population proportions equal their hypothesized values.

The first step in calculating the value of the test statistic is to calculate the expected frequency for each category. That is, we need to estimate the frequencies that we would expect to get if the null hypothesis is true. In general, in order to calculate the expected frequency e_i for category i, we multiply the sample size n by the respective hypothesized value of the population proportion p_i. For example, consider the category Excellent. If H_0 is true, then we expect that 15% ($p_1 = 0.15$) of 250 patrons will find the quality of entrées to be excellent. Therefore, the expected frequency of Excellent responses is 37.5 ($= 250 \times 0.15$), whereas the corresponding observed frequency is 46. Expected frequencies for other responses are found similarly. Ultimately, when computing the value of the test statistic, we compare these expected frequencies to the frequencies we actually observe. The test statistic follows the χ^2 (chi-square) distribution that was discussed in Chapter 11. Because the distribution is characterized by a family of distributions, where each distribution depends on its particular degrees of freedom, df, it is common to make reference to it using the notation χ^2_{df}.

Table 12.2 shows the expected frequency e_i for each category. The condition that each expected frequency e_i must equal five or more is satisfied here. As we will see shortly, sometimes it is necessary to combine data from two or more categories to achieve this result.

TABLE 12.2 Calculation of Expected Frequency for Restaurant Example

	Hypothesized Proportion, p_i	Expected Frequency, $e_i = np_i$
Excellent	0.15	$250 \times 0.15 = 37.5$
Good	0.30	$250 \times 0.30 = 75.0$
Fair	0.45	$250 \times 0.45 = 112.5$
Poor	0.10	$250 \times 0.10 = 25.0$
		$\Sigma e_i = 250$

As a check on the calculations, the sum of the expected frequencies Σe_i must equal the sample size n, which in this example equals 250. Once the expected frequencies are estimated, we are ready to calculate the value of the test statistic.

The χ^2_{df} statistic measures how much the observed frequencies deviate from the expected frequencies. In particular, χ^2_{df} is computed as the sum of the standardized squared deviations. The smallest value that χ^2_{df} can assume is zero—this occurs when each observed frequency equals its expected frequency. Rejection of the null hypothesis occurs when χ^2_{df} is significantly greater than zero. As a result, these tests of hypotheses regarding multiple population proportions (p_1, p_2, p_3, . . .) are always implemented as right-tailed tests. However, since the alternative hypothesis states that not all population proportions equal their hypothesized values, rejection of the null hypothesis does not indicate which proportions differ from these values.

In this example, there are four categories ($k = 4$), so $df = k - 1 = 3$. The value of the test statistic is calculated as

$$\chi^2_{df} = \chi^2_3 = \Sigma \frac{(o_i - e_i)^2}{e_i}$$

$$= \frac{(46 - 37.5)^2}{37.5} + \frac{(83 - 75)^2}{75} + \frac{(105 - 112.5)^2}{112.5} + \frac{(16 - 25)^2}{25}$$

$$= 1.927 + 0.853 + 0.500 + 3.240 = 6.520.$$

Since a goodness-of-fit test is a right-tailed test, we calculate the p-value as $P(\chi^2_3 \geq 6.520)$. We show a portion of the χ^2 table from Appendix B in Table 12.3.

For $df = 3$, we see that 6.520 lies between the values 6.251 and 7.815, implying that the p-value is between 0.05 and 0.10. As explained in Chapter 11, we can use Excel's CHISQ.DIST.RT function or R's pchisq function to find the exact p-value as 0.089. Since the p-value is greater than 0.05, we do not reject H_0. We cannot conclude that the proportions differ from the ones from one year ago at the 5% significance

TABLE 12.3 Portion of the χ^2 table

df	Area in Upper Tail, α									
	0.995	0.990	0.975	0.950	0.900	0.100	0.050	0.025	0.010	0.005
1	0.000	0.000	0.001	0.004	0.016	2.706	3.841	5.024	6.635	7.879
2	0.010	0.020	0.051	0.103	0.211	4.605	5.991	7.378	9.210	10.597
3	0.072	0.115	0.216	0.352	0.584	6.251	7.815	9.348	11.345	12.838

level. Management may find this news disappointing in that the goal of the menu change was to improve customer satisfaction. Responses to other questions on the survey may shed more light on whether the goals of the menu change met or fell short of expectations.

EXAMPLE 12.1

Table 12.4 lists the market shares in 2010 of the five firms that manufacture a particular product. A marketing analyst wonders whether the market shares have changed since 2010. He surveys 200 customers. The last column of Table 12.4 shows the number of customers who recently purchased the product at each firm.

TABLE 12.4 Market Share of Five Firms

Firm	Market Share in 2010	Number of Recent Customers
1	0.40	70
2	0.32	60
3	0.24	54
4	0.02	10
5	0.02	6

a. Specify the competing hypotheses to test whether the market shares have changed since 2010.

b. Calculate the value of the test statistic.

c. Use $a = 0.05$ to determine if the market shares have changed since 2010.

SOLUTION:

a. Let p_i denote the market share for the ith firm. In order to test whether the market shares have changed since 2010, we *initially* set up the competing hypotheses as

H_0: $p_1 = 0.40$, $p_2 = 0.32$, $p_3 = 0.24$, $p_4 = 0.02$, and $p_5 = 0.02$

H_A: Not all market shares equal their hypothesized values.

b. The value of the test statistic is calculated as $\chi^2_{df} = \Sigma \frac{(o_i - e_i)^2}{e_i}$. The last column of Table 12.4 shows each firm's observed frequency o_i, so before applying the formula, we first calculate each firm's expected frequency e_i:

$$e_1 = 200 \times 0.40 = 80$$
$$e_2 = 200 \times 0.32 = 64$$
$$e_3 = 200 \times 0.24 = 48$$
$$e_4 = 200 \times 0.02 = 4$$
$$e_5 = 200 \times 0.02 = 4$$

$\left.\begin{array}{c} \\ \\ \end{array}\right\} 8$

We note that the expected frequencies for firms 4 and 5 are less than five. The test is valid so long as the expected frequencies in each category are five or more. In order to achieve this result, we combine the expected frequencies for firms 4 and 5 to obtain a combined frequency of eight ($e_4 + e_5 = 8$). We could have made other combinations, say e_4 with e_1 and e_5 with e_2, but we preferred to maintain a category for the less dominant firms. After making this combination, we now respecify the competing hypotheses as

H_0: $p_1 = 0.40$, $p_2 = 0.32$, $p_3 = 0.24$, and $p_4 = 0.04$

H_A: Not all market shares equal their hypothesized values.

With $df = k - 1 = 3$, we calculate the value of the test statistic as

$$\chi_3^2 = \Sigma \frac{(o_i - e_i)^2}{e_i} = \frac{(70 - 80)^2}{80} + \frac{(60 - 64)^2}{64} + \frac{(54 - 48)^2}{48} + \frac{(16 - 8)^2}{8}$$
$$= 1.250 + 0.250 + 0.750 + 8.000 = 10.250.$$

c. We calculate the p-value as $P(\chi_3^2 \geq 10.250)$. From Table 12.3, we see that 10.520 lies between the values 9.348 and 11.345, implying that the p-value is between 0.01 and 0.025. Using Excel's CHISQ.DIST.RT function or R's pchisq function, we find that the exact p-value is 0.017. Since the p-value is less than 0.05, we reject H_0. At the 5% significance level, we conclude that some market shares have changed.

As mentioned earlier, one limitation of this type of chi-square test is that we cannot tell which proportions differ from their hypothesized values. However, given the divergence between the observed and expected frequencies for the less dominant firms, it appears that they may be making some headway in this industry. Further testing can be conducted to see if this is the case.

Using R to Conduct a Goodness-of-Fit Test

Unfortunately, the current version of Excel does not provide a simple function to implement a goodness-of-fit test. However, R's **chisq.test** function generates both the value of the test statistic and the p-value for a goodness-of-fit test. Consider the following example.

EXAMPLE 12.2

It has been well documented that women have been underrepresented in earning STEM—science, technology, engineering, and mathematics—degrees. One reason this is important is that STEM graduates earn more than non-STEM graduates, so this outcome further aggravates the gender pay gap (*Women in STEM: A Gender Gap to Innovation*, U.S. Department of Commerce, 2011). Table 12.5 shows the proportions of college degrees awarded to women, categorized by major, in 2010. At this time, only 8% of graduating women earned STEM degrees. A researcher wonders if these proportions have changed since 2010. He collects data on 500 women who have recently graduated from college. The last column of Table 12.5 shows the number of women graduates in each major. At the 5% significance level, can he conclude that the proportions have changed since 2010?

TABLE 12.5 College Degrees Awarded to Women by Major

Major	2010 Proportions	Recent Numbers
Business	0.19	80
Education	0.09	35
Healthcare	0.12	85
Social Sciences	0.22	105
STEM	0.08	55
Other	0.30	140

Source: The 2010 proportions come from Table 322.50 in *Digest of Education Statistics,* 2011.

SOLUTION: We let p_i denote the proportion of college degrees awarded to women within the ith major. In order to test whether the proportions have changed since 2010, we set up the competing hypotheses as

H_0: $p_1 = 0.19$, $p_2 = 0.09$, $p_3 = 0.12$, $p_4 = 0.22$, $p_5 = 0.08$, and $p_6 = 0.30$

H_A: Not all proportions equal their hypothesized values.

Using R

a. Import the **STEM** data into a data frame (table) in R.

b. We use R's **chisq.test** function to calculate the value of the test statistic and the p-value. Within the **chisq.test** function, we use the option p to indicate the location of the hypothesized proportions.

```
> chisq.test(STEM$'Recent Numbers',
  p=STEM$'2010 Proportions')
```

And R returns:

```
Chi-squared test for given probabilities
data: STEM$"Recent Numbers"
X-squared = 21.526, df = 5, p-value = 0.0006441
```

The value of the test statistic is $\chi_5^2 = 21.526$ with a p-value of 0.001; both values are put in boldface. Since the p-value is less than 0.05, we can reject the null hypothesis. At the 5% significance level, we can conclude that the proportions have changed since 2010. Further research will need to be conducted to determine whether there has been an increase in the proportion of women who have received STEM degrees.

EXERCISES 12.1

Mechanics

1. Consider a multinomial experiment with $n = 250$ and $k = 4$. The null hypothesis to be tested is H_0: $p_1 = p_2 = p_3 = p_4 = 0.25$. The observed frequencies resulting from the experiment are

Category	1	2	3	4
Frequency	70	42	72	66

a. Specify the alternative hypothesis.

b. Calculate the value of the test statistic and the p-value.

c. At the 5% significance level, what is the conclusion to the hypothesis test?

2. Consider a multinomial experiment with $n = 400$ and $k = 3$. The null hypothesis is H_0: $p_1 = 0.60$, $p_2 = 0.25$, and $p_3 = 0.15$. The observed frequencies resulting from the experiment are

Category	1	2	3
Frequency	250	94	56

a. Specify the alternative hypothesis.

b. Calculate the value of the test statistic and the p-value.

c. At the 5% significance level, what is the conclusion to the hypothesis test?

3. A multinomial experiment produced the following results:

Category	1	2	3	4	5
Frequency	57	63	70	55	55

Can we conclude at the 1% significance level that not all population proportions are equal to 0.20?

4. A multinomial experiment produced the following results:

Category	1	2	3
Frequency	128	87	185

At the 1% significance level, can we reject H_0: $p_1 = 0.30$, $p_2 = 0.20$, and $p_3 = 0.50$?

Applications

5. You suspect that an unscrupulous employee at a casino has tampered with a die; that is, he is using a loaded die. In order to test this claim, you roll the die 200 times and obtain the following frequencies:

Category	1	2	3	4	5	6
Frequency	40	35	33	30	33	29

a. Specify the null and alternative hypotheses in order to test your claim.
b. Calculate the value of the test statistic and the p-value.
c. At the 10% significance level, can you conclude that the die is loaded?

6. A study conducted in September and October of 2010 found that fewer than half of employers who hired new college graduates last academic year plan to definitely do so again (*The Wall Street Journal*, November 29, 2010). Suppose the hiring intentions of the respondents were as follows:

Definitely Hire	Likely to Hire	Hire Uncertain	Will not Hire
37%	17%	28%	18%

Six months later, a sample of 500 employers were asked their hiring intentions and gave the following responses:

Definitely Hire	Likely to Hire	Hire Uncertain	Will not Hire
170	100	120	110

a. Specify the competing hypotheses to test whether the proportions from the initial study have changed.

b. Calculate the value of the test statistic and the p-value.
c. At the 5% significance level, what is the conclusion to the hypothesis test? Interpret your results.

7. A rent-to-own (RTO) agreement appeals to low-income and financially distressed consumers. It allows immediate access to merchandise, and by making all payments, the consumer acquires the merchandise. At the same time, goods can be returned at any point without penalty. Suppose a recent study documents that 65% of RTO contracts are returned, 30% are purchased, and the remaining 5% default. In order to test the validity of this claim, an RTO researcher looks at the transaction data of 420 RTO contracts, of which 283 are returned, 109 are purchased, and the rest defaulted.

a. Set up the competing hypothesis to test whether the return, purchase, and default probabilities of RTO contracts differ from 0.65, 0.30, and 0.05, respectively.
b. Compute the value of the test statistic.
c. Conduct the test at the 5% level of significance, and interpret the test results.

8. Despite Zimbabwe's shattered economy, with endemic poverty and widespread political strife and repression, thousands of people from overseas still head there every year (*BBC News*, August 27, 2008). Main attractions include the magnificent Victoria Falls, the ruins of Great Zimbabwe, and herds of roaming wildlife. A tourism director claims that Zimbabwe visitors are equally represented by Europe, North America, and the rest of the world. Records show that of the 380 tourists who recently visited Zimbabwe, 148 were from Europe, 106 were from North America, and 126 were from the rest of the world.

a. A recent visitor to Zimbabwe believes that the tourism director's claim is wrong. Set up the competing hypotheses to test the visitor's belief.
b. Conduct the test at the 5% significance level. Do the sample data support the visitor's belief?

9. In 2003, *The World Wealth Report* first started publishing market shares of global millionaires (*The Wall Street Journal*, June 25, 2008). At this time, the distribution of the world's people worth $1 million or more was as follows:

Region	Millionaires
Europe	35.7%
North America	31.4%
Asia Pacific	22.9%
Latin America	4.3%
Middle East	4.3%
Africa	1.4%

Source: *The Wealth Report*, 2003.

A recent sample of 500 global millionaires produces the following results:

Region	Number of Millionaires
Europe	153
North America	163
Asia Pacific	139
Latin America	20
Middle East	20
Africa	5

a. Test whether the distribution of millionaires today is different from the distribution in 2003 at $\alpha = 0.05$.

b. Would the conclusion change if we tested it at $\alpha = 0.10$?

10. An Associated Press/GfK Poll shows that 38% of American drivers favor U.S. cars, while 33% prefer Asian brands, with the remaining 29% going for other foreign cars (www.msnbc.com, April 21, 2010). A researcher wonders whether the preferences for cars have changed since the Associated Press/GfK Poll. He surveys 200 Americans and finds that the number of respondents in the survey who prefer American, Asian, and other foreign cars are 66, 70, and 64, respectively. At the 5% significance level, can the researcher conclude that preferences have changed since the Associated Press/GfK Poll?

11. The quality department at an electronics company has noted that, historically, 92% of the units of a specific product pass a test operation, 6% fail the test but are able to be repaired, and 2% fail the test and need to be scrapped. Due to recent process improvements, the quality department would like to test if the rates have changed. A recent sample of 500 parts revealed that 475 parts passed the test, 18 parts failed the test but were repairable, and 7 parts failed the test and were scrapped.

a. State the null and alternative hypotheses to test if the current proportions are different than the historical proportions.

b. Calculate the value of the test statistic and the p-value.

c. At the 5% significance level, what is your conclusion? Would your conclusion change at the 1% significance level?

12. An agricultural grain company processes and packages various grains purchased from farmers. A high-volume conveyor line contains four chutes at the end, each of which is designed to receive and dispense equal proportions of grain into bags. Each bag is then stamped with a date code and the number of the chute from which it came. If the chute output proportions are not relatively equal, then a bottleneck effect is created upstream and the conveyor cannot function at peak output. Recently, a series of repairs and modifications have led management to question whether the grains still are being equally distributed among the chutes. Packaging records from 800 bags yesterday indicate that 220 bags came from Chute 1, 188 bags from Chute 2, 218 bags from Chute 3, and 174 bags from Chute 4.

a. State the null and alternative hypotheses to test if the proportion of bags filled by any of the chutes is different from 0.25.

b. Calculate the value of the test statistic and the p-value.

c. What is your conclusion at the 10% significance level? Would your conclusion change at the 5% significance level?

12.2 CHI-SQUARE TEST FOR INDEPENDENCE

LO 12.2

Recall from Chapter 4 that a contingency table is a useful tool when we want to examine or compare two qualitative variables defined on the same population.

Conduct a test for independence.

CONTINGENCY TABLE

A contingency table generally shows frequencies for two qualitative (categorical) variables, x and y, where each cell represents a mutually exclusive combination of the pair of x and y values.

In this section, we use the data in a contingency table to conduct a hypothesis test that determines whether the two qualitative variables depend upon one another. Whereas a goodness-of-fit test examines a single qualitative variable, a **test for independence**—also called a **chi-square test of a contingency table**—assesses the relationship between two qualitative variables. Many examples of the use of this test arise, especially in marketing, biomedical research, and courts of law. For instance, a retailer may be trying to determine whether there is a relationship between the age of its clientele and where it chooses to advertise. Doctors might want to investigate whether or not losing weight through stomach surgery can extend the lives of severely obese patients. Or one party in a discrimination lawsuit may be trying to show that a person's sex and promotion are related. All of these examples lend themselves to applications of the hypothesis test discussed in this section.

In the introductory case study, we are presented with a contingency table cross-classified by the variables Age Group and Brand Name. Specifically, we want to determine whether or not the age of a consumer influences his/her decision to buy a garment from Under Armour, Nike, or Adidas. We will conduct this test at the 5% significance level.

In general, the competing hypotheses for a statistical test for independence are formulated such that rejecting the null hypothesis leads to the conclusion that the two qualitative variables are dependent. Formally,

H_0: The two qualitative variables are independent.

H_A: The two qualitative variables are dependent.

Since the criteria upon which we classify the data are Age Group and Brand Name, we write the competing hypotheses as

H_0: Age Group and Brand Name are independent.

H_A: Age Group and Brand Name are dependent.

Table 12.6 reproduces Table 12.1 of the introductory case. The variable Age Group has two possible categories: (1) Under 35 years and (2) 35 years or older. The variable Brand Name has three possible categories: (1) Under Armour, (2) Nike, and (3) Adidas. Each cell in this table represents an observed frequency o_{ij}, where the subscript ij refers to the ith row and the jth column. Thus, o_{13} refers to the cell in the first row and the third column. Here, $o_{13} = 90$, or, equivalently, 90 customers under 35 years of age purchased an Adidas product.

TABLE 12.6 Purchases of Compression Garments Based on Age and Brand Name

Age Group	Brand Name		
	Under Armour	Nike	Adidas
Under 35 years	174	132	90
35 years or older	54	72	78

We will use the independence assumption postulated under the null hypothesis to derive an expected frequency for each cell from the sample data. In other words, we first estimate values as if no relationship exists between the age of a consumer and the brand name of the clothing purchased. Then we will compare these expected frequencies with the observed values to compute the value of the test statistic.

Calculating Expected Frequencies

For ease of exposition, we let events A_1 and A_2 represent "Under 35 years" and "35 years or older," respectively; events B_1, B_2, and B_3 stand for Under Armour, Nike, and Adidas, respectively. We then sum the frequencies for each column and row. For instance, the sum of the frequencies for Event A_1 is 396; this is obtained by summing the values in row A_1: 174, 132, and 90. Totals for the other rows and columns are shown in Table 12.7.

TABLE 12.7 Row and Column Totals

Age Group	Brand Name			Row Total
	B_1	B_2	B_3	
A_1	e_{11}	e_{12}	e_{13}	396
A_2	e_{21}	e_{22}	e_{23}	204
Column Total	228	204	168	600

Our goal is to calculate the expected frequency e_{ij} for each cell, where again the subscript ij refers to the ith row and the jth column. Thus, e_{13} refers to the cell in the first row and the third column, or the expected number of customers who are under 35 years of age and purchase an Adidas product.

Before we can arrive at the expected frequencies, we first calculate marginal row probabilities (the proportion of people under 35 years of age and those 35 years old or older) and marginal column probabilities (the proportion of people purchasing from each brand name). We calculate a marginal row (column) probability by dividing the row (column) sum by the total sample size:

Marginal Row Probabilities:

$$P(A_1) = \frac{396}{600} \quad \text{and} \quad P(A_2) = \frac{204}{600}$$

Marginal Column Probabilities:

$$P(B_1) = \frac{228}{600}, P(B_2) = \frac{204}{600}, \text{and } P(B_3) = \frac{168}{600}$$

We can now calculate each cell probability by applying the multiplication rule for independent events from Chapter 4. That is, if two events are independent, say events A_1 and B_1 (our assumption under the null hypothesis), then their joint probability is

$$P(A_1 \cap B_1) = P(A_1)P(B_1) = \left(\frac{396}{600}\right)\left(\frac{228}{600}\right) = 0.2508.$$

Multiplying this joint probability by the sample size yields the expected frequency for e_{11}; that is, the expected number of customers who are under 35 years of age and purchase an Under Armour product is

$$e_{11} = 600(0.2508) = 150.48.$$

CALCULATING EXPECTED FREQUENCIES FOR A TEST FOR INDEPENDENCE

We use the following general formula to calculate the expected frequencies for each cell in a contingency table:

$$e_{ij} = \frac{(\text{Row } i \text{ total})(\text{Column } j \text{ total})}{\text{Sample Size}},$$

where e_{ij} is the expected frequency for each cell in a contingency table, and the subscript ij refers to the ith row and the jth column.

Applying the formula, we calculate all expected frequencies as

$$e_{11} = \frac{(396)(228)}{600} = 150.48 \quad e_{12} = \frac{(396)(204)}{600} = 134.64 \quad e_{13} = \frac{(396)(168)}{600} = 110.88$$

$$e_{21} = \frac{(204)(228)}{600} = 77.52 \quad e_{22} = \frac{(204)(204)}{600} = 69.36 \quad e_{23} = \frac{(204)(168)}{600} = 57.12$$

Table 12.8 shows the expected frequency e_{ij} for each cell. In order to satisfy subsequent assumptions, each expected frequency e_{ij} *must equal five or more*. This condition is satisfied here. As we saw in Example 12.1, it may be necessary to combine two or more rows or columns to achieve this result in other applications.

TABLE 12.8 Expected Frequencies for Contingency Table

Age Group	Brand Name			Row Total
	B_1	B_2	B_3	
A_1	150.48	134.64	110.88	396
A_2	77.52	69.36	57.12	204
Column Total	228	204	168	600

When conducting a test for independence, we calculate the value of the chi-square test statistic χ^2_{df}. Analogous to the discussion in Section 12.1, χ^2_{df} measures how much the observed frequencies deviate from the expected frequencies. The smallest value that χ^2_{df} can assume is zero—this occurs when each observed frequency equals its expected frequency. Thus, a test for independence is also implemented as a *right-tailed test*.

TEST STATISTIC FOR A TEST FOR INDEPENDENCE

For a test for independence applied to a contingency table with r rows and c columns, the value of the test statistic is calculated as

$$\chi^2_{df} = \sum_i \sum_j \frac{(o_{ij} - e_{ij})^2}{e_{ij}},$$

where $df = (r - 1)(c - 1)$, and o_{ij} and e_{ij} are the observed frequency and the expected frequency, respectively, for each cell in a contingency table.

Note: This test is valid when the expected frequencies for each cell are five or more.

With two rows and three columns in the contingency table, degrees of freedom are calculated as $df = (r - 1)(c - 1) = (2 - 1)(3 - 1) = 2$. We apply the formula to compute the value of the test statistic as

$$\chi^2_2 = \frac{(174 - 150.48)^2}{150.48} + \frac{(132 - 134.64)^2}{134.64} + \frac{(90 - 110.88)^2}{110.88}$$
$$+ \frac{(54 - 77.52)^2}{77.52} + \frac{(72 - 69.36)^2}{69.36} + \frac{(78 - 57.12)^2}{57.12}$$
$$= 3.6762 + 0.0518 + 3.9319 + 7.1361 + 0.1005 + 7.6326 = 22.529.$$

For $df = 2$, we calculate the p-value as $P(\chi^2_2 \geq 22.529)$. From Table 12.3, we see that 22.529 is greater than 10.597, implying that the p-value is less than 0.005. As discussed in Section 12.1, we can use Excel's CHISQ.DIST.RT function or R's pchisq function to find the exact p-value as 0 (approximately). Since the p-value is less than 0.05, we reject H_0. At the 5% significance level, we conclude that the two qualitative variables are dependent; that is, there is a relationship between the age of a consumer and the brand name of the apparel purchased.

SYNOPSIS OF INTRODUCTORY CASE

Under Armour pioneered clothing in the compression-gear market. Compression garments are meant to keep moisture away from a wearer's body during athletic activities in warm and cool weather. Wicking moisture is a secondary characteristic of compression gear. Wicking materials were in widespread use before Under Armour and are used in most noncompression athletic wear. The characteristic that defines *compression* gear is that it is tight to help compress muscles, which supposedly helps them work better, avoid injury, and recover faster. Under Armour has experienced exponential growth since the firm went public in November 2005 (*USA Today*, June 16, 2010); however, Nike and Adidas have aggressively entered the compression-gear market as well. An analysis was conducted to examine whether the age of the customer matters when making a purchase in the compression-gear market. This information is relevant not only for Under Armour and how the firm may focus its advertising efforts, but also to competitors and retailers in this market. Data were collected on 600 recent purchases in the compression-gear market; the data were then cross-classified by age group and brand name. A test for independence was conducted at the 5% significance level. The results suggest that a customer's age and the brand name purchased are related to one another. Given that age influences the brand name purchased, it is not surprising that Under Armour signed NFL quarterback Tom Brady (http://cnbc.com, October 6, 2010) to endorse its products, a move likely to attract a younger consumer. Brady had spent most of his career with Nike before breaking away to go with Under Armour.

©Jean Baptiste Lacroix/ WireImage/Getty Images

EXAMPLE 12.3

In general, Latinos and Caucasians use social media networks equally, but there are some differences in their preferences for specific social media sites (www.pewresearch.org, February 5, 2015). In particular, Instagram is more popular among Latinos while Pinterest is more popular among Caucasians. Kate Dawson, a junior in college, decides to test if similar differences exist among students on her campus. She collects data on 400 students cross-classified by Race (Latinos versus Caucasians) and Social Media Preference (Instagram versus Pinterest). The results are shown in Table 12.9. At the 10% significance level, determine whether the sample data support racial differences in social media preferences.

TABLE 12.9 Social Media Preference by Race

Race	Social Media Preference		Row Total
	Instagram	Pinterest	
Latinos	50	60	110
Caucasians	120	170	290
Column Total	170	230	400

SOLUTION: In order to determine whether social media preference depends on race, we specify the competing hypotheses as

H_0: Race and Social Media Preference are independent.

H_A: Race and Social Media Preference are dependent.

The value of the test statistic is calculated as $\chi^2_{df} = \sum_i \sum_j \frac{(o_{ij} - e_{ij})^2}{e_{ij}}$. Table 12.9 provides each cell's observed frequency o_{ij}, so before applying the formula, we first calculate each cell's expected frequency e_{ij}:

$$e_{11} = \frac{(110)(170)}{400} = 46.75 \qquad e_{12} = \frac{(110)(230)}{400} = 63.25$$

$$e_{21} = \frac{(290)(170)}{400} = 123.25 \qquad e_{22} = \frac{(290)(230)}{400} = 166.75$$

With two rows and two columns in the contingency table, degrees of freedom are calculated as $df = (r-1)(c-1) = (2-1)(2-1) = 1$. The value of the test statistic is calculated as

$$\chi^2_1 = \frac{(50 - 46.75)^2}{46.75} + \frac{(60 - 63.25)^2}{63.25} + \frac{(120 - 123.25)^2}{123.25} + \frac{(170 - 166.75)^2}{166.75}$$

$$= 0.2259 + 0.1670 + 0.0857 + 0.0633 = 0.542.$$

Using Excel's CHISQ.DIST.RT function or R's pchisq function, we find that the exact p-value, $P(\chi^2_1 \geq 0.542)$, is equal to 0.462. Since the p-value is greater than 0.10, we do not reject H_0. At the 10% significance level, the sample data do not support racial differences in social media preferences.

Using R to Conduct a Test for Independence

In addition to being used in goodness-of-fit tests, R's **chisq.test** function also simplifies a test for independence by providing the value of the test statistic and the p-value. Consider the following example.

FILE
STEM2

EXAMPLE 12.4

The dean at a large university would like to examine whether one's sex influences the field choice within the STEM major. She samples 500 recent graduates cross-classified by one's sex and STEM field. At the 5% significance level, can the dean conclude that field choice depends on one's sex?

TABLE 12.10 STEM Degrees by Sex

STEM Field	Female	Male
Sciences	120	100
Technology	15	75
Engineering	30	125
Math	15	20

SOLUTION: We specify the competing hypotheses as

H_0: Sex and Field Choice are independent.

H_A: Sex and Field Choice are dependent.

Using R

a. Import the **STEM2** data into a data frame (table) in R.

b. We use R's **chisq.test** function to calculate the value of the test statistic, as well as the p-value. Within the **chisq.test** function, we indicate that the relevant data are in columns 2 and 3 of the data frame; we also set the option *correct* to FALSE since we are not interested in applying a continuity correction factor. We enter

```
> chisq.test(STEM2[, 2:3], correct=FALSE)
```

And R returns:

```
 Pearson's Chi-squared test
 data: STEM2[, 2:3]
 X-squared = 66.795, df = 3, p-value = 2.072e-14
```

The value of the test statistic is $\chi_3^2 = 66.795$, with a *p*-value equal to 0 (approximately); both values are put in boldface. Since the *p*-value is less than 0.05, we can reject the null hypothesis. At the 5% significance level, we can conclude that one's sex does influence field choice within the STEM major. A common misconception with this conclusion is that men outnumber women in all STEM fields. Recent research suggests that men outnumber women in technology and engineering, but the opposite is true in the sciences (www.pbs.org, April 17, 2015). Other tests, such as statistical inference with respect to the population proportion, can be conducted that capture specific differences within the STEM fields.

EXERCISES 12.2

Mechanics

13. Given the following contingency table, conduct a test for independence at the 5% significance level.

	Variable A	
Variable B	1	2
1	23	47
2	32	53

14. Given the following contingency table, conduct a test for independence at the 1% significance level.

	Variable A			
Variable B	1	2	3	4
1	120	112	100	110
2	127	115	120	124
3	118	115	110	124

Applications

15. According to an online survey by Harris Interactive for job site CareerBuilder.com (InformationWeek.com, September 27, 2007), more than half of IT workers say they have fallen asleep at work. The same is also true for government workers. Assume that the following contingency table is representative of the survey results.

	Job Category	
Slept on the Job?	IT Professional	Government Professional
Yes	155	256
No	145	144

a. Specify the competing hypotheses to determine whether sleeping on the job is associated with job category.

b. Calculate the value of the test statistic.

c. Find the *p*-value.

d. At the 5% significance level, can you conclude that sleeping on the job depends on job category?

16. A market researcher for an automobile company suspects differences in preferred color between male and female buyers. Advertisements targeted to different groups should take such differences into account, if they exist. The researcher examines the most recent sales information of a particular car that comes in three colors.

	Sex of Automobile Buyer	
Color	Male	Female
Silver	470	280
Black	535	285
Red	495	350

a. Specify the competing hypotheses to determine whether color preference depends on the automobile buyer's sex.

b. Calculate the value of the test statistic and the *p*-value.

c. Does your conclusion suggest that the company should target advertisements differently for males versus females? Explain.

17. The following sample data reflect shipments received by a large firm from three different vendors and the quality of those shipments.

Vendor	Defective	Acceptable
1	14	112
2	10	70
3	22	150

a. Specify the competing hypotheses to determine whether quality is associated with the source of the shipments.

b. Conduct the test at the 1% significance level.

c. Should the firm be concerned about the source of the shipments? Explain.

18. A marketing agency would like to determine if there is a relationship between union membership and type of vehicle owned (domestic or foreign brand). The goal is to develop targeted advertising campaigns for particular vehicle brands likely to appeal to specific groups of customers. A survey of 500 potential customers revealed the following results.

	Union Member	Not Union Member
Domestic brand	133	147
Foreign brand	67	153

a. Specify the competing hypotheses to determine whether vehicle brand (domestic, foreign) is associated with union membership.

b. Conduct the test at the 10% significance level. What is your conclusion?

c. Is the conclusion reached in part (b) sensitive to the choice of significance level?

19. The quality manager believes there may be a relationship between the experience level of an inspector and whether a product passes or fails inspection. Inspection records were reviewed for 630 units of a particular product, and the number of units which passed and failed inspection was determined based on three inspector experience levels. The results are shown in the following table.

	Experience Level		
Decision	Low (< 2 years)	Medium (2–8 years)	High (> 8 years)
Pass	152	287	103
Fail	16	46	26

a. Specify the competing hypotheses to determine whether the inspector pass/fail decision depends on experience level.

b. Calculate the value of the test statistic.

c. Find the *p*-value.

d. At the 5% significance level, what is your conclusion? Does your conclusion change at the 1% significance level?

20. According to a 2008 survey by the Pew Research Center, people in China are highly satisfied with their roaring economy and the direction of their nation (*USA Today*, July 22, 2008). Eighty-six percent of those who were surveyed expressed positive views of the way China is progressing and described the economic situation as good. A political analyst wants to know if this optimism among the Chinese depends on age. In an independent survey of 280 Chinese residents, the respondents are asked how happy they are with the direction that their country is taking. Their responses are tabulated in the following table.

Age	Very Happy	Somewhat Happy	Not Happy
20 up to 40	23	50	18
40 up to 60	51	38	16
60 and older	19	45	20

a. Set up the hypotheses to test the claim that optimism regarding China's direction depends on the age of the respondent.

b. Calculate the value of the test statistic.

c. Find the *p*-value.

d. At the 1% level of significance, can we infer that optimism among the Chinese is dependent on age?

21. A study by the Massachusetts Community & Banking Council found that blacks, and, to a lesser extent, Latinos, remain largely unable to borrow money at the same interest rate as whites (*The Boston Globe*, February 28, 2008). The following contingency table shows representative data for the city of Boston, cross-classified by race and type of interest rate received:

	Type of Interest Rate on Loan	
Race	High Interest Rate	Low Interest Rate
Black	553	480
Latino	265	324
White	491	3,701

At the 5% significance level, do the data indicate that the interest rate received on a loan is dependent on race? Provide the details.

22. Founded in February 2004, Facebook is a social utility that helps people communicate with their friends and family. In just six years, Facebook had acquired more than 500 million active users, of which 50% logged on to Facebook in any given day. In a survey of 3,000 Facebook users, the designers looked at why Facebook users break up in a relationship (*The Wall Street Journal*, November 27–28, 2010).

Reasons for Breakup	Sex of Respondent	
	Percentage of Men	Percentage of Women
Nonapproval	3	4
Distance	21	16
Cheating	18	22
Lost Interest	28	26
Other	30	32

Source: Internal survey of 3,000 Facebook users.

Suppose the survey consisted of 1,800 men and 1,200 women. Use the data to determine whether the reasons for breakup depend on one's sex at the 1% significance level. Provide the details.

12.3 CHI-SQUARE TESTS FOR NORMALITY

The goodness-of-fit test for a multinomial experiment can also be used to test a hypothesis that a population has a particular probability distribution. For instance, we can use this test to determine whether the sample data fit the binomial or the Poisson distributions. However, due to its wide applicability, we focus on the normal distribution. We first describe the **goodness-of-fit test for normality**. We then introduce another chi-square test for normality referred to as the Jarque-Bera test.

The Goodness-of-Fit Test for Normality

Suppose an economist claims that annual household income in a small Midwestern city is not normally distributed. We will use the representative data (in $1,000s) in Table 12.11 to test this claim at the 5% significance level.

Conduct a goodness-of-fit test for normality.

TABLE 12.11 Household Income (in $1,000s)

90	15	85	54	62	38	38	55	62	210
19	38	57	78	98	42	19	62	66	90
25	38	14	65	77	110	22	18	180	52
44	17	45	99	250	78	58	35	57	45
37	58	62	44	35	78	35	82	94	58

Household_Income

We first use the data to compute the sample mean and the sample standard deviation as

$$\bar{x} = 63.80 \quad \text{and} \quad s = 45.78.$$

Since we want to determine whether or not the given data represent a random sample from a population having a normal distribution, we specify the null and the alternative hypotheses accordingly.

H_0: Income (in $1,000s) follows a normal distribution with mean $63.80 and standard deviation $45.78.

H_A: Income (in $1,000s) does not follow a normal distribution with mean $63.80 and standard deviation $45.78.

The null hypothesis implies that the underlying distribution is normal and that the population mean and the population standard deviation equal their estimates, or, equivalently, $\mu = 63.80$ and $\sigma = 45.78$. As discussed in Section 12.1, the goodness-of-fit test for a multinomial experiment deals with a single population of qualitative data. Since observations that follow the normal distribution are quantitative, we essentially need to convert the data into a qualitative format. After computing the sample mean and the sample standard deviation, we divide the data into k non-overlapping intervals (categories); in other words, we construct a frequency distribution. The intervals are chosen somewhat arbitrarily. The first two columns of Table 12.12 show the frequency distribution for the raw data from Table 12.11, divided up into five non-overlapping intervals.

TABLE 12.12 Calculations for the Normality Test Example

Income (in $1,000s)	Observed Frequency, o_i	p_i if H_0 is True	Expected Frequency, $e_i = n \times p_i$	Standardized Squared Deviation, $\frac{(o_i - e_i)^2}{e_i}$
Income < 20	6	0.1685	$50 \times 0.1685 = 8.425$	$\frac{(6 - 8.43)^2}{8.43} = 0.6980$
$20 \le$ Income < 40	10	0.1330	$50 \times 0.1330 = 6.650$	1.6876
$40 \le$ Income < 60	13	0.1666	$50 \times 0.1666 = 8.330$	2.6181
$60 \le$ Income < 80	10	0.1687	$50 \times 0.1687 = 8.435$	0.2904
Income ≥ 80	11	0.3632	$50 \times 0.3632 = 18.160$	2.8230
	$\Sigma o_i = 50$	$\Sigma p_i = 1$	$\Sigma e_i = 50$	$\Sigma \frac{(o_i - e_i)^2}{e_i} = 8.117$

Earlier, we were able to calculate expected frequencies by multiplying the sample size n by the hypothesized probabilities (proportions) p_i under the null hypothesis. Here, we first calculate the probabilities under the assumption that the null hypothesis is true and then use them to calculate expected frequencies. For example, under the null hypothesis that income is normally distributed with $\mu = 63.80$ and $\sigma = 45.78$, we reference the z table to find the probability that an individual's income is less than 20, or

$$P(X < 20) = P\left(\frac{X - \mu}{\sigma} < \frac{20 - 63.80}{45.78}\right) = P(Z < -0.96) = 0.1685.$$

We proceed with the other intervals in a like manner.

$$P(20 \le X < 40) = P(-0.96 \le Z < -0.52) = 0.1330$$
$$P(40 \le X < 60) = P(-0.52 \le Z < -0.08) = 0.1666$$
$$P(60 \le X < 80) = P(-0.08 \le Z < 0.35) = 0.1687$$
$$P(X \ge 80) = P(Z \ge 0.35) = 0.3632$$

The third column of Table 12.12 shows these probabilities. We are then able to compute the expected frequencies for each interval as $n \times p_i$. The fourth column of Table 12.12 shows the values for the expected frequencies. It is important to ensure that the expected frequency is five or more in each interval. In this example, this condition is satisfied; however in other applications, it may be necessary to combine adjacent intervals until this condition is achieved.

As in Section 12.1, the appropriate test statistic follows the χ^2_{df} distribution, and its value is calculated as $\chi^2_{df} = \Sigma \frac{(o_i - e_i)^2}{e_i}$. The only difference is that the degrees of freedom is equal to the number of intervals k minus one, minus the number of parameters estimated. Since we estimate two parameters—the population mean and the population standard deviation—from the sample data, the degrees of freedom for the chi-square test for normality is always $k - 1 - 2 = k - 3$. In this example we formed five intervals ($k = 5$); therefore, we calculate $df = 5 - 3 = 2$.

As shown in the last column of Table 12.12, we sum the standardized squared deviations to find the value of the chi-square test statistic as $\chi_{df}^2 = \chi_2^2 = 8.117$. Like before, the goodness-of-fit test for normality is a right-tailed test. Using Excel's CHISQ.DIST.RT function or R's pchisq function, we find that the p-value, $P(\chi_2^2 \geq 8.117)$, is equal to 0.017. Since the p-value is less than 0.05, we reject H_0. At the 5% significance level, we conclude that income in this Midwestern city does not follow a normal distribution with a mean of \$63,800 and a standard deviation of \$45,780.

The Jarque-Bera Test

A criticism of the goodness-of-fit test for normality is that we first have to convert raw data into a frequency distribution by grouping them into a set of arbitrary intervals or categories. The resulting value of the chi-square test statistic depends on how the data are grouped. An alternative to the goodness-of-fit test for normality is the **Jarque-Bera test**. In this test, it is not necessary to convert the quantitative data into a qualitative form.

For the Jarque-Bera test, we first calculate the **skewness coefficient** S and the (excess) **kurtosis coefficient** K of the sample data. A skewness coefficient of zero indicates that the data are symmetric about the mean. The kurtosis coefficient measures whether a distribution is more or less peaked than a normal distribution. The skewness coefficient and the kurtosis coefficient for the normal distribution are both equal to zero.

When testing whether sample data are derived from the normal distribution, the null hypothesis consists of the joint hypothesis that both the skewness coefficient and the kurtosis coefficient are zero. It can be shown that the Jarque-Bera test statistic follows the χ_{df}^2 distribution with two degrees of freedom.

THE TEST STATISTIC FOR THE JARQUE-BERA TEST

When testing whether data are derived from a normal distribution using the Jarque-Bera (JB) test, the value of the test statistic is calculated as

$$JB = \chi_2^2 = (n/6)[S^2 + K^2/4],$$

where $df = 2$, n is the sample size, S is the skewness coefficient, and K is the (excess) kurtosis coefficient.

FILE

Household_Income

EXAMPLE 12.5

Using the **Household_Income** data from Table 12.11 and the Jarque-Bera test, determine whether or not annual household income is normally distributed at the 1% significance level.

SOLUTION: The competing hypotheses take the following form:

$$H_0: S = 0 \text{ and } K = 0$$
$$H_A: S \neq 0 \text{ or } K \neq 0$$

In order to compute the value of the test statistic, we first need to compute the skewness and (excess) kurtosis coefficients, S and K. We use Excel's SKEW and KURT functions to find that $S = 2.3190$ and $K = 6.7322$. (We discuss how to use R for the goodness-of-fit test for normality and the Jarque-Bera test next.) The value of the test statistic is calculated as

$$JB = \chi_2^2 = (n/6)[S^2 + K^2/4] = (50/6)[2.3190^2 + 6.7322^2/4] = 139.237.$$

Using Excel's CHISQ.DIST.RT function or R's pchisq function, we find that the exact p-value, $P(\chi_2^2 \geq 139.237)$, is equal to 0 (approximately). Since the p-value is less than 0.01, we reject H_0. At the 1% significance level, we conclude that income in this Midwestern city does not follow a normal distribution.

In the preceding examples, the conclusion with the Jarque-Bera test and the goodness-of-fit test for normality is the same. This result is not surprising, as it is fairly well documented that income distribution, in general, is skewed to the right (not normally distributed), with a few households accounting for most of the total income. For this reason, we prefer to use the median rather than the mean to get a more accurate reflection of income.

Using R to Conduct a Goodness-of-Fit Test for Normality and the Jarque-Bera Test

R offers a number of options when testing for normality. Here, we focus on the goodness-of-fit test for normality and the Jarque-Bera test. It is important to note that R internally finds the nonoverlapping intervals (categories) for the goodness-of-fit test for normality. In addition, R calculates the Jarque-Bera test statistic using slightly different formulas for the skewness and (excess) kurtosis coefficients, as compared to the ones used by Excel. In general, the R results for both tests are consistent with the ones we obtain using the formulas outlined in this section. Consider the following example.

EXAMPLE 12.6

FILE

Janus_Funds

A financial analyst would like to compare the annual return data for two mutual funds from the Janus Capital Group. The Balance Fund consists of stocks and bonds and its goal is diversification. It has historically produced solid long-term returns through different market cycles. The Janus Overseas Fund invests in overseas companies based on their individual merits instead of their geography or industry sector. Table 12.13 shows a portion of the annual return data for each fund from 2000–2016 ($n = 17$). Before conducting any valid statistical inference with respect to the risk or the reward from investing in either of these funds, the analyst first wants to determine whether the annual return data follow the normal distribution. At the 5% significance level, use the goodness-of-fit test for normality and the Jarque-Bera test to make conclusions about normality assumptions for the annual return data for each fund.

TABLE 12.13 Returns (in percent) for Janus Funds

Year	Balanced	Overseas
2000	−2.16	−18.57
2001	−5.04	−23.11
⋮	⋮	⋮
2016	4.51	−6.91

Source: www.finance.yahoo.com, data retrieved March 1, 2017.

SOLUTION: For the goodness-of-fit test for normality and the Jarque-Bera test, we can generalize the competing hypotheses as

H_0: The annual return data are normally distributed.

H_A: The annual return data are not normally distributed.

Using R

a. Import the ***Janus_Funds*** data into a data frame (table) in R.

b. In order to conduct the two different tests for normality, we need to install and load two packages: *nortest* and *fBasics*.

```
> install.packages(c("nortest", "fBasics"))
> library(nortest)
> library(fBasics)
```

c. In order to run the goodness-of-fit test for normality, we use the **pearson. test** function from the nortest package.

```
> pearson.test(Janus_Funds$'Balanced')
> pearson.test(Janus_Funds$'Overseas')
```

For clarity, we have condensed the R output as follows:

Pearson chi-square normality test for the Balanced Fund:
    $P = 4$, p-value $= 0.406$

Pearson chi-square normality test for the Overseas Fund:
    $P = 4.8235$, p-value $= 0.3059$

Since the p-values for both funds are greater than 0.05, we cannot reject the null hypothesis of normality for either fund.

d. In order to run the Jarque-Bera test, we use the **jarqueberaTest** function from the fBasics package.

```
> jarqueberaTest(Janus_Funds$'Balanced')
> jarqueberaTest(Janus_Funds$'Overseas')
```

For clarity, we have condensed the R output as follows:

Test Results for Balanced Fund:
    STATISTIC: X-squared: 0.2119
    P VALUE: Asymptotic p Value: 0.8995

Test Results for Overseas Fund:
    STATISTIC: X-squared: 0.3159
    P VALUE: Asymptotic p Value: 0.8539

The results from the Jarque-Bera test are consistent with the results from the goodness-of-fit test for normality. Again, the p-values for both funds are greater than 0.05, so we cannot conclude that the annual return data are not normally distributed.

EXERCISES 12.3

Mechanics

23. Consider the following sample data with mean and standard deviation of 20.5 and 5.4, respectively.

Class	Frequency
Less than 10	25
10 up to 20	95
20 up to 30	65
30 or more	15
	$n = 200$

a. Using the goodness-of-fit test for normality, specify the competing hypotheses in order to determine whether or not the data are normally distributed.

b. Calculate the value of the test statistic and the p-value.

c. What is the conclusion at the 5% significance level?

24. The following frequency distribution has a sample mean of -3.5 and a sample standard deviation of 9.7.

Class	Frequency
Less than –10	70
–10 up to 0	40
0 up to 10	80
10 or more	10

At the 1% significance level, use the goodness-of-fit test for normality to determine whether or not the data are normally distributed.

25. You are given the following summary statistics from a sample of 50 observations:

Mean	77.25
Standard Deviation	11.36
Skewness	1.12
Kurtosis	1.63

a. Using the Jarque-Bera test, specify the null and alternative hypotheses to determine whether or not the data are normally distributed.

b. Calculate the value of the test statistic and the p-value.

c. At the 5% significance level, what is the conclusion? Can you conclude that the data do not follow the normal distribution? Explain.

Applications

26. An economics professor states on her syllabus that final grades will be distributed using the normal distribution. The final averages of 300 students are calculated, and she groups the data into a frequency distribution as shown in the accompanying table. The mean and the standard deviation of the final are $\bar{x} = 72$ and $s = 10$.

Final Averages	Frequency
F: Less than 50	5
D: 50 up to 70	135
C: 70 up to 80	105
B: 80 up to 90	45
A: 90 or above	10
	Total = 300

a. Using the goodness-of-fit test for normality, state the competing hypotheses in order to determine if the normal distribution is inappropriate for making grades.

b. Calculate the value of the test statistic and the p-value.

c. At the 5% significance level, what is the conclusion to the test?

27. Fifty cities provided information on vacancy rates (in percent) in local apartments in the following frequency distribution. The sample mean and the sample standard deviation are 9% and 3.6%, respectively.

Vacancy Rate	Frequency
Less than 6	10
6 up to 9	10
9 up to 12	20
12 or more	10

Apply the goodness-of-fit test for normality at the 5% significance level. Do the sample data suggest that vacancy rates do not follow the normal distribution?

28. The quality department at an electronics component manufacturer must ensure that their components will operate at prespecified levels. The accompanying table shows a frequency distribution with measured resistance values (in ohms) for a sample of 520 resistors. The sample mean and the sample standard deviation are 4,790 ohms and 40 ohms, respectively.

Resistance	Frequency
Under 4,740	44
4,740 up to 4,780	145
4,780 up to 4,820	197
4,820 up to 4,860	107
4,860 or more	27
	Total = 520

a. Using the goodness-of-fit test for normality, state the competing hypotheses to test if the sample data suggest that resistance does not follow the normal distribution.

b. At $\alpha = 0.05$, what is the conclusion to the test?

c. Would your conclusion change at the 10% significance level?

29. **FILE** *Shaft_Diameter.* Fabco, a precision machining shop, uses statistical process control (SPC) techniques to ensure quality and consistency of their steel shafts. The control limits used in their SPC charts are based on the assumption that shaft diameters are normally distributed. To verify this assumption, a quality engineer has measured the diameters for a sample of 50 of its popular 1/2-inch shafts.

a. Using the Jarque-Bera test, state the competing hypotheses in order to determine whether or not the data follow the normal distribution.

b. Calculate the value of the Jarque-Bera test statistic and the p-value.

c. At $\alpha = 0.10$, can you conclude that the shaft diameters are not normally distributed?

d. Would your conclusion change at the 5% significance level?

30. Total 2005 CEO compensation (in $ millions) for the largest U.S. companies by revenue is reported in the following frequency distribution. Total compensation includes salary, bonuses, stock and incentives, the potential value of stock options, and gains from stock options exercised.

Total Compensation	Frequency
Less than 5	43
5 up to 10	65
10 up to 15	32
15 up to 20	38
20 or more	60
	n = 238

Other summary statistics for CEO compensation are as follows:

Mean (in $ millions)	Median (in $ millions)	Standard Deviation (in $ millions)	Skewness	Kurtosis
19.03	11.02	27.61	5.26	35.53

a. Conduct a goodness-of-fit test for normality of CEO compensation at the 1% significance level. Does total compensation of CEOs for the largest U.S. companies not follow the normal distribution?

b. Conduct the Jarque-Bera test at the 1% significance level. Does total compensation of CEOs for the largest U.S. companies not follow the normal distribution?

31. The following frequency distribution shows the distribution of monthly returns (in %) for Starbucks Corp. for the years 2003 through 2007.

Monthly Return	Frequency
Less than −5	14
−5 up to 0	9
0 up to 5	18
5 up to 10	11
10 or more	8
	n = 60

Source: www.yahoo.finance.com.

Over this time period, the following summary statistics are provided:

Mean	Median	Standard Deviation	Skewness	Kurtosis
1.16%	1.79%	7.38%	−0.31	−0.65

a. Conduct a goodness-of-fit test for normality at the 5% significance level. Can you conclude that monthly returns do not follow the normal distribution?

b. Conduct the Jarque-Bera test at the 5% significance level. Can you conclude that monthly returns do not follow the normal distribution?

32. **FILE** *Home_Depot.* The data that accompany this exercise show weekly stock prices for Home Depot.

a. Using the Jarque-Bera test, state the competing hypotheses in order to determine whether or not Home Depot's weekly stock prices follow the normal distribution.

b. Calculate the value of the Jarque-Bera test statistic and the p-value.

c. At $\alpha = 0.05$, can you conclude that Home Depot's stock prices are not normally distributed?

33. **FILE** *MPG.* The data that accompanies this exercise show miles per gallon (MPG) for a sample of 25 cars.

a. Using the Jarque-Bera test, state the competing hypotheses in order to determine whether or not MPG follows the normal distribution.

b. Calculate the value of the Jarque-Bera test statistic and the p-value.

c. At $\alpha = 0.05$, can you conclude that MPG is not normally distributed?

WRITING WITH STATISTICS

©JGI/Blend Images/Getty Images RF

FILE
50_Largest_Funds

Javier Gonzalez is in the process of writing a comprehensive analysis on the three-year returns for the 50 largest mutual funds. Before he makes any inferences concerning the return data, he would first like to determine whether or not the data follow a normal distribution. Table 12.14 shows a portion of the three-year return data (in %) for the 50 largest mutual funds.

TABLE 12.14 Three-Year Returns (in %) for the 50 Largest Mutual Funds

Mutual Fund	Return
American Growth	5.7
Pimco Total Return	4.7
⋮	⋮
Loomis Sayles Bond	5.4

Source: *The Boston Sunday Globe*, August 17, 2008.

Javier wants to use the sample information to

1. Conduct the goodness-of-fit test for normality that determines, at the 5% significance level, whether or not three-year returns follow a normal distribution.

2. Conduct the Jarque-Bera test that determines, at the 5% significance level, whether or not three-year returns follow a normal distribution.

Sample Report— Assessing Whether Data Follow the Normal Distribution

As part of a broader report concerning the mutual fund industry in general, three-year return data for the 50 largest mutual funds were collected with the objective of determining whether or not the data follow a normal distribution. Information of this sort is particularly useful because much statistical inference is based on the assumption of normality. If the assumption of normality is not supported by the data, it may be more appropriate to use nonparametric techniques to make valid inferences. Table 12.A shows relevant summary statistics for three-year returns for the 50 largest mutual funds.

TABLE 12.A Three-Year Return Summary Measures for the 50 Largest Mutual Funds, August 2008

Mean	Median	Standard Deviation	Skewness	Kurtosis
5.96%	4.65%	3.39%	1.37	2.59

The average three-year return for the 50 largest mutual funds is 5.96%, with a median of 4.65%. When the mean is significantly greater than the median, it is often an indication of a positively skewed distribution. The skewness coefficient of 1.37 seems to support this claim. Moreover, the kurtosis coefficient of 2.59 suggests a distribution that is more peaked than the normal distribution. A formal test will determine whether the conclusion from the sample can be deemed real or due to chance.

The goodness-of-fit test is first applied to check for normality. The raw data are converted into a frequency distribution with five intervals ($k = 5$). Expected frequencies are calculated by multiplying the sample size $n = 50$ by the hypothesized proportions p_i, under the null hypothesis that the data follow the normal distribution with mean 5.96% and standard deviation 3.39%. Finally, the value of the chi-square test statistic is computed by summing the standardized squared deviations. All of these calculations are shown in Table 12.B.

TABLE 12.B Calculations for the Goodness-of-Fit Test for Normality

Return (in %)	Observed Frequency, o_i	p_i if Normally Distributed	Expected Frequency, $e_i = n \times p_i$	Standardized Squared Deviation, $\frac{(o_i - e_i)^2}{e_i}$
Return < 2.5	7	0.1539	7.695	0.0628
$2.5 \leq$ Return < 5.0	20	0.2358	11.790	5.7171
$5.0 \leq$ Return < 7.5	6	0.2839	14.195	4.7311
$7.5 \leq$ Return < 10	11	0.2094	10.470	0.0268
Return ≥ 10	6	0.1170	5.850	0.0038
	$\Sigma o_i = 50$	$\Sigma p_i = 1$	$\Sigma e_i = 50$	$\Sigma \frac{(o_i - e_i)^2}{e_i} = 10.542$

Table 12.C shows the competing hypotheses, the value of the test statistic, and the p-value that result from applying the goodness-of-fit test for normality. At the 5% significance level, the p-value of 0.005 allows us to reject the null hypothesis that returns are normally distributed.

TABLE 12.C Test Statistics and p-values for Hypothesis Tests

Hypotheses	Test Statistic	p-value
Goodness-of-Fit Test: H_0: Returns are normally distributed. H_A: Returns are not normally distributed.	$\chi_2^2 = 10.542$	$P(\chi_2^2 \geq 10.542) = 0.005$
Jarque-Bera Test: H_0: $S = 0$ and $K = 0$ H_A: $S = 0$ or $K = 0$	$\chi_2^2 = 29.616$	$P(\chi_2^2 \geq 29.616) = 0$ (approximately)

Table 12.C also shows the results from conducting the Jarque-Bera (*JB*) test. The value for the *JB* test statistic is 29.616 and its associated p-value is 0 (approximately); thus, at the 5% significance level, the null hypothesis that skewness and kurtosis are both zero is rejected. This result is consistent with the conclusion drawn from the goodness-of-fit test for normality. Both statistical tests reject the null hypothesis of normality—three-year returns do not follow the normal distribution. Statistical inference regarding mutual fund returns would best be conducted using nonparametric techniques that do not require the assumption of normality.

CONCEPTUAL REVIEW

LO 12.1 Conduct a goodness-of-fit test for a multinomial experiment.

A **multinomial experiment** consists of a series of n independent and identical trials such that on each trial there are k possible outcomes, called categories; the probability p_i associated with the ith category remains the same; and the sum of the probabilities is one.

A **goodness-of-fit test** is conducted to determine if the population proportions differ from some predetermined (hypothesized) values. The value of the test statistic is calculated as $\chi^2_{df} = \sum \frac{(o_i - e_i)^2}{e_i}$, where $df = k - 1$, o_i and $e_i = np_i$ are the observed frequency and expected frequency in the ith category, respectively, and n is the number of observations. The test is valid when the expected frequencies for each category are five or more. This test is always implemented as a right-tailed test.

LO 12.2 Conduct a test for independence.

A goodness-of-fit test examines a single qualitative variable, whereas a **test for independence**, also called a **chi-square test of a contingency table**, analyzes the relationship between two qualitative variables defined on the same population. A contingency table shows frequencies for two qualitative variables, x and y, where each cell of the table represents a mutually exclusive combination of the pair of x and y values.

In order to determine whether or not the two variables are related, we again compare observed frequencies with expected frequencies. The expected frequency for each cell, e_{ij}, is calculated as $e_{ij} = \frac{(\text{Row } i \text{ total})(\text{Column } j \text{ total})}{\text{Sample Size}}$, where the subscript ij refers to the ith row and the jth column of the contingency table.

The value of the chi-square test statistic is calculated as $\chi^2_{df} = \sum_i \sum_j \frac{(o_{ij} - e_{ij})^2}{e_{ij}}$, where o_{ij} is the observed frequency. Degrees of freedom is calculated as $(r - 1)(c - 1)$, where r and c refer to the number of rows and columns, respectively, in the contingency table. The test for independence is also implemented as a right-tailed test and is valid when the expected frequencies for each cell are five or more.

LO 12.3 Conduct a goodness-of-fit test for normality.

We can use the **goodness-of-fit test for normality** to contest that a given population follows the normal distribution. For the test, we have to first convert raw data into a frequency distribution. We construct a frequency distribution with k intervals. We then calculate the probability of observing the ith interval p_i under the assumption of a normal distribution, and then use this probability to calculate the expected frequency as $e_i = n \times p_i$. The value of the test statistic is calculated as $\chi^2_{df} = \sum \frac{(o_i - e_i)^2}{e_i}$, with $df = k - 3$. Since it is a goodness-of-fit test, it is implemented as a right-tailed test and is valid when the expected frequencies in each cell are five or more.

LO 12.4 Conduct the Jarque-Bera test.

An alternative to the goodness-of-fit test for normality is the **Jarque-Bera test**. We use the skewness coefficient S and the (excess) kurtosis coefficient K of the sample data to conduct the test. The value of the **Jarque-Bera JB test statistic** is calculated as $JB = \chi^2_2 = (n/6)[S^2 + K^2/4]$, where n is the sample size.

ADDITIONAL EXERCISES AND CASE STUDIES

Exercises

34. The following table lists the market shares of the four firms in a particular industry in 2010 and total sales (in $ billions) for each firm in 2011.

Firm	Market Share in 2010	Total Sales in 2011
1	0.40	200
2	0.30	180
3	0.20	100
4	0.10	70

a. Specify the competing hypotheses to test whether the market shares in 2010 are not valid in 2011.
b. Calculate the value of the test statistic and the p-value.
c. At the 1% significance level, do the sample data suggest that the market shares changed from 2010 to 2011?

35. A study suggests that airlines have increased restrictions on cheap fares by raising overnight requirements (*The Wall Street Journal*, August 19, 2008). This would force business travelers to pay more for their flights, since they tend to need the most flexibility and want to be home on weekends. Eight months ago, the overnight stay requirements were as follows:

One night	Two nights	Three nights	Saturday night
37%	17%	28%	18%

A recent sample of 644 flights found the following restrictions:

One night	Two nights	Three nights	Saturday night
117%	137%	298%	92%

a. Specify the competing hypotheses to test whether the proportions cited by the study have changed.
b. Calculate the value of the test statistic.
c. At the 5% significance level, what is the conclusion to the hypothesis test? Interpret your results.

36. Although founded only in 2004, Facebook has nearly 2 billion active users, of which 50% log on to Facebook on any given day. In a survey by Facebook, young users were asked about their preference for delivering the news about breaking up a relationship (*The Wall Street Journal*, November 27–28, 2010). One of the shocking results was that only 47% of users preferred to break the news in person. A researcher decides to verify the survey results of Facebook by taking her own sample of 200 young Facebook users. The preference percentages from Facebook and the researcher's survey are presented in the following table.

Delivery Method	Facebook Results	Researcher's Results
In Person	47%	55%
Phone	30%	25%
E-mail	4%	6%
Facebook	5%	5%
Instant Message	14%	9%

At the 5% level of significance, test if the researcher's results are inconsistent with the survey results conducted by Facebook. Provide the details.

37. A local TV station claims that 60% of people support Candidate A, 30% support Candidate B, and 10% support Candidate C. A survey of 500 registered voters is taken. The accompanying table indicates how they are likely to vote.

Candidate A	Candidate B	Candidate C
350	125	25

a. Specify the competing hypotheses to test whether the TV station's claim can be rejected by the data.
b. Test the hypothesis at the 1% significance level.

38. A study in the *Journal of the American Medical Association* (February 20, 2008) found that patients who go into cardiac arrest while in the hospital are more likely to die if it happens after 11 pm. The study investigated 58,593 cardiac arrests during the day or evening. Of those, 11,604 survived to leave the hospital. There were 28,155 cardiac arrests during the shift that began at 11 pm, commonly referred to as the graveyard shift. Of those, 4,139 survived for discharge. The following contingency table summarizes the results of the study:

Shift	Survived for Discharge	Did Not Survive for Discharge
Day or Evening Shift	11,604	46,989
Graveyard Shift	4,139	24,016

a. Specify the competing hypotheses to determine whether a patient's survival depends on the time at which he/she experiences cardiac arrest.

b. Calculate the value of the test statistic and the p-value.

c. At the 1% significance level, is the timing of when a cardiac arrest occurs independent of whether or not the patient survives for discharge? Given your answer, what type of recommendations might you give to hospitals?

39. An analyst is trying to determine whether the prices of certain stocks on the NASDAQ are independent of the industry to which they belong. She examines four industries and, within each industry, categorizes each stock according to its price (high-priced, average-priced, low-priced).

Stock Price	Industry			
	I	II	III	IV
High	16	8	10	14
Average	18	16	10	12
Low	7	8	4	9

a. Specify the competing hypotheses to determine whether stock price depends on the industry.

b. Calculate the value of the test statistic and the p-value.

c. At the 1% significance level, what can the analyst conclude?

40. Many parents have turned to St. John's wort, an herbal remedy, to treat their children with attention deficit hyperactivity disorder (ADHD). *The Journal of the American Medical Association* (June 11, 2008) published an article that explored the herb's effectiveness. Children with ADHD were randomly assigned to take either St. John's wort capsules or placebos. The contingency table below broadly reflects the results found in the study.

Treatment	Effect on ADHD	
	No Change in ADHD	Improvement in ADHD
St. John's wort	12	15
Placebo	14	13

At the 5% significance level, do the data indicate that St. John's wort affects children with ADHD?

41. A poll asked 3,228 Americans aged 16 to 21 whether they are likely to serve in the U.S. military. The following table, cross-classified by a person's sex and race, reports those who responded that are likely or very likely to serve in the active-duty military.

Sex	Race		
	Hispanic	Black	White
Male	1,098	678	549
Female	484	355	64

Source: Defense Human Resources Activity telephone poll of 3,228 Americans conducted October through December 2005.

a. State the competing hypotheses to test whether a person's sex and race are dependent when making a choice to serve in the military.

b. Conduct the test at the 5% significance level.

42. Given a shaky economy and high heating costs, more and more households are struggling to pay utility bills (*The Wall Street Journal*, February 14, 2008). Particularly hard hit are households with homes heated with propane or heating oil. Many of these households are spending twice as much to stay warm this winter compared to those who heat with natural gas or electricity. A representative sample of 500 households was taken to investigate if the type of heating influences whether or not a household is delinquent in paying its utility bill. The following table reports the results.

Delinquent in Payment?	Type of Heating			
	Natural Gas	Electricity	Heating Oil	Propane
Yes	50	20	15	10
No	240	130	20	15

At the 5% significance level, test whether the type of heating influences a household's delinquency in payment. Interpret your results.

43. The following frequency distribution shows the monthly stock returns (in percent) for Home Depot for the years 2003 through 2007.

Monthly Returns	Observed Frequency
Less than −5	13
−5 up to 0	16
0 up to 5	20
5 or more	11
	$n = 60$

Source: www.yahoo.finance.com.

Over this time period, the following summary statistics are provided:

Mean	Median	Standard Deviation	Skewness	Kurtosis
0.31%	0.43%	6.49%	0.15	0.38

a. Conduct a goodness-of-fit test for normality at the 5% significance level. Can you conclude that monthly stock returns do not follow the normal distribution?

b. Conduct the Jarque-Bera test at the 5% significance level. Are your results consistent with your answer in part (a)?

44. **FILE** *Arlington_Homes.* The data that accompany this exercise show various variables, including price and square footage, for 36 single-family homes in Arlington, Massachusetts, sold in the first quarter of 2009.

a. Use the Jarque-Bera test to test if house prices are not normally distributed at $\alpha = 0.05$.

b. Use the Jarque-Bera test to test if square footage is not normally distributed at $\alpha = 0.05$.

45. An automotive parts company has been besieged with poor publicity over the past few years due to several highly publicized product recalls that have tarnished its public image. This has prompted a series of quality improvement initiatives. Currently, the marketing manager would like to determine if these initiatives have been successful in changing public perception about the company. Below are results of two surveys, each of 600 random adults. Survey 1 was conducted prior to the quality initiatives. Survey 2 was conducted after the quality initiatives were implemented and publicized.

	Public Perception		
	Negative	Neutral	Positive
Survey 1	324	180	96
Survey 2	246	146	208

a. State the appropriate null and alternative hypotheses to test if the public perception has changed since the quality initiatives have been implemented.

b. Make a conclusion at the 1% significance level.

46. Color coding is often used in manufacturing operations to display production status or to identify/prioritize materials. For example,

suppose "green" status indicates that an assembly line is operating normally, "yellow" indicates it is down waiting on personnel for set up or repair, "blue" indicates it is down waiting on materials to be delivered, and "red" indicates an emergency condition. Management has set realistic goals whereby the assembly line should be operating normally 80% of the time, waiting on personnel 9% of the time, waiting on materials 9% of the time, and in an emergency condition 2% of the time. Based on 250 recent status records, the status was green 185 times, yellow 24 times, blue 32 times, and red 9 times.

a. State the appropriate null and alternative hypotheses to test if the proportions of assembly line statuses differ from the goals set by management.

b. Calculate the value of the test statistic and the p-value.

c. Are management's goals being met at $\alpha = 0.05$? Will your conclusion change at $\alpha = 0.01$?

47. The operations manager at ElectroTech, an electronics manufacturing company, believes that workers on particular shifts may be more likely to phone in "sick" than those on other shifts. To test this belief, she has compiled the following table containing frequencies based on work shift and days absent over the past year.

	First Shift	Second Shift	Third Shift
0–2 days absent	44	20	10
3–6 days absent	38	25	12
7–10 days absent	14	9	13
11 or more days absent	4	6	5

a. Specify the competing hypotheses to determine whether days absent depend on work shift.

b. Calculate the value of the test statistic and the p-value.

c. What is your conclusion at the 5% significance level? What about the 1% significance level?

48. The human resources department would like to consolidate the current set of retirement plan options offered to specific employee pay groups into a single plan for all pay groups (salaried, hourly, or piecework). A sample of 585 employees of various pay groups were asked which of three

potential plans they preferred (A, B, or C). The results are shown in the accompanying table. The human resources department is hoping to conclude that the retirement plan preferred by the majority of employees is independent of pay group, in order to avoid the impression that the preferred plan may favor a particular group.

Preferred Plan	Employee Pay Group		
	Salaried	Hourly	Piecework
A	78	98	37
B	121	95	30
C	51	57	18

a. Specify the competing hypotheses to determine whether the preferred retirement plan depends on employee pay group.
b. Calculate the value of the test statistic and the p-value.
c. What is your conclusion at the 10% significance level? What about the 5% significance level?

49. A software company develops and markets a popular business simulation/modeling program. A random number generator contained in the program provides random values from various probability distributions. The software design group would like to validate that the program is properly generating random numbers. Accordingly, they generated 5,000 random numbers from a normal distribution and grouped the results into the accompanying frequency distribution. The sample mean and sample standard deviation are 100 and 10, respectively.

Value	Frequency
Under 70	12
70 up to 80	99
80 up to 90	658
90 up to 100	1734
100 up to 110	1681
110 up to 120	697
120 up to 130	112
130 or more	7
	Total = 5,000

a. Using the goodness-of-fit test for normality, state the competing hypotheses to test if the random numbers generated do not follow the normal distribution.

b. Calculate the value of the test statistic and the p-value.
c. What is the conclusion to the test at the 1% significance level? Is your conclusion sensitive within the range of typical significance levels?

50. **FILE** *Reorder_Point.* Reorder point decisions for a particular part at an automotive parts distributor are based on the assumption that weekly demand is normally distributed. (Note: "Reorder point" is the inventory level at which a replenishment order is placed; it should be high enough to cover demand during the order fulfillment period, but low enough to avoid excessive inventory holding costs.) To examine the validity of this assumption, the logistics department has compiled weekly demand values for the past year.

a. Using the Jarque-Bera test, state the competing hypotheses in order to determine whether or not weekly demand values follow the normal distribution.
b. Calculate the value of the Jarque-Bera test statistic and the p-value.
c. At $\alpha = 0.05$, can you conclude that the weekly demand values are not normally distributed? Is the conclusion sensitive to the choice of significance level?

51. **FILE** *Degrees.* The value of a college degree is greater than it has been in nearly half a century, at least when compared to the prospect of not getting a degree (www.pewresearch.org, January 28, 2014). Due to this fact, more and more people are obtaining college degrees, despite the soaring costs. The accompanying table shows the proportions of college degrees awarded in 2010 by colleges and universities, categorized by a graduate's race and ethnicity. The race and ethnicity of 500 recent graduates are recorded and shown in the last column of the table.

Race/Ethnicity	2010 Proportions	Recent Numbers
White	0.73	350
Black	0.10	50
Hispanic	0.09	60
Asian	0.08	40

Source: The 2010 proportions come from Table 300 in *Digest of Education Statistics*, 2011.

At the 5% significance level, test if the proportions have changed since 2010.

CASE STUDIES

CASE STUDY 12.1   A detailed study of Americans' religious beliefs and practices by the Pew Forum on Religion & Public Life revealed that religion is quite important in an individual's life (*The Boston Globe*, June 24, 2008). The second column of the accompanying table reports the proportion of Americans who feel a certain way about religion. The study also concludes that Massachusetts residents are the least likely to say that they are religious. In order to test this claim, assume 400 randomly selected Massachusetts residents are asked about the importance of religion in their lives. The results of this survey are shown in the last column of the accompanying table.

Data for Case Study 12.1 Importance of Religion, U.S. versus Massachusetts

Importance of Religion	U.S. Results	Responses of Massachusetts Residents
Very important	0.58	160
Somewhat important	0.25	140
Not too important	0.15	96
Don't know	0.02	4

In a report, use the sample information to

1. Determine whether Massachusetts residents' religious beliefs differ from those based on the United States at the 5% significance level.

2. Discuss whether you would expect to find the same conclusions if you conducted a similar test for the state of Utah or states in the Southern Belt of the United States.

CASE STUDY 12.2   A University of Utah study examined 7,925 severely obese adults who had gastric bypass surgery and an identical number of people who did not have the surgery (*The Boston Globe*, August 23, 2007). The study wanted to investigate whether losing weight through stomach surgery prolonged the lives of severely obese patients, thereby reducing their deaths from heart disease, cancer, and diabetes.

Over the course of the study, 534 of the participants died. Of those who died, the cause of death was classified as either a disease death (disease deaths include heart disease, cancer, and diabetes) or a nondisease death (nondisease deaths include suicide or accident). The following contingency table summarizes the study's findings:

Data for Case Study 12.2 Deaths Cross-Classified by Cause and Method of Losing Weight

Cause of Death	Method of Losing Weight	
	No Surgery	Surgery
Death from disease	285	150
Death from nondisease	36	63

In a report, use the sample information to

1. Determine at the 5% significance level whether the cause of death depends on the method of losing weight.

2. Discuss how the findings of the statistical test used in question 1 might be used by those in the health industry.

CASE STUDY 12.3   Matthew Jordon is a research analyst for a large investment firm. He is preparing a report on the stock performance of Nike, Inc. One aspect of his report will contain inferences concerning monthly stock returns. Before making valid inferences, Matthew first wants to determine whether the return data follow the normal distribution. To this end, he constructs the following frequency distribution on monthly stock returns (in percent) for the years 2006 through 2010.

Monthly Return	Observed Frequency
Less than −5	8
−5 up to 0	20
0 up to 5	14
5 or more	18

Source: www.yahoo.finance.com.

He also calculates the following summary statistics over this time period:

Mean	Median	Standard Deviation	Skewness	Kurtosis
1.50%	1.31%	6.98%	0.11	−0.33

In a report, use the sample information to

1. Conduct the goodness-of-fit test for normality in order to determine whether the monthly stock returns are not normally distributed at the 5% significance level.

2. Conduct the Jarque-Bera test in order to determine whether the monthly stock returns are not normally distributed at the 5% significance level.

APPENDIX 12.1   Guidelines for Other Software Packages

The following section provides brief commands for Minitab, SPSS, and JMP. Where a data file is specified, copy and paste it into the relevant software spreadsheet prior to following the commands.

Minitab

Goodness-of-Fit Test

Share

A. (Replicating Example 12.1) From the menu, choose **Stat > Tables > Chi-Square Goodness-of-Fit Test (One Variable)**.

B. Choose **Observed counts** and then select Number. Under **Test**, select **Proportions specified by historical counts**, and then select Share. Choose **Results** and select **Display test results**.

Test for Independence

STEM2

A. (Replicating Example 12.4) From the menu, choose **Stat > Tables > Cross Tabulation and Chi-Square**.

B. Select "Summarized data in a two-way table." Under **Columns containing the table**, select Females and Males. Choose Chi-Square and select **Chi-square test**.

Test of Normality

A. (Confirming Normality test in Example 12.6) From the menu, choose **Stat > Basic Statistics > Normality Test**.

B. After **Variable**, select Balanced and Overseas. Under **Tests for Normality**, select **Anderson-Darling**.

SPSS

Goodness-of-Fit Test

A. (Replicating Example 12.1) From the menu, choose **Data > Weight Cases**. Select **Weight cases by**, and under **Frequency Variable**, select Number.

B. Select **Analyze > Nonparametric Tests > Legacy Dialogs > Chi-square**.

C. Under **Test Variable List**, select Firm. Under **Expected Values**, select **Values**, and **Add** 0.40, 0.32, 0.24, and 0.04.

Test for Independence

A. (Replicating Example 12.3) In order to conduct this test in SPSS, the data need to be reconfigured. Label Columns 1, 2, and 3 as "Sex," "Field," and "Frequency," respectively. In the first row, enter Female, Sciences, 120; in the second row, enter Female, Technology, 15; and so on, until the last row in the spreadsheet is Male, Math, 20.

B. From the menu, choose **Data > Weight Cases**. Select **Weight cases by**, and under **Frequency Variable**, select Frequency.

C. From the menu, select **Analyze > Descriptive Statistics > Crosstabs**.

D. Under **Rows**, select Sex, and under **Columns**, select Field. Choose **Statistics**, check **Chi-square**.

Test of Normality

A. (Confirming normality test in Example 12.6) From the menu, select **Analyze > Descriptive Statistics > Explore**.

B. Under **Dependent List**, select Balanced and Overseas. Select **Plots**, then select box in front of **Normality plots with tests**.

JMP

Test for Independence

A. (Replicating Example 12.3) In order to conduct this test in JMP, the data need to be reconfigured. Follow Step A under the SPSS instructions for Test for Independence.

B. From the menu, select **Analyze > Fit Y by X**.

C. Under **Select Columns**, select Sex, and then under **Cast Selected Columns into Roles**, select **Y, Response**. Under **Select Columns**, select Field, and then under **Cast Selected Columns into Roles**, select **X, Factor**. Under **Select Columns**, select Frequency, and then under **Cast Selected Columns into Roles**, select **Freq**.

Test of Normality

A. (Confirming normality test in Example 12.6) From the menu, select **Analyze > Distribution**.

B. Under **Select Columns**, select Balanced and Overseas, and then under **Cast Selected Columns into Roles**, select **Y, Columns**.

C. In the red triangles next to Balanced and Overseas, select **Continuous Fit > Normal**. In the red triangle next to **Fitted Normal**, select **Diagnostic Plot** and **Goodness of Fit**.

13 Analysis of Variance

LEARNING OBJECTIVES

After reading this chapter you should be able to:

LO 13.1 Conduct and evaluate a one-way ANOVA test.

LO 13.2 Use Fisher's LSD method and Tukey's HSD method to determine which means differ.

LO 13.3 Conduct and evaluate a two-way ANOVA test with no interaction.

LO 13.4 Conduct and evaluate a two-way ANOVA test with interaction.

n this chapter, we study analysis of variance, which is more commonly referred to as ANOVA. ANOVA is a statistical technique used to determine if differences exist between the means of three or more populations under independent sampling. The ANOVA test is actually a generalization of the two-sample t test with equal but unknown variances discussed in Chapter 10. For instance, we may want to determine if the average miles per gallon of small hybrid cars vary by brand. Or we may wish to compare the effectiveness of different fertilizers on the average yield per acre. These are examples of one-way ANOVA, where we examine the effect of one factor on the mean. We then move on to two-way ANOVA, where the mean may be influenced by two factors. For instance, we may want to determine if the average miles per gallon of small hybrid cars vary by brand and octane rating of gasoline. Or we may wish to determine if the average yield per acre is influenced by the fertilizer and the acidity level of the soil. Tests based on two-way ANOVA can be conducted *with* or *without* the interaction of the factors.

©Huntstock, Inc./Alamy Stock Photo RF

INTRODUCTORY CASE

Public Transportation

Sean Cox, a research analyst at an environmental organization, believes that an upswing in the use of public transportation has taken place due to environmental concerns, the volatility of gas prices, and the general economic climate. He is especially pleased with a study that highlights the average annual cost savings when commuters use public transportation (*The Boston Globe*, May 8, 2009). Commuters who use public transportation save on buying, maintaining, and operating their cars, which comprise the largest household expenditure after housing. The study finds that Boston leads 20 other American cities in the amount that commuters can save if they take public transportation. Sean wonders whether or not cost savings vary dramatically by city. He collects a representative sample of public transit riders in the top four cost-savings cities: Boston, New York, San Francisco, and Chicago. Table 13.1 shows each public transit rider's annual cost savings by city.

TABLE 13.1 Annual Cost Savings (in $) from Using Public Transportation

FILE
Public_Transportation

Boston	New York	San Francisco	Chicago
12500	12450	11800	10595
12640	12500	11745	10740
12600	12595	11700	10850
12625	12605	11800	10725
12745	12650	11700	10740
	12620	11575	
	12560		
	12700		

Sean wants to use the above sample information to

1. Determine whether there are differences in mean cost savings among these four cities at the 5% significance level.

2. Determine which cities' means differ at the 5% significance level, if it is found that differences exist in the mean cost savings among these four cities.

A synopsis of this case is provided in Section 13.2.

Conduct and evaluate a
one-way ANOVA test.

We use an **analysis of variance (ANOVA) test** to determine if differences exist
between the means of three or more populations under independent sampling. The
ANOVA test is actually a generalization of the two-sample t test with equal but
unknown variances discussed in Chapter 10. This test is based on the $F_{(df_1, df_2)}$ distribution that was introduced in Chapter 11. A **one-way ANOVA test** compares population means based on one categorical variable or factor. In general, it is used for
testing c population means under the following assumptions:

1. The populations are normally distributed.
2. The population standard deviations are unknown but assumed equal.
3. The samples are selected independently.

In the public transportation example from the introductory case, we want to determine whether some differences exist in the mean cost savings of using public
transportation in Boston, New York, San Francisco, and Chicago. We thus delineate
cost savings of using public transportation by city (the categorical variable). We formulate the following competing hypotheses:

$$H_0: \mu_1 = \mu_2 = \mu_3 = \mu_4$$

$$H_A: \text{Not all population means are equal.}$$

Note that H_A does not require that all means must differ from one another. In
principle, the sample data may support the rejection of H_0 in favor of H_A even if only
two means differ.

When conducting the equality of means test, you might be tempted to set up a se-
ries of hypothesis tests, comparing μ_1 and μ_2, then μ_1 and μ_3, and so on, and then use
the two-sample t test with equal variances discussed in Section 10.1. However, such an
approach is not only cumbersome, but also flawed. In this example, where we evaluate
the equality of four means, we would have to compare six combinations of two means
at a time. Also, by conducting numerous pairwise comparisons, we inflate the risk of
the Type I error α; that is, we increase the risk of incorrectly rejecting the null hypothesis. In other words, if we conduct all six pairwise tests at the 5% level of significance,
the resulting significance level for the overall test will be greater than 5%.

Fortunately, the ANOVA technique avoids this problem by providing one test that
simultaneously evaluates the equality of several means. In the public transportation
example, if the four population means are equal, we would expect the resulting
sample means, $\bar{x}_1$, $\bar{x}_2$, $\bar{x}_3$, and $\bar{x}_4$, to be relatively close to one another. Figure 13.1a

FIGURE 13.1
The logic of ANOVA

a. Distribution of sample means if H_0 is true

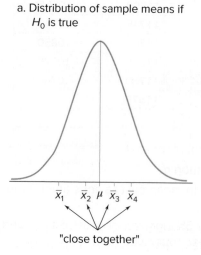

b. Distributions of sample means if H_0 is false

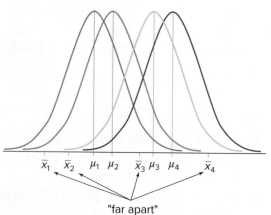

illustrates the distribution of the sample means if H_0 is true. Here, the relatively small variability in the sample means can be explained by chance. What if the population means differ? Figure 13.1b shows the distributions of the sample means if the sample data support H_A. In this scenario, the sample means are relatively far apart since each sample mean is calculated from a population with a different mean. The resulting variability in the sample means cannot be explained by chance alone.

The term *treatments* is often used to identify the c populations being examined. The practice of referring to different populations as different treatments is due to the fact that many ANOVA applications were originally developed in connection with agricultural experiments where different fertilizers were regarded as different treatments applied to soil.

In order to determine if significant differences exist between some of the population means, we develop two independent estimates of the common population variance σ^2. One estimate of σ^2 can be attributed to the variability *between* the sample means. It is referred to as **between-treatments variance**. The other estimate of σ^2 can be attributed to the variability of the data *within* each sample; that is, the variability due to chance. It is referred to as **within-treatments variance**.

If the two independent estimates of σ^2 are relatively close together, then it is likely that the variability of the sample means can be explained by chance and the null hypothesis of equal population means is not rejected. However, if the between-treatments variance is significantly greater than the within-treatments variance, then the null hypothesis of equal population means is rejected. This is equivalent to concluding that the ratio of between-treatments variance to within-treatments variance is significantly greater than one. We will come back to this ratio shortly.

Between-Treatments Estimate of σ^2: MSTR

The between-treatments variance is based on a weighted sum of squared differences between the sample means and the overall mean of the data set, referred to as the **grand mean** and denoted as $\bar{\bar{x}}$. We compute the grand mean by summing all observations in the data set and dividing by the total number of observations.

Each squared difference of a sample mean from the grand mean $(\bar{x}_i - \bar{\bar{x}})^2$ is multiplied by the respective sample size for each treatment n_i. After summing the weighted squared differences, we arrive at a value called the **sum of squares due to treatments** or *SSTR*. When we divide *SSTR* by its degrees of freedom $c - 1$, we obtain the mean square for treatments; or equivalently, the between-treatments estimate of σ^2, which we denote by *MSTR*.

CALCULATIONS FOR *MSTR*

- The grand mean: $\bar{\bar{x}} = \dfrac{\sum\limits_{i=1}^{c} \sum\limits_{j=1}^{n_i} x_{ij}}{n_T}$,

- The sum of squares due to treatments: $SSTR = \sum\limits_{i=1}^{c} n_i(\bar{x}_i - \bar{\bar{x}})^2$, and

- The between-treatments estimate of σ^2: $MSTR = \dfrac{SSTR}{c - 1}$,

where c is the number of populations (treatments), $\bar{x}_i$ and n_i are the sample mean and the sample size of the ith sample, respectively, and n_T is the total sample size.

Referring back to the public transportation example, we first find the sample mean $\bar{x}_i$ and the sample size n_i, for each city. For Boston, New York, San Francisco, and

Chicago, the sample means are 12,622, 12,585, 11,720, and 10,730, respectively. The corresponding sample sizes are 5, 8, 6, and 5, respectively. The calculations for $\bar{\bar{x}}$, $SSTR$, and $MSTR$ for the public transportation example are as follows:

$$\bar{\bar{x}} = \frac{\sum\limits_{j=1}^{c} \sum\limits_{i=1}^{n_j} x_{ij}}{n_T} = \frac{12,500 + 12,640 + \cdots + 10,740}{24} = 11,990.$$

$$SSTR = \sum_{i=1}^{c} n_i(\bar{x}_i - \bar{\bar{x}})^2 = 5(12,622 - 11,990)^2 + 8(12,585 - 11,990)^2$$
$$+ 6(11,720 - 11,990)^2 + 5(10,730 - 11,990)^2$$
$$= 13,204,720.$$

$$MSTR = \frac{SSTR}{c - 1} = \frac{13,204,720}{4 - 1} = 4,401,573.3333.$$

Within-Treatments Estimate of σ^2: MSE

We just calculated a value of $MSTR$ equal to 4,401,573.3333. Is this value of $MSTR$ large enough to indicate that the population means differ? To answer this question, we compare $MSTR$ to the variability that we expect due to chance. We first calculate the sum of squares due to error, or equivalently, the **error sum of squares**, denoted as SSE. SSE provides a measure of the degree of variability that exists even if all population means are the same. We calculate SSE as a weighted sum of the sample variances of each treatment. When we divide SSE by its degrees of freedom $n_T - c$, we arrive at the **mean square error** or, equivalently, the within-treatments estimate of σ^2, which we denote by MSE.

CALCULATIONS FOR MSE

- The error sum of squares: $SSE = \sum\limits_{i=1}^{c} (n_i - 1)s_i^2$, and

- The within-treatments estimate of σ^2: $MSE = \frac{SSE}{n_T - c}$,

where c is the number of populations (treatments), s_i^2 and n_i are the sample variance and the sample size of the ith sample, respectively, and n_T is the total sample size.

Here we first calculate the sample standard deviations for Boston, New York, San Francisco, and Chicago as 87.7924, 80.4008, 83.9643, and 90.6228, respectively. The values of SSE and MSE for the public transportation example are calculated as follows:

$$SSE = \sum_{i=1}^{c} (n_i - 1)s_i^2$$
$$= (5 - 1)(87.7924)^2 + (8 - 1)(80.4008)^2 + (6 - 1)(83.9643)^2$$
$$+ (5 - 1)(90.6228)^2 = 144,180.$$

$$MSE = \frac{SSE}{n_T - c} = \frac{144,180}{24 - 4} = 7,209.$$

As mentioned earlier, if the ratio of the between-treatments variance to the within-treatments variance is significantly greater than one, then this finding provides evidence for rejecting the null hypothesis of equal population means. Equivalently, if this ratio is not significantly greater than one, then we are not able to reject the null hypothesis in favor of the alternative hypothesis. We use this ratio to develop the test statistic for a one-way ANOVA test.

The value of the test statistic for testing whether differences exist between the population means is computed as

$$F_{(df_1, df_2)} = \frac{MSTR}{MSE},$$

where $df_1 = c - 1$, $df_2 = n_T - c$, and n_T is the total sample size; $MSTR$ is the between-treatments variance and MSE is the within-treatments variance.

The values for $MSTR$ and MSE are based on independent samples drawn from c normally distributed populations with a common variance. ANOVA tests are always implemented as right-tailed tests.

We are now in a position to conduct a four-step hypothesis test at the 5% significance level for the public transportation example.

Step 1. Specify the null and the alternative hypothesis. For completeness, we repeat the competing hypotheses to determine whether cost savings in public transportation differ between the four cities:

$$H_0: \mu_1 = \mu_2 = \mu_3 = \mu_4$$
$$H_A: \text{Not all population means are equal.}$$

Step 2. Specify the significance level. We conduct the hypothesis test at the 5% significance level, so $\alpha = 0.05$.

Step 3. Calculate the value of the test statistic and the p-value. Given $MSTR = 4{,}401{,}573.3333$, $MSE = 7{,}209$, $df_1 = c - 1 = 4 - 1 = 3$ and $df_2 = n_T - c = 24 - 4 = 20$, we compute the value of the test statistic as

$$F_{(df_1, df_2)} = F_{(3,20)} = \frac{MSTR}{MSE} = \frac{4{,}401{,}573.3333}{7{,}209} = 610.566.$$

Since the ANOVA test is a right-tailed test, we calculate the p-value as $P(F_{3,20} \geq 610.566)$. We show a portion of the F table from Appendix B in Table 13.2.

TABLE 13.2 Portion of the F table

df_2	Area in Upper Tail	df_1		
		1	2	3
20	0.10	2.97	2.59	2.38
	0.05	4.35	3.49	3.10
	0.025	5.87	4.46	3.86
	0.01	8.10	5.85	4.94

For $df_1 = 3$ and $df_2 = 20$, we see that 610.566 is much greater than 4.94, implying that the p-value is less than 0.01. As explained in Chapter 11, we can use Excel's **F.DIST.RT** function or R's **pf** function to find the exact p-value as 0 (approximately).

Step 4. State the conclusion and interpret the results. Since the p-value is less than 0.05, we reject H_0. Therefore, at the 5% significance level, we conclude that the mean cost savings from using public transportation differs between the four cities.

It is important to note that if we reject the null hypothesis, we can only conclude that not all population means are equal. The one-way ANOVA test does not allow us to infer which individual means differ. Therefore, even though the sample mean is the highest for Boston, we cannot conclude that Boston leads other cities in the amount that commuters save by taking public transportation. Further analysis of the difference between paired population means is addressed in Section 13.2.

The One-Way ANOVA Table

Most software packages summarize the ANOVA calculations in a table. The general format of the ANOVA table is presented in Table 13.3.

TABLE 13.3 General Format of a One-Way ANOVA Table

Source of Variation	SS	df	MS	F	p-value
Between Groups	SSTR	$c - 1$	MSTR	$F_{(df_1, df_2)} = \dfrac{MSTR}{MSE}$	$P\left(F_{(df_1, df_2)} \geq \dfrac{MSTR}{MSE}\right)$
Within Groups	SSE	$n_T - c$	MSE		
Total	SST	$n_T - 1$			

We should also note that **total sum of squares** *SST* is equal to the sum of the squared differences of each observation from the grand mean. This is equivalent to summing *SSTR* and *SSE*; that is, $SST = SSTR + SSE$.

DECOMPOSING TOTAL VARIATION IN A ONE-WAY ANOVA TEST

In a one-way ANOVA test, the total sum of squares, *SST*, of the variable is partitioned into two distinct components: the sum of squares due to treatments, *SSTR*, and the error sum of squares, *SSE*. That is, $SST = SSTR + SSE$.

FILE
Public_Transportation

Using Excel and R to Construct a One-Way ANOVA Table

Fortunately, we can follow simple steps to construct a one-way ANOVA table in Excel and R.

EXAMPLE 13.1

Use Excel and R to obtain the ANOVA table for the public transportation example.

SOLUTION:
Using Excel

a. Open the ***Public_Transportation*** data file.
b. From the menu, choose **Data > Data Analysis > ANOVA: Single Factor**.
c. In the *ANOVA: Single Factor* dialog box, as shown in Figure 13.2, choose the box next to *Input range*, and then select all the data, including the city names. Check the box in front of *Labels in First Row*. Click **OK**.

FIGURE 13.2
Excel's ANOVA: Single Factor dialog box

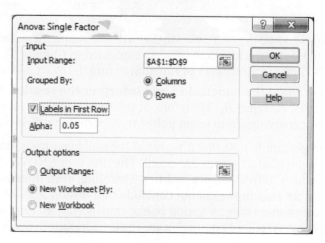

Table 13.4 shows the Excel-produced ANOVA table for the public transportation example. You should verify that all of your calculations match the values produced by Excel. Excel also shows a statistic called "F crit" which would be useful if we were using the critical-value approach to conduct a hypothesis test. Since we use the p-value approach, we can ignore this statistic.

We find that the value of the test statistic, $F_{(3,20)} = 610.566$, and corresponding p-value of 0 (approximately) match our calculations (these values are in boldface in Table 13.4). As concluded before, mean cost savings from using public transportation are not the same for each city.

TABLE 13.4 Excel-Produced ANOVA Table for Public Transportation Example

SUMMARY				
Groups	Count	Sum	Average	Variance
Boston	5	63110	12622	7707.5
New York	8	100680	12585	6464.3
San Francisco	6	70320	11720	7050
Chicago	5	53650	10730	8212.5

ANOVA					
Source of Variation	SS	df	MS	F	p-value
Between Groups	13204720	3	4401573	**610.566**	**7.96E-20**
Within Groups	144180	20	7209		
Total	13348900	23			

Using R

a. Import the ***Public_Transportation*** data into a data frame (table) in R.

b. Install and load the *reshape2* package. We need this package in order to reconfigure the data frame. Enter

```
> install.packages("reshape2")
> library(reshape2)
```

c. We stack the city names and cost values using the **melt** function from the *reshape2* package. We label the reconfigured data frame as Stacked. R displays a warning, which we can ignore. For clarity, we use the **colnames** function to label the columns in Stacked as City and Cost, respectively. Enter

```
> Stacked <- melt(Public_Transportation)
> colnames(Stacked) <- c("City", "Cost")
```

(You can make sure that your data has been properly reconfigured by entering Stacked at the prompt sign.)

d. We then use the **aov** function, which creates an analysis of variance model object; we label this object as Transit. Within the **aov** function, we first specify the quantitative variable of interest as a function of the categorical factor(s) or treatment(s). In this example, we are interested in Cost as a function of City. We also need to specify the data frame. Enter

```
> Transit <- aov(Cost~City,data=Stacked)
```

e. To obtain the ANOVA table, we use the **anova** function with the object created in Step d. Enter

```
> anova(Transit)
```

Table 13.5 shows the R-produced ANOVA results. Note that these results match our calculations as well as the Excel-produced ANOVA table.

TABLE 13.5 R-Produced ANOVA Table for the Public Transportation Example

```
Analysis of Variance Table

Response: Cost
          Df   Sum       Sq Mean   Sq F value   Pr(>F)
City       3   13204720  4401573   610.57       < 2.2e-16 ***
Residuals 20   144180    7209
---
Signif. codes: 0 '***' 0.001 '**' 0.01 '*' 0.05 '.' 0.1 ' ' 1
```

EXERCISES 13.1

Mechanics

1. A random sample of five observations from three normally distributed populations produced the following data:

Treatments		
A	B	C
22	20	19
25	25	22
27	21	24
24	26	21
22	23	19
$\bar{x}_A = 24$	$\bar{x}_B = 23$	$\bar{x}_C = 21$
$s_A^2 = 4.5$	$s_B^2 = 6.5$	$s_C^2 = 4.5$

a. Calculate the grand mean.
b. Calculate *SSTR* and *MSTR*.
c. Calculate *SSE* and *MSE*.
d. Specify the competing hypotheses in order to determine whether some differences exist between the population means.
e. Calculate the value of the $F_{(df_1,df_2)}$ test statistic and the *p*-value.
f. At the 5% significance level, what is the conclusion to the test?

2. Random sampling from four normally distributed populations produced the following data:

Treatments			
A	B	C	D
−11	−8	−8	−12
−13	−13	−13	−13
−10	−15	−8	−15
	−12	−13	
		−10	

a. Calculate the grand mean.
b. Calculate *SSTR* and *MSTR*.
c. Calculate *SSE* and *MSE*.
d. Specify the competing hypotheses in order to determine whether some differences exist between the population means.
e. Calculate the value of the $F_{(df_1,df_2)}$ test statistic and the *p*-value.
f. At the 10% significance level, what is the conclusion to the test?

3. Given the following information obtained from three normally distributed populations, construct an ANOVA table and perform an ANOVA test of mean differences at the 1% significance level.

$$SSTR = 220.7; SSE = 2252.2; c = 3; n_1 = n_2 = n_3 = 8$$

4. Given the following information obtained from four normally distributed populations, construct an ANOVA table and perform an ANOVA test of mean differences at the 5% significance level.

$SST = 70.47$; $SSTR = 11.34$; $c = 4$; $n_1 = n_2 = n_3 = n_4 = 15$

5. An analysis of variance experiment produced a portion of the accompanying ANOVA table.

Source of Variation	SS	df	MS	F	p-value
Between Groups	25.08	3	?	?	0.000
Within Groups	92.64	76	?		
Total	117.72	79			

a. Specify the competing hypotheses in order to determine whether some differences exist between the population means.
b. Fill in the missing statistics in the ANOVA table.
c. At the 5% significance level, what is the conclusion to the test?

6. An analysis of variance experiment produced a portion of the following ANOVA table.

Source of Variation	SS	df	MS	F	p-value
Between Groups		5	?	?	?
Within Groups	4321.11	54	?		
Total	4869.48	59			

a. Specify the competing hypotheses in order to determine whether some differences exist between the population means.
b. Fill in the missing statistics in the ANOVA table.
c. At the 10% significance level, what is the conclusion to the test?

Applications

7. Asian residents in Boston have the highest average life expectancy of any racial or ethnic group—a decade longer than black residents (*The Boston Globe*, August 16, 2010). Suppose sample results indicative of the overall results are as follows.

Asian	Black	Latino	White
$\bar{x}_1 = 83.7$ years	$\bar{x}_2 = 73.5$ years	$\bar{x}_3 = 80.6$ years	$\bar{x}_4 = 79.0$ years
$s_1^2 = 26.3$	$s_2^2 = 27.5$	$s_3^2 = 28.2$	$s_4^2 = 24.8$
$n_1 = 20$	$n_2 = 20$	$n_3 = 20$	$n_4 = 20$

a. Specify the competing hypotheses to test whether there are some differences in average life expectancies between the four ethnic groups.
b. Construct an ANOVA table. Assume life expectancies are normally distributed.
c. At the 5% significance level, what is the conclusion to the test?

8. FILE *Detergent.* A well-known conglomerate claims that its detergent "whitens and brightens better than all the rest." In order to compare the cleansing action of the top three brands of detergents, 24 swatches of white cloth were soiled with red wine and grass stains and then washed in front-loading machines with the respective detergents. The following whiteness readings were obtained:

Detergent		
1	2	3
84	78	87
79	74	80
87	81	91
85	86	77
94	86	78
89	89	79
89	69	77
83	79	78

a. Specify the competing hypotheses to test whether there are some differences in the average whitening effectiveness of the three detergents.
b. At the 5% significance level, what is the conclusion to the test? Assume whiteness readings are normally distributed.

9. A survey by Genworth Financial Inc., a financial-services company, concludes that the cost of long-term care in the United States varies significantly, depending on where an individual lives (*The Wall Street Journal*, May 16, 2009). An economist collects data from the five states with the highest annual costs (Alaska, Massachusetts, New Jersey, Rhode Island, and Connecticut), in order to determine if his sample data are consistent with the survey's conclusions. The economist provides the following portion of an ANOVA table:

Source of Variation	SS	df	MS	F	p-value
Between Groups	635.0542	4	?	?	?
Within Groups	253.2192	20	?		
Total	888.2734	24			

a. Specify the competing hypotheses to test whether some differences exist in the mean long-term care costs in these five states.

b. Complete the ANOVA table. Assume that long-term care costs are normally distributed.

c. At the 5% significance level, do mean costs differ?

10. **FILE** *Sports.* An online survey by the Sporting Goods Manufacturers Association, a trade group of sports retailers and marketers, claimed that household income of recreational athletes varies by sport (*The Wall Street Journal*, August 10, 2009). In order to verify this claim, an economist samples five sports enthusiasts participating in each of four different recreational sports and obtains each enthusiast's income (in $1,000s), as shown in the accompanying table.

Snorkeling	Sailing	Boardsailing/ Windsurfing	Bowling
90.9	87.6	75.9	79.3
86.0	95.0	75.6	75.8
93.6	94.6	83.1	79.6
98.8	87.2	74.4	78.5
98.4	82.5	80.5	73.2

a. Specify the competing hypotheses in order to test the association's claim.

b. Do some average incomes differ depending on the recreational sport? Explain. Assume incomes are normally distributed.

11. The following output summarizes the results of an analysis of variance experiment in which the treatments were three different hybrid cars and the variable measured was the miles per gallon (mpg) obtained while driving the same route. Assume mpg is normally distributed.

Source of Variation	SS	df	MS	F	p-value
Between Groups	1034.51	2	517.26	19.86	4.49E-07
Within Groups	1302.41	50	26.05		
Total	2336.92	52			

At the 5% significance level, can we conclude that average mpg differs between the hybrids? Explain.

12. Do energy costs vary dramatically depending on where you live in the United States? Annual energy costs are collected from 25 households in four regions in the United States. A portion of the ANOVA table is shown.

Source of Variation	SS	df	MS	F	p-value
Between Groups	7531769	3	?	?	7.13E-24
Within Groups	3492385	96	?		
Total	11024154	99			

a. Complete the ANOVA table. Assume energy costs are normally distributed.

b. At the 1% significance level, can we conclude that average annual energy costs vary by region?

13. **FILE** *Buggies.* Wenton Powersports produces dune buggies. They have three assembly lines, "Razor," "Blazer," and "Tracer," named after the particular dune buggy models produced on those lines. Each assembly line was originally designed using the same target production rate. However, over the years, various changes have been made to the lines. Accordingly, management wishes to determine whether the assembly lines are still operating at the same average hourly production rate. Production data (in dune buggies/hour) for the last eight hours are as follows.

Razor	Blazer	Tracer
11	10	9
10	8	9
8	11	10
10	9	9
9	11	8
9	10	7
13	11	8
11	8	9

a. Specify the competing hypotheses to test whether there are some differences in the mean production rates across the three assembly lines.

b. At the 5% significance level, what is the conclusion to the test? What about the 10% significance level? Assume production rates are normally distributed.

14. **FILE** *Fill_Volumes.* In the carbonated beverage industry, dispensing pressure can be an important factor in achieving accurate fill volumes. Too little pressure can slow down the dispensing process. Too much pressure can create excess "fizz" and, thus, inaccurate fill volumes. Accordingly, a leading beverage manufacturer wants to conduct an experiment at three different pressure settings to determine if differences exist in the mean fill volumes. Forty bottles

with a target fill volume of 12 ounces were filled at each pressure setting, and the resulting fill volumes (in ounces) were recorded. A portion of the data is shown in the accompanying table.

Low Pressure (60 psi)	Medium Pressure (80 psi)	High Pressure (100 psi)
12.00	12.00	11.56
11.97	11.87	11.55
⋮	⋮	⋮
12.00	12.14	11.80

a. Specify the competing hypotheses to test whether there are differences in the mean fill volumes across the three pressure settings.
b. At the 5% significance level, what is the conclusion to the test? What about the 1% significance level?

15. **FILE** *Exam_Scores.* A statistics instructor wonders whether significant differences exist in her students' final exam scores in her three different sections. She randomly selects the scores from 10 students in each section. A portion of the data is shown in the accompanying table. Assume exam scores are normally distributed.

Section 1	Section 2	Section 3
85	91	74
68	84	69
⋮	⋮	⋮
74	75	73

Do these data provide enough evidence at the 5% significance level to indicate that there are some differences in final exam scores among these three sections?

16. **FILE** *Patronage.* The accompanying table shows a portion of the number of customers that frequent a restaurant on weekend days over the past 52 weeks.

Fridays	Saturdays	Sundays
391	450	389
362	456	343
⋮	⋮	⋮
443	441	376

At the 5% significance level, can we conclude that the average number of customers that frequent the restaurant differs by weekend day?

17. **FILE** *Nike_Revenues.* The accompanying table shows a portion of quarterly data on Nike's revenue (in $ millions) for the fiscal years 2001 through 2010. Data for Nike's fiscal year refer to the time period from June 1 through May 31. Assume revenue is normally distributed.

	Quarters Ended			
Year	August 31	November 30	February 28	May 31
2001	2637	2199	2170	2483
2002	2614	2337	2260	2682
⋮	⋮	⋮	⋮	⋮
2010	4799	4406	4733	5077

Source: Annual Reports for Nike, Inc.

Use a one-way ANOVA test to determine if the data provide enough evidence at the 5% significance level to indicate that there are quarterly differences in Nike's revenue.

18. **FILE** *Field_Score.* A human resource specialist wants to determine whether the average job satisfaction score (on a scale of 0 to 100) differs depending on a person's field of employment. She collects scores from 30 employees in three different fields. A portion of the data is shown in the accompanying table.

Field 1	Field 2	Field 3
80	76	81
76	73	77
⋮	⋮	⋮
79	67	80

At the 10% significance level, can we conclude that the average job satisfaction differs by field?

13.2 MULTIPLE COMPARISON METHODS

LO 13.2

In the preceding section, we used a one-way ANOVA test to determine whether differences exist between population means. Suppose that for a given sample we reject the null hypothesis of equal means. While the ANOVA test determines that not all population means are equal, it does not indicate which ones differ. To find out which population means differ requires further analysis of the direction and the statistical significance of the difference between paired population means $(\mu_i - \mu_j)$. By constructing confidence intervals for all pairwise differences for the population

Use Fisher's LSD method and Tukey's HSD method to determine which means differ.

means, we can identify which means significantly differ from one another. The first method we discuss is often referred to as **Fisher's Least Significant Difference (LSD) method**.

We also introduce an improved method, developed by the renowned 20th-century statistician John Tukey (1915–2000). This is often referred to as **Tukey's Honestly Significant Difference (HSD) method**. Note that there are no significant differences to find if the ANOVA test does not reject the null hypothesis of equal means.

Fisher's Least Significant Difference (LSD) Method

In Chapter 10, we stated that, when the population variances are unknown but assumed equal, the $100(1 - \alpha)\%$ confidence interval for the difference between two population means $\mu_i - \mu_j$ is

$$(\bar{x}_i - \bar{x}_j) \pm t_{\alpha/2, n_i + n_j - 2}\sqrt{s_p^2\left(\frac{1}{n_i} + \frac{1}{n_j}\right)}.$$

Here, s_p^2 is a pooled estimate of the common population variance and is computed as

$$s_p^2 = \frac{(n_i - 1)s_i^2 + (n_j - 1)s_j^2}{n_i + n_j - 2}.$$

We substitute the mean square error MSE from the one-way ANOVA test for s_p^2 since MSE uses all samples whereas s_p^2 uses only two of the samples for the pairwise comparison. Recall that when we conduct a one-way ANOVA test, we assume that we are sampling from populations that have the same population variance σ^2. We still apply the t_{df} distribution, but we use the degrees of freedom corresponding to MSE, or $df = n_T - c$.

FISHER'S CONFIDENCE INTERVAL FOR $\mu_i - \mu_j$

Fisher's $100(1 - \alpha)\%$ confidence interval for the difference between two population means $\mu_i - \mu_j$ is given by

$$(\bar{x}_i - \bar{x}_j) \pm t_{\alpha/2, n_T - c}\sqrt{MSE\left(\frac{1}{n_i} + \frac{1}{n_j}\right)},$$

where the mean square error MSE is estimated from the one-way ANOVA test.

EXAMPLE 13.2

Using the sample means and the ANOVA test results from the public transportation example of Section 13.1, calculate 95% confidence intervals for the difference between all possible pairings of the four population means. Comment on the direction and the significance of the differences at the 5% level.

SOLUTION: We use the following sample means and sample sizes to derive the confidence intervals:

$$\bar{x}_{\text{Boston}} = 12{,}622 \qquad n_{\text{Boston}} = 5$$
$$\bar{x}_{\text{New York}} = 12{,}585 \qquad n_{\text{New York}} = 8$$
$$\bar{x}_{\text{San Francisco}} = 11{,}720 \qquad n_{\text{San Francisco}} = 6$$
$$\bar{x}_{\text{Chicago}} = 10{,}730 \qquad n_{\text{Chicago}} = 5$$

In addition, $MSE = 7{,}209$ (see Table 13.4 in Section 13.1), $n_T - c = 24 - 4 = 20$, and $t_{\alpha/2, n_T - c} = t_{0.025, 20} = 2.086$. Table 13.6 shows the 95% confidence intervals.

TABLE 13.6 Fisher's 95% Confidence Intervals for Example 13.2

Population Mean Differences	Confidence Interval
$\mu_{Boston} - \mu_{New\ York}$	$(12622 - 12585) \pm 2.086 \sqrt{7209\left(\frac{1}{5} + \frac{1}{8}\right)} = 37 \pm 100.97$ or [−63.97, 137.97]
$\mu_{Boston} - \mu_{San\ Francisco}$	$(12622 - 11720) \pm 2.086 \sqrt{7209\left(\frac{1}{5} + \frac{1}{6}\right)} = 902 \pm 107.25$ or [794.75, 1009.25]
$\mu_{Boston} - \mu_{Chicago}$	$(12622 - 10730) \pm 2.086 \sqrt{7209\left(\frac{1}{5} + \frac{1}{5}\right)} = 1892 \pm 112.02$ or [1779.98, 2004.02]
$\mu_{New\ York} - \mu_{San\ Francisco}$	$(12585 - 11720) \pm 2.086 \sqrt{7209\left(\frac{1}{8} + \frac{1}{6}\right)} = 865 \pm 95.65$ or [769.35, 960.65]
$\mu_{New\ York} - \mu_{Chicago}$	$(12585 - 10730) \pm 2.086 \sqrt{7209\left(\frac{1}{8} + \frac{1}{5}\right)} = 1855 \pm 100.97$ or [1754.03, 1955.97]
$\mu_{San\ Francisco} - \mu_{Chicago}$	$(11720 - 10730) \pm 2.086 \sqrt{7209\left(\frac{1}{6} + \frac{1}{5}\right)} = 990 \pm 107.25$ or [882.75, 1097.25]

The 95% confidence interval for $\mu_{Boston} - \mu_{New\ York}$ is given by 37 ± 100.97, which is [−63.97, 137.97]. Since this interval contains the value zero, we cannot reject the null hypothesis, given by H_0: $\mu_{Boston} - \mu_{New\ York} = 0$, at the 5% significance level. In other words, the average cost savings from using public transportation in Boston and in New York is not significantly different.

For $\mu_{Boston} - \mu_{San\ Francisco}$, the entire interval, ranging from 794.75 to 1,009.25, is above the value zero. Thus, we conclude at the 5% significance level that the average cost savings from using public transportation in Boston is different from the average cost savings in San Francisco. In fact, the remaining intervals are all above zero, suggesting that average cost savings is different between the corresponding cities.

SYNOPSIS OF INTRODUCTORY CASE

A report by the American Public Transportation Association suggests that commuters who use public transportation can save a substantial amount of money annually. Sean Cox, a research analyst at an environmental firm, conducts a survey to determine whether average cost savings differs depending on where the commuters reside. He collects data on public transit riders in the top four cost-savings cities: Boston, New York, San Francisco, and Chicago. Table 13.7 shows summary statistics and relevant ANOVA results.

©Hero Images/Getty Images RF

TABLE 13.7 Summary Statistics and Relevant ANOVA Results

Boston	New York	San Francisco	Chicago
$\bar{x}_1 = 12{,}622$	$\bar{x}_2 = 12{,}585$	$\bar{x}_3 = 11{,}720$	$\bar{x}_4 = 10{,}730$
$s_1 = 87.79$	$s_2 = 80.40$	$s_3 = 83.96$	$s_4 = 90.62$
$n_1 = 5$	$n_2 = 8$	$n_3 = 6$	$n_4 = 5$
Mean Square Error (*MSE*): 7,209			
Calculated *F*-statistic and its *p*-value: 610.6 and 0 (approximately), respectively.			

Sean reports that in all four major cities the sample average cost savings is above $10,000. Since the *p*-value of the ANOVA test is close to zero, he concludes that there are differences in cost savings between the cities at the 5% significance level. Sean also constructs confidence intervals for all pairwise differences to identify pairings of cities that have statistically different cost savings. Commuters in Boston and New York have the highest cost savings; however, at the 5% significance level, their average cost savings do not differ from one another. For every other pairing, average cost savings from using public transportation is statistically different between cities. In other words, he concludes at the 5% significance level that average cost savings from using public transportation is different between Boston and San Francisco, Boston and Chicago, New York and San Francisco, New York and Chicago, and San Francisco and Chicago.

It is important to point out that we can apply Fisher's LSD method only if we rejected the null hypothesis of equal means in the one-way ANOVA test. However, as mentioned earlier, we cannot infer the equality of means by conducting a series of paired tests, even those based on the LSD method. In Example 13.2, we have six paired tests. Therefore, if we use the 5% significance level for each test, the probability that we would make a Type I error (incorrectly rejecting a null hypothesis of equal means) on *at least* one of these individual tests will be greater than 5%. The more means we compare, the more the Type I error becomes inflated.

One way to avoid this problem is to perform each individual paired test at a reduced significance level, which ensures that the overall significance level for the equality of all means does not exceed α. The resulting confidence intervals are wider and, hence, reduce the probability of incorrectly rejecting the null hypothesis of equal means. However, this technique reduces the power of the test and thus results in an increased risk of a Type II error (incorrectly failing to reject a null hypothesis of equal means).

Tukey's Honestly Significant Difference (HSD) Method

An improved multiple comparison technique is Tukey's honestly significant difference (HSD) method. The original Tukey's HSD method was introduced with **balanced** data, but it was subsequently modified for **unbalanced** data. If there are an equal number of observations in each sample—that is, when $n_1 = n_2 = \cdots = n_c$—then the data are balanced. In situations where different numbers of observations occur in each sample—that is, when $n_i \neq n_j$—the data are unbalanced. Tukey's method uses the **studentized range distribution**, which has broader, flatter, and thicker tails than the t_{df} distribution. In other words, for a given probability under the right tail of the distribution, the studentized range value will be larger than the corresponding t_{df} value. Therefore, Tukey's HSD method protects against an inflated risk of a Type I error.

TUKEY'S CONFIDENCE INTERVAL FOR $\mu_i - \mu_j$

Tukey's $100(1 - \alpha)\%$ confidence interval for the difference between two population means $\mu_i - \mu_j$ is given by

- $(\bar{x}_i - \bar{x}_j) \pm q_{\alpha,(c,n_T-c)} \sqrt{\dfrac{MSE}{n}}$ for balanced data $(n = n_i = n_j)$, and

- $(\bar{x}_i - \bar{x}_j) \pm q_{\alpha,(c,n_T-c)} \sqrt{\dfrac{MSE}{n}\left(\dfrac{1}{n_i} + \dfrac{1}{n_j}\right)}$ for unbalanced data $(n_i \neq n_j)$,

where $q_{\alpha,(c,n_T-c)}$ is the studentized range value.

The studentized range value $q_{\alpha,(c,n_T-c)}$ varies with the significance level α, the number of populations c, and $n_T - c$. Table 13.8 shows a portion of the studentized range table; Table 5 in Appendix B provides a more comprehensive table. For example, with $\alpha = 0.05$, $c = 6$, and $n_T - c = 19$, we find $q_{0.05,(6,19)} = 4.47$. With $\alpha = 0.01$, $c = 3$, and $n_T - c = 20$, we find $q_{0.01,(3,20)} = 4.64$. These values are in boldface in Table 13.8. In instances where we do not see values for $n_T - c$ in Table 5, we generally round down, especially for smaller sample sizes. For example, if $n_T - c = 33$, a value that does not appear in Table 5 of Appendix B, we reference the row corresponding to $n_T - c = 30$.

TABLE 13.8 Portion of Values for $q_{\alpha,(c,n_T-c)}$ in Tukey's HSD Method

| $n_T - c$ | α | \multicolumn{8}{c}{c = number of means} | | | | | | | |
		2	3	4	5	6	7	8	9
19	0.05	2.96	3.59	3.98	4.25	**4.47**	4.65	4.79	4.92
	0.01	4.05	4.67	5.05	5.33	5.55	5.73	5.89	6.02
20	0.05	2.95	3.58	3.96	4.23	4.45	4.62	4.77	4.90
	0.01	4.02	**4.64**	5.02	5.29	5.51	5.69	5.84	5.97

FISHER'S LSD METHOD VERSUS TUKEY'S HSD METHOD

When using Fisher's LSD method at some stated significance level α, the probability of committing a Type I error increases as the number of pairwise comparisons increases; that is, the likelihood of incorrectly rejecting the null hypothesis of equal means in at least one of the pairwise comparisons is greater than α. By using the studentized range distribution over the t_{df} distribution, Tukey's HSD method ensures that the probability of a Type I error equals α, irrespective of the number of pairwise comparisons.

EXAMPLE 13.3

A consumer advocate in California is concerned with the price of a common generic drug. Specifically, he feels that one region of the state has significantly different prices for the drug than two other regions. He divides the state into three regions and collects the generic drug's price from 10 pharmacies in each region. He produces the summary statistics and ANOVA results shown in Table 13.9.

TABLE 13.9 Summary Statistics and ANOVA Results for Example 13.3

| \multicolumn{5}{c}{SUMMARY} | | | | |
Groups	Count	Sum	Average	Variance
Region 1	10	359	35.9	3.8778
Region 2	10	343	34.3	4.4556
Region 3	10	398	39.8	1.9556

| \multicolumn{6}{c}{ANOVA} | | | | | |
Source of Variation	SS	df	MS	F	p-value
Between Groups	160.0667	2	80.0333	23.336	1.3E-06
Within Groups	92.60	27	3.4296		
Total	252.6667	29			

a. At the 5% significance level, do differences exist between the mean drug prices in the three regions?

b. If significant differences exist, use Tukey's HSD method to determine which regions' means differ at the 5% significance level.

SOLUTION:

a. In order to test differences between the mean drug prices in the three regions, we specify the competing hypotheses as

$$H_0: \mu_{\text{Region1}} = \mu_{\text{Region2}} = \mu_{\text{Region3}}$$
$$H_A: \text{Not all mean drug prices are equal.}$$

The ANOVA table shows the value of the test statistic as $F_{(2,27)} = 23.336$ with a p-value of 1.3×10^{-6}, or $P(F_{2,27} \geq 23.336) = 0$ (approximately). Since the p-value is less than the significance level of 0.05, we reject H_0 and conclude that not all mean drug prices are equal.

b. We use Tukey's confidence interval for balanced data since each sample size is the same ($n_1 = n_2 = n_3 = 10$). Given $\alpha = 0.05$, $c = 3$, and $n_T - c = 30 - 3 = 27$, we refer to Table 5 in Appendix B to find $q_{\alpha,(c,n_T-c)} = q_{0.05,(3,27)} = 3.51$.

We use $(\bar{x}_i - \bar{x}_j) \pm q_{\alpha,(c,n_T-c)}\sqrt{\frac{MSE}{n}}$ to compute 95% confidence intervals for all pairwise differences of the means. The results are shown in Table 13.10.

TABLE 13.10 Tukey's 95% Confidence Intervals for Example 13.3

Population Mean Differences	Confidence Interval		
$\mu_1 - \mu_2$	$(35.9 - 34.3) \pm 3.51\sqrt{\dfrac{3.4296}{10}}$	or	$[-0.46, 3.66]$
$\mu_1 - \mu_3$	$(35.9 - 39.8) \pm 3.51\sqrt{\dfrac{3.4296}{10}}$	or	$[-5.96, -1.84]^*$
$\mu_2 - \mu_3$	$(34.3 - 39.8) \pm 3.51\sqrt{\dfrac{3.4296}{10}}$	or	$[-7.56, -3.44]^*$

The asterisk * shows that the confidence interval does not include the value zero, thus indicating that the corresponding means are different at the 5% significance level. The consumer advocate's claim is supported by the data. At the 5% significance level, the average price of generic drugs in region 3 is different from the average prices in regions 1 and 2. At the 5% significance level, the consumer advocate cannot conclude that average prices differ in regions 1 and 2.

We also employed Tukey's method for unbalanced data using the ANOVA results from the public transportation example. While the resulting intervals (not reported) became wider than those reported in Table 13.6, the inference regarding the population means remains the same.

Using R to Construct Tukey Confidence Intervals for $\mu_1 - \mu_2$

Unfortunately, Excel does not generate Fisher's LSD or Tukey's HSD confidence intervals. R does generate both types of confidence intervals; however, it is more straightforward, and ultimately more useful, to obtain Tukey's HSD confidence intervals with R. Consider the following example.

EXAMPLE 13.4

Use R to replicate the results from Example 13.3.

SOLUTION:

FILE

Generic

a. Import the *Generic* data into a data frame (table) in R. Then, as we did in Section 13.1, we install and load the *reshape2* package and use the **melt, colnames, aov,** and **anova** functions. We revisit these commands in brief.

b. In order to reconfigure the data frame, we use the **melt** function and label the reconfigured data frame as Stacked2. We use the **colnames** function to label the columns in Stacked2 as Region and Price, respectively. We use the **aov** function to create an analysis of variance model object, which we label as Drug, and specify Price as a function of Region. To obtain the ANOVA table, we use the **anova** function. Enter

```
> Stacked2 <- melt(Generic)
> colnames(Stacked2) <- c("Region", "Price")
> Drug <- aov(Price ~ Region, data=Stacked2)
> anova(Drug)
```

c. We use the **TukeyHSD** function to obtain Tukey's HSD confidence intervals. Within the function, we specify the object from Step b, and we use the option *conf.level* to specify the confidence level. Enter

```
> TukeyHSD(Drug, conf.level = 0.95)
```

Table 13.11 shows the R-produced ANOVA table as well as Tukey's HSD confidence intervals for the regional generic drug prices described in Example 13.3. The ANOVA table is identical to the one obtained from Excel. Note that the only difference in the results for the confidence intervals is the order when finding the differences; this results in inverse values for the lower and upper limits. R also reports the *p*-values for testing pairwise differences, which confirm the results found in Example 13.3. At the 5% significance level, the average generic drug prices do not differ between regions 1 and 2; however, at the 5% significance level, the average generic drug price in region 3 is different from the average prices in regions 1 and 2.

TABLE 13.11 R-Produced ANOVA Table and Tukey Confidence Intervals for Example 13.4

```
Analysis of Variance Table
Response: Price
          Df Sum Sq Mean Sq F value   Pr(>F)
Region     2 160.07  80.033  23.336  1.303e-06 ***
Residuals 27  92.60   3.430
---
Signif. codes: 0 '***' 0.001 '**' 0.01 '*' 0.05 '.'
  0.1 ' ' 1
  Tukey multiple comparisons of means
    95% family-wise confidence level
Fit: aov(formula = Price ~ Region, data = Stacked)
$Region
                  diff      lwr       upr       p adj
Region.2-Region.1 -1.6 -3.65347 0.4534697 0.1491760
Region.3-Region.1  3.9  1.84653 5.9534697 0.0001913
Region.3-Region.2  5.5  3.44653 7.5534697 0.0000012
```

EXERCISES 13.2

Mechanics

19. The following statistics are computed by sampling from three normal populations whose variances are equal:

    $\bar{x}_1 = 25.3$, $n_1 = 8$; $\bar{x}_2 = 31.5$, $n_2 = 10$; $\bar{x}_3 = 32.3$, $n_3 = 6$; $MSE = 27.2$

    a. Calculate 95% confidence intervals for $\mu_1 - \mu_2$, $\mu_1 - \mu_3$, and $\mu_2 - \mu_3$ to test for mean differences with Fisher's LSD approach.
    b. Repeat the analysis with Tukey's HSD approach.
    c. Which of these two approaches would you use to determine whether differences exist between the population means? Explain.

20. The following statistics are calculated by sampling from four normal populations whose variances are equal:

    $\bar{x}_1 = 149$, $n_1 = 10$; $\bar{x}_2 = 154$, $n_2 = 10$; $\bar{x}_3 = 143$, $n_3 = 10$; $\bar{x}_4 = 139$, $n_4 = 10$; $MSE = 51.3$

    a. Use Fisher's LSD method to determine which population means differ at $\alpha = 0.01$.
    b. Use Tukey's HSD method to determine which population means differ at $\alpha = 0.01$.
    c. Do all population means differ? Explain.

21. A one-way analysis of variance experiment produced the following ANOVA table.

SUMMARY		
Groups	Count	Average
Column 1	6	0.57
Column 2	6	1.38
Column 3	6	2.33

Source of Variation	SS	df	MS	F	p-value
Between Groups	9.12	2	4.56	12.84	0.0006
Within Groups	5.33	15	0.36		
Total	14.46	17			

a. Conduct an ANOVA test at the 5% significance level to determine if some population means differ.
b. Calculate 95% confidence interval estimates for $\mu_1 - \mu_2$, $\mu_1 - \mu_3$, and $\mu_2 - \mu_3$ with Tukey's HSD approach.
c. Given your response to part (b), which means significantly differ?

22. A one-way analysis of variance experiment produced the following ANOVA table.

SUMMARY		
Groups	Count	Average
Column 1	10	349
Column 2	10	348
Column 3	10	366
Column 4	10	365

Source of Variation	SS	df	MS	F	p-value
Between Groups	2997.11	3	999.04	15.54	1.2E-06
Within Groups	2314.71	36	64.30		
Total	5311.82	39			

a. Use Fisher's LSD method to determine which means differ at the 5% level of significance.
b. Use Tukey's HSD method to determine which means differ at the 5% level of significance.
c. Given your responses to parts (a) and (b), do the population means differ at the 5% significance level?

23. The following output summarizes the results for a one-way analysis of variance experiment in which the treatments were three different hybrid cars and the variable measured was the miles per gallon (mpg) obtained while driving the same route.

Hybrid 1: $\bar{x}_1 = 38$, $n_1 = 20$
Hybrid 2: $\bar{x}_2 = 48$, $n_2 = 15$
Hybrid 3: $\bar{x}_3 = 39$, $n_3 = 18$

Source of Variation	SS	df	MS	F	p-value
Between Groups	1034.51	2	517.26	19.86	4.49E-07
Within Groups	1302.41	50	26.05		
Total	2336.92	52			

a. At the 5% significance level, can we conclude that average mpg differs between the hybrids?
b. If significant differences exist, use Tukey's HSD method at the 5% significance level to determine which hybrids' means differ.

Applications

24. In an attempt to improve efficiency, Starbucks has implemented "lean" Japanese techniques at many of its 11,000 U.S. stores (*The Wall Street Journal*, August 4, 2009). By reducing the time baristas (employees) spend on bending, reaching, and walking,

they will have more time to interact with customers and improve the Starbucks experience. Suppose Starbucks adopts the lean technique at Store 1 but makes no changes at Stores 2 and 3. On a recent Monday morning between the hours of 7:00 AM and 8:00 AM, the following statistics were obtained relating to average time per order (in seconds):

Store 1: $\bar{x}_1 = 56$, $n_1 = 18$
Store 2: $\bar{x}_2 = 66$, $n_2 = 12$
Store 3: $\bar{x}_3 = 63$, $n_3 = 14$

The following ANOVA table was produced:

Source of Variation	SS	df	MS	F	p-value
Between Groups	811.70	2	405.85	52.11	5.5E-12
Within Groups	319.30	41	7.79		
Total	1131.00	43			

a. Compute 95% confidence interval estimates for all paired differences for the means using Fisher's LSD approach.
b. Repeat the analysis with Tukey's HSD approach.
c. Which of these two approaches is more reliable? Explain.

25. Do energy costs vary dramatically depending on where you live in the United States? Annual energy costs are collected from 25 households in four regions in the United States. Sample means for each region and a portion of the ANOVA table is shown below.

SUMMARY		
Groups	Count	Average
West	25	1491
Northeast	25	2391
Midwest	25	1768
South	25	1758

Source of Variation	SS	df	MS	F	p-value
Between Groups	7531769	3	?	?	7.13E-24
Within Groups	3492385	96	?		
Total	11024154	99			

a. Complete the ANOVA table.
b. At the 1% significance level, can we conclude that average annual energy costs vary by region?
c. If significant differences exist, use Tukey's HSD method at the 1% significance level to determine which regions' means differ.

26. Elastotech, a plastics company, is trying to determine whether four successive daily batches of their Lexan polycarbonate have the same mean hardness value. Four daily samples of polycarbonate were taken, and the resulting hardness values were measured (using the Rockwell R scale). The following output was obtained.

Day 1	Day 2	Day 3	Day 4
$\bar{x}_1 = 115.75$	$\bar{x}_2 = 108.00$	$\bar{x}_3 = 121.39$	$\bar{x}_4 = 119.53$
$n_1 = 20$	$n_2 = 16$	$n_3 = 18$	$n_4 = 17$

Source of Variation	SS	df	MS	F	p-value
Between Groups	1751.62	3	583.87	19.29	0.000
Within Groups	2028.26	67	30.27		
Total	3779.89	70			

a. At the 1% significance level, can we conclude that the mean hardness differs among the four daily batches?
b. If significant differences exist, use Tukey's HSD method at the 1% significance level to determine which batches have different mean hardness values.

27. Producers of a new grass seed called Pearl's Premium claim that grass grown using its seed blend requires less maintenance as compared to other brands (*The Boston Globe*, July 4, 2009). For instance, grass grown using Pearl's Premium needs mowing only once a month. Suppose an independent tester wants to test whether the average height of grass after one month's growth is the same between Pearl's Premium and the other two top-selling brands. The independent tester measures 25 grass blades using each of the three seeds (glass blades are measured in inches), and constructs the following ANOVA table with supporting descriptive statistics.

SUMMARY		
Groups	Count	Average
Pearl's Premium	25	4.83
Top Brand 1	25	6.50
Top Brand 2	25	6.99

Source of Variation	SS	df	MS	F	p-value
Between Groups	64.43	2	32.21	121.67	8.09E-24
Within Groups	19.06	72	0.26		
Total	83.49	74			

a. At the 5% significance level, can the independent tester conclude that the average heights of grass blades differ by brand?

b. If significant differences exist, use Tukey's HSD method at the 5% significance level to determine which brands differ.

28. **FILE** *Employee_Absences.* A production manager is examining whether work shift is related to employee absenteeism. The number of days absent over the past year was tallied for random samples of 25 workers on each shift. A portion of the data is shown in the accompanying table.

First Shift	Second Shift	Third Shift
14	5	19
7	10	9
⋮	⋮	⋮
2	9	10

a. At the 5% significance level, can the production manager conclude that the mean days of absenteeism differ

among the three shifts? Does the conclusion change at the 10% significance level?

b. If significant differences exist, use Fisher's LSD method at the 10% significance level to determine which shifts have different mean days of absenteeism.

29. **FILE** *Patronage.* The accompanying table shows a portion of the number of customers that ate at a restaurant on weekend days over the past 52 weeks.

Fridays	Saturdays	Sundays
391	450	389
362	456	343
⋮	⋮	⋮
443	441	376

a. Verify that the average number of customers that frequent the restaurant differs by weekend day at the 5% significance level.

b. Use Tukey's HSD method at the 5% significance level to determine which weekend days differ.

13.3 TWO-WAY ANOVA TEST: NO INTERACTION

Conduct and evaluate a two-way ANOVA test with no interaction.

A one-way ANOVA test is used to compare population means based on one categorical variable or factor. For instance, we can use a one-way ANOVA test to determine whether differences exist in average miles per gallon depending on the brand name of hybrid cars. A **two-way ANOVA test** extends the analysis by measuring the effects of two factors simultaneously. Suppose we want to determine if the brand of a hybrid car and the octane level of gasoline influence average miles per gallon. Whereas a one-way ANOVA test is able to assess either the brand effect or the octane-level effect in isolation, a two-way ANOVA test is able to assess the effect of a factor while controlling for the other factor. The additional factor explains some of the unexplained variation in miles per gallon, or equivalently, reduces the error sum of squares SSE for a more discriminating $F_{(df_1, df_2)}$ test statistic.

Another feature of a two-way ANOVA test is that it can be extended to capture the interaction between the factors. In the above example, if we believe that some brands of a hybrid car react more positively to the octane levels than others, then we can include the interaction of these factors in examining miles per gallon. We use a test that determines whether the factors do indeed interact.

> A two-way ANOVA test is used to simultaneously examine the effect of two factors on the population mean. This test can be conducted with or without the interaction of the factors.

In the following example, we initially conduct a one-way ANOVA test and quickly recognize its limitations. We then introduce a two-way ANOVA test without interaction. In Section 13.4, we discuss a two-way ANOVA test with interaction.

EXAMPLE 13.5

Julia Hayes is an undergraduate who is completely undecided as to what career she should pursue. To help in her decision process, she wants to determine whether or not there are significant differences in annual incomes depending on the field of employment. Initially, she confines her analysis to the following three fields: educational services, financial services, and medical services. As a preliminary experiment, she surveys four workers from each of these three fields and asks how much he/she earns annually. Table 13.12 shows the results (in $1,000s) from the experiment.

TABLE 13.12 Data for Example 13.5

Educational Services	Financial Services	Medical Services
35	58	110
18	90	62
75	25	26
46	45	43

FILE
One-Factor_Income

Conduct a one-way ANOVA test to determine if differences exist among the fields' average incomes at the 5% significance level.

SOLUTION: Table 13.13 shows the relevant results from implementing a one-way ANOVA test.

TABLE 13.13 ANOVA Results for Example 13.5

ANOVA					
Source of Variation	SS	df	MS	F	p-value
Between Groups	579.5	2	289.75	0.330	0.727
Within Groups	7902.75	9	878.0833		
Total	8482.25	11			

In order to determine whether mean incomes differ by field of employment, we specify the following hypotheses:

$$H_0: \mu_{\text{Education}} = \mu_{\text{Financial}} = \mu_{\text{Medical}}$$
$$H_A: \text{Not all population means are equal.}$$

The value of the test statistic is $F_{(2,9)} = 0.330$ with a corresponding p-value of 0.727. Since the p-value is greater than 0.05, we do not reject H_0. At the 5% significance level, we cannot conclude that average incomes differ by field.

Julia is surprised by these results, since she feels that those in the educational services industry probably earn less than those in the other two fields. Julia is advised that she must interpret these results with caution because many other factors influence annual income—one of which is an individual's education level. We can capture the true influence of field of employment on income only when education level is held fixed.

As mentioned earlier, a two-way ANOVA test helps us find a more discriminating $F_{(df_1, df_2)}$ test statistic, since the additional factor reduces the resulting *SSE*. An added requirement for a two-way ANOVA test is that all groups must have the same sample size.

To show how a two-way ANOVA test works, we redo the analysis from Example 13.5, but this time we allow the variation in income to be affected by field (factor A) *and* education level (factor B). We match a worker from each field according to his or her highest degree. For example, we randomly select a worker from the educational services industry whose highest education level is a high school degree. We then randomly select three more workers from this field whose highest education level is a bachelor's degree, a master's degree, and a Ph.D. (or its equivalent), respectively. We repeat this process for the other two fields. The outcomes in this experiment are matched or blocked in the sense that one worker is randomly selected from each field of employment depending on his/her education level. In general, blocks are the levels at which we hold an extraneous factor fixed, so that we can measure its contribution to the total variation of the variable. This experimental design is called a **randomized block design**. The experiment in this example is designed to eliminate the variability in income attributable to differences in education level.

Table 13.14 shows the incomes (in $1,000s) for 12 workers according to their field of employment and highest education level. Also included in the table are the factor means.

Two-Factor_Income

TABLE 13.14 Data for Two-Factor Income Example (No Interaction)

Education Level (Factor B)	Field of Employment (Factor A)			Factor B Means
	Educational Services	Financial Services	Medical Services	
High School	18	25	26	$\bar{x}_{high\ school} = 23.00$
Bachelor's	35	45	43	$\bar{x}_{bachelor's} = 41.00$
Master's	46	58	62	$\bar{x}_{master's} = 53.3333$
Ph.D.	75	90	110	$\bar{x}_{Ph.D.} = 91.6667$
Factor A Means	$\bar{x}_{education} = 43.50$	$\bar{x}_{financial} = 54.50$	$\bar{x}_{medical} = 60.25$	$\bar{\bar{x}} = 52.75$

The goal of the analysis is to answer the following two questions:

- At the 5% significance level, do average annual incomes differ by field of employment?
- At the 5% significance level, do average annual incomes differ by education level?

A one-way ANOVA test is based on one factor for which we used the notation "sum of squares due to treatments $SSTR$" to capture the variability *between* the levels of this factor. Since we are now examining two factors, we use the notation SSA to capture the variability *between* the levels of factor A and SSB to capture the variability *between* the levels of factor B.

DECOMPOSING TOTAL VARIATION IN A TWO-WAY ANOVA TEST WITHOUT INTERACTION

In a two-way ANOVA test without interaction, the total sum of squares, SST, of the variable is partitioned into three distinct components: the sum of squares for factor A, SSA; the sum of squares for factor B, SSB; and the error sum of squares, SSE. That is, $SST = SSA + SSB + SSE$.

The Sum of Squares for Factor A, SSA

We calculate the sum of squares for factor A, SSA, as we did before; that is, we first calculate the sum of the squared differences between the mean for each level of factor A and the grand mean. We then multiply this sum by the number of rows in the randomized block design r. For this example, r equals 4. We calculate SSA as

$$SSA = r\sum_{i=1}^{c}(\bar{x}_i - \bar{\bar{x}})^2$$

$$= 4[(43.50 - 52.75)^2 + (54.50 - 52.75)^2 + (60.25 - 52.75)^2]$$

$$= 579.50.$$

Dividing SSA by its degrees of freedom, $c - 1$, (where c is the number of columns in the randomized block design) yields the mean square for factor A, MSA. For this example, c equals 3, so MSA is

$$MSA = \frac{SSA}{c-1} = \frac{579.50}{3-1} = 289.75.$$

The Sum of Squares for Factor B, SSB

In order to obtain the sum of squares for factor B, SSB, we calculate the sum of the squared differences between the mean for each level of factor B and the grand mean. We multiply this sum by c; thus, we calculate SSB as

$$SSB = c\sum_{j=1}^{r}(x_j - \bar{\bar{x}})^2$$

$$= 3[(23.00 - 52.75)^2 + (41.00 - 52.75)^2 + (55.3333 - 52.75)^2 + (91.6667 - 52.75)^2]$$

$$= 7{,}632.9167.$$

Dividing SSB by its degrees of freedom, $r - 1$, yields the mean square for factor B, MSB, or

$$MSB = \frac{SSB}{r-1} = \frac{7{,}632.9167}{4-1} = 2{,}544.3056$$

The Error Sum of Squares, SSE

As mentioned earlier, in a two-way ANOVA test without interaction, $SST = SSA + SSB + SSE$. We can calculate SSE by rewriting this expression as $SSE = SST - (SSA + SSB)$. We calculate SST as the sum of squared differences between each data point and the grand mean, or equivalently, $SST = \sum_{i=1}^{c}\sum_{j=1}^{r}(x_{ij} - \bar{\bar{x}})^2$. For this example, we calculate SST as

$$SST = \sum_{i=1}^{c}\sum_{j=1}^{r}(x_{ij} - \bar{\bar{x}})^2$$

$$= (18 - 52.75)^2 + (35 - 52.75)^2 + \cdots + (110 - 52.75)^2$$

$$= 8{,}482.25.$$

We then compute SSE as

$$SSE = SST - (SSA + SSB) = 8{,}482.25 - (579.50 + 7{,}632.9167) = 269.8333.$$

We can make some generalizations about the difference in the magnitudes of the SSE values for the one-way ANOVA versus the two-way ANOVA examples. When we used one factor (field of employment) to explain annual incomes, the value of SSE was 7,902.75 (see Table 13.13). By ignoring the second factor (education level), we could not establish that annual incomes were different by field of employment. However, once we include this second factor, the value of SSE declines dramatically to 269.8333. We will show shortly that by accounting for the effect of education level on income, the $F_{(df_1, df_2)}$ test allows Julia to conclude that significant differences do exist among annual incomes by field of employment.

Dividing SSE by its degrees of freedom $(n_T - c - r + 1)$ yields the mean square error, MSE, or

$$MSE = \frac{SSE}{n_T - c - r + 1} = \frac{269.8333}{12 - 3 - 4 + 1} = 44.9722.$$

The test statistics for conducting a two-way ANOVA test without interaction can be summarized as follows.

As we will show shortly, Excel and R easily provide these statistics. Table 13.15 shows the general format of an ANOVA table when conducting a two-way ANOVA test without interaction.

TABLE 13.15 General Format of ANOVA Table for Randomized Block Design

Source of Variation	SS	df	MS	F	p-value
Rows	SSB	$r - 1$	$MSB = \dfrac{SSB}{r - 1}$	$F_{(df_1, df_2)} = \dfrac{MSB}{MSE}$	$P\left(F_{(df_1, df_2)} \geq \dfrac{MSB}{MSE}\right)$
Columns	SSA	$c - 1$	$MSA = \dfrac{SSA}{c - 1}$	$F_{(df_1, df_2)} = \dfrac{MSA}{MSE}$	$P\left(F_{(df_1, df_2)} \geq \dfrac{MSA}{MSE}\right)$
Error	SSE	$n_T - c - r + 1$	$MSE = \dfrac{SSE}{n_T - c - r + 1}$		
Total	SST	$n_T - 1$			

Using Excel and R for a Two-Way ANOVA Test— No Interaction

We rarely use manual calculations to perform a two-way ANOVA test. Consider the following example where we complete the analysis of the two-factor income example.

TwoFactor_Income

EXAMPLE 13.6

Here, we first use Excel and R to obtain the ANOVA table for the two-factor income example. Then, we answer the two questions posed at the beginning of the analysis:

- At the 5% significance level, do average annual incomes differ by field of employment?
- At the 5% significance level, do average annual incomes differ by education level?

SOLUTION:

Using Excel

a. Open the ***Two-factor_Income*** data file.

b. From the menu, choose **Data > Data Analysis > ANOVA: Two Factor Without Replication.**

c. In the *ANOVA: Two Factor Without Replication* dialog box, as shown in Figure 13.3, choose the box next to *Input range*, and then select all the data, including the labels. Check the *Labels* box. Click **OK**.

FIGURE 13.3 Excel's ANOVA: Two-Factor Without Replication dialog box.

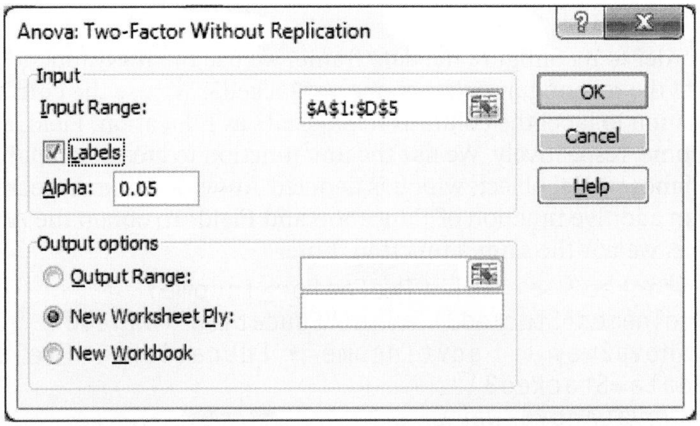

Table 13.16 shows a portion of the Excel-produced results.

TABLE 13.16 Excel-Produced ANOVA Table for Two-Factor Income Example

Source of Variation	SS	df	MS	F	p-value
Rows	7632.9167	3	2544.3056	56.575	8.6E-05
Columns	579.50	2	289.75	6.443	0.032
Error	269.8333	6	44.9722		
Total	8482.25	11			

In order to determine whether annual incomes differ by field of employment, we specify the competing hypotheses as:

$$H_0: \mu_{\text{Education}} = \mu_{\text{Financial}} = \mu_{\text{Medical}}$$
$$H_A: \text{Not all population means are equal.}$$

When testing whether the factor A (column) means differ, the value of the test statistic is $F_{(df_1, df_2)} = \dfrac{MSA}{MSE} = \dfrac{289.75}{44.9722} = 6.443$ where $df_1 = c - 1 = 3 - 1 = 2$ and $df_2 = n_T - c - r + 1 = 12 - 3 - 4 + 1 = 6$; that is, $F_{(2,6)} = 6.443$ with an accompanying p-value of 0.032. Since the p-value is less than 0.05, we reject H_0. Therefore, contrary to the results derived earlier with a one-way ANOVA test, average annual salaries do differ by field of employment at the 5% significance level.

In order to determine whether annual incomes differ by education level, we specify the competing hypotheses as

$$H_0: \mu_{\text{High School}} = \mu_{\text{Bachelor's}} = \mu_{\text{Master's}} = \mu_{\text{Ph.D.}}$$
$$H_A: \text{Not all population means are equal.}$$

When testing whether the factor B (row) means differ, the value of the test statistic is $F_{(df_1, df_2)} = \dfrac{MSB}{MSE} = \dfrac{2,544.3056}{44.9722} = 56.575$ where $df_1 = r - 1 = 4 - 1 = 3$

and $df_2 = n_T - c - r + 1 = 12 - 3 - 4 + 1 = 6$; that is, $F_{(3,6)} = 56.575$ with an accompanying p-value of 0 (approximately). Since the p-value is less than 0.05, we reject H_0. At the 5% significance level, average annual incomes differ by education level. Since education level exerts a significant influence on income, its influence must be incorporated in ANOVA testing.

Using R

a. Import the ***TwoFactor_Income*** data into a data frame (table) in R. Then, as we did in Section 13.1, we install and load the *reshape2* package and use the **melt**, **colnames**, **aov**, and **anova** functions. We revisit these commands in brief.

b. In order to reconfigure the data frame, we use the **melt** function and label the reconfigured data frame as Stacked3. We use the **colnames** function to label the columns in Stacked3 as Education, Field, and Income, respectively. We use the **aov** function to create an analysis of variance model object, which is denoted Anova2way, and specify Income as an additive function of Education and Field. To obtain the ANOVA table, we use the **anova** function. Enter

```
> Stacked3 <- melt(TwoFactor_Income)
> colnames(Stacked3) <- c("Education", "Field", "Income")
> Anova2way <- aov(Income ~ Education + Field,
  data=Stacked3)
> anova(Anova2way)
```

Table 13.17 shows the R-produced ANOVA table. The values are identical to the ones produced by Excel in Table 13.16. Thus, the conclusions to our questions are the same. At the 5% significance level, average annual incomes differ by field of employment as well as by education level.

TABLE 13.17 R-Produced ANOVA Table for Two-Factor Income Example

```
Analysis of Variance Table

Response: Income
            Df Sum Sq  Mean Sq  F value   Pr(>F)
Education    3 7632.9  2544.31  56.5750 8.595e-05 ***
Field        2  579.5   289.75   6.4429   0.03207 *
Residuals    6  269.8    44.97
---
Signif. codes:  0 '***' 0.001 '**' 0.01 '*' 0.05
'.' 0.1 ' ' 1
```

We would like to point out that, analogous to the last section, we can apply the *MSE* estimate from the two-way ANOVA test to construct useful confidence intervals for the paired differences in population means using Fisher's LSD method. The only significant modification to these confidence intervals is with respect to degrees of freedom, which are now given by $df = n_T - c - r + 1$. Similarly, we can also use Tukey's *HSD* method to determine which column means or row means are significantly different from one another. The value for the margin of error in the confidence interval will depend on whether we are assessing differences between the column means or the row means. When constructing the confidence interval for the difference between two column means, we calculate the margin of error as $q_{\alpha,(c,n_T-c)}\sqrt{\frac{MSE}{n}}$, where n is the number of observations in each column. When constructing the confidence interval for the difference between two row means, we calculate the margin of error as $q_{\alpha,(r,n_T-r)}\sqrt{\frac{MSE}{n}}$, where n is the number of observations in each row.

EXERCISES 13.3

Mechanics

30. The following observations were obtained when conducting a two-way ANOVA experiment with no interaction.

	Factor A			
Factor B	1	2	3	$\bar{x}_j$ for Factor B
1	4	8	12	8
2	2	10	3	5
3	0	6	0	2
4	2	4	0	2
$\bar{x}_i$ for Factor A	2	7	3.75	$\bar{\bar{x}} = 4.25$

a. Calculate SST, SSA, SSB, and SSE.
b. Calculate MSA, MSB, and MSE.
c. Construct an ANOVA table.
d. At the 5% significance level, can you conclude that the column means differ?
e. At the 5% significance level, can you conclude that the row means differ?

31. The following observations were obtained when conducting a two-way ANOVA experiment with no interaction.

	Factor A				
Factor B	1	2	3	4	$\bar{x}_j$ for Factor B
1	2	3	2	4	2.75
2	6	5	7	6	6.00
3	8	10	9	10	9.25
$\bar{x}_i$ for Factor A	5.3333	6	6	6.6667	$\bar{\bar{x}} = 6$

a. Calculate SST, SSA, SSB, and SSE.
b. Calculate MSA, MSB, and MSE.
c. Construct an ANOVA table.
d. At the 5% significance level, do the levels of Factor B differ?
e. At the 5% significance level, do the levels of Factor A differ?

32. A two-way analysis of variance experiment with no interaction is conducted. Factor A has four levels (columns) and Factor B has three levels (rows). The results include the following sum of squares terms:

$$SST = 1{,}630.7 \quad SSB = 532.3 \quad SSE = 374.5$$

a. Construct an ANOVA table.
b. At the 1% significance level, can you conclude that the factor A means differ?
c. At the 1% significance level, can you conclude that the factor B means differ?

33. A two-way analysis of variance experiment with no interaction is conducted. Factor A has three levels (columns) and Factor B has five levels (rows). The results include the following sum of squares terms:

$$SST = 311.7 \quad SSA = 201.6 \quad SSE = 69.3$$

a. Construct an ANOVA table.
b. At the 5% significance level, can you conclude that the row means differ?
c. At the 5% significance level, can you conclude that the column means differ?

34. The following table summarizes a portion of the results for a two-way analysis of variance experiment with no interaction.

Source of Variation	SS	df	MS	F	p-value
Rows	1057	5	MSB=?	$F_{Factor\ B}$ = ?	0.006
Columns	7	2	MSA=?	$F_{Factor\ A}$ = ?	0.900
Error	330	10	MSE=?		
Total	1394	17			

a. Find the missing values in the ANOVA table.
b. At the 5% significance level, can you conclude that the column means differ?
c. At the 5% significance level, can you conclude that the row means differ?

35. The following table summarizes a portion of the results for a two-way analysis of variance experiment with no interaction.

Source of Variation	SS	df	MS	F	p-value
Rows	25.17	2	MSB = ?	$F_{Factor\ B}$ = ?	0.083
Columns	142.25	3	MSA = ?	$F_{Factor\ A}$ = ?	0.004
Error	19.50	6	MSE = ?		
Total	186.92	11			

a. Find the missing values in the ANOVA table.
b. At the 5% significance level, can you conclude that the column means differ?
c. At the 5% significance level, can you conclude that the row means differ?

Applications

36. During a typical Professional Golf Association (PGA) tournament, the competing golfers play four rounds of golf, where the hole locations are changed for each round. Here are the scores for the top five finishers at the 2009 U.S. Open.

Golfer	Round 1	Round 2	Round 3	Round 4
Lucas Glover	69	64	70	73
Phil Mickelson	69	70	69	70
David Duval	67	70	70	71
Ricky Barnes	67	65	70	76
Ross Fisher	70	78	79	72
	Grand mean: $\bar{\bar{x}} = 70.45$			

The following statistics were computed:

$$SST = 272.95 \quad SSB = 93.2 \quad SSE = 127.6$$

a. Construct the ANOVA table.
b. At the 5% significance level, can you conclude that the average scores produced by the four different rounds differ?
c. At the 5% significance level, can you conclude that the average scores produced by the five different players differ?

37. The following output summarizes a portion of the results for a two-way analysis of variance experiment with no interaction. Factor A consists of four different kinds of organic fertilizers, factor B consists of three different kinds of soil acidity levels, and the variable measured is the height (in inches) of a plant at the end of four weeks.

Source of Variation	SS	df	MS	F	p-value
Rows	0.13	2	$MSB = ?$	$F_{Factor\ B} = ?$	0.818
Columns	44.25	3	$MSA = ?$	$F_{Factor\ A} = ?$	0.000
Error	1.88	6	$MSE = ?$		
Total	46.26	11			

a. Find the missing values in the ANOVA table.
b. At the 5% significance level, can you conclude that the average growth of the plant differs by organic fertilizer?
c. At the 5% significance level, can you conclude that the average growth of the plant differs by acidity level?

38. **FILE** *Shift_Output.* Metalworks, a supplier of fabricated industrial parts, wants to determine if the average output rate for a particular component is the same across the three work shifts. However, since any of four machines can be used, the machine effect must be controlled for within the sample. The accompanying table shows output rates (in units) for the previous day.

Machine (Factor B)	Shift (Factor A) 1	Shift (Factor A) 2	Shift (Factor A) 3
A	1392	1264	1334
B	1228	1237	1107
C	1173	1108	1186
D	1331	1342	1387

a. At the 5% significance level, can you conclude that the average output rate differs across the work shifts?
b. At the 5% significance level, can you conclude that the average output rate differs across the machines?
c. If significant differences exist across the machines, use Tukey's HSD method at the 5% significance level to determine which machines have different average output rates.

39. **FILE** *Restaurants.* Given a recent outbreak of illness caused by *E. coli* bacteria, the mayor in a large city is concerned that some of his restaurant inspectors are not consistent with their evaluations of a restaurant's cleanliness. In order to investigate this possibility, the mayor has five restaurant inspectors grade (scale of 0 to 100) the cleanliness of three restaurants. The results are shown in the accompanying table.

Inspector	Restaurant 1	Restaurant 2	Restaurant 3
1	72	54	84
2	68	55	85
3	73	59	80
4	69	60	82
5	75	56	84

a. At the 5% significance level, can you conclude that the average grades differ by restaurant?
b. If the average grades differ by restaurant, use Tukey's HSD method at the 5% significance level to determine which averages differ.
c. At the 5% significance level, can you conclude that the average grades differ by inspector? Does the mayor have cause for concern?

40. **FILE** *YumYum.* The marketing manager at YumYum, a large deli chain, is testing the effectiveness of four potential advertising strategies. After a two-week trial period for each advertising strategy, sales were evaluated. However, since some store locations have higher customer traffic than other locations, the effect of location on sales must be controlled for within the sample. The accompanying table shows sales (in $1,000s) achieved over the 2-week trial period using each advertising strategy at three different store locations.

Store Location (Factor B)	Advertising Strategy (Factor A) Newspaper only	Internet only	TV only	Internet & TV
City	511	644	585	712
Suburban	458	548	503	614
Rural	388	298	347	421

a. At the 5% significance level, can you conclude that the mean sales differ among the advertising strategies? What about the 10% significance level?

b. At the 5% significance level, can you conclude that the mean sales differ across the store locations?

c. If significant differences exist across advertising strategies, use Fisher's LSD method at the 10% significance level to find which strategies have different mean sales.

41. **FILE** *Houses.* First National Bank employs three real estate appraisers whose job is to establish a property's market value before the bank offers a mortgage to a prospective buyer. It is imperative that each appraiser values a property with no bias. Suppose First National Bank wishes to check the consistency of the recent values that its appraisers have established. The bank asked the three appraisers to value (in $1,000s) three different types of homes: a cape, a colonial, and a ranch. The results are shown in the accompanying table.

House Type	Appraiser		
	1	2	3
Cape	425	415	430
Colonial	530	550	540
Ranch	390	400	380

a. At the 5% significance level, can you conclude that the average values differ by appraiser? Should the bank be concerned with appraiser inconsistencies?

b. At the 5% significance level, can you conclude that the average values differ by house type?

c. If average values differ by house type, use Tukey's HSD method at the 5% significance level to determine which averages differ.

13.4 TWO-WAY ANOVA TEST: WITH INTERACTION

We use a two-way ANOVA test with interaction to capture the possible relationship between factors A and B. Such a test allows the influence of factor A to change over levels of factor B and the influence of factor B to change over levels of factor A. In the two-factor income example from Section 13.3, field of employment may interact with education level. In other words, the influence of field of employment may vary between levels of education. Similarly, the influence of education level may not be the same for all fields of employment.

Conduct and evaluate a two-way ANOVA test with interaction.

DECOMPOSING TOTAL VARIATION IN A TWO-WAY ANOVA TEST WITH INTERACTION

In a two-way ANOVA test with interaction, the total sum of squares, SST, of the variable is partitioned into four distinct components: the sum of squares for factor A, SSA; the sum of squares for factor B, SSB; the sum of squares for the interaction between the two factors, $SSAB$; and the error sum of squares, SSE. That is,

$$SST = SSA + SSB + SSAB + SSE.$$

While we still use a randomized block design, we need at least two observations for each combination of the ith level of factor A and the jth level of factor B. In other words, we need more than one observation per cell. In a two-way ANOVA test with interaction, we let w equal the number of observations for each combination of the ith level of factor A and the jth level of factor B.

To illustrate two-way ANOVA with interaction, we reanalyze the income example, using new data with three incomes for each combination; thus, $w = 3$. Given the data in Table 13.18, we ultimately want to determine whether interaction is present between education level and field of employment.

TABLE 13.18 Data for Two-Factor Income Example with Interaction

Education Level (Factor B)	Field of Employment (Factor A)		
	Educational Services	Financial Services	Medical Services
High School	20	27	26
	25	25	24
	22	25	25
Bachelor's	30	44	42
	35	46	43
	34	48	45
Master's	46	50	62
	47	58	56
	50	56	60
Ph.D.	79	90	90
	78	92	100
	74	95	105

We are specifically interested in whether field of employment and education level interact with respect to average annual income. In order to find the relevant sum of squares for the test, we first compute the cell means and the factor means. For example, the cell mean for workers in the field of educational services with a high school education is computed as $(20 + 25 + 22)/3 = 22.3333$. Factor means are based on one row or one column of the data. Table 13.19 shows the cell means $\bar{x}_{ij}$, factor means $\bar{x}_i$ and $\bar{x}_j$, and the grand mean $\bar{\bar{x}}$ for the data.

TABLE 13.19 Cell and Factor Means for Two-Factor Income Example with Interaction

Education Level (Factor B)	Field of Employment (Factor A)			
	Educational Services	Financial Services	Medical Services	Factor B Means
High School	22.3333	25.6667	25.00	24.3333
Bachelor's	33.00	46.00	43.3333	40.7778
Master's	47.6667	54.6667	59.3333	53.8889
Ph.D.	77.00	92.3333	98.3333	89.2222
Factor A Means	45.00	54.6667	56.50	$\bar{\bar{x}} = 52.0556$

The Total Sum of Squares, SST

SST is computed as $SST = \sum\limits_{i=1}^{c} \sum\limits_{j=1}^{r} \sum\limits_{k=1}^{w} (x_{ijk} - \bar{\bar{x}})^2$. Using all observations from Table 13.18 and the grand mean from Table 13.19, we calculate

$$SST = (20 - 52.0556)^2 + (25 - 52.0556)^2 + \cdots + (105 - 52.0556)^2$$
$$= 22{,}007.8889$$

The Sum of Squares for Factor A, SSA, and the Sum of Squares for Factor B, SSB

The calculations for SSA and SSB are analogous to the earlier two-way ANOVA discussion, with one minor modification. For two-way ANOVA without interaction, SSA and SSB were calculated as $r \sum\limits_{i=1}^{c} (\bar{x}_i - \bar{\bar{x}})^2$ and $c \sum\limits_{j=1}^{r} (\bar{x}_j - \bar{\bar{x}})^2$, respectively. Now each formula is multiplied by the number of observations per cell w. So,

$SSA = wr \sum\limits_{i=1}^{c}(\bar{x}_i - \bar{\bar{x}})^2$ and $SSB = wc \sum\limits_{j=1}^{r}(\bar{x}_j - \bar{\bar{x}})^2$. Given the means in Table 13.19 with $w = 3$, $c = 3$, and $r = 4$, we calculate

$$SSA = (3 \times 4)[(45.00 - 52.0556)^2 + (54.6667 - 52.0556)^2 + (56.50 - 52.0556)^2]$$
$$= 916.2222,$$

and

$$SSB = (3 \times 3)[(24.3333 - 52.0556)^2 + (40.7778 - 52.0556)^2$$
$$+ (53.8889 - 52.0556)^2 + (89.2222 - 52.0556)^2]$$
$$= 20{,}523.8889.$$

We divide by the respective degrees of freedom to obtain the mean square for factor A, MSA, and the mean square for factor B, MSB, as

$$MSA = \frac{SSA}{c - 1} = \frac{916.2222}{3 - 1} = 458.1111 \quad \text{and}$$

$$MSB = \frac{SSA}{r - 1} = \frac{20{,}523.8889}{4 - 1} = 6{,}841.2963.$$

The Sum of Squares for the Interaction of Factor A and Factor B, $SSAB$

When two factors interact, the effect of one factor on the mean depends upon the specific value or level present for the other factor. Interaction exists between these factors when two mathematical expressions, denoted Expression 1 and Expression 2, are significantly different from one another.

Expression 1 is defined as the difference of a cell mean from the grand mean, or equivalently, $(\bar{x}_{ij} - \bar{\bar{x}})$. Using the data from Table 13.19 with $i = 1$ and $j = 1$, one such difference would be $(\bar{x}_{11} - \bar{\bar{x}}) = (22.3333 - 52.0556)$.

Expression 2 is defined as the *combined* differences of the corresponding factor A mean from the grand mean and the corresponding factor B mean from the grand mean, or equivalently, $(\bar{x}_i - \bar{\bar{x}}) + (\bar{x}_j - \bar{\bar{x}})$. Using the data from Table 13.19 with $i = 1$ and $j = 1$, one such calculation would be $(45.00 - 52.0556) + (24.3333 - 52.0556)$.

If the difference between Expression 1 and Expression 2 is nonzero, then there is evidence of interaction. If we let I denote interaction, then we can measure I as

$$I = (\bar{x}_{ij} - \bar{\bar{x}}) - [(\bar{x}_i - \bar{\bar{x}}) + (\bar{x}_j - \bar{\bar{x}})].$$

This expression can be simplified to

$$I = \bar{x}_{ij} - \bar{x}_i - \bar{x}_j + \bar{\bar{x}}.$$

The sum of squares for the interaction between factor A and factor B, $SSAB$, is then based on a weighted sum of the squared interactions (I^2) where the weight equals the number of observations per cell w:

$$SSAB = w \sum\limits_{i=1}^{c} \sum\limits_{j=1}^{r} (\bar{x}_{ij} - \bar{x}_i - \bar{x}_j + \bar{\bar{x}})^2.$$

Using the means in Table 13.19, we calculate

$$SSAB = 3[(22.3333 - 45.00 - 24.3333 + 52.0556)^2 + (33.00 - 45.00 - 40.7778$$
$$+ 52.0556)^2 + \cdots + (98.3333 - 56.50 - 89.2222 + 52.0666)^2]$$
$$= 318.4444.$$

We obtain the mean square for interaction, $MSAB$, by dividing $SSAB$ by its degrees of freedom $(c - 1)(r - 1)$, or

$$MSAB = \frac{SSAB}{(c - 1)(r - 1)} = \frac{318.4444}{(3 - 1)(4 - 1)} = 53.0741.$$

The Error Sum of Squares, *SSE*

We solve for *SSE* by rearranging $SST = SSA + SSB + SSAB + SSE$; that is,

$$SSE = SST - (SSA + SSB + SSAB) = 22{,}007.8889 - (916.2222 + 20{,}523.8889 + 318.4444) = 249.3334.$$

Finally, we divide *SSE* by its degrees of freedom $rc(w - 1)$ and obtain the mean square error, *MSE*, as

$$MSE = \frac{SSE}{rc(w - 1)} = \frac{249.3333}{(4 \times 3)(3 - 1)} = 10.3889.$$

We now summarize the test statistics when conducting a two-way ANOVA test with interaction. The first two statistics are used to examine the main effects—potential differences in factor *A* means (column means) or potential differences in factor *B* means (row means). The third test statistic is used to test whether there is interaction between factor *A* and factor *B*.

TEST STATISTICS FOR A TWO-WAY ANOVA TEST—WITH INTERACTION

When testing for differences between the factor *A* means (the column means), the value of the test statistic is computed as

$$F_{(df_1, df_2)} = \frac{MSA}{MSE},$$

where $df_1 = c - 1$, $df_2 = rc(w - 1)$, *MSA* is the mean square for factor *A*, and *MSE* is the mean square error.

When testing for differences between the factor *B* means (the row means), the value of the test statistic is computed as

$$F_{(df_1, df_2)} = \frac{MSB}{MSE},$$

where $df_1 = r - 1$, $df_2 = rc(w - 1)$, *MSB* is the mean square for factor *B*, and *MSE* is the mean square error.

When testing for interaction between factor *A* and factor *B*, the value of the test statistic is computed as

$$F_{(df_1, df_2)} = \frac{MSAB}{MSE},$$

where $df_1 = (r - 1)(c - 1)$, $df_2 = rc(w - 1)$, *MSAB* is the mean square for interaction, and *MSE* is the mean square error.

In these tests, *c* represents the number of columns, *r* the number of rows, *w* the number of observations for each combination of the *i*th row and *j*th column, and n_T the total sample size. An ANOVA test is always specified as a right-tailed test.

Using Excel and R for a Two-Way ANOVA Test— With Interaction

Fortunately, Excel and R easily calculate all of the statistics that we have just discussed. Consider the following example where we complete the analysis of the two-factor income with interaction example.

EXAMPLE 13.7

Here, we first use Excel and R to obtain the ANOVA table for the two-factor income with interaction example. Then, we determine whether the field of employment and education level interact with respect to average income at the 5% significance level.

FILE
Income_Interaction

SOLUTION:
Using Excel

a. Open the ***Income_Interaction*** data file.
b. From the menu, choose **Data > Data Analysis > ANOVA: Two Factor With Replication**.
c. In the *ANOVA: Two Factor With Replication* dialog box, as shown in Figure 13.4, choose the box next to *Input range*, and then select all the data, including the labels. Enter 3 for *Rows Per Sample*. Click **OK**.

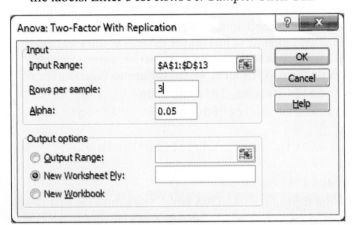

FIGURE 13.4
Excel's ANOVA: Two-Factor With Replication dialog box

Table 13.20 shows a portion of the Excel-produced results. Note that the sum of squares results match the ones we calculated manually.

TABLE 13.20 Excel-Produced ANOVA Table for Two-Factor Income with Interaction Example

Source of Variation	SS	df	MS	F	p-value
Sample (Rows)	20523.8889	3	6841.2963	658.521	3.58E-23
Columns	916.2222	2	458.1111	44.096	9.18E-09
Interaction	318.4444	6	53.0741	5.109	0.002
Within (Error)	249.3333	24	10.3889		
Total	22007.8889	35			

In order to determine whether interaction exists between field of employment and education level, we specify the competing hypotheses as

H_0: There is no interaction between factors A and B.
H_A: There is interaction between factors A and B.

The value of the test statistic is $F_{(df_1, df_2)} = \frac{MSAB}{MSE} = \frac{53.0741}{10.3889} = 5.109$ where $df_1 = (r-1)(c-1) = (4-1)(3-1) = 6$ and $df_2 = rc(w-1) = (4 \times 3)(3-1) = 24$, or $F_{(6,24)} = 5.109$ with a corresponding *p*-value of 0.002. At the 5% significance level, we reject H_0 and conclude that sufficient evidence exists of an interaction effect between the field of employment and education level. This result implies that the average income for attaining an advanced degree is higher in some fields than in others.

Using R

a. Import the ***Income_Interaction*** data into a data frame (table) in R. If you view the data frame, you will notice that there are missing observations in the first column. Each level of education is not repeated three times. In order to correct this issue, we replace the first column using the **rep** function to replicate each entry three times and the **c** function to combine the resulting columns into one larger column. Enter

```
> Income_Interaction[, 1] <- c(rep("High School", 3),
  rep("Bachelor's", 3), rep("Master's", 3),
  rep("Ph.D.", 3))
```

If you view the data frame now, you should see no missing observations.

b. Then, as we did in Section 13.1, we install and load the *reshape2* package and use the **melt**, **colnames**, **aov**, and **anova** functions. We revisit these commands in brief. We use the **melt** function and label the reconfigured data frame as Stacked4. We use the **colnames** function to label the columns in Stacked4 as Education, Field, and Income, respectively. We use the **aov** function to create an analysis of variance model object, which is labeled Interact, and specify Income as a multiplicative function of Education and Field. (Recall when we estimated a two-way ANOVA with no interaction, we used an additive function.) To obtain the ANOVA table, we use the **anova** function. Enter

```
> Stacked4 <- melt(Income_Interaction)
> colnames(Stacked4) <- c("Education", "Field",
  "Income")
> Interact <- aov(Income ~ Education*Field,
  data=Stacked4)
> anova(Interact)
```

Table 13.21 shows the R-produced ANOVA table. The values are identical to the ones produced by Excel in Table 13.20. Again, we are able to conclude that there is interaction between field of employment and education level at the 5% significance level.

TABLE 13.21 R-Produced ANOVA Table for Two-Factor Income with Interaction Example

```
Analysis of Variance Table
Response: Income
              Df   Sum Sq Mean Sq   F value    Pr(>F)
Education      3  20523.9  6841.3  658.5205  < 2.2e-16 ***
Field          2    916.2   458.1   44.0963  9.183e-09 ***
Education:
Field          6    318.4    53.1    5.1087   0.001659 **
Residuals     24    249.3    10.4
---
Signif. codes: 0 '***' 0.001 '**' 0.01 '*' 0.05 '.'
0.1 ' ' 1
```

Note that due to the interaction, the differences between education levels are not the same for all fields of employment. Such an outcome serves to complicate the interpretation of the main effects, since differences in one factor are not consistent across the other factor. This is why we should perform the interaction test before making any conclusions using the other two $F_{(df_1, df_2)}$ statistics. If the interaction effect is not significant, then we can proceed by focusing on the main effects: testing whether or not the row means or the column means differ. If the interaction effect is significant, as it is here, one option is to use another technique called regression analysis. Regression analysis is discussed in the next four chapters.

EXERCISES 13.4

Mechanics

42. A two-way analysis of variance experiment with interaction was conducted. Factor A had four levels (columns), factor B had three levels (rows), and five observations were obtained for each combination. The results include the following sum of squares terms:

$$SST = 2500 \quad SSA = 1200 \quad SSB = 1000 \quad SSE = 280$$

a. Construct an ANOVA table.

b. At the 5% significance level, can you conclude that there is interaction between factor A and factor B?

c. At the 5% significance level, can you conclude that the factor A means differ?

d. At the 5% significance level, can you conclude that the factor B means differ?

43. A two-way analysis of variance experiment with interaction was conducted. Factor A had three levels (columns), factor B had five levels (rows), and six observations were obtained for each combination. The results include the following sum of squares terms:

$$SST = 1558 \quad SSA = 1008 \quad SSB = 400 \quad SSAB = 30$$

a. Construct an ANOVA table.

b. At the 1% significance level, can you conclude that there is interaction between factor A and factor B?

c. At the 1% significance level, can you conclude that the factor A means differ?

d. At the 1% significance level, can you conclude that the factor B means differ?

44. A researcher conducts a two-way ANOVA test with interaction and provides the following ANOVA table.

Source of Variation	SS	df	MS	F	p-value
Sample	30.827	1	30.827	11.690	0.003
Columns	169.861	2	84.930	32.208	1.13E-06
Interaction	4.241	2	2.120	0.804	0.463
Within	47.465	18	2.637		
Total	252.393	23			

a. At the 1% significance level, can you conclude that there is interaction between the two factors?

b. Are you able to conduct tests based on the main effects? If yes, conduct these tests at the 1% significance level. If no, explain.

45. A researcher conducts a two-way ANOVA test with interaction and provides the following ANOVA table.

Source of Variation	SS	df	MS	F	p-value
Sample	752.78	2	$MSB = ?$	$F_{Factor B} = ?$	0.012
Columns	12012.50	1	$MSA = ?$	$F_{Factor A} = ?$	5.62E-09
Interaction	58.33	2	$MSAB = ?$	$F_{Interaction} = ?$	0.612
Within	683.33	12	$MSE = ?$		
Total	13506.94	17			

a. Find the missing values in the ANOVA table.

b. At the 5% significance level, can you conclude that there is an interaction effect?

c. At the 5% significance level, can you conclude that the column means differ?

d. At the 5% significance level, can you conclude that the row (sample) means differ?

Applications

46. The engineering department at a steel mill is studying the tensile strength of a particular grade of steel when fabricated at various pressures (Factor A) and temperatures (Factor B). The accompanying ANOVA table shows a portion of the results from conducting a two-way ANOVA test with interaction.

Source of Variation	SS	df	MS	F	p-value
Sample (B, temperature)	150.22	1	150.22		
Columns (A, pressure)			62.06		
Interaction	24.11	2	12.06		
Within			26.11		
Total	611.78	17			

a. How many levels did pressure have?

b. How many observations were run for each combination of pressure-temperature settings?

c. At the 5% significance level, can you conclude that there is interaction between pressure and temperature?

d. At the 5% significance level, can you conclude that the main effect of pressure is significant?

e. At the 5% significance level, can you conclude that the main effect of temperature is significant?

47. The effects of detergent brand name (factor A) and the temperature of the water (factor B) on the brightness of washed fabrics are being studied. Four brand names and two temperature levels are used; six observations for each combination are examined. The following ANOVA table is produced.

Source of Variation	SS	df	MS	F	p-value
Sample	75	1	75	63.38	8.92E-10
Columns	130.25	3	43.42	36.69	1.45E-11
Interaction	8.67	3	2.89	2.44	0.078
Within	47.33	40	1.18		
Total	261.25	47			

a. Can you conclude that there is interaction between the detergent brand name and the temperature of the water at the 5% significance level?

b. Are you able to conduct tests based on the main effects? If yes, conduct these tests at the 5% significance level. If no, explain.

48. **FILE** *Buy4Less.* The marketing group at Buy4Less, a local retail chain, is examining the effect of advertising at various times of day and on various local television channels. Based on 12-week cycles (4 time periods x 3 local channels), three observations (cycles) of weekly sales data have been obtained for each time period-channel combination. The results (in $1,000s) are shown in the accompanying table.

Local Channel (Factor B)	Time of Day (Factor A)			
	Morning (6am-11am)	Mid-Day (11am-5pm)	Evening (5pm-10pm)	Late Night (10pm-2am)
WTZX	69.6	84.4	83.9	60.0
	74.6	79.9	85.9	63.0
	72.8	73.8	78.0	58.3
WABC	70.1	84.7	81.2	64.4
	68.4	80.0	89.8	69.7
	70.0	82.8	80.2	67.9
WXAQ	76.1	76.0	76.3	56.7
	75.3	83.5	81.4	68.2
	68.7	71.7	81.2	64.4

a. At the 5% significance level, can you conclude that there is interaction between the time of day and the local channel used for advertising?

b. Are you able to conduct tests based on the main effects? If yes, conduct them at the 5% significance level. If no, explain why.

49. **FILE** *Brand_Garage.* A consumer advocate examines whether the longevity of car batteries (measured in years) is affected by the brand name (factor A) and whether or not the car is kept in a garage (factor B). Interaction is suspected. The results are shown in the accompanying table.

Kept in Garage?	Brand Name of Battery		
	A	B	C
Yes	7, 8, 8	6, 7, 7	8, 9, 9
No	5, 6, 6	4, 5, 4	6, 7, 7

a. At the 5% significance level, is there interaction between the brand name and whether a car is garaged?

b. At the 5% significance level, can you conclude that the average battery lives differ by brand name?

c. At the 5% significance level, can you conclude that the average battery lives differ depending on whether a car is garaged?

50. **FILE** *Job_Satisfaction.* A human resource specialist wants to determine whether the average job satisfaction score (on a scale of 0 to 100) is the same for three different industries and three types of work experience. A randomized block experiment with interaction is performed. The results are shown in the accompanying table.

Work Experience	Industry		
	A	B	C
Less than 5 years	77	66	81
	67	58	59
	82	54	64
Five up to 10 years	93	65	57
	92	60	49
	97	68	72
10 years or more	58	75	60
	78	57	45
	91	47	59

a. At the 5% significance level, is there interaction between industry and work experience?

b. At the 5% significance level, can you conclude that job satisfaction differs by industry?

c. At the 5% significance level, can you conclude that job satisfaction differs by work experience?

51. **FILE** *Salaries.* It is generally believed that a practical major such as business or engineering can really pay off for college graduates (CNNMoney.com, July 22, 2010). Other studies have shown that it is not just the major but also how students perform, as measured by their GPA, that influences their salaries. Henry Chen, an employee of PayScale.com, wants to measure the effect of major and GPA on starting salaries of graduates of the University of California at Irvine. He samples starting salaries of five graduates for a given GPA range from the schools of business, engineering, and social sciences. The sample data are shown in the following table.

GPA	Business	Engineering	Social Sciences
3.5–4.0	68	70	44
	54	66	52
	78	62	66
	80	56	42
	58	72	72
3.0–3.5	48	66	48
	76	54	48
	60	70	58
	48	52	56
	64	64	38
<3.0	54	60	44
	42	42	38
	66	48	42
	58	59	52
	66	65	50

a. At the 5% significance level, is there interaction between major and GPA?

b. At the 5% significance level, can you conclude that starting salary differs between majors?

c. At the 5% significance level, can you conclude that starting salary depends on GPA?

WRITING WITH STATISTICS

The Texas Transportation Institute, one of the finest higher-education-affiliated transportation research agencies in the nation, published its highly anticipated *2009 Annual Urban Mobility Report* (July 8, 2009). The study finds that the average U.S. driver languished in rush-hour traffic for 36.1 hours, as compared to 12 hours in 1982 when the records begin. This congestion also wasted approximately 2.81 billion gallons in fuel, or roughly three weeks' worth of gas per traveler. John Farnham, a research analyst at an environmental firm, is stunned by some of the report's conclusions. John is asked to conduct an independent study in order to see if differences exist in congestion depending on the city where the traveler drives. He selects 25 travelers from each of the five cities that suffered from the worst congestion. He asks each traveler to approximate the time spent in traffic (in hours) over the last calendar year. Table 13.22 shows a portion of his sample results.

©Mitchell Funk/Photographer's Choice/Getty Images

TABLE 13.22 Annual Hours of Delay per Traveler in Five Cities

Los Angeles	Washington, DC	Atlanta	Houston	San Francisco
71	64	60	58	57
60	64	58	56	56
⋮	⋮	⋮	⋮	⋮
68	57	57	59	56

Congestion

John wants to use the sample information to

1. Determine whether significant differences exist in congestion, depending on the city where the traveler drives.

2. Use Tukey's method to establish in which of the five cities travelers experience the least and the worst delays.

Sample
Report—
Evaluating
Traffic
Congestion
by City

Does traffic congestion vary by city? *The 2009 Annual Urban Mobility Report* found that traffic congestion, measured by annual hours of delay per traveler, was the worst in Los Angeles, followed by Washington, DC, Atlanta, Houston, and then San Francisco. An independent survey was conducted to verify some of the findings. Twenty-five travelers in each of these cities were asked how many hours they wasted in traffic over the past calendar year. Table 13. A reports the summary statistics. The sample data indicate that Los Angeles residents waste the most time sitting in traffic, with an average of 69.2 hours per year. Washington, DC, residents rank a close second, spending an average of 62 hours per year in traffic. Residents in Atlanta, Houston, and San Francisco spend on average, 57.0, 56.5, and 55.6 hours per year in traffic, respectively. Houston had the highest variability of congestion and San Francisco had the lowest variability, as measured by their respective standard deviations.

TABLE 13.A Summary Statistics

Los Angeles	Washington, DC	Atlanta	Houston	San Francisco
$\bar{x}_1 = 69.24$	$\bar{x}_2 = 61.96$	$\bar{x}_3 = 57.00$	$\bar{x}_4 = 56.52$	$\bar{x}_5 = 55.56$
$s_1 = 4.60$	$s_2 = 4.74$	$s_3 = 4.81$	$s_4 = 5.37$	$s_5 = 3.66$

A one-way ANOVA test was conducted to determine if significant differences exist in the average number of hours spent in traffic in these five worst-congested cities. The value of the test statistic is $F_{4,120} = 37.251$ with a p-value of approximately zero. Therefore, at the 5% level of significance, we reject the null hypothesis of equal means and conclude that traffic congestion does vary by city.

In order to determine which cities had significantly different average delays per traveler, Tukey's *HSD* method was used. The 95% confidence interval for the difference between two population means $\mu_i - \mu_j$ was computed as $(\bar{x}_i - \bar{x}_j) \pm q_{\alpha,(c,n_T-c)}\sqrt{\frac{MSE}{n}}$. Referencing the studentized range table, the approximate value of $q_{0.05,(5,115)}$ is 3.92. The one-way ANOVA test produced an *MSE* of 21.82; thus, the margin of error for the confidence interval was $3.92\sqrt{\frac{21.82}{25}}$, which equals 3.66. Therefore, we can conclude with 95% confidence that travelers in Los Angeles suffered the most hours of congestion, followed by travelers in Washington, DC. Congestion was not significantly different in the cities of Atlanta, Houston, and San Francisco.

CONCEPTUAL REVIEW

LO 13.1 **Conduct and evaluate a one-way ANOVA test.**

A **one-way analysis of variance (ANOVA) test** is used to determine if differences exist between three or more population means. This test examines the amount of variability *between* the samples relative to the amount of variability *within* the samples.

The value of the test statistic for testing for differences between the c population means is calculated as $F_{(df_1,df_2)} = \frac{MSTR}{MSE}$, where *MSTR* is the mean square for treatments, *MSE* is the mean square error, $df_1 = c - 1$, $df_2 = n_T - c$, and n_T is the total sample size. The values for *MSTR* and *MSE* are based on independent samples drawn from c normally distributed populations with a common variance. An ANOVA test is always specified as a right-tailed test.

Use Fisher's LSD method and Tukey's HSD method to determine which means differ.

Fisher's LSD method is implemented by computing $100(1 - \alpha)\%$ confidence intervals for all mean differences $\mu_i - \mu_j$ as $(\bar{x}_i - \bar{x}_j) \pm t_{\alpha/2, n_T - c} \sqrt{MSE\left(\frac{1}{n_i} + \frac{1}{n_j}\right)}$ where MSE is estimated from the ANOVA test. If the computed interval does not include the value zero, then we reject the null hypothesis $H_0: \mu_i - \mu_j = 0$.

When pairwise comparisons are made with Fisher's LSD method, we inflate the risk of the Type I error α. An improved multiple comparison technique is **Tukey's HSD method**, which seeks out "honestly significant differences" between paired means. Tukey's method uses the **studentized range distribution**, which has broader, flatter, and thicker tails than the t_{df} distribution, and therefore protects against an inflated risk of a Type I error. Tukey's $100(1 - \alpha)\%$ confidence interval for $\mu_i - \mu_j$ is computed as $(\bar{x}_i - \bar{x}_j) \pm q_{\alpha,(c,n_T-c)} \sqrt{\frac{MSE}{n}}$ for **balanced data** $(n = n_i = n_j)$ and $(\bar{x}_i - \bar{x}_j) \pm q_{\alpha,(c,n_T-c)} \sqrt{\frac{MSE}{2}\left(\frac{1}{n_i} + \frac{1}{n_j}\right)}$ for **unbalanced data** $(n_i \neq n_j)$, where $q_{\alpha,(c,n_T-c)}$ is the studentized range value.

LO 13.3 Conduct and evaluate a two-way ANOVA test with no interaction.

Whereas a one-way ANOVA test is used to compare population means based on one factor, a **two-way ANOVA test** extends the analysis to measure the effects of two factors simultaneously. The additional factor explains some of the unexplained variation, or equivalently, reduces the error sum of squares SSE for a more discriminating $F_{(df_1, df_2)}$ statistic. A two-way ANOVA test can be conducted with or without interaction between the factors.

In a two-way ANOVA test without interaction, we find the value of two $F_{(df_1, df_2)}$ test statistics. The first test statistic $F_{(df_1, df_2)} = \frac{MSB}{MSE}$, where $df_1 = r - 1$ and $df_2 = n_T - c - r + 1$, is used to test for differences between the factor B means (the row means). The second test statistic $F_{(df_1, df_2)} = \frac{MSA}{MSE}$, where $df_1 = c - 1$ and $df_2 = n_T - c - r + 1$, is used to test for differences between the factor A means (the column means).

LO 13.4 Conduct and evaluate a two-way ANOVA test with interaction.

In a two-way ANOVA test with interaction, we find the values of three $F_{(df_1, df_2)}$ test statistics. Two test statistics are used to examine the main effects—differences in the means of factor B ($F_{(df_1, df_2)} = \frac{MSB}{MSE}$, where $df_1 = r - 1$ and $df_2 = rc(w - 1)$) and differences in the means of factor A ($F_{(df_1, df_2)} = \frac{MSA}{MSE}$, where $df_1 = c - 1$ and $df_2 = rc(w - 1)$). The third test statistic ($F_{(df_1, df_2)} = \frac{MSAB}{MSE}$, where $df_1 = (r - 1)(c - 1)$ and $df_2 = rc(w - 1)$) is used to test for interaction between factor A and factor B.

ADDITIONAL EXERCISES AND CASE STUDIES

52. **FILE** *Transportation.* A government agency wants to determine whether the average salaries of four kinds of transportation operators differ. A random sample of five employees in each of the four categories yields the salary data (in $1,000s) given in the accompanying table.

Engineer	Truck Driver	Bus Driver	Limousine Driver
54.7	40.5	32.4	26.8
53.2	42.7	31.2	27.1
55.1	41.6	30.9	28.3
54.3	40.9	31.8	27.9
51.5	39.2	29.8	29.9

a. Specify the competing hypotheses in order to determine whether the average salaries of the transportation operators differ.

b. At the 5% significance level, what is the conclusion to the test?

53. **FILE** *Foodco.* The Marketing Manager at Foodco, a large grocery store, wants to determine if store display location influences sales of a particular grocery item. He instructs employees to rotate the display location of that item every week and then tallies the weekly sales at each location over a 24-week period (8 weeks per location). The following sales (in $) were obtained.

Front of store	Center of store	Side aisle
947	858	1096
1106	780	1047
1143	786	910
1162	816	823
967	800	919
956	770	924
1057	876	1091
996	802	1027

a. Specify the competing hypotheses to test whether there are some differences in the mean weekly sales across the three store display locations.

b. At the 5% significance level, what is the conclusion to the test?

54. **FILE** *SAT_Ethnicity.* The manager of an SAT review program wonders whether average SAT scores differ depending on the ethnicity of the test taker. Thirty test scores for four ethnicities are collected. A portion of the data is shown in the accompanying table.

White	Black	Asian-American	Mexican-American
1587	1300	1660	1366
1562	1255	1576	1531
⋮	⋮	⋮	⋮
1500	1284	1584	1358

At the 5% significance level, can we conclude that the average SAT scores differ by ethnicity?

55. **FILE** *Concrete_Mixing.* Compressive strength of concrete is affected by several factors, including composition (sand, cement, etc.), mixer type (batch vs. continuous), and curing procedure. Accordingly, a concrete company is conducting an experiment to determine

how mixing technique affects the resulting compressive strength. Four potential mixing techniques have been identified. Subsequently, samples of 20 specimens have been subjected to each mixing technique, and the resulting compressive strengths (in pounds per square inch, psi) were measured. A portion of the data is shown in the accompanying table.

Mix Tech. 1	Mix Tech. 2	Mix Tech. 3	Mix Tech. 4
2972	2794	2732	2977
2818	3162	2905	2986
⋮	⋮	⋮	⋮
2665	2837	3073	3081

a. Specify the competing hypotheses to test whether there are some differences in the mean compressive strengths across the four mixing techniques.

b. At the 5% significance level, what is the conclusion to the test? What about the 1% significance level?

56. **FILE** *Plywood.* An engineer wants to determine whether the average strength of plywood boards (in pounds per square inch, psi) differs depending on the type of glue used. For three types of glue, she measures the strength of 20 plywood boards. A portion of the data is shown in the accompanying table.

Glue 1	Glue 2	Glue 3
38	41	42
34	38	38
⋮	⋮	⋮
38	49	50

At the 5% significance level, can she conclude that the average strength of the plywood boards differs by the type of glue used? Assume that the strength of plywood boards is normally distributed.

57. **FILE** *Route.* An employee of a small software company in Minneapolis bikes to work during the summer months. He can travel to work using one of three routes and wonders whether the average commute times (in minutes) differ between the three routes. He obtains the following data after traveling each route for one week.

Route 1	29	30	33	30	32
Route 2	27	32	28	30	29
Route 3	25	27	24	29	26

a. Determine at the 1% significance level whether the average commute times differ between the three routes. Assume that commute times are normally distributed.

b. If differences exist, use Tukey's *HSD* method at the 1% significance level to determine which routes' average times differ.

58. **FILE** *PEratios.* An economist wants to determine whether average price/earnings (P/E) ratios differ for firms in three industries. Independent samples of five firms in each industry show the following results:

Industry A	12.19	12.44	7.28	9.96	10.51
Industry B	14.34	17.80	9.32	14.90	9.41
Industry C	26.38	24.75	16.88	16.87	16.70

a. At the 5% significance level, determine whether average P/E ratios differ in the three industries.

b. If differences exist, use Tukey's method at the 5% significance level to determine which industries' mean P/E ratios differ.

59. Before the Great Recession, job-creating cities in the Sunbelt, like Las Vegas, Phoenix, and Orlando saw their populations, income levels, and housing prices surge. Las Vegas, however, offered something that often eluded these other cities: upward mobility for the working class. For example, hard-working hotel maids were able to prosper during the boom times. According to the Bureau of Labor Statistics, the average hourly rate for hotel maids was $14.25 in Las Vegas, versus $9.25 in Phoenix and $8.84 in Orlando (*The Wall Street Journal*, July 20, 2009). Suppose the following summary statistics and ANOVA table were produced for $\alpha = 0.05$ from a sample of hourly wages of 25 hotel maids in each city.

SUMMARY					
Groups	**Count**	**Average**			
Las Vegas	25	13.91			
Phoenix	25	8.82			
Orlando	25	8.83			

Source of Variation	SS	df	MS	F	p-value
Between Groups	430.87	2	215.44	202.90	2.58E-30
Within Groups	76.44	72	1.06		
Total	507.31	74			

a. At the 5% significance level, do mean hourly rates for hotel maids differ between the three cities?

b. If differences exist, use Tukey's method to determine which cities' mean hourly rates differ at the 5% significance level.

60. The marketing department for an upscale retail catalog company wants to determine if there are differences in the mean customer purchase amounts across the available purchase sources (Internet, phone, or mail-in). Accordingly, samples were taken for 20 random orders for each purchase source. The following output was compiled. Assume purchase amounts are normally distributed.

Internet Purchase	Phone Purchase	Mail-in Purchase
$\bar{x}_1 = 214.05$	$\bar{x}_2 = 212.45$	$\bar{x}_3 = 182.40$
$n_1 = 20$	$n_2 = 20$	$n_3 = 20$

Source of Variation	SS	df	MS	F	p-value
Between Groups	12715.23	2	6357.62	0.433	0.651
Within Groups	836704.70	57	14679.03		
Total	849419.93	59			

a. At the 5% significance level, can we conclude that the mean purchase amount is different across the three purchase sources?

b. If significant differences exist, use Fisher's LSD method at the 5% significance level to determine which purchase sources have different mean purchase amounts.

61. An accounting professor wants to know if students perform the same on the departmental final exam irrespective of the accounting section they attend. She randomly selects the exam scores of 20 students from three sections. A portion of the output from conducting a one-way ANOVA test is shown in the accompanying table. Assume exam scores are normally distributed.

Source of Variation	SS	df	MS	F	p-value
Between Groups	57.39	2	MSTR = ?	$F_{2,57} = ?$	0.346
Within Groups	SSE = ?	57	MSE = ?		
Total	1570.19	59			

a. Find the missing values in the ANOVA table.

b. At the 5% significance level, can you conclude that average grades differ in the accounting sections?

62. **FILE** *Website.* A data analyst for an online store wonders whether average customer visits to the store's website vary by day of the week. He collects daily unique visits to the website for a 12-week period; a portion of the data is shown in the accompanying table. At the 5% significance level, what conclusion can the data analyst make?

Sunday	Monday	Tuesday	Wednesday	Thursday	Friday	Saturday
3088	2203	2331	1977	2036	2272	3065
2953	2288	2450	1912	2097	2205	2922
⋮	⋮	⋮	⋮	⋮	⋮	⋮
3047	2233	2395	1913	2175	2279	2994

63. **FILE** *Battery_Times.* Electrobat, a battery manufacturer, is investigating how storage temperature affects the performance of one of its popular deep-cell battery models used in recreational vehicles. Samples of 30 fully charged batteries were subjected to a light load under each of four different storage temperature levels. The hours until deep discharge (meaning $\leq 20\%$ of charge remaining) were measured. A portion of the data is shown in the accompanying table.

0 degrees F	30 degrees F	60 degrees F	90 degrees F
3	6	12	12
5	8	13	15
⋮	⋮	⋮	⋮
4	9	9	15

a. At the 5% significance level, can you conclude that mean discharge times differ across the four storage temperature levels? What about the 1% significance level?

b. If significant differences exist, use Tukey's HSD method at the 5% significance level to determine which temperature levels have different mean discharge times.

64. The accompanying table shows a portion of the results from conducting a two-way ANOVA test with no interaction in which five different production methods (factor A, columns) were evaluated in terms of labor cost per unit. Operator experience was used as a blocking factor (factor B, rows) and was considered at four levels.

Source of Variation	SS	df	MS	F	p-Value
Rows (Experience level)	$SSB = ?$	3	$MSB = ?$	$F_B = ?$	$p\text{-}val_B = ?$
Columns (Prod. method)	$SSA = ?$	$df_A = ?$	$MSA = 0.720$	$F_A = ?$	$p\text{-}val_A = ?$
Error	3.072	12	$MSE = ?$		
Total	10.998	19			

a. Find the missing values in the ANOVA table.

b. At the 5% significance level, can you conclude that labor cost per unit differs by production method? What about the 10% significance level?

c. At the 5% significance level, can you conclude that labor cost per unit differs by operator experience level?

65. The following output summarizes a portion of the results for a two-way ANOVA test without interaction where factor A (column) represents three income categories (low, medium, high), factor B (rows) consists of three different kinds of political parties (Democrat, Republican, Independent), and the variable measured was the amount (in $) contributed to the political party during the 2016 presidential election.

Source of Variation	SS	df	MS	F	p-value
Rows	25416.67	2	$MSB = ?$	$F_{\text{Factor B}} = ?$	0.099
Columns	42916.67	2	$MSA = ?$	$F_{\text{Factor A}} = ?$	0.046
Error	11666.67	4	$MSE = ?$		
Total	80000	8			

a. Find the missing values in the ANOVA table.

b. At the 5% significance level, can you conclude that average contributions differ by political party?

c. At the 5% significance level, can you conclude that average contributions differ by income level?

66. **FILE** *Headlight_Design.* An automotive parts manufacturer is testing three potential halogen headlight designs, one of which ultimately will be promoted as providing best-in-class nighttime vision. The distance at which a traffic sign can be read in otherwise total darkness is the variable of interest. Since older drivers often have lower visual acuity, driver age must be controlled in this experiment. The following results (in feet) were obtained from sampling 12 drivers (four age groups for each headlight design).

Driver Age (Factor B)	Headlight Design (Factor A)		
	Design 1	Design 2	Design 3
Below 30	293	268	270
30–45	254	243	254
46–59	224	249	231
60–up	238	214	205

a. At the 5% significance level, can you conclude that the mean nighttime viewing distance is different among the headlight designs? Practically speaking, what does your conclusion imply?

b. At the 5% significance level, was including the blocking variable *Driver Age* beneficial to this experiment? Explain.

67. **FILE** *Gymnastics.* At a gymnastics meet, three judges evaluate the balance beam performances of five gymnasts. The judges use a scale of 1 to 10, where 10 is a perfect score. A statistician wants to examine the objectivity and consistency of the judges. Assume scores are normally distributed.

	Judge 1	Judge 2	Judge 3
Gymnast 1	8.0	8.5	8.2
Gymnast 2	9.5	9.2	9.7
Gymnast 3	7.3	7.5	7.7
Gymnast 4	8.3	8.7	8.5
Gymnast 5	8.8	9.2	9.0

a. At the 1% significance level, can you conclude that average scores differ by judge? Can you conclude that the judges seem inconsistent with their scoring?

b. At the 1% significance level, can you conclude that average scores differ by gymnast?

c. If average scores differ by gymnast, use Tukey's HSD method at the 1% significance level to determine which gymnasts' performances differ.

68. **FILE** *Fuel_Hybrid.* An environmentalist wants to examine whether average fuel consumption (measured in miles per gallon) is affected by fuel type (factor *A*) and type of hybrid (factor *B*). A two-way ANOVA experiment with interaction is performed. The results are shown in the accompanying table.

Car Type	Fuel A	Fuel B	Fuel C
	40	47	60
Hybrid I	36	43	50
	43	41	52
	48	46	49
Hybrid II	48	44	45
	51	48	56
	31	51	50
Hybrid III	41	43	42
	47	38	50

a. At the 5% significance level, is there interaction between fuel type and hybrid type?

b. At the 5% significance level, can you conclude that average fuel consumption differs by fuel type?

c. At the 5% significance level, can you conclude that average fuel consumption differs by type of hybrid?

69. A management consultant wants to determine whether the age and gender of a restaurant's wait staff influence the size of the tip the customer leaves. Three age brackets (factor *A* in columns: young, middle-age, older) and gender (factor *B* in rows: male, female) are used to construct a two-way ANOVA experiment with interaction. For each combination, the percentage of the total bill left as a tip for 10 wait staff is examined. The following ANOVA table is produced.

Source of Variation	SS	df	MS	F	p-value
Sample	0.04278	1	0.04278	16.595	0.000
Columns	0.01793	2	0.00897	3.479	0.038
Interaction	0.00561	2	0.00281	1.089	0.344
Within	0.1392	54	0.00258		
Total	0.20552	59			

a. Can you conclude that there is interaction between age and gender at the 1% significance level?

b. Are you able to conduct tests based on the main effects? If yes, conduct these tests at the 1% significance level. If no, explain.

70. **FILE** *Training_Experience.* A production manager is investigating whether the operator training method (factor *A*) will affect the resulting output for a particular product. Three training methods were studied: a full-day workshop (most intensive), in-line training, and as-needed training (least intensive). Since the value of training likely depends on the operator experience level, experience level (factor *B*) was also studied. Five operators for each training method-experience level category were randomly chosen. The accompanying table shows the total output rates (in units produced) for the previous week.

a. At the 5% significance level, can you conclude that there is interaction between the training method and operator experience level? Explain why this is reasonable from a practical standpoint.

b. Are you able to conduct tests based on the main effects? If yes, conduct them at the 5% significance level. If no, explain why. Explain why your conclusion is reasonable from a practical standpoint.

Experience Level (Factor B)	Training Method (Factor A)		
	Full-Day Workshop	In-Line Training	As Needed Training
Under 3 months	492	405	363
	460	408	313
	433	384	325
	483	447	378
	439	370	338
3–6 months	495	482	425
	457	478	381
	523	435	414
	539	489	387
	497	501	422
Over 6 months	562	511	526
	518	527	526
	567	511	525
	533	599	577
	588	534	547

three different depth-of-cut settings and two different feed rate settings.

Feed Rate (Factor B)	Depth of Cut (Factor A)		
	0.8 mm	1.0 mm	1.2 mm
6 cm/minute	10	10	12
	10	11	10
	8	10	11
	9	9	12
	9	10	12
	9	11	11
8 cm/minute	12	13	15
	12	10	12
	9	14	15
	13	13	13
	11	13	15
	9	12	14

71. **FILE** *BestCuts.* The cutting department at BestCuts, a furniture manufacturer, is examining the effect of depth of cut and feed rate on the surface roughness of table legs used in a popular dining room table model. The accompanying table shows the surface roughness results for six replicates involving

a. At the 5% significance level, can you conclude that there is interaction between depth of cut and feed rate?

b. Are you able to conduct tests based on the main effects? If yes, conduct them at the 5% significance level. If no, explain why.

c. Explain why your conclusion in part (b) is reasonable from a practical standpoint.

CASE STUDIES

CASE STUDY 13.1   Lisa Grattan, a financial analyst for a small investment firm, collects annual stock return data for 10 firms in the energy industry, 13 firms in the retail industry, and 16 firms in the utilities industry. A portion of the data is shown in the accompanying table.

FILE
Industry_Returns

Data for Case Study 13.1 Annual Stock Returns (in %)

Energy	Retail	Utilities
12.5	6.6	3.5
8.2	7.4	6.4
⋮	⋮	⋮
6.9	7.9	4.3

In a report, use the sample information to

1. Determine whether significant differences exist in the annual returns for the three industries at the 5% significance level.

2. Construct 95% confidence intervals for the difference between annual returns for each pairing using Tukey's HSD method.

3. Evaluate which means (if any) significantly differ from one another using the results from part 2.

CASE STUDY 13.2 In 2007, the United States experienced the biggest jump in food prices in 17 years (*The Wall Street Journal*, April 1, 2008). A variety of reasons led to this result, including rising demand for meat and dairy products in emerging overseas markets, increased use of grains for alternative fuels, and bad weather in some parts of the world. A survey compared prices (in $) of selected products at grocery stores in the Boston area. The accompanying table shows the results.

Data for Case Study 13.2 Prices of Select Groceries at Three Stores

FILE
Grocery_Prices

Item	Crosby's	Shaw's	Market Basket
Two-liter Coke	1.79	1.59	1.50
Doritos chips	4.29	4.99	3.50
Cheerios cereal	3.69	2.99	3.00
Prince spaghetti	1.59	1.69	1.99
Skippy peanut butter	5.49	4.49	3.99
Cracker Barrel cheese	4.99	4.99	3.49
Pepperidge Farm white bread	3.99	3.99	3.99
Oreo cookies	4.69	3.39	3.00
One dozen eggs*	2.49	2.69	1.59
Coffee*	4.49	4.79	3.99
Gallon of milk*	3.69	3.19	1.59

*Store brand items; data collected October 5–6, 2011.

In a report, use the sample information to

1. Determine whether differences exist in the average prices of products sold at the three stores at the 5% significance level.

2. Determine whether differences exist in the average prices of the 11 products at the 5% significance level.

3. Determine which stores' prices differ using Tukey's HSD method, if it is found that differences exist in the average prices among these three stores. Use a 5% significance level.

CASE STUDY 13.3 The manager of an SAT review program wonders whether the ethnic background of a student and the program's instructor affect the student's performance on the SAT. Four ethnicities and three instructors are examined. Ten student scores for each combination are sampled. A portion of the data is shown in the following table.

Data for Case Study 13.3 Ethnic Background and SAT Scores

FILE
ANOVA_SAT

	White	Black	Asian-American	Mexican-American
Instructor A	1587	1300	1660	1366
	1562	1255	1576	1531
	⋮	⋮	⋮	⋮
Instructor B	1598	1296	1535	1345
	1539	1286	1643	1357
	⋮	⋮	⋮	⋮
Instructor C	1483	1289	1641	1400
	1525	1272	1633	1421
	⋮	⋮	⋮	⋮

In a report, use the sample information and $\alpha = 0.05$ to

1. Determine if there is any interaction between instructor and ethnicity.

2. Establish whether average SAT scores differ by instructor.

3. Establish whether average SAT scores differ by ethnicity.

The following section provides brief commands for Minitab, SPSS, and JMP. Copy and paste the specified data file into the relevant software spreadsheet prior to following the commands.

Minitab

One-Way ANOVA; Fisher and Tukey Confidence Intervals

FILE
Public_Transportation

A. (Replicating Examples 13.1 and 13.2) From the menu, choose **Stat > ANOVA > One-Way**.

B. Select "**Response data are in a separate column for each factor level**."

C. Under **Responses**, select Boston, NY, SF, and Chicago. Choose **Comparisons**. Enter the value 5 after **Error rate for comparisons**. After **Comparisons procedures assuming equal variances**, select **Tukey** and **Fisher**.

Two-Way ANOVA (No Interaction)

FILE
TwoFactor_Income

A. (Replicating Example 13.6) Stack all salary values into Column 1 and label Salary. In Column 2 (label Education), denote all salary values associated with a high school education with H, all salary values associated with a bachelor's degree with B, all salary values associated with a master's degree with M, and all salary values associated with a PhD with P. In Column 3 (label Field), denote all income values associated with Education with E, all salary values associated with Financial with F, and all salary values associated with Medical with Med.

B. From the menu, choose **Stat > ANOVA > Balanced ANOVA**.

C. For **Response**, select Salary, and for **Model,** select Education and Field.

Two-Way ANOVA (with Interaction)

FILE
Income_Interaction

A. (Replicating Example 13.7) In order to arrange the data, follow the Minitab instructions for Two-Way ANOVA (No Interaction), step A.

B. From the menu, choose **Stat > ANOVA > General Linear Model > Fit General Linear Model**.

C. For **Response**, select Salary, and for **Factors**, select Education and Field.

D. Choose **Model**, and under **Factors and covariates**, select Education and Field, then **Add**.

SPSS

One-Way ANOVA; Fisher and Tukey Confidence Intervals

FILE
Public_Transportation

A. (Replicating Examples 13.1 and 13.2) Stack all cost values in one column and label Cost. In adjacent column (label City), denote all Boston costs with value 1, all New York costs with value 2, etc.

B. From the menu, choose **Analyze > Compare Means > One-Way ANOVA**.

C. Under **Dependent**, **List**, select Cost, and under **Factor**, select City. Choose **Post Hoc**, and select **LSD** (Fisher) and **Tukey**.

Two-Way ANOVA (No Interaction)

FILE
TwoFactor_Income

A. (Solving Example 13.6) In order to arrange the data, follow the Minitab instructions for Two-Way ANOVA (No Interaction), step A.

B. From the menu, select **Analyze > General Linear Model > Univariate**.

C. Under **Dependent Variable**, select Salary, and under **Fixed Factor(s)**, select Education and Field. Choose **Model**. In the Model dialog box, select **Custom**. Under **Model**, select Education and Field. Under **Type**, select **All 2-way**. Deselect **Include Intercept in Model**.

Two-Way ANOVA (with Interaction)

A. (Replicating Example 13.7) In order to arrange the data, follow the Minitab instructions for Two-Way ANOVA (No Interaction), step A.

B. From the menu, select **Analyze > General Linear Model > Univariate**.

C. In the Univariate dialog box, under **Dependent Variable**, select Salary, and under **Fixed Factor(s)**, select Education and Field. Choose **Model**. In the Model dialog box, select **Full factorial**. Deselect **Include Intercept in Model**. Click **Continue**, and then click **OK**.

JMP

One-Way ANOVA; Fisher and Tukey Confidence Intervals

A. (Replicating Examples 13.1 and 13.2) In order to arrange the data, follow the SPSS instructions for One-Way ANOVA, step A.

B. From the menu, select **Analyze > Fit Y by X**.

C. Under **Select Columns**, select Pooled, then under **Cast Selected Columns into Roles**, select **Y, Columns**. Under **Select Columns**, select Group, then under **Cast Selected Columns into Roles**, select **X, Factor**.

D. Click on the red triangle next to **Oneway Analysis of Pooled by Group** and select **Means/Anova**.

E. For Fisher confidence intervals, click on the red triangle next to **Oneway Analysis of Pooled by Group** and select **Compare Means > Each Pair, Student's t**.

F. For Tukey confidence intervals, click on the red triangle next to **Oneway Analysis of Pooled by Group** and select **Compare Means > All Pairs, Tukey HSD**.

Two-Way ANOVA (No Interaction)

A. (Replicating Example 13.6) In order to arrange the data, follow the Minitab instructions for Two-Way ANOVA (No Interaction), step A.

B. From the menu, select **Analyze > Fit Model**.

C. Under **Select Columns**, select Salary, and then under **Pick Role Variables**, select **Y**. Under **Select Columns**, simultaneously select Education and Field, and then select **Macros > Full Factorial**. Double-click on Education*Field in order to deselect this variable.

Two-Way ANOVA (with Interaction)

A. (Replicating Example 13.7) In order to arrange the data, follow the Minitab instructions for Two-Way ANOVA (No Interaction), step A.

B. From the menu, select **Analyze > Fit Model**.

C. Under **Select Columns**, select Salary, and then under **Pick Role Variables**, select Y. Under **Select Columns**, simultaneously select Education and Field, and then select **Macros > Full Factorial**.

14 Regression Analysis

LEARNING OBJECTIVES

After reading this chapter you should be able to:

LO **14.1** Conduct a hypothesis test for the population correlation coefficient.

LO **14.2** Discuss the limitations of correlation analysis.

LO **14.3** Estimate and interpret a simple linear regression model.

LO **14.4** Estimate and interpret a multiple linear regression model.

LO **14.5** Interpret the standard error of the estimate.

LO **14.6** Interpret the coefficient of determination, R^2.

LO **14.7** Differentiate between R^2 and adjusted R^2.

As researchers or analysts, we often need to examine the relationship between two or more variables. We begin this chapter with a review of the correlation coefficient, first discussed in Chapter 3, and then conduct a hypothesis test to determine if two variables are correlated. Although the correlation analysis may establish a linear relationship between two variables, it does not demonstrate that one variable causes change in the other variable. In this chapter, we introduce regression analysis, which captures the causal relationship between two or more variables and has applications in a wide range of fields, including business, engineering, and social sciences. We first explore the procedures for estimating a linear relationship between two variables, referred to as the simple linear regression model. We then extend the simple linear regression model to the case involving several variables, referred to as the multiple linear regression model. Finally, since we often must choose between various regression models, we examine a number of goodness-of-fit measures in order to assess how well an estimated model fits the data.

©Blend Images-JGI/Jamie Grill/Band X Pictures/Getty Images RF

INTRODUCTORY CASE

Consumer Debt Payments

A study of 26 metropolitan areas found that American consumers are making average monthly debt payments of $983 (Experian.com, November 11, 2010). However, it turns out that the actual amount a consumer pays depends a great deal on where the consumer lives. For instance, residents of Washington, D.C., pay the most ($1,285 per month), while Pittsburgh residents pay the least ($763 per month). Madelyn Davis, an economist at a large bank, believes that income differences between cities are the primary reason for the disparate debt payments. For example, the Washington, D.C., area's high incomes have likely contributed to its placement on the list. She is unsure about the likely effect of the unemployment rate on consumer debt payments. On the one hand, higher unemployment rates may reduce consumer debt payments, as consumers forgo making major purchases such as large appliances and cars. On the other hand, higher unemployment rates may raise consumer debt payments as consumers struggle to pay their bills. In order to analyze the relationship between consumer debt payments, income, and the unemployment rate, Madelyn gathers data on average consumer debt (Debt in $), the annual median household income (Income in $1,000s), and the monthly unemployment rate (Unemployment in %) from the same 26 metropolitan areas used in the debt payment study. Table 14.1 shows a portion of the data.

TABLE 14.1 Average Consumer Debt, Median Income, and the Unemployment Rate, 2010–2011

Metropolitan Area	Debt	Income	Unemployment
Washington, D.C.	1285	103.50	6.3
Seattle	1135	81.70	8.5
⋮	⋮	⋮	⋮
Pittsburgh	763	63.00	8.3

Source: Experian.com collected average monthly consumer debt payments in August 2010 and published the data in November 2010; eFannieMae.com reports 2010–2011 Area Median Household Incomes; bls.com gives monthly unemployment rates for August 2010.

Madelyn would like to use the sample information in Table 14.1 to

1. Determine if debt payments and income are correlated.
2. Use regression analysis to make predictions for debt payments for given values of income and the unemployment rate.
3. Use various goodness-of-fit measures to determine the regression model that best fits the data.

A synopsis of this case is provided at the end of Section 14.3.

14.1 HYPOTHESIS TEST FOR THE CORRELATION COEFFICIENT

It will be useful in this section to review a scatterplot, as well as the sample covariance and the sample correlation coefficient—these concepts were discussed in Chapters 2 and 3. A scatterplot graphically shows the relationship between two variables, while the covariance and the correlation coefficient are measures that quantify the linear relationship between two variables.

Using the data from the introductory case, Figure 14.1 shows a scatterplot depicting the relationship between debt payments and income. We may infer that the two variables have a positive relationship; as one increases, the other one tends to increase. (See Section 2.3 in Chapter 2 for directions on how to construct a scatterplot in Excel and R.)

FIGURE 14.1
Scatterplot of debt payments against income

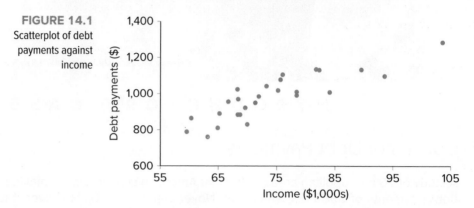

The **sample covariance** s_{xy} measures the direction of the linear relationship between two variables x and y. (See Section 3.8 for the calculation of s_{xy}.) A positive value of the sample covariance implies that, on average, when one variable is above its mean, the other variable is also above its mean; in other words, x and y have a positive linear relationship. Similarly, a negative value suggests that, on average, when x is above its mean, y is below its mean; in other words, x and y have a negative linear relationship. Further interpretation of the covariance is difficult because it is sensitive to the units of measurement. For instance, the covariance between two variables might be 100 and the covariance between two other variables might be 1,000, yet all we can conclude is that both sets of variables are positively related. In other words, we cannot comment on the strength of the linear relationships.

An easier measure to interpret is the **sample correlation coefficient** r_{xy}, which describes both the direction and strength of the linear relationship between x and y.

THE SAMPLE CORRELATION COEFFICIENT

The sample correlation coefficient gauges the direction and the strength of the linear relationship between two variables x and y. We calculate the sample correlation coefficient r_{xy} as

$$r_{xy} = \frac{s_{xy}}{s_x s_y},$$

where s_{xy} is the sample covariance, s_x and s_y are the sample standard deviations of x and y, respectively, and $-1 \le r_{xy} \le 1$.

In short, the sample correlation coefficient r_{xy} is unit-free and its value falls between -1 and 1. If r_{xy} equals 1, then a perfect positive linear relationship exists between x and y. Similarly, a perfect negative linear relationship exists if r_{xy} equals -1.

If r_{xy} equals zero, then no linear relationship exists between x and y. Other values for r_{xy} must be interpreted with reference to -1, 0, and 1. As the absolute value of r_{xy} approaches 1, the stronger the linear relationship. For instance, $r_{xy} = -0.80$ indicates a strong negative relationship, whereas $r_{xy} = 0.12$ indicates a weak positive relationship. However, we should comment on the direction of the relationship only if the correlation coefficient is found to be statistically significant—a topic which we address next.

Testing the Correlation Coefficient ρ_{xy}

We conduct a hypothesis test to determine whether the apparent relationship between the two variables, implied by the sample correlation coefficient, is real or due to chance. Let ρ_{xy} denote the population correlation coefficient. When testing whether the population correlation coefficient differs from zero, is greater than zero, or is less than zero, the competing hypotheses will take one of the following forms:

Two-Tailed Test	Right-Tailed Test	Left-Tailed Test
$H_0: \rho_{xy} = 0$	$H_0: \rho_{xy} \leq 0$	$H_0: \rho_{xy} \geq 0$
$H_A: \rho_{xy} \neq 0$	$H_A: \rho_{xy} > 0$	$H_A: \rho_{xy} < 0$

As in all hypothesis tests, the next step is to specify and calculate the value of the test statistic.

TEST STATISTIC FOR ρ_{XY}

The value of the test statistic for the hypothesis test concerning the population correlation coefficient ρ_{xy} is calculated as

$$t_{df} = \frac{r_{xy}}{s_r},$$

where $df = n - 2$ and $s_r = \sqrt{(1 - r_{xy}^2)/(n - 2)}$ is the standard error of the sample correlation coefficient, r_{xy}.

Or, equivalently,

$$t_{df} = \frac{r_{xy}\sqrt{n - 2}}{\sqrt{1 - r_{xy}^2}}.$$

Using Excel and R to Conduct a Hypothesis Test for ρ_{xy}

In Chapter 3, we manually calculated the sample correlation coefficient. Here, we rely on Excel and R to calculate the sample correlation coefficient and help us conduct a hypothesis test concerning the population correlation coefficient. Consider the following example.

EXAMPLE 14.1

Use the **Debt_Payments** data from the introductory case to solve the following problems.

a. Calculate and interpret the correlation coefficient between debt payments and income.

b. At the 5% significance level, determine whether the correlation coefficient is significant.

FILE

Debt_Payments

SOLUTION:

Using Excel

a. Open the ***Debt_Payments*** data file. Note that the data for debt payments are in cells B2 through B27 (array1), and the data for income are in cells C2 through C27 (array2). We use Excel's **CORREL** function to calculate the correlation coefficient. So, we enter "=CORREL(B2:B27, C2:C27)," and Excel returns 0.8675. The correlation coefficient of 0.8675 indicates that income and debt payments have a positive linear relationship.

b. When testing whether the correlation coefficient between income (x) and debt payments (y) is significant, we set up the following competing hypotheses:

$$H_0: \rho_{xy} = 0$$
$$H_A: \rho_{xy} \neq 0$$

In order to find the value of the test statistic, $t_{df} = \frac{r_{xy}\sqrt{n-2}}{\sqrt{1-r_{xy}^2}}$, we enter "=(CORREL(B2:B27, C2:C27)*sqrt(26-2))/(sqrt(1-CORREL(B2:B27, C2:C27)^2))." Excel returns 8.544, so $t_{24} = 8.544$. Since $t_{df} > 0$, we find the p-value for this two-tailed test by entering "=2*T.DIST.RT(8.544, 24)," and Excel returns 9.661E-09. Since the p-value is less than 0.05, we reject H_0. At the 5% significance level, we conclude that the population correlation coefficient between debt payments and income differs from zero.

Using R

Import the ***Debt_Payments*** data into a data frame (table) in R.

a and b. It is possible to use R's **cor** function, first introduced in Chapter 3, to find the correlation coefficient. However, the **cor.test** function generates the correlation coefficient as well as the value of the test statistic and the p-value. Within the function, we first specify the x variable, and then we specify the y variable. We use the option *alternative* to denote the specification of the alternative hypothesis (specified as "two.sided" for a two-tailed test, "less" for a left-tailed test, and "greater" for a right-tailed test). For Example 14.1, enter

```
> cor.test(Debt_Payments$'Income', Debt_Payments$'Debt', alternative="two.sided")
```

Table 14.2 shows the R output. We have put the sample correlation coefficient, the value of the test statistic, and the p-value in boldface. The results are identical to the Excel output. That is, the correlation between debt payments and income, found at the bottom of Table 14.2, is 0.8675. Also, since the p-value is approximately 0, we reject the null hypothesis. At the 5% significance level, we conclude that the population correlation coefficient between debt payments and income differs from zero.

TABLE 14.2 R's Output for Hypothesis Test Concerning the Correlation Coefficient

```
             Pearson's product-moment correlation
data: Debt_Payments[, "Income"] and Debt_Payments[, "Debt"]
t = 8.544, df = 24, p-value = 9.66e-09
alternative hypothesis: true correlation is not equal to 0
95 percent confidence interval:
0.7231671 0.9392464
sample estimates:
   cor
0.8675115
```

Limitations of Correlation Analysis

LO **14.2**

Discuss the limitations of correlation analysis.

Several limitations apply to correlation analysis.

A. The correlation coefficient captures only a linear relationship. Two variables can have a very low correlation coefficient yet have a strong *nonlinear* relationship. Consider the following sample data:

x	−20	−15	−10	−5	0	5	10	15	20
y	380	210	90	20	0	30	110	240	420

The sample correlation coefficient for these data is $r_{xy} = 0.09$, implying an extremely weak positive linear relationship. However, further analysis of the data would reveal a perfect nonlinear relationship given by $y_i = x_i + x_i^2$.

B. The correlation coefficient may not be a reliable measure when *outliers* are present in one or both of the variables. Recall that outliers are a small number of extreme high or low values in the data set. As a general rule, we must determine whether the sample correlation coefficient varies dramatically by removing a few outliers. However, we must use judgment to determine whether those outliers contain important information about the relationship between the two variables (and should be included in the correlation analysis) or do not contain important information (and should be excluded).

C. Correlation does not imply causation. Even if two variables are highly correlated, one does not necessarily cause the other. *Spurious correlation* can make two variables appear closely related when no causal relation exists. Spurious correlation between two variables is *not* based on any theoretical relationship, but rather on a relation that arises in the data solely because each of the two variables is related to some third variable. For example, Robert Matthews in his article "Storks Bring Babies" (*Teaching Statistics*, Summer 2000) finds that the correlation coefficient between stork breeding pairs and the human birth rate for 17 European countries is 0.62. Further, he finds that the correlation is different from zero at the 5% significance level. He stresses that the most plausible explanation for this observed correlation—and absurd conclusion—is the existence of a confounding factor, namely land area. That is, we are likely to see higher human birth rates in more densely populated areas. More densely populated areas also provide more chimneys, where stork breeding pairs prefer to nest. See *www.tylervigen.com/spurious-correlations* for other outrageous examples of spurious correlation.

EXERCISES 14.1

Mechanics

1. The covariance between two random variables x and y is 100. The sample standard deviation for x is 10 and the sample standard deviation for y is 12.5. Calculate and interpret the correlation coefficient.

2. The covariance between two random variables x and y is −250. The sample standard deviation for x is 40 and the sample standard deviation for y is 50. Calculate and interpret the correlation coefficient.

3. Consider the following competing hypotheses:

$$H_0: \rho_{xy} = 0$$
$$H_A: \rho_{xy} \neq 0$$

The sample consists of 25 observations and the sample correlation coefficient is 0.15.

   a. Calculate the value of the test statistic and the *p*-value.
   b. At the 5% significance level, what is the conclusion to the test? Explain.

4. Consider the following competing hypotheses:

$$H_0: \rho_{xy} \geq 0$$
$$H_A: \rho_{xy} < 0$$

The sample consists of 30 observations and the sample correlation coefficient is −0.60.

   a. Calculate the value of the test statistic and the *p*-value.
   b. At the 5% significance level, what is the conclusion to the test? Explain.

5. A sample of 10 observations provides the following statistics:

$$s_x = 13, \quad s_y = 18, \quad \text{and} \quad s_{xy} = 117.22$$

   a. Calculate and interpret the sample correlation coefficient r_{xy}.
   b. Specify the competing hypotheses to determine whether the population correlation coefficient is positive.
   c. Calculate the value of the test statistic and the p-value.
   d. At the 5% significance level, what is the conclusion to the test? Explain.

6. A sample of 25 observations provides the following statistics:

$$s_x = 2, \quad s_y = 5, \quad \text{and} \quad s_{xy} = -1.75$$

   a. Calculate and interpret the sample correlation coefficient r_{xy}.
   b. Specify the competing hypotheses in order to determine whether the population correlation coefficient differs from zero.
   c. Make a conclusion at the 5% significance level.

Applications

7. **FILE** *Rain.* In June 2009, an onslaught of miserable weather in New England played havoc with people's plans and psyches. However, the dreary weather brought a quiet benefit to many city neighborhoods. Police reported that the weather was a key factor in reducing fatal and nondeadly shootings (*The Boston Globe*, July 3, 2009). For instance, it rained in Boston on 22 days in June, when 15 shootings occurred. In 2008, the city saw rain on only eight days, and 38 shootings occurred. The accompanying table shows the number of rainy days and the number of shootings that occurred in June from 2005 to 2009.

	Number of Rainy Days	Number of Shootings
June 2005	7	31
June 2006	15	46
June 2007	10	29
June 2008	8	38
June 2009	22	15

Source: *The Boston Globe*, July 3, 2009.

   a. Calculate the sample correlation coefficient between the number of rainy days and crime.
   b. Specify the competing hypotheses in order to determine whether the population correlation coefficient between the number of rainy days and crime is negative.
   c. Calculate the value of the test statistic and the p-value.
   d. At the 5% significance level, what is the conclusion to the test? Does it appear that dreary weather and crime are negatively correlated?

8. **FILE** *2010_StockReturns.* Diversification is considered important in finance because it allows investors to reduce risk by investing in a variety of assets. It is especially effective when the correlation between the assets is low. Consider the accompanying table, which shows a portion of monthly data on closing stock prices of four companies in 2010.

Month	Microsoft	Coca Cola	Bank of America	General Electric
Jan	27.61	49.52	15.13	15.64
Feb	28.22	54.88	16.61	15.72
⋮	⋮	⋮	⋮	⋮
Dec	27.91	55.58	13.34	18.29

Source: finance.yahoo.com.

   a. Calculate the sample correlation coefficients between all pairs of stock prices.
   b. Suppose an investor already has a stake in Microsoft and would like to add another asset to her portfolio. Which of the remaining three assets will give her the maximum benefit of diversification? (*Hint*: Find the asset with the lowest correlation with Microsoft.)
   c. Suppose an investor does not own any of these four stocks. Pick two stocks so that she gets the maximum benefit of diversification.

9. **FILE** *Property_Taxes.* A realtor studies the relationship between the size of a house (in square feet) and the property taxes (in $) owed by the owner. The accompanying table shows a portion of the data for 20 homes in a suburb 60 miles outside of New York City.

Property Taxes	Size
21928	2449
17339	2479
⋮	⋮
29235	2864

   a. Calculate and interpret r_{xy}.
   b. Specify the competing hypotheses in order to determine whether the population correlation coefficient between the size of a house and property taxes differs from zero.
   c. Calculate the value of the test statistic and the p-value.
   d. At the 5% significance level, what is the conclusion to the test?

10. **FILE** *Happiness_Age.* Many attempts have been made to relate happiness with various factors. One such study relates happiness with age and finds that holding everything else constant, people are least happy when they are in their

mid-40s (*The Economist*, December 16, 2010). The accompanying table shows a portion of data on a respondent's age and his/her perception of well-being on a scale from 0 to 100.

Happiness	Age
62	49
66	51
⋮	⋮
72	69

a. Calculate and interpret the sample correlation coefficient between age and happiness.
b. Is the correlation coefficient statistically significant at the 1% level?
c. Construct a scatterplot to point out a flaw with the above correlation analysis.

11. **FILE** *Points.* The following table lists the National Basketball Association's leading scorers, their average points per game (PPG), and their average minutes per game (MPG) for 2008.

	PPG	MPG
D. Wade	30.2	38.6
L. James	28.4	37.7
K. Bryant	26.8	36.1
D. Nowitzki	25.9	37.3
D. Granger	25.8	36.2
K. Durant	25.3	39.0
C. Paul	22.8	38.5
C. Anthony	22.8	34.5
C. Bosh	22.7	38.0
B. Roy	22.6	37.2

Source: www.espn.com.

a. Calculate and interpret the sample correlation coefficient between PPG and MPG.
b. Specify the competing hypotheses in order to determine whether the population correlation coefficient between PPG and MPG is positive.
c. Calculate the value of the test statistic and the p-value.
d. At the 5% significance level, what is the conclusion to the test? Is this result surprising? Explain.

14.2 THE LINEAR REGRESSION MODEL

LO 14.3

The correlation coefficient may establish a linear relationship between two variables, but the measure does not suggest that one variable causes change in the other variable. With **regression analysis**, we change the emphasis from correlation to causation. Here, we explicitly assume that one variable, called the **response variable**, is influenced or caused by other variables, called the **explanatory variables**. Consequently, we use information on the explanatory variables to predict and/or describe changes in the response variable. Alternative names for the explanatory variables are independent variables, predictor variables, control variables, and regressors, while the response variable is often referred to as the dependent variable, the explained variable, the predicted variable, or the regressand.

Estimate and interpret a simple linear regression model.

Regression analysis is one of the most widely used statistical methodologies in business, engineering, and the social sciences. In the introductory case, Madelyn is interested in examining how income and the unemployment rate might influence debt payments. In another scenario, we may want to predict a firm's sales based on its advertising; estimate an individual's salary based on education and years of experience; predict the selling price of a house on the basis of its size and location; or describe auto sales with respect to consumer income, interest rates, and price discounts. In all of these examples, we can use regression analysis to describe the causal relationship between the variables of interest.

No matter the response variable that we choose to examine, we cannot expect to predict its exact value. If the value of the response variable is uniquely determined by the values of the explanatory variables, we say that the relationship between the variables is **deterministic**. This is often the case in the physical sciences. For example, momentum p is the product of the mass m and velocity v of an object; that is, $p = mv$. In most fields of research, however, we tend to find that the relationship between the explanatory variables and the response variable is **stochastic**, due to the omission of relevant factors (sometimes not measurable) that influence the response variable. For instance, debt payments are likely to be influenced by costs associated with the household size—a variable that is not included in the introductory case. Similarly, when trying to predict an individual's salary, the individual's natural ability is often omitted since it is extremely difficult, if not impossible, to quantify.

> **DETERMINISTIC VERSUS STOCHASTIC RELATIONSHIPS**
>
> The relationship between the response variable and the explanatory variables is deterministic if the value of the response variable is uniquely determined by the explanatory variables; otherwise, the relationship is stochastic.

Our objective is to develop a mathematical model that captures the relationship between the response variable y and the k explanatory variables $x_1, x_2, \ldots, x_k$. The model must also account for the stochastic nature of the relationship. In order to develop a linear regression model, we start with a deterministic component that approximates the relationship we want to model, and then add a random term to it, making the relationship stochastic.

The Simple Linear Regression Model

We first focus on the **simple linear regression model**, which uses one explanatory variable, denoted x_1, to explain the variation in the response variable, denoted y. For ease of exposition when discussing the simple linear regression model, we often drop the subscript on the explanatory variable and refer to it solely as x. We then extend the simple linear regression model to the **multiple linear regression model**, where more than one explanatory variable is presumed to have a linear relationship with the response variable.

A fundamental assumption underlying the simple linear regression model is that the expected value of y lies on a straight line, denoted by $\beta_0 + \beta_1 x$, where β_0 and β_1 (the Greek letters read as betas) are the unknown intercept and slope parameters, respectively. (You have actually seen this relationship before, but you just used different notation. Recall the equation for a line: $y = mx + b$, where b and m are the intercept and the slope, respectively, of the line.)

The expression $\beta_0 + \beta_1 x$ is the deterministic component of the simple linear regression model, which can be thought of as the expected value of y for a given value of x. In other words, conditional on x, $E(y) = \beta_0 + \beta_1 x$. The slope parameter β_1 determines whether the linear relationship between x and $E(y)$ is positive ($\beta_1 > 0$) or negative ($\beta_1 < 0$); $\beta_1 = 0$ indicates that there is no linear relationship. Figure 14.2 shows the expected value of y for various values of the intercept β_0 and the slope β_1 parameters.

FIGURE 14.2
Various examples of a simple linear regression model

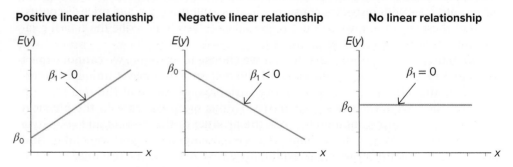

Positive linear relationship   Negative linear relationship   No linear relationship

As noted earlier, the observed value y may differ from the expected value $E(y)$. Therefore, we add a random error term ε (the Greek letter read as epsilon) to develop a simple linear regression model.

THE SIMPLE LINEAR REGRESSION MODEL

The simple linear regression model is defined as

$$y = \beta_0 + \beta_1 x + \varepsilon,$$

where y and x are the response variable and the explanatory variable, respectively, and ε is the random error term. The coefficients β_0 and β_1 are the unknown parameters to be estimated.

The population parameters β_0 and β_1 used in the simple linear regression model are unknown, and, therefore, must be estimated. As always, we use sample data to estimate the population parameters of interest. Here sample data consist of n pairs of observations on y and x.

Let b_0 and b_1 represent the estimates of β_0 and β_1, respectively. We form the sample regression equation as $\hat{y} = b_0 + b_1 x$, where $\hat{y}$ (read as y-hat) is the predicted value of the response variable given a specified value of the explanatory variable x. For a given value of x, the observed and the predicted values of the response variable are likely to be different since many factors besides x influence y. We refer to the difference between the observed and the predicted values of y, that is $y - \hat{y}$, as the **residual** e.

THE SAMPLE REGRESSION EQUATION FOR THE SIMPLE LINEAR REGRESSION MODEL

The sample regression equation for the simple linear regression model is denoted as

$$\hat{y} = b_0 + b_1 x,$$

where b_0 and b_1 are the estimates of β_0 and β_1, respectively.

The difference between the observed and the predicted values of y represents the residual e—that is, $e = y - \hat{y}$.

Before estimating a simple linear regression model, it is useful to visualize the relationship between y and x by constructing a scatterplot. Here, we explicitly place y on the vertical axis and x on the horizontal axis, implying that x influences the variation in y. In Figure 14.3, we use the data from the introductory case to show a scatterplot of debt payments against income. We then superimpose a linear trendline through the points on the scatterplot.

The superimposed line in Figure 14.3 is the sample regression equation, $\hat{y} = b_0 + b_1 x$, where y and x represent debt payments and income, respectively. The upward slope of the line suggests that as income increases, the predicted debt payments also increase. Also, the vertical distance between any data point on the scatterplot (y) and the corresponding point on the line ($\hat{y}$) represents the residual, $e = y - \hat{y}$.

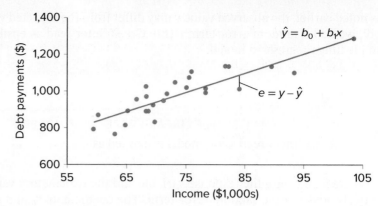

FIGURE 14.3
Scatterplot with a superimposed trendline

A common approach to fitting a line to the scatterplot is the **method of least squares**, also referred to as **ordinary least squares (OLS)**. In other words, we use OLS to estimate the parameters β_0 and β_1. OLS estimators have many desirable properties if certain assumptions hold (these assumptions are discussed in the next chapter). The OLS method chooses the line whereby the **error sum of squares**, **SSE**, is minimized, where $SSE = \Sigma(y_i - \hat{y}_i)^2 = \Sigma e_i^2$. SSE is the sum of the squared differences between the observed values y and their predicted values $\hat{y}$ or, equivalently, the sum of the squared distances from the regression equation. Thus, using this distance measure, we say that the OLS method produces the straight line that is "closest" to the data. In the context of Figure 14.3, the superimposed line has been estimated by OLS.

Using calculus, equations have been developed for b_0 and b_1 that satisfy the OLS criterion. These equations, or formulas, are as follows.

CALCULATING THE REGRESSION COEFFICIENTS b_1 AND b_0

The slope b_1 and the intercept b_0 of the sample regression equation are calculated as

$$b_1 = \frac{\Sigma(x_i - \bar{x})(y_i - \bar{y})}{\Sigma(x_i - \bar{x})^2} \quad \text{and}$$

$$b_0 = \bar{y} - b_1\bar{x}.$$

Fortunately, virtually every statistical software package produces values for b_1 and b_0. So we can focus on interpreting these regression coefficients rather than performing the grueling calculations. The slope estimate b_1 represents the change in $\hat{y}$ when x increases by one unit. As we will see in the following example, it is not always possible to provide an economic interpretation of the intercept estimate b_0; mathematically, however, it represents the predicted value of $\hat{y}$ when x has a value of zero.

Debt_Payments

EXAMPLE 14.2

Using the data from Table 14.1, let debt payments represent the response variable and income represent the explanatory variable in a simple linear regression model.

a. What is the sample regression equation?
b. Interpret b_1.
c. Interpret b_0.
d. Predict debt payments if income is $80,000.

SOLUTION: Table 14.3 shows the Excel-produced output from estimating the model: Debt $= \beta_0 + \beta_1$ Income $+ \varepsilon$, or simply, $y = \beta_0 + \beta_1 x + \varepsilon$, where y and x represent debt payments and income, respectively. We will provide Excel and R instructions for obtaining this output shortly.

TABLE 14.3 Excel-Produced Regression Results for Example 14.2

Regression Statistics					
Multiple R	0.8675				
R Square	0.7526				
Adjusted R Square	0.7423				
Standard Error	63.2606				
Observations	26				

ANOVA					
	df	SS	MS	F	Significance F
Regression	1	292136.91	292136.91	72.9996	9.66E-09
Residual	24	96045.55	4001.90		
Total	25	388182.46			

	Coefficients	Standard Error	t Stat	p-Value	Lower 95%	Upper 95%
Intercept	**210.2977**	91.3387	2.3024	0.0303	21.78	398.81
Income	**10.4411**	1.2220	8.5440	9.66E-09	7.92	12.96

FILE
Debt_Payments

a. As Table 14.3 shows, Excel produces quite a bit of information. In order to formulate the sample regression equation, we need estimates for β_0 and β_1, which are found at the bottom of the table (see values in boldface). We will address the remaining information in the next section of this chapter, as well as in Chapter 15. We find that $b_0 = 210.2977$ and $b_1 = 10.4411$. Thus, the sample regression equation is $\hat{y} = 210.2977 + 10.4411x$; that is, $\widehat{\text{Debt}} = 210.2977 + 10.4411 \text{Income}$.

b. The estimated slope coefficient of 10.4411 suggests a positive relationship between income and debt payments. If median household income increases by $1,000 (since income is measured in $1,000s), then we predict consumer debt payments to increase by b_1—that is, by $10.44.

c. The estimated intercept coefficient of 210.2977 suggests that if income equals zero, then predicted debt payments are $210.30. In this particular application, this conclusion makes some sense, since a household with no income still needs to make debt payments for any credit card use, automobile loans, and so on. However, we should be careful about predicting y when we use a value for x that is not included in the sample range of x. In the **Debt_Payments** data set, the lowest and highest values for income (in $1,000s) are 59.40 and 103.50, respectively; plus, the scatterplot suggests that a line fits the data well within this range of the explanatory variable. Unless we assume that income and debt payments will maintain the same linear relationship at income values less than 59.40 and more than 103.50, we should refrain from making predictions based on values of the explanatory variable outside the sample range.

d. Recall that income is measured in $1,000s. So if we are predicting debt payments for an income of $80,000, then we input the value of 80 for Income in the sample regression equation. Thus, we find

$$\widehat{\text{Debt}} = 210.2977 + 10.4411 \times 80 = 1{,}045.59.$$

That is, debt payments are predicted to be $1,045.59.

Using Excel and R to Estimate a Simple Linear Regression Model

Debt_Payments

We replicate Table 14.3 from Example 14.2.

Using Excel

A. Open the ***Debt_Payments*** data file.

B. Choose **Data** > **Data Analysis** > **Regression** from the menu.

C. See Figure 14.4. In the *Regression* dialog box, click on the box next to *Input Y Range*, and then select the Debt data, including its heading. For *Input X Range*, select the Income data, including its heading. Check *Labels*. Click **OK**. Your results should be identical to Table 14.3.

FIGURE 14.4 Excel's Regression dialog box

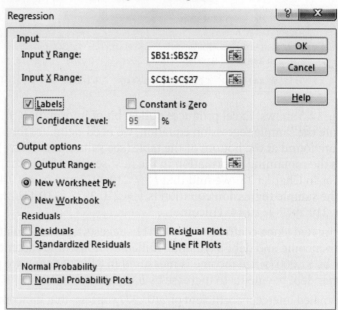

Using R

A. Import the ***Debt_Payments*** data into a data frame (table) in R.

B. We use the **lm** function to create a linear model. In R terminology, this is referred to as an object. We label this object as Simple. You will not see output after you implement this step. Enter

```
> Simple <- lm(Debt~Income, data=Debt_Payments)
```

C. We use the **summary** function to view the regression output. Enter:

```
> summary(Simple)
```

Table 14.4 shows the R regression output. We have put the intercept and the slope coefficients in boldface. As expected, these values are identical to the ones obtained using Excel.

TABLE 14.4 R-Produced Regression Output for Example 14.2

```
Call:
lm(formula = Debt ~ Income, data = Debt_Payments)

Residuals:
      Min        1Q    Median       3Q       Max
  -107.087   -38.767    -5.828   50.137   101.619

Coefficients:
              Estimate Std.    Error    t value    Pr(>|t|)
(Intercept)     210.298       91.339      2.302      0.0303 *
Income           10.441        1.222      8.544    9.66e-09 ***
---
Signif. codes:  0 '***' 0.001 '**' 0.01 '*' 0.05 '.' 0.1 ' ' 1

Residual standard error: 63.26 on 24 degrees of freedom
Multiple R-squared:  0.7526,  Adjusted R-squared:  0.7423
F-statistic:  73 on 1 and 24 DF, p-value: 9.66e-09
```

The Multiple Linear Regression Model

LO 14.4

Estimate and interpret the multiple linear regression model.

The simple linear regression model allows us to analyze the linear relationship between one explanatory variable and the response variable. However, by restricting the number of explanatory variables to one, we sometimes reduce the potential usefulness of the model. In Chapter 15, we will discuss how the OLS estimates can be quite misleading when important explanatory variables are excluded. A multiple linear regression model allows us to examine how the response variable is influenced by two or more explanatory variables. The choices of the explanatory variables are based on economic theory, intuition, and/or prior research. The multiple linear regression model is a straightforward extension of the simple linear regression model.

THE MULTIPLE LINEAR REGRESSION MODEL

The multiple linear regression model is defined as

$$y = \beta_0 + \beta_1 x_1 + \beta_2 x_2 + \cdots + \beta_k x_k + \varepsilon,$$

where y is the response variable, $x_1, x_2, \ldots, x_k$ are the k explanatory variables, and ε is the random error term. The coefficients $\beta_0, \beta_1, \ldots, \beta_k$ are the unknown parameters to be estimated.

As in the case of the simple linear regression model, we apply the OLS method that minimizes SSE, where $SSE = \Sigma(y_i - \hat{y}_i)^2 = \Sigma e_i^2$.

THE SAMPLE REGRESSION EQUATION FOR THE MULTIPLE LINEAR REGRESSION MODEL

The sample regression equation for the multiple linear regression model is denoted as

$$\hat{y} = b_0 + b_1 x_1 + b_2 x_2 + \cdots + b_k x_k,$$

where $b_0, b_1, \ldots, b_k$ are the estimates of $\beta_0, \beta_1, \ldots, \beta_k$.

The difference between the observed and the predicted values of y represents the residual e—that is, $e = y - \hat{y}$.

For each explanatory variable x_j ($j = 1, \ldots, k$), the corresponding slope coefficient b_j is the estimate of β_j. We slightly modify the interpretation of the slope coefficients in the context of a multiple linear regression model. Here b_j measures the change in the predicted value of the response variable $\hat{y}$ given a unit increase in the associated explanatory variable x_j, *holding all other explanatory variables constant*. In other words, it represents the partial influence of x_j on $\hat{y}$.

EXAMPLE 14.3

In this example we analyze how debt payments may be influenced by income *and* the unemployment rate.

a. Given the data from Table 14.1, estimate the multiple linear regression model with debt payments as the response variable and income and the unemployment rate as the explanatory variables.

b. Interpret the regression coefficients.

c. Predict debt payments if income is $80,000 and the unemployment rate is 7.5%.

SOLUTION:

a. Table 14.5 shows the Excel-produced output from estimating the model: $Debt = \beta_0 + \beta_1 Income + \beta_2 Unemployment + \varepsilon$. We will provide Excel and R instructions for obtaining this output shortly.

TABLE 14.5 Excel-Produced Regression Output for Example 14.3

Regression Statistics	
Multiple R	0.8676
R Square	0.7527
Adjusted R Square	0.7312
Standard Error	64.6098
Observations	26

ANOVA					
	df	SS	MS	F	Significance F
Regression	2	292170.77	146085.39	34.9954	1.05E-07
Residual	23	96011.69	4174.42		
Total	25	388182.46			

	Coefficients	Standard Error	t Stat	p-Value	Lower 95%	Upper 95%
Intercept	**198.9956**	156.3619	1.2727	0.2159	−124.46	522.45
Income	**10.5122**	1.4765	7.1120	2.98E-07	7.46	13.57
Unemployment	**0.6186**	6.8679	0.0901	0.9290	−13.59	14.83

Using the boldface estimates from Table 14.5, $b_0 = 198.9956$, $b_1 = 10.5122$, and $b_2 = 0.6186$, we derive the sample regression equation as

$$\widehat{Debt} = 198.9956 + 10.5122 Income + 0.6186 Unemployment.$$

b. The regression coefficient of Income is 10.5122. Since income is measured in $1,000s, the model suggests that if income increases by $1,000, then debt payments are predicted to increase by $10.51, holding the unemployment rate constant. Similarly, the regression coefficient of Unemployment is 0.6186, implying that a 1 percentage point increase in the unemployment rate leads to a predicted increase in debt payments of $0.62, holding income constant. It seems that the predicted impact of Unemployment, with Income held constant, is rather small. In fact, the influence of the unemployment rate is not even statistically significant at any reasonable level; we will discuss such tests of significance in the next chapter.

c. If income is \$80,000 and the unemployment rate is 7.5%, we find

$$\widehat{\text{Debt}} = 198.9956 + 10.5122 \times 80 + 0.6186 \times 7.5 = 1{,}044.61.$$

That is, debt payments are predicted to be \$1,044.61.

Using Excel and R to Estimate a Multiple Linear Regression Model

We replicate Table 14.5 from Example 14.3. When using either Excel or R, there are very small modifications when estimating a simple linear regression as compared to a multiple linear regression. For these reasons, we are brief.

Using Excel

A. Open the **Debt_Payments** data file.

B. Choose **Data** > **Data Analysis** > **Regression** from the menu.

C. See Figure 14.4. In the *Regression* dialog box, click on the box next to *Input Y Range*, then select the Debt data, including its heading. For *Input X Range*, *simultaneously* select the Income and the Unemployment data (including both headings). Check *Labels*. Click **OK**. Your results should be identical to Table 14.5.

Using R

A. Import the **Debt_Payments** data into a data frame (table) in R.

B. We use the **lm** function to create a linear model. We label this object as Multiple. Enter

```
> Multiple <-lm(Debt~Income+Unemployment,
  data=Debt_Payments)
```

C. We use the **summary** function to view the regression output. Enter:

```
> summary(Multiple)
```

Table 14.6 shows the R regression output. We have put the intercept and the slope coefficients in boldface. As expected, these values are identical to the ones obtained using Excel.

TABLE 14.6 R-Produced Regression Output for Example 14.3

```
Call:
lm(formula = Debt ~ Income + Unemployment, data = Debt_Payments)
Residuals:
      Min        1Q     Median        3Q        Max
  -110.456    -38.454    -5.836     51.156    102.121
Coefficients:
               Estimate Std.    Error     t value    Pr(>|t|)
(Intercept)     198.9956      156.3619      1.273       0.216
Income           10.5122        1.4765      7.120     2.98e-07  ***
Unemployment      0.6186        6.8679      0.090       0.929
---
Signif. codes:  0 '***' 0.001 '**' 0.01 '*' 0.05 '.' 0.1 ' ' 1

Residual standard error: 64.61 on 23 degrees of freedom
Multiple R-squared:  0.7527,  Adjusted R-squared:  0.7312
F-statistic:  35 on 2 and 23 DF, p-value: 1.054e-07
```

EXERCISES 14.2

Mechanics

12. In a simple linear regression, the following sample regression equation is obtained:

$$\hat{y} = 15 + 2.5x.$$

   a. Predict y if x equals 10.
   b. What happens to this prediction if x doubles in value to 20?

13. In a simple linear regression, the following sample regression equation is obtained:

$$\hat{y} = 436 - 17x.$$

   a. Interpret the slope coefficient.
   b. Predict y if x equals -15.

14. In a multiple regression, the following sample regression equation is obtained:

$$\hat{y} = -8 + 2.6x_1 - 47.2x_2.$$

   a. Predict y if x_1 equals 40 and x_2 equals -10.
   b. Interpret the slope coefficient of x_2.

15. In a multiple regression, the following sample regression equation is obtained:

$$\hat{y} = 152 + 12.9x_1 + 2.7x_2.$$

   a. Predict y if x_1 equals 20 and x_2 equals 35.
   b. Interpret the slope coefficient of x_1.

16. Thirty observations were used to estimate $y = \beta_0 + \beta_1 x + \varepsilon$. A portion of the results is shown in the accompanying table.

	Coefficients	Standard Error	t Stat	p-value
Intercept	41.82	8.58	4.87	3.93E-05
x	0.49	0.10	4.81	4.65E-05

   a. What is the estimate for β_1? Interpret this value.
   b. What is the sample regression equation?
   c. If $x = 30$, what is $\hat{y}$?

17. Twenty-four observations were used to estimate $y = \beta_0 + \beta_1 x + \varepsilon$. A portion of the regression results is shown in the accompanying table.

	Coefficients	Standard Error	t Stat	p-value
Intercept	2.25	2.36	0.95	0.3515
x	-0.16	0.30	-0.53	0.6017

   a. What is the estimate for β_1? Interpret this value.
   b. What is the sample regression equation?
   c. What is the predicted value for y if $x = 2$? If $x = -2$?

18. Thirty observations were used to estimate $y = \beta_0 + \beta_1 x_1 + \beta_2 x_2 + \varepsilon$. A portion of the regression results is shown in the accompanying table.

	Coefficients	Standard Error	t Stat	p-value
Intercept	21.97	2.98	7.37	6.31E-08
x_1	30.00	2.23	13.44	1.75E-13
x_2	-1.88	0.27	-6.96	1.75E-07

   a. What is the estimate for β_1? Interpret this value.
   b. What is the sample regression equation?
   c. If $x_1 = 30$ and $x_2 = 20$, what is $\hat{y}$?

19. Forty observations were used to estimate $y = \beta_0 + \beta_1 x_1 + \beta_2 x_2 + \varepsilon$. A portion of the regression results is shown in the accompanying table.

	Coefficients	Standard Error	t Stat	p-value
Intercept	13.83	2.42	5.71	1.56E-06
x_1	-2.53	0.15	-16.87	5.84E-19
x_2	0.29	0.06	4.83	2.38E-05

   a. What is the estimate for β_1? Interpret this value.
   b. What is the sample regression equation?
   c. What is the predicted value for y if $x_1 = -9$ and $x_2 = 25$?

Applications

20. If a firm spends more on advertising, is it likely to increase sales? Data on annual sales (in \$100,000s) and advertising expenditures (in \$10,000s) were collected for 20 firms in order to estimate the model Sales $= \beta_0 + \beta_1$Advertising $+ \varepsilon$. A portion of the regression results is shown in the accompanying table.

	Coefficients	Standard Error	t Stat	p-value
Intercept	-7.42	1.46	-5.09	7.66E-05
Advertising	0.42	0.05	8.70	7.26E-08

   a. Is the sign on the slope as expected? Explain.
   b. What is the sample regression equation?
   c. Predict the sales for a firm that spends \$500,000 annually on advertising.

21. The owner of several used-car dealerships believes that the selling price of a used car can best be predicted using the car's age. He uses data on the recent selling price (in \$) and age of 20 used sedans to estimate Price $= \beta_0 + \beta_1$Age $+ \varepsilon$. A portion of the regression results is shown in the accompanying table.

	Coefficients	Standard Error	t Stat	p-value
Intercept	21187.94	733.42	28.89	1.56E-16
Age	-1208.25	128.95	-9.37	2.41E-08

   a. What is the estimate for β_1? Interpret this value.
   b. What is the sample regression equation?
   c. Predict the selling price of a 5-year-old sedan.

22. On the first day of class, an economics professor administers a test to gauge the math preparedness of her students. She believes that the performance on this math test and the number of hours studied per week on the course are the

primary factors that predict a student's score on the final exam. Using data from her class of 60 students, she estimates $Final = \beta_0 + \beta_1 Math + \beta_2 Hours + \varepsilon$. A portion of the regression results is shown in the following table.

	Coefficients	Standard Error	t Stat	p-value
Intercept	40.55	3.37	12.03	2.83E-17
Math	0.25	0.04	6.06	1.14E-07
Hours	4.85	0.57	8.53	9.06E-12

a. What is the slope coefficient of Hours?
b. What is the sample regression equation?
c. What is the predicted final exam score for a student who has a math score of 70 and studies 4 hours per week?

23. Using data from 50 workers, a researcher estimates $Wage = \beta_0 + \beta_1 Education + \beta_2 Experience + \beta_3 Age + \varepsilon$, where Wage is the hourly wage rate and Education, Experience, and Age are the years of higher education, the years of experience, and the age of the worker, respectively. A portion of the regression results is shown in the following table.

	Coefficients	Standard Error	t Stat	p-value
Intercept	7.87	4.09	1.93	0.0603
Education	1.44	0.34	4.24	0.0001
Experience	0.45	0.14	3.16	0.0028
Age	−0.01	0.08	−0.14	0.8920

a. Interpret the estimates for β_1 and β_2.
b. What is the sample regression equation?
c. Predict the hourly wage rate for a 30-year-old worker with 4 years of higher education and 3 years of experience.

24. A sociologist believes that the crime rate in an area is significantly influenced by the area's poverty rate and median income. Specifically, she hypothesizes crime will increase with poverty and decrease with income. She collects data on the crime rate (crimes per 100,000 residents), the poverty rate (in %), and the median income (in $1,000s) from 41 New England cities. A portion of the regression results is shown in the following table.

	Coefficients	Standard Error	t Stat	p-value
Intercept	−301.62	549.71	−0.55	0.5864
Poverty	53.16	14.22	3.74	0.0006
Income	4.95	8.26	0.60	0.5526

a. Are the signs as expected on the slope coefficients?
b. Interpret the slope coefficient for Poverty.
c. Predict the crime rate in an area with a poverty rate of 20% and a median income of $50,000.

25. Osteoporosis is a degenerative disease that primarily affects women over the age of 60. A research analyst wants to forecast sales of StrongBones, a prescription drug for treating this debilitating disease. She uses the model $Sales = \beta_0 + \beta_1 Population + \beta_2 Income + \varepsilon$, where Sales refers to the sales of StrongBones (in $1,000,000s), Population is the number of women over the age of 60 (in millions), and Income is the average income of women over the age of 60 (in $1,000s). She collects data on 38 cities across the United States and obtains the following regression results:

	Coefficients	Standard Error	t Stat	p-value
Intercept	10.35	4.02	2.57	0.0199
Population	8.47	2.71	3.12	0.0062
Income	7.62	6.63	1.15	0.2661

a. What is the sample regression equation?
b. Interpret the slope coefficients.
c. Predict sales if a city has 1.5 million women over the age of 60 and their average income is $44,000.

26. **FILE** *GPA.* The director of graduate admissions at a large university is analyzing the relationship between scores on the math portion of the Graduate Record Examination (GRE) and subsequent performance in graduate school, as measured by a student's grade point average (GPA). She uses a sample of 24 students who graduated within the past five years. A portion of the data is as follows:

GPA	GRE
3.0	700
3.5	720
⋮	⋮
3.5	780

a. Find the sample regression equation for the model: $GPA = \beta_0 + \beta_1 GRE + \varepsilon$.
b. What is a student's predicted GPA if he/she scored 710 on the math portion of the GRE?

27. **FILE** *Education.* A social scientist would like to analyze the relationship between educational attainment (in years of higher education) and annual salary (in $1,000s). He collects data on 20 individuals. A portion of the data is as follows:

Salary	Education
40	3
53	4
⋮	⋮
38	0

a. Find the sample regression equation for the model: $Salary = \beta_0 + \beta_1 Education + \varepsilon$.
b. Interpret the coefficient for Education.
c. What is the predicted salary for an individual who completed 7 years of higher education?

28. **FILE** *Consumption_Function.* The consumption function, first developed by John Maynard Keynes, captures one of the key relationships in economics. It expresses consumption as a function of disposable income, where disposable income is income after taxes. The accompanying table shows a portion of average U.S. annual consumption (in $) and disposable income (in $) for the years 1985–2006.

	Consumption	Disposable Income
1985	23490	22887
1986	23866	23172
⋮	⋮	⋮
2006	48398	58101

Source: *The Statistical Abstract of the United States.*

a. Estimate the model: Consumption $= \beta_0 + \beta_1$Disposable Income $+ \varepsilon$.

b. In this model, the slope coefficient is called the marginal propensity to consume. Interpret its meaning.

c. What is predicted consumption if disposable income is $57,000?

29. **FILE** *MLB_Pitchers.* The following table lists a portion of Major League Baseball's (MLB's) leading pitchers, each pitcher's salary (In $ millions), and earned run average (ERA) for 2008.

	Salary	ERA
J. Santana	17.0	2.53
C. Lee	4.0	2.54
⋮	⋮	⋮
C. Hamels	0.5	3.09

Source: www.ESPN.com.

a. Estimate the model: Salary $= \beta_0 + \beta_1$ERA $+ \varepsilon$ and interpret the coefficient of ERA.

b. Use the estimated model to predict the salary for each player, given his ERA. For example, use the sample regression equation to predict the salary for J. Santana with ERA $= 2.53$.

c. Derive the corresponding residuals and explain why the residuals might be so high.

30. **FILE** *Happiness_Age.* Refer to the accompanying data file on happiness and age to answer the following questions.

a. Estimate a simple linear regression model with Happiness as the response variable and Age as the explanatory variable.

b. Use the sample regression equation to predict Happiness when Age equals 25, 50, and 75.

c. Construct a scatterplot of Happiness against Age. Discuss why your predictions might not be accurate.

31. **FILE** *Property_Taxes.* The accompanying table shows a portion of data that refers to the property taxes owed by a homeowner (in $) and the size of the home (in square feet) in an affluent suburb 30 miles outside New York City.

Property Taxes	Size
21928	2449
17339	2479
⋮	⋮
29235	2864

a. Estimate the sample regression equation that enables us to predict property taxes on the basis of the size of the home.

b. Interpret the slope coefficient.

c. Predict the property taxes for a 1,500-square-foot home.

32. **FILE** *Test_Scores.* The accompanying table shows a portion of the scores that 32 students obtained on the final and the midterm in a course in statistics.

Final	Midterm
86	78
94	97
⋮	⋮
91	47

a. Estimate the sample regression equation that enables us to predict a student's final score on the basis of his/her midterm score.

b. Predict the final score of a student who received an 80 on the midterm.

33. **FILE** *Fertilizer.* A horticulturist is studying the relationship between tomato plant height and fertilizer amount. Thirty tomato plants grown in similar conditions were subjected to various amounts of fertilizer (in ounces) over a four-month period, and then their heights (in inches) were measured. A portion of the data is shown in the accompanying table.

Height	Fertilizer
20.4	1.9
49.2	5.0
⋮	⋮
46.4	3.1

a. Estimate the model: Height $= \beta_0 + \beta_1$Fertilizer $+ \varepsilon$.

b. Interpret the coefficient of Fertilizer. Does the y-intercept make practical sense?

c. Use the estimated model to predict, after four months, the height of a tomato plant which received 3.0 ounces of fertilizer.

34. **FILE** *Dexterity.* Finger dexterity, the ability to make precisely coordinated finger movements to grasp or assemble very small objects, is important in jewelry making. Thus, the manufacturing manager at Gemco, a manufacturer of high-quality watches, wants to develop a regression model to predict the productivity (in watches per shift) of new employees based on dexterity. He has subjected a sample of 20 current employees to the O'Connor dexterity test in which the time required to place 3 pins in each of 100 small holes using tweezers is measured in seconds. A portion of the data is shown in the accompanying table.

Watches	Time
23	513
19	608
⋮	⋮
20	437

a. Estimate the model: Watches $= \beta_0 + \beta_1$Time $+ \varepsilon$.
b. Interpret the coefficient of Time.
c. Explain why the y-intercept makes no practical sense in this particular problem.
d. Suppose a new employee takes 550 seconds on the dexterity test. How many watches per shift is she expected to produce?

35. **FILE** *Arlington_Homes.* A realtor in Arlington, Massachusetts, is analyzing the relationship between the sale price of a home (Price in $), its square footage (Sqft), the number of bedrooms (Beds), and the number of bathrooms (Baths). She collects data on 36 sales in Arlington in the first quarter of 2009 for the analysis. A portion of the data is shown in the accompanying table.

Price	Sqft	Beds	Baths
840000	2768	4	3.5
822000	2500	4	2.5
⋮	⋮	⋮	⋮
307500	850	1	1

Source: http://Newenglandmoves.com.

a. Estimate the model Price $= \beta_0 + \beta_1$Sqft $+ \beta_2$Beds $+ \beta_3$Baths $+ \varepsilon$.
b. Interpret the slope coefficients.
c. Predict the price of a 2,500-square-foot home with three bedrooms and two bathrooms.

36. **FILE** *Engine_Overhaul.* The maintenance manager at a trucking company wants to build a regression model to forecast the time (in years) until the first engine overhaul based on four explanatory variables: (1) annual miles driven (in 1,000s of miles), (2) average load weight (in tons), (3) average driving speed (in mph), and (4) oil change interval (in 1,000s of miles). Based on driver logs and onboard computers, data have been obtained for a sample of 25 trucks. A portion of the data is shown in the accompanying table.

Time until First Engine Overhaul	Annual Miles Driven	Average Load Weight	Average Driving Speed	Oil Change Interval
7.9	42.8	19	46	15
0.9	98.5	25	46	29
⋮	⋮	⋮	⋮	⋮
6.1	61.2	24	58	19

a. For each explanatory variable, discuss whether it is likely to have a positive or negative causal effect on time until the first engine overhaul.
b. Estimate the regression model (use all four explanatory variables).
c. Based on part (a), are the signs of the regression coefficients logical?
d. Predict the time before the first engine overhaul for a particular truck driven 60,000 miles per year with an average load of 22 tons, an average driving speed of 57 mph, and 18,000 miles between oil changes.

37. **FILE** *MCAS.* Education reform is one of the most hotly debated subjects on both state and national policy makers' list of socioeconomic topics. Consider a linear regression model that relates school expenditures and family background to student performance in Massachusetts using 224 school districts. The response variable is the mean score on the MCAS (Massachusetts Comprehensive Assessment System) exam given in May 1998 to 10th graders. Four explanatory variables are used: (1) STR is the student-to-teacher ratio in %, (2) TSAL is the average teacher's salary in $1,000s, (3) INC is the median household income in $1,000s, and (4) SGL is the percentage of single-parent households. A portion of the data is shown in the accompanying table.

Score	STR	TSAL	INC	SGL
227.00	19.00	44.01	48.89	4.70
230.67	17.90	40.17	43.91	4.60
⋮	⋮	⋮	⋮	⋮
230.67	19.20	44.79	47.64	5.10

Source: Massachusetts Department of Education and the Census of Population and Housing.

a. For each explanatory variable, discuss whether it is likely to have a positive or negative causal effect on Score.
b. Find the sample regression equation. Are the signs of the slope coefficients as expected?
c. What is the predicted score if STR $= 18$, TSAL $= 50$, INC $= 60$, SGL $= 5$?
d. What is the predicted score if everything else is the same as in part (c) except INC $= 80$?

38. **FILE** *Electricity_Cost.* The facility manager at a pharmaceutical company wants to build a regression model to forecast monthly electricity cost. Three main variables are thought to dictate electricity cost (in $): (1) average outdoor temperature (Avg Temp in °F), (2) working days per month, and (3) tons of product produced. A portion of the past year's monthly data is shown in the accompanying table.

Cost	Avg Temp	Work Days	Tons Produced
24100	26	24	80
23700	32	21	73
⋮	⋮	⋮	⋮
26000	39	22	69

a. For each explanatory variable, discuss whether it is likely to have a positive or negative causal effect on monthly electricity cost.

b. Estimate the regression model.

c. Are the signs of the regression coefficients as expected? If not, speculate as to why this could be the case.

d. What is the predicted electricity cost in a month during which the average outdoor temperature is 65°, there are 23 working days, and 76 tons are produced?

39. **FILE** *Quarterback_Salaries.* American football is the highest paying sport on a per-game basis. The quarterback, considered the most important player on the team, is appropriately compensated. A sports statistician wants to use 2009 data to estimate a multiple linear regression model that links the quarterback's salary (in $ millions) with his pass completion percentage (PCT), total touchdowns scored (TD), and his age. A portion of the data is shown in the accompanying table.

Name	Salary	PCT	TD	Age
Philip Rivers	25.5566	65.2	28	27
Jay Cutler	22.0441	60.5	27	26
⋮	⋮	⋮	⋮	⋮
Tony Romo	0.6260	63.1	26	29

Source: *USA Today* database for salaries; http://NFL.com for other data.

a. Estimate the model defined as Salary $= \beta_0 + \beta_1\text{PCT} + \beta_2\text{TD} + \beta_3\text{Age} + \varepsilon$.

b. Are you surprised by the estimated coefficients?

c. Drew Brees earned 12.9895 million dollars in 2009. According to the model, what is his predicted salary if PCT $= 70.6$, TD $= 34$, and Age $= 30$?

d. Tom Brady earned 8.0073 million dollars in 2009. According to the model, what is his predicted salary if PCT $= 65.7$, TD $= 28$, and Age $= 32$?

e. Compute and interpret the residual salary for Drew Brees and Tom Brady.

40. **FILE** *AnnArbor_Rental.* The accompanying table shows a portion of data consisting of the rent, the number of bedrooms, the number of bathrooms, and the square footage for 40 apartments in the college town of Ann Arbor, Michigan.

Rent	Bed	Bath	Sqft
645	1	1	500
675	1	1	648
⋮	⋮	⋮	⋮
2400	3	2.5	2700

a. Determine the sample regression equation that enables us to predict the rent of an Ann Arbor apartment on the basis of the number of bedrooms, the number of bathrooms, and the square footage.

b. Interpret the slope coefficient of Bath.

c. Predict the rent for a 1,500-square-foot apartment with 2 bedrooms and 1 bathroom.

41. **FILE** *Car_Prices.* The accompanying table shows a portion of data consisting of the selling price, the age, and the mileage for 20 used sedans.

Selling Price	Age	Mileage
13590	6	61485
13775	6	54344
⋮	⋮	⋮
11988	8	42408

a. Estimate the sample regression equation that enables us to predict the price of a sedan on the basis of its age and mileage.

b. Interpret the slope coefficient of Age.

c. Predict the selling price of a five-year-old sedan with 65,000 miles.

14.3 GOODNESS-OF-FIT MEASURES

So far we have focused on the estimation and the interpretation of the linear regression models. By simply observing the sample regression equation, we cannot assess how well the explanatory variables explain the variation in the response variable. We rely on several objective "goodness-of-fit" measures that summarize how well the sample regression equation fits the data. If each predicted value $\hat{y}$ is equal to its observed values y, then we have a perfect fit. Since that almost never happens, we evaluate the models on a relative basis.

In the introductory case study, we were interested in analyzing consumer debt payments. In the last section, we estimated the following two linear regression models:

$$\text{Model 1: Debt} = \beta_0 + \beta_1 \text{Income} + \varepsilon$$

$$\text{Model 2: Debt} = \beta_0 + \beta_1 \text{Income} + \beta_2 \text{Unemployment} + \varepsilon$$

For ease of exposition, we use the same notation to refer to the coefficients in Models 1 and 2. We note, however, that these coefficients and their estimates have a different meaning depending on which model we are referencing.

If you had to choose one of these models to predict debt payments, which model would you choose? It may be that by using more explanatory variables, you can better describe the response variable. However, for a given sample, *more* is not always better. In order to select the preferred model, we need to examine goodness-of-fit measures. We will study three goodness-of-fit measures: the standard error of the estimate, the coefficient of determination, and the adjusted coefficient of determination.

The Standard Error of the Estimate

LO 14.5

Interpret the standard error of the estimate.

We first describe goodness-of-fit measures in the context of a simple linear regression model, or Model 1. Figure 14.5 reproduces the scatterplot of debt payments against income, as well as the superimposed sample regression line. Recall that the residual e represents the difference between an observed value and the predicted value of the response variable—that is, $e = y - \hat{y}$. If all the data points had fallen on the line, then each residual would be zero; in other words, there would be no dispersion between the observed and the predicted values. Since in practice we rarely, if ever, obtain this result, we evaluate models on the basis of the relative magnitude of the residuals. The sample regression equation provides a good fit when the dispersion of the residuals is relatively small.

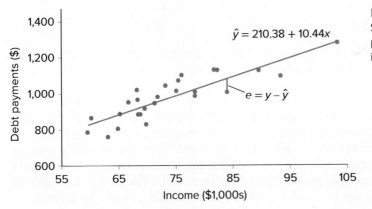

FIGURE 14.5
Scatterplot of debt payments y against income x

A numerical measure that gauges dispersion from the sample regression equation is the sample variance of the residual, denoted s_e^2. This measure is defined as the average squared difference between y_i and $\hat{y}_i$. The numerator of the formula is the error sum of squares, $SSE = \Sigma(y_i - \hat{y}_i)^2 = \Sigma e_i^2$. Dividing SSE by its respective degrees of freedom $n - k - 1$ yields s_e^2. Recall that k denotes the number of explanatory variables in the linear regression model; thus, for a simple linear regression model, k equals one. Instead of s_e^2, we generally report the standard deviation of the residual, denoted s_e, more commonly referred to as the **standard error of the estimate**. As usual, s_e is the positive square root of s_e^2. The less the dispersion, the smaller the s_e, which typically implies that the model provides a good fit for the sample data.

> ## THE STANDARD ERROR OF THE ESTIMATE
>
> The standard error of the estimate s_e is calculated as
>
> $$s_e = \sqrt{s_e^2} = \sqrt{\frac{SSE}{n - k - 1}},$$
>
> where SSE is the error sum of squares. Theoretically, s_e can assume any value between zero and infinity, $0 \leq s_e < \infty$. The closer s_e is to zero, the better the model fits the sample data.

For a given sample size n, increasing the number k of the explanatory variables reduces both the numerator (SSE) and the denominator ($n - k - 1$) in the formula for s_e. The net effect, shown by the value of s_e, allows us to determine if the added explanatory variables improve the fit of the model.

Virtually all statistical software packages report s_e. Excel reports s_e in the *Regression Statistics* portion of the regression output and refers to it as Standard Error. R reports s_e in the bottom portion of the regression output and refers to it as Residual standard error. The last row of Table 14.7 reports s_e for Model 1 and for Model 2.

TABLE 14.7 Goodness-of-Fit Measures for Model 1 and Model 2

	Model 1	Model 2
Multiple R	0.8675	0.8676
R Square	0.7526	0.7527
Adjusted R Square	0.7423	0.7312
Standard Error	63.2606	64.6098

EXAMPLE 14.4

Refer back to Table 14.7. As measured by the standard error of the estimate, does Model 1 or Model 2 provide a better fit for explaining debt payments? Explain.

SOLUTION: Our objective in adding another explanatory variable to the linear regression model is to increase the model's usefulness. In Model 2, we use income x_1 and the unemployment rate x_2 to explain debt payments y. If Model 2 is an improvement over Model 1, then we would expect it to have a smaller standard error of the estimate. We note that the standard error of the estimate for Model 2 is actually greater than that for Model 1 ($64.6098 > 63.2606$). In other words, Model 1 provides a better fit for the sample data. In general, we use the standard error of the estimate in conjunction with other measures to judge the overall usefulness of a model.

LO **14.6**

Interpret the coefficient of determination, R^2.

The Coefficient of Determination, R^2

In Example 14.4, we calculated $s_e = 63.2606$ for Model 1. It is difficult to interpret this value in isolation. The fact that a value closer to 0 implies a better fit does not allow us to determine how close a value of 63.2606 is to zero. The standard error of the estimate is a useful goodness-of-fit measure when we are comparing various models—the model with the smaller s_e provides the better relative fit. However, it proves less useful when we are assessing a single model. One reason for this is due to the fact that s_e has no predefined upper limit—that is, $0 \le s_e < \infty$. The **coefficient of determination**, commonly referred to as R^2, is another goodness-of-fit measure that is easier to interpret than the standard error of the estimate. As we will see shortly, R^2 has both lower and upper bounds that make its interpretation more intuitive.

Like the standard error of the estimate, the coefficient of determination evaluates how well the sample regression equation fits the data. In particular, R^2 quantifies the sample variation in the response variable y that is explained by the sample regression equation. It is computed as the ratio of the explained variation of the response variable to its total variation. For example, if $R^2 = 0.72$, we say that 72% of the sample variation in the response variable is explained by the sample regression equation. Other factors, which have not been included in the model, account for the remaining 28% of the sample variation.

We use analysis of variance (ANOVA) in the context of the linear regression model, to derive R^2. We denote the total variation in y as $\Sigma(y_i - \bar{y})^2$, which is the numerator in the formula for the variance of y. This value, called the **total sum of squares, SST**, can be broken down into two components: explained variation and unexplained variation. Figure 14.6 illustrates the decomposition of the total variation in y into its two components for a simple linear regression model.

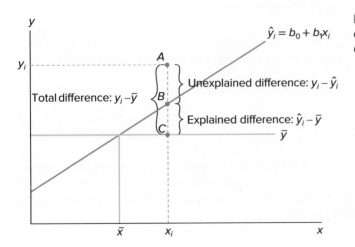

FIGURE 14.6 Total, explained, and unexplained differences

For ease of exposition, we show a scatterplot with all the points removed except one (point A). Point A refers to the observation (x_i, y_i). The blue line represents the estimated regression equation based on the entire sample data; the horizontal and vertical green lines represent the sample means $\bar{y}$ and $\bar{x}$, respectively. The vertical distance between the data point A and $\bar{y}$ (point C) is the difference $y_i - \bar{y}$ (distance AC). For each data point, we square these differences and then find their sum—this amounts to $SST = \Sigma(y_i - \bar{y})^2$. As mentioned above, SST is a measure of the total variation in y.

Now, we focus on the distance between the predicted value $\hat{y}_i$ (point B) and $\bar{y}$; that is, the explained difference (distance BC). It is called "explained" because the difference between $\hat{y}_i$ and $\bar{y}$ can be explained by the difference between x_i and $\bar{x}$. Squaring all such differences and summing them yields the **regression sum of squares, SSR**, where $SSR = \Sigma(\hat{y}_i - \bar{y})^2$. SSR is a measure of the explained variation in y.

The distance between the particular observation and its predicted value (distance AB) is the unexplained difference. This is the portion that remains unexplained; it is due to random error or chance. Squaring all such differences and summing them yields the familiar error sum of squares, $SSE = \Sigma(y_i - \hat{y}_i)^2$. SSE is a measure of the unexplained variation in y.

Thus, the total variation in y can be decomposed into explained and unexplained variation as follows:

$$SST = SSR + SSE.$$

Dividing both sides by SST and rearranging yields:

$$\frac{SSR}{SST} = 1 - \frac{SSE}{SST}.$$

Each side of the above equation shows two equivalent formulas for the coefficient of determination R^2; that is, $R^2 = SSR/SST$ or $R^2 = 1 - SSE/SST$. The value of R^2 falls between zero and one, $0 \leq R^2 \leq 1$. The closer R^2 is to one, the stronger the fit; the closer it is to zero, the weaker the fit.

THE COEFFICIENT OF DETERMINATION, R^2

The coefficient of determination, R^2, is the proportion of the sample variation in the response variable that is explained by the sample regression equation. We compute R^2 as

$$R^2 = \frac{SSR}{SST}, \text{ or equivalently, } R^2 = 1 - \frac{SSE}{SST},$$

where $SSR = \Sigma(\hat{y} - \bar{y})^2$, $SSE = \Sigma(y_i - \hat{y}_i)^2$, and $SST = \Sigma(y_i - \bar{y})^2$. R^2 can also be computed as $R^2 = r_{y\hat{y}}^2$, where $r_{y\hat{y}}$ is the sample correlation coefficient between y and $\hat{y}$.

The value of R^2 falls between zero and one; the closer the value is to one, the better the fit.

Most statistical packages, including Excel and R, report the coefficient of determination. Excel reports R^2 in the *Regression Statistics* portion of the regression output and refers to it as R Square. R reports R^2 in the bottom portion of the regression output and refers to it as Multiple R-squared.

EXAMPLE 14.5

Refer back to Table 14.7. Interpret the coefficient of determination for Model 1.

SOLUTION: The coefficient of determination, or R^2, for Model 1 is 0.7526. This means that 75.26% of the sample variation in debt payments is explained by changes in income.

Another interesting statistic in Table 14.7 is **Multiple R**. (This statistic is explicitly reported in Excel-produced regression output, but not in R-produced regression output.) Multiple R is simply the sample correlation coefficient between the response variable y and its predicted value $\hat{y}$ which, using our earlier notation, implies that Multiple $R = r_{y\hat{y}}$. Note that R^2 is the square of Multiple R—that is, $R^2 = r_{y\hat{y}}^2$.

In Chapter 16, we will use several examples to compute $r_{y\hat{y}}$ from scratch. Here, we simply note that Multiple R in Table 14.7 implies that the sample correlation coefficient between y and $\hat{y}$ for Model 2, for example, is $r_{y\hat{y}} = 0.8676$. Thus, $R^2 = r_{y\hat{y}}^2 = 0.8676^2 = 0.7527$, which is the same value for R^2 that is shown in Table 14.7.

Recall that the standard error of the estimate for Model 1 ($s_e = 63.2606$) was smaller than that for Model 2 ($s_e = 64.6098$), suggesting that Model 1 provides a better fit. Since the coefficient of determination for Model 2 ($R^2 = 0.7527$) is slightly greater than that of Model 1 ($R^2 = 0.7526$), one may think that Model 2 explains more of the variation in debt payments. How do we resolve these apparently conflicting results? It turns out that we cannot use R^2 for model comparison when the competing models do not include the same number of explanatory variables. Unlike s_e, R^2 never decreases as we add more explanatory variables to the model. A popular model selection method in such situations is to choose a model that has the highest adjusted R^2 value.

The Adjusted R^2

LO **14.7**

Differentiate between R^2 and adjusted R^2.

Since R^2 never decreases as we add more explanatory variables to the linear regression model, it is possible to increase its value unintentionally by including a group of explanatory variables that may have no economic or intuitive foundation in the linear regression model. This is true especially when the number of explanatory variables k is large relative to the sample size n. In order to avoid the possibility of R^2 creating a false impression, virtually all software packages, including Excel and R, include **adjusted R^2**. Unlike R^2, adjusted R^2 explicitly accounts for the number of explanatory variables k. It is common to use adjusted R^2 for model selection because it imposes a penalty for any additional explanatory variable that is included in the analysis.

ADJUSTED R^2

The adjusted coefficient of determination is calculated as

$$\text{Adjusted } R^2 = 1 - (1 - R^2)\left(\frac{n-1}{n-k-1}\right).$$

Adjusted R^2 is used to compare competing linear regression models with different numbers of explanatory variables; the higher the adjusted R^2, the better the model.

If *SSE* is substantially greater than zero and k is large compared to n, then adjusted R^2 will differ substantially from R^2. Adjusted R^2 may be negative if the correlation between the response variable and the explanatory variables is sufficiently low.

We would also like to point out that both the standard error of the estimate and the adjusted R^2 are useful for comparing the linear regression models with different numbers of explanatory variables. Adjusted R^2, however, is the more commonly used criterion for model selection.

EXAMPLE 14.6

Refer back to Table 14.7. As measured by the adjusted R^2, does Model 1 or Model 2 provide a better fit for explaining debt payments? Explain.

SOLUTION: We note from Table 14.7 that Model 1 has an adjusted R^2 of 0.7423, whereas it is 0.7312 for Model 2. Therefore, given its higher adjusted R^2, we choose Model 1 to predict debt payments.

SYNOPSIS OF INTRODUCTORY CASE

©Andy Dean Photography/Alamy Stock Photo RF

A study shows substantial variation in consumer debt payments depending on where the consumer resides (Experian.com, November 11, 2010). A possible explanation is that a linear relationship exists between consumer debt payments and an area's median household income. In order to substantiate this claim, relevant data on 26 metropolitan areas are collected. The correlation coefficient between debt payments and income is computed as 0.87, suggesting a strong positive linear relationship between the two variables. A simple test confirms that the correlation coefficient is statistically significant at the 5% level.

Two regression models are also estimated for the analysis. A simple linear regression model (Model 1), using consumer debt payments as the response variable and median household income as the explanatory variable, is estimated as $\widehat{Debt} = 210.30 + 10.44 Income$. For every \$1,000 increase in median household income, consumer debt payments are predicted to increase by \$10.44. In an attempt to improve upon the prediction, a multiple regression model (Model 2) is proposed, where median household income and the unemployment rate are used as explanatory variables. The sample regression line for Model 2 is $\widehat{Debt} = 199.00 + 10.51 Income + 0.62 Unemployment$. Given its slope coefficient of only 0.62, the economic impact of the unemployment rate on consumer debt payments, with median household income held fixed, seems extremely weak. Goodness-of-fit measures confirm that Model 1 provides a better fit than Model 2. The standard error of the estimate is smaller for Model 1, suggesting less dispersion of the data from the sample regression equation. In addition, the adjusted R^2 is higher for Model 1, implying that more of the sample variation in consumer debt payments is explained by the simple linear regression model. Using Model 1 and an area's median household income of \$80,000, consumer debt payments are predicted to be about \$1,046.

EXERCISES 14.3

Mechanics

42. In a simple linear regression based on 25 observations, it is found that $SSE = 1,250$ and $SST = 1,500$.
    a. Calculate s_e^2 and s_e.
    b. Calculate R^2.

43. In a simple linear regression based on 30 observations, it is found that $SSE = 2,540$ and $SST = 13,870$.
    a. Calculate s_e^2 and s_e.
    b. Calculate R^2.

44. In a multiple regression with two explanatory variables, and 50 observations, it is found that $SSE = 35$ and $SST = 90$.
    a. Calculate the standard error of the estimate s_e.
    b. Calculate the coefficient of determination R^2.

45. In a multiple regression with four explanatory variables and 100 observations, it is found that $SSR = 4.75$ and $SST = 7.62$.
    a. Calculate the standard error of the estimate s_e.
    b. Calculate the coefficient of determination R^2.
    c. Calculate adjusted R^2.

46. The accompanying table lists goodness-of-fit measures that were obtained when estimating the following two simple linear regression models:

$$\text{Model 1: } y = \beta_0 + \beta_1 x_1 + \varepsilon$$
$$\text{Model 2: } y = \beta_0 + \beta_1 x_2 + \varepsilon$$

	Model 1	Model 2
R^2	0.459	0.496
Adjusted R^2	0.445	0.483
s_e	104.914	101.274

Which model provides a better fit for y? Justify your response with two goodness-of-fit measures.

47. The accompanying table lists goodness-of-fit measures that were obtained when estimating the following simple linear regression model and multiple linear regression model:

$$\text{Model 1: } y = \beta_0 + \beta_1 x_1 + \varepsilon$$
$$\text{Model 2: } y = \beta_0 + \beta_1 x_1 + \beta_2 x_2 + \varepsilon$$

	Model 1	Model 2
R^2	0.751	0.752
Adjusted R^2	0.748	0.747
s_e	13.652	13.694

Which model provides a better fit for y? Justify your response with two goodness-of-fit measures.

48. The accompanying table lists goodness-of-fit measures that were obtained when estimating the following simple linear regression model and multiple linear regression model:

$$\text{Model 1: } y = \beta_0 + \beta_1 x_1 + \varepsilon$$
$$\text{Model 2: } y = \beta_0 + \beta_1 x_1 + \beta_2 x_2 + \beta_3 x_3 + \varepsilon$$

	Model 1	Model 2
R^2	0.804	0.828
Adjusted R^2	0.801	0.819
s_e	17.746	16.924

Which model provides a better fit for y? Justify your response with two goodness-of-fit measures.

49. The accompanying table lists goodness-of-fit measures that were obtained when estimating the following multiple linear regression models:

$$\text{Model 1: } y = \beta_0 + \beta_1 x_1 + \beta_2 x_2 + \varepsilon$$
$$\text{Model 2: } y = \beta_0 + \beta_1 x_3 + \beta_2 x_4 + \varepsilon$$

	Model 1	Model 2
R^2	0.640	0.610
Adjusted R^2	0.627	0.597
s_e	34.706	36.103

Which model provides a better fit for y? Justify your response with two goodness-of-fit measures.

Applications

50. An analyst estimates the sales of a firm as a function of its advertising expenditures using the model: Sales $= \beta_0 + \beta_1$Advertising $+ \varepsilon$. Using 20 observations, he finds that $SSR = 199.93$ and $SST = 240.92$.
   a. What proportion of the sample variation in sales is explained by advertising expenditures?
   b. What proportion of the sample variation in sales is unexplained by advertising expenditures?

51. **FILE** *Test_Scores.* The accompanying data file shows the midterm and final scores for 32 students in a statistics course.
   a. Estimate a student's final score as a function of his/her midterm score.
   b. Find the standard error of the estimate.
   c. Find and interpret the coefficient of determination.

52. The director of college admissions at a local university is trying to determine whether a student's high school GPA or SAT score is a better predictor of the student's subsequent college GPA. She formulates two models:

$$\text{Model 1. College GPA} = \beta_0 + \beta_1\text{High School GPA} + \varepsilon$$
$$\text{Model 2. College GPA} = \beta_0 + \beta_1\text{SAT Score} + \varepsilon$$

She estimates these models and obtains the following goodness-of-fit measures.

	Model 1	Model 2
R^2	0.5595	0.5322
Adjusted R^2	0.5573	0.5298
s_e	40.3684	41.6007

Which model provides a better fit for y? Justify your response with two goodness-of-fit measures.

53. **FILE** *Property_Taxes.* The accompanying data file shows the square footage and associated property taxes for 20 homes in an affluent suburb 30 miles outside New York City.
   a. Estimate a home's property taxes as a linear function of the size of the home (measured by its square footage).
   b. What proportion of the sample variation in property taxes is explained by the home's size?
   c. What proportion of the sample variation in property taxes is unexplained by the home's size?

54. **FILE** *Car_Prices.* The accompanying data file shows the selling price of a used sedan, its age, and its mileage. Estimate two models:

$$\text{Model 1: Price} = \beta_0 + \beta_1 x_1 \text{Age} + \varepsilon$$
$$\text{Model 2: Price} = \beta_0 + \beta_1\text{Age} + \beta_2\text{Mileage} + \varepsilon$$

Which model provides a better fit for y? Justify your response with two goodness-of-fit measures.

55. For a sample of 41 New England cities, a sociologist studies the crime rate in each city (crimes per 100,000 residents) as a function of its poverty rate (in %) and its median income (in $1,000s). He finds that $SSE = 4{,}182{,}663$ and $SST = 7{,}732{,}451$.
   a. Calculate the standard error of the estimate.
   b. What proportion of the sample variation in crime rate is explained by the variability in the explanatory variables? What proportion is unexplained?

56. A financial analyst uses the following model to estimate a firm's stock return: Return $= \beta_0 + \beta_1\text{P/E} + \beta_2\text{P/S} + \varepsilon$, where P/E is a firm's price-to-earnings ratio and P/S is a firm's price-to-sales ratio. For a sample of 30 firms, she finds that $SSE = 4{,}402.786$ and $SST = 5{,}321.532$.
   a. Calculate the standard error of the estimate.
   b. Calculate and interpret the coefficient of determination.
   c. Calculate the adjusted R^2.

57. **FILE** *Football.* Is it defense or offense that wins football games? Consider the following portion of data, which includes a team's winning record (Win in %), the average number of yards gained, and the average number of yards allowed during the 2009 NFL season.

Team	Win	Yards Gained	Yards Allowed
Arizona Cardinals	62.50	344.40	346.40
Atlanta Falcons	56.30	340.40	348.90
⋮	⋮	⋮	⋮
Washington Redskins	25.00	312.50	319.70

Source: NFL website.

   a. Compare two simple linear regression models, where Model 1 predicts the winning percentage based on Yards Gained and Model 2 uses Yards Allowed.

   b. Estimate a multiple linear regression model, Model 3, that applies both Yards Gained and Yards Allowed to forecast the winning percentage. Is this model an improvement over the other two models? Explain.

58. **FILE** *Executive_Compensation.* Executive compensation has risen dramatically beyond the rising levels of an average worker's wage over the years. The government is even considering a cap on high-flying salaries for executives (*The New York Times*, February 9, 2009). Consider the following portion of data which links total compensation (in $ millions) of the 455 highest-paid CEOs in 2006 with three measures: industry-adjusted return on assets (ROA), industry-adjusted stock return (Return) and the firm's size (Total Assets in $ millions).

Compensation	ROA	Return	Total Assets
16.58	2.53	−0.15	20917.5
26.92	1.27	0.57	32659.5
⋮	⋮	⋮	⋮
2.3	0.45	0.75	44875.0

Source: SEC website and Compustat.

   a. Estimate three simple linear regression models that use Compensation as the response variable with ROA, Return, or Total Assets as the explanatory variable. Which model do you select? Explain.

   b. Estimate multiple linear regression models that use various combinations of two, or all three, explanatory variables. Which model do you select? Explain.

WRITING WITH STATISTICS

©Kick Images/Getty Images

Matthew Farnham is an investment consultant who always recommends a well-diversified portfolio of mutual funds to his clients. He knows that a key concept in benefiting from diversification is correlation. Correlation is the extent to which assets perform in relation to one another. If all of an investor's assets move in lockstep, or are highly correlated, then the investor is either all right or all wrong. In order to reduce risk, it is considered good practice to invest in assets whose values rise and fall independently of one another. Matthew is approached by a client who has already invested in Vanguard's 500 Index Fund—a fund that mimics the Standard & Poor's 500 Index. She seeks advice for choosing her next investment from one of the following Vanguard funds:

- Inflation-Protected Securities Index
- Intermediate-Term Bond Index
- Real Estate Investment Trust Index
- Small Cap Index

Matthew collects 10 years of monthly return data for each mutual fund for the analysis. A portion of the data is shown in Table 14.8.

TABLE 14.8 Monthly Return Data for Five Mutual Funds, January 2001–December 2010

FILE
Vanguard_Funds

	500 Index	Inflation-Protected Securities	Intermediate-Term Bond	Real Estate	Small Cap
January 2001	0.0342	0.0205	0.0181	0.0044	0.0527
February 2001	−0.1007	0.0161	0.0129	−0.0175	−0.0658
⋮	⋮	⋮	⋮	⋮	⋮
December 2010	0.0585	−0.0284	−0.0320	0.0355	0.0663

Source: finance.yahoo.com; data retrieved January 4, 2011.

Matthew would like to use the sample information in Table 14.8 to

1. Calculate and interpret the sample correlation coefficient of each fund with Vanguard's 500 Index.

2. Make a recommendation for a mutual fund that is not correlated with Vanguard's 500 Index.

In attempting to create a well-diversified portfolio, an analysis of the correlation between the assets' returns is crucial. The correlation coefficient measures the direction and the strength of the linear relationship between the assets' returns. This statistic can aid in the hunt for assets to consider when forming a portfolio. An investor has already chosen Vanguard's 500 Index mutual fund as part of her portfolio. When choosing to add to her portfolio, she considers these four mutual funds from the Vanguard family:

- Inflation-Protected Securities Index
- Intermediate-Term Bond Index
- Real Estate Investment Trust Index
- Small Cap Index

Ten years of monthly return data for each of these prospective funds, as well as the 500 Index, are collected. The first row of Table 14.A shows the sample correlation coefficients between the 500 Index and each mutual fund.

TABLE 14.A Analysis of Correlations between the 500 Index and Each Mutual Fund

	Inflation-Protected Securities	Intermediate-Term Bond	Real Estate	Small Cap
Correlation Coefficient	0.0796	−0.0408	0.6630	0.9030
Test Statistic	0.868	−0.444	9.621	2.835
p-value	0.387	0.658	0.000	0.000

The correlation coefficient always assumes a value between −1 and 1; an absolute value close to 1 implies that the two assets move in sync. In this sample, the highest sample correlation coefficient is between the 500 Index and the Small Cap Index, with a value of 0.9030. Next on the list is the correlation coefficient 0.6630 between the 500 Index and the Real Estate Index. Investors often choose to invest across a range of asset classes that earn respectable returns but are relatively uncorrelated. This way, if one asset in a portfolio suffers, the rest may be unaffected. Given that the Inflation-Protected Securities Index and the Intermediate-Term Bond Index have correlation coefficients close to zero, these may prove to be desirable additions to the investor's portfolio.

A hypothesis test is conducted to determine whether the fund returns are correlated at the 5% significance level. The null hypothesis is that the returns are uncorrelated and the alternative hypothesis suggests either a positive or a negative correlation. Rows 2 and 3 of Table 14.A show the value of the test statistics and the corresponding p-values. For instance, given a p-value of 0.387, the correlation coefficient between the 500 Index and the Inflation-Protected Securities Index is not different from zero at the 5% significance level. This same conclusion holds for the correlation coefficient between the 500 Index and the Intermediate-Term Bond Index. On the other hand, given p-values of 0.000 for both of the test statistics associated with the correlation coefficient between the 500 Index and the Real Estate Index and the 500 Index and the Small Cap Index, we can conclude that the returns of these funds are correlated with the returns of the 500 Index fund.

Assuming that the correlation between assets is likely to remain stable in the future, then it appears that the investor should add either the Inflation-Protected Securities Index or the Intermediate Bond Index to her portfolio. Compared to the other two funds, these funds would offer the maximum benefit from diversification in the sense of reducing volatility.

Sample Report– Making Investment Decisions by Diversifying

CONCEPTUAL REVIEW

LO 14.1 **Conduct a hypothesis test for the population correlation coefficient.**

The **sample correlation coefficient** r_{xy} is a unit-free measure that gauges both the direction and the strength of the linear relationship between two variables x and y; its value falls between -1 and 1. We calculate the sample correlation coefficient as $r_{xy} = \frac{s_{xy}}{s_x s_y}$, where s_{xy} is the sample covariance, and s_x and s_y are the sample standard deviations of x and y, respectively.

When conducting tests concerning the population correlation coefficient ρ_{xy}, the value of the test statistic is calculated as $t_{df} = \dfrac{r_{xy}\sqrt{n-2}}{\sqrt{1-r_{xy}^2}}$, where n is the sample size and $df = n - 2$.

LO 14.2 **Discuss the limitations of correlation analysis.**

There are several limitations to correlation analysis. These include: (1) two variables may have a very low correlation coefficient, yet a strong *nonlinear* relation; (2) the existence of *outliers* may blur the interpretation of the correlation coefficient; and (3) *spurious correlation* can make two variables appear closely related when no causal relationship exists.

LO 14.3 **Estimate and interpret the simple linear regression model.**

Regression analysis explicitly assumes that one variable, called the **response variable**, is influenced by other variables, called the **explanatory variables**. The **simple linear regression model** uses only one explanatory variable to predict and/or describe changes in the response variable. The model is expressed as $y = \beta_0 + \beta_1 x + \varepsilon$, where y and x are the response variable and the explanatory variable, respectively, and ε is the random error term. The coefficients β_0 and β_1 are the unknown parameters to be estimated.

We apply the **ordinary least squares (OLS)** method to find a sample regression equation $\hat{y} = b_0 + b_1 x$, where $\hat{y}$ is the predicted value of the response variable and b_0 and b_1 are the estimates of β_0 and β_1, respectively. The estimated slope coefficient b_1 represents the change in $\hat{y}$ when x changes by one unit. The units of b_1 are the same as those of y.

LO 14.4 **Estimate and interpret the multiple linear regression model.**

The **multiple linear regression model** allows more than one explanatory variable to be linearly related with the response variable y. It is defined as $y = \beta_0 + \beta_1 x_1 + \beta_2 x_2 + \cdots + \beta_k x_k + \varepsilon$, where y is the response variable, $x_1, x_2, \ldots, x_k$ are the k explanatory variables, and ε is the random error term. The coefficients $\beta_0, \beta_1, \ldots, \beta_k$ are the unknown parameters to be estimated. We again use the OLS method to arrive at the following sample regression equation: $\hat{y} = b_0 + b_1 x_1 + b_2 x_2 + \cdots + b_k x_k$, where b_0, $b_1, \ldots, b_k$ are the estimates of $\beta_0, \beta_1, \ldots, \beta_k$, respectively.

For each explanatory variable x_j ($j = 1, \ldots, k$), the corresponding slope coefficient b_j is the estimated regression coefficient. It measures the change in the predicted value of the response variable $\hat{y}$, given a unit increase in the associated explanatory variable x_j, *holding all other explanatory variables constant*. In other words, it represents the partial influence of x_j on $\hat{y}$.

LO 14.5 **Interpret the standard error of the estimate.**

The **standard error of the estimate** s_e is the standard deviation of the residual and is calculated as $s_e = \sqrt{\dfrac{SSE}{n-k-1}}$, where SSE is the error sum of squares. Theoretically,

s_e can assume any value between zero and infinity, $0 \leq s_e < \infty$; the closer s_e is to zero, the better the model fits the sample data. Since s_e has no predetermined upper limit, it is difficult to interpret it in isolation. The standard error of the estimate is a useful goodness-of-fit measure when comparing models; the model with the smaller s_e provides the better fit.

LO 14.6 Interpret the coefficient of determination, R^2.

The **coefficient of determination R^2** is the proportion of the sample variation in the response variable that is explained by the sample regression equation. It falls between 0 and 1; the closer the value is to 1, the better the model fits the sample data.

We compute the coefficient of determination as $R^2 = SSR/SST = 1 - \frac{SSE}{SST}$, where SSR is the regression sum of squares, SSE is the error sum of squares, and SST is the total sum of squares. Alternatively, we can compute it as $R^2 = r_{y\hat{y}}^2$, where $r_{y\hat{y}}$ is the sample correlation coefficient between y and $\hat{y}$.

LO 14.7 Differentiate between R^2 and adjusted R^2.

Adjusted R^2 adjusts R^2 by accounting for the number of explanatory variables k used in the regression. It is calculated as adjusted $R^2 = 1 - (1 - R^2)\left(\frac{n-1}{n-k-1}\right)$. In comparing competing models with different numbers of explanatory variables, the preferred model will have the highest adjusted R^2.

ADDITIONAL EXERCISES AND CASE STUDIES

59. **FILE** *Energy_Health.* The following table shows a portion of the monthly returns data (in percent) for 2010–2016 for two of Vanguard's mutual funds: the Vanguard Energy Fund and the Vanguard Healthcare Fund.

Date	Energy	Healthcare
Jan-10	−4.86	−0.13
Feb-10	1.50	0.58
⋮	⋮	⋮
Dec-16	−0.30	−5.26

Source: www.finance.yahoo.com.

a. Calculate and interpret the sample correlation coefficient r_{xy}.
b. Specify the competing hypotheses in order to determine whether the population correlation coefficient is different from zero.
c. At the 5% significance level, what is the conclusion to the test? Are the returns on the mutual funds correlated?

60. **FILE** *Yields.* In response to the Great Recession, Federal Reserve leaders continue to keep the short-run target interest rate near zero. While the Fed controls short-term interest rates, long-term interest rates essentially depend on supply and

demand dynamics, as well as longer-term interest rate expectations. For the 2001–2010 period, the accompanying table shows a portion of data for the annualized rates for the 10-year Treasury yield (in %) and the 3-month Treasury yield (in %).

Year	10-Year Yield	3-Month Yield
2001	5.02	3.47
2002	4.61	1.63
⋮	⋮	⋮
2010	3.21	0.14

Source: Federal Reserve Bank of Dallas.

a. Construct and interpret a scatterplot of the 10-year treasury yield against the 3-month yield.
b. Calculate and interpret the sample correlation coefficient. Use $\alpha = 0.05$ to test if the population correlation coefficient is different from zero.
c. Estimate and interpret a sample regression equation using the 10-year yield as the response variable and the 3-month yield as the explanatory variable.

61. **FILE** *Home_Ownership.* The homeownership rate in the U.S. was 67.4% in 2009. In order to determine if homeownership is linked with income, 2009 state-level data on the homeownership rate (Ownership

in %) and median household income (Income in $) were collected. A portion of the data is shown in the accompanying table.

State	Ownership	Income
Alabama	74.1	39980
Alaska	66.8	61604
⋮	⋮	⋮
Wyoming	73.8	52470

Source: www.census.gov.

a. Estimate and interpret the model: Ownership = $\beta_0 + \beta_1 \text{Income} + \varepsilon$.
b. What is the standard error of the estimate?
c. Interpret the coefficient of determination.

62. **FILE** *Dow_2010.* A research analyst is trying to determine whether a firm's price-earnings (P/E) and price-sales (P/S) ratios can explain the firm's stock performance over the past year. A P/E ratio is calculated as a firm's share price compared to the income or profit earned by the firm per share. Generally, a high P/E ratio suggests that investors are expecting higher earnings growth in the future compared to companies with a lower P/E ratio. The P/S ratio is calculated by dividing a firm's share price by the firm's revenue per share for the trailing 12 months. In short, investors can use the P/S ratio to determine how much they are paying for a dollar of the firm's sales rather than a dollar of its earnings (P/E ratio). In general, the lower the P/S ratio, the more attractive the investment. The accompanying table shows the year-to-date returns (Return in %) and the P/E and P/S ratios for a portion of the 30 firms included in the Dow Jones Industrial Average.

Return	P/E	P/S
4.4	14.37	2.41
−4.5	11.01	0.78
⋮	⋮	⋮
16.3	13.94	1.94

Source: The 2010 returns (January 1, 2010–December 31, 2010) were obtained from *The Wall Street Journal,* January 3, 2010; the P/E ratios and the P/S ratios were obtained from finance.yahoo.com on January 20, 2011.

a. Estimate: Return = $\beta_0 + \beta_1 \text{P/E} + \beta_2 \text{P/S} + \varepsilon$. Are the signs on the coefficients as expected? Explain.
b. Interpret the slope coefficient of the P/S ratio.
c. What is the predicted return for a firm with a P/E ratio of 10 and a P/S ratio of 2?
d. What is the standard error of the estimate?
e. Interpret R^2.

63. **FILE** *SAT.* There has been a lot of discussion regarding the relationship between Scholastic Aptitude Test (SAT) scores and test-takers' family income (*The New York Times,* August 27, 2009). It is generally believed that the wealthier a student's family, the higher the SAT score. Another commonly used predictor for SAT scores is the student's grade point average (GPA). Consider the following portion of data collected on 24 students.

SAT	Income	GPA
1651	47000	2.79
1581	34000	2.97
⋮	⋮	⋮
1940	113000	3.96

a. Estimate three models:
   (i) SAT = $\beta_0 + \beta_1 \text{Income} + \varepsilon$,
   (ii) SAT = $\beta_0 + \beta_1 \text{GPA} + \varepsilon$, and
   (iii) SAT = $\beta_0 + \beta_1 \text{Income} + \beta_2 \text{GPA} + \varepsilon$.
b. Use goodness-of-fit measures to select the best-fitting model.
c. Use the preferred model to predict SAT given the mean value of the explanatory variable(s).

64. **FILE** *Startups.* Many of today's leading companies, including Google, Microsoft, and Facebook, are based on technologies developed within universities. Lisa Fisher is a business school professor who would like to analyze university factors that enhance innovation. She collects data on 143 universities in 2008 for a regression where the response variable is the number of startups (Startups), which is used as a measure for innovation. The explanatory variables include the university's research expenditure (Research in $ millions), the number of patents issued (Patents), and the age of its technology transfer office (Duration in years). A portion of the data is shown in the accompanying table.

Startups	Research	Patents	Duration
1	145.52	8	23
1	237.52	16	23
⋮	⋮	⋮	⋮
1	154.38	3	9

Source: Association of University Managers and National Science Foundation.

a. Estimate: Startups = $\beta_0 + \beta_1 \text{Research} + \beta_2 \text{Patents} + \beta_3 \text{Duration} + \varepsilon$.
b. Predict the number of startups for a university that spent $120 million on research, that was

issued 8 patents, and has had a technology transfer office for 20 years.

c. How much more research expenditure is needed for the university to have an additional predicted startup, with everything else being the same?

Wage	EDUC	EXPER	AGE	Male
37.85	11	2	40	1
21.72	4	1	39	0
⋮	⋮	⋮	⋮	⋮
24.18	8	11	64	0

65. **FILE** *Wage.* A researcher interviews 50 employees of a large manufacturer and collects data on each worker's hourly wage (Wage in $), years of higher education (EDUC), years of experience (EXPER), and age (AGE). A portion of the data is shown in the accompanying table (Note: You do not need the variable Male in this problem).

a. Estimate: $Wage = \beta_0 + \beta_1 EDUC + \beta_2 EXPER + \beta_3 AGE + \varepsilon$.
b. Are the signs as expected?
c. Interpret the coefficient of EDUC.
d. Interpret the coefficient of determination.
e. Predict the hourly wage of a 40-year-old employee who has 5 years of higher education and 8 years of experience.

CASE STUDIES

CASE STUDY 14.1   A local university offers its employees the following Fidelity investment products for their retirement plans:

- Fidelity Total Bond Fund
- Fidelity Short-Term Bond Fund
- Fidelity Magellan Fund
- Fidelity International Small Cap Fund
- Fidelity Freedom Income Fund

After working at the university for a year, Minori Vardan is now eligible to participate in the retirement plan. She has already decided to invest a portion of her retirement funds in the Magellan fund. She would like to choose one other fund that has the smallest correlation, preferably zero, with the Magellan fund. She collects 5 years of monthly return data for each mutual fund, a portion of which is shown in the accompanying table.

Data for Case Study 14.1 Monthly Return Data for Five Mutual Funds

Fidelity_Retirement

	Magellan	Total Bond	Short-Term Bond	Int'l Small Cap	Freedom Income
January 2006	0.0477	0.0026	0.0013	0.0904	0.0107
February 2006	−0.0149	0.0026	0.0027	−0.0152	0.0000
⋮	⋮	⋮	⋮	⋮	⋮
December 2010	0.0586	−0.0183	−0.0035	0.0478	0.0036

Source: finance.yahoo.com; data retrieved January 6, 2011.

In a report, use the sample information to

1. Calculate and interpret the sample correlation coefficient of each fund with Magellan.
2. Discuss the statistical significance of the correlation coefficients.
3. Make an investment recommendation for Minori.

CASE STUDY 14.2 Akiko Hamaguchi, the manager at a small sushi restaurant in Phoenix, Arizona, is concerned that the weak economic environment has hampered foot traffic in her area, thus causing a dramatic decline in sales. Her cousin in San Francisco, Hiroshi Sato, owns a similar restaurant, but he has seemed to prosper during these rough economic times. Hiroshi agrees that higher unemployment rates have likely forced some customers to dine out less frequently, but he maintains an aggressive marketing campaign to thwart this apparent trend. For instance, he advertises in local papers with valuable two-for-one coupons and promotes early-bird specials over the airwaves. Despite the fact that advertising increases overall costs, he believes that this campaign has positively affected sales at his restaurant. In order to support his claim, Hiroshi provides his restaurant's monthly sales (in $1,000s) and advertising costs (in $), as well as the monthly unemployment rate (in %) from San Francisco County. A portion of the data is shown in the accompanying table.

Data for Case Study 14.2 Hiroshi's Sales, Advertising Costs, and Unemployment Data

Month	Year	Sales	Advertising Costs	Unemployment Rate
January	2006	27.0	550	4.6
February	2008	24.2	425	4.3
⋮	⋮	⋮	⋮	⋮
May	2009	27.4	550	9.1

Source for unemployment rate data: Development Department, State of California, June 2009.

In a report, use the sample information to

1. Estimate a simple regression model, $\text{Sales} = \beta_0 + \beta_1 \text{Advertising} + \varepsilon$, as well as a multiple regression model, $\text{Sales} = \beta_0 + \beta_1 \text{Advertising} + \beta_2 \text{Unemployment} + \varepsilon$.
2. Show that the multiple regression model is more appropriate for making predictions.
3. Make predictions for sales with an unemployment rate of 6% and advertising costs of $400 and $600.

CASE STUDY 14.3 Megan Hanson, a realtor in Brownsburg, Indiana, would like to use estimates from a multiple regression model to help prospective sellers determine a reasonable asking price for their homes. She believes that the following four factors influence the asking price (Price) of a house: (1) the square footage of the house (SQFT), (2) the number of bedrooms (Bed), (3) the number of bathrooms (Bath), and (4) the lot size (LTSZ) in acres. She randomly collects online listings for 50 single-family homes. A portion of the data is presented in the accompanying table.

Data for Case Study 14.3 Real Estate Data for Brownsburg, Indiana

Price	SQFT	Bed	Bath	LTSZ
399900	5026	4	4.5	0.3
375000	3200	4	3	5
⋮	⋮	⋮	⋮	⋮
102900	1938	3	1	0.1

Source: *Indianapolis Star*, February 27, 2008.

In a report, use the sample information to

1. Provide summary statistics on the asking price, square footage, the number of bedrooms, the number of bathrooms, and the lot size.
2. Estimate and interpret a multiple regression model where the asking price is the response variable and the other four factors are the explanatory variables.
3. Interpret the resulting coefficient of determination.

APPENDIX 14.1   Guidelines for Other Software Packages

The following section provides brief commands for specific software packages: Minitab, SPSS, and JMP. Copy and paste the specified data file into the relevant software spreadsheet prior to following the commands.

Minitab

Simple Linear Regression

(Replicating Example 14.2) From the menu, choose **Stat > Regression > Regression > Fit Regression Model**. Select Debt for **Responses**, and select Income for **Continuous predictors**.

Multiple Regression

(Replicating Example 14.3) From the menu, choose **Stat > Regression > Regression > Fit Regression Model**. Select Debt for **Responses**, and select Income and Unemployment for **Continuous predictors**.

SPSS

Simple Linear Regression

(Replicating Example 14.2) From the menu, choose **Analyze > Regression-Linear**. Select Debt as **Dependent**, and Income as **Independent(s)**.

FILE
Debt_Payments

Multiple Regression

(Replicating Example 14.3) From the menu, choose **Analyze > Regression-Linear**. Select Debt as **Dependent**, and Income and Unemployment as **Independent(s)**.

JMP

Simple Linear Regression

A. (Replicating Example 14.2) From the menu, choose **Analyze > Fit Y by X**. Select Debt as **Y, Response**, and select Income as **X, Factor**.

FILE
Debt_Payments

B. Click on the red triangle next to the header that reads **Bivariate Fit of Debt by Income** and select **Fit line**.

Multiple Regression

(Replicating Example 14.3) From the menu, choose **Analyze > Fit Model**. Under **Pick Role Variables**, select Debt, and under **Construct Model Effects**, select Income and Unemployment, and choose **Add**.

15 Inference with Regression Models

n Chapter 14, we employed simple and multiple linear regression models to capture a relationship between a response variable and one or more explanatory variables. We also studied goodness-of-fit measures that assess how well the sample regression equation fits the data. While the estimated regression models and goodness-of-fit measures are useful, it is not clear if the relationships inferred from the estimated coefficients are real or due to chance. In this chapter, we focus on statistical inference with regression models. In particular, we develop hypothesis tests that enable us to determine the individual and joint significance of the explanatory variables. We also develop interval estimates for a prediction from the sample regression equation. Finally, we examine the importance of the assumptions on the statistical properties of the ordinary least squares (OLS) estimator, as well as the validity of the testing procedures. We address common violations to the model assumptions, the consequences when these assumptions are violated, and offer some remedial measures.

©Rob Tringali/MLB Photos via Getty Images

INTRODUCTORY CASE

Analyzing the Winning Percentage in Baseball

On a recent radio talk show, two sports analysts quarreled over which statistic was a better predictor of a Major League Baseball team's winning percentage (Win). One argued that the team's batting average (BA) was a better predictor of a team's success since the team with the higher batting average has won approximately 75% of the World Series contests. The other insisted that a team's pitching is clearly the main factor in determining wins—the lower a team's earned run average (ERA), the higher the team's winning percentage. In order to determine if these claims are backed by the data, relevant information is collected for the 14 American League (AL) and 16 National League (NL) teams during the regular season of 2010. A portion of the data is shown in Table 15.1.

TABLE 15.1 Winning Percentage, Batting Average, and Earned Run Average in Baseball

FILE
Baseball

Team	League	Win	BA	ERA
Baltimore Orioles	AL	0.407	0.259	4.59
Boston Red Sox	AL	0.549	0.268	4.20
⋮	⋮	⋮	⋮	⋮
Washington Nationals	NL	0.426	0.250	4.13

Source: mlb.mlb.com.

Use the sample information to

1. Employ goodness-of-fit measures to determine the best-fitting regression model for the winning percentage.
2. Determine the statistical significance of the batting average and earned run average variables.

A synopsis of this case is provided at the end of Section 15.1.

In this section we continue to assess linear regression models. We first revisit goodness-of-fit measures, and then we turn our attention to hypothesis testing about the unknown parameters (coefficients) $\beta_0, \beta_1, \ldots, \beta_k$. In particular, we test for the individual and joint significance of the regression coefficients to determine whether there is evidence of a linear relationship between the response and the explanatory variables. We note that for the tests to be valid, the ordinary least squares (OLS) estimators $b_0, b_1, \ldots, b_k$ must be normally distributed. This condition is satisfied if the random error term, ε, is normally distributed. If we cannot assume the normality of ε, then the tests are valid only for large sample sizes. We discuss the underlying assumptions of the linear regression model in Section 15.4.

The objective outlined in the introductory case study is to predict a baseball team's winning percentage, denoted Win, either on the basis of its batting average BA or its earned run average ERA, or jointly by BA and ERA. For those readers who do not follow baseball, BA is a ratio of hits divided by times at bat, and ERA is the average number of earned runs given up by a pitcher per nine innings pitched. A priori, we expect that a higher BA positively influences a team's winning percentage, while a higher ERA negatively affects a team's winning percentage. We define

Model 1 as Win $= \beta_0 + \beta_1 BA + \varepsilon$,

Model 2 as Win $= \beta_0 + \beta_1 ERA + \varepsilon$, and

Model 3 as Win $= \beta_0 + \beta_1 BA + \beta_2 ERA + \varepsilon$.

Before we develop the tests of significance, we will use goodness-of-fit measures discussed in Chapter 14 to choose the appropriate model. Table 15.2 shows the relevant goodness-of-fit measures for the three models; we advise you to replicate these results using the sample data in Table 15.1.

TABLE 15.2 Goodness-of-Fit Measures for the Models

	Model 1	Model 2	Model 3
R Square	0.2112	0.4656	0.7156
Adjusted R Square	0.1830	0.4465	0.6945
Standard Error	0.0614	0.0505	0.0375

We choose Model 3 to predict the winning percentage because it has the lowest standard error of the estimate and the highest adjusted R^2. Remember, we cannot compare these models on the basis of R^2, because Models 1 and 2 use only one explanatory variable, whereas Model 3 uses two.

Test of Individual Significance

LO **15.1**

Conduct a test of individual significance.

A **test of individual significance** can be implemented in the context of the simple and the multiple regression models. Consider the following multiple regression model, which links the response variable y with k explanatory variables $x_1, x_2, \ldots, x_k$:

$$y = \beta_0 + \beta_1 x_1 + \beta_2 x_2 + \cdots + \beta_k x_k + \varepsilon.$$

If the slope coefficient β_j equals zero, then the explanatory variable x_j basically drops out of the above equation, implying that x_j does not influence y. In other words, if β_j equals zero, there is no linear relationship between x_j and y. Conversely, if β_j does not equal zero, then x_j influences y.

Following the hypothesis testing methodology introduced in earlier chapters, we want to test whether the population coefficient β_j is different from, greater than, or less than β_{j0}, where β_{j0} is the hypothesized value of β_j. That is, the competing hypotheses take one of the following forms:

Two-Tailed Test	Right-Tailed Test	Left-Tailed Test
$H_0: \beta_j = \beta_{j0}$	$H_0: \beta_j \leq \beta_{j0}$	$H_0: \beta_j \geq \beta_{j0}$
$H_A: \beta_j \neq \beta_{j0}$	$H_A: \beta_j > \beta_{j0}$	$H_A: \beta_j < \beta_{j0}$

When testing whether x_j significantly influences y, we set $\beta_{j0} = 0$ and specify a two-tailed test as $H_0: \beta_j = 0$ and $H_A: \beta_j \neq 0$. We could easily specify one-tailed competing hypotheses for a positive linear relationship ($H_0: \beta_j \leq 0$ and $H_A: \beta_j > 0$) or a negative linear relationship ($H_0: \beta_j \geq 0$ and $H_A: \beta_j < 0$).

Although tests of significance are commonly based on $\beta_{j0} = 0$, in some situations we might wish to determine whether the slope coefficient differs from a nonzero value. For instance, if we are analyzing the relationship between students' exam scores on the basis of hours studied, we may want to determine if an extra hour of review before the exam will increase a student's score by more than 5 points. Here, we formulate the hypotheses as $H_0: \beta_j \leq 5$ and $H_A: \beta_j > 5$; in this example, $\beta_{j0} = 5$. Finally, although in most applications we are interested in conducting hypothesis tests on the slope coefficient(s), there are instances where we may also be interested in testing the intercept, β_0. The testing framework for the intercept remains the same; that is, if we want to test whether the intercept differs from zero, we specify the competing hypotheses as $H_0: \beta_0 = 0$ and $H_A: \beta_0 \neq 0$.

As in all hypothesis tests, the next essential piece of information is how we define the appropriate test statistic.

TEST STATISTIC FOR THE TEST OF INDIVIDUAL SIGNIFICANCE

The value of the test statistic for a test of individual significance is calculated as

$$t_{df} = \frac{b_j - \beta_{j0}}{se(b_j)},$$

where $df = n - k - 1$, n is the sample size, k is the number of explanatory variables, b_j is the estimate for β_j, $se(b_j)$ is the standard error of the estimator b_j, and β_{j0} is the hypothesized value of β_j. If $\beta_{j0} = 0$, the value of the test statistic reduces to $t_{df} = \frac{b_j}{se(b_j)}$.

As mentioned earlier, tests of significance can be implemented in the context of the simple and the multiple regression models. In Example 15.1 and Example 15.2, the tests are based on the multiple regression model; Example 15.3 uses the simple regression model for the test.

EXAMPLE 15.1

Let's revisit Model 3, Win $= \beta_0 + \beta_1 BA + \beta_2 ERA + \varepsilon$, estimated with the sample data in Table 15.1. We reproduce a portion of the regression results in Table 15.3. Conduct a hypothesis test to determine whether batting average influences winning percentage at the 5% significance level.

TABLE 15.3 Portion of Regression Results for Model 3: Win $= \beta_0 + \beta_1 BA + \beta_2 ERA + \varepsilon$

	Coefficients	Standard Error	t Stat	p-value	Lower 95%	Upper 95%
Intercept	0.1269	0.1822	0.696	0.492	−0.2470	0.5008
BA	3.2754	0.6723	4.872	0.000	1.8960	4.6549
ERA	−0.1153	0.0167	−6.920	0.000	−0.1494	−0.0811

Using a Confidence Interval to Determine Individual Significance

In earlier chapters, we constructed a confidence interval to conduct a two-tailed hypothesis test. When assessing whether the regression coefficient differs from zero, we can apply the same methodology.

CONFIDENCE INTERVAL FOR β_j

A $100(1 - \alpha)\%$ confidence interval for the regression coefficient β_j is computed as

$$b_j \pm t_{\alpha/2, df} se(b_j) \quad \text{or} \quad [b_j - t_{\alpha/2, df} se(b_j), \, b_j + t_{\alpha/2, df} se(b_j)],$$

where $se(b_j)$ is the standard error of b_j and $df = n - k - 1$.

Excel automatically provides a 95% confidence interval for the regression coefficients; it will provide other levels if prompted. In R, we can easily obtain confidence intervals for the regression coefficients using the **confint** function. As explained in Chapter 14, if we have estimated Model 3 by constructing an object labeled Multiple, then at the prompt sign we would enter "confint(Multiple, level = 0.95)"; R would return 95% confidence intervals for all regression coefficients. In general, if the confidence interval for the slope coefficient contains the value zero, then the explanatory variable associated with the regression coefficient is not significant. Conversely, if the confidence interval does not contain the value zero, then the explanatory variable associated with the regression coefficient is statistically significant. The next example is based on the confidence interval approach.

EXAMPLE 15.2

Let's revisit Model 3 with a portion of the regression results in Table 15.3. Construct the 95% confidence interval to determine whether earned run average is significant in explaining winning percentage.

SOLUTION: For testing whether earned run average is statistically significant, we set up the following competing hypotheses:

$$H_0: \beta_2 = 0$$
$$H_A: \beta_2 \neq 0$$

For the 95% confidence interval, $\alpha = 0.05$ and $\alpha/2 = 0.025$. With $n = 30$ and $k = 2$, we use $df = 30 - 2 - 1 = 27$ and reference the t table to find $t_{\alpha/2,df} = t_{0.025,27} = 2.052$. Given $b_2 = -0.1153$ and $se(b_2) = 0.0167$ (from Table 15.3), the 95% confidence interval for the population coefficient β_2 is

$$b_2 \pm t_{\alpha/2,df} se(b_2) = -0.1153 \pm 2.052 \times 0.0167 = -0.1153 \pm 0.0343.$$

Thus, the lower and upper limits of the confidence interval are -0.1496 and -0.0810, respectively. Note that Table 15.3 also provides these values. (Slight differences are due to rounding.) Since the 95% confidence interval does not contain the value zero, we can conclude that earned run average is significant in explaining the winning percentage at $\alpha = 0.05$.

So far, we have only considered examples of two-tailed tests to determine if a regression coefficient differs from zero. As mentioned earlier, for such standard cases, we can use the computer-generated value of the test statistic as well as the corresponding p-value. For a one-tailed test with $\beta_{j0} = 0$, the value of the test statistic is valid, but the p-value is not; in most cases, the computer-generated p-value must be divided in half. For a one- or two-tailed test to determine if the regression coefficient differs from a nonzero value, both the computer-generated value of the test statistic and the p-value become invalid. These facts are summarized below.

COMPUTER-GENERATED TEST STATISTIC AND THE P-VALUE

Excel, R, and virtually all other statistical computer packages report a value of the test statistic and its associated p-value for a two-tailed test that assesses whether the regression coefficient differs from zero.

- If we specify a one-tailed test, then we need to divide the computer-generated p-value in half.

- If we test whether the coefficient differs from a nonzero value, then we cannot use the value of the computer-generated test statistic and its p-value.

We would also like to point out that for a one-tailed test with $\beta_{j0} = 0$, there are rare instances when the computer-generated p-value is invalid. This occurs when the sign of b_j (and the value of the accompanying test statistic) is not inconsistent with the null hypothesis. For example, for a right-tailed test, $H_0: \beta_j \leq 0$ and $H_A: \beta_j > 0$, the null hypothesis cannot be rejected if the estimate b_j (and the value of the accompanying test statistic t_{df}) is negative. Similarly, no further testing is necessary if $b_j > 0$ (and thus $t_{df} > 0$) for a left-tailed test.

A Test for a Nonzero Slope Coefficient

In Examples 15.1 and 15.2, the null hypothesis included a zero value for the slope coefficient; that is, $\beta_{j0} = 0$. We now motivate a test where the hypothesized value is not zero by using a renowned financial application—the **capital asset pricing model (CAPM)**.

Let R represent the return on a stock or portfolio of interest. Given the market return R_M and the risk-free return R_f, the CAPM expresses the risk-adjusted return of an asset, $R - R_f$, as a function of the risk-adjusted market return, $R_M - R_f$. It is common to use the return of the S&P 500 index for R_M and the return on a Treasury bill for R_f. For empirical estimation, we express the CAPM as

$$R - R_f = \alpha + \beta(R_M - R_f) + \varepsilon.$$

We can rewrite the model as $y = \alpha + \beta x + \varepsilon$, where $y = R - R_f$ and $x = R_M - R_f$. Note that this is essentially a simple linear regression model that uses α and β, in place of the usual β_0 and β_1, to represent the intercept and the slope coefficients, respectively. The slope coefficient β, called the stock's **beta**, measures how sensitive the stock's return is to changes in the level of the overall market. When β equals 1, any change in the market return leads to an identical change in the given stock return. A stock for which $\beta > 1$ is considered more "aggressive" or riskier than the market, whereas one for which $\beta < 1$ is considered "conservative" or less risky. We also give importance to the intercept coefficient α, called the stock's **alpha**. The CAPM theory predicts α to be zero, and thus a nonzero estimate indicates abnormal returns. Abnormal returns are positive when $\alpha > 0$ and negative when $\alpha < 0$.

EXAMPLE 15.3

Johnson & Johnson (J&J) was founded more than 120 years ago on the premise that doctors and nurses should use sterile products to treat people's wounds. Since that time, J&J products have become staples in most people's homes. Consider the CAPM where the J&J risk-adjusted stock return $R - R_f$ is used as the response variable and the risk-adjusted market return $R_M - R_f$ is used as the explanatory variable. A portion of 60 months of data is shown in Table 15.4.

TABLE 15.4 Risk-Adjusted Stock Return of J&J and Market Return

Date	$R - R_f$	$R_M - R_f$
1/1/2006	−4.59	2.21
2/1/2006	0.39	−0.31
⋮	⋮	⋮
12/1/2010	0.48	2.15

Source: finance.yahoo.com and U.S. Treasury.

a. Since consumer staples comprise many of the products sold by J&J, its stock is often considered less risky; that is, people need these products whether the economy is good or bad. At the 5% significance level, is the beta coefficient less than one?

b. At the 5% significance level, are there abnormal returns? In other words, is the alpha coefficient significantly different from zero?

SOLUTION: Using the CAPM notation, we estimate the model, $R - R_f = \alpha + \beta(R_M - R_f) + \varepsilon$; the relevant portion of the regression output is presented in Table 15.5.

TABLE 15.5 Portion of CAPM Regression Results for J&J

	Coefficients	Standard Error	t Stat	p-value
Intercept	0.2666	0.4051	0.658	0.513
$R_M - R_f$	0.5844	0.0803	7.276	0.000

a. The estimate for the beta coefficient is 0.5844 and its standard error is 0.0803. Interestingly, our estimate is identical to the beta reported in the popular press (www.dailyfinance.com, March 4, 2011). In order to determine whether the beta coefficient is significantly less than one, we formulate the hypotheses as

$$H_0: \beta \geq 1$$
$$H_A: \beta < 1$$

Given 60 data points, $df = n - k - 1 = 60 - 1 - 1 = 58$. We cannot use the test statistic value reported in Table 15.5, since the hypothesized value of β is not zero. We calculate the value of the test statistic as $t_{58} = \frac{b_j - \beta_{j0}}{se(b_j)} = \frac{0.5844 - 1}{0.0803} = -5.176$. We can use the t table to approximate the p-value, $P(T_{58} \leq -5.176)$, as a value that is less than 0.005. Using statistical software, we find that the exact p-value is approximately zero. Since the p-value $< \alpha = 0.05$, we reject H_0 and conclude that β is significantly less than one; that is, the return on J&J stock is less risky than the return on the market.

b. Abnormal returns exist when α is significantly different from zero. Thus, the competing hypotheses are $H_0: \alpha = 0$ versus $H_A: \alpha \neq 0$. Since it is a standard case, where the hypothesized value of the coefficient is zero, we can use the reported test statistic value of 0.658 with an associated p-value of 0.513. We cannot reject H_0 at any reasonable level of significance. Therefore, we cannot conclude that there are abnormal returns for J&J stock.

Test of Joint Significance

LO 15.2

Conduct a test of joint significance.

So far, we have considered a test of individual significance. For instance, we used a t-test to determine whether the batting average has a statistically significant influence on the winning percentage. When we assess a multiple linear regression model, it is also important to conduct a **test of joint significance**. A test of joint significance is often regarded as a test of the overall usefulness of a regression. This test determines whether the explanatory variables $x_1, x_2, \ldots, x_k$ have a joint statistical influence on y.

In the null hypothesis of the test of joint significance, *all* of the slope coefficients are assumed zero. The competing hypotheses for a test of joint significance are specified as

$$H_0: \beta_1 = \beta_2 = \cdots = \beta_k = 0$$
$$H_A: \text{At least one } \beta_j \neq 0.$$

You might be tempted to implement this test by performing a series of tests of individual significance with the t statistic. However, such an option is not appropriate. The test of joint significance determines if at least one of the explanatory variables is significant. Therefore, it is not clear if one or all of the explanatory variables must be significant in order to document a joint significance. In addition, recall from the discussion of ANOVA in Chapter 13 that if we conduct many individual tests at (say) a 5% level of significance, the resulting significance level for the joint test will be greater than 5%.

> Testing a series of individual hypotheses is not equivalent to testing the same hypotheses jointly.

To conduct the test of joint significance, we employ a right-tailed F test. (Recall that the $F_{(df_1, df_2)}$ distribution was used for hypothesis testing in Chapters 11 and 13.) The test statistic measures how well the regression equation explains the variability in the response variable. It is defined as the ratio of the **mean square regression (MSR)** to the **mean square error (MSE)** where $MSR = SSR/k$ and $MSE = SSE/(n - k - 1)$. Recall from Chapter 14 that SSR is the regression sum of squares and SSE is the error sum of squares.

In general, a large value of $F_{(df_1, df_2)}$ indicates that a large portion of the sample variation in y is explained by the regression model; thus, the model is useful. A small value of $F_{(df_1, df_2)}$ implies that a large portion of the sample variation in y remains unexplained. In fact, the test of joint significance is sometimes informally referred to as the test of the significance of R^2. Note that while the test of joint significance is important for a multiple regression model, it is redundant for a simple regression model. In fact, in a simple regression model, the p-value of the F test is identical to that of the t-test; we advise you to verify this fact.

Most statistical computer packages, including Excel and R, produce an ANOVA table that decomposes the total variability of the response variable y into two components: (1) the variability explained by the regression and (2) the variability that is unexplained. In addition, the value for the $F_{(df_1, df_2)}$ test statistic and its p-value are also provided. Table 15.6 shows the general format of an ANOVA table. Excel explicitly provides an ANOVA table with its regression output, with the p-value reported under the heading *Significance F*. R provides the value for the $F_{(df_1, df_2)}$ test statistic and its p-value with its regression output, which is sufficient to conduct a test of joint significance. If we use R's **anova** function discussed in Chapter 13, R generates an ANOVA table that is even more detailed than the one provided by Excel—it breaks down the contribution of each explanatory variable in explaining the total variability in the response variable.

TABLE 15.6 General Format of an ANOVA Table for Regression

ANOVA	df	SS	MS	F	Significance F
Regression	k	SSR	$MSR = \dfrac{SSR}{k}$	$F_{(df_1, df_2)} = \dfrac{MSR}{MSE}$	$P\left(F_{(df_1, df_2)} \geq \dfrac{MSR}{MSE}\right)$
Residual	$n - k - 1$	SSE	$MSE = \dfrac{SSE}{n - k - 1}$		
Total	$n - 1$	SST			

EXAMPLE 15.4

Let's revisit Model 3, $\text{Win} = \beta_0 + \beta_1 \text{BA} + \beta_2 \text{ERA} + \varepsilon$, estimated with the sample data in Table 15.1. We reproduce the ANOVA portion of the regression results in Table 15.7. Conduct a test to determine if batting average and earned run average are jointly significant in explaining winning percentage at $\alpha = 0.05$.

TABLE 15.7 Portion of Regression Results for Model 3: $\text{Win} = \beta_0 + \beta_1 \text{BA} + \beta_2 \text{ERA} + \varepsilon$

ANOVA	df	SS	MS	F	Significance F
Regression	2	0.0958	0.0479	33.966	0.000
Residual	27	0.0381	0.0014		
Total	29	0.1338			

SOLUTION: When testing whether the explanatory variables are jointly significant in explaining winning percentage, we set up the following competing hypotheses:

$$H_0: \beta_1 = \beta_2 = 0$$
$$H_A: \text{At least one } \beta_j \neq 0.$$

Given $n = 30$ and $k = 2$, we find that $df_1 = k = 2$ and $df_2 = n - k - 1 = 27$. From Table 15.7, we find that

$$F_{(2,27)} = \frac{SSR/k}{SSE/(n-k-1)} = \frac{MSR}{MSE} = \frac{0.0958/2}{0.0381/(30-2-1)} = \frac{0.0479}{0.0014} = 34.214$$

Note that the computer-generated value of the test statistic is reported as 33.966; manual calculations differ slightly due to rounding. The p-value, $P(F_{(2,27)} \geq 33.966)$, is equal to 0.000. Since the p-value is less than $\alpha = 0.05$, we reject H_0. At the 5% significance level, batting average and earned run average are jointly significant in explaining winning percentage. The result is not surprising since both BA and ERA were found to be individually significant in Examples 15.1 and 15.2. It is worth noting that sometimes we may find joint significance when only one, or sometimes even none, of the explanatory variables is individually significant.

Reporting Regression Results

Regression results are often reported in a "user-friendly" table. Table 15.8 reports the regression results for the three models that attempt to explain a baseball team's winning percentage. The explanatory variables are batting average in Model 1, earned run average in Model 2, and both batting average and earned run average in Model 3. If we were supplied with only this table, we would be able to compare these models, construct the sample regression equation of the chosen model, and perform a respectable assessment of the model with the statistics provided. Many tables contain a Notes section at the bottom explaining some of the notation. We choose to put the p-values in parentheses under all estimated coefficients; however, some researchers place the standard errors of the coefficients or the values of the test statistics in parentheses. Whichever format is chosen, it must be made clear to the reader in the Notes section.

TABLE 15.8 Estimates of the Alternative Regression Models for Explaining Winning Percentage

Variable	Model 1	Model 2	Model 3
Intercept	−0.2731 (0.342)	0.9504* (0.000)	0.1269 (0.492)
Batting Average	3.0054* (0.011)	NA	3.2754* (0.000)
Earned Run Average	NA	−0.1105* (0.000)	−0.1153* (0.000)
s_e	0.0614	0.0505	0.0375
R^2	0.2112	0.4656	0.7156
Adjusted R^2	0.1830	0.4465	0.6945
F-test (p-value)			33.966* (0.000)

Notes: Parameter estimates are in the top half of the table with the p-values in parentheses; * represents significance at the 5% level. NA denotes not applicable. The lower part of the table contains goodness-of-fit measures.

SYNOPSIS OF INTRODUCTORY CASE

©Mark Cunningham/MLB Photos via Getty Images

Two sports analysts have conflicting views over how best to predict a Major League Baseball team's winning percentage. One argues that the team's batting average is a better predictor of a team's success, since the team with the higher batting average has won approximately 75% of the World Series contests. The other analyst insists that a team's pitching is clearly the main factor in determining wins. Three regression models are used to analyze a baseball team's winning percentage (Win). The explanatory variables are batting average (BA) in Model 1, earned run average (ERA) in Model 2, and both BA and ERA in Model 3.

After estimating the models using data from 14 American League teams and 16 National League teams during the regular season of 2010, it is found that Model 2 has a lower standard error and a higher R^2 than Model 1. Therefore, if simply choosing between these two models, Model 2 appears better for prediction. However, Model 3 provides the best overall fit, as measured by its highest adjusted R^2 value. The sample regression equation for Model 3 is $\widehat{Win} = 0.13 + 3.28BA - 0.12ERA$. Further testing of this preferred model reveals that the two explanatory variables are jointly as well as individually significant in explaining the winning percentage at the 5% significance level. It appears that neither analyst is totally right or totally wrong. Given $R^2 = 0.7156$, approximately 72% of the sample variability in the winning percentage is explained by the estimated Model 3. However, 28% of the sample variability in the winning percentage remains unexplained. This is not entirely surprising, since other factors, besides batting average and earned run average, influence a baseball team's winning percentage.

EXERCISES 15.1

Mechanics

1. In a simple linear regression based on 30 observations, it is found that $b_1 = 3.25$ and $se(b_1) = 1.36$. Consider the hypotheses:

$$H_0: \beta_1 = 0 \text{ and } H_A: \beta_1 \neq 0.$$

a. Calculate the value of the test statistic.
b. Find the p-value.
c. At the 5% significance level, what is the conclusion? Is the explanatory variable statistically significant?

2. In a simple linear regression based on 25 observations, it is found that $b_1 = 0.5$ and $se(b_1) = 0.3$. Consider the hypotheses:

$$H_0: \beta_1 \leq 0 \text{ and } H_A: \beta_1 > 0.$$

a. Calculate the value of the test statistic and the p-value.
b. At the 5% significance level, what is the conclusion to the test?

3. In a simple linear regression based on 30 observations, it is found that $b_1 = 7.2$ and $se(b_1) = 1.8$. Consider the hypotheses:

$$H_0: \beta_1 \geq 10 \text{ and } H_A: \beta_1 < 10.$$

a. Calculate the value of the test statistic and the p-value.
b. At the 5% significance level, what is the conclusion to the test?

4. Consider the following regression results based on 20 observations.

	Coefficients	Standard Error	t Stat	p-value
Intercept	34.2123	4.5665	7.420	0.000
x_1	0.1223	0.1794	0.682	0.504

a. Specify the hypotheses to determine if the intercept differs from zero. Perform this test at the 5% significance level.
b. Construct the 95% confidence interval for the slope coefficient. At the 5% significance level, does the slope differ from zero? Explain.

5. Consider the following regression results based on 40 observations.

	Coefficients	Standard Error	t Stat	p-value
Intercept	43.1802	12.6963	3.401	0.002
x_1	0.9178	0.9350	0.982	0.333

a. Specify the hypotheses to determine if the slope differs from minus one.

b. Calculate the value of the test statistic and the p-value.

c. At the 5% significance level, does the slope differ from minus one? Explain.

6. When estimating a multiple linear regression model based on 30 observations, the following results were obtained.

	Coefficients	Standard Error	t Stat	p-value
Intercept	152.27	119.70	1.272	0.214
x_1	12.91	2.68	4.817	5.06E-05
x_2	2.74	2.15	1.274	0.213

a. Specify the hypotheses to determine whether x_1 is linearly related to y. At the 5% significance level, are x_1 and y linearly related?

b. What is the 95% confidence interval for β_2? Using this confidence interval, is x_2 significant in explaining y? Explain.

c. At the 5% significance level, can you conclude that β_1 is less than 20? Show the relevant steps of the hypothesis test.

7. The following ANOVA table was obtained when estimating a multiple linear regression model.

ANOVA	df	SS	MS	F	Significance F
Regression	2	22016.75	11008.375		0.0228
Residual	17	39286.93	2310.996		
Total	19	61303.68			

a. How many explanatory variables were specified in the model? How many observations were used?

b. Specify the hypotheses to determine whether the explanatory variables are jointly significant.

c. Compute the value of the test statistic.

d. At the 5% significance level, what is the conclusion to the test? Explain.

Applications

8. A marketing manager analyzes the relationship between the annual sales of a firm (in $100,000s) and its advertising expenditures (in $10,000s). He collects data from 20 firms and estimates Sales $= \beta_0 + \beta_1$Advertising $+ \varepsilon$. A portion of the regression results is shown in the accompanying table.

	Coefficients	Standard Error	t Stat	p-value
Intercept	-7.42	1.46	-5.082	7.66E-05
Advertising	0.42	0.05		1.21E-07

a. Specify the competing hypotheses in order to determine whether advertising expenditures and sales have a positive linear relationship.

b. Calculate the value of the test statistic.

c. At the 5% significance level, do advertising expenditures and sales have a positive linear relationship?

9. In order to examine the relationship between the selling price of a used car and its age, an analyst uses data from 20 recent transactions and estimates Price $= \beta_0 + \beta_1$Age $+ \varepsilon$. A portion of the regression results is shown in the accompanying table.

	Coefficients	Standard Error	t Stat	p-value
Intercept	21187.94	733.42	28.889	1.56E-16
Age	-1208.25	128.95		2.41E-08

a. Specify the competing hypotheses in order to determine whether the selling price of a used car and its age are linearly related.

b. Calculate the value of the test statistic.

c. At the 5% significance level, is the age of a used car significant in explaining its selling price?

d. Conduct a hypothesis test at the 5% significance level in order to determine if β_1 differs from -1000. Show all of the relevant steps.

10. A study on the evolution of mankind shows that, with a few exceptions, world-record holders in the 100-meter dash have progressively gotten bigger over time (*The Wall Street Journal*, July 22, 2009). The following table shows runners who have held the record, along with their record-holding times (in seconds) and heights (in inches):

Record Holder/Year	Time	Height
Eddie Tolan (1932)	10.30	67
Jesse Owens (1936)	10.20	70
Charles Greene (1968)	9.90	68
Eddie Hart (1972)	9.90	70
Carl Lewis (1991)	9.86	74
Asafa Powell (2007)	9.74	75
Usain Bolt (2008)	9.69	77

A portion of the regression results from estimating Time $= \beta_0 + \beta_1$Height $+ \varepsilon$ is:

	Coefficients	Standard Error	t Stat	p-value
Intercept	13.353	1.1714	11.399	9.1E-05
Height	-0.0477	0.0163		

a. Specify the sample regression equation.

b. Specify the hypotheses to determine whether Height is linearly related to Time.

c. Calculate the value of the test statistic.

d. At the 5% significance level, is Height statistically significant? Explain.

11. An economist examines the relationship between changes in short-term interest rates and long-term interest rates. He believes that changes in short-term rates are significant in explaining long-term interest rates. He estimates the model $Dlong = \beta_0 + \beta_1 Dshort + \varepsilon$, where Dlong is the change in the long-term interest rate (10-year Treasury bill) and Dshort is the change in the short-term interest rate (3-month Treasury bill). Monthly data from January 2006 through December 2010 ($n = 60$) were obtained from the St. Louis Federal Reserve's website. A portion of the regression results is shown in the accompanying table.

	Coefficients	Standard Error	t Stat	p-value
Intercept	−0.0038	0.0088	−0.427	0.671
Dshort	0.0473	0.0168	2.813	0.007

Use a 5% significance level to determine whether there is a linear relationship between Dshort and Dlong.

12. For a sample of 20 New England cities, a sociologist studies the crime rate in each city (crimes per 100,000 residents) as a function of its poverty rate (in %) and its median income (in $1,000s). A portion of the regression results is shown in the accompanying table.

ANOVA	df	SS	MS	F	Significance F
Regression	2	188246.8	94123.40	35.20	9.04E-07
Residual	17	45457.32	2673.96		
Total	19	233704.1			

	Coefficients	Standard Error	t Stat	p-value
Intercept	−301.7927	549.7135	−0.549	0.590
Poverty	53.1597	14.2198	3.738	0.002
Income	4.9472	8.2566	0.599	0.557

a. Specify the sample regression equation.
b. At the 5% significance level, show whether the poverty rate and the crime rate are linearly related.
c. Construct the 95% confidence interval for the slope coefficient of income. Using the confidence interval, determine whether income influences the crime rate at the 5% significance level.
d. At the 5% significance level, are the poverty rate and income jointly significant in explaining the crime rate?

13. Akiko Hamaguchi is a manager at a small sushi restaurant in Phoenix, Arizona. Akiko is concerned that the weak economic environment has hampered foot traffic in her area, thus causing a dramatic decline in sales. In order to offset the decline in sales, she has pursued a strong advertising campaign. She believes advertising expenditures have a positive influence on sales. To support her claim, Akiko estimates the following linear regression model: Sales $= \beta_0 + \beta_1 Unemployment + \beta_2 Advertising + \varepsilon$. A portion of the regression results is shown in the accompanying table.

ANOVA	df	SS	MS	F	Significance F
Regression	2	72.6374	36.3187	8.760	0.003
Residual	14	58.0438	4.1460		
Total	16	130.681			

	Coefficients	Standard Error	t Stat	p-value
Intercept	17.5060	3.9817	4.397	0.007
Unemployment	−0.6879	0.2997	−2.296	0.038
Advertising	0.0266	0.0068	3.932	0.002

a. At the 5% significance level, test whether the explanatory variables jointly influence sales.
b. At the 1% significance level, test whether the unemployment rate is negatively related with sales.
c. At the 1% significance level, test whether advertising expenditures are positively related with sales.

14. A researcher estimates the following model relating the return on a firm's stock as a function of its price-to-earnings ratio and its price-to-sales ratio: Return $= \beta_0 + \beta_1 P/E + \beta_2 P/S + \varepsilon$. A portion of the regression results is shown in the accompanying table.

ANOVA	df	SS	MS	F	Significance F
Regression	2	918.746	459.3728	2.817	0.077
Residual	27	4402.786	163.0661		
Total	29	5321.532			

	Coefficients	Standard Error	t Stat	p-value
Intercept	−12.0243	7.886858	−1.525	0.139
P/E	0.1459	0.4322	0.338	0.738
P/S	5.4417	2.2926	2.374	0.025

a. Specify the sample regression equation.
b. At the 10% significant level, are P/E and P/S jointly significant? Show the relevant steps of the test.
c. Are both explanatory variables individually significant at the 10% significance level? Show the relevant steps of the test.

15. **FILE** *Test_Scores.* The accompanying data file shows midterm and final grades for 32 students. Estimate a student's final grade as a linear function of a student's midterm grade. At the 1% significance level, is a student's midterm grade significant in explaining a student's final grade? Show the relevant steps of the test.

16. **FILE** *Property_Taxes.* The accompanying data file shows the square footage and associated property taxes for 20 homes in an affluent suburb 30 miles outside of New York City. Estimate a home's property taxes as a linear function of its square footage. At the 5% significance level, is square footage significant in explaining property taxes? Show the relevant steps of the test.

17. **FILE** *Fertilizer.* A horticulturist is studying the relationship between tomato plant height and fertilizer amount. Thirty tomato plants grown in similar conditions were subjected to various amounts of fertilizer (in ounces) over a four-month period, and then their heights (in inches) were measured.

a. Estimate the regression model:
   $Height = \beta_0 + \beta_1 Fertilizer + \varepsilon$.
b. At the 5% significance level, determine if an ounce of fertilizer increases height by more than 3 inches. Show the relevant steps of the test.

18. **FILE** *Dexterity.* Finger dexterity, the ability to make precisely coordinated finger movements to grasp or assemble very small objects, is important in jewelry making. Thus, the manufacturing manager at Gemco, a manufacturer of high-quality watches, wants to develop a regression model to predict the productivity, measured by watches per shift, of new employees based on the time required (in seconds) to place 3 pins in each of 100 small holes using tweezers. He has subjected a sample of 20 current employees to the O'Connor dexterity test in which the time required to place the pins and the number of watches produced per shift are measured.

a. Estimate the regression model:
   $Watches = \beta_0 + \beta_1 Time + \varepsilon$.
b. The manager claims that for every extra second taken on placing the pins, the number of watches produced decreases by more than 0.02. Test this claim at the 5% significance level. Show the relevant steps of the test.

19. **FILE** *Engine_Overhaul.* The maintenance manager at a trucking company wants to build a regression model to forecast the time until the first engine overhaul (Time in years) based on four explanatory variables: (1) annual miles driven (Miles in 1,000s), (2) average load weight (Load in tons), (3) average driving speed (Speed in mph), and (4) oil change interval (Oil in 1,000s miles). Based on driver logs and onboard computers, data have been obtained for a sample of 25 trucks.

a. Estimate the time until the first engine overhaul as a function of all four explanatory variables.
b. At the 10% significance level, are the explanatory variables jointly significant? Show the relevant steps of the test.
c. Are the explanatory variables individually significant at the 10% significance level? Show the relevant steps of the test.

20. **FILE** *Electricity_Cost.* The facility manager at a pharmaceutical company wants to build a regression model to forecast monthly electricity cost. Three main variables are thought to dictate electricity cost: (1) average outdoor temperature (Temp in °F), (2) working days per month (Days), and (3) tons of product produced (Tons).

a. Estimate the regression model.
b. At the 10% significance level, are the explanatory variables jointly significant? Show the relevant steps of the test.
c. Are the explanatory variables individually significant at the 10% significance level? Show the relevant steps of the test.

21. **FILE** *Caterpillar.* Caterpillar, Inc. manufactures and sells heavy construction equipment worldwide. The performance of Caterpillar's stock is likely to be strongly influenced by the economy. For instance, during the subprime mortgage crisis, the value of Caterpillar's stock plunged dramatically. Monthly data for Caterpillar's risk-adjusted return ($R - R_f$) and the risk-adjusted market return ($R_M - R_f$) are collected for a five-year period ($n = 60$). A portion of the data is shown in the accompanying table.

Date	$R - R_f$	$R_M - R_f$
1/1/2006	17.66	2.21
2/1/2006	7.27	−0.31
⋮	⋮	⋮
11/1/2010	3.37	2.15

Source: http://finance.yahoo.com and U.S. Treasury.

a. Estimate the CAPM model for Caterpillar, Inc. Show the regression results in a well-formatted table.
b. At the 5% significance level, determine if investment in Caterpillar is riskier than the market (beta significantly greater than 1).
c. At the 5% significance level, is there evidence of abnormal returns?

22. **FILE** *Arlington_Homes.* A realtor examines the factors that influence the price of a house in Arlington, Massachusetts. He collects data on recent house sales (Price) and notes each house's square footage (Sqft) as well as its number of bedrooms (Beds) and number of bathrooms (Baths). A portion of the data is shown in the accompanying table.

Price	Sqft	Beds	Baths
840000	2768	4	3.5
822000	2500	4	2.5
⋮	⋮	⋮	⋮
307500	850	1	1

a. Estimate: $Price = \beta_0 + \beta_1 Sqft + \beta_2 Beds + \beta_3 Baths + \varepsilon$. Show the regression results in a well-formatted table.
b. At the 5% significance level, are the explanatory variables jointly significant in explaining Price?
c. At the 5% significance level, are all explanatory variables individually significant in explaining Price?

23. **FILE** *Final_Test.* On the first day of class, an economics professor administers a test to gauge the math preparedness of her students. She believes that the performance on this math test and the number of hours studied per week on the course are the primary factors that predict a student's score on the final exam. She collects data from 60 students, a portion of which is shown in the accompanying table.

Final	Math	Hours
94	92	5
74	90	3
⋮	⋮	⋮
63	64	2

a. Estimate the sample regression equation that enables us to predict a student's final exam score on the basis of his/her math score and the number of hours studied per week.

b. At the 5% significance level, are a student's math score and the number of hours studied per week jointly significant in explaining a student's final exam score?

c. At the 5% significance level, is each explanatory variable individually significant in explaining a student's final exam score?

15.2 A GENERAL TEST OF LINEAR RESTRICTIONS

Conduct a general test of linear restrictions.

The significance tests discussed in the preceding section can also be referred to as tests of linear restrictions. For example, the two-tailed t-test is a test of one linear restriction that determines whether or not a slope coefficient differs from zero. Similarly, the F test is a test of k linear restrictions that determines whether or not at least one of the slope coefficients is nonzero. In this section, we introduce a general **test of linear restrictions**; the resulting F test is often referred to as the **partial F test**. We can apply this test to any subset of the regression coefficients.

Consider a multiple regression model with three explanatory variables:

$$y = \beta_0 + \beta_1 x_1 + \beta_2 x_2 + \beta_3 x_3 + \varepsilon.$$

As mentioned earlier, we use a t-test for a test of one restriction, $\beta_j = 0$, and an F test for a test of three restrictions, $\beta_1 = \beta_2 = \beta_3 = 0$. What if we wanted to test if x_2 and x_3 are jointly significant? This is an example of a test of two restrictions, $\beta_2 = \beta_3 = 0$. Similarly, we may wish to test if the influence of x_3 is identical to that of x_2. This would be a test of one restriction, $\beta_2 = \beta_3$. When conducting a partial F test, the null hypothesis implies that the restrictions are valid. In these two examples, the null hypothesis would be specified as $H_0: \beta_2 = \beta_3 = 0$ and $H_0: \beta_2 = \beta_3$, respectively. As usual, the alternative hypothesis implies that the null hypothesis is not true. We conclude that the restrictions implied by the null hypothesis are not valid if we reject the null hypothesis.

In order to conduct the partial F test, we estimate the model with and without the restrictions. The **restricted model** is a reduced model where we do not estimate the coefficients that are restricted to a specific value under the null hypothesis. The **unrestricted model** is a complete model that imposes no restrictions on the coefficients; therefore, all coefficients are estimated. If the restrictions are valid—that is, the null hypothesis is true—then the error sum of squares of the restricted model SSE_R will not be significantly larger than the error sum of squares of the unrestricted model SSE_U. With the partial F test, we basically analyze the ratio of $(SSE_R - SSE_U)$ to SSE_U. If this ratio, suitably adjusted for the degrees of freedom, is significantly large, then we reject the null hypothesis and conclude that the restrictions implied by the null hypothesis are not valid.

We will consider two examples of the partial F test.

EXAMPLE 15.5

A manager at a car wash company in Missouri wants to measure the effectiveness of price discounts and various types of advertisement expenditures on sales. For the analysis, he uses varying price discounts (Discount) and advertisement expenditures on radio (Radio) and newspapers (Newspaper) in 40 counties in Missouri. A portion of the monthly data on sales (in $1,000s), price discounts (in percent), and advertisement expenditures (in $1,000s) on radio and newspapers are shown in Table 15.9. At the 5% level, determine if the advertisement expenditures on radio and newspapers have a statistically significant influence on sales.

TABLE 15.9 Sales, Price Discounts, and Advertising Expenditures, $n = 40$

County	Sales	Discount	Radio	Newspaper
1	62.72	40	2.27	3.00
2	49.65	20	3.78	1.78
⋮	⋮	⋮	⋮	⋮
40	49.95	40	3.57	1.57

Car_Wash

SOLUTION: Consider the unrestricted model (U) that does not impose restrictions on the coefficients and is specified as

(U)   Sales $= \beta_0 + \beta_1 \text{Discount} + \beta_2 \text{Radio} + \beta_3 \text{Newspaper} + \varepsilon$.

A test that determines whether advertisement expenditures on radio and newspapers have a significant influence on sales is equivalent to a test that determines whether the Radio and Newspaper variables are jointly significant. We formulate the competing hypotheses as

$$H_0: \beta_2 = \beta_3 = 0$$
$$H_A: \text{At least one of the coefficients is nonzero.}$$

In order to implement the partial F test, we then create the restricted (R) model. Note that we do not estimate the coefficients that are restricted to zero under the null hypothesis. Therefore, we exclude Radio and Newspaper and specify the model as

(R)   Sales $= \beta_0 + \beta_1 \text{Discount} + \varepsilon$.

For ease of exposition, we use the same notation to refer to the coefficients in models U and R. We note, however, that these coefficients and their estimates have a different meaning depending on which model we are referencing. Table 15.10 shows the relevant portion of the regression results.

TABLE 15.10 Relevant Regression Output for Example 15.5

Variable	Restricted	Unrestricted
Intercept	43.4541* (0.000)	6.7025 (0.356)
Discount	0.4016* (0.000)	0.3417* (0.000)
Radio	NA	6.0624* (0.001)
Newspaper	NA	9.3968* (0.000)
SSE	2,182.5649	1,208.1348

Notes: Parameter estimates are in the main body of the table with the p-values in parentheses; * represents significance at the 5% level. NA denotes not applicable. The last row presents the error sum of squares.

We use $df_1 = 2$, since we are testing for two restrictions, $\beta_2 = 0$ and $\beta_3 = 0$, and $df_2 = n - k - 1 = 40 - 3 - 1 = 36$. Taking the appropriate SSE values from Table 15.10, we calculate the value of the test statistic as

$$F_{(2,36)} = \frac{(SSE_R - SSE_U)/df_1}{SSE_U/df_2} = \frac{(2,182.5649 - 1,208.1348)/2}{1,208.1348/36} = 14.518.$$

We can use the F table to approximate the p-value, $P(F_{(2,36)} \geq 14.518)$, as a value that is less than 0.01. Using statistical software, we find that the exact p-value is approximately zero. Since the p-value $< \alpha = 0.05$, we reject H_0. At the 5% level, we conclude that the advertisement expenditures on radio and newspapers have a significant influence on sales.

FILE
Car_Wash

EXAMPLE 15.6

In Example 15.5, we showed that the advertisement expenditures on radio and newspapers have a statistically significant influence on sales. The manager believes that the influence of the advertisement expenditure on radio differs from the influence of the advertisement expenditure on newspapers. Conduct the appropriate partial F test at the 5% level to verify the manager's belief.

SOLUTION: We again specify the unrestricted model (U) as

(U)   Sales $= \beta_0 + \beta_1$Discount $+ \beta_2$Radio $+ \beta_3$Newspaper $+ \varepsilon$.

Because β_2 and β_3 capture the influence of the advertisement expenditures on radio and newspapers, respectively, we formulate the competing hypotheses as

$$H_0: \beta_2 = \beta_3$$
$$H_A: \beta_2 \neq \beta_3$$

In order to implement the partial F test, we then create the restricted (R) model. Note that under the restriction that $\beta_2 = \beta_3$, so the unrestricted model simplifies to

Sales $= \beta_0 + \beta_1$Discount $+ \beta_2$Radio $+ \beta_2$Newspaper $+ \varepsilon$; that is,

(R)   Sales $= \beta_0 + \beta_1$Discount $+ \beta_2$(Radio $+$ Newspaper) $+ \varepsilon$.

Thus, the restricted model uses only two explanatory variables, where the new second explanatory variable is defined as the sum of Radio and Newspaper. For this regression, we have to first create a new explanatory variable by adding up the Radio and Newspaper values. Further, given the restriction, $\beta_2 = \beta_3$, the estimated coefficient for this new explanatory variable applies to both Radio and Newspaper.

Note that the restricted model imposes one restriction, as there is one fewer coefficient to estimate. Table 15.11 presents the relevant portion of the regression results.

TABLE 15.11 Relevant Regression Output for Example 15.6

Variable	Restricted	Unrestricted
Intercept	7.9524 (0.274)	6.7025 (0.356)
Discount	0.3517* (0.000)	0.3417* (0.000)
Radio	NA	6.0624* (0.001)
Newspaper	NA	9.3968* (0.000)
Radio + Newspaper	7.1831* (0.000)	NA
SSE	1,263.6243	1,208.1348

Notes: Parameter estimates are in the main body of the table with the *p*-values in parentheses; * represents significance at the 5% level. NA denotes not applicable. The last row presents the error sum of squares.

We use $df_1 = 1$ since we are testing for only one restriction, and $df_2 = n - k - 1 = 40 - 3 - 1 = 36$. Using the appropriate SSE values from Table 15.11, we calculate the value of the test statistic as

$$F_{(1,36)} = \frac{(SSE_R - SSE_U)/df_1}{SSE_U/df_2} = \frac{(1{,}263.6243 - 1{,}208.1348)/1}{1{,}208.1348/36} = 1.653.$$

We can use the F table to approximate the *p*-value, $P(F_{(1,36)} \geq 1.653)$, as a value that is greater than 0.10. Using statistical software, we find that the exact *p*-value is 0.207. Since the *p*-value $> \alpha = 0.05$, we do not reject H_0. At the 5% significance level, we cannot conclude that the influence of the advertisement expenditures on radio is different from the influence of the advertisement expenditures on newspapers.

EXERCISES 15.2

Mechanics

24. Consider the multiple linear regression model, $y = \beta_0 + \beta_1 x_1 + \beta_2 x_2 + \beta_3 x_3 + \varepsilon$. You wish to test whether the slope coefficients β_1 and β_3 are jointly significant. Define the restricted and unrestricted models needed to conduct the test.

25. Consider the multiple linear regression model, $y = \beta_0 + \beta_1 x_1 + \beta_2 x_2 + \beta_3 x_3 + \varepsilon$. You wish to test whether the slope coefficients β_1 and β_3 are statistically different from each other. Define the restricted and unrestricted models needed to conduct the test.

26. Consider the multiple linear regression model, $y = \beta_0 + \beta_1 x_1 + \beta_2 x_2 + \varepsilon$. Define the restricted and unrestricted models if the hypotheses are

$H_0: \beta_1 + \beta_2 = 1$ and $H_A: \beta_1 + \beta_2 \neq 1$.

27. Consider a portion of simple linear regression results,

$\hat{y} = 105.40 + 39.17 x_1;$ $SSE = 407{,}308;$ $n = 30$

In an attempt to improve the results, two explanatory variables are added. The relevant regression results are the following:

$\hat{y} = 4.87 + 19.47 x_1 - 26.31 x_2 + 7.31 x_3;$

$SSE = 344{,}784;$ $n = 30$

a. Formulate the hypotheses to determine whether x_2 and x_3 are jointly significant in explaining y.

b. Calculate the value of the test statistic and the *p*-value.

c. At the 5% significance level, what is the conclusion to the test?

Applications

28. A real estate analyst estimates the following regression, relating a house price to its square footage (Sqft):

$\widehat{Price} = 48.39 + 52.74 Sqft;$ $SSE = 56{,}944;$ $n = 50$

In an attempt to improve the results, he adds two more explanatory variables: the number of bedrooms (Beds) and the number of bathrooms (Baths). The estimated regression equation is

$\widehat{Price} = 28.11 + 40.17 Sqft + 10.08 Beds + 16.14 Baths;$

$SSE = 48{,}074;$ $n = 50$

a. Formulate the hypotheses to determine whether Beds and Baths are jointly significant in explaining Price.

b. Calculate the value of the test statistic and the p-value.

c. At the 5% significance level, what is the conclusion to the test?

29. A financial analyst believes that the best way to predict a firm's returns is by using the firm's price-to-earnings ratio (P/E) and its price-to-sales ratio (P/S) as explanatory variables. He estimates the following regression, using 30 large firms:

$$\widehat{Return} = -33.40 + 3.97P/E - 3.37P/S;$$
$$SSE = 5,021.63; \quad n = 30$$

A colleague suggests that he can improve on his prediction if he also includes the P/E-to-growth ratio (PEG) and the dividend yield (DIV). He re-estimates the model by including these explanatory variables and obtains

$$\widehat{Return} = -31.84 + 4.26P/E - 2.16P/S - 11.49PEG$$
$$+ 3.82DIV; \quad SSE = 4,149.21; \quad n = 30$$

At the 5% significance level, is the colleague's claim substantiated by the data? Explain.

30. Lisa Fisher is a business school professor who would like to analyze university factors that enhance innovation. She collects data on 143 universities in 2008 for a regression where the response variable is the number of startups (Startups), which is used as a measure for innovation. Lisa believes that the amount of money that a university directs toward research (Research) is the most important factor influencing Startups. She estimates Startups as a function of Research and obtains

$$\widehat{Startups} = 0.21 + 0.01Research; \quad SSE = 1,434.78; \quad n = 143$$

Two other explanatory variables are also likely to influence Startups: the number of patents issued (Patents), and the age of its technology transfer office in years (Duration). Lisa then includes these additional variables in the model and obtains

$$\widehat{Startups} = 0.42 + 0.01Research + 0.05Patents$$
$$- 0.02Duration; \quad SSE = 1,368.14; \quad n = 143$$

At the 5% significance level, should Lisa include Patents and Duration in the model predicting Startups?

31. **FILE** *Wage.* A researcher interviews 50 employees of a large manufacturer and collects data on each worker's hourly wage (Wage in $), years of higher education (EDUC), experience (EXPER), and age (AGE). A portion of the data is shown in the accompanying table.

Wage	EDUC	EXPER	AGE
37.85	11	2	40
21.72	4	1	39
⋮	⋮	⋮	⋮
24.18	8	11	64

a. Estimate:
$$Wage = \beta_0 + \beta_1 EDUC + \beta_2 EXPER + \beta_3 AGE + \varepsilon.$$

b. The researcher wonders if the influence of experience is different from that of age, or if $\beta_2 \neq \beta_3$. Specify the competing hypotheses for this test.

c. What is the restricted model given that the null hypothesis is true? Estimate this model.

d. At the 5% significance level, can you conclude that the influence of experience is different from that of age?

32. **FILE** *Mobile_Phones.* The manager of a local Costo store is in the process of making hiring decisions for selling mobile phone contracts. She believes that the sale of mobile phone contracts depends crucially on the number of hours clocked by male and female employees. She collects the weekly data on last year's sales of mobile phone contracts (Sale) along with work hours of male (Hours Males) and female (Hours Females) employees. A portion of the data is shown in the accompanying table.

Sale	Hours Males	Hours Females
59	30	32
65	33	36
⋮	⋮	⋮
64	35	35

a. Report the sample regression equation of the appropriate model.

b. At the 5% significance level, are the explanatory variables jointly significant? Are they individually significant?

c. The manager would like to determine whether there is a difference in productivity of male and female employees. In other words, for the same work hours, whether the number of sales of mobile contracts varies between male and female employees. Conduct the appropriate test at the 5% level of significance. Provide the details.

33. **FILE** *Football.* A multiple regression model is used to predict an NFL team's winning record (Win in %). For the explanatory variables, the average rushing yards (Rush) and the average passing yards (Pass) are used to capture offense, and the average yards allowed are used to capture defense (Yards Allowed). A portion of the data for the 2009 NFL season is shown in the accompanying table.

Team	Win	Rush	Pass	Yards Allowed
Arizona Cardinals	62.50	93.40	251.00	346.40
Atlanta Falcons	56.30	117.21	223.19	348.90
⋮	⋮	⋮	⋮	⋮
Washington Redskins	25.00	94.38	218.13	319.70

Source: NFL website.

a. Estimate the model: $Win = \beta_0 + \beta_1 Rush + \beta_2 Pass + \beta_3 Yards\ Allowed + \varepsilon$.

b. Conduct a test at the 10% significance level to determine whether the impact of Rush is different from that of Pass in explaining Win, or $\beta_1 \neq \beta_2$.

34. **FILE** *Union_Pay.* An automotive workers union, in conjunction with top management, is negotiating a new hourly pay policy for union workers based on three variables: (1) job class, (2) years with the company, and (3) years as a union member at any company. The goal is to develop an equitable model that can objectively specify hourly pay, thereby reducing pay disparity grievances. Fifty union workers have been sampled and will be used as the basis for the pay model. A portion of the data is shown in the accompanying table.

Hourly Pay	Job Class	Years with Company	Years in Union
15.90	24	12	7
23.70	52	17	14
⋮	⋮	⋮	⋮
26.70	43	2	2

a. Report the sample regression equation of the appropriate model.

b. At the 5% significance level, are the explanatory variables jointly significant? Are they individually significant?

c. Predict hourly pay for a worker in Job Class 48 with 18 years experience at the company and 14 years with the union.

d. A manager wonders if the years with the company and the years as a union member matter in negotiating hourly pay. At the 5% significance level, can you conclude that the influence of these two explanatory variables is jointly significant? Provide the details.

15.3 INTERVAL ESTIMATES FOR THE RESPONSE VARIABLE

LO 15.4

In the introductory case, we analyzed the winning percentage of a baseball team on the basis of its batting average (BA) and earned run average (ERA). We estimated the most appropriate model to be $\widehat{Win} = 0.1269 + 3.2754BA - 0.1153ERA$. Suppose we want to predict a team's winning percentage given its batting average of 0.25 and earned run average of 4. We can use the above estimated model with BA = 0.25 and ERA = 4 to derive the predicted winning percentage as

$$\widehat{Win} = 0.1269 + 3.2754 \times 0.25 - 0.1153 \times 4 = 0.4846.$$

Calculate and interpret confidence intervals and prediction intervals.

Predictions, such as the one above, are certainly useful, but we need to be aware that such predictions are subject to sampling variations. In other words, the prediction will change if we use a different sample to estimate the regression model. Recall from Chapter 8 that the point estimate along with the margin of error is used to construct the relevant interval estimate. In the above example, 0.4846 represents the point estimate.

In this section, we will make a distinction between the interval estimate for the mean (expected value) of the response variable y and the interval estimate for the individual value of y. It is common to refer to the former as the **confidence interval** and the latter as the **prediction interval**. For given values of the explanatory variables, we can think of the confidence interval as the range that contains the mean of y and the prediction interval as the range that contains the individual value of y. We use the same point estimate for constructing both interval estimates. In the context of the above example, 0.4846 is the point estimate for the mean winning percentage as well as the individual winning percentage given the team's batting average of 0.25 and earned run average of 4. Due to the added uncertainty in predicting the individual value of y, the prediction interval is always wider than the corresponding confidence interval.

CONFIDENCE INTERVAL AND PREDICTION INTERVAL

We construct two types of interval estimates regarding the response variable y for given values of the explanatory variables. The interval estimate for the mean (expected value) of y is referred to as the confidence interval. It is common to refer to the interval estimate for an individual value of y as the prediction interval. The prediction interval is always wider than the corresponding confidence interval.

We will now describe the general procedure for constructing the confidence interval and the prediction interval. For the sake of simplicity, we let x's denote all explanatory variables. In the context of the preceding example, x_1 and x_2 represent the team's batting average and earned run average, respectively.

Consider a multiple regression model $y = \beta_0 + \beta_1 x_1 + \beta_2 x_2 + \cdots + \beta_k x_k + \varepsilon$ with k explanatory variables, $x_1, x_2, \ldots, x_k$.

Moreover, let

$$y^0 = \beta_0 + \beta_1 x_1^0 + \beta_2 x_2^0 + \cdots + \beta_k x_k^0 + \varepsilon^0,$$

where $x_1^0, x_2^0, \ldots, x_k^0$ denote specific values for $x_1, x_2, \ldots, x_k$ at which y^0 is evaluated and ε^0 is the (unobserved) random error term. In the baseball example, we used $x_1^0 = 0.25$ and $x_2^0 = 4$. Alternatively, we can evaluate the expected value of the response variable at $x_1^0, x_2^0, \ldots, x_k^0$ as

$$E(y^0) = \beta_0 + \beta_1 x_1^0 + \beta_2 x_2^0 + \cdots + \beta_k x_k^0.$$

The expected value equation uses the fact that the expected value of the random error term is assumed to be zero; that is, $E(\varepsilon^0) = 0$. We discuss this assumption in the next section. Note that the prediction interval is wider than the confidence interval because it also incorporates the additional uncertainty due to ε^0. We first derive the confidence interval for $E(y^0)$, followed by the prediction interval for y^0.

The predicted value, $\hat{y}^0 = b_0 + b_1 x_1^0 + b_2 x_2^0 + \cdots + b_k x_k^0$, is the point estimate for $E(y^0)$. In the baseball example, 0.4846 is the point estimate of $E(y^0)$ when $x_1^0 = 0.25$ and $x_2^0 = 4$. We form the $100(1 - \alpha)\%$ confidence interval for $E(y^0)$ as $\hat{y}^0 + t_{\alpha/2,df}se(\hat{y}^0)$, where $se(\hat{y}^0)$ is the estimated standard error of $\hat{y}^0$. While there is a simple formula to compute the standard error $se(\hat{y}^0)$ for a simple linear regression model, it is very cumbersome to do so for a multiple linear regression model. Next we describe a relatively easy way to construct a confidence interval that works for both simple and multiple linear regression models.

CONFIDENCE INTERVAL FOR THE EXPECTED VALUE OF Y

For specific values of $x_1, x_2, \ldots, x_k$, denoted by $x_1^0, x_2^0, \ldots, x_k^0$, the $100(1 - \alpha)\%$ confidence interval for the expected value of y is computed as

$$\hat{y}^0 + t_{\alpha/2,df}se(\hat{y}^0),$$

where $\hat{y}^0 = b_0 + b_1 x_1^0 + b_2 x_2^0 + \cdots + b_k x_k^0$, $se(\hat{y}^0)$ is the standard error of $\hat{y}^0$, and $df = n - k - 1$.

To derive $\hat{y}^0$ together with $se(\hat{y}^0)$, we first estimate a modified regression model where y is the response variable and the explanatory variables are defined as $x_1^* = x_1 - x_1^0, x_2^* = x_2 - x_2^0, \ldots, x_k^* = x_k - x_k^0$. The resulting estimate of the intercept and its standard error equal $\hat{y}^0$ and $se(\hat{y}^0)$, respectively.

EXAMPLE 15.7

We again reference the data from Table 15.1 and the regression model Win $= \beta_0 + \beta_1$BA $+ \beta_2$ERA $+ \varepsilon$. Construct the 95% confidence interval for expected winning percentage if BA is 0.25 and ERA is 4.

SOLUTION: Let y, x_1, and x_2 denote Win, BA, and ERA, respectively. In order to construct a confidence interval for $E(y^0)$, we follow the above-mentioned procedure to derive $\hat{y}^0$ as well as $se(\hat{y}^0)$. First, given $x_1^0 = 0.25$ and $x_2^0 = 4$, we define two modified explanatory variables as $x_1^* = x_1 - 0.25$ and $x_2^* = x_2 - 4$. Table 15.12 shows a portion of the computed values.

TABLE 15.12 Computing the Values of Modified Explanatory Variables (Example 15.7)

y	x_1	x_2	$x_1^* = x_1 - 0.25$	$x_2^* = x_2 - 4$
0.407	0.259	4.59	$0.259 - 0.25 = 0.009$	$4.59 - 4 = 0.59$
0.549	0.268	4.20	$0.268 - 0.25 = 0.018$	$4.20 - 4 = 0.20$
⋮	⋮	⋮	⋮	⋮
0.426	0.250	4.13	$0.250 - 0.25 = 0.000$	$4.13 - 4 = 0.13$

The regression output for a multiple regression model that uses y as the response variable and x_1^* and x_2^* as the explanatory variables is presented in Table 15.13.

TABLE 15.13 Regression Results with Modified Explanatory Variables (Example 15.7)

Regression Statistics		
Multiple R	0.8459	
R Square	0.7156	
Adjusted R Square	0.6945	
Standard Error	**0.0375**	
Observations	30	

ANOVA					
	df	SS	MS	F	Significance F
Regression	2	0.0958	0.0479	33.966	4.25E-08
Residual	27	0.0381	0.0014		
Total	29	0.1338			

	Coefficients	Standard Error	t Stat	p-value	Lower 95%	Upper 95%
Intercept	**0.4847**	**0.0085**	57.258	0.000	**0.4673**	**0.5021**
x_1^*	3.2754	0.6723	4.872	0.000	1.8960	4.6549
x_2^*	−0.1153	0.0167	−6.920	0.000	−0.1494	−0.0811

We note that the modified regression output is identical to the original regression output (refer to the summarized results for Model 3 in Table 15.8), except for the estimates of the intercept term. Here the intercept estimate is 0.4847 and its standard error is 0.0085 (see values in boldface in Table 15.13). Therefore, we use $\hat{y}^0 = 0.4847$ and $se(\hat{y}^0) = 0.0085$ in constructing the confidence interval. Note that the computer-generated calculation for $\hat{y}^0$ is the same as our earlier estimate, $\hat{y}^0 = 0.1269 + 3.2754 \times 0.25 - 0.1153 \times 4 = 0.4846$, except for rounding.

For the 95% confidence level and $df = n - k - 1 = 30 - 2 - 1 = 27$, we find $t_{\alpha/2,df} = t_{0.025,27} = 2.052$. The 95% confidence interval for $E(y^0)$ is

$$\hat{y}^0 \pm t_{\alpha/2,df}se(\hat{y}^0) = 0.4847 \pm 2.052 \times 0.0085 = 0.4847 \pm 0.0174.$$

Or, with 95% confidence,

$$0.4673 \le E(y^0) \le 0.5021.$$

Using this 95% confidence interval, we can state that the mean winning percentage of a team with a batting average of 0.25 and earned run average of 4 falls between 0.4673 and 0.5021. Note that the lower and upper confidence limits for the 95% confidence interval for $E(y^0)$ are identical to the lower and upper confidence limits for the 95% confidence interval for the intercept (see values in boldface in Table 15.13).

As mentioned earlier, the prediction interval pertains to the individual value of the response variable defined for specific explanatory variables as $y^0 = \beta_0 + \beta_1 x_1^0 + \beta_2 x_2^0 + \cdots + \beta_k x_k^0 + \varepsilon^0$. The prediction interval is wider than the confidence interval because it incorporates the variability of the random error term ε^0.

For specific values of $x_1, x_2, \ldots, x_k$, denoted by $x_1^0, x_2^0, \ldots, x_k^0$, the $100(1 - \alpha)\%$ prediction interval for an individual value of y is computed as

$$\hat{y}^0 \pm t_{\alpha/2,df}\sqrt{(se(\hat{y}^0))^2 + s_e^2},$$

where $df = n - k - 1$, $se(\hat{y}^0)$ is the standard error of $\hat{y}^0$, and s_e is the standard error of the estimate.

Note that the standard error of the estimate, s_e, captures the variability of the random error term, ε^0.

EXAMPLE 15.8

Reconsider the estimated model, $\hat{y}^0 = 0.1269 + 3.2754x_1 - 0.1153x_2$, where y, x_1, and x_2 denote Win, BA, and ERA, respectively.

a. Construct the 95% prediction interval for Win if BA is 0.25 and ERA is 4.
b. Comment on any differences between this prediction interval and the confidence interval constructed in Example 15.7.

SOLUTION:

a. As in the calculation for the confidence interval, we compute $\hat{y}^0 = 0.4847$, $se(\hat{y}^0) = 0.0085$, and $t_{\alpha/2,df} = t_{0.025,27} = 2.052$. The only thing missing from the prediction interval formula is the standard error of the estimate s_e. From Table 15.13, we extract the value, $s_e = 0.0375$ (see value in boldface). The 95% prediction interval is then

$$\hat{y}^0 \pm t_{\alpha/2,df}\sqrt{(se(\hat{y}^0))^2 + s_e^2} = 0.4847 \pm 2.052\sqrt{0.0085^2 + 0.0375^2}$$
$$= 0.4847 \pm 0.0789.$$

Or, with 95% confidence,

$$0.4058 \le y^0 \le 0.5636.$$

b. Using this 95% prediction interval, we can state that the winning percentage of a team with a batting average of 0.25 and earned run average of 4 falls between 0.4058 and 0.5636. In the previous example, we used the 95% confidence interval to state that the mean winning percentage of a team with a batting average of 0.25 and earned run average of 4 falls between 0.4673 and 0.5021. As expected, the prediction interval is wider than the corresponding confidence interval. In forming the prediction interval, we also have to account for a very important source of variability caused by the random error term. This is captured by the standard error of the estimate, s_e, in the prediction interval formula. The higher variability makes it more difficult to predict accurately, thus necessitating a wider interval.

EXERCISES 15.3

Mechanics

35. In a simple linear regression based on 30 observations, the following information is provided: $\hat{y} = -6.92 + 1.35x$ and $s_e = 2.78$. Also, $se(\hat{y}^0)$ evaluated at $x = 30$ is 1.02.
    a. Construct the 95% confidence interval for $E(y)$ if $x = 30$.
    b. Construct the 95% prediction interval for y if $x = 30$.
    c. Which interval is narrower? Explain.

36. In a simple linear regression based on eight observations, the following sample regression is obtained: $\hat{y} = 9.15 + 1.46x$ with $s_e = 2.67$. Also, when x equals 15, $se(\hat{y}^0) = 1.06$.
    a. Construct the 95% confidence interval for $E(y)$ if $x = 15$.
    b. Construct the 95% prediction interval for y if $x = 15$.
    c. Which interval is wider? Explain.

37. In a multiple linear regression with 40 observations, the following sample regression equation is obtained: $\hat{y} = 12.8 + 2.6x_1 - 1.2x_2$ with $s_e = 5.84$. Also, when x_1 equals 15 and x_2 equals 6, $se(\hat{y}^0) = 2.20$.

   a. Construct the 95% confidence interval for $E(y)$ if x_1 equals 15 and x_2 equals 6.

   b. Construct the 95% prediction interval for y if x_1 equals 15 and x_2 equals 6.

   c. Which interval is wider? Explain.

38. In a multiple linear regression based on eight observations, the following sample regression is obtained: $\hat{y} = 22.81 + 0.85x_1 - 0.71x_2$ with $s_e = 4.69$. Also, when x_1 equals 50 and x_2 equals 20, $se(\hat{y}^0) = 2.18$.

   a. Construct the 95% confidence interval for $E(y)$ if $x_1 = 50$ and $x_2 = 20$.

   b. Construct the 95% prediction interval for y if $x_1 = 50$ and $x_2 = 20$.

   c. Which interval is narrower? Explain.

Applications

39. **FILE** *Education.* Estimate: Salary $= \beta_0 + \beta_1$Education $+ \varepsilon$, where Salary is measured in $1,000s and Education refers to years of higher education.

   a. Construct the 90% confidence interval for the expected salary for an individual who completed 6 years of higher education.

   b. Construct the 90% prediction interval for salary for an individual who completed 6 years of higher education.

   c. Comment on the difference in the widths of these intervals.

40. **FILE** *Fertilizer.* Estimate: Height $= \beta_0 + \beta_1$Fertilizer $+ \varepsilon$, where Height is a tomato plant's height (in inches) and Fertilizer is the fertilizer amount (in ounces).

   a. Calculate and interpret the 90% confidence interval for the mean height of a tomato plant that receives 3.0 ounces of fertilizer.

   b. Calculate and interpret the 90% prediction interval for a tomato plant that receives 3.0 ounces of fertilizer.

41. **FILE** *GPA.* Estimate: GPA $= \beta_0 + \beta_1$GRE $+ \varepsilon$, where GRE is a student's score on the math portion of the Graduate Record

Examination (GRE) score and GPA is the student's grade point average in graduate school.

   a. Construct the 90% confidence interval for the expected GPA for an individual who scored 710 on the math portion of the GRE.

   b. Construct the 90% prediction interval for GPA for an individual who scored 710 on the math portion of the GRE.

42. **FILE** *Debt_Payments.* Estimate: Debt $= \beta_0 + \beta_1$Income $+ \varepsilon$, where Debt (in $) is the average debt payments for a household in a particular city and Income (in $1,000s) is the city's median income.

   a. Construct the 95% confidence interval for expected debt payments if income is $80,000.

   b. Construct the 95% prediction interval for debt payments if income is $80,000.

43. **FILE** *Arlington_Homes.* Estimate: Price $= \beta_0 + \beta_1$Sqft $+ \beta_2$Beds $+ \beta_2$Baths $+ \varepsilon$, where Price, Sqft, Beds, and Baths refer to home price, square footage, number of bedrooms, and number of bathrooms, respectively. Construct the 95% confidence interval for the expected price of a 2,500-square-foot home in Arlington, Massachusetts, with three bedrooms and two bathrooms. Construct the corresponding prediction interval for an individual home. Interpret both intervals.

44. **FILE** *Engine_Overhaul.* The maintenance manager at a trucking company wants to build a regression model to forecast the time until the first engine overhaul (Time in years) based on four explanatory variables: (1) annual miles driven (Miles in 1,000s), (2) average load weight (Load in tons), (3) average driving speed (Speed in mph), and (4) oil change interval (Oil in 1,000s miles). Based on driver logs and onboard computers, data have been obtained for a sample of 25 trucks.

   a. Estimate the regression model to predict the time before the first engine overhaul for a truck driven 60,000 miles per year with an average load of 22 tons, an average driving speed of 57 mph, and 18,000 miles between oil changes. (Note that both annual miles driven and oil change interval are measured in 1,000s.)

   b. Use the above prediction to calculate and interpret the 90% confidence interval for the mean time before the first engine overhaul.

   c. Calculate and interpret the corresponding 90% prediction interval for the time before the first engine overhaul.

15.4 MODEL ASSUMPTIONS AND COMMON VIOLATIONS

LO 15.5

So far we have focused on the estimation and the assessment of linear regression models. It is important to understand that the statistical properties of the ordinary least squares (OLS) estimator, as well as the validity of the testing procedures, depend on the assumptions of the classical linear regression model. In this section, we

Explain the role of the assumptions on the OLS estimators.

discuss these assumptions. We also address common violations to the assumptions, discuss the consequences when the assumptions are violated, and, where possible, offer some remedies.

Under the assumptions of the classical linear regression model, the OLS estimators have desirable properties. In particular, the OLS estimators of the regression coefficients β_j are unbiased; that is, $E(b_j) = \beta_j$. Moreover, among all linear unbiased estimators, they have minimum variations between samples. These desirable properties of the OLS estimators become compromised as one or more model assumptions are violated. Aside from coefficient estimates, the validity of the significance tests is also impacted by the assumptions. For certain violations, the estimated standard errors of the OLS estimators are inappropriate; in these cases it is not possible to make meaningful inferences from the t and the F test results.

The assumptions of the classical linear regression model are, for the most part, based on the error term ε. Since the residuals, or the observed error term, $e = y - \hat{y}$, contain useful information regarding ε, it is common to use the residuals to investigate the assumptions. In this section, we will rely on **residual plots** to detect some of the common violations to the assumptions. These graphical plots are easy to use and provide informal analysis of the estimated regression models. Formal tests are beyond the scope of this text.

It is common to plot the residuals e on the vertical axis and the explanatory variable x_j, or the predicted values $\hat{y}$ on the horizontal axis. Such plots are useful for detecting departures from linearity as well as constant variability. If the regression is based on time series data, we can plot the residuals sequentially to detect if the observations are correlated.

Residual plots can also be used to detect outliers. Recall that outliers are observations that stand out from the rest of the data. For an outlier observation, the resulting residual will appear distinct in a plot; it will stand out from the rest. While outliers can greatly impact the estimates, it is not always clear what to do with them. As mentioned in Chapter 3, outliers may indicate bad data due to incorrectly recorded (or included) observations in the data set. In such cases, the relevant observation should be corrected or simply deleted. Alternatively, outliers may just be due to random variations, in which case the relevant observations should remain. In any event, residual plots help us identify potential outliers so that we can take corrective actions, if needed.

In Figure 15.1, we present a hypothetical residual plot when none of the assumptions has been violated. Note that all the points are randomly dispersed around the zero value of the residuals. Also, there is no evidence of outliers since no residual stands out from the rest. Any discernible pattern of the residuals indicates that one or more assumptions have been violated.

FIGURE 15.1
Residual plot of a correctly specified model

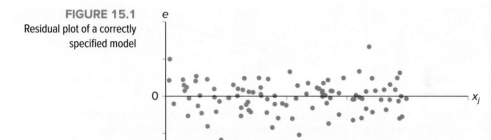

We discuss how to obtain residual plots in Excel and R at the end of this section, but first we describe common violations of the assumptions and offer remedies.

Common Violation 1: Nonlinear Patterns

Linear regression models are often justified on the basis of their computational simplicity. The simple linear regression model $y = \beta_0 + \beta_1 x + \varepsilon$ implies that if x goes up by one unit, we expect y to change by β_1, irrespective of the value of x. However, in many applications, the relationship cannot be represented by a straight line and, therefore, must be captured by an appropriate curve. It is always good to rely on economic theory and intuition to determine if the linearity assumption is appropriate. We confirm our intuition by analyzing scatterplots or residual plots. The OLS estimates can be quite misleading if there are obvious nonlinear patterns in the data.

Detection

We can use residual plots to identify nonlinear patterns. Linearity is justified if the residuals are randomly dispersed across the values of an explanatory variable. A discernible trend in the residuals is indicative of nonlinear patterns.

LO 15.6

Describe common violations of the assumptions and offer remedies.

EXAMPLE 15.9

A sociologist wishes to study the relationship between age and happiness. He interviews 24 individuals and collects data on age and happiness, measured on a scale from 0 to 100. A portion of the data is shown in Table 15.14. Examine the linearity assumption in the regression model, Happiness $= \beta_0 + \beta_1 \text{Age} + \varepsilon$.

TABLE 15.14 Happiness and Age

Happiness	Age
62	49
66	51
⋮	⋮
72	69

SOLUTION: We start the analysis with a scatterplot of Happiness against Age. Figure 15.2 shows the scatterplot and the superimposed trend line, which is based on the sample regression equation, $\widehat{\text{Happiness}} = 56.18 + 0.28\text{Age}$. It is fairly clear from Figure 15.2 that the linear regression model does not appropriately capture the relationship between Happiness and Age. In other words, it is misleading to conclude that a person's happiness increases by 0.28 units every year.

FIGURE 15.2 Scatterplot and the superimposed trendline (Example 15.9)

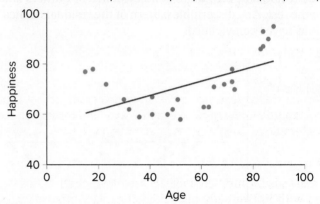

A residual plot, shown in Figure 15.3, further explores the linearity assumption of the regression model.

FIGURE 15.3 Residual plot against Age (Example 15.9)

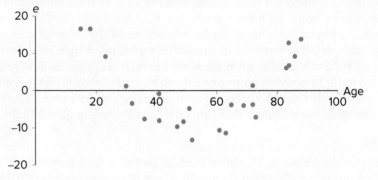

The above residual plot shows that there is an obvious trend with the residuals decreasing until the age of 50 and steadily increasing thereafter. The linear regression model is inappropriate as it underestimates at lower and higher age levels and overestimates in the middle. This result is consistent with a report that shows that happiness initially decreases with age and then increases with age (*The Economist*, December 16, 2010).

Remedy

Linear regression models are often used as a first pass for most empirical work. In many instances, they provide a very good approximation for the actual relationship. However, if residual plots exhibit strong nonlinear patterns, the inferences made by a linear regression model can be quite misleading. In such instances, we should employ nonlinear regression methods based on simple transformations of the response and the explanatory variables; these methods are discussed in the next chapter.

Common Violation 2: Multicollinearity

Perfect multicollinearity exists when two or more explanatory variables have an exact linear relationship. Consider the model $y = \beta_0 + \beta_1 x_1 + \beta_2 x_2 + \varepsilon$, where y is bonus, x_1 is the number of cars sold, and x_2 is the number of cars remaining in the lot. If all car salesmen started with the same inventory, we have a case of *perfect* multicollinearity ($x_2 = \text{Constant} - x_1$). Perfect multicollinearity is easy to detect because the model cannot be estimated. However, if x_2 represents the proportion of positive reviews from customers, we have *some* **multicollinearity** since the number of cars sold and the proportion of positive reviews are likely to be correlated. In most applications, some degree of correlation exists between the explanatory variables.

The problem with (non-perfect) multicollinearity is similar to that of small samples. Multicollinearity does not violate any of the assumptions; however, its presence results in imprecise estimates of the slope coefficients. In other words, multicollinearity makes it difficult to disentangle the separate influences of the explanatory variables on the response variable. If multicollinearity is severe, we may find insignificance of important explanatory variables; some coefficient estimates may even have wrong signs.

Detection

The detection methods for multicollinearity are mostly informal. The presence of a high R^2 coupled with individually insignificant explanatory variables can indicate multicollinearity. Sometimes researchers examine the correlations between the explanatory variables to detect severe multicollinearity. One such guideline suggests that multicollinearity is severe if the sample correlation coefficient between any two explanatory variables is more than 0.80 or less than −0.80. Seemingly wrong signs of the estimated regression coefficients may also indicate multicollinearity.

EXAMPLE 15.10

Examine the multicollinearity issue in a linear regression model that uses median home values (in $) as the response variable and median household incomes (in $), per capita incomes (in $), and the proportion of owner-occupied homes (in %) as the explanatory variables. A portion of 2010 data for all states in the United States is shown in Table 15.15.

TABLE 15.15 Home Values and Other Factors

State	Home Value	HH Income	Per Cap Inc	Pct Owner Occ
Alabama	117600	42081	22984	71.1
Alaska	229100	66521	30726	64.7
⋮	⋮	⋮	⋮	⋮
Wyoming	174000	53802	27860	70.2

Source: 2010 U.S. Census.

FILE

Home_Values

SOLUTION: We estimate three models to examine the multicollinearity issue; Table 15.16 presents the regression results.

TABLE 15.16 Summary of Model Estimates (Example 15.10)

Variable	Model 1	Model 2	Model 3
Intercept	417,892.04*	348,187.14*	285,604.08
	(0.001)	(0.002)	(0.083)
HH Income	9.04*	7.74*	NA
	(0.000)	(0.000)	
Per Cap Inc	−3.27	NA	13.21*
	(0.309)		(0.000)
Pct Owner Occ	−8,744.30*	−8,027.90*	−6,454.08*
	(0.000)	(0.000)	(0.001)
Adjusted R^2	0.8071	0.8069	0.6621

Notes: The table contains parameter estimates with p-values in parentheses; * represents significance at the 5% level. NA denotes not applicable. Adjusted R^2, reported in the last row, is used for model selection.

Model 1 uses all three explanatory variables to explain home values. Surprisingly, the per capita income variable has a negative estimated coefficient of −3.27 and, with a p-value of 0.31, is not even statistically significant at the 5% level. Multicollinearity might be the reason for this surprising result since household income and per capita income are likely to be correlated. We compute the sample correlation coefficient between these two variables as 0.8582, which suggests that multicollinearity is severe. We estimate two more models where one of these collinear variables is removed; Model 2 removes per capita income and Model 3 removes household income. Note that per capita income in Model 3 now exerts a positive and significant influence on home values. Between these two models, Model 2 is preferred to Model 3 because of its higher adjusted R^2 (0.8069 > 0.6621). The choice between Model 1 and Model 2 is unclear. In general, Model 1, with the highest adjusted R^2 value of 0.8071, is preferred if the sole purpose of the analysis is to make predictions. However, if the coefficient estimates need to be evaluated, then Model 2 may be the preferred choice.

Remedy

Inexperienced researchers tend to include too many explanatory variables in their quest not to omit anything important and in doing so may include redundant variables that essentially measure the same thing. When confronted with multicollinearity, a good remedy is to drop one of the collinear variables. The difficult part is to decide which of the collinear variables is redundant and, therefore, can safely be removed. Another option is to obtain more data, since the sample correlation may get weaker as we include more observations. Sometimes it helps to express the explanatory variables differently so that they are not collinear. At times, the best approach may be to *do nothing* when there is a justification to include all explanatory variables. This is especially so if the estimated model yields a high R^2, which implies that the estimated model is good for prediction.

Common Violation 3: Changing Variability

The assumption of constant variability of observations often breaks down in studies with cross-sectional data. Consider the model $y = \beta_0 + \beta_1 x + \varepsilon$, where y is a household's consumption expenditure and x is its disposable income. It may be unreasonable to assume that the variability of consumption is the same across a cross-section of household incomes. For example, we would expect higher-income households to have a higher variability in consumption as compared to lower-income households. Similarly, home prices tend to vary more as homes get larger, and sales tend to vary more as firm size increases.

In the presence of **changing variability**, the OLS estimators are still unbiased. However, the estimated standard errors of the OLS estimators are inappropriate. Consequently, we cannot put much faith in the standard t or F tests since they are based on these estimated standard errors.

Detection

We can use residual plots to gauge changing variability. The residuals are generally plotted against each explanatory variable x_j; for a multiple regression model, we can also plot them against the predicted value $\hat{y}$. There is no violation if the residuals are randomly dispersed across the values of x_j. On the other hand, there is a violation if the variability increases or decreases over the values of x_j.

EXAMPLE 15.11

Consider a simple regression model that relates monthly sales (Sales in $1,000s) from a chain of convenience stores with the square footage (Sqft) of the store. A portion of the data used for the analysis is shown in Table 15.17. Estimate the model and use a residual plot to determine if the observations have a changing variability.

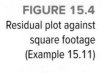

TABLE 15.17 Sales and Square Footage of Convenience Stores

Sales	Sqft
140	1810
160	2500
⋮	⋮
110	1470

SOLUTION: The sample regression is given by

$$\widehat{\text{Sales}} = 22.0795 + 0.0591\text{Sqft},$$
$$(se) \quad (10.4764) \quad (0.0057)$$

where we have put the standard errors of the coefficients in parentheses. We will reference these values when we incorporate R instructions at the end of this section.

A residual plot of the estimated model is shown in Figure 15.4. Note that the residuals seem to fan out across the horizontal axis. Therefore, we conclude that changing variability is a likely problem in this application relating sales to square footage. This result is not surprising, since you would expect sales to vary more as square footage increases. For instance, a small convenience store is likely to include only bare essentials for which there is a fairly stable demand. A larger store, on the other hand, may include specialty items, resulting in more fluctuation in sales.

FIGURE 15.4
Residual plot against square footage
(Example 15.11)

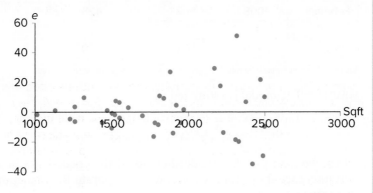

Remedy

As mentioned earlier, in the presence of changing variability, the OLS estimators are unbiased but their estimated standard errors are inappropriate. Therefore, OLS still provides reasonable coefficient estimates, but the t and the F tests are no longer valid. This has prompted some researchers to use the OLS estimates along with a correction for the standard errors, often referred to as robust standard errors. Unfortunately, the current version of Excel does not include a correction for the standard errors. However, it is available on many statistical computer packages, including R. At the end of this section, we use R to make the necessary correction in Example 15.11. With robust standard errors, we can then perform legitimate t-tests.

Common Violation 4: Correlated Observations

When obtaining the OLS estimators, we assume that the observations are uncorrelated. This assumption often breaks down in studies with time series data. Variables such as GDP, employment, and asset returns exhibit business cycles. As a consequence, successive observations are likely to be correlated.

In the presence of **correlated observations**, the OLS estimators are unbiased, but their estimated standard errors are inappropriate. Generally, these standard errors are distorted downward, making the model look better than it really is with a spuriously high R^2. Furthermore, the t and F tests may suggest that the explanatory variables are individually and jointly significant when this is not true.

Detection

We can plot the residuals sequentially over time to look for correlated observations. If there is no violation, then the residuals should show no pattern around the horizontal axis. A violation is indicated when a positive residual in one period is followed by positive residuals in the next few periods, followed by negative residuals for a few periods, then positive residuals, and so on. Although not as common, a violation is also indicated when a positive residual is followed by a negative residual, then a positive residual, and so on.

EXAMPLE 15.12

Consider $y = \beta_0 + \beta_1 x_1 + \beta_2 x_2 + \varepsilon$ where y represents sales (in \$1000s) at a sushi restaurant and x_1 and x_2 represent advertising costs (in \$) and the unemployment rate (in %), respectively. A portion of monthly data from January 2008 to June 2009 is given in Table 15.18. Inspect the behavior of the residuals in order to comment on serial correlation.

TABLE 15.18 Sales, Advertising Costs, and Unemployment Data for Example 15.12

Sushi_Restaurant

Month	Year	Sales	Advertising Costs	Unemployment Rate
January	2008	27.0	550	4.6
February	2008	24.2	425	4.3
⋮	⋮	⋮	⋮	⋮
May	2009	27.4	550	9.1

Source for the unemployment rate data: Development Department, State of California, June 2009.

SOLUTION: The model is estimated as

$$\hat{y} = 17.5060 + 0.0266x_1 - 0.6879x_2,$$
$$(se) \quad (3.9817) \quad (0.0068) \quad (0.2997)$$

where we have put the standard errors of the coefficients in parentheses. We will reference these values when we incorporate R instructions at the end of this section.

In order to detect serial correlation, we plot the residuals sequentially against time t, where t is given by 1, 2, . . . , 17 for the 17 months of time series data. Figure 15.5 shows a wavelike movement in the residuals over time, first clustering below the horizontal axis, then above the horizontal axis, and so on. Given this pattern around the horizontal axis, we conclude that the observations are correlated.

FIGURE 15.5 Scatterplot of residuals against time t

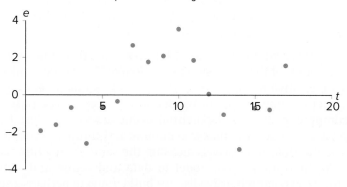

Remedy

As mentioned earlier, in the presence of correlated observations, the OLS estimators are unbiased but their standard errors are inappropriate and generally distorted downward, making the model look better than it really is. Therefore, OLS still provides reasonable coefficient estimates, but the t and the F tests are no longer valid. This has prompted some researchers to use the OLS estimates but correct the standard errors using the Newey-West procedure. As in the case of changing variability, the current version of Excel does not include this correction. However, it is available on many statistical computer packages, including R. At the end of this section, we use R to make the necessary correction in Example 15.12. We can perform legitimate t-tests once the standard errors have been corrected.

Common Violation 5: Excluded Variables

Another crucial assumption in a linear regression model is that the error term is not correlated with the explanatory variables. In general, this assumption breaks down when important explanatory variables are excluded. If one or more of the relevant explanatory variables are excluded, then the resulting OLS estimators are biased. The extent of the bias depends on the degree of the correlation between the included and the excluded explanatory variables.

Suppose we want to estimate $y = \beta_0 + \beta_1 x + \varepsilon$, where y is salary and x is years of education. This model excludes innate ability, which is an important ingredient for salary. Since ability is omitted, it gets incorporated in the error term and the resulting error term is likely to be correlated with years of education. Now consider someone who is highly educated and also commands a high salary. The model will associate high salary with education, when, in fact, it may be the person's unobserved high level of innate ability that has raised both education and salary. In sum, this violation leads to unreliable coefficient estimates; some estimates may even have the wrong signs.

Remedy

It is important that we include all relevant explanatory variables in the regression model. An important first step before running a regression model is to compile a comprehensive list of potential explanatory variables. We can then build down to perhaps a smaller list of explanatory variables using the adjusted R^2 criterion. Sometimes, due to data limitations, we are unable to include all relevant variables. For example, innate ability may be an important explanatory variable for a model that explains salary, but we are unable to include it since innate ability is not observable. In such instances, we use a technique called the instrumental variable technique, which is outside the scope of this text.

Summary

Regression models are an integral part of business statistics. It takes practice to become an effective user of the regression methodology. We should think of regression modeling as an iterative process. We start with a clear understanding of what the regression model is supposed to do. We define the relevant response variable and compile a comprehensive list of potential explanatory variables. The emphasis should be to pick a model that makes economic and intuitive sense and avoid explanatory variables that more or less measure the same thing, thus causing multicollinearity. We then apply this model to data and refine and improve its fit. Specifically, from the comprehensive list, we build down to perhaps a smaller list of explanatory variables using significance tests and goodness-of-fit measures such as the standard error of the estimate and the adjusted R^2. It is important that we explore residual plots to look for signs of changing variability and correlated observations in cross-sectional and time series studies, respectively. If we identify any of these two violations, we can still trust the point estimates of the regression coefficients. However, we cannot place much faith in the standard t or F tests of significance unless we employ the necessary correction.

Using Excel and R to Construct Residual Plots

We first replicate Figure 15.4 from Example 15.11 in Excel and R. Since we found that changing variability was an issue in Example 15.11, we show how to calculate White's standard errors in R.

We then replicate Figure 15.5 from Example 15.12. Since we found that correlated observations were an issue in Example 15.12, we show how to calculate Newey-West standard errors in R.

Convenience_Stores

Using Excel to Replicate Figure 15.4

A. Open the ***Convenience_Stores*** data file.

B. Choose **Data > Data Analysis > Regression** from the menu.

C. For *Input Y Range*, select the Sales data, and for *Input X Range*, select the Sqft data.

D. Select *Residual Plots*.

E. Click **OK**. You should see a graph very similar to Figure 15.4. Formatting (regarding colors, axes, etc.) can be done by selecting **Format** from the menu.

Using R to Replicate Figure 15.4 and Obtain White's Standard Errors

A. Import the ***Convenience_Stores*** data into a data frame (table) in R.

B. Install and load the *sandwich* package. We use this package to calculate robust standard errors. Enter:

```
> install.packages("sandwich")
> library(sandwich)
```

C. As shown in Chapter 14, we use the **lm** function to create a simple linear model or, in R terminology, an object. We label this object as Simple. Enter:

```
> Simple <- lm(Sales~Sqft, data=Convenience_Stores)
```

D. We use the **resid** function to obtain the residuals from the simple linear model or object. We label these residuals as Simple_Residuals. Enter:

```
> Simple_Residuals <- resid(Simple)
```

E. We use the **plot** function to create a scatterplot of the residuals against the explanatory variable, Sqft. We use the *xlab* and *ylab* options to add labels to the x- and y-axes. Enter:

```
> plot(Simple_Residuals ~ Convenience_Stores$'Sqft',
  xlab ="Sqft", ylab ="e")
```

The scatterplot that R returns should look very similar to Figure 15.4.

F. Given the residual plot from Figure 15.4, changing variability is an issue in the simple linear regression model of Sales as a function of Sqft. We use the **vcovHC** function in the *sandwich* package to calculate robust standard errors for the OLS estimators. By using the option *type* = "HC1," we are asking R to apply a widely used formula for calculating robust standard errors (other designations within *type* are available in R). Enter:

```
> vcovHC(Simple, type="HC1")
```

R returns:

```
                 (Intercept)           Sqft
 (Intercept)  91.45127988  -6.095285e-02
 Sqft          -0.06095285   4.149344e-05
```

The above output represents the variance-covariance matrix, where the diagonal elements contain the variances and the off-diagonal elements contain the covariances of the OLS estimators. Since we are interested in the standard errors, we simply take the square roots of the diagonal values of the matrix (see values in boldface). In order to find the standard errors, labeled as Simple_SE, enter:

```
> Simple_SE <- diag(vcovHC(Simple,type="HC1"))^0.5
> Simple_SE
```

```
  (Intercept)        Sqft
  9.56301625   0.00644154
```

So now the corrected standard errors for the intercept and Sqft are 9.5630 and 0.0064, respectively. Recall from Example 15.11 that the OLS-generated standard errors for the intercept and Sqft were 10.4764 and 0.0057, respectively. We can easily compute the t test of significance using the OLS estimates with the corrected standard errors.

Using Excel to Replicate Figure 15.5

A. Open the **Sushi_Restaurant** data file.

B. Choose **Data > Data Analysis > Regression** from the menu.

C. For *Input Y Range*, select the Sales data, and for *Input X Range*, simultaneously select the AdsCost and Unemp data.

D. Select *Residuals*. Click **OK**.

E. Given the regression output, select the residual data and choose **Insert > Scatter**; choose the option on the top left. (If you are having trouble finding this option after selecting **Insert**, look for the graph with data points above **Charts**.) You should see a graph very similar to Figure 15.5. Formatting (regarding colors, axes, etc.) can be done by selecting **Format** from the menu.

A. Follow steps A through D from the instructions for Replicating Figure 15.4, except import the ***Sushi_Restaurant*** data file and create an object, labeled Multiple, which expresses Sales as a function of AdsCost and Unemp. Retrieve the residuals and label them as Multiple_Residuals.

B. We use the **seq** function to create a time variable, labeled as T, that has the same number of observations as Multiple_Residuals, and then we use the **plot** function. We also use the **abline** function to insert a line at the x-axis. Enter:

```
> T <- seq(from = 1, to = length(Multiple_Residuals))
> plot(Multiple_Residuals ~ T, xlab = "time", ylab = "e")
> abline(h = 0)
```

The scatterplot that R returns should look very similar to Figure 15.5.

C. Given the scatterplot, correlated observations are an issue in the multiple linear regression model of Sales as a function of AdsCost and Unemp. We use the **NeweyWest** function in the *sandwich* package to calculate corrected standard errors for the OLS estimators. By using the option *prewhite*=FALSE, we are asking for the most basic correction (many other options are available in R). Enter:

```
> NeweyWest(Multiple, prewhite=FALSE)
```

R returns:

```
              (Intercept)        AdsCost         Unemp
(Intercept)  18.10230474  -2.342228e-02  -5.592667e-01
AdsCost      -0.02342228   4.056877e-05  -9.819913e-05
Unemp        -0.55926668  -9.819913e-05   9.036499e-02
```

As in the case of White's correction, the above output represents the variance-covariance matrix, where the diagonal elements contain the variances and the off-diagonal elements contain the covariances of the OLS estimators. Since we are interested in the standard errors, we simply take the square roots of the diagonal values of the matrix (see values in boldface). In order to find the standard errors, labeled as Multiple_SE, enter:

```
> Multiple_SE<-diag(NeweyWest(Multiple))^0.5
> Multiple_SE
(Intercept)      AdsCost        Unemp
4.773375748 0.006961572 0.354646071
```

So now the corrected standard errors for the intercept, AdsCost, and Unemp are 4.7734, 0.0070, and 0.3546, respectively. Recall from Example 15.12 that the OLS-generated standard errors for the intercept, AdsCost, and Unemp were 3.9817, 0.0068, and 0.2997, respectively. The corrected standard errors are all higher than the OLS estimates, which is typically what we expect when correlated observations are an issue in a regression model. We can easily compute the t test of significance using the OLS estimates with the corrected standard errors.

EXERCISES 15.4

Mechanics

45. Using 20 observations, the multiple regression model $y = \beta_0 + \beta_1 x_1 + \beta_2 x_2 + \varepsilon$ was estimated. A portion of the regression results is as follows:

	df	SS	MS	F	Significance F
Regression	2	2.12E+12	1.06E+12	56.556	3.07E-08
Residual	17	3.19E+11	1.88E+10		
Total	19	2.44E+12			

	Coefficients	Standard Error	t Stat	p-value	Lower 95%	Upper 95%
Intercept	−987557	131583	−7.505	0.000	−1265173	−709941
x_1	29233	32653	0.895	0.383	−39660	98125
x_2	30283	32645	0.928	0.367	−38592	99158

    a. At the 5% significance level, are the explanatory variables jointly significant?

    b. At the 5% significance level, is each explanatory variable individually significant?

    c. What is the likely problem with this model?

46. A simple linear regression, $y = \beta_0 + \beta_1 x + \varepsilon$, is estimated with cross-sectional data. The resulting residuals e along with the values of the explanatory variable x are shown in the accompanying table.

x	1	2	5	7	10	14	15	20	24	30
e	−2	1	−3	2	4	−5	−6	8	11	−10

    a. Graph the residuals e against the values of the explanatory variable x and look for any discernible pattern.

    b. Which assumption is being violated? Discuss its consequences and suggest a possible remedy.

47. A simple linear regression, $y = \beta_0 + \beta_1 x + \varepsilon$, is estimated with time series data. The resulting residuals e and the time variable t are shown in the accompanying table.

t	1	2	3	4	5	6	7	8	9	10
e	−5	−4	−2	3	6	8	4	−5	−3	−2

    a. Graph the residuals against time and look for any discernible pattern.

    b. Which assumption is being violated? Discuss its consequences and suggest a possible remedy.

Applications

48. **FILE** *Television.* Numerous studies have shown that watching too much television hurts school grades. Others have argued that television is not necessarily a bad thing for children (*Mail Online*, July 18, 2009). Like books and stories, television not only entertains, it also exposes a child to new information about the world. While watching too much television is harmful, a little bit may actually help. Researcher

Matt Castle gathers information on the grade point average (GPA) of 28 middle-school children and the number of hours of television they watched per week. Examine the linearity assumption in the regression model, GPA $= \beta_0 + \beta_1$Hours $+ \varepsilon$.

49. **FILE** *Delivery.* Quick2U, a delivery company, would like to standardize its delivery charge model for shipments (Charge in $) such that customers will better understand their delivery costs. Three explanatory variables are used: (1) distance (in miles), (2) shipment weight (in lbs), and (3) number of boxes. A sample of 30 recent deliveries is collected; a portion of the data is shown in the accompanying table.

Charge	Distance	Weight	Boxes
92.50	29	183	1
157.60	96	135	3
⋮	⋮	⋮	⋮
143.00	47	117	7

    a. Estimate the model Charge $= \beta_0 + \beta_1$Distance $+ \beta_2$Weight $+ \beta_3$Boxes $+ \varepsilon$ and examine the joint and individual significance of the explanatory variables at the 1% level.

    b. Is there any evidence of multicollinearity?

    c. Graph the residuals against the predicted values and determine if there is any evidence of changing variability.

50. Consider the results of a survey where students were asked about their GPA and also to break down their typical 24-hour day into study, leisure (including work), and sleep. Consider the model GPA $= \beta_0 + \beta_1$Study $+ \beta_2$Leisure $+ \beta_3$Sleep $+ \varepsilon$.

    a. What is wrong with this model?

    b. Suggest a simple way to reformulate the model.

51. **FILE** *AnnArbor_Rental.* Consider the monthly rent (Rent in $) of a home in Ann Arbor, Michigan, as a function of the number of bedrooms (Beds), the number of bathrooms (Baths), and square footage (Sqft).

    a. Estimate: Rent $= \beta_0 + \beta_1$Beds $+ \beta_2$Baths $+ \beta_3$Sqft $+ \varepsilon$.

    b. Which of the explanatory variables might cause changing variability? Explain.

    c. Use residual plots to verify your economic intuition.

52. **FILE** *Work_Experience.* Consider the data on salary (in $) and work experience (in years) of 100 employees in a marketing firm. Estimate the model: Salary $= \beta_0 + \beta_1$Experience $+ \varepsilon$.

    a. Explain why you would be concerned about changing variability in this application.

    b. Use a residual plot to confirm your economic intuition.

53. **FILE** *Healthy_Living.* Healthy living has always been an important goal for any society. In an ad campaign for Walt Disney, former First Lady Michelle Obama shows parents

and children that eating well and exercising can also be fun (*USA Today*, September 30, 2010). Consider a regression model that conjectures that fruits and vegetables and regular exercising have a positive effect on health and smoking has a negative effect on health. The sample consists of the percentage of these variables observed in various states in the United States in 2009. A portion of the data is shown in the accompanying table.

State	Healthy	Fruits/Vegetables	Exercise	Smoke
AK	88.7	23.3	60.6	14.6
AL	78.3	20.3	41.0	16.4
⋮	⋮	⋮	⋮	⋮
WY	87.5	23.3	57.2	15.2

Source: Centers for Disease Control and Prevention.

a. Estimate the model Healthy $= \beta_0 + \beta_1$Fruits/Vegetables $+ \beta_2$Exercise $+ \beta_3$Smoke $+ \varepsilon$.

b. Analyze the data to determine if multicollinearity and changing variability are present.

54. **FILE** *Johnson_Johnson.* A capital asset pricing model (CAPM) for Johnson & Johnson (J&J) was discussed in Example 15.3. The model uses the risk-adjusted stock return $R - R_f$ for J&J as the response variable and the risk-adjusted market return $R_M - R_f$ as the explanatory variable. Since serial correlation may occur with time series data, it is prudent to inspect the behavior of the residuals. Construct a scatterplot of the residuals against time to comment on correlated observations.

55. **FILE** *Consumption_Quarterly.* The consumption function is one of the key relationships in economics, where consumption y depends on disposable income x. Consider the quarterly data for these seasonally adjusted variables, measured in billions of dollars. A portion of the data is shown in the accompanying table.

Date	Consumption	Disposable Income
2006:01	9148.2	9705.2
2006:02	9266.6	9863.8
⋮	⋮	⋮
2010:04	10525.2	11514.7

Source: U.S. Department of Commerce.

a. Estimate Consumption $= \beta_0 + \beta_1$Disposable Income $+ \varepsilon$. Plot the residuals against time to determine if there is a possibility of correlated observations.

b. Discuss the consequences of correlated observations and suggest a possible remedy.

56. **FILE** *Mowers.* The marketing manager at Turfco, a lawn mower company, believes that monthly sales across all outlets (stores, online, etc.) are influenced by three key variables: (1) outdoor temperature (in °F), (2) advertising expenditures (in $1,000s), and (3) promotional discounts (in %). A portion of the monthly sales data for the past two years is shown in the accompanying table.

Sales	Temperature	Advertising	Discount
17235	33	15	5.0
19854	42	25	5.0
⋮	⋮	⋮	⋮
22571	44	21	5.0

a. Estimate the model Sales $= \beta_0 + \beta_1$Temperature $+ \beta_2$Advertising $+ \beta_3$Discount $+ \varepsilon$, and test for the joint and individual significance of the explanatory variables at the 5% level.

b. Examine the data for evidence of multicollinearity. Provide two reasons why it might be best to do nothing about multicollinearity in this application.

c. Examine the residual plots for evidence of changing variability.

WRITING WITH STATISTICS

Ben Leach is a statistician for a Major League Baseball (MLB) team. One aspect of his job is to assess the value of various players. At the moment, Ben's team is in dire need of an outfielder. Management is ready to make an offer to a certain prospect but asks Ben for some input concerning salary. Management believes that a player's batting average (BA), runs batted in (RBI), and years of experience playing professional baseball (Experience) are the most important factors that influence a player's salary. Management is focusing on a player who has played professional baseball for seven years and whose average BA and RBI over this time have been 266 and 50, respectively. Ben collects data on salary (in $1,000s), BA, RBI, and Experience for 138 outfielders in 2008. Table 15.19 shows a portion of the data.

TABLE 15.19 Major League Baseball Outfielder Data, $n = 138$

Player	Salary	BA	RBI	Experience
1. Nick Markakis	455	299	87	3
2. Adam Jones	390	261	23	3
⋮	⋮	⋮	⋮	⋮
138. Randy Winn	8875	288	53	11

Notes: All data collected from usatoday.com or http://espn.com; BA and RBI are averages over the player's professional life through 2008. For exposition, BA has been multiplied by 1000.

Ben would like to use information in Table 15.19 to

1. Summarize Salaries, BAs, RBIs, and Experience of current outfielders. Examine the potential multicollinearity problem.

2. Address management's claim that BA, RBI, and Experience have a statistically significant influence on salary.

3. Evaluate the expected salary for the prospective player, given his values for BA, RBI, and Experience.

Sample Report— Baseball Salaries

In an attempt to assess the factors that influence an outfielder's salary in Major League Baseball (MLB), data were collected from 138 current players. Management believes that an outfielder's salary is best predicted using the outfielder's overall batting average (BA), runs batted in (RBI), and years of experience (Experience) as an MLB player. Table 15.A provides some descriptive statistics on these relevant variables.

TABLE 15.A Descriptive Statistics on Salary, BA, RBI, and Experience, $n = 138$

	Salary	BA	RBI	Experience
Mean	3,459	271	43	6
Minimum	390	152	1	1
Maximum	18,623	331	102	20

The average salary of an MLB outfielder in 2008 is a staggering $3,459,000; however, the minimum salary of $390,000 and the maximum salary of $18,623,000 suggest quite a bit of variability in salary. The average outfielder has a BA of 271 with 43 RBIs in a season. Experience of outfielders in 2008 varied from only 1 year to 20 years, with an average of 6 years.

Table 15.B provides regression results from estimating a model where BA, RBI, and Experience are the explanatory variables and Salary is the response variable. All sample correlation coefficients (not reported), between explanatory variables, are less than 0.50, indicating that multicollinearity is not a serious problem in this application.

TABLE 15.B Analysis of Salary of Baseball Players

Variable	Coefficient
Intercept	−4,769.40 (0.130)
BA	4.76 (0.698)
RBI	80.44* (0.000)
Experience	539.67* (0.000)
$R^2 = 0.5795$	
$F_{(3,133)} = 61.544$ (associated p-value = 0.000)	

Notes: p-values are in parentheses; * denotes significance at the 5% level.

The slope coefficients suggest that BA, RBI, and Experience exert a positive influence on Salary. For instance, the slope coefficient of Experience indicates that if an outfielder stays in the major leagues for one additional year, then, on average, his salary will increase by \$539,670, holding BA and RBI constant. The p-value associated with the value of the $F_{(3,133)}$ test statistic shows that the explanatory variables are jointly significant at the 5% level. Upon testing the explanatory variables individually, the extremely small p-values associated with RBI and Experience reveal that these variables have a significant linear relationship with Salary; surprisingly, BA is not significant at the 5% level. The coefficient of determination R^2 shows that approximately 58% of Salary is explained by the estimated regression model, leaving 42% of the variability in Salary unexplained.

Lastly, for an MLB player with seven years' experience and an average BA and RBI of 266 and 50, respectively, the model predicts a salary of \$4,295,320. With 95% confidence, expected salary will lie between \$3,731,360 and \$4,859,280. Perhaps before management makes an offer to the player, the model should consider including other factors that may significantly influence a player's salary. One possible explanatory variable for inclusion is a player's on-base percentage.

CONCEPTUAL REVIEW

LO 15.1 Conduct a test of individual significance.

A test of individual significance determines whether the explanatory variable x_j has an individual statistical influence on y. The value of the test statistic is calculated as $t_{df} = \frac{b_j - \beta_{j0}}{se(b_j)}$, where $df = n - k - 1$, $se(b_j)$ is the standard error of the OLS estimator b_j, and β_{j0} is the hypothesized value of β_j. If $\beta_{j0} = 0$, the value of the test statistic reduces to $t_{df} = \frac{b_j}{se(b_j)}$. Excel, R, and virtually all other statistical packages report a value of the test statistic and its associated p-value for a two-tailed test that assesses whether the regression coefficient differs from zero.

- If we specify a one-tailed test, then we need to divide the computer-generated p-value in half.
- If we test whether the coefficient differs from a nonzero value, then we cannot use the value of the computer-generated test statistic and its p-value.

The $100(1 - \alpha)\%$ confidence interval for the regression coefficient β_j is given by $b_j \pm t_{\alpha/2,df} se(b_j)$, where $df = n - k - 1$.

LO 15.2 Conduct a test of joint significance.

A **test of joint significance** determines whether the explanatory variables $x_1, x_2, \ldots, x_k$ in a multiple regression model have a joint statistically significant influence on y. The value of the test statistic is calculated as $F_{(df_1,df_2)} = \frac{MSR}{MSE}$, where $df_1 = k$, $df_2 = n - k - 1$, MSR is the mean square regression, and MSE is the mean square error. Excel, R, and virtually all other statistical packages report both the value of the test statistic and its associated p-value.

LO 15.3 Conduct a general test of linear restrictions.

When **testing linear restrictions**, the value of the test statistic is calculated as $F_{(df_1,df_2)} = \frac{(SSE_R - SSE_U)/df_1}{SSE_U/df_2}$, where df_1 is equal to the number of linear restrictions, $df_2 = n - k - 1$ (k is the number of explanatory variables in the unrestricted model), and SSE_R and SSE_U are the error sum of squares of the restricted and unrestricted models, respectively. If the null hypothesis is rejected, then the linear restrictions are not valid.

Calculate and interpret confidence intervals and prediction intervals.

For specific values of $x_1, x_2, \ldots, x_k$, denoted by $x_1^0, x_2^0, \ldots, x_k^0$, the $100(1 - \alpha)\%$ **confidence interval for the expected value of** y is given by $\hat{y}^0 \pm t_{\alpha/2,df} se(\hat{y}^0)$, where $df = n - k - 1$ and $se(\hat{y}^0)$ is the standard error of $\hat{y}^0$. To derive $\hat{y}^0$ together with $se(\hat{y}^0)$, we first estimate a modified regression model where y is the response variable and the explanatory variables are defined as $x_1^* = x_1 - x_1^0, x_2^* = x_2 - x_2^0, \ldots, x_k^* = x_k - x_k^0$. The resulting estimate of the intercept and its standard error equal $\hat{y}^0$ and $se(\hat{y}^0)$, respectively.

For specific values of $x_1, x_2, \ldots, x_k$, denoted by $x_1^0, x_2^0, \ldots, x_k^0$, the $100(1 - \alpha)\%$ **prediction interval for an individual value of** y is given by $\hat{y} \pm t_{\alpha/2,df} \sqrt{(se(\hat{y}^0))^2 + s_e^2}$, where $df = n - k - 1$, $se(\hat{y}^0)$ is the standard error of $\hat{y}^0$, and s_e is the standard error of the estimate.

LO 15.5 **Explain the role of the assumptions on the OLS estimators.**

Under the assumptions of the classical linear regression model, OLS provides the best estimates. However, the desirable properties of the OLS estimators become compromised as one or more model assumptions are violated. In addition, for certain violations, it is not possible to make meaningful inferences from the t and F test results.

LO 15.6 **Describe common violations of the assumptions and offer remedies.**

Common violations of the OLS assumptions include: nonlinear patterns, multicollinearity, changing variability, correlated observations, and excluded variables. Residual plots are used to identify some of these violations; they also help identify outliers. The model is adequate if the residuals are randomly dispersed around the zero value.

If **nonlinear patterns** exist in the data, yet we estimate a linear relationship between the response and the explanatory variables, the resulting OLS estimates can be quite misleading. Often, a plot of the residuals against the explanatory variable(s) will reveal whether or not a nonlinear relationship should be incorporated into the model.

Some degree of **multicollinearity** is present in most applications. A high R^2 coupled with insignificant explanatory variables is often indicative of multicollinearity. Multicollinearity is considered serious if the sample correlation coefficient between any two explanatory variables is more than 0.80 or less than -0.80. We can drop one of the collinear variables if its omission can be justified. We can obtain more data, as that may weaken the correlation. Another option is to express the explanatory variables differently. At times the best approach may be to do nothing, especially if the estimated model yields a high R^2.

The assumption of **constant variability** often breaks down in cross-sectional studies. The resulting OLS estimators are unbiased, but the standard errors of the OLS estimators are inappropriate, making the standard t or F tests invalid. This assumption is violated if the variability of the residuals increases or decreases over the values of an explanatory variable. Researchers often use the OLS estimates along with corrected standard errors, often referred to as robust standard errors.

The assumption of **uncorrelated observations** often breaks down in time series studies. The resulting OLS estimators are unbiased but their standard errors are inappropriate. In general, correlated observations make the model look better than it really is with a spuriously high R^2. Furthermore, the t and the F test results may incorrectly suggest significance of the explanatory variables. This assumption is violated if the residuals show a pattern around the horizontal time axis. Researchers often use the OLS estimates along with a correction for the standard errors, using the Newey-West procedure.

It is important that the regression model incorporates all relevant explanatory variables. In the case of **excluded variables**, the OLS estimators are generally biased.

ADDITIONAL EXERCISES AND CASE STUDIES

Exercises

57. In an attempt to determine whether or not a linear relationship exists between the price of a home (in $1,000s) and the number of days it takes to sell the home, a real estate agent collected data from recent sales in his city and estimated the following model: Price $= \beta_0 + \beta_1\text{Days} + \varepsilon$. A portion of the regression results is shown in the accompanying table.

	Coefficients	Standard Error	t Stat	p-value
Intercept	−384.9281	574.6456	−0.670	0.528
Days	5.3154	1.0242	5.190	0.002

Specify the hypotheses to determine whether Days is significant in explaining a house's price. At the 5% significance level, what is the conclusion to the test? Explain.

58. **FILE** *Quotations.* The labor estimation group at Sturdy Electronics, a contract electronics manufacturer of printed circuit boards, wants to simplify the process it uses to quote production costs to potential customers. They have identified the primary drivers for production time (and thus production cost) as being the number of electronic parts that can be machine-installed and the number of parts that must be manually installed. Accordingly, they wish to develop a multiple regression model to predict production time, measured as minutes per board, using a random sample of 25 recent product quotations. A portion of the data is shown in the accompanying table.

Production Time	Machine Parts	Manual Parts
9.1	275	14
10.8	446	12
⋮	⋮	⋮
15.5	618	16

a. What is the sample regression equation?
b. Predict production time for a circuit board with 475 machine-installed components and 16 manually installed components.
c. What proportion of the sample variability in production time is explained by the two explanatory variables?
d. At the 5% significance level, are the explanatory variables jointly significant? Are they individually significant?

59. **FILE** *Happiness_Age.* A sociologist wishes to study the relationship between happiness and age. He interviews 24 individuals and collects data on age and happiness, measured on a scale from 0 to 100. Estimate: Happiness $= \beta_0 + \beta_1\text{Age} + \varepsilon$. At the 1% significance level, is Age significant in explaining Happiness?

60. **FILE** *Home_Ownership.* The home ownership rate in the U.S. was 67.4% in 2009. In order to determine if home ownership is linked with income, 2009 state-level data on the home ownership rate (Ownership in %) and median household income (Income in $) were collected. A portion of the data is shown in the accompanying table.

State	Ownership	Income
Alabama	74.1	39980
Alaska	66.8	61604
⋮	⋮	⋮
Wyoming	73.8	52470

Source: www.census.gov.

a. Estimate: Ownership $= \beta_0 + \beta_1\text{Income} + \varepsilon$.
b. At the 5% significance level, is Income linearly related to Ownership?
c. Construct the 95% confidence interval for the expected value of Ownership if Income is $50,000.
d. Compare the above confidence interval with the 95% prediction interval for Ownership if Income is $50,000.

61. **FILE** *SAT.* A researcher studies the relationship between SAT scores, the test-taker's family income (Income), and his/her grade point average (GPA). Data are collected from 24 students. A portion of the data is shown in the accompanying table.

SAT	Income	GPA
1651	47000	2.79
1581	34000	2.97
⋮	⋮	⋮
1940	113000	3.96

Estimate: SAT $= \beta_0 + \beta_1\text{Income} + \beta_2\text{GPA} + \varepsilon$.
a. At the 5% significance level, are Income and GPA jointly significant?
b. At the 5% significance level, are Income and GPA individually significant?

c.   With 95% confidence, construct the prediction interval for the individual SAT score if Income is $80,000 and GPA is 3.5.

62.   **FILE** *Turnover_Expense.* George believes that the returns of mutual funds are influenced by annual turnover rates and annual expense ratios. In order to substantiate his claim, he randomly selects 20 mutual funds and collects data on each fund's five-year annual return (Return), its annual holding turnover rate (Turnover), and its annual expense ratio (Expense). All variables are measured in percentages. A portion of the data is shown in the accompanying table.

	Return	Turnover	Expense
First Eagle Gold A	−7.32	16	1.27
Dodge&Cox Int'l	10.14	17	0.64
⋮	⋮	⋮	⋮
Brandes Int'l Equity	8.94	18	1.18

Source: All data as of May 15, 2017 from finance.yahoo.com.

a.   Estimate: $Return = \beta_0 + \beta_1 Turnover + \beta_2 Expense + \epsilon$. Conduct appropriate tests to verify George's theory at the 5% significance level.

b.   Discuss the potential problems of multicollinearity and changing variability.

63.   **FILE** *Crime.* A government researcher examines the factors that influence a city's crime rate. For 41 cities, she collects the crime rate (crimes per 100,000 residents), the poverty rate (in %), the median income (in $1,000s), the percent of residents younger than 18, and the percent of residents older than 65. A portion of the data is shown in the accompanying table.

Crime	Poverty	Income	Under 18	Over 65
710.6	3.8	58.422	18.3	23.4
1317.7	16.7	48.729	19.0	10.3
⋮	⋮	⋮	⋮	⋮
139.7	3.9	59.445	19.7	16

a.   Estimate: $Crime = \beta_0 + \beta_1 Poverty + \beta_2 Income + \beta_3 Under\ 18 + \beta_4 Over\ 65 + \epsilon$. Discuss the individual and joint significance of the explanatory variables at the 5% significance level.

b.   At the 5% level, conduct a partial F test to determine if the influence of Under 18 is different from that of Over 65.

c.   Which explanatory variables are likely to be collinear? Find their sample correlation coefficients to confirm.

64.   **FILE** *DOW_2010.* A research analyst is trying to determine whether a firm's price-earnings (P/E) and price-sales (P/S) ratios can explain the firm's stock performance over the past year. Generally, a high P/E ratio suggests that investors are expecting higher earnings growth in the future compared to companies with a lower P/E ratio. Investors use the P/S ratio to determine how much they are paying for a dollar of the firm's sales rather than a dollar of its earnings. In short, the higher the P/E ratio and the lower the P/S ratio, the more attractive the investment. The accompanying table shows a portion of the 30 firms included in the Dow Jones Industrial Average with each firm's annual return (in %), P/E ratio, and P/S ratio.

Return	P/E	P/S
4.4	14.37	2.41
−4.5	11.01	0.78
⋮	⋮	⋮
16.3	13.94	1.94

Source: The 2010 returns (January 1, 2010–December 31, 2010) were obtained from *The Wall Street Journal*, January 3, 2011; the P/E ratios and the P/S ratios were obtained from finance.yahoo.com on January 20, 2011.

a.   Estimate: $Return = \beta_0 + \beta_1 P/E + \beta_2 P/S + \epsilon$. Show the regression results in a well-formatted table.

b.   Determine whether P/E and P/S are jointly significant at the 5% significance level.

c.   Establish whether the explanatory variables are individually significant at the 5% significance level.

d.   What is the predicted return for a firm with a P/E ratio of 10 and a P/S ratio of 2? Use these values to construct the 95% confidence interval for the expected return.

65.   **FILE** *Smoking.* A nutritionist wants to understand the influence of income and healthy food on the incidence of smoking. He collects 2009 data on the percentage of smokers in each state in the U.S. and the corresponding median income (in $) and the percentage of the population that regularly eats fruits and vegetables. A portion of the data is shown in the accompanying table.

State	Smoke	Fruits/ Vegetables	Median Income
AK	14.6	23.3	61604
AL	16.4	20.3	39980
⋮	⋮	⋮	⋮
WY	15.2	23.3	52470

Source: Centers for Disease Control and Prevention and U.S. Census Bureau.

a. Estimate: Smoke $= \beta_0 + \beta_1$Fruits/Vegetables $+ \beta_2$Median Income $+ \varepsilon$.

b. At the 5% level of significance, are the explanatory variables individually and jointly significant? Explain.

c. Use the sample correlation coefficients to evaluate the potential problem of multicollinearity.

66. **FILE** *PerCapita.* Consider a regression model for per capita income, y. The explanatory variables consist of the percentage of the population in the U.S. that is (a) without a high school diploma, x_1, (b) foreign born, x_2, and (c) non-English speaking, x_3. A portion of the data is shown in the accompanying table.

State	Per capita Income	No High School	Foreign Born	No English
Alabama	22984	18.6	3.4	4.9
Alaska	30726	9.3	7.2	16.5
⋮	⋮	⋮	⋮	⋮
Wyoming	27860	8.7	3.1	6.7

Source: 2010 U.S. Census

a. Estimate the model, $y = \beta_0 + \beta_1 x_1 + \beta_2 x_2 + \beta_3 x_3 + \varepsilon$, and test for the joint and individual significance of the explanatory variables at the 5% level.

b. What proportion of the sample variability in per capita income is explained by the explanatory variables?

c. Do you suspect multicollinearity in the model? Use sample data to confirm.

67. **FILE** *MCAS.* A researcher examines the factors that influence student performance. She gathers data on 224 school districts in Massachusetts. The response variable is the students' mean score on a standardized test (Score). She uses four explanatory variables in her analysis: the student-to-teacher ratio (STR in %), the average teacher's salary (TSAL in $1,000s), the median household income (INC in $1,000s), and the percentage of single family households (SGL). A portion of the data is shown in the accompanying table.

Score	STR	TSAL	INC	SGL
227.00	19.00	44.01	48.89	4.70
230.67	17.90	40.17	43.91	4.60
⋮	⋮	⋮	⋮	⋮
230.67	19.20	44.79	47.64	5.10

Source: Massachusetts Department of Education and the Census of Population and Housing.

a. Estimate: Score $= \beta_0 + \beta_1$STR $+ \beta_2$TSAL $+ \beta_3$INC $+ \beta_4$SGL $+ \varepsilon$. Show the regression results in a well-formatted table.

b. Suppose you want to test if school input factors, STR and TSAL, are significant in explaining Score. Specify the competing hypotheses. Estimate the restricted model. At the 5% significance level, can you conclude that STR and TSAL are jointly significant?

c. Suppose you want to test if socioeconomic factors, INC and SGL, are significant in explaining Score. Specify the competing hypotheses. Estimate the restricted model. At the 5% significance level, can you conclude that INC and SGL are jointly significant?

CASE STUDIES

CASE STUDY 15.1 American football is the highest-paying sport on a per-game basis. Given that the quarterback is considered the most important player on the team, he is typically well-compensated. A sports statistician examines the factors that influence a quarterback's salary. He believes that a quarterback's pass completion rate is the most important variable affecting salary. He also wonders how total touchdowns scored and a quarterback's age might impact salary. The statistician collects data on salary (in $ millions), pass completion rate (PC in %), total touchdowns scored (TD), and age for 32 quarterbacks during the 2009 season. A portion of the data is shown in the accompanying table.

FILE

Quarterback_Salaries

Data for Case Study 15.1 Quarterback Salary Data, 2009

Name	Salary	PC	TD	Age
Philip Rivers	25.5566	65.2	28	27
Jay Cutler	22.0441	60.5	27	26
⋮	⋮	⋮	⋮	⋮
Tony Romo	0.6260	63.1	26	29

Source: USA Today database for salaries; NFL.com for other data.

In a report, use the sample information to

1. Estimate and interpret the model: $\text{Salary} = \beta_0 + \beta_1 PC + \beta_2 TD + \beta_3 Age + \varepsilon$.

2. Discuss the individual and joint significance of the explanatory variables at the 5% level.

3. Determine whether TD and Age are jointly significant at the 5% significance level.

4. Construct the 95% confidence interval for the expected salary of a quarterback using average values of PC, TD, and Age.

CASE STUDY 15.2   Apple Inc. has established a unique reputation in the consumer electronics industry with its development of products such as the iPod, the iPhone, and the iPad. As of May 2010, Apple had surpassed Microsoft as the most valuable company in the world (*The New York Times*, May 26, 2010). Michael Gomez is a stock analyst and wonders if the return on Apple's stock is best modeled using the CAPM model. He collects five years of monthly data, a portion of which is shown in the accompanying table.

Data for Case Study 15.2 Apple Return Data, $n = 60$

Date	$R - R_f$	$R_M - R_f$
1/1/2006	4.70	2.21
2/1/2006	−9.65	−0.31
⋮	⋮	⋮
11/1/2010	1.68	2.15

Source: finance.yahoo.com and U.S. Treasury.

FILE
Apple

In a report, use the sample information to

1. Estimate and interpret CAPM: $R - R_f = \beta_0 + \beta_1(R_M - R_f) + \varepsilon$. Search for Apple's reported Beta on the Web and compare it with your estimate.

2. At the 5% significance level, is the stock return for Apple riskier than that of the market? At the 5% significance level, do abnormal returns exist? Explain.

3. Use a residual plot to analyze the potential problem of correlated observations.

CASE STUDY 15.3   According to a report by the government, new home construction fell to an 18-month low in October 2010 (CNNMoney.com, November 17, 2010). Housing starts, or the number of new homes being built, experienced an 11.7% drop in its seasonally adjusted annual rate. Urmil Singh works for a mortgage company in Madison, Wisconsin. She wants to better understand the quantitative relationship between housing starts (in 1,000s), the mortgage rate (in %), and the unemployment rate (in %). She gathers seasonally adjusted monthly data on these variables from 2006:01–2010:12. A portion of the data is shown in the accompanying table.

Data for Case Study 15.3 Housing Starts and Other Factors, $n = 60$

Date	Housing Starts	Mortgage	Unemployment
2006–01	2273	6.15	4.7
2006–02	2119	6.25	4.8
⋮	⋮	⋮	⋮
2010–12	520	4.71	9.4

Source: Census Bureau and Board of Governors.

FILE
Housing_Starts

In a report, use the sample information to

1. Estimate a multiple regression model for housing starts using the mortgage rate and the unemployment rate as the explanatory variables.

2. At the 5% significance level, evaluate the individual and joint significance of the explanatory variables.

3. Discuss the potential problems of multicollinearity and correlated observations in this time series data application.

APPENDIX 15.1   Guidelines for Other Software Packages

The following section provides brief commands for Minitab, SPSS, and JMP. Copy and paste the specified data file into the relevant software spreadsheet prior to following the commands.

Minitab

Residual Plots—Changing Variability

Convenience_Stores

A. (Replicating Figure 15.4) From the menu, choose **Stat > Regression > Regression > Fit Regression Model**.

B. Next to **Response**, select Sales, and next to **Continuous predictors**, select Sqft. Choose **Graphs**. Under **Residuals Plots**, select **Individual plots**, and under **Residuals versus the variables**, select Sqft.

Residual Plots—Correlated Observations

Sushi_Restaurant

A. (Replicating Figure 15.5) From the menu, choose **Stat > Regression > Regression > Fit Regression Model**.

B. Next to **Response**, select Sales, and next to **Continuous predictors**, select AdsCost and Unemp. Choose **Graphs**. Under **Residuals Plots**, select **Individual plots**, and then select **Residuals versus order**.

Assessing Multicollinearity with a Correlation Matrix

Home_Values

(Replicating Example 15.10) From the menu, choose **Stat > Basic Statistics > Correlation**. Under **Variables**, select HH Income and Per Cap Inc.

SPSS

Residual Plots—Changing Variability

Convenience_Stores

A. (Replicating Figure 15.4) From the menu, choose **Analyze > Regression > Linear**.

B. Under **Dependent**, select Sales, and under **Independent(s)**, select Sqft. Choose **Save**, and under **Residuals**, select **Unstandardized**.

C. From the menu, choose **Graphs > Legacy Dialogs > Scatter/Dot > Simple Scatter**.

D. Under **Y Axis**, select Unstandardized Residual, and under **X Axis**, select Sqft.

Residual Plots—Correlated Observations

Sushi_Restaurant

A. (Replicating Figure 15.5) Add a column to data labeled "time" and number from 1 to 17.

B. From the menu, choose **Analyze > Regression > Linear**.

C. Under **Dependent**, select Sales, and under **Independent(s)**, select AdsCost and Unempl. Choose **Save,** and under **Residuals**, select **Unstandardized**.

D. From the menu, choose **Graphs > Legacy Dialogs > Scatter/Dot > Simple Scatter**.

E. Under **Y Axis**, select Unstandardized Residual, and under **X Axis**, select time.

Assessing Multicollinearity with a Correlation Matrix

A. (Replicating Example 15.10) From the menu, choose **Analyze > Correlate > Bivariate**.

B. Under **Variables**, select HH Income and Per Cap Inc.

FILE
Home_Values

JMP

Residual Plots—Simple Linear Regression

A. (Replicating Example 15.4) From the menu, choose **Analyze > Fit Y by X**.

B. Under **Select Columns**, select Sales, and then under **Cast Selected Columns Into Roles**, select **Y, Response**. Under **Select Columns**, select Sqft, and then under **Cast Selected Columns Into Roles**, select **X, Factor**.

C. Click on the red triangle next to **Bivariate Fit Sales by Sqft**, and select **Fit Line**.

D. Click on the red triangle next to **Linear Fit**, and select **Plot Residuals**.

FILE
Convenience_Stores

Residual Plots—Multiple Regression

A. (Replicating Figure 15.5) From the menu, choose **Analyze > Fit Model**.

B. Under **Select Columns**, select Sales, and then under **Pick Role Variables**, select **Y**. Under **Select Columns**, select AdsCost and Unemp, and then under **Construct Model Effects**, select **Add**.

C. Click on the red triangle next to **Response Sales**, select **Role Diagnostics > Plot Residual by Row**.

FILE
Sushi_Restaurant

Assessing Multicollinearity with a Correlation Matrix

(Replicating Example 15.10) From the menu, choose **Analyze > Multivariate Methods > Multivariate**. Under **Select Columns**, select HH Income and Per Cap Inc, and under **Cast Selected Columns into Roles**, select **Y, Columns**.

FILE
Home_Values

16

Regression Models for Nonlinear Relationships

LEARNING OBJECTIVES

After reading this chapter you should be able to:

LO **16.1** Use and evaluate polynomial regression models.

LO **16.2** Use and evaluate log-transformed models.

LO **16.3** Describe the method used to compare linear models with log-transformed models.

R egression analysis is one of the most widely used statistical techniques in business, engineering, and the social sciences. It empirically validates not only whether a relationship exists between variables, but also quantifies the strength of the relationship. So far, we have considered only linear regression models. There are numerous applications where the relationship between the explanatory variable and the response variable cannot be represented by a straight line and, therefore, must be captured by an appropriate curve. In fact, the choice of a functional form is a crucial part of specifying a regression model. In this chapter, we discuss some common nonlinear regression models by making simple transformations of the variables. These transformations include squares and natural logarithms, which capture interesting nonlinear relationships while still allowing easy estimation within the framework of a linear regression model. We use goodness-of-fit measures to choose between alternative model specifications.

©Yellow Dog Productions/Digital Vision/Getty Images RF

INTRODUCTORY CASE

Rental Market in Ann Arbor, Michigan

Real estate investment in college towns continues to promise good returns (*The Wall Street Journal*, September 24, 2010). First, students offer a steady stream of rental demand as cash-strapped public universities are unable to house their students beyond freshman year. Second, this demand is projected to grow as more children of baby boomers head to college. Marcela Treisman works for an investment firm in Michigan. Her assignment is to analyze the rental market in Ann Arbor, which is home to the main campus of the University of Michigan. She knows that with a third of its population consisting of university students, Ann Arbor is consistently rated as one of the best places to live in the United States. Marcela wants to understand what kind of off-campus homes promise good rental income. She gathers data on monthly rent (Rent, in $) for 2011, along with three characteristics of the home: number of bedrooms (Beds), number of bathrooms (Baths), and square footage (Sqft). A portion of the data is shown in Table 16.1.

TABLE 16.1 Rental Data for Ann Arbor, Michigan; $n = 40$

Rent	Beds	Baths	Sqft
645	1	1	500
675	1	1	648
⋮	⋮	⋮	⋮
2400	3	2.5	2700

FILE *AnnArbor*

Source: www.zillow.com.

Marcela would like to use the information in Table 16.1 to

1. Evaluate various models that quantify the relationship between rent and home characteristics.
2. Use model selection criteria to select the most appropriate model.
3. Make predictions for rental income for specific values of home characteristics.

A synopsis of this case is provided at the end of Section 16.2.

16.1 POLYNOMIAL REGRESSION MODELS

Linear regression models are often justified on the basis of their computational simplicity. An implication of a simple linear regression model, $y = \beta_0 + \beta_1 x + \varepsilon$, is that if x goes up by one unit, the expected value of y changes by β_1, irrespective of the value of x. However, in many applications, the relationship cannot be represented by a straight line and, therefore, must be captured by an appropriate curve. We note that the linearity assumption discussed in Chapter 15 places the restriction of linearity on the parameters and not on the variables. Consequently, we can capture many interesting nonlinear relationships, within the framework of a linear regression model, by simple transformations of the response and/or the explanatory variables.

If you ever studied microeconomics, you may have learned that a firm's (or industry's) average cost curve tends to be "U-shaped." Due to economies of scale, the average cost y of a firm initially decreases as output x increases. However, as x increases beyond a certain point, its impact on y turns positive. Other applications show the influence of the explanatory variable initially positive but then turning negative, leading to an "inverted U shape." The **quadratic regression model** is appropriate when the slope, capturing the influence of x on y, changes in magnitude as well as sign.

A quadratic regression model with one explanatory variable is specified as $y = \beta_0 + \beta_1 x + \beta_2 x^2 + \varepsilon$; we can easily extend it to include multiple explanatory variables. The expression $\beta_0 + \beta_1 x + \beta_2 x^2$ is the deterministic component of a quadratic regression model. In other words, conditional on x, $E(y) = \beta_0 + \beta_1 x + \beta_2 x^2$. This model can easily be estimated as a regression of y on x and x^2.

THE QUADRATIC REGRESSION MODEL

In a quadratic regression model $y = \beta_0 + \beta_1 x + \beta_2 x^2 + \varepsilon$, the coefficient β_2 determines whether the relationship between x and y is U-shaped ($\beta_2 > 0$) or inverted U-shaped ($\beta_2 < 0$).

Predictions with a quadratic model are made by $\hat{y} = b_0 + b_1 x + b_2 x^2$. It is advisable to use unrounded coefficients (or rounded to at least four decimal places) for making predictions.

Figure 16.1 highlights some representative shapes of a quadratic regression model.

FIGURE 16.1
Representative shapes of a quadratic regression model:
$y = \beta_0 + \beta_1 x + \beta_2 x^2 + \varepsilon$

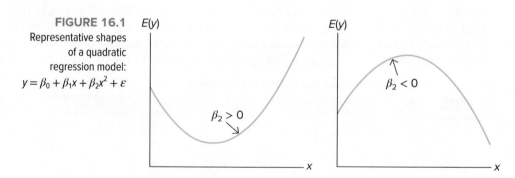

It is important to be able to determine whether a quadratic regression model provides a better fit than the linear regression model. As we learned in Chapter 14, we cannot compare these models on the basis of their respective R^2 values because the quadratic regression model uses one more parameter than the linear regression model. For comparison purposes, we use adjusted R^2, which imposes a penalty for the additional parameter.

EXAMPLE 16.1

Table 16.2 shows a portion of the average cost (in $) and annual output (in millions of units) for 20 manufacturing firms. We also include a column of $Output^2$, which will be used for estimating the quadratic regression model.

TABLE 16.2 Average Cost and Output Data for 20 Manufacturing Firms

Average Cost	Output	Output²
9.61	4	16
9.55	5	25
⋮	⋮	⋮
9.62	11	121

a. Plot average cost (AC) against output.

b. Estimate the linear and the quadratic regression models. Determine which model fits the data best.

c. Use the best-fitting model to predict the average cost for a firm that produces 7 million units.

SOLUTION:

a. It is always informative to begin with a scatterplot of the response variable against the explanatory variable. Make sure that the response variable is on the vertical axis. Figure 16.2 shows average cost against output. We also superimpose linear and quadratic trends on the scatterplot (in Excel, right-click on the scatterpoints, add Trendline, and choose Linear and Polynomial with Order 2). At lower and higher levels of output, average costs are highest. It appears that the average cost in this industry would best be estimated using a quadratic regression model.

FIGURE 16.2 Scatterplot of average cost versus output

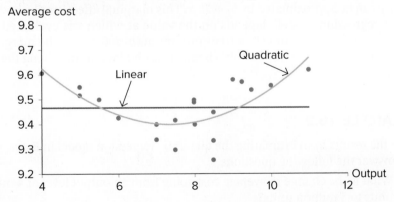

b. The second column of Table 16.3 shows the regression results for the linear regression model: $AC = \beta_0 + \beta_1 Output + \varepsilon$. The linear regression model provides a poor fit, which is not surprising given the scatterplot in Figure 16.2. Not only is Output statistically insignificant, the adjusted R^2 is negative. In order to estimate a quadratic regression model, we have to first create data on the squared Output variable. A portion of these data, computed by squaring Output, is shown in Table 16.2. The third column of Table 16.3 shows the regression results for the quadratic regression model: $AC = \beta_0 + \beta_1 Output + \beta_2 Output^2 + \varepsilon$. In the quadratic regression model, Output is now significant. In addition, the slope coefficient of $Output^2$ is positive and significant, indicating a U-shaped relationship between average cost and output.

TABLE 16.3 Estimates of the Linear and the Quadratic Regression Models for Example 16.1

Variable	Linear Regression Model	Quadratic Regression Model
Intercept	9.4461* (0.000)	10.5225* (0.000)
Output	0.0029 (0.841)	−0.3073* (0.001)
Output^2	NA	0.0210* (0.001)
Adjusted R^2	−0.0531	0.4540

Notes: Parameter estimates are in the main body of the table with the *p*-values in parentheses; NA denotes not applicable; * represents significance at the 5% level. The last row presents adjusted R^2 for model comparison.

Given the adjusted R^2 of 0.4540, the quadratic regression model is clearly better than the linear regression model in explaining average cost.

c. Using the quadratic regression model, the predicted average cost for a firm that produces 7 million units is

$$\widehat{AC} = 10.5225 - 0.3073(7) + 0.0210(7^2) = \$9.40.$$

Interpretation of coefficients in the quadratic regression model: It does not make sense to think of β_1 in the quadratic regression model of Example 16.1 as being the effect of changing a firm's output, holding the square of the firm's output constant. In nonlinear models, the sample regression equation is best interpreted by calculating, and even graphing, the predicted effect on the response variable over a range of values for the explanatory variable. We will elaborate on this point in Examples 16.2 and 16.3.

Evaluating the marginal effect of *x* on *y* in the quadratic regression model: It is important to evaluate the estimated marginal (partial) effect of the explanatory variable x on the predicted value of the response variable; that is, we want to evaluate the change in $\hat{y}$ due to a one unit increase in x. In a linear regression model, $y = \beta_0 + \beta_1 x + \varepsilon$, the marginal effect is constant, estimated by the slope coefficient b_1. In a quadratic regression model, it can be shown with calculus that the marginal effect of x on $\hat{y}$ can be approximated by $b_1 + 2b_2 x$. This marginal effect, unlike in the case of a linear regression model, depends on the value at which x is evaluated. In addition, $\hat{y}$ reaches a maximum ($b_2 < 0$) or minimum ($b_2 > 0$) when the marginal effect equals zero. The value of x when this happens is obtained from solving the equation $b_1 + 2b_2 x = 0$ as $x = \frac{-b_1}{2b_2}$.

EXAMPLE 16.2

Use the results from estimating the quadratic regression model in Example 16.1 to answer the following questions.

a. What is the change in average cost going from an output level of 4 million units to 5 million units?

b. What is the change in average cost going from an output level of 8 million units to 9 million units? Compare this result to the result found in part a.

c. What is the output level that minimizes average cost?

SOLUTION:

a. The predicted average cost for a firm that produces 4 million units is:

$$\widehat{AC} = 10.5225 - 0.3073(4) + 0.0210(4^2) = \$9.63.$$

The predicted average cost for a firm that produces 5 million units is:

$$\widehat{AC} = 10.5225 - 0.3073(5) + 0.0210(5^2) = \$9.51.$$

An increase in output from 4 to 5 million units (a one-unit increase in x) results in a \$0.12 decrease (\$9.63 − \$9.51) in predicted average cost.

b. The predicted average cost for a firm that produces 8 million units is:

$$\widehat{AC} = 10.5225 - 0.3073(8) + 0.0210(8^2) = \$9.41.$$

The predicted average cost for a firm that produces 9 million units is:

$$\widehat{AC} = 10.5225 - 0.3073(9) + 0.0210(9^2) = \$9.46.$$

An increase in output from 8 to 9 million units (a one-unit increase in x) results in a \$0.05 increase in predicted average cost. Comparing this result to the one found in part a, we note that a one-unit change in x depends on the value at which x is evaluated. A one-unit increase in output from 4 to 5 million units results in a \$0.12 decrease in predicted average cost, while a one-unit increase in output from 8 to 9 million units results in a \$0.05 increase in predicted average cost. Depending on the value at which x is evaluated, a one-unit change in x may have a positive or negative influence on y, and the magnitude of this effect is not constant.

c. Given $b_1 = -0.3073$ and $b_2 = 0.0210$, the output level that minimizes average cost is $x = \frac{-b_1}{2b_2} = \frac{-(-0.3073)}{2 \times 0.0210} = 7.32$ million units. This result is not surprising if we look back at Figure 16.2.

Let's now turn to an example with an inverted U-shaped relationship.

EXAMPLE 16.3

In the United States, age discrimination is illegal, but its occurrence is hard to prove (*Newsweek*, March 17, 2010). Even without discrimination, it is widely believed that wages of workers decline as they get older. A young worker can expect wages to rise with age only up to a certain point, beyond which wages begin to fall. Ioannes Papadopoulos works in the human resources department of a large manufacturing firm and is examining the relationship between wages (in \$), education (in years of school), and age. Specifically, he wants to verify the quadratic effect of age on wages. He gathers data on 80 workers in his firm with information on their hourly wage, education, and age. A portion of the data is shown in Table 16.4.

TABLE 16.4 Data for Example 16.3 on Hourly Wage, Education, and Age; $n = 80$

Wage	Education	Age
17.54	12	76
20.93	10	61
⋮	⋮	⋮
23.66	12	49

FILE
Quadratic

a. Plot Wage against Age and evaluate whether a linear or quadratic regression model better captures the relationship. Verify your choice by using the appropriate goodness-of-fit measure.

b. Use the appropriate model to predict hourly wages for someone with 16 years of education and age equal to 30, 50, or 70.

c. According to the model, at what age will someone with 16 years of education attain the highest wages?

SOLUTION:

a. Figure 16.3 shows a scatterplot of Wage against Age. We superimpose linear and quadratic trends on the scatterplot. It seems that the quadratic regression model provides a better fit for the data as compared to the linear regression model.

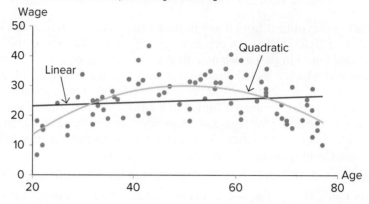

FIGURE 16.3 Scatterplot of Wage versus Age

We estimate two models.

Linear Regression Model: $Wage = \beta_0 + \beta_1 Education + \beta_2 Age + \varepsilon$

Quadratic Regression Model: $Wage = \beta_0 + \beta_1 Education + \beta_2 Age + \beta_3 Age^2 + \varepsilon$

Note that in order to estimate the quadratic regression model, we first create data on Age^2. For ease of exposition, we use the same notation for the coefficients in the linear and the quadratic models even though they have a different meaning depending on the model we reference. Table 16.5 shows the relevant regression results for the linear and the quadratic regression models.

TABLE 16.5 Estimates of the Linear and the Quadratic Regression Models for Example 16.3

Variable	Linear Regression Model	Quadratic Regression Model
Intercept	2.6381 (0.268)	−22.7219* (0.000)
Education	1.4410* (0.000)	1.2540* (0.000)
Age	0.0472 (0.127)	1.3500* (0.000)
Age^2	NA	−0.0133* (0.000)
Adjusted R^2	0.6088	0.8257

Notes: Parameter estimates are in the main body of the table with the *p*-values in parentheses; NA denotes not applicable; * represents significance at the 5% level. The last row presents adjusted R^2 for model comparison.

Note that in the linear regression model, Age has an estimated coefficient of only 0.0472, which is not statistically significant (*p*-value = 0.127) even at the 10% significance level. However, results change dramatically when Age^2 is included along with Age. In the quadratic regression model, both of these variables, with *p*-values of approximately zero, are statistically significant at any reasonable level. Also, the adjusted R^2 is higher for the quadratic regression model (0.8257 > 0.6088), making it a better choice for prediction. This conclusion is consistent with our visual impression from the scatterplot in Figure 16.3, which suggested a weak linear but strong quadratic relationship between age and hourly wage.

b. From Table 16.5, the estimated regression equation for the quadratic regression model is

$$\widehat{Wage} = -22.7219 + 1.2540Education + 1.3500Age - 0.0133Age^2.$$

Therefore, the predicted hourly wage for a 30-year-old person with 16 years of education is

$$\widehat{Wage} = -22.7219 + 1.2540 \times 16 + 1.3500 \times 30 - 0.0133 \times 30^2 = \$25.87.$$

Similarly, the predicted hourly wage for a 50- and a 70-year-old person is $31.59 and $26.67, respectively. Note that, consistent with the estimates, the hourly wage increases as a person ages from 30 to 50, but then decreases as a person ages from 50 to 70.

c. In part b, we predicted the hourly wage for a 30-, 50-, and 70-year-old person with 16 years of education. Therefore, of the three ages considered, a 50-year-old person earns the highest wage. In Figure 16.4, we plot the predicted wage with 16 years of education and vary age from 20 to 80 with increments of 1.

FIGURE 16.4 Predicted wages with 16 years of education and varying age

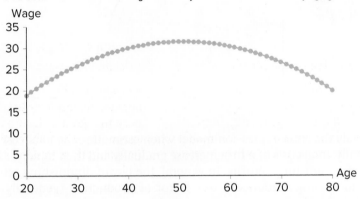

In order to determine the optimal age at which wage is maximized, we also solve $x = \frac{-b_2}{2b_3} = \frac{-(1.3500)}{2(-0.0133)} = 50.75$. The optimal age at which the wage is maximized is about 51 years, with a wage of about $31.60. It is worth noting that at a different education level, predicted wages will not be the same, yet the highest wage will still be achieved at the same 51 years of age. We advise you to plot a similar graph with 12 years of education and varying age levels.

The quadratic regression model allows one sign change of the slope capturing the influence of x on y. It is a special case of a **polynomial regression model**. Polynomial regression models describe various numbers of sign changes. Sometimes a quadratic regression model with one sign change is referred to as a polynomial regression model of order 2. In fact, a linear regression model is a polynomial regression model of order 1, which, with a constant slope coefficient, does not allow any sign change.

The linear and the quadratic regression models are the most common polynomial regression models. Sometimes, researchers use a polynomial regression model of order 3, also called the **cubic regression model**. The cubic regression model allows for two changes in slope.

A cubic regression model, $y = \beta_0 + \beta_1 x + \beta_2 x^2 + \beta_3 x^3 + \varepsilon$, allows two sign changes of the slope capturing the influence of x on y.

Predictions with a cubic model are made by $\hat{y} = b_0 + b_1 x + b_2 x^2 + b_3 x^3$. It is advisable to use unrounded coefficients (or rounded to at least four decimal places) for making predictions.

The expression $\beta_0 + \beta_1 x + \beta_2 x^2 + \beta_3 x^3$ is the deterministic component of a cubic regression model; equivalently, conditional on x, $E(y) = \beta_0 + \beta_1 x + \beta_2 x^2 + \beta_3 x^3$. The shape of a cubic relationship depends on the coefficients. Figure 16.5 highlights a representative shape of a cubic regression model when $\beta_1 > 0$, $\beta_2 < 0$, and $\beta_3 > 0$.

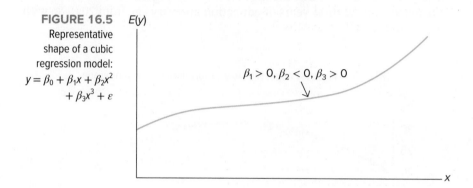

FIGURE 16.5 Representative shape of a cubic regression model: $y = \beta_0 + \beta_1 x + \beta_2 x^2 + \beta_3 x^3 + \varepsilon$

$E(y)$

$\beta_1 > 0, \beta_2 < 0, \beta_3 > 0$

x

We often apply the cubic regression model when estimating the total cost curve of a firm. Generally, total costs of a firm increase gradually and then rapidly, as predicted by the law of diminishing returns. In general, the law of diminishing returns states that when increasing amounts of one factor of production (generally labor) are employed in a production process along with a fixed amount of another factor (generally capital), then, after some point, the resulting increases in output of the product become smaller and smaller. A common example is adding more workers to a job, such as assembling a car in a factory. At some point, adding more workers will result in inefficiency as workers get in each other's way or wait for access to a machine. Producing one more unit of output will eventually cost increasingly more, due to inputs being used less and less effectively. We can think of Figure 16.5 as a firm's typical total cost curve where x and y represent a firm's output and total cost, respectively.

A cubic regression model can easily be estimated within the framework of a linear regression model where we use y as the response variable and x, x^2, and x^3 as the explanatory variables. It is easy to estimate a cubic regression model after we have created data on x^2 and x^3. As before, we can compare polynomial models of various orders on the basis of adjusted R^2.

EXAMPLE 16.4

Table 16.6 shows a portion of data on the total cost (in $1,000s) and output for producing a particular product. We also include a portion of the squared output and cubed output variables; these variables will be used in the estimation process.

a. Use a cubic regression model to estimate total cost (TC).

b. Predict the total cost if a firm produces 11 units of the product.

TABLE 16.6 Data for Example 16.4 on Total Cost y and Output x, $n = 40$

Total Cost	Output	Output^2	Output^3
37.49	9	81	729
37.06	7	49	343
⋮	⋮	⋮	⋮
33.92	4	16	64

SOLUTION:

a. In order to estimate a cubic regression model, we first create data on the squared output and the cubed output variables (see Table 16.6). We then estimate $TC = \beta_0 + \beta_1 Output + \beta_2 Output^2 + \beta_3 Output^3 + \varepsilon$. Table 16.7 shows the relevant regression results. All variables are significant at the 5% level. In addition, the adjusted R^2 (not shown) is 0.8551, which is higher than the adjusted R^2 of 0.6452 and 0.8289 for the linear and the quadratic regression models, respectively. We advise you to verify these results.

TABLE 16.7 Estimates of the Cubic Regression Model for Example 16.4

Variable	Cubic Regression Model
Intercept	17.1836* (0.000)
Output	6.4570* (0.000)
Output^2	−0.7321* (0.000)
Output^3	0.0291* (0.009)

Notes: p-values are in parentheses; * represents significance at the 5% level.

b. We calculate the total cost of production for a firm that produces 11 units of the product as $\widehat{TC} = 17.1836 + 6.4570 \times 11 - 0.7321 \times 11^2 + 0.0291 \times 11^3 = 38.37$, or \$38,370.

EXERCISES 16.1

Mechanics

1. Consider the following two estimated models:

$$\hat{y} = 25 + 1.2x$$
$$\hat{y} = 30 + 1.4x - 0.12x^2$$

For each of the estimated models, predict y when x equals 5 and 10.

2. Consider the following three models:

$$\hat{y} = 80 + 1.2x$$
$$\hat{y} = 200 + 2.1x - 0.6x^2$$
$$\hat{y} = 100 + 16x - 2.2x^2 + 0.08x^3$$

For each of the estimated models, predict y when x equals 10 and 15.

3. Consider the following sample regressions for the linear and quadratic models along with their respective R^2 and adjusted R^2.

	Linear	Quadratic
Intercept	13.3087	1.7656
x	0.3392	4.0966
x^2	NA	−0.2528
R^2	0.1317	0.5844
Adjusted R^2	0.0232	0.4657

a. Use the appropriate goodness-of-fit measure to justify which model fits the data best.

b. Given the best-fitting model, predict y for $x = 4$, 8, and 12.

4. Consider the following sample regressions for the linear and quadratic models along with their respective R^2 and adjusted R^2.

	Linear	Quadratic
Intercept	1.1006	12.1338
x	0.5828	−3.1034
x^2	NA	0.2565
R^2	0.4814	0.7843
Adjusted R^2	0.4166	0.7226

    a. Use the appropriate goodness-of-fit measure to justify which model fits the data best.

    b. Given the best-fitting model, predict y for $x = 4, 6$, and 12.

5. Consider the following sample regressions for the linear, the quadratic, and the cubic models along with their respective R^2 and adjusted R^2.

	Linear	Quadratic	Cubic
Intercept	9.66	10.00	10.06
x	2.66	2.75	1.83
x^2	NA	−0.31	−0.33
x^3	NA	NA	0.26
R^2	0.810	0.836	0.896
Adjusted R^2	0.809	0.833	0.895

    a. Predict y for $x = 1$ and 2 with each of the estimated models.

    b. Select the most appropriate model. Explain.

6. Consider the following sample regressions for the linear, the quadratic, and the cubic models along with their respective R^2 and adjusted R^2.

	Linear	Quadratic	Cubic
Intercept	19.80	20.08	20.07
x	1.35	1.50	1.58
x^2	NA	−0.31	−0.27
x^3	NA	NA	−0.03
R^2	0.640	0.697	0.698
Adjusted R^2	0.636	0.691	0.689

    a. Predict y for $x = 2$ and 3 with each of the estimated models.

    b. Select the most appropriate model. Explain.

Applications

7. **FILE** *Television.* Numerous studies have shown that watching too much television hurts school grades. Others have argued that television is not necessarily a bad thing for children (*Mail Online*, July 18, 2009). Like books and stories, television not only entertains, it also exposes a child to new information about the world. While watching too much television is harmful, a little bit may actually help. Researcher Matt Castle gathers information on the grade point average (GPA) of 28 middle school children and the number of hours of television they watched per week. A portion of the data is shown in the accompanying table.

GPA	Hours
3.24	19
3.10	21
⋮	⋮
3.31	4

    a. Estimate a quadratic regression model where the GPA of middle school children is regressed on hours and hours-squared.

    b. Is the quadratic term in this model justified? Explain.

    c. Find the optimal number of weekly hours of TV for middle school children.

8. **FILE** *Crew_Size.* The project manager at a construction company is evaluating how crew size affects the productivity of framing jobs. He has experimented with varying crew size (the number of workers) on a weekly basis over the past 27 weeks and has recorded productivity (jobs/week). A portion of the data is shown in the accompanying table.

Crew Size	Productivity
2	10
3	12
⋮	⋮
10	12

    a. Create a scatterplot of the data. Based on the scatterplot alone, what crew size(s) seems optimal?

    b. Estimate the linear and the quadratic regression models. Evaluate the two models in terms of variable significance and adjusted R^2. Which model provides the best fit? Provide an intuitive justification for the chosen model.

    c. Use the best-fitting model to predict how many jobs a crew of 5 could be expected to complete in a week.

    d. Estimate the cubic regression model. Does it improve the fit as compared to the quadratic regression model?

9. **FILE** *Bids.* Consider a sample comprised of firms that were targets of tender offers during the period 1978–1985. Conduct an analysis where the response variable represents the number of bids (Bids) received prior to the takeover of the firm. The explanatory variables include the bid premium (Premium) and firm size (Size in $ billions). It is generally believed that a high initial bid premium, defined as the percentage excess of the firm's stock price, would deter subsequent bids. Moreover, while tender offers for large firms are likely to receive more media coverage and thereby attract the attention of opportunistic

bidders, it also is a wealth constraint to potential bidders. A portion of the data is shown in the accompanying table.

Bids	Premium	Size
3	1.1905	0.7668
1	1.0360	0.1625
⋮	⋮	⋮
2	1.0329	3.4751

Source: Compustat and *The Wall Street Journal* Index.

a. Estimate the model, $Bids = \beta_0 + \beta_1 Premium + \beta_2 Size + \beta_2 Size^2 + \varepsilon$.

b. Justify the inclusion of the quadratic term in the model.

c. What firm size is likely to get the highest number of bids?

10. **FILE** *Inspection.* A lead inspector at ElectroTech, an electronics assembly shop, wants to convince management that it takes longer, on a per-component basis, to inspect large devices with many components than it does to inspect small devices because it is difficult to keep track of which components have already been inspected. To prove her point, she has collected data on the inspection time (Time in seconds) and the number of components per device (Components) from the last 25 devices. A portion of the data is shown in the accompanying table.

Time	Components
84	32
49	13
⋮	⋮
70	23

a. Estimate the linear, quadratic, and cubic regression models. Evaluate each model in terms of variable significance and adjusted R^2. Which model provides the best fit?

b. Use the best model to predict the time required to inspect a device with 35 components.

11. **FILE** *Debt_Payments.* You collect data on 26 metropolitan areas to analyze average monthly debt payments (Debt in $) in terms of income (Inc in $1,000s) and the unemployment rate (Unemp in %). A portion of the data is shown in the accompanying table.

Metropolitan Area	Debt	Inc	Unemp
Washington, D.C.	1285	103.50	6.3
Seattle	1135	81.70	8.5
⋮	⋮	⋮	⋮
Pittsburgh	763	63.00	8.3

Source: eFannieMae.com; bls.com; and Experian.com.

a. Estimate the model $Debt = \beta_0 + \beta_1 Inc + \beta_2 Unemp + \varepsilon$. Is unemployment significant at the 5% level?

b. You are told that the unemployment rate might have a quadratic influence on monthly debt payments. Provide an intuitive justification for this claim.

c. Estimate $Debt = \beta_0 + \beta_1 Inc + \beta_2 Unemp + \beta_3 Unemp^2 + \varepsilon$ to determine if Unemp and $Unemp^2$ are jointly significant at the 5% level.

16.2 REGRESSION MODELS WITH LOGARITHMS

In the preceding section, we squared, and in some instances, cubed the explanatory variable in order to capture nonlinearities between the response variable and the explanatory variable. Another commonly used transformation is based on the natural logarithm. You may recall from your math courses that the natural logarithmic function is the inverse of the exponential function. It is useful to briefly review exponential and logarithmic functions before using them in regression models.

Use and evaluate log-transformed models.

The exponential function is defined as

$$y = \exp(x) = e^x,$$

where $e \approx 2.718$ is a constant and x is the function argument. We can use a computer or a calculator to compute, for example, $e^2 = 7.3891$, or $e^5 = 148.4132$.

The inverse of the exponential function is the natural logarithm (or simply, log); that is, the logarithm with the base $e \approx 2.718$. In other words,

$$\text{if } y = e^x, \quad \text{then} \quad \ln(y) = x,$$

where $\ln(y)$ is the natural log of y. For example, if $y = e^2 = 7.3891$, then $\ln(y) = \ln(7.3891) = 2$. Similarly, if $y = e^5 = 148.4132$, then $\ln(y) = \ln(148.4132) = 5$. Since $\exp(\ln(x)) = x$, the exponential function is sometimes referred to as the anti-log function. Finally, the log of a negative or zero value is not defined. Therefore, we can log-transform only those values that are positive.

As mentioned earlier, in many applications, linearity is not justifiable. For instance, consider an estimated linear regression of annual food expenditure y on annual income x: $\hat{y} = 9{,}000 + 0.20x$. An estimated slope coefficient value of $b_1 = 0.20$ implies that a \$1,000 increase in annual income would lead to a \$200 increase in annual food expenditure, irrespective of whether the income increase is from \$20,000 to \$21,000 or from \$520,000 to \$521,000. Since we would expect the impact to be smaller at high income levels, it may be more meaningful to analyze what happens to food expenditure as income increases by a certain percentage rather than by a certain dollar amount.

Logarithms convert changes in variables into percentage changes, which is useful since many relationships are naturally expressed in terms of percentages. For instance, it is common to log-transform variables such as incomes, house prices, and sales. On the other hand, variables such as age, experience, and scores are generally expressed in their original form. We rely both on economic intuition as well as statistical measures to find the appropriate form for the variables.

We first illustrate log models with only one explanatory variable, which we later extend to a multiple regression model.

A Log-Log Model

In a **log-log model**, both the response variable and the explanatory variable are transformed into natural logs. We can write this model as

$$\ln(y) = \beta_0 + \beta_1 \ln(x) + \varepsilon,$$

where $\ln(y)$ is the log-transformed response variable and $\ln(x)$ is the log-transformed explanatory variable. With these transformations, the relationship between y and x is captured by a curve whose shape depends on the sign and magnitude of the slope coefficient β_1. Figure 16.6 shows a couple of representative shapes of a log-log regression model.

FIGURE 16.6 Representative shapes of a log-log model: $\ln(y) = \beta_0 + \beta_1 \ln(x) + \varepsilon$

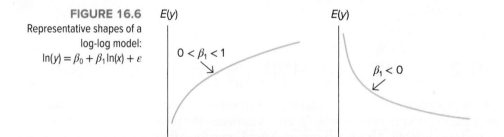

For $0 < \beta_1 < 1$, the log-log model implies a positive relationship between x and $E(y)$; as x increases, $E(y)$ increases at a slower rate. This may be appropriate in the earlier example, where we expect food expenditure to react positively to changes in income, with the impact diminishing at higher income levels. If $\beta_1 < 0$, it suggests a negative relationship between x and $E(y)$; as x increases, $E(y)$ decreases at a slower rate. Finally, $\beta_1 > 1$ implies a positive and increasing relationship between x and y; this case is not shown in Figure 16.6. For any application, the estimated value of β_1 is determined by the data.

Note that while the log-log regression model is nonlinear in the variables, it is still linear in the coefficients, thus satisfying the requirement of the linear regression model. The only requirement is that we have to first transform both variables into logs before running the regression. We should also point out that in a log-log regression model, the slope coefficient β_1 measures the percentage change in y for a small percentage change in x. In other words, β_1 is a measure of elasticity. In a log-log model, if y represents the quantity demanded of a particular good and x is its unit price, then β_1 measures the price elasticity of demand, a parameter of considerable economic interest. Suppose $\beta_1 = -1.2$; then a 1% increase in the price of this good is expected to lead to about a 1.2% decrease in its quantity demanded.

Finally, even though the response variable is transformed into logs, we still make predictions in regular units. Given $\widehat{\ln(y)} = b_0 + b_1 \ln(x)$, you may be tempted to use the anti-log function, to make predictions in regular units as $\hat{y} = \exp(\widehat{\ln(y)}) = \exp(b_0 + b_1 \ln(x))$, where b_0 and b_1 are the coefficient estimates. However, this transformation is known to systematically underestimate the expected value of y. One relatively simple correction is to make predictions as $\hat{y} = \exp(b_0 + b_1 \ln(x) + s_e^2/2)$, where s_e is the standard error of the estimate from the log-log model. This correction is easy to implement since virtually all statistical packages report s_e.

THE LOG-LOG REGRESSION MODEL

A log-log model is specified as $\ln(y) = \beta_0 + \beta_1 \ln(x) + \varepsilon$, and β_1 measures the approximate percentage change in $E(y)$ when x increases by 1%.

Predictions with a log-log model are made by $\hat{y} = \exp(b_0 + b_1 \ln(x) + s_e^2/2)$, where b_0 and b_1 are the coefficient estimates and s_e is the standard error of the estimate. It is advisable to use unrounded coefficients (or rounded to at least four decimal places) for making predictions.

EXAMPLE 16.5

Refer back to the food expenditure example where y represents expenditure on food and x represents income. Let the sample regression be $\widehat{\ln(y)} = 3.64 + 0.50 \ln(x)$ with the standard error of the estimate $s_e = 0.18$.

a. What is the predicted food expenditure for an individual whose income is $20,000?

b. What is the predicted food expenditure if income increases to $21,000?

c. Interpret the slope coefficient, $b_1 = 0.50$.

SOLUTION: For this log-log model, we make predictions as $\hat{y} = \exp(b_0 + b_1 \ln(x) + s_e^2/2)$.

a. For income $x = 20,000$, we predict food expenditure as $\hat{y} = \exp(3.64 + 0.50 \times \ln(20,000) + 0.18^2/2) = 5,474.98$.

b. For $x = 21,000$, we find $\hat{y} = \exp(3.64 + 0.50 \times \ln(21,000) + 0.18^2/2) = 5,610.18$.

c. In the log-log model, a slope coefficient of $b_1 = 0.50$ implies that a 1% increase in income will lead to a 0.5% increase in predicted food expenditure. Here, as income increases from $20,000 to $21,000, or by 5%, the predicted food expenditure increases from $5,474.98 to $5,610.18, or by about 2.5%. This is consistent with the elasticity interpretation of the slope coefficient; that is, a 5% increase in income will lead to approximately a 2.5% ($= 5 \times 0.5$) increase in the predicted food expenditure.

The Logarithmic Model

A log-log specification transforms all variables into logs. It is also common to employ a **semi-log** model, in which not all variables are transformed into logs. We will discuss two types of semi-log models in the context of the simple linear regression model. A semi-log model that transforms only the explanatory variable is called the **logarithmic model,** and a semi-log model that transforms only the response variable is called the **exponential model**. We can have many variants of semi-log models when we extend the analysis to include multiple explanatory variables.

The logarithmic model is defined as

$$y = \beta_0 + \beta_1 \ln(x) + \varepsilon.$$

Like the log-log model, this model implies that an increase in x will lead to an increase ($\beta_1 > 0$) or decrease ($\beta_1 < 0$) in $E(y)$ at a decreasing rate. These models are especially attractive when only the explanatory variable is better captured in percentages. Figure 16.7 highlights some representative shapes of this model. Since the log-log and the logarithmic model can allow similar shapes, the choice between the two models can be tricky. We will compare models later in this section.

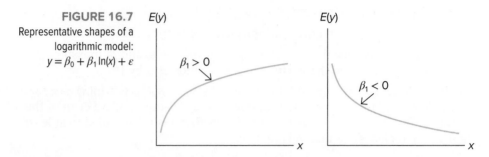

FIGURE 16.7 Representative shapes of a logarithmic model: $y = \beta_0 + \beta_1 \ln(x) + \varepsilon$

In the logarithmic model, the response variable is specified in regular units, but the explanatory variable is transformed into logs. Therefore, $\beta_1/100 = \beta_1 \times 0.01$ measures the approximate unit change in $E(y)$ when x increases by 1%. For example, if $\beta_1 = 5{,}000$, then a 1% increase in x leads to a 50 unit ($= 5{,}000 \times 0.01$) increase in $E(y)$. Since the response variable is already specified in regular units, no further transformation is necessary when making predictions.

> **THE LOGARITHMIC MODEL**
>
> A logarithmic model is specified as $y = \beta_0 + \beta_1 \ln(x) + \varepsilon$, and $\beta_1/100 = \beta_1 \times 0.01$ measures the approximate change in $E(y)$ when x increases by 1%.
>
> Predictions with a logarithmic model are made by $\hat{y} = b_0 + b_1 \ln(x)$, where b_0 and b_1 are the coefficient estimates. It is advisable to use unrounded coefficients (or rounded to at least four decimal places) for making predictions.

EXAMPLE 16.6

Continuing with the earlier example of food expenditure, let the estimated regression be $\hat{y} = 12 + 566\ln(x)$.

a. What is the predicted food expenditure for an individual whose income is $20,000?

b. What is the predicted food expenditure if income increases to $21,000?

c. Interpret the slope coefficient, $b_1 = 566$.

SOLUTION: For this logarithmic model, we make predictions as $\hat{y} = b_0 + b_1 \ln(x)$.

a. For income $x = 20{,}000$, we predict food expenditure as
$\hat{y} = 12 + 566 \times \ln(20{,}000) = 5{,}617.37$.

b. For $x = 21{,}000$, we find $\hat{y} = 12 + 566 \times \ln(21{,}000) = 5{,}644.99$.

c. With a 5% increase in income from \$20,000 to \$21,000, the predicted food expenditure increases from \$5,617.37 to \$5,644.99, or by about \$28. This is consistent with the interpretation of the slope coefficient; that is, $b_1 = 566$ implies that a 5% increase in income will lead to approximately a \$28 ($= 5 \times 566 \times 0.01$) increase in predicted food expenditure.

The Exponential Model

Unlike the logarithmic model, in which we were interested in finding the unit change in $E(y)$ for a 1% increase in x, the exponential model allows us to estimate the percent change in $E(y)$ when x increases by one unit. The exponential model is defined as

$$\ln(y) = \beta_0 + \beta_1 x + \varepsilon.$$

Figure 16.8 shows some representative shapes of this model.

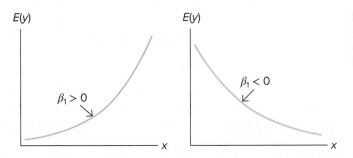

FIGURE 16.8
Representative shapes of an exponential model: $\ln(y) = \beta_0 + \beta_1 x + \varepsilon$

For an exponential model, $\beta_1 \times 100$ measures the approximate percentage change in $E(y)$ when x increases by one unit. For example, a value of $\beta_1 = 0.05$ implies that a one-unit increase in x leads to a 5% ($= 0.05 \times 100$) increase in $E(y)$. In applied work, we often see this model used to describe the rate of growth of certain economic variables, such as population, employment, wages, productivity, and the gross national product (GNP). As in the case of a log-log model, we make a correction for making predictions, since the response variable is measured in logs.

THE EXPONENTIAL MODEL

An exponential model is specified as $\ln(y) = \beta_0 + \beta_1 x + \varepsilon$, and $\beta_1 \times 100$ measures the approximate percentage change in $E(y)$ when x increases by one unit.

Predictions with an exponential model are made by $\hat{y} = \exp(b_0 + b_1 x + s_e^2/2)$, where b_0 and b_1 are the coefficient estimates and s_e is the standard error of the estimate. It is advisable to use unrounded coefficients (or rounded to at least four decimal places) for making predictions.

EXAMPLE 16.7

Continuing again with the example of food expenditure, let the estimated regression be $\widehat{\ln(y)} = 7.60 + 0.00005x$ with the standard error of the estimate, $s_e = 0.20$.

a. What is the predicted food expenditure for an individual whose income is \$20,000?

b. What is the predicted food expenditure if income increases to \$21,000?

c. Interpret the slope coefficient, $b_1 = 0.00005$.

SOLUTION: For this exponential model, we make predictions as $\hat{y} = \exp(b_0 + b_1 x + s_e^2/2)$.

a. For income $x = 20{,}000$, we predict food expenditure as
$\hat{y} = \exp(7.60 + 0.00005 \times 20{,}000 + 0.20^2/2) = 5{,}541.39$.

b. For $x = 21{,}000$, we find $\hat{y} = \exp(7.60 + 0.00005 \times 21{,}000 + 0.20^2/2) = 5{,}825.50$.

c. With a \$1,000 increase in income, the predicted food expenditure increases from \$5,541.39 to \$5,825.50, or by about 5%. This result is consistent with the interpretation of the slope coefficient; that is, $b_1 = 0.00005$ implies that a \$1,000 increase in income will lead to approximately a 5% ($= 1000 \times 0.00005 \times 100$) increase in predicted food expenditure.

While these log models are easily estimated within the framework of a linear regression model, care must be exercised in making predictions and interpreting the estimated slope coefficient. When interpreting the slope coefficient, keep in mind that logs essentially convert changes in variables into percentage changes. Table 16.8 summarizes the results.

TABLE 16.8 Summary of the Linear, Log-Log, Logarithmic, and Exponential Models

Model	Predicted Value	Estimated Slope Coefficient
$y = \beta_0 + \beta_1 x + \varepsilon$	$\hat{y} = b_0 + b_1 x$	b_1 measures the change in $\hat{y}$ when x increases by one unit.
$\ln(y) = \beta_0 + \beta_1 \ln(x) + \varepsilon$	$\hat{y} = \exp(b_0 + b_1 \ln(x) + s_e^2/2)$	b_1 measures the approximate percentage change in $\hat{y}$ when x increases by 1%.
$y = \beta_0 + \beta_1 \ln(x) + \varepsilon$	$\hat{y} = b_0 + b_1 \ln(x)$	$b_1 \times 0.01$ measures the approximate change in $\hat{y}$ when x increases by 1%.
$\ln(y) = \beta_0 + \beta_1 x + \varepsilon$	$\hat{y} = \exp(b_0 + b_1 x + s_e^2/2)$	$b_1 \times 100$ measures the approximate percentage change in $\hat{y}$ when x increases by one unit.

It is advisable to use unrounded coefficients (or rounded to at least four decimal places) for making predictions.

AnnArbor

EXAMPLE 16.8

The objective outlined in the introductory case was to evaluate the influence of the number of bedrooms (Beds), the number of bathrooms (Baths), and the square footage (Sqft) on monthly rent (Rent). Use the Ann Arbor rental data in Table 16.1 to solve the following:

a. Plot rent against each of the three explanatory variables and evaluate whether the relationship is best captured by a line or a curve. Identify variables that may require a log-transformation.

b. Estimate the linear and the relevant log models to predict rent for a 1,600-square-foot home with three bedrooms and two bathrooms.

SOLUTION: Given the nature of Beds and Baths, we will specify these variables only in regular units. We will, however, consider log-transformations for Rent and Sqft, since their changes are often expressed in percentages.

a. In Figure 16.9, we plot Rent against (a) Beds and (b) Baths and superimpose linear and exponential curves (recall that an exponential model log-transforms only the response variable).

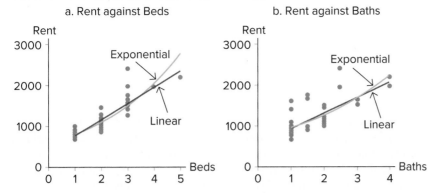

FIGURE 16.9 Comparing Rent against (a) Beds and (b) Baths

a. Rent against Beds

b. Rent against Baths

It is hard to tell from Figure 16.9 whether the relationship between Rent and Beds or Rent and Baths is better captured by a line or a curve. We will use goodness-of-fit measures for the selection.

We now plot Rent against Sqft in Figure 16.10.

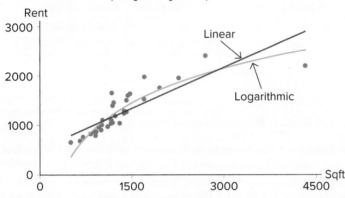

FIGURE 16.10 Comparing Rent against Sqft

Here it appears that the relationship between Rent and Sqft is better captured by a curve than a line. Figure 16.10 shows that a logarithmic model that log-transforms Sqft fits the data better than the linear model, suggesting that as square footage increases, rent increases at a decreasing rate. In other words, the increase in Rent is higher when Sqft increases from 1,000 to 2,000 than from 2,000 to 3,000. Two other models worth considering are the exponential model, where only Rent is log-transformed, and a log-log model, where both Rent and Sqft are log-transformed. In order to avoid a "cluttered" figure, these curves are not superimposed on the scatterplot; however, we will formally evaluate all models.

b. While the preceding visual tools are instructive, we evaluate four models and use goodness-of-fit measures to select the most appropriate model for prediction.

$$\text{Model 1: Rent} = \beta_0 + \beta_1\text{Beds} + \beta_2\text{Baths} + \beta_3\text{Sqft} + \varepsilon$$
$$\text{Model 2: Rent} = \beta_0 + \beta_1\text{Beds} + \beta_2\text{Baths} + \beta_3\ln(\text{Sqft}) + \varepsilon$$
$$\text{Model 3: } \ln(\text{Rent}) = \beta_0 + \beta_1\text{Beds} + \beta_2\text{Baths} + \beta_3\text{Sqft} + \varepsilon$$
$$\text{Model 4: } \ln(\text{Rent}) = \beta_0 + \beta_1\text{Beds} + \beta_2\text{Baths} + \beta_3\ln(\text{Sqft}) + \varepsilon$$

In order to estimate these models, we first log-transform Rent and Sqft; see the last two columns of Table 16.9.

TABLE 16.9 Transforming Rent and Sqft into Logs

Rent	Beds	Baths	Sqft	ln(Rent)	ln(Sqft)
645	1	1	500	6.4693	6.2146
675	1	1	648	6.5147	6.4739
⋮	⋮	⋮	⋮	⋮	⋮
2400	3	2.5	2700	7.7832	7.9010

In Models 1 and 2, we use Rent as the response variable with Beds and Baths, along with Sqft in Model 1 and ln(Sqft) in Model 2, as the explanatory variables. Similarly, in Models 3 and 4, we use ln(Rent) as the response variable with Beds and Baths, along with Sqft in Model 3 and ln(Sqft) in Model 4, as the explanatory variables. Model estimates are summarized in Table 16.10.

TABLE 16.10 Regression Results for Example 16.8

	Response Variable: Rent		Response Variable: ln(Rent)	
	Model 1	Model 2	Model 3	Model 4
Intercept	300.4116* (0.001)	−3,909.7415* (0.001)	6.3294* (0.000)	3.3808* (0.000)
Beds	225.8100* (0.001)	131.7781* (0.040)	0.2262* (0.000)	0.1246* (0.009)
Baths	89.2661 (0.119)	36.4255 (0.494)	0.0831 (0.060)	0.0254 (0.514)
Sqft	0.2096* (0.028)	NA	0.0001 (0.362)	NA
ln(Sqft)	NA	675.2648* (0.000)	NA	0.4742* (0.001)
s_e	193.1591	172.2711	0.1479	0.1262
R^2	0.8092	0.8482	0.8095	0.8613

Notes: Parameter estimates are followed with the p-values in parentheses; NA denotes not applicable; * represents significance at the 5% level.

For the most part, the number of bedrooms and the square footage of the house are statistically significant at the 5% level, while the number of bathrooms is insignificant. We use the model results to predict rent for a 1,600-square-foot home with three bedrooms and two bathrooms. In order to make a prediction with Models 3 and 4, which are both based on ln(Rent), we will add the correction term $s_e^2/2$.

Model 1: $\widehat{\text{Rent}} = 300.4116 + 225.8100(3) + 89.2661(2) + 0.2096(1{,}600)$
$= \$1{,}492$

Model 2: $\widehat{\text{Rent}} = -3{,}909.7415 + 131.7781(3) + 36.4255(2) + 675.2648$
$\times \ln(1{,}600) = \$1{,}540$

Model 3: $\widehat{\text{Rent}} = \exp(6.3294 + 0.2262(3) + 0.0831(2) + 0.0001(1{,}600)$
$+ 0.1479^2/2) = \$1{,}549$

Model 4: $\widehat{\text{Rent}} = \exp(3.3808 + 0.1246(3) + 0.0254(2) + 0.4742$
$\times \ln(1{,}600) + 0.1262^2/2) = \$1{,}498$

The predicted rent ranges from \$1,492 in Model 1 to \$1,549 in Model 3. We would like to know which model provides the best prediction, as we discuss next.

Comparing Linear and Log-Transformed Models

As seen in Example 16.8, it is often not clear which regression model is best suited for an application. While we can use economic intuition and scatterplots for direction, we also justify our selection on the basis of goodness-of-fit measures. In Chapter 14, we introduced R^2 to compare models based on the same number of explanatory variables; we compared adjusted R^2 if the number of explanatory variables was different. Such comparisons are valid only when the response variable of the competing models is the same. Since R^2 measures the percentage of sample variations of the response variable explained by the model, we cannot compare the percentage of explained variations of y with that of $\ln(y)$. Comparing models based on the computer-generated R^2, that does not differentiate between y and $\ln(y)$, is like comparing apples with oranges. For a valid comparison, we need to compute the percentage of explained variations of y even though the estimated model uses $\ln(y)$ as the response variable. To do this, it will help to revisit the formula for calculating R^2. Recall that an easy way to compute R^2 is by squaring the sample correlation coefficient of y and $\hat{y}$.

REVISITING THE CALCULATION OF THE COEFFICIENT OF DETERMINATION, R^2

The coefficient of determination, R^2, can be computed as $R^2 = (r_{y\hat{y}})^2$ where $r_{y\hat{y}}$ is the sample correlation coefficient between y and $\hat{y}$.

Example 16.9 elaborates on the method with the use of Excel and R.

Using Excel and R to Compare Linear and Log-Transformed Models

---

EXAMPLE 16.9

Revisit the four regression models in Example 16.8 and determine which model is best suited for making predictions.

SOLUTION: From Table 16.10, Model 4 has the highest computer-generated R^2 value of 0.8613. However, this does not mean that Model 4 is necessarily the best, since R^2 is based on Rent for Models 1 and 2 and on $\ln(\text{Rent})$ for Models 3 and 4. Therefore, while we can infer that Model 2 is superior to Model 1 ($0.8482 > 0.8092$) and Model 4 is superior to Model 3 ($0.8613 > 0.8095$), we cannot directly compare Models 2 and 4 based on the computer-generated R^2. For a valid comparison, we compute R^2 for Model 4 from scratch; that is, R^2 is based on Rent, even though it uses $\ln(\text{Rent})$ for estimation.

   For Model 4, we first compute $\widehat{\text{Rent}} = \exp(b_0 + b_1\text{Beds} + b_2\text{Baths} + b_3\ln(\text{Sqft}) + s_e^2/2)$ for the given sample values of the explanatory variables. For example, for the first sample observation, with Beds $= 1$, Baths $= 1$, and Sqft $= 500$, the predicted rent is computed as

$$\widehat{\text{Rent}} = \exp(3.3808 + 0.1246(1) + 0.0254(1) + 0.4742 \times \ln(500) + 0.1262^2/2)$$
$$= \$656.$$

Excel and R are quite useful in performing the calculations for the predicted values for Rent, as well as generating a value of R^2 for Model 4 based on Rent rather than $\ln(\text{Rent})$.

FILE
AnnArbor

Using Excel

a. Open the ***AnnArbor*** data file. Convert the Rent and Sqft variables into their respective logarithms by using Excel's **ln** function.

b. Estimate Model 4 by choosing **Data > Data Analysis > Regression** from the menu. For *Input Y Range*, select the $\ln(\text{Rent})$ data, and for *Input X*

Range, simultaneously select the Beds, Baths, and ln(Sqft) data. If you check the *Residuals* box, then Excel provides the predicted values for the ln(Rent), or $\widehat{\ln(\text{Rent})}$. So check this box, and then click **OK**.

c. For convenience, paste the values for $\widehat{\ln(\text{Rent})}$ next to the observed values for Rent on the spreadsheet; the first two columns of Table 16.11 show a portion of the results. Next, we want to calculate: $\widehat{\text{Rent}} = \exp(b_0 + b_1\text{Beds} + b_2\text{Baths} + b_3\ln(\text{Sqft}) + s_e^2/2)$. Given the Excel-produced predicted values for ln(Rent), this equation simplifies to $\widehat{\text{Rent}} = \exp(\widehat{\ln(\text{Rent})} + s_e^2/2)$. Substituting the value for the standard error of the estimate from Model 4 into this equation yields: $\widehat{\text{Rent}} = \exp(\widehat{\ln(\text{Rent})} + 0.1262^2/2)$. (For a more precise estimate, you can use the unrounded value for s_e from the regression output.) The third column of Table 16.11 shows a portion of the results.

TABLE 16.11 Excel-Produced Predicted Values for Model 4

Rent	ln(Rent)	$\widehat{\text{Rent}} = \exp(\ln(\text{Rent}) + 0.1262^2/2)$
645	6.4778	655.7334
675	6.6007	742.5210
⋮	⋮	⋮
2400	7.5648	1944.5760

d. Finally, use Excel's **CORREL** function to calculate the correlation between Rent and $\widehat{\text{Rent}}$ (columns 1 and 3 in Table 16.11) as $r_{y\hat{y}} = 0.8691$. Square the sample correlation coefficient to find the coefficient of determination, $R^2 = (0.8691)^2 = 0.7554$. We can now compare this value with the computer-generated value for Model 2 that is correctly based on Rent and conclude that Model 2 is better suited for making predictions, since $0.8482 > 0.7554$.

Using R

a. Import the ***Ann_Arbor*** data into a data frame (table) in R.

b. As shown in Chapter 14, we use the **lm** function to create a regression model or, in R terminology, an object. We label this object as Model_4. We also use the **log** function to transform the variables Rent and Sqft. Enter:

```
> Model_4 <- lm(log(Rent) ~ Bed+Bath+log(Sqft),
  data=AnnArbor)
> summary(Model_4)
```

c. We then generate predicted values for Model_4, or $\widehat{\ln(\text{Rent})}$, using the **predict** function. Within the function, we indicate the name of the model or object. We label $\widehat{\ln(\text{Rent})}$ as Pred_ln_rent. Enter:

```
> Pred_ln_rent<-predict(Model_4)
```

d. Next, we want to calculate the predicted values for Rent: $\widehat{\text{Rent}} = \exp(\widehat{\ln(\text{Rent})} + s_e^2/2)$. We label $\widehat{\text{Rent}}$ as Pred_rent. We could use the standard error of 0.1262 that is provided in the model summary output. However, we obtain the unrounded value, which provides a more precise estimate; we label this value as SE. Enter:

```
> SE<-summary(Model_4)$sigma
> Pred_rent<-exp(Pred_ln_rent+SE^2/2)
```

e. Finally, we use R's **cor** function to calculate the correlation between Rent and $\widehat{\text{Rent}}$. We square this value to find the coefficient of determination, R^2. Enter:

```
> cor(AnnArbor$'Rent', Pred_rent)^2
```

And R returns: 0.7554188. This result is the same as one that we obtained with Excel; it would be identical to the last digit if we had used the unrounded value for s_e from the Excel output. We again conclude that Model 2, with an R^2 equal to 0.8482, is better suited than Model 4 for making predictions.

SYNOPSIS OF INTRODUCTORY CASE

The recession-resistance of campus towns has prompted many analysts to call investment in off-campus student housing a smart choice (*The Wall Street Journal*, September 24, 2010). First, there is a stable source of demand in college towns, as cash-strapped public universities are unable to house all students. Second, this demand may actually improve due to a projected increase in college enrollment. In this study, Ann Arbor, which is home to the main campus of the University of Michigan, is used to study rental opportunities. Four regression models analyze the monthly rent (Rent) on the basis of the number of bedrooms (Beds), the number of bathrooms (Baths), and the square footage (Sqft) of off-campus houses. Nonlinearities between the variables are captured by transforming Rent and/or Sqft into natural logs. The coefficient of deter-

©Cultura Creative/Alamy Stock Photo RF

mination R^2, computed in the original units, is used to select the best model. The selected model is estimated as $\widehat{\text{Rent}} = -3909.74 + 131.78\text{Beds} + 36.43\text{Baths} + 675.26\ln(\text{Sqft})$. The bedroom coefficient implies that for every additional bedroom, the monthly rent is predicted to go up by about \$132, holding other factors constant. Similarly, for every 1% increase in square footage, the monthly rent is predicted to increase by about \$6.75 (675×0.01). This sample regression model can also be used to make predictions for rent. For example, a 1,000-square-foot house with two bedrooms and one bathroom is predicted to rent for \$1,055. Similarly, a 1,600-square-foot house with three bedrooms and two bathrooms is predicted to rent for \$1,540. These results are useful to any investor interested in off-campus housing in Ann Arbor.

EXERCISES 16.2

Mechanics

12. Consider the following four estimated models:

$$\hat{y} = 500 - 4.2x$$
$$\hat{y} = 1370 - 280\ln(x)$$
$$\widehat{\ln(y)} = 8.4 - 0.04x; s_e = 0.13$$
$$\widehat{\ln(y)} = 8 - 0.8\ln(x); s_e = 0.11$$

a. Interpret the slope coefficient in each of these estimated models.

b. For each model, what is the predicted change in y when x increases by 1%, from 100 to 101?

13. Consider the following estimated models:

$$\hat{y} = 10 + 4.4x$$
$$\hat{y} = 2 + 23\ln(x)$$
$$\widehat{\ln(y)} = 3.0 + 0.1x; s_e = 0.07$$
$$\widehat{\ln(y)} = 2.6 + 0.6\ln(x); s_e = 0.05$$

a. Interpret the slope coefficient in each of these estimated models.

b. For each model, what is the predicted change in y when x increases by 5%, from 10 to 10.5?

14. Consider the sample regressions for the linear, the logarithmic, the exponential, and the log-log models. For each of the estimated models, predict y when x equals 100.

	Response Variable: y		Response Variable: $\ln(y)$	
	Model 1	Model 2	Model 3	Model 4
Intercept	240.42	−69.75	1.58	0.77
x	4.68	NA	0.05	NA
$\ln(x)$	NA	162.51	NA	1.25
s_e	83.19	90.71	0.12	0.09

15. Consider the sample regressions for the linear, the logarithmic, the exponential, and the log-log models. For each of the estimated models, predict y when x equals 50.

	Response Variable: y		Response Variable: $\ln(y)$	
	Model 1	Model 2	Model 3	Model 4
Intercept	18.52	−6.74	1.48	1.02
x	1.68	NA	0.06	NA
$\ln(x)$	NA	29.96	NA	0.96
s_e	23.92	19.71	0.12	0.10

16. Consider the following sample regressions for the linear and the logarithmic models.

	Linear	Logarithmic
Intercept	6.7904	−5.6712
x	1.0607	NA
$\ln(x)$	NA	10.5447*
s_e	2.4935	1.5231
R^2	0.8233	0.9341
Adjusted R^2	0.8013	0.9259

a. Justify which model fits the data best.
b. Use the selected model to predict y for $x = 10$.

17. Consider the following sample regressions for the log-log and the exponential models.

	Log-Log	Exponential
Intercept	1.8826	2.0219
x	NA	0.0513
$\ln(x)$	0.3663	NA
s_e	0.3508	0.2922
R^2	0.5187	0.6660
Adjusted R^2	0.4585	0.6242

a. Justify which model fits the data best.
b. Use the selected model to predict y for $x = 20$.

Applications

18. An economist is interested in examining how an individual's cigarette consumption (C) may be influenced by the price for a pack of cigarettes (P) and the individual's annual income (I). Using data from 50 individuals, she estimates a log-log model and obtains the following regression results.

$$\widehat{\ln(C)} = 3.90 - 1.25\ln(P) + 0.18\ln(I)$$
$$p\text{-values} = (0.000) \quad (0.005) \quad (0.400)$$

a. Interpret the value of the elasticity of demand for cigarettes with respect to price.
b. At the 5% significance level, is the price elasticity of demand statistically significant?
c. Interpret the value of the income elasticity of demand for cigarettes.
d. At the 5% significance level, is the income elasticity of demand statistically significant? Is this result surprising? Explain.

19. **FILE** *BMI.* According to the *World Health Organization*, obesity has reached epidemic proportions globally. While obesity has generally been linked with chronic disease and disability, researchers argue that it may also affect wages. Body Mass Index (BMI) is a widely used weight measure that also adjusts for height. A person is considered normal weight if BMI is between 18.5 to 25, overweight if BMI is between 25 to 30, and obese if BMI is over 30. The accompanying table shows a portion of data on the salary (in $1,000s) of 30 college-educated men with their respective BMIs.

Salary	BMI
34	33
43	26
⋮	⋮
45	21

a. Estimate a linear model with salary as the response variable and BMI as the explanatory variable. What is the estimated salary of a college-educated man with a BMI of 25? With a BMI of 30?
b. Estimate an exponential model using log of salary as the response variable and BMI as the explanatory variable. What is the estimated salary of a college-educated man with a BMI of 25? With a BMI of 30?
c. Which of the above two models is more appropriate for this application? Use R^2 for comparison.

20. **FILE** *Dexterity.* A manufacturing manager uses a dexterity test on 20 current employees in order to predict watch production based on time to completion (in seconds). A portion of the data is shown below.

Watches	Time
23	513
19	608
⋮	⋮
20	437

a. Estimate the linear model: Watches $= \beta_0 + \beta_1 \text{Time} + \varepsilon$. Interpret the slope coefficient. If the time required to complete the dexterity test is 550 seconds, what is the predicted watch production?

b. Estimate the logarithmic model: Watches $= \beta_0 + \beta_1 \ln(\text{Time}) + \varepsilon$. Interpret the slope coefficient. If the time required to complete the dexterity test is 550 seconds, what is the predicted watch production?

c. Which model provides a better fit? Explain.

21. **FILE** *Wine_Pricing.* Professor Orley Ashenfelter of Princeton University is a pioneer in the field of wine economics. He claims that, contrary to old orthodoxy, the quality of wine can be explained mostly in terms of weather conditions. Wine romantics accuse him of undermining the whole wine-tasting culture. In an interesting co-authored paper that appeared in *Chance* magazine in 1995, he ran a multiple regression model where quality, measured by the average vintage price relative to 1961, is used as the response variable y. The explanatory variables were the average temperature x_1 (in degrees Celsius), the amount of winter rain x_2 (in millimeters), the amount of harvest rain x_3 (in millimeters), and the years since vintage x_4. A portion of the data is shown in the accompanying table.

y	x_1	x_2	x_3	x_4
0.3684	17.1167	600	160	31
0.6348	16.7333	690	80	30
⋮	⋮	⋮	⋮	⋮
0.1359	16.0000	578	74	3

Source: www.liquidasset.com.

a. Estimate the linear model: $y = \beta_0 + \beta_1 x_1 + \beta_2 x_2 + \beta_3 x_3 + \beta_4 x_4 + \varepsilon$. What is the predicted price if $x_1 = 16$, $x_2 = 600$, $x_3 = 120$, and $x_4 = 20$?

b. Estimate the exponential model: $\ln(y) = \beta_0 + \beta_1 x_1 + \beta_2 x_2 + \beta_3 x_3 + \beta_4 x_4 + \varepsilon$. What is the predicted price if $x_1 = 16$, $x_2 = 600$, $x_3 = 120$, and $x_4 = 20$?

c. Use R^2 to select the appropriate model for prediction.

22. **FILE** *Electricity_Cost.* The facility manager at a pharmaceutical company wants to build a regression model to forecast monthly electricity cost (Cost in $). Three main variables are thought to influence electricity cost: (1) average outdoor temperature (Temp in °F), (2) working days per month (Days), and (3) tons of product produced (Tons). A portion of the past year's monthly data is shown in the accompanying table.

Cost	Temp	Days	Tons
24100	26	24	80
23700	32	21	73
⋮	⋮	⋮	⋮
26000	39	22	69

a. Estimate the linear model: Cost $= \beta_0 + \beta_1 \text{Temp} + \beta_2 \text{Days} + \beta_3 \text{Tons} + \varepsilon$. What is the predicted electricity cost in a month during which the average outdoor temperature is 65°, there are 23 working days, and 76 tons are produced?

b. Estimate the exponential model: $\ln(\text{Cost}) = \beta_0 + \beta_1 \text{Temp} + \beta_2 \text{Days} + \beta_3 \text{Tons} + \varepsilon$. What is the predicted electricity cost in a month during which the average outdoor temperature is 65°, there are 23 working days, and 76 tons are produced?

c. Based on R^2, which model provides the better fit?

23. **FILE** *Davis_Rental.* Chad Dobson has heard about the positive outlook for real estate investment in college towns. He is interested in investing in Davis, California, which houses one of the University of California campuses. He uses zillow.com to access data on 2011 monthly rents (in $) for 27 houses, along with three characteristics of the home: number of bedrooms (Beds), number of bathrooms (Baths), and square footage (Sqft). A portion of the data is shown in the accompanying table.

Rent	Beds	Baths	Sqft
2950	4	4	1453
2400	4	2	1476
⋮	⋮	⋮	⋮
744	2	1	930

Source: www.zillow.com.

a. Estimate a linear model that uses Rent as the response variable. Estimate an exponential model that uses log of Rent as the response variable.

b. Compute the predicted rent for a 1,500-square-foot house with three bedrooms and two bathrooms for the linear and the exponential models (ignore the significance tests).

c. Use R^2 to select the appropriate model for prediction.

24. **FILE** *Life_Expectancy.* Life expectancy at birth is the average number of years that a person is expected to live. There is a huge variation in life expectancies between countries, with the highest being in Japan, and the lowest in some African countries. An important factor for such variability is the availability of suitable health care. One measure of a person's access to health care is the people-to-physician ratio. We expect life expectancy to be lower for countries where this ratio is high. The accompanying table lists a portion of life expectancy of males and females in 40 countries and their corresponding people-to-physician ratio.

Country	Male Life Expectancy	Female Life Expectancy	People/Physician
Argentina	67	74	370
Bangladesh	54	53	6166
⋮	⋮	⋮	⋮
Zaire	52	56	23193

Source: *The World Almanac and Book Facts*, 1993.

a. Construct a scatterplot of female life expectancy against the people-to-physician ratio. Superimpose a linear trend and a logarithmic trend to determine the appropriate model.

b. Estimate a simple linear regression model with life expectancy of females as the response variable and the people-to-physician ratio as the explanatory variable. What happens to life expectancy of females as the people-to-physician ratio decreases from 1,000 to 500?

c. Estimate a logarithmic regression model with the natural log of the people-to-physician ratio as the explanatory variable. What happens to the life expectancy of females as the people-to-physician ratio decreases from 1,000 to 500?

d. Use R^2 to determine which of the preceding two models is more appropriate.

25. **FILE** *Life_Expectancy.* Use the data in Exercise 24 to answer the same four questions regarding life expectancy of males. Who is more likely to benefit from adding more physicians to the population? Explain.

26. **FILE** *Production_Function.* Economists often examine the relationship between the inputs of a production function and the resulting output. A common way of modeling this relationship is referred to as the Cobb–Douglas production function. This function can be expressed as $\ln(Q) = \beta_0 + \beta_1 \ln(L) + \beta_2 \ln(K) + \varepsilon$, where Q stands for output, L for labor, and K for capital. The accompanying table lists a portion of data relating to the U.S. agricultural industry in the year 2004.

State	Output	Labor	Capital
AL	3.1973	2.7682	3.1315
AR	7.7006	4.9278	4.7961
⋮	⋮	⋮	⋮
WY	1.2993	1.6525	1.5206

Source: www.ers.usda.gov/Data/AgProductivity; see Tables 3, 8, 10. Values in table are indices.

Estimate $\ln(Q) = \beta_0 + \beta_1 \ln(L) + \beta_2 \ln(K) + \varepsilon$.

a. What is the predicted change in output if labor increases by 1%, holding capital constant?

b. Holding capital constant, can we conclude at the 5% level that a 1% increase in labor will increase the output by more than 0.5%?

WRITING WITH STATISTICS

©Photodisc/Getty Images RF

Numerous attempts have been made to relate happiness to various factors. Since there is no unique way to quantify happiness, researchers generally rely on surveys to capture a subjective assessment of well-being. One study relates happiness with age and finds that holding everything else constant, people seem to be least happy when they are in their mid- to upper-40s (*The Economist*, December 16, 2010). Perhaps with greater age comes maturity that contributes to a better sense of overall well-being. With regard to the influence of money, a study from Princeton University's Woodrow Wilson School suggests that money does buy happiness, but its effect diminishes as incomes rise above $75,000 a year (*Time Magazine*, September 6, 2010). Perhaps people do not need more than $75,000 to do what matters most to their emotional well-being, such as spending time with friends and family and meeting their basic food, health, and leisure needs. Nick Fisher is a young business school graduate who is fascinated by these reports. He decides to collect his own data to better comprehend and also verify the results of these studies. He surveys working adults in his hometown and inputs information on the respondent's self-assessed happiness on a scale of 0 to 100, along with age and family income. A portion of the data is shown in Table 16.12.

TABLE 16.12 Happiness, Age, and Income Data, $n = 100$.

Respondent	Happiness	Age	Family Income
1	69	49	52000
2	83	47	123000
⋮	⋮	⋮	⋮
100	79	31	105000

Nick would like to use the above sample information to

1. Find the appropriate functional form to capture the influence of age and family income on happiness.

2. Predict happiness associated with varying levels of age for a family with income of $80,000.

3. Predict happiness associated with varying levels of family income for a 60-year-old working adult.

Sample
Report—
Understanding
Happiness

In a survey of 100 working adults, respondents were asked to report their age and family income, as well as rate their happiness on a scale of 0 to 100. This report summarizes the analysis of several regression models that examine the influence of age and income on the perceived happiness of respondents. The models used various transformations to capture interesting non-linearities suggested by recent research reports. For example, one such report shows that people get happier as they get older, despite the fact that old age is associated with a loss of hearing, vision, and muscle tone (*The New York Times*, May 31, 2010). In addition, while people start out feeling pretty good about themselves in their 20s, their self-assessed happiness deteriorates until around age 50 and then improves steadily thereafter. In order to quantify this possible quadratic effect, both age and age-squared variables are used for the regression. Also, the natural log of income is considered in order to capture the possible diminishing effect on happiness of incomes above $75,000 (*Time Magazine*, September 6, 2010). The results of the various regression models are summarized in Table 16.A.

TABLE 16.A Regression Results

	Model 1	Model 2	Model 3	Model 4
Intercept	49.1938* (0.00)	118.5285* (0.00)	−81.0939* (0.00)	−13.3021 (0.39)
Age	0.2212* (0.00)	−2.4859* (0.00)	0.2309* (0.00)	−2.4296* (0.00)
Age-squared	NA	0.0245* (0.00)	NA	0.0241* (0.00)
Income	0.0001* (0.00)	0.0001* (0.00)	NA	NA
ln(Income)	NA	NA	12.6761* (0.00)	12.7210* (0.00)
Adjusted R^2	0.4863	0.6638	0.5191	0.6907

Notes: Parameter estimates are in the top portion of the table with the *p*-values in parentheses; NA denotes not applicable; * represents significance at the 5% level. The last row presents the adjusted R^2 values for model comparison.

Model 4 was selected as the most appropriate model because it has the highest adjusted R^2 value of 0.6907. The estimated parameters of this model were used to make predictions. For instance, with family income equal to $80,000, the predicted happiness for a 30-, 50-, and 70-year-old is 79.09, 69.00, and 78.17, respectively. Note that these results are consistent with those suggesting that happiness first decreases and then increases with age. Specifically, using the estimated coefficients for Age, a person is least happy at 50.4 years of age. These results are shown graphically in Figure 16.A(a), where Happiness is plotted against Age, holding Income fixed at $80,000.

The regression results were also used to analyze the income effect. For instance, for a 60-year-old, the predicted happiness with family income of $50,000, $75,000, and

$100,000 is 65.20, 70.36, and 74.02, respectively. Note that there is a greater increase in Happiness when income increases from $50,000 to $75,000 than when it increases from $75,000 to $100,000. These results are shown in Figure 16.A(b), where predicted Happiness is plotted against Income, holding Age fixed at 60 years. Overall, the results support recent research findings.

FIGURE 16.A Predicted Happiness using Model 4 regression results

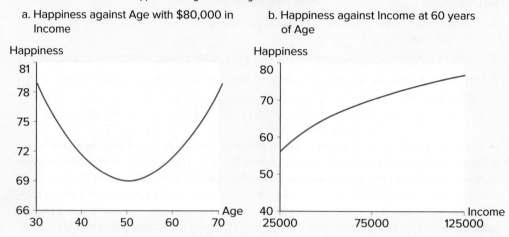

a. Happiness against Age with $80,000 in Income

b. Happiness against Income at 60 years of Age

CONCEPTUAL REVIEW

LO 16.1 Use and evaluate polynomial regression models.

In a **quadratic regression model**, $y = \beta_0 + \beta_1 x + \beta_2 x^2 + \varepsilon$, the sign of the coefficient β_2 determines whether the relationship between x and $E(y)$ is U-shaped ($\beta_2 > 0$) or inverted U-shaped ($\beta_2 < 0$). Predictions are made by $\hat{y} = b_0 + b_1 x + b_2 x^2$.

In a quadratic regression model, the marginal effect of x on $\hat{y}$ is approximated by $b_1 + 2b_2 x$; so this effect depends on the value of x. The quadratic equation reaches a maximum (if $b_2 < 0$) or minimum (if $b_2 > 0$) at $x = \frac{-b_1}{2b_2}$.

A **cubic regression model**, $y = \beta_0 + \beta_1 x + \beta_2 x^2 + \beta_3 x^3 + \varepsilon$, allows two sign changes of the slope capturing the influence of x on $E(y)$. Predictions are made by $\hat{y} = b_0 + b_1 x + b_2 x^2 + b_3 x^3$.

It is advisable to use unrounded coefficients (or rounded to at least four decimal places) for making predictions. We compare polynomial regression models of various orders on the basis of adjusted R^2.

LO 16.2 Use and evaluate log-transformed models.

Many interesting nonlinear relationships can be captured by transforming the response and/or the explanatory variables into natural logs. These regression models are summarized as follows:

In a **log-log model**, $\ln(y) = \beta_0 + \beta_1 \ln(x) + \varepsilon$, the slope coefficient β_1 measures the approximate percentage change in $E(y)$ when x increases by 1%. Predictions are made by $\hat{y} = \exp(b_0 + b_1 \ln(x) + s_e^2/2)$, where b_0 and b_1 are the coefficient estimates and s_e is the standard error of the estimate.

In a **logarithmic model**, $y = \beta_0 + \beta_1 \ln(x) + \varepsilon$, $\beta_1 \times 0.01$ measures the approximate change in $E(y)$ when x increases by 1%. Predictions are made by $\hat{y} = b_0 + b_1 \ln(x)$, where b_0 and b_1 are the coefficient estimates.

In an **exponential model**, $\ln(y) = \beta_0 + \beta_1 x + \varepsilon$, $\beta_1 \times 100$ measures the approximate percentage change in $E(y)$ when x increases by one unit. Predictions are made by $\hat{y} = \exp(b_0 + b_1 x + s_e^2/2)$, where b_0 and b_1 are the coefficient estimates and s_e is the standard error of the estimate.

It is advisable to use unrounded coefficients (or rounded to at least four decimal places) for making predictions.

LO 16.3 Describe the method used to compare linear models with log-transformed models.

We use the coefficient of determination R^2 to compare models that employ the same number of explanatory variables and use adjusted R^2 if the number of explanatory variables differs. Such comparisons are valid only when the response variable of the competing models is the same. In other words, we cannot compare the percentage of explained variations of y with that of $\ln(y)$. For a valid comparison, for any model that uses $\ln(y)$ as the response variable, we compute R^2 as $R^2 = (r_{y\hat{y}})^2$, where $r_{y\hat{y}}$ is the sample correlation coefficient between y and $\hat{y}$.

ADDITIONAL EXERCISES AND CASE STUDIES

Exercises

27. **FILE** *Quarterback_Salaries.* A sports enthusiast wants to examine the factors that influence a quarterback's salary (Salary in $ millions). In particular, he wants to assess the influence of the pass completion rate (PC), the total touchdowns scored (TD), and a quarterback's age (Age) on Salary. He uses 2009 data, a portion of which is shown in the accompanying table.

Name	Salary	PC	TD	Age
Philip Rivers	25.5566	65.2	28	27
Jay Cutler	22.0441	60.5	27	26
⋮	⋮	⋮	⋮	⋮
Tony Romo	0.6260	63.1	26	29

Source: *USA Today* database for salaries; NFL.com for other data.

a. Estimate and interpret the model: Salary $= \beta_0 + \beta_1 PC + \beta_2 TD + \beta_3 Age + \varepsilon$. Show that this model is preferable to a model that uses log of salary as the response variable.

b. Consider the quadratic effect of Age by adding Age^2 in the regression. Use a partial F test to determine the joint statistical significance of Age and Age^2.

28. **FILE** *Fertilizer2.* A horticulturist is studying the relationship between tomato plant height and fertilizer amount. Thirty tomato plants grown in similar conditions were subjected to various amounts of fertilizer (in ounces) over a four-month period, and then their heights (in inches) were measured. A portion of the results is shown in the accompanying table.

Height	Fertilizer
20.4	1.9
29.1	5.0
⋮	⋮
36.4	3.1

a. Estimate the linear regression model: Height $= \beta_0 + \beta_1$Fertilizer $+ \varepsilon$.

b. Estimate the quadratic regression model: Height $= \beta_0 + \beta_1$Fertilizer $+ \beta_2$Fertilizer$^2 + \varepsilon$. Find the fertilizer amount at which the height reaches a minimum or maximum.

c. Use the best-fitting model to predict, after a four-month period, the height of a tomato plant that received 3.0 ounces of fertilizer.

29. **FILE** *Arlington_Homes.* A realtor examines the factors that influence the price of a house. He collects data on the prices (in $) for 36 single-family homes in Arlington, Massachusetts, sold in the first quarter of 2009. For explanatory variables, he uses the house's square footage (Sqft), as well as its number of bedrooms (Beds) and bathrooms (Baths). A portion of the data is shown in the accompanying table.

Price	Sqft	Beds	Baths
840000	2768	4	3.5
822000	2500	4	2.5
⋮	⋮	⋮	⋮
307500	850	1	1

Source: NewEnglandMoves.com.

a. Estimate the linear model: $\text{Price} = \beta_0 + \beta_1\text{Sqft} + \beta_2\text{Beds} + \beta_3\text{Baths} + \varepsilon$. Estimate the exponential model: $\ln(\text{Price}) = \beta_0 + \beta_1\text{Sqft} + \beta_2\text{Beds} + \beta_3\text{Baths} + \varepsilon$.

b. Interpret the slope coefficients of the estimated models.

c. Use the coefficient of determination to choose the preferred model.

30. **FILE** *Circuit_Boards.* The operators manager at an electronics company believes that the time required for workers to build a circuit board is not necessarily proportional to the number of parts on the board. He wants to develop a regression model to predict time (in minutes) based on part quantity. He has collected data for the last 25 boards. A portion of this data is shown in the accompanying table.

Time	Parts
30.8	62
9.8	32
⋮	⋮
29.8	60

a. Estimate the linear regression model to predict time as a function of the number of parts (Parts). Then estimate the quadratic regression model to predict time as a function of Parts and Parts squared.

b. Evaluate the two models in terms of variable significance ($\alpha = 0.05$) and adjusted R^2.

c. Use the best-fitting model to predict how long it would take to build a circuit board consisting of 48 parts.

31. **FILE** *Smoking.* A nutritionist wants to understand the influence of income and healthy food on the incidence of smoking. He collects 2009 data on the percentage of smokers in each state in the U.S., the percentage of the state's population that regularly eats fruits and vegetables and the state's median income (in $). A portion of the data is shown in the accompanying table.

State	Smoke	Fruits/ Vegetables	Income
AK	14.6	23.3	61604
AL	16.4	20.3	39980
⋮	⋮	⋮	⋮
WY	15.2	23.3	52470

Source: Centers for Disease Control and Prevention and U.S. Census Bureau.

a. Estimate: $\text{Smoke} = \beta_0 + \beta_1\text{Fruits/Vegetables} + \beta_2\text{Income} + \varepsilon$.

b. Compare this model with a model that log-transforms the income variable.

32. **FILE** *Savings_Rate.* The accompanying table shows a portion of the monthly data on the personal savings rate (Savings in %) and personal disposable income (Income in $ billions) in the U.S. from January 2007 to November 2010.

Date	Savings	Income
2007–01	2.2	10198.2
2007–02	2.3	10252.9
⋮	⋮	⋮
2010–11	5.5	11511.9

Source: Bureau of Economic Analysis.

a. Estimate the linear model, $\text{Savings} = \beta_0 + \beta_1\text{Income} + \varepsilon$, and a log-log model, $\ln(\text{Savings}) = \beta_0 + \beta_1\ln(\text{Income}) + \varepsilon$.

b. Which is the preferred model? Explain.

33. **FILE** *Inventory_Cost.* The inventory manager at a warehouse distributor wants to predict inventory cost (Cost in $) based on order quantity (Quantity in units). She thinks it may be a nonlinear relationship since its two primary components move in opposite directions: (1) order processing cost (costs of procurement personnel, shipping, transportation), which *decreases* as order quantity increases (due to fewer orders needed), and (2) holding cost (costs of capital, facility, warehouse personnel, equipment), which *increases* as order quantity increases (due to more inventory held). She has collected monthly inventory costs and order quantities for the past 36 months. A portion of the data is shown in the accompanying table.

Cost	Quantity
844	54.4
503	52.1
⋮	⋮
870	55.5

a. Create a scatterplot of inventory cost as a function of quantity. Superimpose a linear trendline and quadratic trendline.
b. Estimate the linear regression model to predict inventory cost as a function of order quantity. Then estimate the quadratic regression model to predict inventory cost as a function of order quantity and order quantity squared.
c. Evaluate the two models in terms of significance tests ($\alpha = 0.05$) and adjusted R^2.
d. Use the best-fitting model to predict monthly inventory cost for an order quantity of 800 units.

34. **FILE** *Learning_Curve.* Learning curves are used in production operations to estimate the time required to complete a repetitive task as an operator gains experience. Suppose a production manager has compiled 30 time values (in minutes) for a particular operator as she progressed down the learning curve during the first 100 units. A portion of this data is shown in the accompanying table.

Time per Unit	Unit Number
18.30	3
17.50	5
⋮	⋮
5.60	100

a. Create a scatterplot of time per unit against units built. Superimpose a linear trendline and a logarithmic trendline to determine visually the best-fitting model.
b. Estimate a simple linear regression model and a logarithmic regression model for explaining time per unit using unit number as the explanatory variable.
c. Based on R^2, use the best-fitting model to predict the time that was required for the operator to build Unit 50.

CASE STUDIES

CASE STUDY 16.1   Executive compensation has risen dramatically beyond the rising levels of an average worker's wage over the years. Consider the following portion of data that link total compensation (in $ millions) of the 455 highest-paid CEOs in 2006 with two performance measures (industry-adjusted return on assets (Adj ROA in %) and industry-adjusted stock return (Adj Return in %)) and the firm's total assets (in $ millions).

Data for Case Study 16.1 Executive Compensation and Other Factors, $n = 455$

Compensation	Adj ROA	Adj Return	Total Assets
16.58	2.53	−0.15	20917.5
26.92	1.27	0.57	32659.5
⋮	⋮	⋮	⋮
2.30	0.45	0.75	44875.0

Source: SEC website and Compustat.

In a report, use the sample information to

1. Estimate two models, where each model uses Compensation as the response variable and Adj ROA and Adj Return as the explanatory variables along with Total Assets in Model 1 and natural log of Total Assets in Model 2.

2. Use the preferred model to predict compensation given the average values of the explanatory variables.

CASE STUDY 16.2 Brendan Connolly, a statistician for a Major League Baseball (MLB) team, wants to elaborate on the salary of baseball players. Excluding pitchers from his analysis, he believes that a baseball player's batting average (BA), runs batted in (RBI), and years of experience playing professional baseball (Experience) are the most important factors that influence a player's salary. Further, he believes that salaries rise with experience only up to a point, beyond which they begin to fall; in other words, experience has a quadratic effect on salaries. Brendan collects data on salary (in $1,000s), BA, RBI, and experience for 138 outfielders in 2008. A portion of the data is shown in the accompanying table.

MLB_Salary

Data for Case Study 16.2 Major League Baseball Outfielder Data, $n = 138$

Player	Salary	BA	RBI	Experience
Nick Markakis	455	299	87	3
Adam Jones	390	261	23	3
⋮	⋮	⋮	⋮	⋮
Randy Winn	8875	288	53	11

Notes: All data collected from usatoday.com or espn.com; BA and RBI are averages over the player's professional life through 2008. For exposition, BA has been multiplied by 1,000.

In a report, use the sample information to

1. Estimate a quadratic regression model using Salary as the response variable and BA, RBI, Experience, and Experience^2 as the explanatory variables.

2. Compare the above quadratic regression model with a linear model that uses BA, RBI, and Experience as the explanatory variables.

CASE STUDY 16.3 According to a report by the government, new home construction fell to an 18-month low in October 2010 (CNNMoney.com, November 17, 2010). Housing starts, or the number of new homes being built, experienced an 11.7% drop in the seasonally adjusted annual rate. Beena Singh works for a mortgage company in Madison, Wisconsin. She wants to better understand the quantitative relationship between housing starts (in 1000s), the mortgage rate (in %), and the unemployment rate (in %). She gathers monthly data on these variables from 2006:01–2010:12. A portion of the data is shown in the accompanying table.

Housing_Starts

Data for Case Study 16.3 Housing Starts and Other Factors, $n = 60$

Date	Housing Starts	Mortgage	Unemployment
2006–01	2273	6.15	4.7
2006–02	2119	6.25	4.8
⋮	⋮	⋮	⋮
2010–12	520	4.71	9.4

Source: Census Bureau and Board of Governors.

In a report, use the sample information to

1. Construct scatterplots to quantify the relationship of housing starts with the mortgage rate and the unemployment rate.

2. Estimate a linear regression model and an exponential regression model and use goodness-of-fit measures to select the most appropriate model for prediction.

3. Discuss the potential problems of correlated observations in this time series data application.

APPENDIX 16.1 Guidelines for Other Software Packages

The following section provides brief commands for Minitab, SPSS, and JMP. Copy and paste the specified data file into the relevant software spreadsheet prior to following the commands.

Minitab

Estimating Polynomial Regression Models

A. (Replicating Example 16.3) To create the variable Age^2, from the menu, select **Calc > Calculator**. After **Store result in variable**, enter AgeSqu. After **Expression**, select Age, select *, and select Age.

B. Estimate the regression model using the standard commands.

FILE
Quadratic

Estimating Logarithmic Regression Models

A. (Replicating Example 16.8, Model 4) To create the variable ln(Rent), from the menu, select **Calc > Calculator**. After **Store result in variable**, enter ln(Rent). Under **Functions**, select **Natural log**, then select Rent. Repeat these steps to create the variable ln(Sqft).

B. Estimate the regression model using the standard commands.

FILE
AnnArbor

Calculating a Comparable R^2

A. (Replicating Example 16.9) Create the variables ln(Rent) and ln(Sqft).

B. From the menu, choose **Stat > Regression > Regression > Fit Regression Model**. After **Responses**, select ln(Rent), and after **Continuous predictors**, select Bed, Bath, and ln(Sqft). Choose **Storage**, and then select **Fits**.

C. From the menu, select **Calc > Calculator**. After **Store result in variable**, enter yhat. After **Expression**, enter Exp(FITS1+0.1262*0.1262/2). (Recall that 0.1262 is the standard error of the estimate.)

D. From the menu, select **Stat > Basic Statistics > Correlation**. Under **Variables**, select Rent and yhat. Square the correlation coefficient to obtain R^2.

FILE
AnnArbor

SPSS

Estimating Polynomial Regression Models

A. (Replicating Example 16.3) To create the variable Age^2, from the menu, select **Transform > Compute Variables**. Under **Target Variable**, enter

FILE
Quadratic

AgeSqu. In the **Numeric Expression** dialog box, select Age, select *, and select Age.

B. Estimate the regression model using the standard commands.

Estimating Logarithmic Regression Models

AnnArbor

A. (Replicating Example 16.8, Model 4) To create the variable ln(Rent), from the menu, select **Transform > Compute Variables**. Under **Target Variable**, enter lnRent. Under **Function group**, select **Arithmetic**, and under **Functions and Special Variables**, double-click on **Ln**. Under **Numeric Expression**, select Rent. Repeat these steps to calculate ln(Sqft).

B. Estimate the regression model using the standard commands.

Calculating a Comparable R^2

AnnArbor

A. (Replicating Example 16.9) Create the variables lnRent and lnSqft.

B. From the menu, select **Analyze > Regression > Linear**.

C. Under **Dependent**, select lnRent, and under **Independent(s)**, select Bed, Bath, and lnSqft. Choose **Save** and select **Predicted Values – Unstandardized**.

D. From the menu, select **Transform > Compute Variables**. Under **Target Variable**, enter yhat. Under **Numeric Expression**, input EXP(PRE_1+0.1262 ** 2/2). (Recall that 0.1262 is the standard error.)

E. From the menu, select **Analyze > Correlate > Bivariate**. Under **Variables**, select Rent and yhat. Square the correlation coefficient to obtain R^2.

JMP

Estimating Polynomial Regression Models

Quadratic

A. (Replicating Example 16.3) To create the variable Age^2, right-click on a new column and select **New Column**, and label it AgeSqu. Right-click on AgeSqu, and select **Formula**. Under **Table Columns**, select Age, select ×, and select Age.

B. Estimate the regression model using the standard commands.

Estimating Logarithmic Regression Models

AnnArbor

A. (Replicating Example 16.8, Model 4) To create the variable ln(Rent), right-click on a new column and select **New Column**, and label it ln(Rent). Right-click on ln(Rent), and select **Formula**. Under **Functions (grouped)**, select **Transcendental > Log**, and then select Rent in the bracket. Repeat these steps to create the variable ln(Sqft).

B. Estimate the regression model using the standard commands.

Calculating a Comparable R^2

A. (Replicating Example 16.9) Create the variables ln(Rent) and ln(Sqft).

B. From the menu, choose **Analyze > Fit Model**.

C. Under **Select Columns**, select ln(Rent), and then under **Pick Role Variables**, select **Y**. Under **Select Columns**, select Bed, Bath, and ln(Sqft), and then under **Construct Model Effect**, select **Add**.

D. In the red triangle next to **Response ln(Rent)**, select **Save Columns > Predicted Values**. A new column named Predicted ln(Rent) should appear in the JMP spreadsheet.

E. In the JMP spreadsheet, right-click on a new column, select **New Column**, and enter yhat as the column name. Right-click on yhat, input **Formula > Transcendental > Exp**. In the bracket, input Predicted ln(Rent) + 0.1262 × 0.1262/2. (Recall that 0.1262 is the standard error.)

F. From the menu, select **Analyze > Multivariate Methods > Multivariate**.

G. Under **Select Columns**, select Rent and yhat, and under **Cast Selected Columns into Roles**, select **Y, Columns**. Square the correlation coefficient to obtain R^2.

17 Regression Models with Dummy Variables

LEARNING OBJECTIVES

After reading this chapter you should be able to:

LO **17.1** Use a dummy variable to represent a qualitative explanatory variable.

LO **17.2** Test for differences between the categories of a qualitative variable.

LO **17.3** Use a dummy variable to capture the interaction between a qualitative explanatory variable and a quantitative explanatory variable.

LO **17.4** Estimate and interpret a linear probability model.

LO **17.5** Estimate and interpret a logit model.

U p until now, regression analysis has allowed us to answer questions such as: How much does an extra year of education contribute to salary? What is the contribution of advertisement expenditures on sales of electronic goods? Is a student's SAT score a good predictor of his/her college GPA? All of these questions use response and explanatory variables that are quantitative. There are other important applications that use qualitative variables representing two or more categories. For instance, we may want answers to questions such as: Do women get paid as much as men for the same work? Are sales of electronic goods higher in the 4th quarter than in the other quarters? What is the influence of family income on the probability of buying a house? In order to answer these questions, the regression analysis must incorporate qualitative explanatory variables and/or a qualitative response variable. This chapter examines these kinds of situations, using dummy variable models and binary choice probability models.

©Asia Images Group/Getty Images RF

INTRODUCTORY CASE

Is There Evidence of Wage Discrimination?

A few years ago, three female professors at Seton Hall University filed a lawsuit alleging that the University paid better salaries to younger instructors and male professors. Even though this particular case was eventually dismissed, other universities took notice (www.nj.com, November 23, 2010). Hannah Benson, a human resource specialist at a large liberal arts college, was asked by the college's president to test for differences in salaries due to the professor's sex or age. For 42 professors, Hannah gathered information on annual salary (Salary in $1,000s), years of experience (Experience), whether or not the professor was male or female (Male equals 1 if male, 0 otherwise), and whether or not the professor was at least 60 years of age (Age equals 1 if at least 60 years of age, 0 otherwise). A portion of the data is shown in Table 17.1.

TABLE 17.1 Salary and Other Information on 42 Professors

FILE
Professor

Salary	Experience	Male	Age
67.50	14	1	0
53.51	6	1	0
⋮	⋮	⋮	⋮
73.06	35	0	1

Hannah would like to use the sample information in Table 17.1 to

1. Determine whether salary differs by a fixed amount between male and female professors.
2. Determine whether there is evidence of age discrimination in salaries.
3. Determine whether the salary difference between male and female professors increases with experience.

A synopsis of this case is provided in Section 17.2.

17.1 DUMMY VARIABLES

Up until now, the explanatory variables and the response variable used in the regression applications have been quantitative; in other words, they assume meaningful numerical values. For example, in Chapter 14, we used income and unemployment to explain variations in consumer debt (all quantitative variables). In empirical work, however, it is common to include some variables that are qualitative. Although qualitative variables can be described by several categories, they are commonly described by only two categories. Examples include a person's sex (male or female), homeownership (own or do not own), shipment (rejected or not rejected), and admission (yes or no). In the first two sections of this chapter we focus on incorporating qualitative explanatory variables into a regression model. In the last section, we discuss how to estimate and interpret a regression model that is based on a qualitative response variable.

> ### QUANTITATIVE VERSUS QUALITATIVE VARIABLES IN REGRESSION
> Variables employed in a regression can be quantitative or qualitative. Quantitative variables assume meaningful numerical values, whereas qualitative variables represent categories.

Given the professor salary data in the introductory case, we can estimate the model as $\hat{y} = 48.83 + 1.15x$ where y represents salary (in \$1,000s) and x is the usual quantitative variable, representing experience (in years). The sample regression equation implies that the predicted salary increases by about \$1,150 ($1.15 \times 1{,}000$) for every year of experience. Arguably, in addition to experience, variations in salary are also caused by qualitative explanatory variables such as a person's sex (male or female) and age (under or over 60 years).

A Qualitative Explanatory Variable with Two Categories

A qualitative explanatory variable with two categories can be associated with a **dummy variable**, also referred to as an **indicator variable**. A dummy variable d is defined as a variable that assumes a value of 1 for one of the categories and 0 for the other. For example, in the case of a dummy variable categorizing a person's sex, we can define 1 for male and 0 for female. Alternatively, we can define 1 for female and 0 for male, with no change in inference. Sometimes we define a dummy variable by converting a quantitative variable to a qualitative variable. In the introductory case, the qualitative variable age (under or over 60 years) was defined from the quantitative variable age. Similarly, in studying teen behavior, we may have access to quantitative information on age, but we can generate a dummy variable that equals 1 for ages between 13 and 19 and 0 otherwise.

> ### A DUMMY VARIABLE
> A dummy variable d is defined as a variable that takes on values of 1 or 0. It is commonly used to describe a qualitative variable with two categories.

LO 17.1

Use a dummy variable to represent a qualitative explanatory variable.

For the sake of simplicity, we will first consider a model containing one quantitative explanatory variable and one dummy variable. As we will see shortly, the model can easily be extended to include additional variables.

Consider the following model:

$$y = \beta_0 + \beta_1 x + \beta_2 d + \varepsilon,$$

where x is a quantitative variable and d is a dummy variable with values of 1 or 0. We can use sample data to estimate the model as

$$\hat{y} = b_0 + b_1 x + b_2 d.$$

For a given x and $d = 1$, we can compute the predicted value as

$$\hat{y} = b_0 + b_1x + b_2 = (b_0 + b_2) + b_1x.$$

Similarly, for $d = 0$,

$$\hat{y} = b_0 + b_1x.$$

Observe that the two regression lines, $\hat{y} = (b_0 + b_2) + b_1x$ and $\hat{y} = b_0 + b_1x$, have the same slope b_1. Thus, the sample regression equation $\hat{y} = b_0 + b_1x + b_2d$ accommodates two parallel lines; that is, the dummy variable d affects the intercept but not the slope. The difference between the intercepts is b_2 when d changes from 0 to 1. Figure 17.1 shows the two regression lines when $b_2 > 0$.

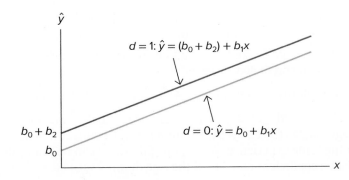

FIGURE 17.1
Using d for an intercept shift

EXAMPLE 17.1

The objective outlined in the introductory case is to determine if there are differences in salaries due to a professor's sex or age at a large liberal arts college. Use the data in Table 17.1 to answer the following questions.

FILE
Professor

a. Estimate $y = \beta_0 + \beta_1x + \beta_2d_1 + \beta_3d_2 + \varepsilon$, where y is the annual salary (in \$1,000s) of a professor, x is the number of years of experience, d_1 is the Male dummy variable that equals 1 if the professor is male and 0 otherwise, and d_2 is the Age dummy variable that equals 1 if the professor is at least 60 years of age and 0 otherwise.

b. Compute the predicted salary of a 50-year-old male professor with 10 years of experience. Compute the predicted salary of a 50-year-old female professor with 10 years of experience. Discuss the impact of Male on predicted salary.

c. Compute the predicted salary of a 65-year-old female professor with 10 years of experience. Discuss the impact of Age on predicted salary.

SOLUTION:

a. Table 17.2 shows a portion of the regression results.

TABLE 17.2 Regression Results for Example 17.1

	Coefficients	Standard Error	t Stat	p-Value
Intercept	40.6060	3.6919	10.999	0.000
Experience (x)	1.1279	0.1790	6.300	0.000
Male (d_1)	13.9240	2.8667	4.857	0.000
Age (d_2)	4.3428	4.6436	0.935	0.356

The estimated model is $\hat{y} = 40.6060 + 1.1279x + 13.9240d_1 + 4.3428d_2$.

b. The predicted salary of a 50-year-old male professor ($d_1 = 1$ and $d_2 = 0$) with 10 years of experience ($x = 10$) is

$$\hat{y} = 40.6060 + 1.1279(10) + 13.9240(1) + 4.3428(0) = 65.809, \text{ or } \$65,809.$$

The corresponding salary of a 50-year-old female professor ($d_1 = 0$ and $d_2 = 0$) is

$$\hat{y} = 40.6060 + 1.1279(10) + 13.9240(0) + 4.3428(0) = 51.885, \text{ or } \$51,885.$$

The predicted difference in salary between a male and a female professor with 10 years of experience is $13,924 (65,809 − 51,885). This difference can also be inferred from the estimated coefficient 13.924 of the Male dummy variable d_1. Note that the salary difference does not change with experience. For instance, the predicted salary of a 50-year-old male with 20 years of experience is $77,088. The corresponding salary of a 50-year-old female is $63,164, for the same difference of $13,924.

c. For a 65-year-old female professor ($d_1 = 0$ and $d_2 = 1$) with 10 years of experience ($x = 10$), the predicted salary is

$$\hat{y} = 40.6060 + 1.1279(10) + 13.9240(0) + 4.3428(1) = 56.228, \text{ or } \$56,228.$$

Prior to any statistical testing, it appears that an older female professor earns, on average, $4,343 (56,228 − 51,885) more than a younger female professor with the same experience. Again, this difference can be inferred from the estimated coefficient of 4.343 of the Age dummy variable d_2.

LO 17.2

Test for differences between the categories of a qualitative variable.

Dummy variables are treated just like other explanatory variables; that is, all statistical tests discussed in Chapter 15 remain valid. In particular, we can examine whether a particular dummy variable is statistically significant by using the standard t test. Here, the statistical significance indicates that the response variable depends on the two categories of the dummy variable.

TESTING THE SIGNIFICANCE OF A DUMMY VARIABLE

In a model, $y = \beta_0 + \beta_1 x + \beta_2 d_1 + \beta_3 d_2 + \varepsilon$, we can perform the t test to determine the significance of each dummy variable.

EXAMPLE 17.2

Refer to the regression results in Table 17.2.

a. Determine whether a male professor's salary differs from a female professor's salary at the 5% significance level.

b. Determine whether an older professor's salary differs from a younger professor's salary at the 5% significance level.

SOLUTION:

a. In order to test for a salary difference between male and female professors, we set up the competing hypotheses as $H_0: \beta_2 = 0$ against $H_A: \beta_2 \neq 0$. Given a value of the t_{df} test statistic of 4.857 with a p-value ≈ 0, we reject the null hypothesis and conclude that the Male dummy variable is statistically significant at the 5% level. We conclude that male and female professors do not make the same salary, holding other variables constant.

b. Here the competing hypotheses take the form $H_0: \beta_3 = 0$ against H_A: $\beta_3 \neq 0$. Given a value of the t_{df} test statistic of 0.935 with a p-value $= 0.356$, we cannot reject the null hypothesis. At the 5% significance level, we cannot conclude that an older professor's salary differs from a younger professor's salary.

We now turn our attention to selecting the preferred model for the analysis. Regression results are summarized in Table 17.3.

TABLE 17.3 Summary of Model Estimates

Variable	Model 1	Model 2	Model 3
Intercept	48.8274*	39.4333*	40.6060*
	(0.000)	(0.000)	(0.000)
Experience (x)	1.1455*	1.2396*	1.1279*
	(0.000)	(0.000)	(0.000)
Male (d_1)	NA	13.8857*	13.9240*
		(0.000)	(0.000)
Age (d_2)	NA	NA	4.3428
			(0.356)
Adjusted R^2	0.5358	0.7031	0.7022

Notes: The table contains parameter estimates with p-values in parentheses; NA denotes not applicable; * represents significance at the 5% level; adjusted R^2, reported in the last row, is used for model selection.

Model 1 uses only the quantitative variable, Experience. In addition to Experience, Model 2 includes the Male dummy variable, and Model 3 includes Experience and the two dummy variables, Male and Age. This raises an important question: which of the above three models should we use for making predictions? As discussed in Chapter 14, we usually rely on adjusted R^2 to compare models with different numbers of explanatory variables. Based on the adjusted R^2 values of the models, reported in the last row of Table 17.3, we select Model 2 as the preferred model because it has the highest adjusted R^2 value of 0.7031. This is consistent with the test results that showed that the Male dummy variable is significant, but the Age dummy variable is not significant, at the 5% level.

A Qualitative Explanatory Variable with Multiple Categories

So far we have used dummy variables to describe qualitative explanatory variables with only two categories. Sometimes, a qualitative explanatory variable may be defined by more than two categories. In such cases, we use multiple dummy variables to capture all categories. For example, the mode of transportation used to commute to work may be described by three categories: Public Transportation, Driving Alone, and Car Pooling. We can then define two dummy variables d_1 and d_2, where d_1 equals 1 for Public Transportation, 0 otherwise, and d_2 equals 1 for Driving Alone, 0 otherwise. For this three-category case, we need to define only two dummy variables; Car Pooling is indicated when $d_1 = d_2 = 0$.

Consider the following regression model:

$$y = \beta_0 + \beta_1 x + \beta_2 d_1 + \beta_3 d_2 + \varepsilon,$$

where y represents commuting expenditure, x represents distance to work, and d_1 and d_2 represent the Public Transportation and Driving Alone dummy variables, respectively. We can use sample data to estimate the model as

$$\hat{y} = b_0 + b_1 x + b_2 d_1 + b_3 d_2.$$

For $d_1 = 1$, $d_2 = 0$ (Public Transportation), $\hat{y} = b_0 + b_1 x + b_2 = (b_0 + b_2) + b_1 x$.

For $d_1 = 0$, $d_2 = 1$ (Driving Alone), $\hat{y} = b_0 + b_1 x + b_3 = (b_0 + b_3) + b_1 x$.

For $d_1 = d_2 = 0$ (Car Pooling), $\hat{y} = b_0 + b_1 x$.

Here we use Car Pooling as the reference category in the estimated regression line with the intercept b_0. The intercept changes to $(b_0 + b_2)$ for Public Transportation and $(b_0 + b_3)$ for Driving Alone. Therefore, we account for all three categories with just two dummy variables.

Given the intercept term, we exclude one of the dummy variables from the regression, where the excluded variable represents the reference category against which the others are assessed. If we include as many dummy variables as there are categories, then their sum will equal one. For instance, if we add a third dummy variable d_3 that equals 1 to denote Car Pooling, then for all observations, $d_1 + d_2 + d_3 = 1$. This creates the problem called perfect multicollinearity, a topic discussed in Chapter 15; recall that such a model cannot be estimated. This situation is sometimes referred to as the **dummy variable trap**.

AVOIDING THE DUMMY VARIABLE TRAP

Assuming that the linear regression model includes an intercept, the number of dummy variables representing a qualitative variable should be *one less than the number of categories* of the variable.

EXAMPLE 17.3

In 2015, 64 groups filed a complaint with the U.S. Department of Justice claiming that Asian Americans are held to a higher standard than other students when applying for admission at elite universities (*The Los Angeles Times*, June 9, 2015). A researcher from the Center for Equal Opportunity wants to determine if SAT scores of admitted students at a large state university differed by ethnic background. She collects data on SAT scores and ethnic background for 200 admitted students. A portion of the data is shown in Table 17.4.

TABLE 17.4 SAT Scores and Ethnic Background; $n = 200$

Individual	SAT	White	Black	Asian	Hispanic
1	1515	1	0	0	0
2	1530	0	0	0	1
⋮	⋮	⋮	⋮	⋮	⋮
200	1614	1	0	0	0

a. Estimate the model $y = \beta_0 + \beta_1 d_1 + \beta_2 d_2 + \beta_3 d_3 + \varepsilon$, where y represents a student's SAT score; d_1 equals 1 if the student is white, 0 otherwise; d_2 equals 1 if the student is black, 0 otherwise; and d_3 equals 1 if the student is Asian, 0 otherwise. Note that the reference category is Hispanic.

b. What is the predicted SAT score for an Asian student? For a Hispanic student?

c. Do SAT scores vary by ethnic background at the 5% significance level? Explain.

SOLUTION:

a. We report a portion of the regression results of this model in Table 17.5.

TABLE 17.5 Regression Results for Example 17.3

	Coefficients	Standard Error	t Stat	p-Value
Intercept	1388.8919	9.3567	148.438	0.000
White (d_1)	201.1447	12.9056	15.586	0.000
Black (d_2)	−31.4544	22.1913	−1.417	0.158
Asian (d_3)	264.8581	17.8584	14.831	0.000

b. For an Asian student, we set $d_1 = 0$, $d_2 = 0$, $d_3 = 1$ and calculate $\hat{y} = 1388.8919 + 264.8581 = 1653.75$. Thus, the predicted SAT score for an Asian student is approximately 1654. The predicted SAT score for a Hispanic student ($d_1 = d_2 = d_3 = 0$) is $\hat{y} = 1388.89$, or approximately 1389.

c. Since the p-values corresponding to d_1 and d_3 are approximately zero, we conclude at the 5% level that the SAT scores of admitted white and Asian students are different from those of Hispanic students. However, with a p-value of 0.158, we cannot conclude that the SAT scores of admitted black and Hispanic students are statistically different.

EXAMPLE 17.4

Let's reformulate the model from Example 17.3 to determine if the SAT scores of white students are lower than the SAT scores of Asian students. We will conduct the test at the 5% significance level and, as in Example 17.3, we consider all ethnic categories for the analysis.

SAT_Ethnicity

SOLUTION: We note that the regression results reported in Table 17.5 cannot be used to determine if the SAT scores of white students are lower than the SAT scores of Asian students. In order to conduct the relevant test, we must use either Asians or whites as the reference category against which the others are assessed. We estimate the model as $y = \beta_0 + \beta_1 d_1 + \beta_2 d_2 + \beta_3 d_3 + \varepsilon$, where d_1 and d_2 are again dummy variables corresponding to the categories of white and black students, respectively, but now d_3 equals 1 if the student is Hispanic, 0 otherwise. Here the reference category is Asian. We report a portion of the regression results of this model in Table 17.6.

TABLE 17.6 Regression Results for Example 17.4

	Coefficient	Standard Error	t Stat	p-Value
Intercept	1653.7500	15.2111	108.720	0.000
White (d_1)	−63.7134	17.6177	−3.616	0.000
Black (d_2)	−296.3125	25.2247	−11.747	0.000
Hispanic (d_3)	−264.8581	17.8584	−14.831	0.000

For an Asian student, we set $d_1 = d_2 = d_3 = 0$ to find the predicted SAT score as 1653.75, which is the same as derived earlier. In fact, we can show that all predicted SAT scores are identical to those found in Example 17.3. This shows that the choice of the reference category does not matter for making predictions. The results in Table 17.6, however, can be used to determine if the SAT scores of white students are lower than the SAT scores of Asian students. We specify the competing hypotheses for a left-tailed test as $H_0: \beta_1 \geq 0$ against $H_A: \beta_1 < 0$. The p-value for this one-tailed test is calculated as $0.000/2 \approx 0$. Since the p-value $< \alpha = 0.05$, we reject the null hypothesis. Therefore, we conclude that the SAT scores of admitted white students are less than the SAT scores of admitted Asian students at the 5% significance level.

EXERCISES 17.1

Mechanics

1. Consider a linear regression model where y represents the response variable, x is a quantitative explanatory variable, and d is a dummy variable. The model is estimated as $\hat{y} = 14.8 + 4.4x - 3.8d$.
   a. Interpret the dummy variable coefficient.
   b. Compute $\hat{y}$ for $x = 3$ and $d = 1$.
   c. Compute $\hat{y}$ for $x = 3$ and $d = 0$.

2. Consider a linear regression model where y represents the response variable and d_1 and d_2 are dummy variables. The model is estimated as $\hat{y} = 160 + 15d_1 + 32d_2$.
   a. Compute $\hat{y}$ for $d_1 = 1$ and $d_2 = 1$.
   b. Compute $\hat{y}$ for $d_1 = 0$ and $d_2 = 0$.

3. Using 50 observations, the following regression output is obtained from estimating $y = \beta_0 + \beta_1 x + \beta_2 d_1 + \beta_3 d_2 + \varepsilon$.

	Coefficients	Standard Error	t Stat	p-Value
Intercept	−0.61	0.23	−2.75	0.007
x	3.12	1.04	3.01	0.003
d_1	−13.22	15.65	−0.85	0.401
d_2	5.35	1.25	4.27	0.000

   a. Compute $\hat{y}$ for $x = 250$, $d_1 = 1$, and $d_2 = 0$; compute $\hat{y}$ for $x = 250$, $d_1 = 0$, and $d_2 = 1$.
   b. Interpret d_1 and d_2. Are both dummy variables individually significant at the 5% level? Explain.

Applications

4. An executive researcher wants to better understand the factors that explain differences in salaries for marketing majors. He decides to estimate two models: $y = \beta_0 + \beta_1 d_1 + \varepsilon$ (Model 1) and $y = \beta_0 + \beta_1 d_1 + \beta_2 d_2 + \varepsilon$ (Model 2). Here y represents salary, d_1 is a dummy variable that equals 1 for male employees, and d_2 is a dummy variable that equals 1 for employees with an MBA.
   a. What is the reference group in Model 1?
   b. What is the reference group in Model 2?
   c. In the above models, would it matter if d_1 equaled 1 for female employees?

5. House price y is estimated as a function of the square footage of a house x and a dummy variable d that equals 1 if the house

has ocean views. The estimated house price, measured in $1,000s, is given by $\hat{y} = 118.90 + 0.12x + 52.60d$.
   a. Compute the predicted price of a house with ocean views and square footage of 2,000 and 3,000, respectively.
   b. Compute the predicted price of a house without ocean views and square footage of 2,000 and 3,000, respectively.
   c. Discuss the impact of ocean views on the house price.

6. **FILE** *Urban.* A sociologist is studying the relationship between consumption expenditures of families in the United States (Consumption in $), family income (Income in $), and whether or not the family lives in an urban or rural community (Urban = 1 if urban, 0 otherwise). She collects data on 50 families, a portion of which is shown in the accompanying table.

Consumption	Income	Urban
62336	87534	0
60076	94796	1
⋮	⋮	⋮
59055	100908	1

   a. Estimate Consumption $= \beta_0 + \beta_1$Income $+ \beta_2$Urban $+ \varepsilon$. Use the estimated model to predict the consumption expenditure of urban families with an income of $80,000. What is the corresponding consumption expenditure of rural families?
   b. Estimate Consumption $= \beta_0 + \beta_1$Income $+ \beta_2$Rural $+ \varepsilon$ where the dummy variable Rural equals 1 if rural, 0 otherwise. Use the estimated model to predict the consumption expenditure of urban families with an income of $80,000. What is the corresponding consumption expenditure of rural families?
   c. Interpret the results of the preceding two models.

7. **FILE** *IPO.* One of the theories regarding initial public offering (IPO) pricing is that the initial return y (the percentage change from offer to open price) on an IPO depends on the price revision x (the percentage change from pre-offer to offer price). Another factor that may influence the initial return is a high-tech dummy variable that equals 1 for high-tech firms and 0 otherwise. The following table shows a portion of the data on 264 IPO firms from January 2001 through September 2004.

Initial Return	Price Revision	High-Tech
33.93	7.14	0
18.68	−26.39	0
⋮	⋮	⋮
0.08	−29.41	1

Source: www.ipohome.com; www.nasdaq.com.

a. Estimate $y = \beta_0 + \beta_1 x + \beta_2 d + \varepsilon$ where the dummy variable d equals 1 for firms that are high-tech. Use the estimated model to predict the initial return of a high-tech firm with a 10% price revision. Find the corresponding predicted return of a firm that is not high-tech.

b. Estimate $y = \beta_0 + \beta_1 x + \beta_2 d + \varepsilon$ where the dummy variable d equals 1 for firms that are not high-tech. Use the estimated model to predict the initial return of a high-tech firm with a 10% price revision. Find the corresponding predicted return of a firm that is not high-tech.

c. In the above two models, determine if the dummy variable is significant at the 5% level.

8. **FILE** *BMI.* According to the World Health Organization, obesity has reached epidemic proportions globally. While obesity has generally been linked with chronic disease and disability, researchers argue that it may also affect salaries. In other words, the body mass index (BMI) of an employee is a predictor for salary. (A person is considered overweight if his/her BMI is at least 25 and obese if BMI exceeds 30.) The accompanying table shows a portion of salary data (in $1,000s) for 30 college-educated men with their respective BMI and a dummy variable that equals 1 for a white man and 0 otherwise.

Salary	BMI	White
34	33	1
43	26	1
⋮	⋮	⋮
45	21	1

a. Estimate a model for Salary using BMI and White as the explanatory variables. Determine if BMI influences salary at the 5% level of significance.

b. What is the estimated salary of a white college-educated man with a BMI of 30? Compute the corresponding salary of a nonwhite man.

9. **FILE** *Wage.* A researcher wonders whether males get paid more, on average, than females at a large firm. She interviews 50 employees and collects data on each employee's hourly wage (Wage in $), years of higher education (EDUC), years of experience (EXPER), age (Age), and a Male dummy variable that equals 1 if male, 0 otherwise. A portion of the data is shown in the accompanying table.

Wage	EDUC	EXPER	Age	Male
37.85	11	2	40	1
21.72	4	1	39	0
⋮	⋮	⋮	⋮	⋮
24.18	8	11	64	0

a. Estimate: Wage $= \beta_0 + \beta_1$EDUC $+ \beta_2$EXPER $+ \beta_3$Age $+ \beta_4$Male $+ \varepsilon$.

b. Predict the hourly wage of a 40-year-old male employee with 10 years of higher education and 5 years experience. Predict the hourly wage of a 40-year-old female employee with the same qualifications.

c. Interpret the estimated coefficient for Male. Is the variable Male significant at the 5% level? Do the data suggest that sex discrimination exists at this firm?

10. **FILE** *Nicknames.* In the United States, baseball has always been a favorite pastime and is rife with statistics and theories. While baseball purists may disagree, to an applied statistician no topic in baseball is too small or hypothesis too unlikely. Researchers at Wayne State University showed that major league players who have nicknames live 2½ years longer than those without them (*The Wall Street Journal,* July 16, 2009). The following table shows a portion of data on the lifespan (Years) of a player and a Nickname dummy variable that equals 1 if the player had a nickname and 0 otherwise.

Years	Nickname
74	1
62	1
⋮	⋮
64	0

a. Create two subsamples, with one consisting of players with a nickname and the other one without a nickname. Calculate the average longevity for each subsample.

b. Estimate a linear regression model of Years on the Nickname dummy variable. Compute the predicted longevity of players with and without a nickname.

c. Conduct a one-tailed test at the 5% level to determine if players with a nickname live longer.

11. **FILE** *SAT.* The SAT has gone through many revisions over the years. People argue that female students generally do worse on math tests but better on writing tests. Consider the following portion of data on 20 students who took the SAT test last year. Information includes each student's score on the writing and math sections of the exam, the student's GPA, and a Female dummy variable that equals 1 if the student is female, 0 otherwise.

Writing	Math	GPA	Female
620	600	3.44	0
570	550	3.04	0
⋮	⋮	⋮	⋮
540	520	2.84	0

a. Estimate a linear regression model with Writing as the response variable and GPA and Female as the explanatory variables.

b. Compute the predicted writing score for a male student with a GPA of 3.5. Repeat the computation for a female student.

c. At the 5% significance level, determine if there is a difference in writing scores between males and females.

12. **FILE** *SAT.* Use the accompanying data to estimate a linear regression model with Math as the response variable and GPA and Female as the explanatory variables.

a. Compute the predicted math score for a male student with a GPA of 3.5. Repeat the computation for a female student.

b. At the 5% significance level, determine if there is a difference in math scores between males and females.

13. **FILE** *Ice_Cream.* A manager at an ice cream store is trying to determine how many customers to expect on any given day. Overall business has been relatively steady over the past several years, but the customer count seems to have ups and downs. He collects data over 30 days and records the number of customers, the high temperature (in degrees Fahrenheit), and whether the day fell on a weekend (Weekend equals 1 if weekend, 0 otherwise). A portion of the data is shown in the accompanying table.

Customers	Temperature	Weekend
376	75	0
433	78	0
⋮	⋮	⋮
401	68	0

a. Estimate: Customers $= \beta_0 + \beta_1$Temperature $+ \beta_2$Weekend $+ \varepsilon$.

b. How many customers should the manager expect on a Sunday with a forecasted high temperature of 80°?

c. Interpret the estimated coefficient for Weekend. Is it significant at the 5% level? How might this affect the store's staffing needs?

14. In an attempt to "time the market," a financial analyst studies the quarterly returns of a stock. He uses the model $y = \beta_0 + \beta_1 d_1 + \beta_2 d_2 + \beta_3 d_3 + \varepsilon$ where y is the quarterly return of a stock, d_1 is a dummy variable that equals 1 if quarter 1 and 0 otherwise, d_2 is a dummy variable that equals 1 if quarter 2 and 0 otherwise, and d_3 is a dummy variable that equals 1 if

quarter 3 and 0 otherwise. The following table shows a portion of the regression results.

	Coefficients	Standard Error	t Stat	p-Value
Intercept	10.62	5.81	1.83	0.08
d_1	−7.26	8.21	−0.88	0.38
d_2	−1.87	8.21	−0.23	0.82
d_3	−9.31	8.21	−1.13	0.27

a. Given that there are four quarters in a year, why doesn't the analyst include a fourth dummy variable in his model? What is the reference category?

b. At the 5% significance level, are the dummy variables individually significant? Explain.

c. Explain how you would reformulate the model to determine if the quarterly return is higher in quarter 2 than in quarter 3, still accounting for all quarters.

15. **FILE** *Industry.* The issues regarding executive compensation have received extensive media attention (*The New York Times*, February 9, 2009). Consider a regression model that links CEO compensation (in $ millions) with the total assets of the firm (in $ millions) and the firm's industry. Dummy variables are used to represent four industries: Manufacturing Technology d_1, Manufacturing Other d_2, Financial Services d_3, and Nonfinancial Services d_4. A portion of the data for the 455 highest-paid CEOs in 2006 is shown in the accompanying table.

Compensation	Assets	d_1	d_2	d_3	d_4
16.58	20917.5	1	0	0	0
26.92	32659.5	1	0	0	0
⋮	⋮	⋮	⋮	⋮	⋮
2.30	44875.0	0	0	1	0

Source: SEC website and Compustat.

a. Estimate the model: $y = \beta_0 + \beta_1 x + \beta_2 d_1 + \beta_3 d_2 + \beta_4 d_3 + \varepsilon$, where y and x denote compensation and assets, respectively. Here the reference category is the nonfinancial services industry.

b. Interpret the estimated coefficients.

c. Use a 5% level of significance to determine which industries, relative to the nonfinancial services industry, have different executive compensation.

d. Reformulate the model to determine, at the 5% significance level, if compensation is higher in Manufacturing Other than in Manufacturing Technology. Your model must account for total assets and all industry types.

16. **FILE** *QuickFix.* The general manager of QuickFix, a chain of quick-service, no-appointment auto repair shops, wants to

develop a model to forecast monthly vehicles served at any particular shop based on four factors: garage bays, population within 5-mile radius (Population in 1,000s), interstate highway access (Access equals 1 if convenient, 0 otherwise), and time of year (Winter equals 1 if winter, 0 otherwise). He believes that, all else equal, shops near an interstate will service more vehicles and that more vehicles will be serviced in the winter due to battery and tire issues. A sample of 19 locations has been obtained. A portion of the data is shown in the accompanying table.

Vehicles Served	Garage Bays	Population	Access	Winter
200	3	15	0	0
351	3	22	0	1
⋮	⋮	⋮	⋮	⋮
464	6	74	1	1

a. Estimate the regression equation relating vehicles serviced to the four explanatory variables.
b. Interpret each of the slope coefficients.
c. At the 5% significance level, are the explanatory variables jointly significant? Are they individually significant? What about at the 10% significance level?
d. What proportion of the variability in vehicles served is explained by the four explanatory variables?
e. Predict vehicles serviced in a non-winter month for a particular location with 5 garage bays, a population of 40,000, and convenient interstate access.

17. **FILE** *Retail.* A government researcher is analyzing the relationship between retail sales (in $ millions) and the gross national product (GNP in $ billions). He also wonders whether there are significant differences in retail sales related to the quarters of the year. He collects 10 years of quarterly data. A portion is shown in the accompanying table.

Year	Quarter	Retail Sales	GNP
2001	1	696048	9740.5
2001	2	753211	9983.5
⋮	⋮	⋮	⋮
2009	4	985649	14442.8

Source: Retail sales obtained from www.census.gov; GNP obtained from http://research.stlouisfed.org.

a. Estimate $y = \beta_0 + \beta_1 x + \beta_2 d_1 + \beta_3 d_2 + \beta_4 d_3 + \varepsilon$ where y is retail sales, x is GNP, d_1 is a dummy variable that equals 1 if quarter 1 and 0 otherwise, d_2 is a dummy variable that equals 1 if quarter 2 and 0 otherwise, and d_3 is a dummy variable that equals 1 if quarter 3 and 0 otherwise. Here the reference category is quarter 4.
b. Predict retail sales in quarters 2 and 4 if GNP equals $13,000 billion.
c. Which of the quarterly sales are significantly different from those of the 4th quarter at the 5% level?
d. Reformulate the model to determine, at the 5% significance level, if sales differ between quarter 2 and quarter 3. Your model must account for all quarters.

17.2 INTERACTIONS WITH DUMMY VARIABLES

LO 17.3

Use a dummy variable to capture the interaction between a qualitative explanatory variable and a quantitative explanatory variable.

So far we have used a dummy variable d to allow for a shift in the intercept. In other words, d allows the predicted y to differ between the two categories of a qualitative variable by a fixed amount across the values of x. We can also use d to create an **interaction variable**, which allows the predicted y to differ between the two categories of a qualitative variable by a varying amount across the values of x. The interaction variable is a product term xd that captures the interaction between a quantitative variable x and a dummy variable d. Together, the variables d and xd allow the intercept as well as the slope of the estimated linear regression line to vary between the two categories of a qualitative variable.

Consider the following regression model:

$$y = \beta_0 + \beta_1 x + \beta_2 d + \beta_3 xd + \varepsilon.$$

We can use sample data to estimate the model as

$$\hat{y} = b_0 + b_1 x + b_2 d + b_3 xd.$$

For a given x and $d = 1$, we can compute the predicted value as

$$\hat{y} = b_0 + b_1 x + b_2 + b_3 x = (b_0 + b_2) + (b_1 + b_3)x.$$

Similarly, for $d = 0$,

$$\hat{y} = b_0 + b_1 x.$$

The use of the dummy variable d along with the interaction variable xd affects the intercept as well as the slope of the estimated regression line. Note that the estimated intercept b_0 and slope b_1 when $d = 0$ shift to $(b_0 + b_2)$ and $(b_1 + b_3)$, respectively, when $d = 1$. Figure 17.2 shows a shift in the intercept and the slope of the estimated regression line when $d = 0$ changes to $d = 1$, given $b_2 > 0$ and $b_3 > 0$.

FIGURE 17.2 Using d and xd for intercept and slope shifts

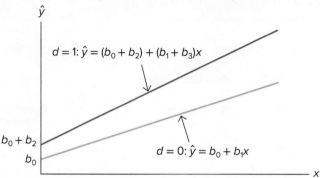

Prior to estimation, we use sample data to generate two variables, d and xd, which we use along with other explanatory variables in the regression. Tests of significance are performed as before.

TESTING THE SIGNIFICANCE OF A DUMMY VARIABLE AND AN INTERACTION VARIABLE

In a model $y = \beta_0 + \beta_1 x + \beta_2 d + \beta_3 xd + \varepsilon$, we can perform a t test for the individual significance of the dummy variable d and the interaction variable xd. Similarly, we can perform the partial F test for the joint significance of d and xd.

EXAMPLE 17.5

Professor

In Section 17.1, we estimated a regression model to test for differences in salaries depending on a professor's sex and age. We found that the number of years of experience x and the Male dummy variable d_1 were significant in explaining salary differences; however, the Age dummy variable d_2 was insignificant. In an attempt to refine the model explaining salary, we drop d_2 and estimate three models using the data from Table 17.1, where y represents annual salary (in \$1,000s).

$$\text{Model 1: } y = \beta_0 + \beta_1 x + \beta_2 d_1 + \varepsilon$$
$$\text{Model 2: } y = \beta_0 + \beta_1 x + \beta_2 xd_1 + \varepsilon$$
$$\text{Model 3: } y = \beta_0 + \beta_1 x + \beta_2 d_1 + \beta_3 xd_1 + \varepsilon$$

a. Estimate and interpret each of the three models.
b. Select the most appropriate model.
c. Use the selected model to predict salaries for males and females over various years of experience.

SOLUTION:

a. In order to estimate the three models, we first generate data on xd_1; Table 17.7 shows a portion of the data.

TABLE 17.7 Generating xd_1 from the Data in Table 17.1

y	x	d_1	xd_1
67.50	14	1	$14 \times 1 = 14$
53.51	6	1	$6 \times 1 = 6$
⋮	⋮	⋮	⋮
73.06	35	0	$35 \times 0 = 0$

Table 17.8 summarizes the regression results for the three models.

TABLE 17.8 Summary of Model Estimates

	Model 1	Model 2	Model 3
Intercept	39.4333* (0.000)	47.0725* (0.000)	49.4188* (0.000)
Experience (x)	1.2396* (0.000)	0.8466* (0.000)	0.7581* (0.000)
Male (d_1)	13.8857* (0.000)	NA	−4.0013 (0.422)
Experience × Male (xd_1)	NA	0.7716* (0.000)	0.9303* (0.000)
Adjusted R^2	0.7031	0.7923	0.7905

Notes: The top portion of the table contains parameter estimates with p-values in parentheses; NA denotes not applicable; * represents significance at the 5% level; Adjusted R^2, reported in the last row, is used for model selection.

Model 1 uses a Male dummy variable d_1 to allow salaries between males and females to differ by a fixed amount, irrespective of experience. It is estimated as $\hat{y} = 39.4333 + 1.2396x + 13.8857d_1$. Since d_1 is associated with a p-value ≈ 0, we conclude at the 5% level that d_1 has a statistically significant influence on salary. The estimated model implies that, on average, males earn about \$13,886 (13.8857 × 1,000) more than females at all levels of experience.

Model 2 uses an interaction variable xd_1 to allow the difference in salaries between males and females to vary with experience. It is estimated as $\hat{y} = 47.0725 + 0.8466x + 0.7716xd_1$. Since xd_1 is associated with a p-value ≈ 0, we conclude that it is statistically significant at the 5% level. With every extra year of experience, the estimated difference in salaries between males and females increases by about \$772 (0.7716 × 1,000).

Model 3 uses d_1 along with xd_1 to allow a fixed as well as a varying difference in salaries between males and females. The estimated regression equation is $\hat{y} = 49.4188 + 0.7581x - 4.0013d_1 + 0.9303xd_1$. Interestingly, with a p-value of 0.422, the variable d_1 is no longer statistically significant at the 5% level. However, the variable xd_1 is significant, suggesting that with every extra year of experience, the estimated difference in salaries between males and females increases by about \$930 (0.9303 × 1,000).

b. While Model 1 shows that the Male dummy variable d_1 is significant and Model 2 shows that the interaction variable xd_1 is significant, Model 3 provides somewhat conflicting results. This raises an important question:

which model should we trust? It is not uncommon to contend with such scenarios in business applications. As discussed earlier, we usually rely on adjusted R^2 to compare models that have a different number of explanatory variables. Based on the adjusted R^2 values of the models, reported in the last row of Table 17.8, we select Model 2 as the preferred model because it has the highest value of 0.7923.

c. In order to interpret the results further, we use Model 2 to estimate salaries with varying levels of experience for both males and females. For example, with 10 years of experience, the predicted salary for males ($d_1 = 1$) is

$$\hat{y} = 47.0725 + 0.8466(10) + 0.7716(10 \times 1) = 63.25, \text{ or } \$63{,}250.$$

The corresponding predicted salary for females ($d_1 = 0$) is

$$\hat{y} = 47.0725 + 0.8466(10) + 0.7716(10 \times 0) = 55.54, \text{ or } \$55{,}540.$$

Therefore, with 10 years of experience, the salary difference between males and females is about $7,710. Predicted salaries (in $) for both males and females, and their salary difference, at other levels of experience are presented in Table 17.9.

TABLE 17.9 Predicted Salaries at Various Levels of Experience

Experience	Males	Females	Difference
1	48,690	47,920	770
2	50,310	48,770	1,540
3	51,930	49,610	2,320
4	53,550	50,460	3,090
5	55,160	51,310	3,850
10	63,250	55,540	7,710
15	71,350	59,770	11,580
20	79,440	64,000	15,440
25	87,530	68,240	19,290
30	95,620	72,470	23,150

Note that as experience increases, the salary difference between males and females becomes wider. For instance, the difference is $3,850 with 5 years of experience. However, the difference increases to $19,290 with 25 years of experience. This is consistent with the inclusion of the interaction variable in Model 2. The shift in the slope, implied by the predicted salaries in Table 17.9, is shown in Figure 17.3.

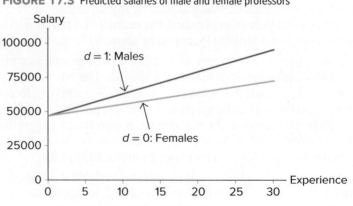

FIGURE 17.3 Predicted salaries of male and female professors

A lawsuit brought against Seton Hall University by three female professors alleged that the university engaged in both age and sex discrimination with respect to salaries (www.nj.com, November 23, 2010). Despite the fact that the case was eventually dismissed, another university wonders if the same can be said about its practices. For 42 professors, information is collected on annual salary, experience, whether a professor is male or female, and whether or not the professor is at least 60 years of age. A regression of annual salary against experience, a Male dummy variable, and an Age dummy variable reveal that the professor's sex is significant in explaining variations in salary, but the professor's age is not significant.

©Hero Images/Getty Images RF

In an attempt to refine the model describing annual salary, various models are estimated that remove the Age dummy variable but use the Male dummy variable to allow both fixed and changing effects on salary. The sample regression line that best fits the data does not include the Male dummy variable for a fixed effect. However, the interaction variable, defined as the product of Male and experience, is significant at any reasonable level, implying that males make about $772 more than females for every year of experience. While the estimated difference in salaries between males and females is only $772 with 1 year of experience, the difference increases to $19,290 with 25 years of experience. In sum, the findings suggest that salaries do indeed differ by one's sex, and this difference increases with every extra year of experience.

EXERCISES 17.2

Mechanics

18. Consider a linear regression model where y represents the response variable and x and d are the explanatory variables; d is a dummy variable assuming values 1 or 0. A model with the dummy variable d and the interaction variable xd is estimated as $\hat{y} = 5.2 + 0.9x + 1.4d + 0.2xd$.
    a. Compute $\hat{y}$ for $x = 10$ and $d = 1$.
    b. Compute $\hat{y}$ for $x = 10$ and $d = 0$.

19. Using 20 observations, the following regression output is obtained from estimating $y = \beta_0 + \beta_1 x + \beta_2 d + \beta_3 xd + \varepsilon$.

	Coefficients	Standard Error	t Stat	p-Value
Intercept	13.56	3.31	4.09	0.001
x	4.62	0.56	8.31	0.000
d	−5.15	4.97	−1.04	0.316
xd	2.09	0.79	2.64	0.018

    a. Compute $\hat{y}$ for $x = 10$ and $d = 1$; compute $\hat{y}$ for $x = 10$ and $d = 0$.
    b. Are the dummy variable d and the interaction variable xd individually significant at the 5% level? Explain.

Applications

20. The annual salary of an employee y (in $1,000s) is estimated as a function of years of experience x; a dummy variable d that equals 1 for college graduates and 0 for those graduating from high school but not college; and the interaction variable xd. The estimated salary is given by $\hat{y} = 30.3 + 1.2x + 15.5d + 2.0xd$.
    a. What is the predicted salary of a college graduate who has 5 years of experience? What is the predicted salary of a college graduate who has 15 years of experience?
    b. What is the predicted salary of a non-college graduate who has 5 years of experience? What is the predicted salary of a non-college graduate who has 15 years of experience?
    c. Discuss the impact of a college degree on salary.

21. House price y is estimated as a function of the square footage of a house x; a dummy variable d that equals 1 if the house has ocean views and 0 otherwise; and the interaction variable xd. The estimated house price, measured in $1,000s, is given by $\hat{y} = 80 + 0.12x + 40d + 0.01xd$.
    a. Compute the predicted price of a house with ocean views and square footage of 2,000 and 3,000, respectively.

b. Compute the predicted price of a house without ocean views and square footage of 2,000 and 3,000, respectively.

c. Discuss the impact of ocean views on the house price.

22. **FILE** *Urban.* A sociologist is looking at the relationship between consumption expenditures of families in the United States (Consumption in \$), family income (Income in \$), and whether or not the family lives in an urban or rural community (Urban = 1 if urban, 0 otherwise). She collects data on 50 families across the United States, a portion of which is shown in the accompanying table.

Consumption	Income	Urban
62336	87534	0
60076	94796	1
⋮	⋮	⋮
59055	100908	1

a. Estimate: Consumption = $\beta_0 + \beta_1$Income + ε. Compute the predicted consumption expenditures of a family with income of \$75,000.

b. Include a dummy variable Urban to predict consumption for a family with income of \$75,000 in urban and rural communities.

c. Include a dummy variable Urban and an interaction variable (Income × Urban) to predict consumption for a family with income of \$75,000 in urban and rural communities.

d. Which of the preceding models is most suitable for the data? Explain.

23. **FILE** *BMI.* According to the World Health Organization, obesity has reached epidemic proportions globally. While obesity has generally been linked with chronic disease and disability, researchers argue that it may also affect wages. In other words, the body mass index (BMI) of an employee is a predictor for salary. (A person is considered overweight if his/her BMI is at least 25 and obese if BMI exceeds 30.) The accompanying table shows a portion of salary data (in \$1,000s) for 30 college-educated men with their respective BMI and a dummy variable that represents 1 for a white man and 0 otherwise.

Salary	BMI	White
34	33	1
43	26	1
⋮	⋮	⋮
45	21	1

a. Estimate a model for Salary with BMI and White as the explanatory variables.

b. Reestimate the model with BMI, White, and a product of BMI and White as the explanatory variables.

c. Which of the models is most suitable? Explain. Use this model to estimate the salary for a white college-educated man with a BMI of 30. Compute the corresponding salary for a nonwhite man.

24. **FILE** *Pick_Errors.* The distribution center for an online retailer has been experiencing quite a few "pick errors" (i.e., retrieving the wrong item). Although the warehouse manager thinks most errors are due to inexperienced workers, she believes that a training program also may help to reduce them. Before sending all employees to training, she examines data from a pilot study of 30 employees. Information is collected on the employee's annual pick errors (Errors), experience (Exper in years), and whether or not the employee attended training (Train equals 1 if the employee attended training, 0 otherwise). A portion of the data is shown in the accompanying table.

Errors	Exper	Train
13	9	0
3	27	0
⋮	⋮	⋮
4	24	1

a. Estimate two models:
Errors = $\beta_0 + \beta_1$ Exper + β_2 Train + ε, and
Errors = $\beta_0 + \beta_1$ Exper + β_2 Train + β_3 Exper × Train + ε.

b. Which model provides a better fit in terms of adjusted R^2 and the significance of the explanatory variables at the 5% level?

c. Use the chosen model to predict the number of pick errors for an employee with 10 years of experience who attended the training program, and for an employee with 20 years of experience who did not attend the training program.

d. Give a practical interpretation for the positive interaction coefficient.

25. **FILE** *IPO.* One of the theories regarding initial public offering (IPO) pricing is that the initial return (the percentage change from offer to open price) on an IPO depends on the price revision (the percentage change from pre-offer to offer price). Another factor that may influence the initial return is a dummy variable that equals 1 for high-tech firms and 0 otherwise. The following table shows a portion of data on 264 IPO firms from January 2001 through September 2004.

Initial Return	Price Revision	High Tech
33.93	7.14	0
18.68	−26.39	0
⋮	⋮	⋮
0.08	−29.41	1

Source: www.ipohome.com, www.nasdaq.com.

a.	Estimate a model with the initial return as the response variable and the price revision and the high-tech dummy variable as the explanatory variables.

b.	Reestimate the model with price revision along with the dummy variable and the product of the dummy variable and the price revision.

c.	Which of these models is the preferred model? Explain. Use this model to estimate the initial return for a high-tech firm with a 15% price revision. Compute the corresponding initial return for a firm that is not high-tech.

26.	**FILE** *Savings.* The following table shows a portion of monthly data on the personal savings rate (Savings in %) and personal disposable income (Income in $ billions) in the U.S. from January 2007 to November 2010.

Date	Savings	Income
2007–01	2.2	10198.2
2007–02	2.3	10252.9
⋮	⋮	⋮
2010–11	5.5	11511.9

Source: Bureau of Economic Analysis.

a.	Estimate and interpret a log-log model, ln (Savings) = $\beta_0 + \beta_1 \ln$ (Income) + ε. What is the predicted percentage change in savings when personal disposable income increases by 1%?

b.	Suppose we want to test whether or not there has been a structural shift due to the financial crisis that erupted in the fall of 2008. Consider a dummy variable d that assumes a value 0 before August 2008 and a value of 1 starting August 2008 onwards. Estimate: ln (Savings) = $\beta_0 + \beta_1 \ln$ (Income) + $\beta_2 d$ + $\beta_3 \ln$ (Income) $\times d + \varepsilon$. What is the predicted percentage change in savings when personal disposable income increases by 1% prior to August 2008? What is the corresponding predicted percentage change starting in August 2008 onward?

c.	At the 5% significance level, conduct the partial F test to determine whether or not β_2 and β_3 are jointly significant. Has there been a structural shift?

17.3 BINARY CHOICE MODELS

So far we have considered regression models where dummy (binary) variables are used as explanatory variables. In this section, we analyze **binary choice models** where the response variable is binary. These models are also referred to as **discrete choice models** or **qualitative response models**. The consumer choice literature is replete with applications such as whether or not to buy a house, join a health club, or go to graduate school. At the firm level, managers make decisions such as whether or not to replace equipment, restructure debt, or approve a loan. In all such applications, the response variable is binary, where one of the choices can be designated as 1 and the other as 0. Usually, this choice can be related to a host of factors—the explanatory variables. For instance, whether or not a family buys a house depends on explanatory variables such as household income, mortgage rates, and so on.

> BINARY CHOICE MODELS
>
> Regression models that use a dummy (binary) variable as the response variable are called binary choice models. They are also referred to as discrete choice models or qualitative response models.

The Linear Probability Model

LO 17.4

Estimate and interpret a linear probability model.

Consider a simple linear regression model $y = \beta_0 + \beta_1 x + \varepsilon$, where y is a binary variable; we can easily extend the model to include multiple explanatory variables. A linear regression model applied to a binary response variable is called a **linear probability model (LPM)**. While we know that the relationship implied by this model is linear, it may not be obvious why it is also called a probability model. Recall that in the above simple linear regression model, the expression $\beta_0 + \beta_1 x$ is its deterministic component, which is the expected value of y for a given value of x. In other words, conditional on x, $E(y) = \beta_0 + \beta_1 x$. Here, since y is a discrete random variable with possible values 0 and 1, its expected value conditional on x can also be computed as $E(y) = 0 \times P(y = 0) + 1 \times P(y = 1) = P(y = 1)$, where $P(y = 1)$ is often referred to as the probability of success. Therefore, we can write $y = \beta_0 + \beta_1 x + \varepsilon = P(y = 1) + \varepsilon$, where $P(y = 1)$, or simply P, is a linear function of the explanatory variable.

> ### A LINEAR PROBABILITY MODEL
>
> A linear probability model (LPM) is specified as $y = \beta_0 + \beta_1 x + \varepsilon = P(y = 1) + \varepsilon$, where y assumes a 1 or 0 value and $P(y = 1)$ is the probability of success. Predictions with this model are made by $\hat{P} = \hat{y} = b_0 + b_1 x$, where b_0 and b_1 are the estimates of the population parameters β_0 and β_1.

EXAMPLE 17.6

The subprime mortgage crisis forced financial institutions to be extra stringent in granting mortgage loans. Thirty recent mortgage applications are obtained to analyze the mortgage approval rate. The response variable y equals 1 if the mortgage loan is approved, 0 otherwise. It is believed that approval depends on the percentage of the down payment x_1 and the percentage of the income-to-loan ratio x_2. Table 17.10 shows a portion of the data.

FILE

Mortgage

TABLE 17.10 Mortgage Application Data

y	x_1	x_2
1	16.35	49.94
1	34.43	56.16
⋮	⋮	⋮
0	17.85	26.86

a. Estimate and interpret the linear probability model $y = \beta_0 + \beta_1 x_1 + \beta_2 x_2 + \varepsilon$.
b. Predict the loan approval probability for an applicant with a 20% down payment and a 30% income-to-loan ratio. What if the down payment was 30%?

SOLUTION:

a. Table 17.11 shows a portion of the regression results. The estimated regression equation is $\hat{P} = \hat{y} = -0.8682 + 0.0188x_1 + 0.0258x_2$. With p-values of 0.012 and 0.000, respectively, both explanatory variables exert a positive and statistically significant influence on loan approval, at a 5% level. Also, $b_1 = 0.0188$ implies that a 1-percentage-point increase in down payment increases the approval probability by 0.0188, or by 1.88%. Similarly, a 1-percentage-point increase in the income-to-loan ratio increases the approval probability by 0.0258, or by 2.58%.

TABLE 17.11 LPM Model Results for Example 17.6

	Coefficients	Standard Error	t Stat	p-Value
Intercept	−0.8682	0.2811	−3.089	0.005
x_1	0.0188	0.0070	2.695	0.012
x_2	0.0258	0.0063	4.107	0.000

b. The predicted loan approval probability for an applicant with a 20% down payment and a 30% income-to-loan ratio is $\hat{P} = -0.8682 + 0.0188 \times 20 + 0.0258 \times 30 = 0.2818$. Similarly, the predicted loan approval probability with a down payment of 30% is $\hat{P} = -0.8682 + 0.0188 \times 30 + 0.0258 \times 30 = 0.4698$. In other words, as down payment increases by 10 percentage points, the predicted probability of loan approval increases by $0.1880 (= 0.4698 - 0.2818)$, which is essentially the estimated slope, 0.0188, multiplied by 10. The estimated slope coefficient for the percentage of income-to-loan variable can be interpreted similarly.

Although it is easy to estimate and interpret a linear probability model, it has some shortcomings. The major shortcoming is that it can produce predicted probabilities that are greater than 1 or less than 0. For instance, for a down payment of 60%, with the same income-to-loan ratio of 30%, we get a predicted loan approval probability of $\hat{P} = -0.8682 + 0.0188 \times 60 + 0.0258 \times 30 = 1.0338$, a probability greater than one! Similarly, for a down payment of 5%, the model predicts a negative probability, $\hat{P} = -0.8682 + 0.0188 \times 5 + 0.0258 \times 30 = -0.0002$. Furthermore, the linearity of the relationship may also be questionable. For instance, we would expect a big increase in the probability of loan approval if the applicant makes a down payment of 30% instead of 20%. This increase in probability is likely to be much smaller if the same 10-percentage-point increase in down payment is from 60% to 70%. The LPM cannot differentiate between these two scenarios. For these reasons, we introduce the logit model, which is a more appropriate probability model for binary choice variables.

The Logit Model

LO 17.5

Estimate and interpret a logit model.

Recall that in an LPM model with a single explanatory variable, $y = \beta_0 + \beta_1 x + \varepsilon$, the following relationship is implied: $P = \beta_0 + \beta_1 x$. Here, the influence of x on P, captured by the slope β_1, is constant. As mentioned earlier, one shortcoming of the LPM model is that for any given slope, we can find some value of x for which the predicted probability is outside the [0,1] interval. We basically want a nonlinear specification that constrains the predicted probability between 0 and 1.

Consider

$$P = \frac{\exp(\beta_0 + \beta_1 x)}{1 + \exp(\beta_0 + \beta_1 x)},$$

where $\exp(\beta_0 + \beta_1 x) = e^{\beta_0 + \beta_1 x}$ and $e \approx 2.718$. This specification is the cumulative distribution function of the logistic distribution. Thus, the resulting regression model is called a logistic model, or simply a **logit model**. The logit model ensures that the probability is between 0 and 1 for all values of x.

The logit model cannot be estimated with standard ordinary least squares (OLS) procedures. Instead, we rely on the method of **maximum likelihood estimation (MLE)** to estimate a logit model. While the MLE of the logit model is not supported by Excel, it can easily be estimated with most statistical packages, including R. Given the relevance of the logit model in business applications, it is important to be able to interpret and make predictions with the estimated logit model.

THE LOGIT MODEL

The logit model is a nonlinear model that can be estimated with most statistical packages. Predictions with this model are made by

$$\hat{P} = \frac{\exp(b_0 + b_1 x)}{1 + \exp(b_0 + b_1 x)},$$

where b_0 and b_1 are the estimates of the population parameters β_0 and β_1.

Figure 17.4 highlights the relationship between the predicted probability $\hat{P}$ and the explanatory variable x for an LPM and a logit model, given $b_1 > 0$. Note that in an LPM, the probability falls below 0 for small values of x and exceeds 1 for large values of x. The probabilities implied by a logit model, however, are always constrained in the [0,1] interval. (For ease of exposition, we use the same notation to refer to the coefficients in the LPM and logit model. We note, however, that these coefficients and their estimates have a different meaning depending on which model we are referencing.)

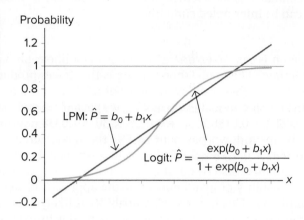

FIGURE 17.4 Predicted probabilities with an LPM and a logit model

It is important to be able to interpret the regression coefficients of a logit model. In an LPM, the interpretation of a regression coefficient is straightforward. For instance, if the estimated LPM is $\hat{P} = -0.20 + 0.03x$, it implies that for every 1-unit increase in x, the predicted probability $\hat{P}$ increases by 0.03. We note that $\hat{P}$ increases by 0.03, whether x increases from 10 to 11 or from 20 to 21.

Now consider the estimated logit model, $\hat{P} = \frac{\exp(-2.10 + 0.18x)}{1 + \exp(-2.10 + 0.18x)}$. Since the regression coefficient $b_1 = 0.18$ is positive, we can infer that x exerts a positive influence on $\hat{P}$. However, the exact impact based on the estimated regression coefficient is not obvious. A useful method to interpret the estimated coefficient is to highlight the changing impact of x on $\hat{P}$. For instance, given $x = 10$, we compute the predicted probability as $\hat{P} = \frac{\exp(-2.10 + 0.18 \times 10)}{1 + \exp(-2.10 + 0.18 \times 10)} = 0.4256$. Similarly, for $x = 11$, the predicted probability is $\hat{P} = 0.4700$. Therefore, as x increases by one unit from 10 to 11, the predicted probability increases by 0.0444. However, the increase in $\hat{P}$ will not be the same if x increases from 20 to 21. We can show that $\hat{P}$ increases from 0.8176 when $x = 20$ to 0.8429 when $x = 21$, for a smaller increase of 0.0253.

EXAMPLE 17.7

There is a declining interest among teenagers in pursuing a career in science (*U.S. News & World Report*, May 23, 2011). In a survey, 50% of high school students showed no interest in the sciences. An educator wants to determine if a student's interest in science is linked with the student's GPA. She estimates a logit model where the choice of field (1 for choosing science, 0 otherwise) depends on the student's GPA. She collects data from 120 students and uses R to produce the logit regression results shown in Table 17.12. (Instructions for estimating a logit model with R are provided at the end of this section.)

Sciences

TABLE 17.12 Logit Regression Results for Example 17.7

	Estimate	Std. Error	z value	P(>|z|)
(Intercept)	−3.4759	1.2699	−2.737	0.006
GPA	1.3394	0.4134	3.240	0.001

a. Use a 5% level of significance to determine if GPA has a statistically significant influence on the probability of pursuing a career in science.

b. Compute and interpret the probability that a student will pursue a career in science given a GPA of 3.0, 3.5, and 4.0.

SOLUTION:

a. In order to determine the significance of GPA, we specify the competing hypotheses as $H_0: \beta_1 = 0$ against $H_A: \beta_1 \neq 0$. Since the p-value = 0.001 is less than $\alpha = 0.05$, we reject H_0 and conclude that GPA influences the probability that a student pursues a career in science. (In maximum likelihood estimation, the significance tests are valid only with large samples. Consequently, we conduct the z test, in place of the usual t test, to evaluate the statistical significance of a coefficient.)

b. Since the estimated regression coefficient for GPA is positive ($b_1 = 1.3394$), it suggests that GPA exerts a positive influence on the predicted probability of pursuing a career in science. For a student with a GPA = 3.0, we compute the predicted probability as

$$\hat{P} = \frac{\exp(-3.4759 + 1.3394 \times 3.0)}{1 + \exp(-3.4759 + 1.3394 \times 3.0)} = 0.6323.$$

Similarly, we compute the predicted probabilities for a student with GPA = 3.5 and GPA = 4.0 as 0.7707 and 0.8678, respectively. Note that the predicted probability increases by 0.1384 (= 0.7707 − 0.6323) when GPA increases from 3.0 to 3.5. The increase is only 0.0971 (= 0.8678 − 0.7707) when GPA increases from 3.5 to 4.0.

FILE
Mortgage

EXAMPLE 17.8

Let's revisit Example 17.6.

a. Estimate and interpret the logit model for the loan approval outcome y based on the applicant's percentage of down payment x_1 and the income-to-loan ratio x_2.

b. Predict the loan approval probability for an applicant with a 20% down payment and a 30% income-to-loan ratio. What if the down payment is 30%?

c. Compare the results of the estimated logit model with the estimated LPM in Example 17.6.

SOLUTION:

a. We again use R to produce the logit regression results shown in Table 17.13.

TABLE 17.13 Logit Regression Results for Example 17.8

	Estimate	Std. Error	z value	P(>|z|)
(Intercept)	−9.3671	3.1958	−2.931	0.003
x_1	0.1349	0.0640	2.107	0.035
x_2	0.1782	0.0646	2.758	0.006

The estimated probability equation is computed as

$$\hat{P} = \frac{\exp(-9.3671 + 0.1349x_1 + 0.1782x_2)}{1 + \exp(-9.3671 + 0.1349x_1 + 0.1782x_2)}.$$

As in the case of the linear probability model, both explanatory variables exert a positive and statistically significant influence on loan approval at a 5% level, given positive estimated coefficients and p-values of 0.035 and 0.006, respectively.

b. The predicted loan approval probability with $x_1 = 20$ and $x_2 = 30$ is

$$\hat{P} = \frac{\exp(-9.3671 + 0.1349 \times 20 + 0.1782 \times 30)}{1 + \exp(-9.3671 + 0.1349 \times 20 + 0.1782 \times 30)} = 0.2103.$$

Similarly, the predicted loan approval probability with $x_1 = 30$ and $x_2 = 30$ is 0.5065.

c. Table 17.14 provides predicted probabilities based on the linear probability model, estimated in Example 17.6, and the logit model for selected values of x_1 given $x_2 = 30$.

TABLE 17.14 Predicted Probabilities with a LPM versus a Logit Model

x_1	x_2	LPM	Logit Model
5	30	−0.0002	0.0340
20	30	0.2818	0.2103
30	30	0.4698	0.5065
60	30	1.0338	0.9833

As discussed earlier, with a linear probability model, the predicted probabilities can be negative or greater than one. The probabilities based on a logit model stay between zero and one for all possible values of the explanatory variables. Therefore, whenever possible, it is preferable to use the logit model over the linear probability model for binary choice models.

FILE
Mortgage

Using R to Estimate a Logit Model

A. Import the ***Mortgage*** data into a data frame (table) in R.

B. We use the **glm** function to construct a logit model object, which is a generalized version of the **lm** function; we label this object as Logit_Model. Within the function, we first specify y as a function of x1 and x2 and then use the *family* option to denote the type of model. Finally, we specify the data frame. Like the **lm** function, we will not see any immediate output after we enter the command. We use the summary function to obtain the output. Enter:

```
> Logit_Model <- glm(y ~ x1 + x2, family = binomial(link = "logit"), data = Mortgage)
> summary(Logit_Model)
```

EXERCISES 17.3

Mechanics

27. Consider a binary response variable y and an explanatory variable x that varies between 0 and 4. The linear model is estimated as $\hat{y} = -1.11 + 0.54x$.

   a. Compute the estimated probability for $x = 2$ and $x = 3$.

   b. For what values of x is the estimated probability negative or greater than one?

28. Consider a binary response variable y and an explanatory variable x that varies between 0 and 50. The linear probability model is estimated as $\hat{y} = 0.92 - 0.02x$.

   a. Compute the estimated probability for $x = 25$ and $x = 40$.

   b. For what values of x is the estimated probability negative?

29. Consider a binary response variable y and an explanatory variable x. The following table contains the parameter estimates of the linear probability model (LPM) and the logit model, with the associated p-values shown in parentheses.

Variable	LPM	Logit
Constant	−0.72 (0.04)	−6.20 (0.04)
x	0.05 (0.06)	0.26 (0.02)

a. Test for the significance of the intercept and the slope coefficients at the 5% level in both models.
b. What is the predicted probability implied by the linear probability model for $x = 20$ and $x = 30$?
c. What is the predicted probability implied by the logit model for $x = 20$ and $x = 30$?

30. Consider a binary response variable y and an explanatory variable x. The following table contains the parameter estimates of the linear probability model (LPM) and the logit model, with the associated p-values shown in parentheses.

Variable	LPM	Logit
Constant	−0.40 (0.03)	−4.50 (0.01)
x	0.32 (0.04)	1.54 (0.03)

a. Use both models to predict the probability of success as x varies from 1 to 5 with increments of 1.
b. Comment on the suitability of the linear probability model in modeling binary outcomes.

31. Consider a binary response variable y and two explanatory variables x_1 and x_2. The following table contains the parameter estimates of the linear probability model (LPM) and the logit model, with the associated p-values shown in parentheses.

Variable	LPM	Logit
Constant	−0.40 (0.03)	−2.20 (0.01)
x_1	0.32 (0.04)	0.98 (0.06)
x_2	−0.04 (0.01)	−0.20 (0.01)

a. Comment on the significance of the variables.
b. What is the predicted probability implied by the linear probability model for $x_1 = 4$ with x_2 equal to 10 and 20?
c. What is the predicted probability implied by the logit model for $x_1 = 4$ with x_2 equal to 10 and 20?

32. Using 30 observations, the following regression output is obtained from estimating the linear probability model $y = \beta_0 + \beta_1 x + \varepsilon$.

	Coefficients	Standard Error	t Stat	p-Value
Intercept	1.31	0.31	4.17	0.000
x	−0.04	0.01	−2.67	0.013

a. What is the predicted probability when $x = 20$?
b. Is x significant at the 5% level?

33. Using 30 observations, the following output was obtained when estimating the logit model.

Predictor	Coef	SE	z	P
Constant	−0.188	0.083	2.27	0.024
x	3.852	1.771	2.18	0.030

a. What is the predicted probability when $x = 0.40$?
b. Is x significant at the 5% level?

34. Using 40 observations, the following output was obtained when estimating the logit model.

Predictor	Coef	SE	z	P
Constant	1.609	1.405	1.145	0.252
x_1	−0.194	0.143	−1.357	0.177
x_2	0.202	0.215	0.940	0.348
x_3	0.223	0.086	2.593	0.010

a. What is the predicted probability when $x_1 = 15$, $x_2 = 10$, and $x_3 = -2$?
b. At the 5% significance level, which of the explanatory variables are significant?

Applications

35. **FILE** *Purchase.* Annabel, a retail analyst, has been following Under Armour, Inc., the pioneer in the compression-gear market. Compression garments are meant to keep moisture away from a wearer's body during athletic activities in warm and cool weather. Annabel believes that the Under Armour brand attracts a younger customer, whereas the more

established companies, Nike and Adidas, draw an older clientele. In order to test her belief, she collects data on the age of the customers and whether or not they purchased Under Armour (1 for Under Armour, 0 otherwise). A portion of the data is shown in the accompanying table.

Under Armour	Age
1	30
0	19
⋮	⋮
1	24

a. Estimate a linear probability model using Under Armour as the response variable and Age as the explanatory variable.

b. Compute the predicted probability of an Under Armour purchase for a 20-year-old customer and a 30-year-old customer.

c. Test Annabel's belief that the Under Armour brand attracts a younger customer, at the 5% level.

36. **FILE** *Purchase.* Refer to the previous exercise for a description of the data set. Estimate the logit model where the Under Armour purchase depends on age.

a. Compute the predicted probability of an Under Armour purchase for a 20-year-old customer and a 30-year-old customer.

b. Test Annabel's belief that the Under Armour brand attracts a younger customer, at the 5% level.

37. **FILE** *Health.* Nearly nine out of 10 Americans now have health insurance since the Affordable Care Act (also known as "Obamacare") took effect in 2014 (www.cnn.com, April 13, 2015). However, 22% of those making less than $36,000 still do not have coverage. Also, the rising insurance premiums have made it difficult for small employers to offer insurance, and those that do offer insurance, are contributing a smaller share of the premium. Consider a portion of data in the following table relating to insurance coverage (1 for coverage, 0 for no coverage) for 30 working individuals in Atlanta, Georgia. Also included in the table is the percentage of the premium paid by the employer and the individual's income (in $1,000s).

Insurance	Premium Percentage	Income
1	0	88
0	0	60
⋮	⋮	⋮
0	60	60

a. Analyze a linear probability model for insurance coverage with premium percentage and income used as the explanatory variables.

b. Consider an individual with an income of $60,000. What is the probability that she has insurance coverage if her employer contributes 50% of the premium? What if her employer contributes 75% of the premium?

38. **FILE** *Health.* Refer to the previous exercise for a description of the data set. Estimate the logit model where insurance coverage depends on premium percentage and income. Consider an individual with an income of $60,000. What is the probability that she has insurance coverage if her employer contributes 50% of the premium? What if her employer contributes 75% of the premium?

39. **FILE** *Divorce.* According to an estimate, the divorce rate in England has fallen to a 26-year low (*The Guardian*, August 29, 2008). However, it is documented that the rate of divorce is more than twice as high for men and women aged 25 to 29. John Haddock is a sociologist from Sussex University who wants to analyze the divorce rate based on the individual's age, family income (in £1,000's), and the number of children that the couple has. He collects data on 30 individuals in a small town near Brighton, a portion of which is shown in the accompanying table.

Divorce	Age	Income	Children
0	1	19	3
0	0	46	3
⋮	⋮	⋮	⋮
0	0	26	0

a. Estimate and interpret a linear probability model where divorce (1 for divorce; 0 otherwise) depends on age (1 if 25–29 years old; 0 otherwise), family income (in £1,000s), and the number of children.

b. Do the data support the article's claim that the divorce rate is higher for those aged 25–29 years old? Explain.

c. Use the above estimates to predict the probability of divorce for an individual who is 27 years old, has £60,000 of family income, and has one child. Recalculate the probability with three children.

40. **FILE** *Divorce.* Refer to the previous exercise for a description of the data set. Estimate the logit model where divorce depends on age, income, and the number of children.

a. Do the data support the article's claim that the divorce rate is higher for those aged 25–29 years old? Explain.

b. Use the above estimates to predict the probability of divorce for an individual who is 27 years old, has £60,000 of family income, and has one child. Recalculate the probability with three children.

During the 2009–2010 NBA season, the Los Angeles Lakers had the highest offensive production throughout the league. Led by Kobe Bryant, the Lakers beat the Boston Celtics in game seven of the championships for the 2010 NBA title. Jacqueline Thomsen, an amateur statistician, would like to examine the factors that led to the Lakers' success. Specifically, Jacqueline wishes to predict the likelihood of a Lakers win as a function of field goal percentage (FG), rebounds (Rebounds), and turnovers (Turnovers). The probability of winning should be positively influenced by FG and Rebounds but negatively affected by Turnovers. In addition, she wonders if there is a home court advantage in that playing at home significantly influences the team's chances of winning. Table 17.15 shows a portion of data on the Lakers' 82-game regular season.

©Dean Bertoncelj/Shutterstock RF

TABLE 17.15 Statistics on the Los Angeles Lakers' 2009–2010 Regular Season

Game	Win	FG	Rebounds	Turnovers	Home
1	1	41.2	47	16	1
2	0	39.5	40	19	1
⋮	⋮	⋮	⋮	⋮	⋮
82	0	39.5	49	14	0

Source: www.nba.com.

FILE
Lakers

Jacqueline would like to use the above sample information to

1. Choose an appropriate model to predict the probability of winning.
2. Determine whether there is a home court advantage.
3. Predict the probability of winning if the Lakers are playing at home or away, with average values of FG, Rebounds, and Turnovers.

Sample Report— Predicting the Probability of Winning

With the highest offensive production throughout the league during the 2009–2010 season, it is not surprising that the Los Angeles Lakers won the 2010 NBA championship. Other teams might benefit if they could unravel the factors that led to the Lakers' success. In an attempt to examine the factors that influence a team's chances of winning, regression analysis is conducted on the Lakers' 82-game regular season. The response variable is Win (equals 1 for a win, 0 otherwise), and the explanatory variables include

- The team's field goal percentage (FG),
- The number of rebounds,
- The number of turnovers, and
- A Home dummy variable that equals 1 for a home game and 0 otherwise.

The probability of winning should be positively influenced by FG and rebounds, but negatively affected by turnovers. In addition, if there truly is a home court advantage, then playing at home should positively influence the team's chances of winning.

Two models are evaluated that link the probability of winning with the explanatory variables: the linear probability model and the logit model. The parameter estimates of both models are shown in Table 17.A.

TABLE 17.A Regression Results of the Linear Probability Model and the Logit Model

Response Variable: Win (equals 1 if Lakers win, 0 otherwise)		
	LPM	Logit
Constant	−2.3915* (0.000)	−28.7560* (0.000)
FG	0.0473* (0.000)	0.4890* (0.000)
Rebounds	0.0194* (0.005)	0.1715* (0.015)
Turnovers	−0.0040 (0.684)	−0.0371 (0.705)
Home	0.2324* (0.005)	1.8182* (0.019)

Notes: Parameter estimates of both models are presented with p-values in parentheses; * represents significance at the 5% level.

The linear probability model is estimated as $\widehat{Win} = -2.3915 + 0.0473FG + 0.0194Rebounds - 0.0040Turnovers + 0.2324Home$. All signs on the estimated slope coefficients are as expected; that is, the field goal percentage, the number of rebounds, and playing at home exert a positive influence on the chances of winning; the number of turnovers suggests a negative relationship with the chances of winning. Upon testing the explanatory variables individually, the extremely small p-values associated with FG, Rebounds, and Home reveal that these variables influence the probability of winning; Turnovers is not significant at the 5% level. The slope coefficient of Home indicates that the likelihood of winning increases by approximately 23% if the Lakers play at home. While the results of the linear probability model seem reasonable, some values of the explanatory variables may yield predicted probabilities that are either negative or greater than one. In order to avoid this possibility, the logit model is preferred.

The logit model is estimated as

$$\widehat{Win} = \frac{\exp(-28.7560 + 0.4890FG + 0.1715Rebounds - 0.0371Turnovers + 1.8182Home)}{1 + \exp(-28.7560 + 0.4890FG + 0.1715Rebounds - 0.0371Turnovers + 1.8182Home)}.$$

As in the case of the linear probability model, FG, Rebounds, and Home are again individually significant at the 5% level; thus, the significance of Home supports the belief of a home field advantage. Over the 82-game season, the averages for field goal percentage, the number of rebounds, and the number of turnovers were 45%, 44, and 13, respectively. If the Lakers are playing an "average" game away from home, then the model predicts a 57.75% chance of winning. However, if they are playing an "average" game at home, then their likelihood of winning jumps to 89.39%. In sum, the home court advantage overwhelmingly puts the likelihood of success in their favor.

CONCEPTUAL REVIEW

LO 17.1 Use a dummy variable to represent a qualitative explanatory variable.

A **dummy variable** d is defined as a variable that takes on values of 1 or 0. Dummy variables are used to represent categories of a qualitative variable. The number of dummy variables needed should be one less than the number of categories of the variable.

A regression model with a quantitative variable x and a dummy variable d is specified as $y = \beta_0 + \beta_1 x + \beta_2 d + \varepsilon$. The dummy variable d allows the predicted y to differ between the two categories of a qualitative variable by a fixed amount across the values of x. We estimate this model to make predictions as $\hat{y} = (b_0 + b_2) + b_1 x$ for $d = 1$ and as $\hat{y} = b_0 + b_1 x$ for $d = 0$.

LO 17.2 **Test for differences between the categories of a qualitative variable.**

Using $y = \beta_0 + \beta_1 x + \beta_2 d + \varepsilon$, we can perform a standard t test to determine whether differences exist between the two categories of the qualitative variable d.

LO 17.3 **Use a dummy variable to capture the interaction between a qualitative explanatory variable and a quantitative explanatory variable.**

A regression model with a dummy variable d, a quantitative variable x, and an interaction variable xd is specified by $y = \beta_0 + \beta_1 x + \beta_2 d + \beta_3 xd + \varepsilon$. We estimate this model to make predictions as $\hat{y} = (b_0 + b_2) + (b_1 + b_3)x$ for $d = 1$, and as $\hat{y} = b_0 + b_1 x$ for $d = 0$. The interaction variable xd allows the predicted y to differ between the two categories of a qualitative variable by a varying amount across the values of x. In addition to performing a t test to determine the individual significance of d or xd, we can also implement the partial F test to determine their joint significance.

LO 17.4 **Estimate and interpret a linear probability model.**

Models that use a dummy (binary) variable as the response variable are called binary choice models. A **linear probability model (LPM)** is specified as $y = \beta_0 + \beta_1 x_1 + \beta_2 x_2 + \cdots + \beta_k x_k + \varepsilon = P(y = 1) + \varepsilon$, where y assumes values of 1 or 0 and $P(y = 1)$ is the probability of success. Predictions with this model are made by $\hat{P} = \hat{y} = b_0 + b_1 x + b_2 x_2 + \cdots + b_k x_k$, where $b_0, b_1, b_2, \ldots, b_k$ are the estimates. The major shortcoming of the LPM is that it can produce predicted probabilities that are greater than one or less than zero.

LO 17.5 **Estimate and interpret a logit model.**

A **logit model** is a nonlinear model that can be estimated with most statistical packages, including R. Predictions with this model are made by $\hat{P} = \frac{\exp(b_0 + b_1 x_1 + b_2 x_2 + \cdots + b_k x_k)}{1 + \exp(b_0 + b_1 x_1 + b_2 x_2 + \cdots + b_k x_k)}$, where $b_0, b_1, b_2, \ldots, b_k$ are the estimates. The estimated model ensures that the predicted probability falls between zero and one.

ADDITIONAL EXERCISES AND CASE STUDIES

Exercises

41. **FILE** *Magellan.* A financial analyst would like to determine whether the return on Fidelity's Magellan mutual fund varies depending on the quarter; that is, if there is a seasonal component describing return. He collects 10 years of quarterly return data. A portion is shown in the accompanying table.

Year	Quarter	Return	d_1	d_2	d_3
2000	1	4.85	1	0	0
2000	2	−3.96	0	1	0
⋮	⋮	⋮	⋮	⋮	⋮
2009	4	4.06	0	0	0

Source: http://finance.yahoo.com.

a. Estimate $y = \beta_0 + \beta_1 d_1 + \beta_2 d_2 + \beta_3 d_3 + \varepsilon$, where y is Magellan's quarterly return, d_1 is a dummy variable that equals 1 if quarter 1 and 0 otherwise, d_2 is a dummy variable that equals 1 if quarter 2 and 0 otherwise, and d_3 is a dummy variable that equals 1 if quarter 3 and 0 otherwise.

b. Interpret the slope coefficients of the dummy variables.

c. Predict Magellan's stock return in quarters 2 and 4.

42. **FILE** *Hiring.* In a seminal study, researchers documented race-based hiring in the Boston and Chicago labor markets (*American Economic Review*, September 2004). They sent out identical resumes to employers, half with traditionally African American names and the other half with traditionally Caucasian names. Interestingly, there was a 53% difference in call-back rates between the two groups of people. A research fellow at an institute in Santa Barbara decides to repeat the same experiment with names along with age in the Los Angeles labor market. She repeatedly sends out resumes for sales positions in the city that are identical except for the difference in the names and ages of the applicants. She also records the call-back rate for each candidate. The accompanying table shows a portion of data on call-back rate (in %), age, and a Caucasian dummy that equals 1 for a Caucasian-sounding name, 0 otherwise.

Call-back	Age	Caucasian
12	60	1
9	56	0
⋮	⋮	⋮
15	38	0

a. Estimate a linear regression model with call-back as the response variable, and age and the Caucasian dummy variable as the explanatory variables.

b. Compute the call-back rate for a 30-year-old applicant with a Caucasian-sounding name. What is the corresponding call-back rate for a non-Caucasian?

c. Conduct a test for race discrimination at the 5% significance level.

43. An analyst studies quarterly data on the relationship between retail sales (y, in \$ millions), gross national product (x, in \$ billions), and a quarterly dummy d that equals 1 if the sales are for the 4th quarter, 0 otherwise. He estimates the

model $y = \beta_0 + \beta_1 x + \beta_2 d + \beta_3 xd + \varepsilon$. Relevant regression results are shown in the accompanying table.

	Coefficients	Standard Error	t Stat	p-Value
Intercept	186553.3	56421.1	3.31	0.002
x	55.0	4.6	12.08	0.000
d	112605.8	117053.0	0.96	0.342
xd	−4.7	9.3	−0.50	0.618

a. Interpret the dummy variable, d. Is it significant at the 5% level?

b. Interpret the interaction variable. Is it significant at the 5% level?

44. **FILE** *Study.* A researcher in the education department wants to determine if the number of hours that business students study per week at a state university varies by term. He conducts a survey where business students are asked how much they study per week in each of the three terms. He defines a dummy variable Fall that equals 1 if the survey was conducted in the fall term and 0 otherwise. The dummy variables Winter and Spring are defined similarly. The accompanying table shows a portion of the data for 120 students.

Study Hours	Fall	Winter	Spring
15	0	0	1
16	0	1	0
⋮	⋮	⋮	⋮
14	0	0	1

a. Estimate the appropriate model to determine, at the 5% significance level, if students study the least in the spring term.

b. Find the predicted number of hours that students study per week in the fall, winter, and spring terms.

45. **FILE** *Longevity.* According to the Center for Disease Control and Prevention, life expectancy at age 65 in America is about 18.7 years. Medical researchers have argued that while excessive drinking is detrimental to health, drinking a little alcohol every day, especially wine, may be associated with an increase in life expectancy. Others have also linked longevity with income and a person's sex. The accompanying table shows a portion of data relating to the length of life after 65, average income (in \$1,000s) at a retirement age of 65, a Female dummy variable, that equals 1 if the individual is female, 0 otherwise, and the average number of alcoholic drinks consumed per day.

Life	Income	Female	Drinks
19.00	64	0	1
19.30	43	1	3
⋮	⋮	⋮	⋮
20.24	36	1	0

BMI	Female	Black
28.70	0	1
28.31	0	0
⋮	⋮	⋮
24.90	0	1

a. Use the data to model life expectancy at 65 on the basis of Income, Female, and Drinks.

b. Conduct a one-tailed test at $\alpha = 0.01$ to determine if females live longer than males.

c. Predict the life expectancy at 65 of a male with an income of $40,000 and an alcoholic consumption of two drinks per day; repeat the prediction for a female.

46. **FILE** *Shifts.* The manager of a diner wants to reevaluate his staffing needs depending on variations in customer traffic during the day. He collects data on the number of customers served, along with four dummy variables representing the morning, afternoon, evening, and night shifts. The dummy variable Morning equals 1 if the number of customers served was from the morning shift and 0 otherwise; other dummy variables are defined similarly. The accompanying table shows a portion of the data.

Customers	Morning	Afternoon	Evening	Night
99	0	0	0	1
148	0	1	0	0
⋮	⋮	⋮	⋮	⋮
111	0	1	0	0

a. Estimate a regression model using the number of customers as the response variable and the shift dummy variables as the explanatory variables; use Night as the reference category.

b. What is the predicted number of customers served during the morning, afternoon, evening, and night shifts?

47. **FILE** *Overweight.* According to the U.S. Department of Health and Human Services, African American women have the highest rates of being overweight compared to other groups in the United States. Individuals are considered overweight if their body mass index (BMI) is 25 or greater. Data are collected from 120 individuals. The following table shows a portion of data on each individual's BMI, a Female dummy variable that equals 1 if the individual is female, 0 otherwise, and a Black dummy variable that equals 1 if the individual is African American, 0 otherwise.

a. Estimate the model, BMI $= \beta_0 + \beta_1$Female $+ \beta_2$Black $+ \beta_3$(Female $\times$ Black) $+ \varepsilon$, to predict the BMI for white males, white females, black males, and black females.

b. Is the difference between white females and white males statistically significant at the 5% level?

c. Is the difference between white males and black males statistically significant at the 5% level?

48. **FILE** *Compensation.* To encourage performance, loyalty, and continuing education, the human resources department at a large company wants to develop a regression-based compensation model (Comp in $ per year) for mid-level managers based on three variables: (1) business unit-profitability (Profit in $1000's per year), (2) years with the company (Years), and (3) whether or not the manager has a graduate degree (Grad equals 1 if graduate degree, 0 otherwise). The accompanying table shows a portion of data collected for 36 managers.

Comp	Profit	Years	Grad
118100	4500	37	1
90800	5400	5	1
⋮	⋮	⋮	⋮
85000	4200	29	0

a. Estimate the following model for compensation:
Comp $= \beta_0 + \beta_1$Profit $+ \beta_2$Years $+ \beta_3$Grad $+ \beta_4$Profit $\times$ Grad $+ \beta_5$Years $\times$ Grad $+ \varepsilon$.

b. At the 5% significance level, is the overall regression model significant?

c. Which predictor variables and interaction terms are significant at $\alpha = 0.05$?

d. Use the (full) model to determine compensation for a manager having 15 years with the company, a graduate degree, and a business-unit profit of $4,800(000) last year.

49. **FILE** *Assembly.* Since assembly line work can be tedious and repetitive, it is not suited for

everybody. Consequently, a production manager is developing a binary choice regression model to predict whether a newly hired worker will stay in the job for at least one year (Stay equals 1 if a new hire stays for at least one year, 0 otherwise). Three explanatory variables will be used: (1) Age, (2) a Female dummy variable that equals 1 if the new hire is female, 0 otherwise, and (3) an Assembly dummy variable that equals 1 if the new hire has worked on an assembly line before, 0 otherwise. Records have been obtained for the past 32 assembly line workers hired. A portion of the data is shown in the accompanying table.

Stay	Age	Female	Assembly
0	35	1	0
0	26	1	0
⋮	⋮	⋮	⋮
1	38	0	1

a. Estimate a linear probability model in which being in the job one year later depends on Age, Female, and Assembly. Use this model to predict the probability that (1) a 45-year-old female who has not worked on an assembly line before will still be in the job one year later, and (2) a 35-year-old male who has worked on an assembly line will still be in the job one year later.

b. Estimate a logit model where being in the job one year later depends on Age, Female, and Assembly. Use this model to predict the probability that (1) a 45-year-old female who has not worked on an assembly line before will still be in the job one year later, and (2) a 35-year-old male who has worked on an assembly line will still be in the job one year later.

c. At $\alpha = 0.05$, compare the significance of the parameters in both models. What do the significance results imply from a practical standpoint?

50. **FILE** *SetonHall.* Seton Hall University is a Roman Catholic university situated in New Jersey, with easy access to New York City. Like most universities, it uses SAT scores and high school GPA as primary criteria for admission. The accompanying table shows a portion of data concerning information on admission (Admission equals 1 if admitted, 0 otherwise), SAT score, and GPA for 30 students who had recently applied to Seton Hall.

Admission	SAT	GPA
1	1700	3.39
1	2020	2.65
⋮	⋮	⋮
0	1300	2.47

a. Estimate the linear probability model where admission is a function of the SAT score and high school GPA. Analyze the significance of the variables at the 5% level.

b. Predict the probability of admission for an individual with a GPA of 3.5 and an SAT score of 1700.

c. Predict the probability of admission for an individual with a GPA of 3.5 and an SAT score of 1800.

51. **FILE** *SetonHall.* Refer to the previous exercise for a description of the data set. Estimate the logit probability model where admission is a function of the SAT score and high school GPA.

a. Analyze the significance of the variables at the 5% level.

b. Predict the probability of admission for an individual with a GPA of 3.5 and an SAT score of 1700.

c. Predict the probability of admission for an individual with a GPA of 3.5 and an SAT score of 1800.

52. **FILE** *Parole.* More and more parole boards are using risk assessment tools when trying to determine an individual's likelihood of returning to crime (*The Boston Globe*, February 20, 2011). Most of these models are based on a range of character traits and biographical facts about an individual. Many studies have found that older people are less likely to re-offend than younger ones. In addition, once released on parole, women are not likely to re-offend. A sociologist collects data on 20 individuals who were released on parole two years ago. She notes if the parolee committed another crime over the last two years (Crime equals 1 if crime committed, 0 otherwise), the parolee's age at the time of release, and the parolee's sex (Male equals 1 if male, 0 otherwise). The accompanying table shows a portion of the data.

Crime	Age	Male
1	25	1
0	42	1
⋮	⋮	⋮
0	30	1

a. Estimate the linear probability model where crime depends on age and the parolee's sex.

b. Are the results consistent with the claims of other studies with respect to age and the parolee's sex?

c. Predict the probability of a 25-year-old male parolee committing another crime; repeat the prediction for a 25-year-old female parolee.

53. **FILE** *Parole*. Refer to the previous exercise for a description of the data set.

a. Estimate the logit model where crime depends on age and the parolee's sex.

b. Are the results consistent with the claims of other studies with respect to age and the parolee's sex?

c. Predict the probability of a 25-year-old male parolee committing another crime; repeat the prediction for a 25-year-old female parolee.

CASE STUDIES

CASE STUDY 17.1   A study examined "sidewalk rage" in an attempt to find insight into anger's origins and offer suggestions for anger-management treatments (*The Wall Street Journal*, February 15, 2011). "Sidewalk ragers" tend to believe that pedestrians should behave in a certain way. For instance, slower pedestrians should keep to the right or should step aside to take a picture. If pedestrians violate these "norms," then ragers feel that the "violaters" are breaking the rules of civility. Since anger is associated with a host of negative health consequences, psychologists suggest developing strategies to quell the rage. One possible strategy is to avoid slow walkers. A portion of the study looked at the average speed of walkers (feet per second) in Lower Manhattan and found that average speeds differ when the pedestrian is distracted by other activities (smoking, talking on a cell phone, tourism, etc.) or exhibits other traits (elderly, obese, etc.). Sample data were obtained from 50 pedestrians in Lower Manhattan. Each pedestrian's speed was calculated (feet per second). In addition, it was noted if the pedestrian was smoking (equaled 1 if smoking, 0 otherwise), was a tourist (equaled 1 if tourist, 0 otherwise), was elderly (equaled 1 if over 65 years old, 0 otherwise), or was obese (equaled 1 if obese, 0 otherwise). In the sample, each pedestrian was associated with no more than one of these four characteristics/traits. The accompanying table shows a portion of the data.

Data for Case Study 17.1   Pedestrian Speeds with Defining Characteristics/Traits

Speed	Smoking	Tourist	Elderly	Obese
3.76	0	1	0	0
3.82	0	1	0	0
⋮	⋮	⋮	⋮	⋮
5.02	0	0	0	0

FILE
PedSpeeds

In a report, use the sample information to

1. Estimate $Speed = \beta_0 + \beta_1 Smoking + \beta_2 Tourist + \beta_3 Elderly + \beta_4 Obese + \varepsilon$.

2. Interpret the slope coefficient of Tourist. Interpret the intercept. Predict the speed of an elderly pedestrian. Predict the speed of an obese pedestrian.

3. Are the explanatory variables jointly significant in explaining speed at the 5% significance level? Are all explanatory variables individually significant at the 5% level? What type of pedestrian should a "sidewalk rager" avoid?

CASE STUDY 17.2   Jack Sprague is the relocation specialist for a real estate firm in the town of Arlington, Massachusetts. He has been working with a client who wishes to purchase a single-family home in Arlington. After seeing the information that Jack provided, the client is perplexed by the variability of home prices in Arlington. She is especially puzzled by the premium that a colonial house commands. (A colonial house is a style dating back to the time of the American colonies, with a simple rectangular structure and a peaked roof.) Despite Jack's eloquent explanations, it seems that the client will not be satisfied until she understands the quantitative relationship between house prices and house characteristics. Jack decides to use a multiple regression model to provide the client with the necessary information. He collects data on the prices (in $) for 36 single-family homes in Arlington sold in the first quarter of 2009. Also included in the data is the information on square footage, the number of bedrooms, the number of bathrooms, and whether or not the house is a colonial (1 for colonial, 0 otherwise). A portion of the data is shown in the accompanying table.

Data for Case Study 17.2 Sales Information of Single-Family Homes in Arlington, MA

FILE

Arlington

Price	Square feet	Bedrooms	Baths	Colonial
840000	2768	4	3.5	1
822000	2500	4	2.5	1
⋮	⋮	⋮	⋮	⋮
307500	850	1	1	0

Source: NewEnglandMoves.com.

In a report, use the sample information to

1. Estimate and interpret three models, where d is the colonial dummy variable.

    Model 1: $\text{Price} = \beta_0 + \beta_1\text{Sqft} + \beta_2\text{Beds} + \beta_3\text{Baths} + \beta_4 d + \varepsilon$.

    Model 2: $\text{Price} = \beta_0 + \beta_1\text{Sqft} + \beta_2\text{Beds} + \beta_3\text{Baths} + \beta_4(\text{Sqft} \times d) + \varepsilon$.

    Model 3: $\text{Price} = \beta_0 + \beta_1\text{Sqft} + \beta_2\text{Beds} + \beta_3\text{Baths} + \beta_4 d + \beta_5(\text{Sqft} \times d) + \varepsilon$.

2. Choose which model is most reliable in predicting the price of a house. Provide at least one reason for your choice. Are price differences between colonial homes versus other styles fixed and/or changing at the 5% significance level?

3. Use this model to make predictions for a colonial home versus other styles, given the average values of the explanatory variables.

CASE STUDY 17.3 The Chartered Financial Analyst (CFA) designation is fast becoming a requirement for serious investment professionals. Although it requires successfully completing three levels of grueling exams, it also promises great careers with lucrative salaries. Susan Wayne works as a research analyst at Fidelity Investments. She is thinking about taking the CFA exam in the summer and wants to understand why the recent pass rate for Level I has been under 40%. She firmly believes that those who were good students in college have a better chance of passing. She has also been told that work experience helps. She has access to the information on 30 Fidelity employees who took the test last year, including the employee's success on the exam (1 for pass, 0 for fail), the employee's college GPA, and years of work experience. A portion of the data is shown in the accompanying table.

Data for Case Study 17.3 Information on Individuals Who Took CFA Exam

FILE

CFA

Pass	GPA	Experience
1	3.64	12
0	3.16	5
⋮	⋮	⋮
0	2.64	4

In a report, use the sample information to

1. Analyze a linear probability model to explain the probability of success. Predict the probability of passing the CFA exam for a candidate with various values of college GPA and years of experience.

2. Analyze the logit model to explain the probability of success. Predict the probability of passing the CFA exam for a candidate with various values of college GPA and years of experience.

3. Which model is more reliable for predicting the probability of passing the CFA exam? Provide at least one reason for your choice.

APPENDIX 17.1   Guidelines for Other Software Packages

The following section provides brief commands for Minitab, SPSS, and JMP. Where a data file is specified, copy and paste it into the relevant software spreadsheet prior to following the commands.

Minitab

Estimating a Logit Model

(Replicating Example 17.8) From the menu, choose **Stat > Regression > Binary Logistic Regression > Fit Binary Logistic Model**. Select **Response in binary response/frequency format**, and after **Response**, select y. After **Continuous predictors**, select x1 and x2. Choose **Results**, and after **Display of results**, select **Expanded tables**.

FILE
Mortgage

SPSS

Estimating a Logit Model

(Replicating Example 17.8) From the menu, select **Analyze > Regression > Binary Logistic**. Under **Dependent**, select y, and under **Covariates**, select x1 and x2.

FILE
Mortgage

JMP

Estimating a Logit Model

A. (Replicating Example 17.8) Right-click on y, and under **Data Type**, select **Character**, and under **Modeling Type**, select **Nominal**.

B. From the menu, choose **Analyze > Fit Model**.

C. Under **Select Columns**, select y, and then under **Pick Role Variables**, select **Y**. Under **Select Columns**, select x1 and x2, and then under **Construct Model Effect**, select **Add**. Note that under **Personality**, you now see **Nominal Logistic** rather than **Standard Least Squares**. (Note: By default, JMP fits the 0 response. Thus, the results have opposite signs from those in the text.)

FILE
Mortgage

18 Time Series and Forecasting

LEARNING OBJECTIVES

After reading this chapter you should be able to:

LO **18.1** Distinguish among the various models used in forecasting.

LO **18.2** Use smoothing techniques to make forecasts.

LO **18.3** Use trend regression models to make forecasts.

LO **18.4** Calculate and interpret seasonal indices and use them to seasonally adjust a time series.

LO **18.5** Use decomposition analysis to make forecasts.

LO **18.6** Use trend regression models with seasonal dummy variables to make forecasts.

LO **18.7** Use causal forecasting models to make forecasts.

Forecasting is an important aspect of statistical analysis, providing guidance for decisions in all areas of business. Examples include forecasting product sales, product defects, the inflation rate, the price of a financial asset, or a company's cash flows. In fact, the success of any business or government agency depends on the ability to accurately forecast many vital variables. Sound forecasts not only improve the quality of business plans, but also help identify and evaluate potential risks. The field of forecasting has developed rapidly over the last few decades, with some approaches requiring highly sophisticated techniques. In this chapter, we focus on some of the easier approaches, which nevertheless provide a flavor and insight into this fascinating field. In particular, we use simple smoothing techniques for making forecasts when short-term fluctuations in the data represent random departures from the overall pattern with no discernible trend or seasonal fluctuations. Special forecasting methods are introduced when trend and seasonal fluctuations are present in the data. We will also explain a regression approach that uses lagged variables for forecasting.

INTRODUCTORY CASE

Nike Revenue Forecast

Chad Moriarty, a research analyst at a small investment firm, is evaluating Nike Inc.'s performance by analyzing the firm's revenues. Some analysts argue that Nike's revenue may slow down due to the global economic crisis and increased competition from emerging brands. Others believe that with a strong and free cash flow, Nike will likely survive this current environment and emerge stronger as some of the weaker competitors get squeezed. Chad fully understands that nobody really knows how well this Oregon-based sportswear company will perform in a softening global economy. However, he believes that Nike's past performance will aid in predicting its future performance. He collects quarterly data on Nike's revenue for the fiscal years 1999 through 2008. A portion of the data is shown in Table 18.1.

TABLE 18.1 Quarterly Revenue for Nike Inc. (in $ millions)

FILE
Nike_Revenues

Period	Revenue
1999:01	2505
1999:02	1913
⋮	⋮
2008:04	5088

Source: Annual Reports for Nike, Inc.

Chad would like to use the information in Table 18.1 to

1. Determine whether revenue exhibits any sort of trend.
2. Determine whether revenue exhibits a significant seasonal component.
3. Forecast revenue for fiscal year 2009.

A synopsis of this case is provided at the end of Section 18.4.

Distinguish among the various models used in forecasting.

In this chapter, we focus our attention on **time series** data. Observations of any variable recorded over time in sequential order are considered a time series. The time period can be expressed in terms of a year, a quarter, a month, a week, a day, an hour, or even a second. Examples of time series include the *hourly* volume of stocks traded on the New York Stock Exchange (NYSE) on four consecutive days; the number of *daily* visitors that frequent the Statue of Liberty over the month of June; the *monthly* sales for a retailer over a five-year period; and the growth rate of a country over the past 15 *years*.

> A time series is a set of sequential observations of a variable over time.

Let $y_1, y_2, \ldots, y_T$ represent a sample of T observations of a variable y with y_t denoting the value of y at time t. With time series data, it is customary to use the notation T, instead of n, to represent the number of sample observations and to use a subscript t to identify time. For instance, if the number of daily visitors (in 1,000s) to the Statue of Liberty over five days are 100, 94, 98, 110, 102, then $y_1 = 100, y_2 = 94, \ldots, y_5 = 102$.

Forecasting Methods

Forecasting methods are broadly classified as quantitative or qualitative. **Qualitative forecasting** methods are based on the judgment of the forecaster, who uses prior experience and expertise to make forecasts. On the other hand, **quantitative forecasting** methods use a formal model along with historical data for the variable of interest.

Qualitative forecasting is especially attractive when historical data are not available. For instance, a manager may use qualitative forecasts when she attempts to project sales for a brand new product. Similarly, we rely on qualitative forecasts when future results are suspected to depart markedly from results in prior periods and therefore cannot be based on historical data. For example, major changes in market conditions or government policies will render the analysis from historical data obsolete.

Although attractive in certain scenarios, qualitative forecasts are often criticized on the grounds that they are prone to some well-documented biases such as optimism and overconfidence. Decisions based on the judgment of an overly optimistic manager may prove costly to the business. Also, qualitative forecasting is difficult to document, and its quality is totally dependent on the judgment and skill of the forecaster. Two people with access to similar information may offer different qualitative forecasts.

In this chapter, we focus on quantitative forecasting. Formal quantitative models have been used extensively to forecast variables such as sales, defects, stock price, cash flows, inflation, and housing starts. These models are further split up into causal and noncausal models. **Causal models** are based on a regression framework, where the variable of interest is related to a single or multiple explanatory variables. In other words, forecasts are "caused" by the known values of the explanatory variables. **Noncausal models,** also referred to as purely time series models, do not present any explanation of the mechanism generating the variable of interest and simply provide a method for projecting historical data. Despite the lack of theory, noncausal models can provide sound forecasts. However, they provide no guidance on the likely effects of changes in policy (explanatory) variables. Both types of quantitative forecasting methods are discussed in this chapter, although the emphasis is on noncausal methods.

> ### TYPES OF FORECASTING METHODS
> Forecasting methods are broadly classified as quantitative or qualitative. Quantitative forecasting models are further divided into causal and noncausal models. Noncausal models are also referred to as purely time series models.

Model Selection Criteria

Numerous models can be used to make a forecast, with each model well-suited to capture a particular feature of the time series. It would be easy to choose the right model if we knew which feature truly describes the given series. Unfortunately, the truth is almost never known. Because we do not know *a priori* which of the competing models is likely to provide the best forecast, it is common to consider several models. Model selection is one of the most important steps in forecasting. Therefore, it is important to understand model selection criteria before we even introduce any of the formal models.

Two types of model selection criteria are used to compare the performance of competing models. These are broadly defined as in-sample criteria and out-of-sample criteria. These criteria give rise to two important questions: How well does a model explain the given sample data? And how well does a model make out-of-sample forecasts? Ideally, the chosen model is best in terms of its in-sample predictability *and* its out-of-sample forecasting ability. In this chapter we will focus on in-sample criteria.

Let y_t denote the value of the series at time t and let $\hat{y}_t$ represent its in-sample forecast. The in-sample forecast is also referred to as the predicted or fitted value. For every forecasting model, the sample forecast is likely to differ from the actual series. In other words, $\hat{y}_t$ will not equal y_t. Recall that we define $e_t = y_t - \hat{y}_t$ as the residual. All in-sample model selection criteria compare competing models on the basis of these residuals.

> The in-sample forecast $\hat{y}_t$ is also called the predicted or fitted value of y_t. Competing models are compared on the basis of the residuals, computed as $e_t = y_t - \hat{y}_t$.

In the earlier chapters on regression, we used the coefficient of determination R^2 as a goodness-of-fit measure. We cannot always use R^2 or adjusted R^2 in noncausal models because some are not based on a regression model framework. A commonly used goodness-of-fit measure for the comparison of competing forecasting models is the **mean square error (MSE)**, which is the error (residual) sum of squares divided by the number of residuals n.[1] As we will see shortly, it is not uncommon for n to be less than the number of observations T in the series. Another measure is the **mean absolute deviation (MAD)**, which is the mean of the absolute residuals. The preferred model will have the lowest MSE and MAD.

> ### MODEL SELECTION CRITERIA
>
> The mean square error (MSE) and the mean absolute deviation (MAD) are computed as
>
> $$MSE = \frac{\Sigma(y_t - \hat{y}_t)^2}{n} = \frac{\Sigma e_t^2}{n} \quad \text{and}$$
>
> $$MAD = \frac{\Sigma|y_t - \hat{y}_t|}{n} = \frac{\Sigma|e_t|}{n},$$
>
> where n is the number of residuals used in the computation. We choose the model with the lowest MSE and MAD.

In the following sections we employ various forecasting models and compare them on the basis of the above goodness-of-fit measures.

---

[1]Here the MSE formula is different from the one defined in the context of regression analysis in Chapter 15, where the error sum of squares, SSE, was divided by the appropriate degrees of freedom.

Use smoothing techniques to make forecasts.

Time series generally consist of systematic and unsystematic patterns. **Systematic patterns** are caused by a set of three identifiable components: the trend, the seasonal, and the cyclical components. Unsystematic patterns are difficult to identify because they are caused by the presence of a random error term. In this section, we focus on applications where the time series is described primarily by unsystematic patterns. In the following sections, we discuss systematic patterns.

As mentioned earlier, a time series is a sequence of observations that are ordered in time. Inherently, any data collected over time is likely to exhibit some form of random variation. For instance, the checkout time at a campus bookstore or weekly sales at a convenience store encounter random variations for no apparent reason.

A simple plot of the time series provides insights into its components. A jagged appearance, caused by abrupt changes in the series, indicates random variations. Smoothing techniques are employed to reduce the effect of random fluctuations. These techniques can also be used to provide forecasts if short-term fluctuations represent random departures from the structure, with no discernible systematic patterns. These techniques are especially attractive when forecasts of multiple variables need to be updated frequently. For example, consider a manager of a convenience store who has to update the inventories of numerous items on a weekly basis. It is not practical in such situations to develop complex forecasting models for each item. We discuss two distinct smoothing techniques: the moving average and the exponential smoothing techniques.

TIME SERIES PATTERNS

Time series consist of systematic and unsystematic patterns. Systematic patterns are caused by the trend, the seasonal, and the cyclical components. Unsystematic patterns are difficult to identify because they are caused by the presence of a random error term.

Moving Average Methods

Due to its simplicity, the **moving average method** ranks among the most popular techniques for processing time series. The method is based on computing the average from a fixed number m of the most recent observations. For instance, a 3-period moving average is formed by averaging the three most recent observations. The term "moving" is used because as a new observation becomes available, the average is updated by including the newest observation and dropping the oldest observation.

CALCULATING A MOVING AVERAGE

An m-period moving average is computed as

$$\text{Moving Average} = \frac{\text{Sum of the } m \text{ most recent observations}}{m}.$$

Here, we focus on the calculation of odd-numbered moving averages, such as 3-period, 5-period, and so on. In Section 18.4, we will use even-numbered moving averages to extract the seasonal component of a time series.

EXAMPLE 18.1

According to the Energy Information Administration, the United States consumes about 21 million barrels (882 million gallons) of petroleum each day. About half of this consumption is in the form of gasoline. Table 18.2 shows a portion of weekly U.S. finished motor gasoline production, measured in thousands of barrels per day.

a. Construct a 3-period moving average series for the data.

b. Plot production and its corresponding 3-period moving average, and comment on any differences.

c. Using the 3-period moving average series, forecast gasoline production on May 29, 2009 (week 22).

d. Calculate the mean square error, *MSE,* and the mean absolute deviation, *MAD.*

TABLE 18.2 Weekly U.S. Finished Motor Gasoline Production

Date	Week	Production
January 2, 2009	1	9115
January 9, 2009	2	8813
January 16, 2009	3	8729
January 23, 2009	4	8660
January 30, 2009	5	8679
⋮	⋮	⋮
May 8, 2009	19	8710
May 15, 2009	20	8735
May 22, 2009	21	9378

Source: Energy Information Administration.

SOLUTION:

a. We would like to point out that the calculations are based on unrounded values even though we show rounded values in the text. For notational simplicity, let production be denoted by y_t and the corresponding moving average be denoted by $\bar{y}_t$. We form a 3-period moving average series by averaging all sets of three consecutive values of the original series. The first value of a 3-period moving average is calculated as

$$\bar{y}_2 = \frac{y_1 + y_2 + y_3}{3} = \frac{9{,}115 + 8{,}813 + 8{,}729}{3} = 8{,}885.67.$$

We designate this value $\bar{y}_2$ because it represents the average in weeks 1 through 3. The next moving average, representing the average in weeks 2 through 4, is

$$\bar{y}_3 = \frac{y_2 + y_3 + y_4}{3} = \frac{8{,}813 + 8{,}729 + 8{,}660}{3} = 8{,}734.00.$$

Other values of $\bar{y}_t$ are calculated similarly and are presented in column 3 of Table 18.3. Note that we lose one observation at the beginning and one observation at the end of the 3-period moving average series $\bar{y}_t$. (If it were a 5-period moving average, we would lose two observations at the beginning and two at the end.)

TABLE 18.3 3-Period Moving Averages, Forecasts, and Residuals

Week (1)	y (2)	ȳ (3)	ŷ (4)	$e = y - \hat{y}$ (5)	e^2 (6)	$\lvert e \rvert$ (7)
1	9115	—	—	—	—	—
2	8813	8885.67	—	—	—	—
3	8729	8734.00	—	—	—	—
4	8660	8689.33	8885.67	−225.67	50925.44	225.67
5	8679	8610.33	8734.00	−55.00	3025.00	55.00
⋮	⋮	⋮	⋮	⋮	⋮	⋮
19	8710	8787.67	8932.00	−222.00	49284.00	222.00
20	8735	8941.00	8806.00	−71.00	5041.00	71.00
21	9378	—	8787.67	590.33	348493.44	590.33
Total					953509.78	3312.67

b. In Figure 18.1, we plot production and its corresponding 3-period moving average against weeks. Note that the original production series has a jagged appearance, suggesting the presence of an important random component of the series. The series of moving averages, on the other hand, presents a much smoother picture.

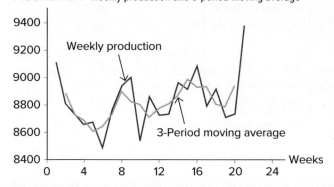

FIGURE 18.1 Weekly production and 3-period moving average

c. As mentioned earlier, if the series exhibits primarily random variations, we can use moving averages to generate forecasts. Since $\bar{y}_2$ represents the average in weeks 1 through 3, it is the most updated estimate of the series prior to period 4. Therefore, we use $\hat{y}_4 = \bar{y}_2$ where $\hat{y}_4$ is the in-sample forecast for period 4. Similarly, $\hat{y}_5 = \bar{y}_3$ is the forecast for period 5, where $\bar{y}_3$ is the average in weeks 2 through 4, and so on. These forecasts, derived as $\hat{y}_t = \frac{y_{t-3} + y_{t-2} + y_{t-1}}{3}$, are shown in column 4 of Table 18.3. Following this simple process, we compute the out-of-sample forecast in week 22 as

$$\hat{y}_{22} = \bar{y}_{20} = \frac{y_{19} + y_{20} + y_{21}}{3} = \frac{8{,}710 + 8{,}735 + 9{,}378}{3} = 8{,}941.$$

Therefore, the forecast for gasoline production on May 29, 2009 (week 22) is 8,941 thousand barrels. One potential weakness when using the moving average technique is that all future forecasts take on the same value as the first out-of-sample forecast; that is, the forecast for week 23 is also 8,941 thousand barrels.

d. To calculate the mean square error, *MSE,* and the mean absolute deviation, *MAD,* we first compute the residuals as $e_t = y_t - \hat{y}_t$, shown in column 5 of

Table 18.3. These residuals are squared (see column 6) and then summed to compute MSE as

$$MSE = \frac{\Sigma e_t^2}{n} = \frac{953{,}509.78}{18} = 52{,}973.$$

The absolute values of the residuals, presented in column 7, are used to compute MAD as

$$MAD = \frac{\Sigma |e_t|}{n} = \frac{3{,}312.67}{18} = 184.$$

While it is difficult to interpret the numerical values of MSE and MAD, they are useful in comparing alternative models.

Exponential Smoothing Methods

Although the moving average approach is popular, it has some shortcomings. First, the choice of the order m is arbitrary, although we can use trial and error to choose the value of m that results in the smallest MSE and MAD. Second, it may not be appropriate to give equal weight to all recent m observations. Whereas the moving average method weighs all recent observations equally, the method called **exponential smoothing** assigns exponentially decreasing weights as the observations get older. As in the case of moving averages, exponential smoothing is a procedure for continually revising a forecast in the light of more recent observations.

Let A_t denote the estimated level of the series at time t, where A_t is defined as

$$A_t = \alpha y_t + \alpha(1 - \alpha)y_{t-1} + \alpha(1 - \alpha)^2 y_{t-2} + \alpha(1 - \alpha)^3 y_{t-3} + \cdots, \text{ where } 0 < \alpha < 1.$$

That is, A_t is simply a weighted average of exponentially declining weights, with α dictating the speed of decline. For example, with $\alpha = 0.8$,

$$A_t = 0.8y_t + 0.16y_{t-1} + 0.032y_{t-2} + 0.0064y_{t-3} + \cdots .$$

Similarly, with $\alpha = 0.2$,

$$A_t = 0.2y_t + 0.16y_{t-1} + 0.128y_{t-2} + 0.1024y_{t-3} + \cdots .$$

Note that the speed of decline is higher when $\alpha = 0.8$ as compared to when $\alpha = 0.2$.

Using algebra, it can be shown that the initial equation simplifies to

$$A_t = \alpha y_t + (1 - \alpha)A_{t-1}.$$

We generally use this representation to define the formula for exponential smoothing. Because A_t represents the most updated level at time t, we can use it to make a one-period-ahead forecast as $\hat{y}_{t+1} = A_t$.

CALCULATING AN EXPONENTIALLY SMOOTHED SERIES

The exponential smoothing procedure continually updates the level of the series as

$$A_t = \alpha y_t + (1 - \alpha)A_{t-1},$$

where α represents the speed of decline. Forecasts are made as $\hat{y}_{t+1} = A_t$.

In order to implement this method, we need to determine α and the initial value of the series A_1. Typically, the initial value is set equal to the first value of the time series, that is, $A_1 = y_1$; the choice of the initial value is less important if the number of observations is large. The optimal value for α is determined by a trial-and-error method. We evaluate various values of α and choose the one that results in the smallest MSE and MAD.

EXAMPLE 18.2

Revisit the **Gas_Production** data on weekly U.S. finished motor gasoline production, measured in thousands of barrels per day.

a. Construct the exponentially smoothed series with $\alpha = 0.20$ and $A_1 = y_1$.

b. Plot production and its corresponding exponentially smoothed series against weeks. Comment on any differences.

c. Using the exponentially smoothed series, forecast gasoline production on May 29, 2009 (week 22).

d. Calculate *MSE* and *MAD*. Compare these values with those obtained using the 3-period moving average method.

SOLUTION: Again, the calculations are based on unrounded values even though we show rounded values in the text.

a. In Column 3 of Table 18.4, we present sequential estimates of A_t with the initial value $A_1 = y_1 = 9,115$. We use $A_t = \alpha y_t + (1 - \alpha)A_{t-1}$ to continuously update the level with $\alpha = 0.2$. For instance, for periods 2 and 3 we calculate

$$A_2 = 0.20(8,813) + 0.80(9,115) = 9,054.60, \text{ and}$$
$$A_3 = 0.20(8,729) + 0.80(9,054.60) = 8,989.48.$$

All other estimates of A_t are found in a like manner.

TABLE 18.4 Exponentially Smoothed Series with $\alpha = 0.20$, Forecasts, and Residuals

Week (1)	y (2)	A_t (3)	$\hat{y}$ (4)	$e = y - \hat{y}$ (5)	e^2 (6)	$|e|$ (7)
1	9115	9115.00	—	—	—	—
2	8813	9054.60	9115.00	−302.00	91204.00	302.00
3	8729	8989.48	9054.60	−325.60	106015.36	325.60
⋮	⋮	⋮	⋮	⋮	⋮	⋮
21	9378	8933.29	8822.11	555.89	309011.71	555.89
Total					1153160.28	3995.40

b. In Figure 18.2, we plot production and its corresponding exponentially smoothed series against weeks. As mentioned earlier, while the original series has the jagged appearance, the exponentially smoothed series removes most of the sharp points and, much like the moving average series, presents a much smoother picture.

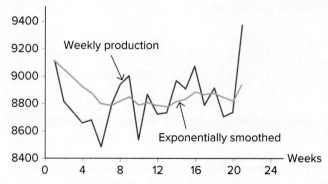

FIGURE 18.2
Weekly production and exponentially smoothed series

c. Forecasts given by $\hat{y}_{t+1} = A_t$ are presented in column 4 of Table 18.4. For instance, for period 2, $\hat{y}_2 = A_1 = 9,115$. Similarly, $A_2 = 9,054.60$ is the forecast for $\hat{y}_3$. Therefore, the forecast for gasoline production on May 29, 2009, is computed as $\hat{y}_{22} = A_{21} = 0.20 \times 9,378 + 0.80 \times 8,822.11 = 8,933.29$, or 8,933.29

thousand barrels. As with the moving average method, any further out-of-sample forecasts also assume this same value; for instance, $\hat{y}_{23} = 8{,}933.29$ thousand barrels.

d. In columns 5, 6, and 7, we present the residuals, their squares, and their absolute values, respectively. We compute model selection measures as

$$MSE = \frac{\Sigma e_t^2}{n} = \frac{1{,}153{,}160.28}{20} = 57{,}658 \quad \text{and}$$

$$MAD = \frac{\Sigma |e_t|}{n} = \frac{3{,}995.40}{20} = 200.$$

The moving average model employed in Example 18.1 outperforms the exponential model, as it yields a lower MSE of 52,973 and a lower MAD of 184. Note that we used the residuals from Weeks 4 to 21 with moving averages and Weeks 2 to 21 with exponential smoothing. For a fair comparison, we recalculated $MSE = 53{,}108$ and $MAD = 187$ with exponential smoothing, using the residuals only from Weeks 4 to 21. The moving average method still outperforms.

There is nothing sacrosanct about $\alpha = 0.2$; we used this value primarily to illustrate the exponential smoothing procedure. As we noted earlier, it is common to evaluate various values of α and choose the one that produces the smallest MSE and MAD for forecasting. In order to illustrate how α is chosen, we generate MSE and MAD with α values ranging from 0.1 to 0.9 with increments of 0.1. The results are summarized in Table 18.5.

TABLE 18.5 Various Values of α and the Resulting MSE and MAD

α	0.1	0.2	0.3	0.4	0.5	0.6	0.7	0.8	0.9
MSE	66,906	57,658	54,368	53,364	53,470	54,200	55,394	57,047	59,235
MAD	209	200	196	194	191	188	185	184	188

Here, the choice of α depends on whether we employ MSE or MAD for comparison, with MSE suggesting $\alpha = 0.4$ and MAD suggesting $\alpha = 0.8$. In instances where MSE and MAD give conflicting results, it is common to choose the procedure with the smallest MSE; we make this choice because MSE penalizes larger deviations more harshly due to squaring. Therefore, we choose α equal to 0.4 since it has the smallest MSE of 53,364. In this application, the moving average model still outperforms the exponential smoothing model, as measured by its lower MSE and MAD values.

Using Excel and R for Moving Averages and Exponential Smoothing

Using Excel

Obtaining the Moving Averages in Table 18.3

A. Open the ***Gas_Production*** data file.

B. From the menu, choose **Data > Data Analysis > Moving Average**.

C. Click on the box next to *Input Y Range*, select the Production data (including the heading), and then check the box in front of *Labels in First Row*. Next to *Interval*, enter 3, since we want to generate a 3-period moving average. Finally, indicate an *Output Range*; we enter D3, thus replicating the forecasts shown in column 4 of Table 18.3.

Obtaining the Exponentially Smoothed Series in Table 18.4

A. Open the ***Gas_Production*** data file.

B. From the menu, choose **Data > Data Analysis > Exponential Smoothing**.

FILE
Gas_Production

C. Click on the box next to *Input Y Range*, select the Production data (including the heading), and then check the box in front of *Labels*. Select the box next to *Damping Factor*. If we want to construct an exponentially smoothed series with $\alpha = 0.2$, then for *Damping Factor* we enter $1 - \alpha = 0.8$. Finally, indicate an *Output Range*; we enter D2, thus replicating the forecasts shown in column 4 of Table 18.4.

Using R

Obtaining the Moving Averages in Table 18.3

A. Import the **Gas_Production** data into a data frame (table) in R.

B. Install and load the *TTR* package (where *TTR* stands for Technical Trading Rules). Enter

```
> install.packages("TTR")
> library(TTR)
```

C. We use the **SMA** function from the *TTR* package to generate a moving average, which we label MA3. Within the function, we set the number of intervals, n, equal to 3. Enter

```
> MA3 <- SMA(Gas_Production$'Production', n=3)
```

Obtaining the Exponentially Smoothed Series in Table 18.4

A. Follow Steps A and B from the moving averages instructions.

B. We use the **EMA** function from the *TTR* package to generate an exponentially smoothed series, which we label ExpSm. Within the function, we set the number of intervals, n, equal to 1 and the *ratio* (α) equal to 0.20. Enter

```
> ExpSm <- EMA(Gas_Production$'Production', n=1,
  ratio=0.2)
```

EXERCISES 18.1

Mechanics

1. **FILE** *Exercise_18.1.* The accompanying data file contains 10 observations for t and y_t.
   a. Construct the 3-period moving average and plot it along with the actual series. Comment on smoothing.
   b. Use the 3-period moving average to make in-sample forecasts and compute the resulting *MSE* and *MAD*.
   c. Make a forecast for period 11.

2. **FILE** *Exercise_18.2.* The accompanying data file contains 20 observations for t and y_t.
   a. Construct the 5-period moving average and plot it along with the actual series. Comment on smoothing.
   b. Use the 5-period moving average to make in-sample forecasts and compute the resulting *MSE* and *MAD*.
   c. Make a forecast for period 21.

3. **FILE** *Exercise_18.3.* The accompanying data file contains 20 observations for t and y_t.
   a. Plot the series and discuss the presence of random variations.
   b. Use the exponential smoothing method to make in-sample forecasts with $\alpha = 0.2$. Compute the resulting *MSE* and *MAD*.
   c. Repeat the process with $\alpha = 0.4$.
   d. Use the appropriate value of α to make a forecast for period 21.

4. **FILE** *Exercise_18.4.* The accompanying data file contains 20 observations for t and y_t.
   a. Use the 3-period moving average to make in-sample forecasts and compute the resulting *MSE* and *MAD*.
   b. Use the exponential smoothing method to make in-sample forecasts with $\alpha = 0.4$. Compute the resulting *MSE* and *MAD*.
   c. Use the preferred method to make a forecast for period 21.

Applications

5. **FILE** *Rock_Music.* Rock and roll is a form of music that evolved in the United States and quickly spread to the rest of the world. The interest in rock music, like any other genre,

has gone through ups and downs over the years. The Recording Industry Association of America (RIAA) reports consumer trends on the basis of annual data on genre, format, age, and gender of purchasers and place of purchase. The accompanying table lists a portion of the percentage (share) of total shipment of music that falls in the category of rock music from 1991–2008.

Year	Share
1991	34.8
1992	31.6
⋮	⋮
2008	31.8

Source: www.riaa.com.

a. Plot the series and discuss the presence of random variations.
b. Use the 3-period moving average to make a forecast for the share of rock music in 2009.
c. Use the 5-period moving average to make a forecast for the share of rock music in 2009.
d. Use the *MSE* to pick the appropriate moving average for making a forecast for the share of rock and roll music in 2009.

6. **FILE** *Rock_Music.* Refer to the previous exercise for a description of the data set.
a. Make a forecast for the share of rock music in 2009 using the exponential smoothing method with $\alpha = 0.4$.
b. Make a forecast for the share of rock music in 2009 using the exponential smoothing method with $\alpha = 0.6$.
c. Use the *MSE* to pick the appropriate speed of decline for making a forecast for the share of rock music in 2009.

7. **FILE** *Poverty_Rate.* According to the Census Bureau, the number of people below the poverty level has been steadily increasing (CNN, September 16, 2010). This means many families are finding themselves there for the first time. The following table shows a portion of the percent of families in the United States who were below the poverty level from 1986–2009.

Year	Poverty Rate
1986	10.9
1987	10.7
⋮	⋮
2009	11.1

Source: U.S. Census Bureau.

a. Plot the series and comment on its shape.
b. Use the 3-period moving average to make in-sample forecasts. Compute the resulting *MSE* and *MAD*.
c. Use the exponential smoothing method to make in-sample forecasts with $\alpha = 0.6$. Compute the resulting *MSE* and *MAD*.
d. Choose the appropriate model to make a forecast of the poverty rate in 2010.

8. **FILE** *S&P_Price.* Consider the following table, which shows a portion of the closing prices of the S&P 500 Index for 21 trading days in November 2010.

Date	S&P Price
1-Nov	1184.38
2-Nov	1193.57
⋮	⋮
30-Nov	1180.55

Source: finance.yahoo.com.

a. Use the 3-period moving average to make a price forecast for December 1, 2010.
b. Use the exponential smoothing method to make a price forecast for December 1, 2010. Use $\alpha = 0.4$.
c. Which of the above smoothing methods results in a lower *MSE*?

9. **FILE** *Unemployment_Inflation.* The accompanying table shows a portion of monthly data on seasonally adjusted inflation and unemployment rates in the United States from January 2009 to November 2010.

Year	Month	Unemployment	Inflation
2009	Jan	7.7	0.3
2009	Feb	8.2	0.4
⋮	⋮	⋮	⋮
2010	Nov	9.8	0.1

Source: Bureau of Labor Statistics.

a. Use the 3-period moving average and exponential smoothing with $\alpha = 0.6$ to make in-sample forecasts for unemployment. Use the more appropriate smoothing method to forecast unemployment for December 2010.
b. Use the 3-period moving average and exponential smoothing with $\alpha = 0.6$ to make in-sample forecasts for inflation. Use the more appropriate smoothing method to forecast inflation for December 2010.

18.3 TREND FORECASTING MODELS

The smoothing techniques discussed in Section 18.2 are used when the time series represent random fluctuations with no discernible trend or seasonal fluctuations. When trend and seasonal variations are present, we need to use special models for the analysis. In this section, we focus on **trend** analysis, which extracts long-term upward or downward movements of the series.

The Linear Trend

We estimate a **linear trend model** using the regression techniques described in earlier chapters. Let y_t be the value of the response variable at time t. Here we use t as the explanatory variable corresponding to consecutive time periods, such as 1, 2, 3, and so on. Example 18.3 shows how to use this model to make forecasts.

THE LINEAR TREND MODEL

A linear trend model is used for a time series that is expected to grow by a fixed amount each time period. It is specified as $y_t = \beta_0 + \beta_1 t + \varepsilon_t$, where y_t is the value of the series at time t. The estimated model is used to make forecasts as $\hat{y}_t = b_0 + b_1 t$, where b_0 and b_1 are the coefficient estimates.

EXAMPLE 18.3

The United States continues to increase in diversity, with more than a third of its population belonging to a minority group (CNN.com, May 14, 2009). Hispanics are the fastest-growing minority segment, comprising one out of six residents in the country. Table 18.6 shows a portion of data relating to the number (in 1,000s) as well as the median income (in $) of Hispanic households from 1975 through 2007.

TABLE 18.6 Number and Median Income of Hispanics, 1975–2007

Year	Number	Income
1975	2948	8865
1976	3081	9569
⋮	⋮	⋮
2007	13339	38679

Source: United States Census Bureau.

a. Use the sample data to estimate the linear trend model for the number (Regression 1) and the median income (Regression 2) of Hispanic households. Interpret the slope coefficients.

b. Forecast the number and the median income of Hispanic households in 2008.

SOLUTION: In order to estimate the linear trend models, it is advisable to first relabel the 33 years of observations from 1 to 33. In other words, make the explanatory variable t assume values 1, 2, . . . , 33 rather than 1975, 1976, . . . , 2007. Table 18.7 shows a portion of the data.

TABLE 18.7 Generating the Time Variable *t*

Year	t	Number	Income
1975	1	2948	8865
1976	2	3081	9569
⋮	⋮	⋮	⋮
2007	33	13339	38679

The regression results are presented in Table 18.8.

TABLE 18.8 Regression Results for Example 18.3

	Response Variable: Number (Regression 1)	Response Variable: Income (Regression 2)
	Coefficients	Coefficients
Intercept	1,657.8428* (0.000)	7,796.9186* (0.000)
t	327.4709* (0.000)	887.7249* (0.000)

Notes: Parameter estimates are followed by the *p*-values in parentheses; * represents significance at 5%.

a. The slope coefficient in Regression 1 implies that the number of Hispanic households has grown, on average, by approximately 327 (in 1,000s) each year. Regression 2 shows that the median income for Hispanic households has grown, on average, by approximately $888 each year. The slope coefficients in both regressions are significant at any level, since the *p*-values approximate zero in both regressions.

b. Using the estimates from Regression 1, we forecast the number of Hispanic households in 2008 ($t = 34$) as $1{,}657.8428 + 327.4709 \times 34 = 12{,}791.85$ (in 1,000s). Similarly, using the estimates from Regression 2, the forecast for the median income of Hispanic households in 2008 is $7{,}796.9186 + 887.7249 \times 34 = \$37{,}979.57$. Forecasts for other years can be computed similarly.

The Exponential Trend

A linear trend model uses a straight line to capture the trend, thus implying that for each period, the value of the series is expected to change by a fixed amount, given by the estimated coefficient b_1. For example, in Example 18.3 we concluded that the predicted median income of Hispanic households grows by approximately $888 each year. The **exponential trend model** is attractive when the expected increase in the series gets larger over time. Figure 18.3 compares linear and exponential trends. While both graphs have positive slopes, the exponential trend, unlike the linear trend, allows the series to grow by an increasing amount over time.

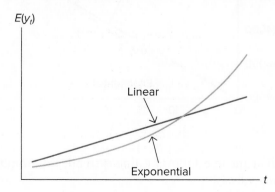

FIGURE 18.3
Linear and exponential trends

Recall from Chapter 16 that we specify an exponential model as $\ln(y_t) = \beta_0 + \beta_1 t + \varepsilon_t$. In order to estimate this model, we first generate the series in natural logs, $\ln(y_t)$, and then run a regression of $\ln(y_t)$ on t. Since in the exponential model, the response variable is measured in logs, we make forecasts in regular units as $\hat{y}_t = \exp(b_0 + b_1 t + s_e^2/2)$, where s_e is the standard error of the estimate.

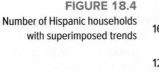

THE EXPONENTIAL TREND MODEL

An exponential trend model is commonly used for a time series that is expected to grow by an increasing amount each time period. It is specified as $\ln(y_t) = \beta_0 + \beta_1 t + \varepsilon_t$, where $\ln(y_t)$ is the natural log of y_t. The estimated model is used to make forecasts as $\hat{y}_t = \exp(b_0 + b_1 t + s_e^2/2)$, where b_0 and b_1 are the coefficient estimates and s_e is the standard error of the estimate.

It is always advisable to inspect the data visually as a first step to gauge whether a linear or an exponential trend provides a better fit. Figures 18.4 and 18.5 are scatterplots of the number and the median income of Hispanic households from 1975 through 2007. These plots are based on the **Hispanic_Characteristics** data. We relabel the 33 years of annual observations from 1 to 33 and also superimpose the linear and the exponential trends to the data.

FIGURE 18.4
Number of Hispanic households with superimposed trends

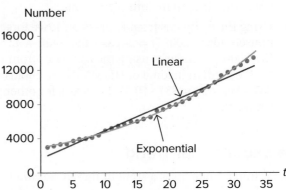

FIGURE 18.5
Median income of Hispanic households with superimposed trends

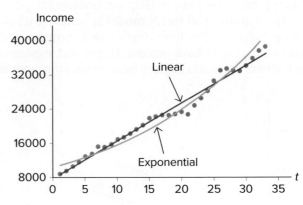

It appears that while the median income follows a linear trend, the number of Hispanics seems to grow exponentially.

EXAMPLE 18.4

FILE

Hispanic_Characteristics

a. Revisit the **Hispanic_Characteristics** data to estimate the exponential trend model for both the number (Regression 1) and the median income (Regression 2) of Hispanic households. Interpret the slope coefficients.

b. Forecast the number, as well as the median income, of Hispanic households in 2008.

c. Use *MSE* and *MAD* to decide whether the linear or the exponential model is more appropriate for the series.

SOLUTION: In order to estimate the exponential model, we first transform both series to natural logs. Table 18.9 shows a portion of the data where the variables (Number and Income) are transformed into natural logs. The table also includes the explanatory variable t, relabeled from 1 to 33.

TABLE 18.9 Generating the Natural Log of the Series (Example 18.4)

Year	t	Number	Income	ln (Number)	ln (Income)
1975	1	2948	8865	7.9889	9.0899
1976	2	3081	9569	8.0330	9.1663
⋮	⋮	⋮	⋮	⋮	⋮
2007	33	13339	38679	9.4984	10.5631

Relevant regression results for the exponential regression models are presented in Table 18.10.

TABLE 18.10 Regression Results for Example 18.4

	Response Variable: Log of Number (Regression 1)	Response Variable: Log of Income (Regression 2)
	Coefficients	Coefficients
Intercept	7.9706* (0.000)	9.2517* (0.000)
t	0.0479* (0.000)	0.0418* (0.000)
s_e	0.0311	0.0775

Notes: Parameter estimates are followed by the *p*-values in parentheses; * represents significance at the 5% level. The last row shows the standard error of the estimate s_e.

a. Consistent with the results of the linear trend models, the exponential trend models suggest that the number and the median income of Hispanic households are trending upward, since both regressions have positive slope coefficients. The slope coefficient from Regression 1 implies that the number of Hispanic households has grown, on average, by about 4.79% per year. Similarly, the slope coefficient from Regression 2 implies that the median income of Hispanic households has grown, on average, by about 4.18% per year. In addition, both slope coefficients are significant at any level, since the *p*-values approximate zero in both regressions.

b. We make forecasts as $\hat{y}_t = \exp(b_0 + b_1 t + s_e^2/2)$ using unrounded values of the estimates even though we show rounded values in the text. In order to forecast the number of Hispanic households for 2008 ($t = 34$), we compute

$$\hat{y}_{34} = \exp(7.9706 + 0.0479 \times 34 + 0.0311^2/2) = 14{,}750.70 \text{ (in 1,000s)}.$$

Similarly, the forecast for Hispanic median income is computed as

$$\hat{y}_{34} = \exp(9.2517 + 0.0418 \times 34 + 0.0775^2/2) = \$43{,}239.57.$$

Forecasts for other years can be computed similarly. Note that 2008 forecasts with the exponential trend model are higher than those with the linear trend model.

Note: Whenever possible, it is advisable to use unrounded values for making forecasts in an exponential model because even a small difference, when exponentiated, can make a big difference in the forecast. If we had rounded the estimates to 4 decimal places, the forecasts for Number and Income would have been 14,760.11 and $43,209.79, respectively.

c. We compute $\hat{y}$ for the exponential model in regular units and not in natural logs. The resulting $\hat{y}$ also enables us to compare the linear and the exponential models in terms of MSE and MAD; we could have made the comparison in terms of correctly computed R^2. In Table 18.11, we present a portion of the series $\hat{y}_t$, along with y_t, for both models; as mentioned earlier, we did these calculations with unrounded values for the estimates. We then compute $MSE = \frac{\Sigma e_t^2}{n}$ and $MAD = \frac{\Sigma |e_t|}{n}$ where $e_t = y_t - \hat{y}_t$. While these calculations are not reported, the MSE and MAD values for the linear and the exponential models are shown in the last two rows of Table 18.11.

TABLE 18.11 Analysis of Linear and Exponential Trend Models

		Number y			Income y	
t	y	ŷ (Linear)	ŷ (Exponential)	y	ŷ (Linear)	ŷ (Exponential)
1	2948	1985.31	3037.97	8865	8684.64	10899.65
2	3081	2312.79	3186.97	9569	9572.37	11364.43
⋮	⋮	⋮	⋮	⋮	⋮	⋮
33	13339	12464.38	14061.05	38679	37091.84	41471.14
MSE		281255	45939		1508369	2210693
MAD		460	155		881	1289

The exponential trend is better suited to describe the number of Hispanic households, since it has a lower MSE and MAD than the linear trend model. On the other hand, median income is better described by the linear trend model. These findings are consistent with our earlier analysis with Figures 18.4 and 18.5. Therefore, we use the exponential trend model to forecast the number of Hispanic households in 2008 as 14,750.70 (in 1,000s). The linear trend model is used to forecast the median income of Hispanic households in 2008 as $37,980.

Polynomial Trends

Sometimes a time series reverses direction, due to any number of circumstances. A common polynomial function that allows for curvature in the series is a **quadratic trend model**. A quadratic regression model was first introduced in Chapter 16. This model describes one change in the direction of a series and is estimated as

$$\hat{y}_t = \beta_0 + \beta_1 t + \beta_2 t^2 + \varepsilon_t.$$

The coefficient β_2 determines whether the trend is U-shaped or inverted U-shaped. Figure 18.6 depicts possible trends of a quadratic model.

In order to estimate the quadratic trend model, we generate t^2, which is simply the square of t. Then we run a multiple regression model that uses y as the response variable and both t and t^2 as the explanatory variables. The estimated model is used to make forecasts as

$$\hat{y}_t = b_0 + b_1 t + b_2 t^2.$$

FIGURE 18.6
Representative shapes
of a quadratic trend

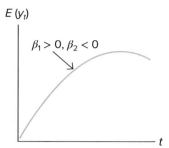
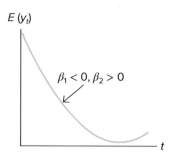

Higher-order polynomial functions can be estimated similarly. For instance, consider a **cubic trend model** specified as

$$y_t = \beta_0 + \beta_1 t + \beta_2 t^2 + \beta_3 t^3 + \varepsilon_t.$$

The cubic trend model allows for two changes in the direction of a series. Figure 18.7 presents possible shapes of a cubic model.

FIGURE 18.7
Representative shapes
of a cubic trend

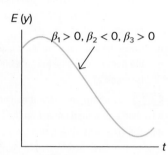
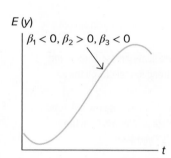

In the cubic trend model, we basically generate two additional variables, t^2 and t^3, for the regression. A multiple regression model is run that uses y as the response variable and t, t^2, and t^3 as the explanatory variables. The estimated model is used to make forecasts as $\hat{y}_t = b_0 + b_1 t + b_2 t^2 + b_3 t^3$.

While we use the *MSE* and the *MAD* of in-sample forecast errors to compare the linear and the exponential models, we cannot use them to compare the linear, quadratic, and cubic trend models. The reason is that the values of *MSE* and *MAD* are always lowest for the highest-order polynomial trend model, since the values decrease as we estimate additional parameters. The problem is similar to that of the coefficient of determination R^2 discussed in earlier chapters. When comparing polynomial trend models, we use adjusted R^2, which imposes a penalty for over-parameterization.

THE POLYNOMIAL TREND MODEL

A polynomial trend model of order q is estimated as

$$y_t = \beta_0 + \beta_1 t + \beta_2 t^2 + \beta_3 t^3 + \cdots + \beta_q t^q + \varepsilon_t.$$

This model specializes to a linear trend model, quadratic trend model, and cubic trend model for $q = 1$, 2, and 3, respectively. The estimated model is used to make forecasts as $\hat{y}_t = b_0 + b_1 t + b_2 t^2 + b_3 t^3 + \cdots + b_q t^q$, where $b_0, b_1, \ldots, b_q$ are the coefficient estimates. We use adjusted R^2 to compare polynomial trend models with different orders.

An application of the polynomial trend model is used in the Writing with Statistics section of this chapter.

EXERCISES 18.2

Mechanics

10. Consider the following estimated trend models. Use them to make a forecast for $t = 21$.

   a. Linear Trend: $\hat{y} = 13.54 + 1.08t$

   b. Quadratic Trend: $\hat{y} = 18.28 + 0.92t - 0.01t^2$

   c. Exponential Trend: $\widehat{\ln(y)} = 1.8 + 0.09t$; $s_e = 0.01$

11. **FILE** *Exercise_18.11.* The accompanying data file contains 20 observations for t and y_t.

   a. Plot the series along with the superimposed linear and quadratic trends. Which trend model do you think describes the data well?

   b. Estimate a linear trend model and a quadratic trend model. Validate your guess from the graphs by comparing their adjusted R^2.

12. **FILE** *Exercise_18.12.* The accompanying data file contains 20 observations for t and y_t.

   a. Plot the series along with the superimposed linear and exponential trends. Which trend model do you think describes the data well?

   b. Estimate a linear trend model and an exponential trend model for the sample. Validate your guess from the graphs by comparing the *MSE* and *MAD*.

Applications

13. **FILE** *Amusement_Park.* Despite the growth in digital entertainment, the nation's 400 amusement parks have managed to hold on to visitors. A manager collects data on the number of visitors (in millions) to amusement parks in the United States. A portion of the data is shown in the accompanying table.

Year	Visitors
2000	317
2001	319
⋮	⋮
2007	341

Source: International Association of
Amusement Parks and Attractions.

   a. Plot the series. Does the linear trend model or the exponential trend model fit the series best?

   b. Estimate both models. Verify your answer in part a by comparing the *MSE* of the models.

   c. Given the model of best fit, make a forecast for visitors to amusement parks in 2008 and 2009.

14. **FILE** *Swine_Flu.* The potentially deadly 2009 Swine Flu outbreak was due to a new flu strain of subtype H1N1 not previously reported in pigs. When the World Health Organization declared a pandemic, the virus continued to spread in the United States, causing illness along with regular seasonal influenza viruses. Data for week 17 to week 26 in 2009 on total Swine Flu cases in the United States are collected. A portion of the data is shown in the accompanying table.

Week	Flu Cases
17	1190
18	2012
⋮	⋮
26	1093

Source: www.cdc.gov.

   a. Plot the series. Estimate the linear and the quadratic trend models. Use their adjusted R^2 to choose the preferred model.

   b. Given the preferred model, make a forecast for the number of Swine Flu cases in the United States for week 27.

15. **FILE** *Recording_Industry.* Rapid advances in technology have had a profound impact on the United States recording industry (*The New York Times, July 28, 2008*). While cassette tapes gave vinyl records strong competition, they were subsequently eclipsed by the introduction of the compact disc (CD) in the early 1980s. Lately, the CD, too, has been in rapid decline, primarily because of Internet music stores. The following data show a portion of year-end shipment statistics on the three formats of the United States recording industry, in particular, the manufacturers' unit shipments, in millions, of vinyl, cassettes, and CDs from 1991 to 2008.

Year	Vinyl	Cassettes	CDs
1991	4.8	360.1	333.3
1992	2.3	366.4	407.5
⋮	⋮	⋮	⋮
2008	2.9	0.1	384.7

Source: www.riaa.com.

   a. Plot the series for cassettes. Estimate the quadratic and the cubic trend models for this series. Make a forecast with the chosen model for 2009.

   b. Plot the series for CDs. Estimate the linear and the quadratic trend models for this series. Make a forecast with the chosen model for 2009.

16. **FILE** *California_Unemployment.* Consider the following table, which lists a portion of the seasonally adjusted monthly unemployment rates (in %) in California from 2007–2010.

Date	Unemployment Rate
Jan-07	4.9
Feb-07	5.0
⋮	⋮
Dec-10	12.5

Source: Bureau of Labor Statistics.

a. Plot the series. Which polynomial trend model do you think is most appropriate?
b. Verify your answer by formally comparing the linear, the quadratic, and the cubic trend models.
c. Use the preferred model to forecast the unemployment rate in California for January 2011.

17. **FILE** *TrueCar.* Investors are always reviewing past pricing history and using it to influence their future investment decisions. On May 16, 2014, online car buying system TrueCar launched its initial public offering (IPO), raising $70 million in the stock offering. An investor, looking for a promising return, analyzes the monthly stock price data of TrueCar from June 2014 to May 2017. A portion of the data is shown in the accompanying table.

Date	Price
Jun-14	14.78
Jul-14	13.57
⋮	⋮
May-17	17.51

Source: finance.yahoo.com; data retrieved May 22, 2017.

a. Plot the stock price data with superimposed linear, quadratic, and cubic trends. Which trend do you think describes the data best?
b. Estimate the linear, the quadratic, and the cubic trend models.
c. Use the preferred model to make a forecast for June 2017.

18. **FILE** *Miles_Traveled.* The number of cars sold in the United States in 2016 reached a record high for the seventh year in a row (CNNMoney, January 4, 2017). Consider monthly total miles traveled (in billions) in the United States from January 2010 to December 2016. A portion of the data is shown in the accompanying table.

Date	Miles
Jan-10	2953.305
Feb-10	2946.689
⋮	⋮
Dec-16	3169.501

Source: Federal Reserve Bank of St. Louis.

a. Plot the data with superimposed linear, quadratic, and cubic trends.
b. Estimate the two best models based on the visual analysis in part a. Use adjusted R^2 to select the best model for making forecasts.
c. Use the chosen model to make a forecast for Miles in January 2017.

19. **FILE** *Café_Sales.* With a new chef and a creative menu, Café Venetian has witnessed a huge surge in sales. The following data show a portion of daily sales (in $) at Café Venetian in the first 100 days after the changes.

Day	Sales
1	263
2	215
⋮	⋮
100	2020

a. Plot the café's sales with superimposed linear and exponential trends. Which trend do you think describes the data better?
b. Estimate the linear and the exponential trend models. Use *MSE* to select the best model for making forecasts.
c. Make a forecast with the chosen model for the 101st. week.

20. **FILE** *Apple_Price.* Apple Inc. has performed extremely well in the last decade. After its stock price dropping to below 90 in May 2016, it made a tremendous come back to reach about 146 by May 2017 (SeekingAlpha.com, May 1, 2017). An investor seeking to gain from the positive momentum of Apple's stock price analyzes 53 weeks of stock price data from 5/30/16 to 5/26/17. A portion of the data is shown in the accompanying table.

Date	Price
5/30/2016	97.92
6/6/2016	98.83
⋮	⋮
5/26/2017	153.57

Source: finance.yahoo.com; data retrieved May 22, 2017.

a. Plot the stock price data with superimposed linear and exponential trends. Which trend do you think describes the data better?
b. Estimate the linear and the exponential trend models. Use *MSE* to select the best model for making forecasts.
c. Make a forecast with the chosen model for the next week (54th week).

As mentioned earlier, time series generally consist of systematic and unsystematic patterns. Smoothing methods prove useful for forecasting a series that is described primarily by an unsystematic component. Systematic patterns are identified by the trend, the seasonal, and the cyclical components. In the preceding section, we focused on trend. We now turn our attention to the other components of systematic patterns.

The **seasonal component** typically represents repetitions over a one-year period. Time series consisting of weekly, monthly, or quarterly observations tend to exhibit seasonal variations that repeat year after year. For instance, every year, sales of retail goods increase during the Christmas season, and the number of vacation packages goes up during the summer. The **cyclical component** represents wavelike fluctuations or business cycles, often caused by expansion and contraction of the economy. Unlike the well-defined seasons, the length of a business cycle varies, as fluctuations may last for several months or years. In addition, even the magnitude of business cycles varies over time. Because cycles vary in length and amplitude, they are difficult to capture with historical data. For these reasons, we ignore the cyclical component in this text.

In this section we will make forecasts based on the seasonal as well as the trend components of a series. As shown in Section 18.3, we simply apply trend forecasting models to time series that do not exhibit seasonal variations or that have been seasonally adjusted.

Decomposition Analysis

Let T, S, and I represent the trend, the seasonal, and the irregular or random components, respectively, of the time series y_t. With seasonal data, it is necessary to model seasonality along with trend. Consider the following multiplicative model, which relates sample observations to T, S, and I:

$$y_t = T_t \times S_t \times I_t.$$

We use sample information to extract the trend and the seasonal components of the series and then project them into the future. Let $\hat{T}_t$ and $\hat{S}_t$ denote the estimated trend and seasonal components, respectively. Note that by their very nature, random variations cannot be identified or predicted. Therefore, we set $\hat{I}_t = 1$ and make forecasts as $\hat{y}_t = \hat{T}_t \times \hat{S}_t$. This process is often referred to as **decomposition analysis**. Alternatively, we can use a multiple regression model to simultaneously estimate trend along with **seasonal dummy variables**. We first elaborate on decomposition analysis, then discuss the use of seasonal dummy variables.

Nike_Revenues

In the introductory case to this chapter, we considered Nike's quarterly revenue from 1999 through 2008. Figure 18.8 is a scatterplot of the data, where we have relabeled the 10 years of quarterly observations from 1 to 40. The graph highlights some important characteristics of Nike's revenue. First, there is a persistent upward movement in the data. Second, the trend does not seem to be linear and is

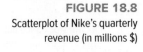

FIGURE 18.8

Scatterplot of Nike's quarterly revenue (in millions $)

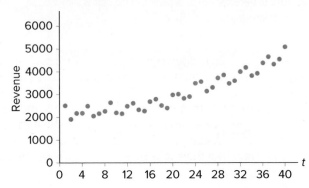

likely to be better captured by an exponential model. Third, a seasonal pattern repeats itself year after year. For instance, revenue is consistently higher in the first and fourth quarters as compared to the second and third quarters.

Extracting Seasonality

LO 18.4

Calculate and interpret seasonal indices and use them to seasonally adjust a time series.

In this section, we employ moving averages to separate the effect of trend from seasonality. Given quarterly data, we use a 4-period moving average by averaging all sets of four consecutive values of the series. Using the earlier notation, let y_t denote revenue at time t and let $\bar{y}_t$ represent its corresponding 4-period moving average. We calculate the first moving average as

$$\bar{y}_{2.5} = \frac{y_1 + y_2 + y_3 + y_4}{4} = \frac{2{,}505 + 1{,}913 + 2{,}177 + 2{,}182}{4} = 2{,}194.25.$$

We designate the first moving average $\bar{y}_{2.5}$ because it represents the average in quarters 1 through 4. The next two moving averages, representing the average in quarters 2 through 5, and quarters 3 through 6, respectively, are

$$\bar{y}_{3.5} = \frac{y_2 + y_3 + y_4 + y_5}{4} = \frac{1{,}913 + 2{,}177 + 2{,}182 + 2{,}501}{4} = 2{,}193.25, \text{ and}$$

$$\bar{y}_{4.5} = \frac{y_3 + y_4 + y_5 + y_6}{4} = \frac{2{,}177 + 2{,}182 + 2{,}501 + 2{,}060}{4} = 2{,}230.00.$$

Other moving averages are calculated similarly.

We note two important points at the outset. First, a 4-period moving average basically represents a quarterly average in one year. The first moving average uses all four quarters of 1999, the second uses three quarters of 1999 and one of 2000, and so on. Since all four quarters are represented in every 4-period moving average, it eliminates seasonal fluctuations in the series. Second, while it is appropriate to designate a moving average in the middle quarter, there is no middle quarter in the original series. For instance, the moving average is represented by $\bar{y}_{2.5}, \bar{y}_{3.5}, \bar{y}_{4.5}$, etc. when the original series is y_1, y_2, y_3, etc.

In order to represent an even-period moving average, we rely on the **centered moving average, CMA**, which is essentially the average of two consecutive moving averages. In the above example, the first 4-period centered moving average is formed as an average of the first two 4-period moving averages. In other words,

$$\bar{y}_3 = \frac{\bar{y}_{2.5} + \bar{y}_{3.5}}{2} = \frac{2{,}194.25 + 2{,}193.25}{2} = 2{,}193.75.$$

Note that this designated centered moving average $\bar{y}_3$ corresponds with y_3 of the actual series. Similarly,

$$\bar{y}_4 = \frac{\bar{y}_{3.5} + \bar{y}_{4.5}}{2} = \frac{2{,}193.25 + 2{,}230.00}{2} = 2{,}211.63.$$

The *CMA* series, $\bar{y}_t$, is shown in column 4 of Table 18.12. As mentioned before, all calculations are based on unrounded values even though we show rounded values in the text.

We note that $\bar{y}_t$ eliminates seasonal variations and also some random variations; that is, $\bar{y}_t$ represents a series that only includes the trend component T_t. Heuristically, since $y_t = T_t \times S_t \times I_t$ and $\bar{y}_t = T_t$, when we divide y_t by $\bar{y}_t$, we are left with $S_t \times I_t$. This series, $y_t/\bar{y}_t$, is called the **ratio-to-moving average** and is presented in column 5 of Table 18.12.

TABLE 18.12 Analysis of Seasonal Data

Period	t	y	Centered Moving Average: $\bar{y}$	Ratio-to-Moving Average: $y/\bar{y}$
1999:01	1	2505	—	—
1999:02	2	1913	—	—
1999:03	3	2177	2193.7500	0.9924
1999:04	4	2182	2211.6250	0.9866
⋮	⋮	⋮	⋮	⋮
2008:01	37	4655	4403.3750	1.0571
2008:02	38	4340	4568.6250	0.9500
2008:03	39	4544	—	—
2008:04	40	5088	—	—

In Table 18.13, we rearrange $y_t/\bar{y}_t$ by quarter from 1999–2008. Note that each quarter has multiple ratios, where each ratio corresponds to a different year. For instance, $y_t/\bar{y}_t$ for the third quarter is 0.9924 in 1999, 0.9541 in 2000, and so on. In this example, each quarter has nine ratios. We use the arithmetic average (sometimes we use the median) to determine a common value for each quarter. By averaging, we basically cancel out the random component and extract the seasonal component of the series. We refer to this summary measure as the unadjusted seasonal index for the quarter. For instance, the average of the ratios for the first quarter is calculated as $(1.1225 + \cdots + 1.0571)/9 = 1.0815$.

TABLE 18.13 Computation of Seasonal Indices

Year	Quarter 1	Quarter 2	Quarter 3	Quarter 4
1999	—	—	0.9924	0.9866
2000	1.1225	0.9206	0.9541	0.9881
⋮	⋮	⋮	⋮	⋮
2008	1.0571	0.9500	—	—
Unadjusted Seasonal Index	1.0815	0.9413	0.9379	1.0377
Adjusted Seasonal Index	1.0819	0.9417	0.9383	1.0381

For ease of interpretation, it is important that the seasonal indices add up to the number of seasons m so that the average equals one. To ensure this requirement, we multiply each unadjusted seasonal index by a multiplier calculated as m divided by the sum of the unadjusted seasonal indices; the resulting value is referred to as the adjusted seasonal index. In the above example with quarterly data,

$$\text{Multiplier} = \frac{4}{1.0815 + 0.9413 + 0.9379 + 1.0377} = 1.0004.$$

Therefore, the adjusted seasonal index for quarter 1 is calculated as $1.0815 \times 1.0004 = 1.0819$. This is the estimate of the seasonal index that will be used for forecasting. Table 18.13 shows adjusted seasonal indices for each quarter. Note that the average of the adjusted seasonal indices equals one.

Let us interpret these adjusted seasonal indices. There is no seasonality if all indices equal their average of one. On the other hand, if the seasonal index for a quarter is greater (less) than one, it implies that the observations in the given quarter are greater (less) than the average quarterly values. In the preceding example, the adjusted seasonal index of 1.0819 for quarter 1 implies that Nike's revenue is about 8.19% higher in the first quarter as compared to the average quarterly revenue. The adjusted seasonal index for the second quarter is 0.9417, suggesting that revenues are about 5.83% lower than the average quarterly revenue. Other adjusted seasonal indices are interpreted similarly.

CALCULATING A SEASONAL INDEX

1. Given the number of seasons m, calculate the moving average, MA (if m is odd), or the centered moving average, CMA (if m is even), of the series. We represent MA or CMA by $\bar{y}_t$.

2. Compute the ratio-to-moving average as $y_t/\bar{y}_t$.

3. Find the average of $y_t/\bar{y}_t$ for each season. This average is referred to as the unadjusted seasonal index.

4. Multiply each unadjusted seasonal index by $m/($Sum of the unadjusted seasonal indices$)$. The resulting value, referred to as the adjusted seasonal index, is the final estimate for the seasonal index.

Extracting Trend

In order to extract the trend from a time series, we first eliminate seasonal variations by dividing the original series y_t by its corresponding adjusted seasonal index $\hat{S}_t$. Here $\hat{S}_t$ represents four quarters of adjusted seasonal indices, repeated over the years. The seasonally adjusted series, $(y_t/\hat{S}_t)$, is shown in column 5 of Table 18.14.

LO 18.5

Use decomposition analysis to make forecasts.

TABLE 18.14 Creating Seasonally Adjusted Series

Period	t	Series: y	Seasonal Index: $\hat{S}$	Seasonally Adjusted Series: $y/\hat{S}$
1999:01	1	2505	1.0819	2315.2871
1999:02	2	1913	0.9417	2031.3911
1999:03	3	2177	0.9383	2320.2372
1999:04	4	2182	1.0381	2101.9668
2000:01	5	2501	1.0819	2311.5900
⋮	⋮	⋮	⋮	⋮
2008:04	40	5088	1.0381	4901.3781

As noted earlier, the adjusted seasonal index of 1.0819 implies that Nike's revenue in the first quarter is about 8.19% higher than average quarterly revenue. Therefore, without the seasonal effect, the revenue would be lower. For instance, the revenue of $2,505 million in 1999:01 is only $2,315.29 million once it has been seasonally adjusted. In Figure 18.9, we plot revenue along with seasonally adjusted revenue.

The seasonally adjusted series is free of seasonal variations, thus highlighting the long-term movement (trend) of the series. Figure 18.9 also confirms that the exponential trend model is better suited for the data than the linear trend model.

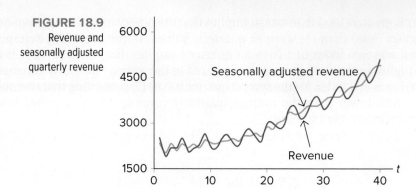

FIGURE 18.9
Revenue and seasonally adjusted quarterly revenue

Seasonally adjusted revenue

Revenue

OBTAINING A SEASONALLY ADJUSTED SERIES

In order to obtain the seasonally adjusted series, we divide the original series by its corresponding seasonal index $(y_t/\hat{S}_t)$. We use the appropriate trend model on the seasonally adjusted series to extract the trend component $\hat{T}_t$.

We estimate the exponential trend model where the response variable is the natural log of the seasonally adjusted revenue $\ln(y_t/\hat{S}_t)$ and the explanatory variable t assumes values 1, 2, . . . , 40, representing 10 years of quarterly data from 1999 to 2008. The relevant portion of the regression output is given in Table 18.15. We encourage you to compare the results of this model with the linear trend model, using the *MSE* and *MAD* criteria.

TABLE 18.15 Exponential Regression Results on Seasonally Adjusted Data

	Coefficients	Standard Error	*t* Stat	*p*-Value
Intercept	7.5571	0.0185	407.516	0.000
t	0.0218	0.0008	27.630	0.000
Standard error of the estimate s_e equals 0.0575.				

Note that the slope coefficient is positive and highly significant (p-value ≈ 0), implying that revenue has grown, on average, by about 2.18% per quarter. We forecast trend for the seasonally adjusted revenue as $\hat{T}_t = \exp(b_0 + b_1 t + s_e^2/2)$. Therefore, a trend forecast for the seasonally adjusted revenue in the first quarter of 2009, with unrounded estimates, is computed as

$$\hat{T}_{2009:01} = \hat{T}_{41} = \exp(7.5571 + 0.0218 \times 41 + 0.0575^2/2) = 4{,}683.1685.$$

Similarly, the seasonally adjusted trend for other quarters is computed as

$$\hat{T}_{2009:02} = \hat{T}_{42} = \exp(7.5571 + 0.0218 \times 42 + 0.0575^2/2) = 4{,}786.2806,$$
$$\hat{T}_{2009:03} = \hat{T}_{43} = \exp(7.5571 + 0.0218 \times 43 + 0.0575^2/2) = 4{,}891.6629, \text{ and}$$
$$\hat{T}_{2009:04} = \hat{T}_{44} = \exp(7.5571 + 0.0218 \times 44 + 0.0575^2/2) = 4{,}999.3655.$$

As mentioned earlier, whenever possible, it is preferable to use unrounded estimates in deriving forecasts with an exponential trend model.

Forecasting with Decomposition Analysis

Now that we have estimated the trend and the seasonal components, we recompose them to make forecasts for Nike's quarterly revenue in 2009. We basically multiply the trend forecast of the seasonally adjusted series with the appropriate seasonal index. This gives us the forecast as $\hat{y}_t = \hat{T}_t \times \hat{S}_t$. The trend forecast of Nike's seasonally adjusted revenue in the first quarter of 2009 is $\hat{T}_{41} = 4{,}683.1685$. We also have $\hat{S}_{41} = 1.0819$, since $t = 41$ represents the first quarter for which we expect the revenue to be 8.19% higher. Therefore, using unrounded estimates, we derive the forecast as

$$\hat{y}_{2009:01} = \hat{y}_{41} = \hat{T}_{41} \times \hat{S}_{41} = 4{,}683.1685 \times 1.0819 = \$5{,}066.90 \text{ million}.$$

Similarly, the forecasts of Nike's revenue for the remaining quarters of 2009 are computed as

$$\hat{y}_{2009:02} = \hat{y}_{42} = \hat{T}_{42} \times \hat{S}_{42} = 4{,}786.2806 \times 0.9417 = \$4{,}507.33 \text{ million},$$
$$\hat{y}_{2009:03} = \hat{y}_{43} = \hat{T}_{43} \times \hat{S}_{43} = 4{,}891.6629 \times 0.9383 = \$4{,}589.68 \text{ million, and}$$
$$\hat{y}_{2009:04} = \hat{y}_{44} = \hat{T}_{44} \times \hat{S}_{44} = 4{,}999.3655 \times 1.0381 = \$5{,}189.72 \text{ million}.$$

EXAMPLE 18.5

A tourism specialist uses decomposition analysis to examine hotel occupancy rates for Bar Harbor, Maine. She collects quarterly data for the past five years ($n = 20$) and finds that the linear trend model best captures the trend of the seasonally adjusted series: $\hat{T}_t = 0.60 + 0.0049t$. In addition, she calculates quarterly indices as $\hat{S}_1 = 0.53$, $\hat{S}_2 = 0.90$, $\hat{S}_3 = 1.40$, and $\hat{S}_4 = 1.17$.

a. Interpret the first and the third quarterly indices.

b. Forecast next year's occupancy rates.

SOLUTION:

a. The first quarter's index of 0.53 implies that the occupancy rate in the first quarter is 47% below the average quarterly occupancy rate, whereas the occupancy rate in the third quarter is 40% above the average quarterly occupancy rate.

b. We calculate the next year's quarterly occupancy rates as $\hat{y}_t = \hat{T}_t \times \hat{S}_t$ or

$$\text{Year 6, Quarter 1: } \hat{y}_{21} = (0.60 + 0.0049 \times 21) \times 0.53 = 0.3725.$$
$$\text{Year 6, Quarter 2: } \hat{y}_{22} = (0.60 + 0.0049 \times 22) \times 0.90 = 0.6370.$$
$$\text{Year 6, Quarter 3: } \hat{y}_{23} = (0.60 + 0.0049 \times 23) \times 1.40 = 0.9978.$$
$$\text{Year 6, Quarter 4: } \hat{y}_{24} = (0.60 + 0.0049 \times 24) \times 1.17 = 0.8396.$$

Seasonal Dummy Variables

LO 18.6

With the method of seasonal dummy variables, we estimate a trend forecasting model that includes dummy variables to capture seasonal variations. In Chapter 17, we used dummy variables to describe a qualitative variable with two or more categories. Recall that a dummy variable is a binary variable that equals 1 for one of the categories and 0 for the other. Here we use dummy variables to describe seasons. For quarterly data, we need to define only three dummy variables. Let d_1, d_2, and d_3 be the dummy variables for the first three quarters, using the fourth quarter as reference. Therefore, for an observation that falls in quarter 1, we use $d_1 = 1$, $d_2 = 0$, and $d_3 = 0$. Similarly, for an observation that falls in quarter 2, $d_1 = 0$, $d_2 = 1$, and $d_3 = 0$, for an observation that falls in quarter 3, $d_1 = 0$, $d_2 = 0$, and $d_3 = 1$, and for an observation that falls in quarter 4, $d_1 = 0$, $d_2 = 0$, and $d_3 = 0$. Seasonal dummy variables for other types of seasonal data, such as monthly data, are implemented in a similar manner.

With quarterly data, the linear and the exponential trend models with seasonal dummy variables are summarized in the following captions. In the captions, we have removed the t subscript to simplify the notation.

Use trend regression models with seasonal dummy variables to make forecasts.

With quarterly data, a linear trend model with seasonal dummy variables is specified as

$$y = \beta_0 + \beta_1 d_1 + \beta_2 d_2 + \beta_3 d_3 + \beta_4 t + \varepsilon.$$

Forecasts based on the estimated model are as follows:

Quarter 1 $(d_1 = 1, d_2 = 0, d_3 = 0)$: $\hat{y}_t = (b_0 + b_1) + b_4 t$

Quarter 2 $(d_1 = 0, d_2 = 1, d_3 = 0)$: $\hat{y}_t = (b_0 + b_2) + b_4 t$

Quarter 3 $(d_1 = 0, d_2 = 0, d_3 = 1)$: $\hat{y}_t = (b_0 + b_3) + b_4 t$

Quarter 4 $(d_1 = 0, d_2 = 0, d_3 = 0)$: $\hat{y}_t = b_0 + b_4 t$

With quarterly data, an exponential trend model with seasonal dummy variables is specified as

$$\ln(y) = \beta_0 + \beta_1 d_1 + \beta_2 d_2 + \beta_3 d_3 + \beta_4 t + \varepsilon.$$

Forecasts based on the estimated model are as follows:

Quarter 1 $(d_1 = 1, d_2 = 0, d_3 = 0)$: $\hat{y}_t = \exp((b_0 + b_1) + b_4 t + s_e^2/2)$

Quarter 2 $(d_1 = 0, d_2 = 1, d_3 = 0)$: $\hat{y}_t = \exp((b_0 + b_2) + b_4 t + s_e^2/2)$

Quarter 3 $(d_1 = 0, d_2 = 0, d_3 = 1)$: $\hat{y}_t = \exp((b_0 + b_3) + b_4 t + s_e^2/2)$

Quarter 4 $(d_1 = 0, d_2 = 0, d_3 = 0)$: $\hat{y}_t = \exp(b_0 + b_4 t + s_e^2/2)$

where s_e is the standard error of the estimate.

EXAMPLE 18.6

Nike_Revenues

Revisit the **Nike_Revenues** data considered in the introductory case. Use the seasonal dummy variable model to make a forecast for Nike's quarterly revenue in 2009.

SOLUTION: Given quarterly data, we first construct relevant variables for the regression. Table 18.16 specifies seasonal dummy variables, along with the time variable t.

TABLE 18.16 Constructing Seasonal Dummy Variables (Example 18.6)

Period	y	ln(y)	t	d_1	d_2	d_3
1999:01	2505	7.8260	1	1	0	0
1999:02	1913	7.5564	2	0	1	0
1999:03	2177	7.6857	3	0	0	1
1999:04	2182	7.6880	4	0	0	0
2000:01	2501	7.8245	5	1	0	0
2000:02	2060	7.6305	6	0	1	0
2000:03	2162	7.6788	7	0	0	1
2000:04	2273	7.7289	8	0	0	0
⋮	⋮	⋮	⋮	⋮	⋮	⋮
2008:03	4544	8.4216	39	0	0	1
2008:04	5088	8.5346	40	0	0	0

As in the case of decomposition analysis, we use the exponential model to capture trend: $\ln(y) = \beta_0 + \beta_1 d_1 + \beta_2 d_2 + \beta_3 d_3 + \beta_4 t + \varepsilon$. Relevant estimates of the regression model are presented in Table 18.17.

TABLE 18.17 Regression Results for Example 18.6

	Coefficients	Standard Error	t Stat	p-Value
Intercept	7.5929	0.0261	290.568	0.000
d_1	0.0501	0.0268	1.870	0.070
d_2	−0.1036	0.0267	−3.874	0.000
d_3	−0.0985	0.0267	−3.687	0.000
t	0.0218	0.0008	26.533	0.000

The standard error of the estimate s_e equals 0.0597.

The coefficients for the seasonal dummy variables indicate that the revenue is about 5% higher in the first quarter and about 10% lower in the second and third quarters as compared to the fourth quarter. The estimated coefficient of 0.0218 for the trend variable t suggests that the predicted quarterly increase in revenue is about 2.18%.

The estimated equation for the exponential trend model with seasonal dummy variables is $\hat{y}_t = \exp(7.5929 + 0.0501 d_1 - 0.1036 d_2 - 0.0985 d_3 + 0.0218t + 0.0597^2/2)$. Using unrounded values for the estimated coefficients, we derive the forecast for the first quarter $(d_1 = 1, d_2 = 0, d_3 = 0)$ of Nike's revenue in 2009 $(t = 41)$ as

$$\hat{y}_{2009:01} = \hat{y}_{41} = \exp(7.5929 + 0.0501 + 0.0218 \times 41 + 0.0597^2/2)$$
$$= \$5,107.16 \text{ million.}$$

Similarly, the forecasts of Nike's revenue for the remaining quarters of 2009 are computed as

$$\hat{y}_{2009:02} = \hat{y}_{42} = \exp(7.5929 - 0.1036 + 0.0218 \times 42 + 0.0597^2/2)$$
$$= \$4,475.87 \text{ million,}$$
$$\hat{y}_{2009:03} = \hat{y}_{43} = \exp(7.5929 - 0.0985 + 0.0218 \times 43 + 0.0597^2/2)$$
$$= \$4,598.06 \text{ million, and}$$
$$\hat{y}_{2009:04} = \hat{y}_{44} = \exp(7.5929 + 0.0218 \times 44 + 0.0597^2/2) = \$5,185.62 \text{ million.}$$

As emphasized earlier, we always use model selection criteria to choose the appropriate forecasting model. In Table 18.18 we present the MSE and MAD based on the residuals, $e_t = y_t - \hat{y}_t$, with decomposition analysis and seasonal dummy variables; again these calculations are based on unrounded values for the estimates. We encourage you to replicate these results.

TABLE 18.18 In-Sample Model Selection Criteria

Model	MSE	MAD
Decomposition Analysis	24,353.95	118.10
Seasonal Dummy Variables	24,843.48	121.32

We select the decomposition analysis method to make forecasts because it has the lower MSE and MAD of in-sample forecast errors. Therefore, the quarterly forecasts for 2009, as derived earlier, are \$5,066.90, \$4,507.33, \$4,589.68, and \$5,189.72 million, respectively. This results in a sum of \$19,353.64 million or \$19.35 billion for fiscal year 2009.

SYNOPSIS OF INTRODUCTORY CASE

©David Paul Morris/Bloomberg via Getty Images

Nike, Inc., is the world's leading supplier and manufacturer of athletic shoes, apparel, and sports equipment. Its revenue in the fiscal year ending May 31, 2008, was $18.627 billion. While some analysts argue that a slowdown of Nike's revenue may occur due to the global economic crisis and increased competition from emerging brands, others believe that with its strong cash flow, Nike will emerge even stronger than before as its competitors get squeezed. This report analyzes the quarterly revenue of Nike from 1999–2008 to make a forecast for fiscal year 2009.

The detailed analysis of the data suggests significant trend and seasonal components in Nike's revenue. For each fiscal year, the revenue is generally higher in the first quarter (June 1–August 31) and the fourth quarter (March 1–May 31). This result is not surprising given that these quarters cover summer and spring seasons, when people most often participate in outdoor activities. Based on various model selection criteria, the decomposition method is chosen as the preferred forecasting technique. It provides forecasts by multiplying the exponential trend estimate with the corresponding seasonal index. The quarterly revenue forecasts for 2009 are $5,066.90, $4,507.33, $4,589.68, and $5,189.72 million, respectively, resulting in $19.35 billion for fiscal year 2009. Interestingly, this forecast, based on a time series analysis of revenue, is extremely close to the actual revenue of $19.20 billion reported by Nike.

EXERCISES 18.3

Mechanics

21. Six years of quarterly data of a seasonally adjusted series are used to estimate a linear trend model as $\hat{T}_t = 128.20 + 1.06t$. In addition, quarterly seasonal indices are calculated as $\hat{S}_1 = 0.93$, $\hat{S}_2 = 0.88$, $\hat{S}_3 = 1.14$, and $\hat{S}_4 = 1.05$.

    a. Interpret the first and the fourth quarterly indices.

    b. Make a forecast for all four quarters of next year.

22. Eight years of quarterly data of a seasonally adjusted series are used to estimate an exponential trend model as $\widehat{\ln(T_t)} = 2.80 + 0.03t$ with a standard error of the estimate, $s_e = 0.08$. In addition, quarterly seasonal indices are calculated as $\hat{S}_1 = 0.94$, $\hat{S}_2 = 1.08$, $\hat{S}_3 = 0.86$, and $\hat{S}_4 = 1.12$.

    a. Interpret the third and the fourth quarterly indices.

    b. Make a forecast for all four quarters of next year.

23. Ten years of monthly data of a seasonally adjusted series are used to estimate a linear trend model as $\hat{T}_t = 24.50 + 0.48t$. In addition, seasonal indices for January and February are calculated as 1.04 and 0.92, respectively. Make a forecast for the first two months of next year.

24. **FILE** *Exercise_18.24.* The accompanying data file contains quarterly observations for 5 years. Calculate and interpret the seasonal indices for quarters 1 and 4.

25. **FILE** *Exercise_18.25.* The accompanying data file contains monthly observations for 5 years. Calculate and interpret the seasonal indices for April and November.

26. **FILE** *Exercise_18.26.* The accompanying data file contains quarterly observations for 5 years.

    a. Plot the series and discuss its trend and seasonal components.

    b. Use decomposition analysis to make in-sample forecasts with the exponential trend and seasonal indices. Compute the *MSE*.

    c. Estimate an exponential trend with seasonal dummies model. Compute the *MSE*.

    d. Use the appropriate model to make forecasts for all four quarters of the next year.

27. **FILE** *Exercise_18.27.* The accompanying data file contains monthly observations for 5 years.
    a. Construct the seasonal indices for the data.
    b. Plot the seasonally adjusted series to recommend the appropriate trend model.
    c. Use the trend and seasonal estimates to make forecasts for the next two months.

28. **FILE** *Exercise_18.28.* The accompanying data file contains monthly observations for 5 years. Use it to estimate (a) a linear trend model with seasonal dummies, and (b) an exponential trend model with seasonal dummies. Which of the two models has a lower *MSE* and *MAD*? Use the appropriate model to make forecasts for the next two months.

Applications

29. **FILE** *Sales_Data.* Hybrid cars have gained popularity because of their fuel economy and the uncertainty regarding the price of gasoline. All automakers, including the Ford Motor Co., have planned to significantly expand their hybrid vehicle lineup (CNN.com, November 9, 2005). The following table contains a portion of quarterly sales of Ford and Mercury hybrid cars.

Year	Quarter	Sales
2006	1	6192
2006	2	5663
⋮	⋮	⋮
2009	1	5337

Source: Internal Revenue Service, United States Department of Treasury.

    a. Plot the series. Comment on the trend and seasonal variation in the sales of hybrid cars.
    b. Calculate and interpret the seasonal indices.

30. **FILE** *Treasury_Bonds.* Consider a portion of monthly return data (in %) on 20-year Treasury Bonds from 2006–2010.

Date	Return
Jan-06	4.65
Feb-06	4.73
⋮	⋮
Dec-10	4.16

Source: Federal Reserve Bank of Dallas.

    a. Plot the series and discuss its seasonal variations.
    b. Calculate the seasonal indices for the data.
    c. Estimate a linear trend model to the seasonally adjusted series.
    d. Use the trend and seasonal estimates to make forecasts for the first three months of 2011.

31. **FILE** *Treasury_Bonds.* Refer to the previous exercise for a description of the data set. Estimate a linear trend model with seasonal dummy variables to make forecasts for the first three months of 2011.

32. **FILE** *Expenses.* The controller of a small construction company is attempting to forecast expenses for the next year. He collects quarterly data on expenses (in $1,000s) over the past five years, a portion of which is shown in the accompanying table.

Year	Quarter	Expenses
2006	1	2136
2006	2	2253
⋮	⋮	⋮
2010	4	3109

    a. Estimate a linear trend model with seasonal dummy variables and compute the *MSE* and *MAD*.
    b. Estimate an exponential trend model with seasonal dummy variables and compute the resulting *MSE* and *MAD*.
    c. Which model is more appropriate? With this model, forecast expenses for year 2011.

33. **FILE** *Blockbuster.* Blockbuster Inc. faced challenges by the growing online market (CNNMoney.com, March 3, 2009). Its revenue from rental stores sagged as customers increasingly got their movies through the mail or high-speed Internet connections. The following table contains a portion of the quarterly revenue from rentals of all formats of movies at Blockbuster Inc. (in $ millions) from 2001 through 2008.

Year	Quarter	Revenue
2001	1	1.403683
2001	2	1.287625
⋮	⋮	⋮
2008	4	1.097712

    a. Compute the seasonal indices.
    b. Estimate linear and quadratic trend models to the seasonally adjusted data. Which model do you prefer?
    c. Use decomposition analysis to make quarterly forecasts for 2009.

34. **FILE** *Blockbuster.* Refer to the previous exercise for a description of the data set.
    a. Estimate a linear trend model with seasonal dummy variables.
    b. Estimate a quadratic trend model with seasonal dummy variables.
    c. Use the appropriate model to make quarterly forecasts for 2009.

35. **FILE** *Consumer_Sentiment.* The following table lists a portion of the University of Michigan's Consumer Sentiment Index. This index is normalized to have a value of 100 in 1965 and is used to record changes in consumer morale.

Date	Consumer Sentiment
Jan-05	95.5
Feb-05	94.1
⋮	⋮
Oct-10	67.7

Source: Federal Reserve Bank of St. Louis.

a. Plot and interpret the series.
b. Calculate and interpret seasonal indices for the series.
c. Estimate linear, quadratic, and cubic trend models to the seasonally adjusted data. Select the best fitting model.
d. Use decomposition analysis to make a forecast for November and December of 2010.

36. **FILE** *Consumer Sentiment.* Refer to the previous exercise for a description of the data set. Fit an appropriate polynomial trend model along with seasonal dummies to make a forecast for November and December of 2010.

18.5 CAUSAL FORECASTING METHODS

Use causal forecasting models to make forecasts.

So far, we have discussed noncausal, or purely time series, models. These models do not offer any explanation of the mechanism generating the variable of interest and simply provide a method for projecting historical data. Although this method can be effective, it provides no guidance on the likely effects of changes in policy (explanatory) variables. Causal forecasting models are based on a regression framework, where the explanatory variables influence the outcome of the response variable. For instance, consider the following simple linear regression model:

$$y_t = \beta_0 + \beta_1 x_t + \varepsilon_t.$$

Here y is the response variable caused by the explanatory variable x. Let the sample observations be denoted by $y_1, y_2, \ldots, y_T$ and $x_1, x_2, \ldots, x_T$, respectively. Once we have estimated this model, we can make a one-step-ahead forecast as

$$\hat{y}_{T+1} = b_0 + b_1 x_{T+1}.$$

Multi-step-ahead forecasts can be made similarly. This causal approach works only if we know, or can predict, the future value of the explanatory variable x_{T+1}. For instance, let sales y be related to expenditure on advertisement x. We can forecast sales $\hat{y}_{T+1}$ only if we know the advertisement budget, x_{T+1}, for the next period.

Lagged Regression Models

For forecasting, sometimes we use a causal approach with lagged values of x and y as explanatory variables. For instance, consider the model

$$y_t = \beta_0 + \beta_1 x_{t-1} + \varepsilon_t,$$

where β_1 represents the slope of the lagged explanatory variable x. Note that if we have T sample observations, the estimable sample will consist of $T - 1$ observations, where $y_2, y_3, \ldots, y_T$ are matched with $x_1, x_2, \ldots, x_{T-1}$. Here a one-step-ahead forecast is easily made as

$$\hat{y}_{T+1} = b_0 + b_1 x_T.$$

This forecast is not conditional on any predicted value of the explanatory variables, since x_T is its last known sample value. We can generalize this model to include more lags of x. For example, we can specify a two-period lagged regression model as $y_t = \beta_0 + \beta_1 x_{t-1} + \beta_2 x_{t-2} + \varepsilon_t$. A one-step-ahead forecast is now made as $\hat{y}_{T+1} = b_0 + b_1 x_T + b_2 x_{T-1}$.

Another popular specification for causal forecasting uses lagged values of the response variable as an explanatory variable. For instance, consider the model

$$y_t = \beta_0 + \beta_1 y_{t-1} + \varepsilon_t,$$

where the parameter β_1 represents the slope of the lagged response variable y. This regression is also referred to as an **autoregressive model** of order one, or simply an AR(1). Higher-order autoregressive models can be constructed similarly. A one-period-ahead forecast is made as

$$\hat{y}_{T+1} = b_0 + b_1 y_T.$$

Finally, we can also use lagged values of both x and y as the explanatory variables. For instance, consider

$$y_t = \beta_0 + \beta_1 x_{t-1} + \beta_2 y_{t-1} + \varepsilon_t.$$

Here, a one-period-ahead forecast is made as

$$\hat{y}_{T+1} = b_0 + b_1 x_T + b_2 y_T.$$

EXAMPLE 18.7

Table 18.19 shows a portion of data on net private housing units sold (Housing in 1,000s), and real per-capita gross domestic product (GDP in $1,000s). Estimate the following three models and use the most suitable model to make a forecast for housing units sold in 2009.

Model 1: $\text{Housing}_t = \beta_0 + \beta_1 \text{GDP}_{t-1} + \varepsilon_t.$

Model 2: $\text{Housing}_t = \beta_0 + \beta_1 \text{Housing}_{t-1} + \varepsilon_t.$

Model 3: $\text{Housing}_t = \beta_0 + \beta_1 \text{GDP}_{t-1} + \beta_2 \text{Housing}_{t-1} + \varepsilon_t.$

TABLE 18.19 Housing and GDP Data

Year	Housing	GDP
1981	436	23.007
1982	412	22.346
1983	623	23.146
⋮	⋮	⋮
2008	509	38.399

Source: The Department of Commerce.

FILE
Housing_Units

SOLUTION: In order to estimate these models, we first have to lag Housing and GDP. Table 18.20 uses a portion of the data to show lagged values. Note that we lose one observation for the regression, since we do not have information on the lagged values for 1981. In order to estimate each model in Excel, we first copy and paste the data as shown in Table 18.20. Then, after choosing **Data > Data Analysis > Regression**, we select the response and explanatory variable(s) corresponding to the years 1982–2008. We provide instructions for R at the end of this section.

TABLE 18.20 Generating Lagged Values

Year	Housing_t	GDP_t	GDP_{t-1}	Housing_{t-1}
1981	436	23.007	—	—
1982	412	22.346	23.007	436
1983	623	23.146	22.346	412
⋮	⋮	⋮	⋮	⋮
2008	509	38.399	38.148	776

Table 18.21 summarizes the regression results of the three models.

TABLE 18.21 Model Evaluation with Causal Forecasting

Parameters	Model 1	Model 2	Model 3
Constant	−112.9093 (0.595)	122.7884 (0.138)	300.0187 (0.068)
GDP_{t-1}	29.0599* (0.000)	NA	−10.9084 (0.203)
$Housing_{t-1}$	NA	0.8433* (0.000)	1.0439* (0.000)
Adjusted R^2	0.3974	0.7264	0.7340

Notes: The top portion of the table contains parameter estimates with p-values in parentheses; NA denotes not applicable; the symbol * denotes significance at the 5% level.

As discussed earlier, it is preferable to compare competing multiple regression models in terms of adjusted R^2 since it appropriately penalizes for the excessive use of explanatory variables. We choose Model 3 because it has the highest adjusted R^2 of 0.7340. The forecast for 2009 is made as

$$\widehat{Housing}_{2009} = b_0 + b_1 GDP_{2008} + b_2 Housing_{2008}$$
$$= 300.0187 − 10.9084 \times 38.399 + 1.0439 \times 509 = 412.51.$$

Therefore, we forecast that about 412,510 net private housing units will be sold in 2009.

Using R to Estimate Lagged Regression Models

Housing_Units

We will use R to estimate Model 3 from Example 18.7.

A. Import the **Housing_Units** data into a data frame (table) in R.

B. Install and load the *dynlm* package (where *dynlm* stands for Dynamic Linear Regression). Enter

```
> install.packages("dynlm")
> library(dynlm)
```

C. We use the **as.ts** function in order to save the Housing and GDP variables as time series objects. Enter

```
> Housing <- as.ts(Housing_Units$'Housing')
> GDP <- as.ts(Housing_Units$'GDP')
```

D. We use the **dynlm** and the **L** functions from the *dynlm* package. The **dynlm** function constructs more versatile types of linear models, and it behaves the same way as the **lm** function that we have used in earlier chapters. The **L** function creates lagged variables. We label the model (or the object in R terminology) as Model3. Enter

```
> Model3 <- dynlm(Housing ~ L(GDP,1) + L(Housing,1))
> summary(Model3)
```

EXERCISES 18.4

Mechanics

37. **FILE** *Exercise_18.37.* Consider the following portion of data on the response variable y and the explanatory variable x.

t	y	x
1	27.96	29.88
2	30.15	21.07
⋮	⋮	⋮
12	24.47	26.41

a. Estimate $y_t = \beta_0 + \beta_1 x_{t-1} + \varepsilon_t$ and $y_t = \beta_0 + \beta_1 x_{t-1} + \beta_2 x_{t-2} + \varepsilon_t$.

b. Use the appropriate model to make a one-step-ahead forecast ($t = 13$) for y.

38. **FILE** *Exercise_18.38.* Consider the following portion of data on the variable y.

t	y
1	29.32
2	30.96
⋮	⋮
24	48.58

a. Estimate an autoregressive model of order 1, $y_t = \beta_0 + \beta_1 y_{t-1} + \varepsilon_t$, to make a one-step-ahead forecast ($t = 25$) for y.

b. Estimate an autoregressive model of order 2, $y_t = \beta_0 + \beta_1 y_{t-1} + \beta_2 y_{t-2} + \varepsilon_t$, to make a one-step-ahead forecast ($t = 25$) for y.

c. Which of the above models is more appropriate for forecasts? Explain.

39. **FILE** *Exercise_18.39.* Consider the following portion of data on y and x.

t	y	x
1	18.23	17.30
2	19.82	16.05
⋮	⋮	⋮
12	22.75	13.66

a. Estimate $y_t = \beta_0 + \beta_1 x_{t-1} + \varepsilon_t$ to make a one-step-ahead forecast for period 13.

b. Estimate $y_t = \beta_0 + \beta_1 y_{t-1} + \varepsilon_t$ to make a one-step-ahead forecast for period 13.

c. Which of the above models is more appropriate for forecasts? Explain.

40. **FILE** *Exercise_18.40.* Consider the following portion of data on y and x.

t	y	x
1	56.96	9171.61
2	57.28	9286.56
⋮	⋮	⋮
12	51.99	9217.94

a. Estimate $y_t = \beta_0 + \beta_1 x_{t-1} + \varepsilon_t$.

b. Estimate $y_t = \beta_0 + \beta_1 y_{t-1} + \varepsilon_t$.

c. Estimate $y_t = \beta_0 + \beta_1 x_{t-1} + \beta_2 y_{t-1} + \varepsilon_t$.

d. Use the most suitable model to make a one-step-ahead forecast ($t = 13$) for y.

Applications

41. Hiroshi Sato, an owner of a sushi restaurant in San Francisco, has been following an aggressive marketing campaign to thwart the effect of rising unemployment rates on business. He used monthly data on sales ($1,000s), advertising costs ($), and the unemployment rate (%) from January 2008 to May 2009 to estimate the following sample regression equation:

$$\widehat{Sales}_t = 17.51 + 0.03\text{Advertising Costs}_{t-1} - 0.69\text{Unemployment Rate}_{t-1}.$$

a. Hiroshi had budgeted $620 toward advertising costs in May 2009. Make a forecast for Sales for June 2009 if the unemployment rate in May 2009 was 9.1%.

b. What will be the forecast if he raises his advertisement budget to $700?

c. Reevaluate the above forecasts if the unemployment rate was 9.5% in May 2009.

42. **FILE** *Phillips_Curve.* The Phillips curve is regarded as a reliable tool for forecasting inflation. It captures the inverse relation between the rate of unemployment and the rate of inflation; the lower the unemployment in an economy, the higher is the inflation rate. Consider the following portion of monthly data on seasonally adjusted inflation and unemployment rates in the United States from January 2009 to November 2010.

Date	Unemployment	Inflation
Jan-09	7.7	0.3
Feb-09	8.2	0.4
⋮	⋮	⋮
Nov-10	9.8	0.1

Source: Bureau of Labor Statistics.

a. Estimate two models, of order 1 and 2, using unemployment as the response variable and lagged inflation as the explanatory variable(s). Should you use either model for forecasting unemployment? Explain.

b. Estimate autoregressive models of order 1 and 2 on unemployment. Choose the appropriate model to make a forecast of unemployment for December 2010.

43. **FILE** *HD_DOW.* A research analyst at an investment firm is attempting to forecast the daily stock price of Home Depot, using causal models. The following table shows a portion of the daily adjusted closing prices of Home Depot y and the

Dow Jones Industrial Average *x* from August 14, 2009, to August 31, 2009.

t	y	x
August 14	26.92	9321.40
August 17	25.89	9135.34
⋮	⋮	⋮
August 31	27.07	9496.28

Source: www.finance.yahoo.

Estimate three models: (a) $y_t = \beta_0 + \beta_1 x_{t-1} + \varepsilon_t$, (b) $y_t = \beta_0 + \beta_1 y_{t-1} + \varepsilon_t$, and (c) $y_t = \beta_0 + \beta_1 x_{t-1} + \beta_2 y_{t-1} + \varepsilon_t$. Use the most suitable model to forecast Home Depot's daily stock price for September 1, 2009.

WRITING WITH STATISTICS

©Skyhobo/E+/Getty Images RF

An important indicator of an economy is its inflation rate, which is generally defined as the percentage change in the consumer price index over a specific period of time. It is well documented that high inflation rates lead to a decline in the real value of money, which in turn can discourage investment and savings. The task of keeping the inflation rate within desired limits is entrusted to monetary authorities, who use various policy instruments to control it. However, their actions depend primarily on their ability to gauge inflationary pressures accurately or, in other words, to correctly forecast the inflation rate.

Pooja Nanda is an economist working for *Creative Thinking*, a well-regarded policy institute based in Washington, DC. She has been given the challenging task of forecasting inflation for January 2017. She has access to monthly inflation rates in the United States from January 2012 to December 2016. A portion of the data is shown in the accompanying table.

TABLE 18.22 Monthly Inflation Rates

Date	Inflation
Jan-12	2.3
Feb-12	2.2
⋮	⋮
Dec-16	2.2

FILE
Inflation_Rates

Source: Bureau of Labor Statistics.

Pooja would like to use the sample information to

1. Evaluate various polynomial trend models for the inflation rate.
2. Use the best-fitting trend model to forecast the inflation rate for January 2017.

Sample Report— Forecasting the Monthly Inflation Rate

Economists generally agree that high levels of inflation are caused by the money supply growing faster than the rate of economic growth. During high inflationary pressures, monetary authorities decrease the money supply, thereby raising short-term interest rates. Sometimes they also have to contend with deflation, or a prolonged reduction in the level of prices. As prices fall, consumers tend to delay purchases until prices fall further, which in turn can depress overall economic activity. This report does not focus on the effectiveness of monetary policy. Instead, a forecast of the inflation rate is made by simply projecting historical data.

A simple plot of the inflation rate from January 2012 to December 2016 is shown in Figure 18.A, where t represents the relabeled monthly observations from 1 (January 2012) through 60 (December 2016). In order to gauge whether a linear or nonlinear trend is appropriate, the linear, the quadratic, and the cubic trend models are superimposed on the inflation rate scatterplot.

FIGURE 18.A Scatterplot of inflation (in percent) and superimposed trends

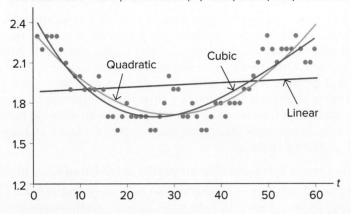

From Figure 18.A, the linear model is clearly inappropriate. Although the cubic model seems to accurately capture the changing trend of the inflation rate over the last 60 months, this finding must be supplemented with a formal model selection criterion.

Two trend models are estimated, where y_t represents the inflation rate.

$$\text{Quadratic Model: } y_t = \beta_0 + \beta_1 t + \beta_2 t^2 + \varepsilon_t$$

$$\text{Cubic Model: } y_t = \beta_0 + \beta_1 t + \beta_2 t^2 + \beta_3 t^3 + \varepsilon_t$$

Table 18.A presents parameter estimates of the two models. Also included in the table is the adjusted R^2 for model comparison.

TABLE 18.A Analysis of the Linear, Quadratic, and Cubic Trend Models

Variable	Quadratic	Cubic
Constant	2.3334* (0.000)	2.4571* (0.000)
t	−0.0421* (0.000)	−0.0654* (0.000)
t^2	0.0007* (0.000)	0.0017* (0.000)
t^3	NA	−0.00001* (0.004)
Adjusted R^2	0.7304	0.7630

Notes: The top portion of the table contains parameter estimates with p-values in parentheses. NA denotes not applicable. The asterisk designates significance at the 5% level. The last row of the table contains adjusted R^2 for model comparison.

Consistent with the informal graphical analysis, the cubic trend provides the best sample fit, as it has a higher adjusted R^2 (0.7630 > 0.7304). Therefore, the estimated cubic trend model is used with unrounded estimates to derive the forecast for January 2017 as

$$\hat{y}_{61} = 2.4571 - 0.0654 \times 61 + 0.0017 \times 61^2 - 0.00001 \times 61^3 = 2.30.$$

Inflation forecasts are widely regarded as key inputs for implementing monetary policy. In this report, we employ basic trend models to project historical data on inflation. We note that the resulting forecast ignores the likely effects of policy changes.

CONCEPTUAL REVIEW

LO 18.1 Distinguish among the various models used in forecasting.

Observations of any variable recorded over time in sequential order are considered a **time series**. The purpose of any forecasting model is to forecast the time series at time t, or $\hat{y}_t$. Forecasting methods are broadly classified as **quantitative** or **qualitative**. While qualitative forecasts are based on prior experience and the expertise of the forecaster, quantitative forecasts use a formal model, along with historical data, for making forecasts. Quantitative forecasting models are further divided into **causal** and **noncausal models**. Causal methods are based on a regression framework, where the variable of interest is related to a single or multiple explanatory variables. Noncausal models, also referred to as purely time series models, do not present any explanation of the mechanism generating the variable of interest and simply provide a method for projecting historical data.

The in-sample forecast $\hat{y}_t$ is also called the **predicted** or **fitted** value of y_t. We use the residuals, computed as $e_t = y_t - \hat{y}_t$, to compute $MSE = \frac{\Sigma e_t^2}{n}$ and $MAD = \frac{\Sigma |e_t|}{n}$, where n is the number of residuals. We select the forecasting model that has the smallest MSE and MAD.

LO 18.2 Use smoothing techniques to make forecasts.

Time series consist of **systematic** and **unsystematic** patterns. Systematic patterns are caused by the **trend**, the **seasonal**, and the **cyclical** components. Unsystematic patterns are difficult to identify and are caused by the presence of a random error term. **Smoothing techniques** are employed to provide forecasts if short-term fluctuations represent random departures from the structure with no discernible systematic patterns.

A **moving average** is the average from a fixed number of the m most recent observations. We use moving averages to make forecasts as $\hat{y}_t = \frac{y_{t-m} + y_{t-m+1} + \cdots + y_{t-1}}{m}$.

Exponential smoothing is a weighted average approach where the weights decline exponentially as they become more distant. The exponential smoothing method continually updates the level of the series as $A_t = \alpha y_t + (1 - \alpha)A_{t-1}$, where α represents the speed of decline. Forecasts are made as $\hat{y}_{t+1} = A_t$.

LO 18.3 Use trend regression models to make forecasts.

For a time series that is expected to grow by a fixed amount each time period, we use the **linear trend model**, $y_t = \beta_0 + \beta_1 t + \varepsilon_t$. We estimate this model to make forecasts as $\hat{y}_t = b_0 + b_1 t$, where b_0 and b_1 are the coefficient estimates.

For a time series that is expected to grow by an increasing amount each time period, we use the **exponential trend model**, $\ln(y_t) = \beta_0 + \beta_1 t + \varepsilon_t$, where $\ln(y_t)$ is the natural log of the series. We estimate this model to make forecasts as $\hat{y}_t = \exp(b_0 + b_1 t + s_e^2/2)$, where b_0 and b_1 are the coefficient estimates and s_e is the standard error of the estimate.

A **polynomial trend model** of order q is estimated as $y_t = \beta_0 + \beta_1 t + \beta_2 t^2 + \beta_3 t^3 + \cdots + \beta_q t^q + \varepsilon_t$. This model specializes to a linear trend model for $q = 1$, to a quadratic trend model for $q = 2$, and to a cubic trend model for $q = 3$. We estimate this model to make forecasts as $\hat{y}_t = b_0 + b_1 t + b_2 t^2 + b_3 t^3 + \cdots + b_q t^q$, where $b_0, b_1, \ldots, b_q$ are the coefficient estimates.

We compare the linear and the exponential trend models on the basis of their MSE and MAD. We use adjusted R^2 to compare various orders of the polynomial trend model.

Calculate and interpret seasonal indices and use them to seasonally adjust a time series.

Centered moving averages, *CMAs*, are often employed to separate the effect of trend from seasonality. We use a centered 4-period moving average for quarterly data and a centered 12-period moving average for monthly data. The **ratio-to-moving average** is calculated as $y_t/\bar{y}_t$, where $\bar{y}_t = CMA_t$. For each season, there are many estimates of the ratio-to-moving average. The unadjusted seasonal index is computed by averaging these ratios over the years. A minor adjustment ensures that the average of adjusted seasonal indices $\hat{S}$ equals one. A **seasonally adjusted series** is computed as $y_t/\hat{S}_t$. We use the appropriate trend model on the seasonally adjusted series to extract $\hat{T}_t$.

LO 18.5 Use decomposition analysis to make forecasts.

We let T, S, and I represent the trend, the seasonal, and the random components, respectively, of the series y_t. Using **decomposition analysis**, we decompose, or isolate, the individual components of the time series to make forecasts. Forecasts are made as $\hat{y}_t = \hat{T}_t \times \hat{S}_t$, where $\hat{T}_t$ and $\hat{S}_t$ represent the estimated trend and the adjusted seasonal index, respectively.

Use trend regression models with seasonal dummy variables to make forecasts.

As an alternative to decomposition analysis, we use a multiple regression model to simultaneously estimate trend along with **seasonal dummy variables**. With quarterly data, a linear trend model with seasonal dummy variables is specified as $y = \beta_0 + \beta_1 d_1 + \beta_2 d_2 + \beta_3 d_3 + \beta_4 t + \varepsilon$. Forecasts based on the estimated model are $\hat{y}_t = (b_0 + b_1) + b_4 t$ (Quarter 1), $\hat{y}_t = (b_0 + b_2) + b_4 t$ (Quarter 2), $\hat{y}_t = (b_0 + b_3) + b_4 t$ (Quarter 3), and $\hat{y}_t = b_0 + b_4 t$ (Quarter 4). With quarterly data, an exponential trend model with seasonal dummy variables is specified as $\ln(y) = \beta_0 + \beta_1 d_1 + \beta_2 d_2 + \beta_3 d_3 + \beta_4 t + \varepsilon$. Forecasts based on the estimated model are $\hat{y}_t = \exp((b_0 + b_1) + b_4 t + s_e^2/2)$ (Quarter 1), $\hat{y}_t = \exp((b_0 + b_2) + b_4 t + s_e^2/2)$ (Quarter 2), $\hat{y}_t = \exp((b_0 + b_3) + b_4 t + s_e^2/2)$ (Quarter 3), and $\hat{y}_t = \exp(b_0 + b_4 t + s_e^2/2)$ (Quarter 4). Forecasts with monthly data can be made similarly.

LO 18.7 Use causal forecasting models to make forecasts.

Causal forecasting models are based on a regression framework. A forecast with a simple regression model, $y_t = \beta_0 + \beta_1 x_t + \varepsilon_t$, can be made as $\hat{y}_{T+1} = b_0 + b_1 x_{T+1}$ only if the future value of the explanatory variable x_{T+1} is known. Sometimes researchers use a causal approach with lagged values of x and y for making forecasts. For instance, we can estimate $y_t = \beta_0 + \beta_1 x_{t-1} + \varepsilon_t$ to make a forecast as $\hat{y}_{T+1} = b_0 + b_1 x_T$. Similarly, we can estimate $y_t = \beta_0 + \beta_1 y_{t-1} + \varepsilon_t$ to make a forecast as $\hat{y}_{T+1} = b_0 + b_1 y_T$. We can also estimate a combined model $y_t = \beta_0 + \beta_1 x_{t-1} + \beta_2 y_{t-1} + \varepsilon_t$ to make a forecast as $\hat{y}_{T+1} = b_0 + b_1 x_T + b_2 y_T$.

ADDITIONAL EXERCISES AND CASE STUDIES

Exercises

44. **FILE** *Yields.* The U.S. housing market remains fragile despite historically low mortgage rates (AARP, July 2, 2010). Since the rate on 30-year mortgages is tied to the 10-year yield on Treasury bonds, it is important to be able to predict this yield accurately. The accompanying table shows a portion of the 10-year yield on Treasury bonds (in %) for 21 trading days in November 2010.

Date	Yield
1-Nov	2.63
2-Nov	2.59
⋮	⋮
30-Nov	2.80

Source: finance.yahoo.com.

Year	Quarter	Spending
2004	1	665924
2004	2	672678
⋮	⋮	⋮
2010	3	695917

Source: U.S. Bureau of Economic Analysis.

a. Use a 3-period moving average to make a forecast for December 1, 2010.

b. Use the exponential smoothing method to make a forecast for December 1, 2010. Use $\alpha = 0.5$.

c. Which of these smoothing methods has a better in-sample performance?

d. The actual 10-year yield on December 1, 2010, was 2.96. Was the forecast performance of the two methods consistent with their in-sample performance in part c?

45. **FILE** *Country_Rap.* The following table lists a portion of the percentage (share) of total shipment of music that falls in the category of country and rap/hip-hop rock music from 1990–2008.

Year	Country	Rap/Hip-hop
1990	9.6	8.5
1991	12.8	10.0
⋮	⋮	⋮
2008	11.9	10.7

Source: www.riaa.com.

a. Plot each of the series and comment on the respective trend.

b. Estimate a linear, a quadratic, and a cubic trend model for the share of country music in the United States. Use adjusted R^2 to choose the preferred model, and, with this model, make a forecast for 2009.

c. Estimate a linear, a quadratic, and a cubic trend model for the share of rap/hip-hop music in the United States. Use adjusted R^2 to choose the preferred model, and, with this model, make a forecast for 2009.

46. **FILE** *Tourism_Spending.* Tourism was hit hard by the international financial crisis that began in the fall of 2008. According to the Bureau of Economic Analysis (December 20, 2010), tourism spending has picked up, but it still remains below its peak, which occurred in 2007. The accompanying table shows a portion of seasonally adjusted data on real tourism spending (in millions of $).

a. Construct seasonal indices for the data.

b. Plot the seasonally adjusted series. Estimate the cubic trend model on the seasonally adjusted series.

c. Use the seasonal and the trend components to forecast tourism spending for the fourth quarter of 2010 and the first three quarters of 2011.

47. **FILE** *GasPrice_Forecast.* Consider the following portion of monthly data on price per gallon of regular unleaded gasoline in the United States from January 2009 to December 2010.

Date	Price Per Gallon
Jan-09	1.79
Feb-09	1.92
⋮	⋮
Dec-10	2.99

Source: U.S. Energy Information Administration.

a. Plot the series to identify an appropriate polynomial trend model. You may ignore seasonality.

b. Compare the adjusted R^2 of the linear, the quadratic, and the cubic trend models.

c. Use the appropriate model to make a forecast for the price of regular unleaded gasoline for January and February of 2011.

48. **FILE** *Loans.* Consider the following portion of data on real estate loans granted by FDIC-insured Commercial Banks in the United States (in $ billions, base = 2007) from 1972 to 2007.

Year	Loans
1972	489.27
1973	567.26
⋮	⋮
2007	3604.03

Source: www2.fdic.gov.

a. Plot the series and comment on the growth of real estate loans.

b. Estimate the linear and the exponential trend models for real estate loans. Use *MSE* to compare these models. Use the preferred model to make a forecast for real estate loans in year 2008.

c. Compare the in-sample performance of the preferred model used in part b with an autoregressive model of order one, AR(1). Make a forecast for real estate loans in year 2008 with this model.

49. **FILE** *Inventory_Sales.* While U.S. inventory levels remain low, there is a slight indication of an increase in the U.S. business inventory-to-sales ratio, due to higher sales (*The Wall Street Journal*, December 15, 2010). The accompanying table shows a portion of seasonally adjusted inventory-to-sales ratios from January 2008 to October 2010.

Date	Inventory-to-Sales
Jan-08	1.28
Feb-08	1.30
⋮	⋮
Oct-10	1.27

Source: U.S. Department of Commerce.

a. Plot the series. Which polynomial trend model do you think is most appropriate?

b. Verify your answer by formally comparing the linear, the quadratic, and the cubic trend models.

c. Make a forecast for the inventory-to-sales ratio for November and December of 2010.

50. **FILE** *Revenue_Miles.* Revenue passenger-miles are calculated by multiplying the number of paying passengers by the distance flown in thousands. The accompanying table shows a portion of monthly data on revenue passenger-miles (in millions) from January 2006 through September 2010.

Date	Revenue
Jan-06	43.1652
Feb-06	44.0447
⋮	⋮
Sep-10	43.7704

Source: Bureau of Transportation Statistics.

a. Plot the series, and comment on its trend and seasonal variations.

b. Compute seasonal indices, and use them to seasonally adjust the series.

c. Fit the appropriate trend model to the seasonally adjusted series.

d. Use decomposition analysis to make monthly forecasts for the last three months of 2010.

51. **FILE** *Revenue_Miles.* Refer to the previous exercise for a description of the data set.

a. Estimate a linear trend model with seasonal dummy variables.

b. Estimate an exponential trend model with seasonal dummy variables.

c. Use *MSE* and *MAD* to compare these models.

d. Use the appropriate model to make monthly forecasts for the last three months of 2010.

52. **FILE** *Lowe's_Sales.* The following data represent a portion of quarterly net sales (in $ millions) of Lowe's Companies, Inc., over five years.

Year	Quarter	Net Sales
2004	1	8861
2004	2	10169
⋮	⋮	⋮
2008	1	9984

Source: All data retrieved from Annual Reports for Lowe's Companies, Inc.

a. Estimate a linear trend model with seasonal dummy variables and compute *MSE* and *MAD*.

b. Estimate an exponential trend model with seasonal dummy variables and compute *MSE* and *MAD*.

c. Which model is more appropriate? Use this model to forecast net sales for Lowe's Companies, Inc., for fiscal year 2009.

53. **FILE** *Genzyme.* The S&P 500 Index is a value-weighted index of prices of 500 large-cap common stocks actively traded in the United States. A research analyst at an investment firm is attempting to forecast the daily stock price of Genzyme Corporation, one of the world's leading biotech companies, using both the S&P 500 Index as well as Genzyme's past stock prices. The following table shows a portion of the daily adjusted closing prices of Genzyme (y) and the S&P 500 Index (x) from December 1, 2010, to December 22, 2010.

Date	y	x
12/1/10	71.14	1206.07
12/2/10	70.97	1221.53
⋮	⋮	⋮
12/22/10	71.52	1258.84

Source: www.finance.yahoo.

Estimate three models: (a) $y_t = \beta_0 + \beta_1 x_{t-1} + \varepsilon_t$, (b) $y_t = \beta_0 + \beta_1 y_{t-1} + \varepsilon_t$, and (c) $y_t = \beta_0 + \beta_1 x_{t-1} + \beta_2 y_{t-1} + \varepsilon_t$. Use the most suitable model to forecast the Genzyme daily stock price for December 23, 2010.

54. **FILE** *Income_Consumption.* The consumption function is one of the key relationships in economics, where consumption (y) depends on disposable income (x). Consider the following table, which presents a portion of quarterly data on personal consumption expenditure and disposable income for the United States. Both variables are measured in billions of dollars and are seasonally adjusted.

Year	Quarter	Consumption (y)	Income (x)
2006	1	9148.2	9705.2
2006	2	9266.6	9863.8
⋮	⋮	⋮	⋮
2010	4	10525.2	11514.7

Source: U.S. Department of Commerce.

a. Plot the consumption series. Estimate the appropriate polynomial trend model to forecast consumption expenditure for the 1st quarter of 2011.

b. Estimate $y_t = \beta_0 + \beta_1 x_{t-1} + \varepsilon_t$ to forecast consumption expenditure for the 1st quarter of 2011.

c. Which of these two models is more appropriate for making forecasts? Explain.

CASE STUDIES

CASE STUDY 18.1   Fried dough is a popular North American food associated with outdoor food stands at carnivals, amusement parks, fairs, festivals, and so on. Usually dusted with powdered sugar and drenched in oil, it is not particularly good for you but it sure is tasty! Jose Sanchez owns a small stall at Boston Commons in Boston, Massachusetts, where he sells fried dough and soft drinks. Although business is good, he is apprehensive about the variation in sales for no apparent reason. He asks a friend to help him make a forecast for fried dough as well as soft drinks. The accompanying table shows a portion of data on the number of plates of fried dough and soft drinks that he sold over the last 20 days.

Data for Case Study 18.1   Data on Fried Dough and Soft Drinks

Day	Fried Dough	Soft Drinks
1	70	150
2	69	145
⋮	⋮	⋮
20	61	153

In a report, use the sample information to

1. Construct the exponentially smoothed series for fried dough and soft drinks using $\alpha = 0.30$ and $\alpha = 0.70$.

2. Calculate *MSE* and *MAD* for each series.

3. Forecast sales of fried dough and soft drinks for day 21 with the best-fitting series.

CASE STUDY 18.2 Madelyn Davis is a research analyst for a large investment firm. She has been assigned the task of forecasting sales for Walmart Stores, Inc., for fiscal year 2011. She collects quarterly sales for Walmart Stores, Inc. (in $ millions) for the 10-year period 2001 through 2010, a portion of which is shown in the accompanying table.

Data for Case Study 18.2 Walmart Quarterly Sales (in millions $)

Period	Sales
2001:01	42985
2001:02	46112
⋮	⋮
2010:04	112826

Source: Annual Reports for Walmart Stores Inc.

In a report, use the sample information to

1. Use a scatterplot to determine which model best depicts trend for Walmart's sales.

2. Determine whether or not a seasonal component exists in the series, using the seasonal dummy variable approach.

3. Given the conclusions on trend and the seasonal component, provide forecast values for the four quarters of 2011 as well as total projected sales for fiscal year 2011.

CASE STUDY 18.3 Gary Martin is a research analyst at an investment firm in Chicago. He follows the oil industry and has developed a pretty sophisticated model that forecasts an oil company's stock price. However, given the recent strife in the Middle East, he wonders if simpler causal models might do a better job at predicting stock prices in the near future. He collects data on the daily adjusted closing price of ExxonMobil Corporation (XOM) as well as the Dow Jones Industrial Average (DJIA) for all trading days in February 2011. A portion of the data is shown in the accompanying table.

Data for Case Study 18.3 XOM and DJIA Adjusted Closing Prices, February 2011

Trading Days	XOM	DJIA
1	83.47	12040.16
2	82.97	12041.97
⋮	⋮	⋮
19	85.53	12226.34

Source: www.finance.yahoo.

In a report, use the sample information to

1. Estimate three models: (a) $XOM_t = \beta_0 + \beta_1 DJIA_{t-1} + \varepsilon_t$, (b) $XOM_t = \beta_0 + \beta_1 XOM_{t-1} + \varepsilon_t$, and (c) $XOM_t = \beta_0 + \beta_1 DJIA_{t-1} + \beta_2 XOM_{t-1} + \varepsilon_t$.

2. Determine which model best fits the data.

3. Use the most appropriate model to forecast the daily stock price for March 1, or trading day 20.

The following section provides brief commands for Minitab, SPSS, and JMP. Copy and paste the specified data file into the relevant software spreadsheet prior to following the commands.

Minitab

Smoothing Techniques – Moving Average

Gas_Production

A. (Replicating Example 18.1) From the menu, choose **Stat > Time Series > Moving Average.**

B. After **Variable**, select Production, and enter 3 after **MA length**. Select **Generate forecasts**, and after **Number of forecasts**, enter 1. Choose **Storage** and select **Moving averages**, **Fits (one-period-ahead forecasts)**, **Residuals**, and **Forecasts**.

Smoothing Techniques – Exponential Smoothing

Gas_Production

A. (Replicating Example 18.2) From the menu, choose **Stat > Time Series > Single Exp Smoothing**.

B. After **Variable**, select Production. Under **Weight to use in smoothing**, select **Use** and enter 0.2. Select **Generate forecasts** and after **Number of forecasts**, enter 1. Choose **Options**, and after **Use average of first K observations K =** enter 1. Choose **Storage** and select **Smoothed Data**, **Fits (one-period-ahead forecasts)**, **Residuals**, and **Forecasts**.

Estimating a Lagged Regression Model

Housing_Units

A. (Replicating Example 18.7 – Model 3) From the menu, choose **Calc > Calculator** in order to create the variable Housing$_{t-1}$. After **Store result in variable**, enter lag(Housing). After **Expression**, enter lag("Housing Units Sold," 1). Repeat these steps in order to create GDP$_{t-1}$.

B. Estimate the regression model using the standard commands.

SPSS

Estimating a Lagged Regression Model

Housing_Units

A. (Replicating Example 18.7 – Model 3) From the menu, choose **Transform > Compute Variable** in order to create the variable Housing$_{t-1}$. Under **Target Variable**, enter lagHousing. Under **Function Group**, select **All**, and under **Functions and Special Variables**, double-click on **Lag(1)**. Under **Numeric Expression**, select Housing. Repeat these steps in order to create GDP$_{t-1}$.

B. Estimate the regression model using the standard commands.

JMP

Smoothing Techniques – Moving Average

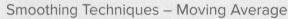
Gas_Production

A. (Replicating Example 18.1) From the menu, choose **Analyze > Modeling > Time Series**.

B. Under **Select Columns**, select Production, and then under **Cast Selected Columns Into Roles**, select **Y, Time Series**. Under **Select Columns**, select Week, and then under **Cast Selected Columns Into Roles**, select **X, Time ID**.

C. Click the red triangle next to **Time Series Production**, then select **Smoothing Model > Simple Moving Average**.

D. Input the value 3 after **Enter smoothing window width**. Deselect **Centered**.

E. Click the red triangle next to **Simple Moving Average**, then select **Smoothing Model > Simple Moving Average**; then select **Save data to table**.

Smoothing Techniques – Exponential Smoothing

Gas_Production

A. (Replicating Example 18.2) From the menu, choose **Analyze > Modeling > Time Series**.

B. Under **Select Columns**, select Production, and then under **Cast Selected Columns Into Roles**, select **Y, Time Series**. Under **Select Columns**, select Week, and then under **Cast Selected Columns Into Roles**, select **X, Time ID**.

C. Click the red triangle next to **Time Series Production**, then select **Smoothing Model > Simple Exponential Smoothing**.

D. When constructing an exponential smoothing series, JMP uses an algorithm to pick the value of w. If you want to specify w, you have to construct the series by defining a formula in a column and using the formula calculator. Here, we allow JMP to pick the value of w. Click **Estimate**.

E. Click the red triangle next to **Model: Simple Exponential Smoothing (Zero to One)**, then select **Save Columns**.

Estimating a Lagged Regression Model

Housing_Units

A. (Replicating Example 18.2) In order to create the variable $Housing_{t-1}$, right-click on a new column in the spreadsheet and label it lag(Housing). Right-click on the column of lag(Housing), and select **Formula**. Under **Functions (grouped)**, select **Row > Lag**. Select Housing in the **Lag** formula. Repeat these steps in order to create GDP_{t-1}.

B. Estimate the regression model using the standard commands.

19

Returns, Index Numbers, and Inflation

LEARNING OBJECTIVES

After reading this chapter you should be able to:

LO **19.1** Define and compute investment returns.

LO **19.2** Use the Fisher equation to convert nominal returns into real returns and vice versa.

LO **19.3** Calculate and interpret a simple price index.

LO **19.4** Calculate and interpret an unweighted aggregate price index.

LO **19.5** Compare the Laspeyres and the Paasche methods for computing a weighted aggregate price index.

LO **19.6** Use price indices to deflate economic time series and derive the inflation rate.

n Chapter 18, we derived seasonal indices to adjust time series for seasonal variations. Policy makers often analyze time series in this deseasonalized format, as they are not particularly interested in its seasonal variations. Other transformations of time series also facilitate interpretation and statistical analysis. For example, financial analysts are interested in the analysis of investment returns. The underlying data may consist of asset prices and income distributions, but these can easily be transformed into investment returns. Similarly, economists are often interested in measuring the magnitude of economic changes over time. They can create index numbers that transform the original data into figures representing percentage changes. Finally, many time series are reported both in nominal as well as real terms. While the nominal values represent dollar amounts, the corresponding real values incorporate inflation to represent the purchasing power of money. In this chapter, we will compute and interpret all such transformed time series.

©imageBROKER/Alamy RF

INTRODUCTORY CASE

Analyzing Beer and Wine Price Changes

Jehanne-Marie Roche is the owner of a convenience store in Mt. Angel, a cozy little town in Oregon, nestled between foothills and farmland. Although Jehanne-Marie sells selected grocery and household items, the major source of revenue is from the sale of liquor. Recently, the store has experienced a significant decline in consumer demand for liquor due to the opening of a supermarket in the neighborhood. Jehanne-Marie has been forced to offer numerous price discounts to sell beer and wine at the store. She asks her nephew to help her understand the price movement of liquor at her store during the 2014–2016 time period. She gives him the average price and quantity information for red wine, white wine, and beer, listed in Table 19.1.

TABLE 19.1 Average Price and Quantity of Wine and Beer

Year		Red Wine	White Wine	6-pack of Beer
2014	Price	$12.30	$11.90	$8.10
	Quantity	1,560	1,410	2,240
2015	Price	$12.10	$11.05	$8.25
	Quantity	1,490	1,390	2,310
2016	Price	$9.95	$10.60	$7.95
	Quantity	1,280	1,010	2,190

Jehanne-Marie wants to use the above information to

1. Determine the percentage price change of red wine, white wine, and beer from 2014 to 2016.

2. Derive and interpret the aggregate price index of liquor.

A synopsis of this case is provided at the end of Section 19.2.

19.1 INVESTMENT RETURN

In earlier chapters, the focus of many examples was on the analysis of **investment returns**. Here we describe a simple method to compute them. The time period used for computing an investment return may be a day, a week, a month, a year, or multiple years, and the investment may be in assets such as stocks, bonds, currencies, Treasury bills, or real estate. The investment may be in an individual asset or a portfolio of assets (for example, a mutual fund). An investment return consists of two components. The income component is the direct cash payments from the underlying asset, such as dividends, interest, or rental income. The price change component is the capital gain or loss resulting from an increase or decrease in the value of the asset.

Consider a share of Mindbody stock that an investor purchased a year ago for $25. If the price of this share jumps to $28 in a year, then $3 ($28 − $25) is the annual capital gain from this stock. In percentage terms, it is computed as $(3/25) \times 100 = 12\%$ and is referred to as the **capital gains yield**. If Mindbody has also paid a dividend of $1 per share during the year, the income component, in percentage terms, is $(1/25) \times 100 = 4\%$ and is referred to as the **income yield**. Therefore, the total annual return from investing in Mindbody is 16% (12% + 4%).

CALCULATING AN INVESTMENT RETURN

An investment return R_t at the end of time t is calculated as

$$R_t = \frac{P_t - P_{t-1} + I_t}{P_{t-1}},$$

where P_t and P_{t-1} are the price of the asset at times t (current) and $t-1$ (prior), respectively, and I_t is the income distributed during the investment period. The ratios $\frac{P_t - P_{t-1}}{P_{t-1}}$ and $\frac{I_t}{P_{t-1}}$ are the capital gains yield and the income yield components, respectively.

The process for computing an investment return is the same for all assets. The income component is dividends for stocks, interest for bonds, and rental income for a real estate investment. For some assets, like Treasury bills, there is no income component and the investment return consists entirely of a capital gain or loss.

EXAMPLE 19.1

Helen Watson purchased a corporate bond for $950 a year ago. She received a coupon payment (interest) of $60 during the year. The bond is currently selling for $975. Compute Helen's (a) capital gains yield, (b) income yield, and (c) investment return.

SOLUTION:

a. We calculate the capital gains yield as $\frac{P_t - P_{t-1}}{P_{t-1}} = \frac{975 - 950}{950} = 0.0263$ or 2.63%.

b. Given the interest payment of $60, we calculate the income yield as $\frac{I_t}{P_{t-1}} = \frac{60}{950} = 0.0632$ or 6.32%.

c. The investment return is the sum of the capital gains yield and the income yield, that is, $0.0263 + 0.0632 = 0.0895$ or 8.95%. We can also compute it directly as $R_t = \frac{P_t - P_{t-1} + I_t}{P_{t-1}} = \frac{975 - 950 + 60}{950} = \frac{85}{950} = 0.0895$ or 8.95%.

EXAMPLE 19.2

Last year, Jim Hamilton bought a stock for \$35 and recently received a dividend of \$1.25. The stock is now selling for \$31. Find Jim's (a) capital gains yield, (b) income yield, and (c) investment return.

SOLUTION:

a. The capital gains yield is $\frac{P_t - P_{t-1}}{P_{t-1}} = \frac{31 - 35}{35} = -0.1143$ or -11.43%.

b. The income yield is $\frac{I_t}{P_{t-1}} = \frac{1.25}{35} = 0.0357$ or 3.57%.

c. The investment return is $-0.1143 + 0.0357 = -0.0786$ or -7.86%.
   Equivalently, we can compute the investment return as
   $$R_t = \frac{P_t - P_{t-1} + I_t}{P_{t-1}} = \frac{31 - 35 + 1.25}{35} = \frac{-2.75}{35} = -0.0786 \text{ or } -7.86\%.$$

Note that the investment return is unaffected by the decision to sell or hold assets. A common misconception is that if you do not sell an asset, there is no capital gain or loss involved, as a given price increase or decrease leads only to paper gain or loss. This misconception often leads an investor to hold a "loser" asset longer than necessary because of the reluctance to admit a bad investment decision. The nonrecognition of the loss is relevant for tax purposes, since only realized income must be reported in tax returns. However, whether or not you have liquidated an asset is irrelevant when measuring its performance.

The Adjusted Closing Price

Historical returns are often used by investors, analysts, and other researchers to assess past performance of a stock. In Example 19.2, we saw that dividend payments also influence stock returns. Therefore, we need the dividend data along with the price data to compute historical returns. Similarly, we need information on stock splits and reverse stock splits in computing returns. Tabulating corporate decisions such as the announcement of dividends, stock splits, and reverse stock splits can be very cumbersome. For these reasons, most data sources for stock price information, such as *http://finance.yahoo.com,* also include data on the **adjusted closing price**. Here, price data are adjusted using appropriate dividend and split multipliers; we recommend an introductory finance book for further details.

Given that the adjustment has been made for all applicable splits and dividend distributions, we can compute the total investment return on the basis of the price appreciation or depreciation of the adjusted closing prices.

> USING ADJUSTED CLOSING PRICES TO
> CALCULATE AN INVESTMENT RETURN
>
> Let P_t^* and P_{t-1}^* represent the adjusted closing price of a stock at times t (current) and $t - 1$ (prior), respectively. The investment return R_t at the end of time t is calculated as
> $$R_t = \frac{P_t^* - P_{t-1}^*}{P_{t-1}^*}.$$

EXAMPLE 19.3

Consider the adjusted closing stock prices of Tesla in Table 19.2. Find the monthly returns for January and February 2017.

TABLE 19.2 Monthly Stock Prices for Tesla

Date	Adjusted Closing Price
January 1, 2017	251.93
February 1, 2017	249.99
March 1, 2017	278.30

Source: finance.yahoo.com; data extracted in June 2017.

SOLUTION: We compute the monthly return for January 2017 as $R_t = \frac{249.99 - 251.93}{251.93} = -0.0077$, or -0.77%. Similarly, the monthly return for February 2017 is $R_t = \frac{278.30 - 249.99}{249.99} = 0.1132$, or 11.32%. The surge in the stock price in February can be explained by President Trump's embrace of U.S. manufacturing that fits nicely with Tesla's businesses, which are becoming major employers of Americans.

LO 19.2

Use the Fisher equation to convert nominal returns into real returns and vice versa.

Nominal versus Real Rates of Return

So far we have focused on **nominal returns**, which make no allowance for inflation. Financial rates, such as interest rates, discount rates, and rates of return, are generally reported in nominal terms. However, the nominal return does not represent a true picture because it does not capture the erosion of the purchasing power of money due to inflation. Consider, for example, an investment of $100 that becomes $105 after one year. While the nominal return on this investment is 5%, the purchasing power of the money is likely to have increased by less than 5%. Once the effects of inflation have been factored in, investors can determine the real, or true, return on their investment. In sum, the **real return** captures the change in the purchasing power, whereas the nominal return simply reflects the change in the number of dollars.

The relationship between the nominal and the real return was developed by Irving Fisher (1867–1947), a prominent economist. The **Fisher equation** is a theoretical relationship between the nominal return, the real return, and the expected inflation rate.

THE FISHER EQUATION

Let R be the nominal rate of return, r the real rate of return, and i the expected inflation rate. The Fisher equation is defined as

$$1 + r = \frac{1 + R}{1 + i}.$$

When the expected inflation rate is relatively low, a reasonable approximation to the Fisher equation is $r = R - i$; we will not be using this approximation in this chapter.

EXAMPLE 19.4

The quoted rate of return on a one-year U.S. Treasury bill in June 2017 is 1.16% (www.ustreas.gov). Compute and interpret the real rate of return that investors can earn if the inflation rate is expected to be 2.1%.

SOLUTION: Using the Fisher equation, $1 + r = \frac{1 + R}{1 + i} = \frac{1.0116}{1.0210} = 0.9908$; we derive the real rate of return as $r = 0.9908 - 1 = -0.0092$, or -0.92%. The negative real rate of return implies that investors are cautious and are willing to accept a small drop in their purchasing power during this period.

EXAMPLE 19.5

A bond produces a real rate of return of 5.30% for a time period when the inflation rate is expected to be 3%. What is the nominal rate of return on the bond?

SOLUTION: The Fisher equation can be rewritten as $1 + R = (1 + r)(1 + i)$. Therefore, given the real rate of return of 5.30% and the inflation rate of 3%, we can easily compute, $1 + R = (1.053)(1.03) = 1.0846$ giving us the nominal return of $R = 1.0846 - 1 = 0.0846$, or 8.46%.

EXERCISES 19.1

1. You borrowed $2,000 to take a vacation in the Caribbean islands. At the end of the year, you had to pay back $2,200. What is the annual interest that you paid on your loan?

2. You bought a corporate bond last year for $980. You received a coupon payment (interest) of $60, and the bond is currently selling for $990. What is the (a) income yield, (b) capital gains yield, and (c) total return on the investment?

3. The year-end price and dividend information on a stock is given in the following table.

Year	Price	Dividend
1	23.50	NA
2	24.80	0.18
3	22.90	0.12

Note: NA denotes not applicable.

  a. What is the nominal return of the stock in years 2 and 3?
  b. What is the corresponding real return if the inflation rates for years 2 and 3 were 2.8% and 1.6%, respectively?

4. The price of a stock has gone up from $24 to $35 in one year. It also paid a year-end dividend of $1.20. What is the stock's (a) income yield, (b) capital gains yield, and (c) total return?

5. A portfolio manager invested $1,500,000 in bonds. In one year, the market value of the bonds dropped to $1,485,000. The interest payments during the year totaled $105,000.
  a. What was the manager's total rate of return for the year?
  b. What was the manager's real rate of return if the inflation rate during the year was 2.3%?

6. Bill Anderson purchased 1,000 shares of Microsoft Corporation stock for $17,100 at the beginning of 2009. At the end of the year, he sold all of his Microsoft shares at $30.48 a share. He also earned a dividend of $0.52 per share during the year.
  a. What is Bill's total return on the investment?
  b. What is the dollar gain from the investment?

7. You would like to invest $20,000 for a year in a risk-free investment. A conventional certificate of deposit (CD) offers a 4.6% annual rate of return. You are also considering an "Inflation-Plus" CD which offers a real rate of return of 2.2% regardless of the inflation rate.
  a. What is the implied (expected) inflation rate?
  b. You decide to invest $10,000 in the conventional CD and $10,000 in the "Inflation-Plus" CD. What is your expected dollar value at the end of the year?
  c. Which of the two CDs is a better investment if the actual inflation rate for the year turns out to be 2.2%?

8. Consider the following adjusted closing stock prices for Intel Corporation. Find the monthly returns for January and February of 2017.

Date	Adjusted Closing Price
January 1, 2017	36.82
February 1, 2017	36.20
March 1, 2017	36.07

Source: finance.yahoo.com; data extracted in June 2017.

Date	Ford	GM
1/1/2017	12.36	36.61
2/1/2017	12.53	36.84
3/1/2017	11.64	35.36
4/1/2017	11.47	34.64
5/1/2017	11.12	33.93
6/1/2017	11.35	34.45

Source: finance.yahoo.com; data extracted in June 2017.

9. Consider the following adjusted closing stock prices for Ford Motor Company (Ford) and General Motors Company (GM). Compute and compare the monthly returns for both companies from January 2017 to May 2017.

19.2 INDEX NUMBERS

An **index number** is an easy-to-interpret numerical value that reflects a percentage change in price or quantity from a base value. In this chapter, we focus on price indices. The base value for a price index is set equal to 100 for the selected base period, and values in other periods are adjusted in proportion to the base. Thus, if the price index for a given year is 125, it implies that the price has increased by 25% from the base year. Similarly, a price index of 90 implies that the price has decreased by 10% from the base year. By working in a manner similar to percentages, index numbers make changes over time easier to compare. Index numbers enable policy makers and analysts to focus on the movements in variables rather than on their raw absolute values.

Simple Price Indices

Consider the price of a hamburger that increases from \$3.25 in 1995 to \$4.75 in 2010. We can easily determine that the price of a hamburger has increased by $\frac{4.75 - 3.25}{3.25} = 0.46$, or 46%. Alternatively, if we use 1995 as the base year with an index value of 100, then the corresponding index value for 2010 is 146, indicating a 46% increase in price. This is an example of a **simple price index**.

> **A SIMPLE PRICE INDEX**
>
> A simple price index for any item is the ratio of the price in period t, p_t, and the price in the base period, p_0, expressed as a percentage. It is calculated as $\frac{p_t}{p_0} \times 100$.

EXAMPLE 19.6

Consider the data presented in the introductory case of this chapter in Table 19.1. Use the base year of 2014 to compute and interpret the 2015 and 2016 simple price indices for:

a. Red wine
b. White wine
c. A 6-pack of beer

SOLUTION: Since 2014 is the base year, we set the corresponding index value equal to 100. The index values for other years are computed below.

a. For red wine, the simple price index for 2015 is

$$\frac{\text{Price in 2015}}{\text{Price in 2014}} \times 100 = \frac{12.10}{12.30} \times 100 = 98.37.$$

Similarly, for 2016, it is

$$\frac{\text{Price in 2016}}{\text{Price in 2014}} \times 100 = \frac{9.95}{12.30} \times 100 = 80.89.$$

Therefore, the average price of red wine in 2015 and 2016 was 98.37% and 80.89%, respectively, of what it was in 2014. In other words, as compared to 2014, the price of red wine dropped by 1.63% in 2015 and 19.11% in 2016.

b. For white wine, the simple price index for 2015 is $(11.05/11.90) \times 100 = 92.86$ and $(10.60/11.90) \times 100 = 89.08$ for 2016. Therefore, relative to 2014, the average price of white wine dropped by 7.14% in 2015 and 10.92% in 2016.

c. The simple price index for a six-pack of beer for 2015 is $(8.25/8.10) \times 100 = 101.85$ and $(7.95/8.10) \times 100 = 98.15$ for 2016. Interestingly, while the prices of both red and white wines experienced substantial declines, the price of beer stayed fairly stable. Relative to the base year of 2014, there was a 1.85% increase in the price of beer in 2015 and a 1.85% decline in 2016.

EXAMPLE 19.7

Table 19.3 shows the average price and corresponding price index for gasoline from 2000 to 2008. Interpret the price indices for 2001 and 2008.

TABLE 19.3 Price and Corresponding Price Index for Unleaded Gasoline in U.S., Base Year 2000

Year	2000	2001	2002	2003	2004	2005	2006	2007	2008
Price	1.51	1.46	1.36	1.59	1.88	2.30	2.59	2.80	3.27
Price Index (Base = 2000)	100	96.69	90.07	105.30	124.50	152.32	171.52	185.43	216.56

Source: Bureau of Labor Statistics.

SOLUTION: Since 2000 is treated as the base year, the index number for 2000 is 100. The index number for 2001 is calculated as $(1.46/1.51) \times 100 = 96.69$. Thus, the gasoline price in 2001 was 96.69% of what it was in 2000, or 3.31% lower. Given a price index of 216.56 in 2008, the gasoline price in 2008 was 116.56% higher relative to 2000.

In Figure 19.1, we plot the raw price and price indices for gasoline from 2000 to 2008. Note that although the units of the gasoline price and index number graphs are different, the basic shape of the two graphs is similar. This shows that the main purpose of index numbers is to provide an easy interpretation of the changes of the series over time.

FIGURE 19.1 Price of gasoline and the corresponding index numbers for 2000–2008

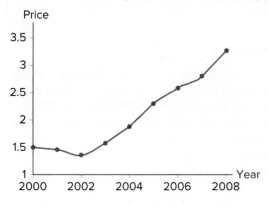
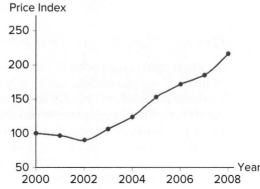

It is important to note that index numbers provide direct comparisons only with respect to the base year. Similar direct comparisons cannot be made between non–base years. For instance, based on the index numbers for 2005 and 2008, we cannot say that prices rose by 64.24% (216.56% − 152.32%) from 2005 to 2008. The actual percentage change from 2005 and 2008 is $\frac{216.56 \ - \ 152.32}{152.32} \times 100 = 42.17$, indicating that prices rose by 42.17% from 2005 to 2008.

Alternatively, we can use index numbers directly to compare prices between 2005 and 2008 by making 2005 the base year. It may be more meaningful to compare 2008 values with those in 2005 rather than the values in 2000. In fact, federal agencies routinely update the base year used in their calculations of statistical indices.

It is fairly simple to revise the base period of an index. We basically transform the index of the newly chosen base period as 100 and values in other periods are adjusted by the same proportion.

REVISING THE BASE PERIOD

A simple index can easily be updated with a revised base period as

$$\text{Updated Index} = \frac{\text{Old Index Value}}{\text{Old Index Value of New Base}} \times 100.$$

EXAMPLE 19.8

Update the index numbers in Table 19.3 with a base year revised from 2000 to 2005.

SOLUTION: With a revised base of 2005, the index number for 2005 is updated from 152.32 to 100. Other indices are adjusted according to the revision rule. For instance, the index number for 2006 is updated as $(171.52/152.32) \times 100 = 112.61$. Table 19.4 contains index numbers that have been similarly updated.

TABLE 19.4 Price Index for Gasoline Using Base Year of 2000 and 2005

Year	2000	2001	2002	2003	2004	2005	2006	2007	2008
Price	1.51	1.46	1.36	1.59	1.88	2.30	2.59	2.80	3.27
Price Index (Base = 2000)	100	96.69	90.07	105.30	124.50	152.32	171.52	185.43	216.56
Price Index (Base = 2005)	65.65	63.48	59.13	69.13	81.74	100.00	112.61	121.74	142.17

With the revised base of 2005, we can directly deduce that the gasoline price in 2008 was 142.17% of what it was in 2005, or 42.17% higher.

Calculate and interpret an unweighted aggregate price index.

Unweighted Aggregate Price Index

An **aggregate price index** is used to represent relative price movements for a group of items. Examples include the closely watched consumer price index (CPI) and the producer price index (PPI). An aggregate price index can be weighted or unweighted. An **unweighted aggregate price index** is based entirely on aggregate prices with no emphasis placed on quantity. In other words, it does not incorporate the information that consumers may not be consuming equal quantities over the years of the items comprising the index. Weighted methods, on the other hand, use quantity as weights in the calculations.

Let p_{it} represent the price of item i in period t, and let p_{i0} be the corresponding price in the base period ($t = 0$). The unweighted aggregate price index in period t is

$$\frac{\Sigma p_{it}}{\Sigma p_{i0}} \times 100.$$

EXAMPLE 19.9

A real estate firm based in Florida collects data on the average selling price of condominiums, single-family homes, and multifamily homes that it sold over the last three years. Table 19.5 shows the results. Compute the unweighted price index for the properties, using 2007 as the base year.

TABLE 19.5 Average Price (in $1,000s) of Properties Sold in Florida (Example 19.9)

Year	Condominiums	Single-family	Multifamily
2007	225	375	440
2008	148	250	390
2009	130	235	400

SOLUTION: In order to find the unweighted aggregate price index, we first aggregate prices for each year by adding up the prices of condominiums, single-family homes, and multifamily homes. For 2007, the aggregate price is computed as $\Sigma p_{0i} = 225 + 375 + 440 = 1040$. Similarly, the aggregate prices are $\Sigma p_{ti} = 148 + 250 + 390 = 788$ for 2008 and $\Sigma p_{ti} = 130 + 235 + 400 = 765$ for 2009. Then, using 2007 as the base year, the unweighted aggregate price indices are computed as

$$\text{Price Index for 2008} = \frac{788}{1{,}040} \times 100 = 75.77 \text{ and}$$

$$\text{Price Index for 2009} = \frac{765}{1{,}040} \times 100 = 73.56.$$

Thus, according to the unweighted aggregate price index, property values in 2008 were 75.77% of what they were in 2007, or equivalently, they were 24.23% lower. Similarly, relative to 2007, property values in 2009 were 26.44% lower. Although the unweighted aggregate price index captures the overall drop in property values in Florida, the drop seems slightly lower than what has been reported in the popular press. A possible explanation is that the unweighted index unfairly treats all property prices equally. The drop in property values would be greater if we take into account the fact that most properties in Florida consisted of condominiums and single-family homes, which witnessed a steeper price decline than multifamily homes.

Weighted Aggregate Price Index

LO 19.5

Compare the Laspeyres and the Paasche methods for computing a weighted aggregate price index.

A **weighted aggregate price index** does not treat prices of different items equally. A higher weight is given to the items that are sold in higher quantities. However, there is no unique way to determine the weights, as they depend on the period in which the quantities are evaluated. One option is to evaluate the changing quantities over the years to derive the weighted average. However, in many applications, the quantity information is not readily available and we have to rely on its evaluation in a single time period. Two popular choices for weights are based on the quantities evaluated in the base period and in the current period. A **Laspeyres price index** uses the quantities evaluated in the base period to compute a weighted aggregate price index.

CALCULATING A WEIGHTED AGGREGATE PRICE INDEX:
THE LASPEYRES PRICE INDEX

Let p_{it} and q_{it} represent the price and quantity of item i in period t, and let p_{i0} and q_{i0} be the corresponding values in the base period ($t = 0$). Using only the base period quantities q_{i0}, the Laspeyres price index for period t is

$$\frac{\sum p_{it} q_{i0}}{\sum p_{i0} q_{i0}} \times 100.$$

EXAMPLE 19.10

Table 19.6 shows the number of condominiums, single-family homes, and multi-family homes sold in Florida. Use these quantities, along with the price information from Table 19.5, to compute the Laspeyres price index for real estate, given a base year of 2007.

TABLE 19.6 Number of Properties Sold in Florida

Year	Condominiums	Single-Family	Multifamily
2007	42	104	20
2008	28	76	16
2009	32	82	10

SOLUTION: Since the Laspeyres price index evaluates the quantities in the base period, we will only use the number of properties sold in 2007 in the calculation. Table 19.7 aids in the calculation of the Laspeyres index.

TABLE 19.7 Calculations for Example 19.10

Year	Weighted Price $= \sum p_{it} q_{i0}$	The Laspeyres Index
2007	$225 \times 42 + 375 \times 104 + 440 \times 20 = 57250$	100
2008	$148 \times 42 + 250 \times 104 + 390 \times 20 = 40016$	$(40016/57250) \times 100 = 69.90$
2009	$130 \times 42 + 235 \times 104 + 400 \times 20 = 37900$	$(37900/57250) \times 100 = 66.20$

Based on the Laspeyres index, the real estate prices in 2008 were 69.90% of what they were in 2007, or equivalently, they were 30.10% lower. Similarly, the real estate prices in 2009 were 33.80% lower. Note that the computed drop in property values based on the Laspeyres price index is sharper than the one inferred from the unweighted aggregate price index.

As mentioned earlier, the choice of weights for a weighted aggregate price index depends on the quantity evaluated in a given period. Whereas a Laspeyres index uses the base period quantities as weights, a **Paasche index** uses the current period quantities in deriving the weights. Since the choice of weights for the two methods are different, the Laspeyres and Paasche indices differ for the period under evaluation.

EXAMPLE 19.11

Consider Tables 19.5 and 19.6, representing the price and quantity data for properties sold in Florida. Use this information to compute the Paasche price index for real estate, given a base year of 2007.

SOLUTION: Since the Paasche price index uses the quantities evaluated in the current period, we use only the numbers of properties sold in 2009 in the calculations. Table 19.8 aids in the calculation of the Paasche index.

TABLE 19.8 Calculations for Example 19.11

Year	Weighted Price = $\Sigma p_{it}q_{in}$	The Paasche Index
2007	$225 \times 32 + 375 \times 82 + 440 \times 10 = 42350$	100
2008	$148 \times 32 + 250 \times 82 + 390 \times 10 = 29136$	$(29136/42350) \times 100 = 68.80$
2009	$130 \times 32 + 235 \times 82 + 400 \times 10 = 27430$	$(27430/42350) \times 100 = 64.77$

The Paasche index is calculated as 68.80 for 2008 and 64.77 for 2009. Therefore, according to the Paasche index with a base year of 2007, property values dropped by 31.20% in 2008 and 35.23% in 2009.

In general, the Laspeyres and Paasche indices provide similar results if the periods being compared are not too far apart. The two indices tend to differ when the length of time between the periods increases, since the relative quantities of items (weights) adjust to the changes in consumer demand over time. Consumers tend to adjust their consumption patterns by decreasing (increasing) the quantity of items that undergo a larger relative price increase (decrease). For instance, a sharp increase in the price of an item is typically accompanied by a decrease in the quantity demanded, making its relative weight go down in value. Similarly, a sharp decrease in the price of an item will make its relative weight go up. Therefore, a Paasche index that uses the updated weights theoretically produces a lower estimate than a Laspeyres index when prices are increasing and a higher estimate when prices are decreasing. Our results regarding property values are consistent with this reasoning. During the period of price decline, the Laspeyres index suggests that relative to 2007, property values have dropped by 30.10% and 33.80% in 2008 and 2009, respectively. According to the Paasche index for the same period, property values had larger drops of 31.20% and 35.23%, respectively.

The Paasche index is attractive because it incorporates current expenditure patterns. However, its data requirements are more stringent than those of the Laspeyres index. The Paasche index requires that the weights be updated each year and the index numbers be recomputed for all of the previous years. The additional cost required to process current expenditure data, needed to revise the weights, can be substantial. It may not always be possible to produce a timely Paasche index. Therefore, the Laspeyres index is a more widely used weighted aggregate price index. The base period is changed periodically to ensure that the Laspeyres index does not become outdated. Here the base period revision involves updated calculations using quantity weights of the new base period.

EXAMPLE 19.12

Let us revisit the introductory case with the data presented in Table 19.1.

a. Using 2014 as the base year, compute and interpret the Laspeyres price index for liquor.

b. Using 2014 as the base year, compute and interpret the Paasche price index for liquor.

SOLUTION: Since 2014 is used as the base year, its value for both indices is set equal to 100.

a. For the Laspeyres price index, the prices are weighted by the quantities evaluated in the base period of 2014. Therefore, the weighted price for 2014 is computed as

$$\Sigma p_{it} q_{i0} = 12.30 \times 1{,}560 + 11.90 \times 1{,}410 + 8.10 \times 2{,}240 = 54{,}111.$$

Similarly, the weighted price equals

$$12.10 \times 1{,}560 + 11.05 \times 1{,}410 + 8.25 \times 2{,}240 = 52{,}936.5 \text{ for 2015 and}$$
$$9.95 \times 1{,}560 + 10.60 \times 1{,}410 + 7.95 \times 2{,}240 = 48{,}276 \text{ for 2016.}$$

The corresponding price index is $(52{,}936.5/54{,}111) \times 100 = 97.83$ for 2015 and $(48{,}276/54{,}111) \times 100 = 89.22$ for 2016. Therefore, based on the Laspeyres index, liquor prices are 97.83% in 2015 and 89.22% in 2016 of what they were in 2014. In other words, relative to 2014, overall liquor prices dropped by 2.17% in 2015 and by 10.78% in 2016.

b. For the Paasche price index, the prices are weighted by the quantities evaluated in the current period, which in our example is 2016. Therefore, the weighted price for 2014 is computed as

$$\Sigma p_{it} q_{in} = 12.30 \times 1{,}280 + 11.90 \times 1{,}010 + 8.10 \times 2{,}190 = 45{,}502.$$

Similarly, the weighted prices equal

$$12.10 \times 1{,}280 + 11.05 \times 1{,}010 + 8.25 \times 2{,}190 = 44{,}716 \text{ for 2015 and}$$
$$9.95 \times 1{,}280 + 10.60 \times 1{,}010 + 7.95 \times 2{,}190 = 40{,}852.5 \text{ for 2016.}$$

The corresponding price index is $(44{,}716/45{,}502) \times 100 = 98.27$ for 2015 and $(40{,}852.5/45{,}502) \times 100 = 89.78$ for 2016. Therefore, based on the Paasche index, liquor prices are 98.27% in 2015 and 89.78% in 2016 of what they were in 2014. In other words, relative to 2014, overall liquor prices dropped by 1.73% in 2015 and by 10.22% in 2016.

SYNOPSIS OF INTRODUCTORY CASE

Small businesses often have to fight an uphill battle to compete with big stores even though they are appealing to customers who value personalized attention. Jehanne-Marie, the owner of a small convenience store in Oregon, has not been spared the effects of stiff competition from a new supermarket. She has been forced to offer numerous price discounts to counter the plummeting demand for liquor. Interestingly, the cutbacks by consumers have not been uniform across red wine, white wine, and beer. While the price of red wine has dropped by 19.11% from 2014 to 2016, the corresponding drop in price has been 10.92% for white wine and only 1.85% for beer. In order to capture the

©Koy Hipster/Shutterstock RF

overall price movement of liquor, two weighted aggregate price indices are also computed. These indices devote a higher weight to the price of items that are sold in higher quantities. The weights are defined by the base period quantities for the Laspeyres index and the current period quantities for the Paasche index. Both indices suggest that, relative to 2014, Jehanne-Marie has experienced an overall price decline of about 2% in 2015 and a larger 10.50% in 2016. In sum, Jehanne-Marie is advised to focus more on beer sales, rather than wine. A comprehensive analysis that includes other grocery items like bread, cheese, and soda would better describe the full impact of the competition from the new supermarket.

EXERCISES 19.2

Mechanics

10. Consider the following simple price index created with a base year of 2004.

Year	2004	2005	2006	2007	2008	2009	2010	2011	2012
Price Index	100	102.2	106.3	110.8	109.4	107.2	108.9	110.5	114.7

   a. Update the index numbers using a revised base year of 2008.

   b. Determine the percentage change in price from 2004 to 2012.

   c. Determine the percentage change in price from 2008 to 2012.

11. Consider the following price data from 1994 to 2002.

Year	1994	1995	1996	1997	1998	1999	2000	2001	2002
Price	62	60	64	67	66	70	74	72	70

   a. Compute the simple price index using 1994 as the base year.

   b. Determine the percentage change in prices from 1994 to 1998.

12. Consider the following price and quantity data for three products from 2008 to 2010.

Year		Product 1	Product 2	Product 3
2008	Price	$14.30	$13.90	$18.10
	Quantity	992	1,110	800
2009	Price	$14.90	$13.70	$18.50
	Quantity	980	1,220	790
2010	Price	$15.50	$13.80	$17.90
	Quantity	140	1,290	810

   a. Compute the simple price index for each product, using 2008 as the base year.

   b. Compare the relative price movements of the three products.

13. Use the price and quantity information in the previous exercise to compute the following aggregate price indices, given a base year of 2008:

   a. The unweighted aggregate price index

   b. The Laspeyres price index

   c. The Paasche price index

Applications

14. Consider the following average monthly prices for regular gasoline in California in 2008.

Month	Jan	Feb	Mar	Apr	May	Jun	Jul	Aug	Sep	Oct	Nov	Dec
Price	3.25	3.18	3.56	3.82	3.97	4.48	4.46	4.16	3.79	3.39	2.46	1.82

Source: www.energyalmanac.ca.gov.

a. Construct a simple price index with January 2008 as the base.

b. Determine the percentage change in the average gasoline price in California from January to June.

15. The following table shows the monthly adjusted closing price per share of Microsoft Corporation for 2009.

Month	Jan	Feb	Mar	Apr	May	Jun	Jul	Aug	Sep	Oct	Nov	Dec
Price	16.6	15.8	18.0	19.8	20.6	23.4	23.2	24.4	25.5	27.5	29.2	30.3

Source: http://finance.yahoo.com.

a. Construct a simple price index with January 2009 as the base.

b. What is the percentage price change in July relative to January?

c. What is the percentage price change in December relative to January?

16. **FILE** *Returns_2009.* According to dollar cost averaging, a fixed amount of money is invested periodically in a portfolio. Consequently, more units of a financial asset are purchased when prices are low and fewer units are purchased when prices are high. Robert Dudek follows dollar cost averaging by making a monthly investment of $500 toward retirement. His monthly investment is divided equally among two T. Rowe Price mutual funds: Equity Income (EqInc) and Short-term Bond (Bond) funds. The following table represents the monthly adjusted closing price of the funds in 2009.

Month	EqInc	Bond	Month	EqInc	Bond
January	14.77	4.47	July	18.40	4.72
February	12.93	4.49	August	19.45	4.75
March	14.14	4.53	September	19.92	4.78
April	16.04	4.58	October	19.53	4.80
May	16.87	4.64	November	20.60	4.85
June	16.89	4.66	December	20.99	4.82

Source: http://finance.yahoo.com.

a. Compute and interpret the Laspeyres price index.

b. Compute and interpret the Paasche price index.

c. Why are the results of the two indices different?

17. The MIT Sloan School of Management is one of the leading business schools in the United States. The following table contains the tuition data for the masters program in the Sloan School of Management.

Year	2004	2005	2006	2007	2008	2009
Tuition	$36,850	$39,844	$42,634	$44,556	$46,784	$48,650

Source: http://web.mit.edu/ir/financial/tuition.html.

a. Use 2004 as the base year to form a simple price index for tuition.

b. Use 2007 as the base year to form a simple price index for tuition.

c. Compare the percentage tuition increase from 2004 through 2007 and 2007 through 2009.

18. JJ Diner is a small mom and pop restaurant in Lincoln, Nebraska. They offer three choices for breakfast: omelets, pancakes, or cereal. The average prices (in $) for these options for 2007, 2008, and 2009 are shown in the accompanying table.

Year	Omelet	Pancakes	Cereal
2007	4.75	3.50	3.50
2008	5.25	4.25	4.00
2009	5.00	4.50	4.25

a. Compute and interpret the simple price index for each breakfast, using 2007 as the base year.

b. Compute and interpret the unweighted aggregate price index for breakfast, using 2007 as the base year.

19. The following table shows the number (in 1,000s) of breakfasts sold at JJ Diner.

Year	Omelet	Pancakes	Cereal
2007	9.26	7.98	2.44
2008	11.82	9.20	2.62
2009	10.48	8.50	2.12

Use this information, along with the price data provided in the previous exercise, to

a. Compute and interpret the Laspeyres price index.

b. Compute and interpret the Paasche price index.

20. With the collapse of house prices that occurred during the Great Recession, the American Dream became a nightmare for many of the 75 million Americans who owned a home (*CBS Evening News,* February 2, 2010). However, the drop in house prices was not uniform across the country. The accompanying table represents median home prices (in $1,000s) by region for 2007, 2008, and 2009.

Region	2007	2008	2009
Northeast	288.1	271.5	240.7
Midwest	161.4	150.5	142.5
South	178.8	169.4	154.6
West	342.5	276.1	224.2

Source: www.realtor.org.

a. Use 2007 as the base year to construct a simple price index for each region.

b. Use the percentage decline in home values to discuss regional differences in price drops.

21. Consider the following table, which reports the sale of homes (in 1,000s) by region for 2007, 2008, and 2009.

Region	2007	2008	2009
Northeast	1,006	849	868
Midwest	1,327	1,129	1,165
South	2,235	1,865	1,913
West	1,084	1,070	1,210

Source: www.realtor.org.

Use this information, along with the price data provided in the previous exercise, to

a. Compute and interpret the Laspeyres aggregate home price index for the United States.

b. Compute and interpret the Paasche aggregate home price index for the United States.

c. Comment on the differences between the two indices.

19.3 USING PRICE INDICES TO DEFLATE A TIME SERIES

LO 19.6

Most business and economic time series are generally reported in nominal terms, implying that they are measured in dollar amounts. Since inflation erodes the value of money over time, the dollar differences over time do not quite tell the whole story. For instance, we cannot directly compare the starting salary of a recent college graduate with that of a college graduate five years ago. Due to price increases, the purchasing power of recent graduates may be lower even if they make more money than their predecessors. Similarly, a hardware store may have doubled its revenue over 20 years, but the true increase in value may be much smaller once it has been adjusted for inflation.

Use price indices to deflate economic time series and derive the inflation rate.

An important function of the price indices, introduced in the previous section, is to serve as deflators. A **deflated time series** is obtained by adjusting the given time series for changes in prices, or inflation. We use the price indices to remove the effect of inflation so that we can evaluate business and economic time series in a more meaningful way.

NOMINAL VERSUS REAL VALUES

A time series that has been deflated is said to be represented in real terms. The unadjusted time series is said to be represented in nominal terms. We use a price index to convert the nominal value of a time series into its real value as

$$\text{Real Value} = \frac{\text{Nominal Value}}{\text{Price Index}} \times 100.$$

Consider the following example. Lisa Redford has worked in a small marketing firm in Florida for the last three years. Due to the economic crisis, her salary has dropped from $80,000 in 2007 to $64,000 in 2009. While her salary has dropped by 20%, a larger drop in property values for the same time period may have made it easier for Lisa to own a home in Florida. In Example 19.10, we used the base year of 2007 to derive the Laspeyres price index of property values for 2009 as 66.20, implying that real estate prices were 33.80% lower in 2009 than in 2007. It is more meaningful to compare Lisa's salary of $80,000 in 2007 (the base year) with the price-adjusted (real) salary of ($64,000/66.20) × 100 = $96,677 in 2009. Using the Laspeyres price index of property values for adjustment, Lisa is actually slightly better off in 2009 than she was in 2007, despite the salary cut. However, it is not reasonable to adjust Lisa's salary solely on the basis of the price index of property values in

Florida. Since her expenditure is not limited to mortgage payments, a more comprehensive price index is needed to make the price adjustment to the salary. In fact, when we say that a series has been deflated, we imply that the series has been adjusted on the basis of the price of a comprehensive basket of goods and services.

The two price indices most commonly used to deflate economic time series are the **Consumer Price Index**, **CPI**, and the **Producer Price Index**, **PPI**. While both the CPI and PPI measure the percentage price change over time for a fixed basket of goods and services, they differ in the composition of the basket and in the types of prices used in the analysis. The general process of computing the CPI and PPI is similar to the method outlined in the preceding section. However, we will not elaborate on their composition in this chapter.

The CPI is perhaps the best-known weighted aggregate price index. The U.S. Bureau of Labor Statistics computes a monthly CPI based on the prices paid by urban consumers for a representative basket of goods and services. Currently, the base period for the CPI is 1982–1984 = 100; that is, all price changes are measured from a base that represents the average index level of the period encompassing 1982, 1983, and 1984. The prices of several hundred consumption items are included in the index. In addition, randomly selected consumers help determine the expenditure for the representative basket of goods and services. The corresponding quantities of items in the base year are used for computing the weights for the index.

The PPI is a weighted aggregate price index of prices measured at the wholesale, or producer level. Prior to 1978, the PPI was called the Wholesale Price Index, WPI. The U.S. Bureau of Labor Statistics computes a monthly PPI based on the selling prices received by domestic producers for their entire marketed output. Currently, the base period for the PPI is 1982 = 100. The target set includes purchases of goods and services by consumers—directly from the producer or indirectly from a retailer—and by other producers as inputs to their production, or as capital investment.

Note that the CPI is based on out-of-pocket expenditures of an urban consumer and the PPI is based on the portion that is actually received by the producer. Therefore, although sales and excise taxes are included in the CPI, they are not included in the PPI because they do not represent revenue to the producer. The differences between the PPI and CPI are consistent with the way these indices are used for deflation. It is common to use the CPI to adjust wages for changes in the cost of living. The PPI, on the other hand, is useful to deflate revenue in order to obtain real growth in output.

It is often assumed that the direction and magnitude of a price change in the PPI for finished goods anticipates a similar change in the CPI for all items. This is not always the case. In Figure 19.2, we use the ***CPI_PPI*** data to plot the annual CPI and PPI from 1960–2010, with a base of 1982–1984. Interestingly, the two indices moved in sync until the early 1980s. Beyond that, changes in prices that consumers paid far exceeded those received by producers, with the difference peaking in 2002. Also noteworthy is the fact that while there was a significant dip in the PPI, the CPI showed a very slight decline during the peak of the financial crisis in 2009.

FIGURE 19.2
CPI and PPI for 1960–2010; base period 1982–1984

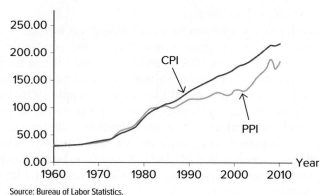

Source: Bureau of Labor Statistics.

EXAMPLE 19.13

Tom Denio has been a project manager in a small construction firm in Atlanta since 2000. He started with a salary of $52,000, which grew to $84,000 in 2008. The revenue of the construction firm also grew over the years, increasing from $13 million in 2000 to $18 million in 2008. According to the Bureau of Labor Statistics, the values of the consumer price index with a base of 1982–1984 for 2000 and 2008 are 172.20 and 215.30, respectively. The corresponding values of the producer price index are 132.70 and 189.60, respectively.

a. Compute and analyze the nominal and real increase in Tom's salary.
b. Compute and analyze the nominal and real revenue growth of the construction firm.

SOLUTION:

a. Tom's nominal salary grew by $\frac{84,000 - 52,000}{52,000} = 0.62$, or by 62% from 2000 to 2008. This nominal salary makes no cost of living adjustment. We use the CPI to compute his real salary as $(52,000/172.20) \times 100 = \$30,197$ in 2000 and $(84,000/215.30) \times 100 = \$39,015$ in 2008. These are Tom's real salaries based on 1982–1984 prices. Thus, while Tom's salary increased by 62% in dollar amounts, his purchasing power increased by only $\frac{39,015 - 30,197}{30,197} = 0.29$, or by 29%.

b. The nominal revenue of the construction firm grew by $\frac{18 - 13}{13} = 0.38$, or by 38% from 2000 to 2008. We use the producer price index to compute the revenue growth in real terms. The real revenue is $(13/132.70) \times 100 = \$9.80$ million in 2000 and $(18/189.60) \times 100 = \$9.49$ million in 2008. Therefore, the real growth in revenue for the construction firm has been $\frac{9.49 - 9.80}{9.80} = -0.03$, or -3%.

Inflation Rate

The **inflation rate** is the percentage rate of change of a price index over time. We generally use the CPI to compute the inflation rate in the United States. Also, although it is common to quote the inflation rate in annual terms, the CPI can be used to calculate the inflation rate for any time period.

CALCULATING THE INFLATION RATE

The reported inflation rate i_t for a given period is generally based on the consumer price index, CPI. It is computed as $i_t = \frac{CPI_t - CPI_{t-1}}{CPI_{t-1}}$.

EXAMPLE 19.14

The consumer price indices for the years 2006, 2007, and 2008 are reported as 201.59, 207.34, and 215.30, respectively (Source: Bureau of Labor Statistics). Use this information to compute the annual inflation rate for 2007 and 2008.

SOLUTION: The inflation rates for 2007 and 2008 are computed as

$$i_{2007} = \frac{CPI_{2007} - CPI_{2006}}{CPI_{2006}} = \frac{207.34 - 201.59}{201.59} = 0.0285 \text{ or } 2.85\%.$$

$$i_{2008} = \frac{CPI_{2008} - CPI_{2007}}{CPI_{2007}} = \frac{215.30 - 207.34}{207.34} = 0.0384 \text{ or } 3.84\%.$$

Therefore, the inflation rate increased from 2.85% in 2007 to 3.84% in 2008.

EXAMPLE 19.15

At the beginning of 2007, Joe Gonzales invested $1,000 in a mutual fund, which grew to $1,050 in a year. The consumer price index, with a base of 1982–1984, is 203.37 for January 2007 and 212.23 for January 2008. Compute the real annual rate of return for Joe.

SOLUTION: The real rate of return is based on the deflated investment values, which for the two years are computed as $\frac{1,000}{203.37} \times 100 = \$491.71$ and $\frac{1,050}{212.23} \times 100 = \$494.75$, respectively. The resulting real return of investment is derived as $\frac{494.75 - 491.71}{491.71} = 0.0062$, or 0.62%.

In Section 19.1, we used the Fisher equation to convert the nominal return into the real return. The Fisher equation will give us this same value for the real return on the investment. The nominal return for Joe is $\frac{1,050 - 1,000}{1,000} = 0.05$, and the corresponding inflation rate is $\frac{212.23 - 203.37}{203.37} = 0.0436$. Therefore, using the Fisher equation, we can compute $1 + r = \frac{1 + R}{1 + i} = \frac{1.05}{1.0436} = 1.0061$ to get the real rate of return $r = 0.0061$, which varies slightly from the previous calculation for the real rate of return due to rounding.

EXERCISES 19.3

Mechanics

22. The nominal values for four years are given by 32, 37, 39, and 42. Convert these values to real terms if the price index values for the corresponding years are given by 100, 102, 103, and 108.

23. An item increases in value from 240 to 280 in one year. What is the percentage change in the value of this item? Compute the percentage change in real terms if overall prices have increased by 5% for the same period.

24. Let revenues increase by 10% from $100,000 to $110,000. Calculate the percentage change in real terms if the relevant price index increases by 4% from 100 to 104.

25. The following table represents the nominal values of an item and the corresponding price index for 2007 and 2008.

Year	Nominal Value	Price Index
2007	38	112
2008	40	120

a. Compute the inflation rate for 2008.
b. Compute the annual percentage change of the item in real terms.

26. The following table represents the nominal values of an item and the corresponding price index from 2009 to 2011.

Year	Nominal Value	Price Index
2009	38	100
2010	40	103
2011	42	112

a. Compare the percentage change in the nominal values with the corresponding real values from 2009 to 2010.
b. Compare the percentage change in the nominal values with the corresponding real values from 2010 to 2011.
c. Use the price data to compute the inflation rate for 2010 and 2011.

Applications

27. **FILE** *Sales_2009.* Economists often look at retail sales data to gauge the state of the economy. This is especially so in a recession year, when consumer spending has decreased. Consider the following table, which shows U.S. monthly nominal retail sales for 2009. Sales are measured in millions of dollars and have been seasonally adjusted. Also included in the table is the corresponding producer price index (PPI) for 2009.

Month	Sales	PPI	Month	Sales	PPI
January	340439	171.2	July	342489	171.6
February	342356	170.9	August	350800	174.1
March	339228	169.6	September	343687	173.3
April	338344	170.6	October	347641	174.0
May	339873	170.6	November	354467	176.6
June	342912	173.7	December	353817	177.3

Source: Federal Reserve Bank of Dallas.

a. How many times were nominal sales below that of the previous month?

b. Use the PPI to compute sales in real terms. How many times were real sales below that of the previous month?

c. Compute the total percentage increase in nominal as well as real retail sales in 2009.

d. Can economists feel optimistic about the economy based on the retail sales data?

28. Japan was the first Asian country to challenge the dominance of the United States in the 1980s. However, since then, its economy has been in a slow but relentless decline (*The New York Times*, October 16, 2010). This country has been trapped in low growth and a downward spiral of prices, known as deflation. Consider the following CPI for Japan for the years 2001 through 2009. Compute and interpret the annual inflation rates in Japan in the 2000s.

Year	2001	2002	2003	2004	2005	2006	2007	2008	2009
CPI	120.1	119.0	118.7	118.7	118.3	118.7	118.7	120.3	118.7

Source: Bureau of Labor Statistics.

29. **FILE** *Earnings_2008.* Each month the Current Employment Statistics (CES) program surveys numerous businesses and government agencies in order to obtain detailed data on earnings of workers. Consider the following data on the national average of hourly earnings for 2008. Also included is the corresponding consumer price index for 2008.

Month	Earnings	CPI	Month	Earnings	CPI
January	21.25	173.3	July	21.66	183.7
February	21.29	173.9	August	21.74	181.9
March	21.43	175.8	September	21.80	182.0
April	21.43	176.5	October	21.84	177.3
May	21.52	178.8	November	21.93	172.3
June	21.60	181.5	December	21.96	169.4

Source: Bureau of Labor Statistics.

a. Use the CPI to deflate the national average of hourly earnings.

b. Compute the percentage change in the nominal as well as real hourly earnings in 2008.

c. Were consumers getting better off over 2008? Explain.

Use the following information on CPI and PPI for Exercises 30, 31, and 32.

Year	CPI (1982–84 =100)	PPI (1982 = 100)
2006	201.59	164.80
2007	207.34	172.70
2008	215.30	189.60
2009	214.54	172.90

Source: Bureau of Labor Statistics.

30. The total revenue for The Walt Disney Company was $35,510,000 for 2007, $37,843,000 for 2008, and $36,149,000 for 2009 (Source: http://finance.yahoo.com).

a. Deflate the total revenue with the relevant price index.

b. Discuss the revenue trend during the 2007–2009 period using nominal as well as real values.

31. According to the New Hampshire Department of Education, the average teacher salary in public school districts in New Hampshire was $46,797 in 2006, $48,310 in 2007, and $46,797 in 2008. Comment on the percentage change in the dollar value (nominal) as well as the purchasing power (real) of salaries.

32. According to Fisher College of Business at The Ohio State University, the starting salary of their graduates in the MBA program in 2008 was $89,156. What must be the starting salary of the MBAs in 2009 if the salary increase makes the exact cost of living adjustment?

WRITING WITH STATISTICS

©Bettmann/Getty Images

Valerie Barnes is a graduate student in the department of political science at Michigan State University. She has been asked to write a brief report on the changes in the economic climate during the presidency of Ronald Reagan from 1981–1989. Valerie collects information on various economic indicators at the beginning and the end of President Reagan's term, as shown in Table 19.9.

TABLE 19.9 Select Economic Indicators during the Reagan Presidency

Economic Indicators	1981	1989
Federal Debt ($ billions)	$994.8	$2,868.0
Median Household Income	$19,074	$28,906
Cost of a New Home	$83,000	$148,800
Dow Jones Industrial Average High	1,024	2,791
Cost of a Gallon of Regular Gasoline	$1.38	$1.12
Consumer Price Index (1982–1984 = 100)	90.9	124

Source: www.1980sflashback.com.

Valerie would like to use the above information to

1. Evaluate the change in prices over the Reagan era, including the annual inflation rate.
2. Calculate and interpret corresponding deflated economic indicators for 1981 and 1989.
3. Comment on changes in select economic indicators during Reagan's presidency.

Sample Report— Economic Indicators during Reagan's Presidency

Ronald Wilson Reagan became the 40th President of the United States in 1981 after serving eight years as governor of California. He took office at a time when the United States was experiencing economic stagnation and inflation. As president, Reagan advocated reduced business regulation and extensive tax cuts to boost economic growth. Arguably, the Reagan era signifies a period of significant growth as the economy recovered from the recession.

Crucial economic indicators were analyzed during Reagan's presidency. The consumer price index (CPI) values indicate that prices were 9.1% lower in 1981 and 24% higher in 1989 than during the base years of 1982–1984. The percentage price increase during Reagan's term is calculated as 36.41%, resulting in an annualized inflation rate of $(1 + 0.3641)^{1/8} - 1 = 3.96\%$. The CPI is also used to deflate crucial economic indicators. For instance, while the median household income increased from $19,074 to $28,906, or by 51.55%, the corresponding deflated incomes increased from $20,984 to $23,311, or by 11.09%. Other similarly deflated economic indicators are presented in Table 19.A.

TABLE 19.A Deflated Economic Indicators

Economic Indicators	1981	1989
Federal Debt ($ billions)	$1,094.4	$2,312.9
Median Household Income	$20,984	$23,311
Cost of a New Home	$91,309	$120,000
Dow Jones Industrial Average High	1,127	2,251
Cost of a Gallon of Regular Gasoline	$1.52	$0.90

The significant increase in the federal debt during the Reagan era is noteworthy. When Reagan took office, he used deficit spending through tax cuts to stimulate the economy. However, the debt continued to grow throughout the boom years. The resulting deflated federal debt rose sharply from $1,094.4 billion in 1981 to $2,312.9 billion in 1989, or by 111%. The deflated cost of a new home grew from $91,309 to $120,000, or by 31.42%. Therefore, despite the 11.09% growth in real income, a higher percentage increase in home values made owning a new home more difficult. Interestingly, the deflated Dow Jones Industrial Average High grew by a whopping 99.73% from 1,127 in 1981 to 2,251 in 1989. Finally, there was a steep decline of 40.79% in the deflated price of gasoline, from $1.52 per gallon to $0.90 per gallon. Perhaps the price decline was the consequence of the falling demand as consumers reacted to the energy crisis of the 1970s.

President Reagan's policies reflected his personal belief in individual freedom. According to Reagan supporters, his policies resulted in the largest peacetime economic boom in American history. His critics, on the other hand, argue that the Reagan era is associated with a widening of inequality, where the rich got richer with little economic gains for most Americans. This argument is partly reflected by a meager 11.09% real increase in the median household income during the supposedly good years.

CONCEPTUAL REVIEW

LO 19.1 Define and compute investment returns.

The **investment return** R_t is calculated as $R_t = \frac{P_t - P_{t-1} + I_t}{P_{t-1}}$, where $\frac{P_t - P_{t-1}}{P_{t-1}}$ and $\frac{I_t}{P_{t-1}}$ are the **capital gains yield** and the **income yield** components, respectively.

The **adjusted closing price** makes appropriate adjustments for dividend distributions, stock splits, and reverse stock splits. Let P_t^* and P_{t-1}^* represent the adjusted closing price of a stock at times t (current) and $t - 1$ (prior), respectively. Using adjusted closing prices, the investment return R_t at the end of time t is calculated as $R_t = \frac{P_t^* - P_{t-1}^*}{P_{t-1}^*}$.

LO 19.2 Use the Fisher equation to convert nominal returns into real returns and vice versa.

The **Fisher equation**, $1 + r = \frac{1 + R}{1 + i}$, represents the relationship between the nominal return R, the real return r, and the expected inflation rate i.

LO 19.3 Calculate and interpret a simple price index.

An **index number** is an easy-to-interpret numerical value that reflects a percentage change in price or quantity from a base value. A **simple price index** is a ratio of the price in period t, p_t, and the price in the base period, p_0, expressed as a percentage. It is calculated as $\frac{p_t}{p_0} \times 100$. It is common to update the base period over time. We update a simple index, with a revised base period, as $\text{Updated Index} = \frac{\text{Old Index Value}}{\text{Old Index Value of New Base}} \times 100$.

LO 19.4 Calculate and interpret an unweighted aggregate price index.

Let p_{it} represent the price of item i in period t, and let p_{i0} be the corresponding price in the base period ($t = 0$). An **unweighted aggregate price index** in period t is $\frac{\Sigma p_{it}}{\Sigma p_{i0}} \times 100$.

Compare the Laspeyres and the Paasche methods for computing a weighted aggregate price index.

Let p_{it} and q_{it} represent the price and quantity of item i in period t, and let p_{i0} and q_{i0} be the corresponding values in the base period ($t = 0$). Using only the base period quantities q_{i0}, the **Laspeyres price index** for period t is $\frac{\Sigma p_{it} q_{i0}}{\Sigma p_{i0} q_{i0}} \times 100$. Using only the current period ($t = n$) quantities q_{in}, the **Paasche price index** for period t is $\frac{\Sigma p_{it} q_{in}}{\Sigma p_{i0} q_{in}} \times 100$.

Use price indices to deflate economic time series and derive the inflation rate.

A **deflated time series** is obtained by adjusting it for changes in prices, or inflation. A time series that has been deflated is said to be represented in **real terms**. The unadjusted time series is said to be represented in **nominal terms**. We use a price index to convert the nominal value of a time series into its real value as

$$\text{Real Value} = \frac{\text{Nominal Value}}{\text{Price Index}} \times 100.$$

Two price indices commonly used to deflate economic time series are the **Consumer Price Index (CPI)** and the **Producer Price Index (PPI)**. It is common to use the CPI to adjust wages for changes in the cost of living. On the other hand, the PPI is useful to deflate revenue in order to obtain real growth in output. The reported **inflation rate** i_t for a given period is generally based on the CPI and is computed as

$$i_t = \frac{CPI_t - CPI_{t-1}}{CPI_{t-1}}.$$

ADDITIONAL EXERCISES AND CASE STUDIES

Exercises

33. Kim Baek invested $20,000 for a year in corporate bonds. Each bond sold for $1,000 and earned a coupon payment of $80 each during the year. The price of the bond at the end of the year has dropped to $980.
    a. Calculate Kim's investment return.
    b. Calculate Kim's total dollar gain or loss on his investment.

34. Toyota Motor Corp., once considered a company synonymous with reliability and customer satisfaction, has been engulfed in a perfect storm with millions of cars recalled (*BBC News*, March 19, 2010). The following table shows the monthly adjusted closing price per share of Toyota from October 2009 to March 2010.

Date	Adjusted Closing Price	Date	Adjusted Closing Price
October 2009	78.89	January 2010	77.00
November 2009	78.54	February 2010	74.83
December 2009	84.16	March 2010	79.56

Source: http://finance.yahoo.com.

a. Form a simple price index with October 2009 as the base.

b. Update the simple price index, using January 2010 as the base.
c. What is the percentage price change from October 2009 to December 2009?
d. What is the percentage price change from January 2010 to March 2010?

35. Consider the following price data from 2002 to 2010.

Year	2002	2003	2004	2005	2006	2007	2008	2009	2010
Price	3.20	3.46	3.51	4.02	4.18	4.30	4.59	4.50	4.70

a. Compute the simple price index using 2002 as the base year.
b. Update the index numbers with a base year revised from 2002 to 2005.
c. Plot the index numbers with a base year of 2002 and a base year of 2005. Compare the two plots.

36. Consider the following price data from 2009 to 2011.

Year	Product 1	Product 2	Product 3
2009	38	94	45
2010	40	92	48
2011	42	98	56

a. Compute and interpret the simple price index for each product, using 2009 as the base year.

b. Compute and interpret the unweighted aggregate price index, using 2009 as the base year.

37. Let the quantities corresponding to the prices in the previous exercise be given by the following table.

Year	Product 1	Product 2	Product 3
2009	90	32	48
2010	82	34	46
2011	76	30	36

a. Compute the Laspeyres price index, using 2009 as the base year.

b. Compute the Paasche price index, using 2009 as the base year.

c. Comment on the differences between the two indices.

38. Lindsay Kelly bought 100 shares of Google, 300 shares of Microsoft, and 500 shares of Nokia in January 2005. The adjusted closing prices of these stocks over the next three years are shown in the accompanying table.

Year	Google	Microsoft	Nokia
2005	195.62	24.11	13.36
2006	432.66	26.14	16.54
2007	505.00	28.83	19.83

Source: http://finance.yahoo.com.

a. Compute and interpret the unweighted aggregate price index for Lindsay's portfolio, using 2005 as the base year.

b. Compute and interpret the corresponding weighted price index using the Laspeyres approach.

c. Why are the results from parts a and b so different?

39. Citigroup, Inc., is a major financial services company based in New York. It suffered huge losses during the global financial crisis and was rescued in November 2008 in a massive bailout by the U.S. government. Consider the following table, representing the net revenue and net income of Citigroup for 2006 to 2009. Both variables are measured in billions of dollars.

Year	Net Revenue	Net Income
2006	146.6	21.2
2007	159.2	3.6
2008	105.8	−27.7
2009	111.0	−1.6

Source: http://money.cnn.com.

a. Compute and interpret the simple price index for net revenue, using 2006 as the base year.

b. Compute and interpret the simple price index for net income, using 2006 as the base year.

40. Consider the following consumer price index (CPI) and producer price index (PPI) for 2006–2009.

Year	CPI (1982–84 =100)	PPI (1982 = 100)
2006	201.59	164.80
2007	207.34	172.70
2008	215.30	189.60
2009	214.54	172.90

Source: Bureau of Labor Statistics.

a. Use the relevant price index to deflate the data on net revenue of Citigroup, given in the previous exercise.

b. Use the relevant price index to deflate the data on net income of Citigroup, given in the previous exercise.

41. The adjusted closing stock prices of Wendy's/Arby's Group, Inc., for the first three months of 2008 are presented in the following table. Assume that these adjusted closing prices are computed at the end of the month. Also included in the table is the corresponding consumer price index (CPI).

Date	Adjusted Closing Price	CPI (Base 1982–1984)
January 2008	8.94	212.225
February 2008	8.29	212.703
March 2008	6.01	213.543

Source: http://finance.yahoo.com; and Bureau of Labor Statistics.

a. Find the real rate of return for February 2008 and March 2008 by first using the CPI to deflate the adjusted closing price.

b. Replicate the above result with Fisher's equation, based on the nominal rate of return and the inflation rate.

42. An investor bought 1,000 shares of Citigroup in January 2009 for $3.55 a share. She sold all of her shares in December 2009 for $3.31 a share.

a. What annual rate of return did the investor earn?

b. Use the CPI information from Exercise 40 to compute the inflation rate for 2009.

c. What is the investor's real rate of return?

CASE STUDIES

CASE STUDY 19.1   The dot-com period, roughly between 1995 and 2000, was characterized by extreme investor optimism for Internet-based businesses. This period was also marked by young, bold managers who made a good deal of money by reaching consumers over the Internet. Arguably, the dot-com boom was a case of too much too fast and was consequently followed by a crash in March 2000. Jose Menges is a business student at a California State University. For his senior seminar course, he has been asked to compare the stock performance of Internet-based companies with non-Internet-based companies during the dot-com boom-bust period. He collects end of the month data on the adjusted closing prices from 1999 to 2000 for four companies. Amazon (AMZN) and eBay (EBAY) are chosen to represent the Internet-based companies, whereas Coca-Cola (COKE) and Johnson and Johnson (JNJ) reflect non-Internet companies. A portion of the data is shown in the accompanying table.

Dotcom

Data for Case Study 19.1 Monthly Adjusted Closing Stock Prices for Four Firms, 1999–2000

Month	AMZN	EBAY	COKE	JNJ
Jan-99	58.47	11.57	44.00	33.93
Feb-99	64.06	13.92	43.80	34.13
⋮	⋮	⋮	⋮	⋮
Dec-00	15.56	8.25	30.84	41.86

Source: http://finance.yahoo.com.

In a report, use the sample information to

1. Compute monthly returns for all companies for February 1999 through December 2000.

2. Compare the stock performance for the Internet-based companies with non-Internet-based companies in the dot-com boom-bust period.

CASE STUDY 19.2   The United States is often blamed for triggering the 2008 global financial crisis because many of the excesses and bad practices originated in the United States. The crisis has had consequences on all aspects of the global economy. According to a recent report by the Brookings Institute, the U.S. economic crisis is linked to a huge drop in world trade. Since U.S. imports have been an important component of world demand, a drop in imports has had repercussions in its exports. Rami Horowitz is a young economist working for a trade policy institute. He wishes to analyze the changes in U.S. imports and exports over the 2007–2009 time period. Rami collects quarterly data on real exports and real imports, where the values are seasonally adjusted and measured in billions of 2005 dollars. A portion of the data is shown in the accompanying table.

Data for Case Study 19.2 U.S. Real Exports and Imports

World_Trade

Period	Real Exports	Real Imports
2007: Quarter 1	1485.9	2190.8
2007: Quarter 2	1504.8	2188.1
⋮	⋮	⋮
2009: Quarter 4	1555.5	1902.7

Source: Federal Reserve Bank of Dallas.

In a report, use the sample information to

1. Create simple indices for real exports and real imports with Quarter 1, 2007, used as the base period.

2. Interpret the percentage changes in real exports and real imports over the three-year period.

CASE STUDY 19.3 The Cheesecake Factory, Inc., is a popular restaurant chain in the United States. Although it started as a small restaurant in 1978, it currently has over 140 branches all over the country. The restaurants are characterized by extensive menus, custom décor, and large portions of food. Jeff Watson works as the kitchen manager in one of their regional branches. He is responsible for managing the operations as well as food and labor costs. He constantly monitors market conditions and, in his annual reports, analyzes the changing retail cost of the ingredients used in cooking. In his current report, he decides to analyze meat prices. He collects data on monthly average retail prices of three varieties of ground beef. This information is important, as the restaurant purchases about 1,400 pounds of regular, 800 pounds of ground chuck, and 500 pounds of lean ground beef each month. A portion of the data is shown in the accompanying table.

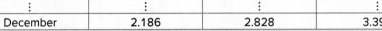 Data for Case Study 19.3 2009 Monthly Retail Cost of Ground Beef (in $ per pound)

Month	Regular Beef	Ground Chuck	Lean Ground Beef
January	2.357	2.961	3.426
February	2.436	3.019	3.440
⋮	⋮	⋮	⋮
December	2.186	2.828	3.391

Source: United States Department of Agriculture.

Ground_Beef

In a report, use the sample information to

1. Compute and interpret simple indices for each variety of meat, using January 2009 as the base period.

2. Compute and interpret the weighted aggregate price index, using January 2009 as the base period.

3. Compare the above indices.

20 Nonparametric Tests

The hypothesis tests presented in earlier chapters make certain assumptions about the underlying population. We refer to these tests as parametric tests. A t or an F test, for example, requires that the observations come from a normal distribution. These tests are quite "robust," in the sense that they are still useful when the assumptions are not exactly fulfilled, especially when the sample size is large. However, in situations when the underlying population is markedly nonnormal and the sample size is not large, we apply distribution-free alternative techniques called nonparametric tests. Nonparametric tests also do not require a level of measurement as strong as that necessary for parametric tests. For instance, we cannot calculate means and variances with ordinal data (required calculations for parametric tests) because the numbers on an ordinal scale have no meaning except to indicate rank order. In this chapter, we explore a variety of nonparametric tests that make fewer assumptions about the distribution of the underlying population and/or treat data of a weaker scale.

©monkeybusinessimages/iStock/Getty Images Plus/Getty Images RF

INTRODUCTORY CASE

Analyzing Mutual Fund Returns

In Chapter 3, we were introduced to Jacqueline Brennan, a financial advisor at a large invest-ment firm. One of her clients has narrowed his investment options to two mutual funds from the Vanguard family: the Growth Index mutual fund (henceforth, Growth) and the Value Index mutual fund (henceforth, Value). He has some final questions for Jacqueline with respect to each mutual fund's return. Jacqueline explains that her analysis will use techniques that do not rely on stringent assumptions concerning the distribution of the underlying population, since return data often diverge from the normal distribution. Table 20.1 shows a portion of the annual return data for each fund and some relevant descriptive statistics for the years 2007–2016.

TABLE 20.1 Annual Returns and Descriptive Statistics (in percent) for Vanguard's Growth and Value Funds, 2007–2016

FILE
Growth_Value

Year	Growth	Value
2007	12.56	0.09
2008	−38.32	−35.97
⋮	⋮	⋮
2016	5.99	16.75
	$\bar{x} = 10.088$ median = 13.015 $s = 20.448$	$\bar{x} = 7.560$ median = 13.655 $s = 18.459$

Source: finance.yahoo.com; data retrieved February 17, 2017.

Jacqueline would like to use the above sample information to

1. Determine whether the median return for each fund is greater than 5%.
2. Determine whether the median difference between the two funds' returns differs from zero.
3. Determine whether the funds' returns are correlated.

A synopsis of this case is provided at the end of Section 20.4.

20.1 TESTING A POPULATION MEDIAN

The parametric tests presented in earlier chapters make certain assumptions about the underlying population. These conventional tests can be misleading if the underlying assumptions are not met. **Nonparametric tests**, also referred to as distribution-free tests, are attractive when the parametric assumptions seem unreasonable. Nonparametric tests use fewer and weaker assumptions than those associated with parametric tests. For instance, these tests do not assume that the sample data originate from a normal distribution. Nonparametric tests are especially useful when sample sizes are small. Finally, while parametric tests require data of interval or ratio scale, nonparametric tests can be performed on data of nominal or ordinal scale. (For a review of these data concepts, refer to Section 3 in Chapter 1.)

Nonparametric tests have disadvantages, too. If the parametric assumptions are valid yet we choose to use a nonparametric test, the nonparametric test is less powerful (more prone to Type II error) than its parametric counterpart. The reason for less power is that a nonparametric test uses the data less efficiently. As we will see shortly, nonparametric tests often focus on the rank of the data rather than the magnitude of the sample values, thus possibly ignoring useful information.

Table 20.2 summarizes some of the parametric tests that we examined in earlier chapters. The first column shows the parametric test of interest, the second column states the underlying assumptions of the test, and the third column lists where the test was covered in the text. Each one of these parametric tests has a nonparametric counterpart. At the end of Section 20.4, we will present a table that lists the corresponding nonparametric test for each parametric test.

TABLE 20.2 Summary of Select Parametric Tests

Parametric Test	Population Characteristics and Other Description	Reference Section
t test concerning the population mean	Sampling from a normal population or large sample; σ unknown	9.3
t test to determine whether the population mean difference differs from some assumed value based on matched-pairs sampling	Sampling from a normal population or large sample	10.2
t test to determine whether two population means differ from some assumed value based on independent sampling	Sampling from normal populations or large samples; σ_1 and σ_2 unknown	10.1
F test to determine whether three or more population means differ	Sampling from normal populations or large samples; $\sigma_1, \sigma_2, \sigma_3, \ldots$ unknown but assumed equal	13.1
t test to determine whether two variables are correlated	Sampling from a normal population or large sample	14.1

The Wilcoxon Signed-Rank Test for a Population Median

In Chapter 9, we used a t test to determine whether the population mean μ (σ unknown) differs from some assumed value. However, as shown in Table 20.2, a t test requires that we sample from a normal distribution. In a small sample, if we cannot assume that the data are normally distributed and/or we want to test whether the population *median* differs from some hypothesized value, we can apply the **Wilcoxon signed-rank test**. The Wilcoxon signed-rank test makes no assumptions concerning the distribution of the population except that it is continuous and symmetric.

Let's revisit the introductory case. In order to analyze the fund return data, Jacqueline chooses nonparametric methods because the distribution of return data often has "fatter tails" as compared to the normal distribution; that is, the likelihood of extreme returns (area under the tail) is higher for a fatter-tailed distribution than for a normal distribution. Figure 20.1 shows a normal distribution versus a distribution with fatter tails. If Jacqueline were to rely on tests that incorrectly assume that the data are normally distributed, then there is a chance that she may make erroneous conclusions. She chooses to use the Wilcoxon signed-rank test for the population median.

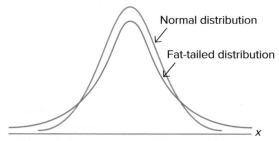

FIGURE 20.1
Normal distribution versus "fat-tailed" distribution

Following the methodology outlined in earlier chapters, when conducting a hypothesis test for the population median m, we want to test whether m differs from, is greater than, or is less than m_0, the value of the population median postulated in the null hypothesis. The null and alternative hypotheses will assume one of the following forms:

Two-Tailed Test	Right-Tailed Test	Left-Tailed Test
$H_0: m = m_0$	$H_0: m \leq m_0$	$H_0: m \geq m_0$
$H_A: m \neq m_0$	$H_A: m > m_0$	$H_A: m < m_0$

For the Growth and the Value fund return data presented in Table 20.1, we would like to determine whether the median return for each fund is greater than 5%. We start with the Growth fund and formulate the competing hypotheses for a one-tailed test as

$$H_0: m \leq 5$$
$$H_A: m > 5$$

To arrive at the sample value for the Wilcoxon signed-rank test statistic T, several calculations are necessary.

A. We first calculate the difference d_i between each observed value and the hypothesized median. In this case, we find $d_i = x_i - 5$. The second column of Table 20.3 shows the results.

TABLE 20.3 Calculations for the Wilcoxon Signed-Rank Test Statistic

Return, x (1)	$d = x - m_0$ (2)	$\lvert d \rvert$ (3)	Rank (4)	Ranks of Negative Differences (5)	Ranks of Positive Differences (6)
12.56	12.56 − 5 = 7.56	7.56	4		4
−38.32	−43.32	43.32	10	10	
36.29	31.29	31.29	9		9
16.96	11.96	11.96	7		7
1.71	−3.29	3.29	3	3	
16.89	11.89	11.89	6		6
32.16	27.16	27.16	8		8
13.47	8.47	8.47	5		5
3.17	−1.83	1.83	2	2	
5.99	0.99	0.99	1		1
				$T^- = 15$	$T^+ = 40$

B. We then take the absolute value of each difference, $|d_i|$; see the third column of Table 20.3. Any differences of zero are discarded from the sample. In this example, there are no zero differences. We calculate $|d_i|$ because if the median is 5 (the null hypothesis is true), then positive or negative differences of a given magnitude are equally likely.

C. Next we rank the absolute value of each difference, assigning 1 to the smallest $|d|$ and n to the largest $|d|$. Note that n would be smaller than the original sample size if there were some zero-difference observations, which would have been discarded. Here, n equals the original sample size of 10. Any ties in the ranks of differences are assigned the average of the tied ranks. For instance, if two observations have the rank of 5 (occupying the 5th and 6th positions), each is assigned the rank of $(5 + 6)/2 = 5.5$. Or, if three observations have a ranking of 1, each is assigned a rank of $(1 + 2 + 3)/3 = 2$. For the Growth fund return data, there are no ties. The rankings for the differences are shown in the fourth column of Table 20.3.

D. We then sum the ranks of the negative differences (denoted T^-) and sum the ranks of the positive differences (denoted T^+). In this example we find three negative differences, whose rank sum is $T^- = 15$, and seven positive differences, whose rank sum is $T^+ = 40$. These calculations are shown in the fifth and sixth columns of Table 20.3.

The sum of T^- and T^+ should equal $n(n + 1)/2$, which is the formula for the sum of consecutive integers from 1 to n. In our example, $T^- + T^+ = 15 + 40 = 55$. Also, $n(n + 1)/2 = 10(10 + 1)/2 = 55$, which is equivalent to the sum of the integers from 1 to n. If the null hypothesis were true, then both T^- and T^+ would equal about half of the total sum of ranks, or about $55/2 = 27.5$. For testing, we could analyze either T^- or T^+. In what follows, we will base the test on T^+. Although we do not use the value of T^- for the test, its calculation can help us avoid errors.

THE TEST STATISTIC T FOR THE WILCOXON SIGNED-RANK TEST

The test statistic T for the Wilcoxon signed-rank test is defined as $T = T^+$, where T^+ denotes the sum of the ranks of the positive differences from the hypothesized median m_0.

There are two scenarios when conducting the Wilcoxon signed-rank test:

1. If $n \leq 10$, then the p-value is found from the sampling distribution of T. Most statistical computer packages, including R, perform this calculation.

2. If $n \geq 10$, the sampling distribution of T can be approximated by the normal distribution with mean $\mu_T = \frac{n(n + 1)}{4}$ and standard deviation $\sigma_T = \sqrt{\frac{n(n + 1)(2n + 1)}{24}}$, and hence the value of the resulting test statistic is computed as $z = \frac{T - \mu_T}{\sigma_T}$.

For ease of exposition, we do not make a distinction between the random variable and the particular outcomes of the random variable. For example, we use the test statistic T to represent a random variable as well as its sample value. We adopt this same practice for the test statistics W, H, r_S, and R that we introduce in later sections.

EXAMPLE 20.1

Given the return data in Table 20.1, determine whether the median return for the Growth fund is greater than 5% with $\alpha = 0.05$.

SOLUTION: As shown earlier, the competing hypotheses for the test are

$$H_0: m \leq 5$$
$$H_A: m > 5$$

In this example, since the sample size equals exactly ten, we can implement the Wilcoxon test with or without the normal distribution approximation. Here, we implement the test without the normal approximation using R. (R instructions will be provided at the end of this section.) Table 20.4 reports a portion of the R output for a right-tailed test. We have put the value of the test statistic and the p-value in boldface. Even though R labels the value of the test statistic as V, it is identical to the one that we calculated manually—that is, $V = T = 40$. So, from Table 20.4 we see that the p-value $= 0.1162$. Since the p-value is greater than $\alpha = 0.05$, we do not reject H_0. At the 5% significance level, we cannot conclude that the median return for the Growth fund is greater than 5%.

TABLE 20.4 R's Output for Example 20.1

```
        Wilcoxon signed rank test
V = 40, p-value = 0.1162
alternative hypothesis: true location is greater
than 5
```

Using a Normal Distribution Approximation for T

As mentioned earlier, the sampling distribution of T can be approximated by the normal distribution if n has at least 10 observations.[1] We can then easily implement a z test with this approximation.

EXAMPLE 20.2

Redo the test specified in Example 20.1, using the normal distribution approximation.

SOLUTION: Again we use the competing hypotheses, $H_0: m \leq 5$ versus $H_A: m > 5$, and the value of the test statistic, $T = 40$. Since there are 10 years of return data ($n = 10$), we calculate the mean and the standard deviation of the sampling distribution of T as

$$\mu_T = \frac{n(n + 1)}{4} = \frac{10(10 + 1)}{4} = 27.50 \text{ and}$$

$$\sigma_T = \sqrt{\frac{n(n + 1)(2n + 1)}{24}} = \sqrt{\frac{10(10 + 1)(2 \times 10 + 1)}{24}} = 9.8107.$$

[1] Since the normality assumption for parametric tests becomes less stringent in large samples, the main appeal of rank-based tests tends to be with relatively small samples. Note, however, the Wilcoxon test requires the sample size to be at least 10, as compared to 30 required for the parametric t-test.

The corresponding value of the test statistic is

$$z = \frac{T - \mu_T}{\sigma_T} = \frac{40 - 27.50}{9.8107} = 1.27.$$

Therefore, with the normal distribution approximation, we find the corresponding p-value as $P(Z \geq 1.27) = 0.1020$. Since the p-value is greater than $\alpha = 0.05$, we do not reject H_0. This conclusion is consistent with the one made in Example 20.1; that is, at the 5% significance level, we cannot conclude that the median return is greater than 5%.

Using R to Test a Population Median

We can use a single function in R, the **wilcox.test** function, which greatly facilitates conducting a Wilcoxon signed-rank test.

EXAMPLE 20.3

Given the return data in Table 20.1, determine whether the median return for the Value fund is greater than 5% with $\alpha = 0.05$.

SOLUTION: The competing hypotheses for the test are

$$H_0: m \leq 5$$
$$H_A: m > 5$$

FILE
Growth_Value

a. Import the **Growth_Value** data into a data frame (table) in R.

b. We use R's **wilcox.test** function to find the value of the test statistic and the p-value. For options within the **wilcox.test** function, we use *mu* to specify the value of the hypothesized median and *alternative* to specify the alternative hypothesis (denoted as "two.sided" for a two-tailed test, "less" for a left-tailed test, and "greater" for a right-tailed test). Enter

```
> wilcox.test(Growth_Value$'Value', mu=5,
    alternative="greater")
```

Table 20.5 shows a portion of the R output.

TABLE 20.5 R's Output for Example 20.3

```
        Wilcoxon signed rank test
data: Growth_Value$Value
V = 39, p-value = 0.1377
alternative hypothesis: true location is greater
than 5
```

The value of the test statistic is $V = T = 39$ with a corresponding p-value of 0.1377 (see values in boldface). Since the p-value > 0.05, we do not reject the null hypothesis. At the 5% significance level, we cannot conclude that the median return for the Value fund is greater than 5%.

We should note that, by default, R generates an exact p-value if the sample size is less than 50 and there are no ties. Otherwise, a normal approximation is used.

EXERCISES 20.1

*For exercises marked with an asterisk, it is advised that you use a statistical software package that accommodates the Wilcoxon signed-rank test.

Mechanics

1. Consider the following sample data:

25	18	21	27	30

   a. Specify the competing hypotheses to determine whether the median differs from 20.
   b. Calculate the value of the test statistic T.
   c. The p-value corresponding to the test statistic in part b is equal to 0.188. At the 5% significance level, does the median differ from 20? Explain.

2. Consider the following sample data:

150	145	138	155	141	152

   a. Specify the competing hypotheses to determine whether the median is greater than 140.
   b. Calculate the value of the test statistic T.
   c. The p-value corresponding to the test statistic in part b is equal to 0.047. At the 5% significance level, is the median greater than 140? Explain.

3. Consider the following sample data.

8	5	11	7	6	5

   a. Specify the competing hypotheses to determine whether the median is less than 10.
   b. Calculate the value of the test statistic T.
   c. The p-value corresponding to the test statistic in part b is approximately equal to 0.029. At the 5% significance level, what is the conclusion to the hypothesis test? Explain.

4. Consider the following competing hypotheses and sample data.

   $H_0: m \le 150$ $n = 30$ $T^- = 200$ $T^+ = 265$
   $H_A: m > 150$

   a. Assuming that the sampling distribution of T is normally distributed, calculate the value of the test statistic.
   b. Calculate the p-value.
   c. At the 5% significance level, what is the conclusion? Explain.

5. Consider the following sample data.

105	90	110	80	85	85	103	70	115	75

   Assume the normal approximation for T.
   a. Specify the competing hypotheses to determine whether the median differs from 100.
   b. Calculate the value of the test statistic and the p-value.
   c. At the 10% significance level, is the median different from 100? Explain.

Applications

6. A random sample of eight drugstores shows the following prices (in $) for a popular pain reliever:

5.00	4.25	3.75	5.50	5.75	6.25	5.25	4.25

   a. Specify the competing hypotheses to determine whether the median price is less than $6.00.
   b. Calculate the value of the test statistic.
   c. The p-value corresponding to the test statistic in part b is approximately equal to 0.012. At the 5% significance level, what is the conclusion to the hypothesis test? Explain.

7. **FILE** *Balanced.* The following table lists a portion of the data representing the annual returns (in percent) over a 10-year period for the Balanced mutual fund, a top-performing mutual fund from the Janus Capital Group.

Year	Return
2007	10.15
2008	−15.22
⋮	⋮
2016	4.51

Source: www.finance.yahoo.com

   a. Specify the competing hypotheses to determine whether the median return is greater than 5%.
   b. Calculate the value of the test statistic, assuming that the sampling distribution of T is normally distributed.
   c. At the 10% significance level, what is the conclusion to the hypothesis test?

8. During the fourth quarter of 2009, rents declined in almost all major cities in the United States. The largest fall was in New York, where average rents fell nearly 20% to $44.69 per square foot annually (*The Wall Street Journal*, January 8, 2010). The following table lists the average rent per square foot (in $) for 10 cities during the fourth quarter of 2009.

City	Rent	City	Rent
New York	45	Miami	24
Washington, D.C.	42	Seattle	24
San Francisco	30	Chicago	21
Boston	30	Houston	20
Los Angeles	27	Philadelphia	20

a. Specify the competing hypotheses to determine whether the median rent is greater than $25 per square foot.
b. Calculate the value of the test statistic. Assume the normal approximation for *T*.
c. Calculate the *p*-value.
d. At the 1% significance level, can you conclude that the median rent exceeds $25 per square foot?

9.* **FILE** *Wage.* An economist wants to test whether the median hourly wage is less than $22.
a. Specify the competing hypotheses for the test.
b. At the 5% significance level, can you conclude that the median hourly wage is less than $22? Explain.

10.* **FILE** *MV_Houses.* A realtor in Mission Viejo, California, believes that the median price of a house is more than $500,000. The accompanying data is in $1,000s.
a. Specify the competing hypotheses for the test.
b. At the 5% significance level, is the realtor's claim supported by the data? Explain.

11.* **FILE** *Convenience.* An entrepreneur examines monthly sales (in $1,000s) for 40 convenience stores in Rhode Island.
a. Specify the competing hypotheses to determine whether median sales differ from $130,000.
b. At the 5% significance level, do median sales differ from $130,000? Explain.

20.2 TESTING TWO POPULATION MEDIANS

In Chapter 10, we presented *t* tests to determine whether significant differences existed between population means from matched-pairs and independent samples. When using a *t* test, we assume that we are sampling from normal populations. If we wish to compare central tendencies from nonnormal populations, then the **Wilcoxon signed-rank test** serves as the nonparametric counterpart to the matched-pairs *t* test. The **Wilcoxon rank-sum test**, also referred to as the **Mann-Whitney test**, is used for independent samples. We again note that if the normality assumption is not unreasonable, then these tests are less powerful than the parametric *t* tests. We begin this section by examining the Wilcoxon signed-rank test for a matched-pairs experiment, followed by the Wilcoxon rank-sum test for independent samples.

LO 20.3

Make inferences about the population median difference based on matched-pairs sampling.

The Wilcoxon Signed-Rank Test for a Matched-Pairs Sample

In this application of matched-pairs sampling, the parameter of interest is referred to as the median difference m_D, where $D = X - Y$, and the random variables X and Y are matched in a pair. We refer you to Chapter 10 for details on matched-pairs sampling. When we wish to test whether m_D differs from, is greater than, or is less than 0, we set up the competing hypotheses as follows.

Two-Tailed Test	Right-Tailed Test	Left-Tailed Test
$H_0: m_D = 0$	$H_0: m_D \leq 0$	$H_0: m_D \geq 0$
$H_A: m_D \neq 0$	$H_A: m_D > 0$	$H_A: m_D < 0$

The Wilcoxon signed-rank test for a matched-pairs sample is nearly identical to its use for a single sample. The only added step is that we first find the difference between each pairing. We illustrate the Wilcoxon signed-rank test for a matched-pairs sample using the *Growth_Value* data from the introductory case.

FILE
Growth_Value

We must first recognize that these samples are dependent, in that each return observation is blocked by year. We apply the Wilcoxon signed-rank test to determine whether significant differences exist between the median difference of the returns and formulate the two-tailed test as

$$H_0: m_D = 0$$
$$H_A: m_D \neq 0$$

Table 20.6 summarizes the method for calculating the value of the T statistic; that is, we first calculate differences between the returns (column 4), find absolute differences (column 5), and determine rankings (column 6). Then we compute the sum of the ranks of negative differences (column 7, $T^- = 15$) and the sum of the ranks of positive differences (column 8, $T^+ = 40$). The value of the test statistic T is $T = T^+ = 40$.

TABLE 20.6 Calculations for Wilcoxon Signed-Rank Test

Year (1)	Growth x (2)	Value y (3)	d = x − y (4)	|d| (5)	Rank (6)	Ranks of Negative Differences (7)	Ranks of Positive Differences (8)
2007	12.56	0.09	12.47	12.47	9		9
2008	−38.32	−35.97	−2.35	2.35	5	5	
2009	36.29	19.58	16.71	16.71	10		10
2010	16.96	14.28	2.68	2.68	6		6
2011	1.71	1.00	0.71	0.71	3		3
2012	16.89	15.00	1.89	1.89	4		4
2013	32.16	32.85	−0.69	0.69	2	2	
2014	13.47	13.05	0.42	0.42	1		1
2015	3.17	−1.03	4.20	4.2	7		7
2016	5.99	16.75	−10.76	10.76	8	8	
						$T^- = 15$	$T^+ = 40$

The p-value for the resulting T test statistic is found from the sampling distribution of T. In Example 20.4, we show how R is used to implement the Wilcoxon signed-rank test for a matched-pairs sample.

Using R to Test for Median Differences from a Matched-Pairs Sample

EXAMPLE 20.4

Using the **Growth_Value** data from the introductory case, determine whether the median difference between the funds' returns differs from zero at the 5% significance level.

SOLUTION: As discussed earlier, the competing hypotheses for the test are $H_0: m_D = 0$ versus $H_A: m_D \neq 0$.

a. Import the **Growth_Value** data into a data frame (table) in R.

b. As discussed in Section 20.1, we again use R's **wilcox.test** function to test m_D. For options within the **wilcox.test** function, we use *alternative* and *paired*. Enter:

Growth_Value

```
> wilcox.test(Growth_Value$'Growth', Growth_
Value$'Value', alternative="two.sided", paired=TRUE)
```

Table 20.7 reports the R output when testing whether the median return difference between the Growth fund and the Value fund differs from zero. We have put the value of the test statistic and the p-value in boldface.

TABLE 20.7 R's Output for Example 20.3

```
        Wilcoxon signed rank test
V = 40, p-value = 0.2324
alternative hypothesis: true location shift is
not equal to 0
```

The value of the test statistic is identical to the one that we calculated manually— that is, $V = T = 40$. We have also prompted R to find the p-value for a two-tailed test. Since the p-value is equal to 0.2324, which is greater than $\alpha = 0.05$, we do not reject H_0. At the 5% significance level, we cannot conclude that the median difference between the funds' returns differs from zero.

LO 20.4

Make inferences about the difference between two population medians based on independent sampling.

The Wilcoxon Rank-Sum Test for Independent Samples

Now we discuss whether significant differences exist between two population medians when the underlying populations are nonnormal and the samples are independent. In this situation, we use the Wilcoxon rank-sum test. The parameter of interest is the difference between two population medians $m_1 - m_2$. When we wish to test whether $m_1 - m_2$ differs from, is greater than, or is less than 0, we set up the competing hypotheses as follows.

Two-Tailed Test	Right-Tailed Test	Left-Tailed Test
$H_0: m_1 - m_2 = 0$	$H_0: m_1 - m_2 \leq 0$	$H_0: m_1 - m_2 \geq 0$
$H_A: m_1 - m_2 \neq 0$	$H_A: m_1 - m_2 > 0$	$H_A: m_1 - m_2 < 0$

We illustrate the Wilcoxon rank-sum test with the following example.

An undergraduate at a local university has narrowed her choice of major to computer science or finance. She wonders whether her choice will influence her salary upon graduation. She gathers salary data (in $1,000s) on 10 recent graduates who majored in computer science and 10 recent graduates who majored in finance. The data are shown in Table 20.8.

TABLE 20.8 Salary Information on Computer Science and Finance Graduates (in $1,000s)

Computer Science		Finance	
66	59	61	55
60	67	52	52
58	64	54	52
65	68	50	47
70	69	62	46

In order to determine whether salaries differ across majors, we apply the Wilcoxon rank-sum test. Let m_1 and m_2 denote the population median salary for computer science and finance majors, respectively. We formulate the two-tailed test as

$$H_0: m_1 - m_2 = 0$$
$$H_A: m_1 - m_2 \neq 0$$

To arrive at the value of the test statistic for the Wilcoxon rank-sum test W, several steps are necessary.

A. We first pool the data from sample 1 (Computer Science) and sample 2 (Finance), with n_1 and n_2 observations, and arrange **all** the data in ascending order of magnitude. That is, we treat the independent samples as if they are one large sample of size $n_1 + n_2 = n$. See column 1 of Table 20.9.

B. We then rank the observations from smallest to largest, assigning the numbers 1 to n. Since we have a multiple tie at ranks 4, 5, and 6, we assign to each of the tied observations the mean of the ranks which they jointly occupy, or $(4 + 5 + 6)/3 = 5$. See columns 2 and 3 of Table 20.9. We note that the finance salaries occupy the lower ranks, whereas the computer science salaries occupy the higher ranks.

C. We then sum the ranks of the computer science salaries (denoted W_1) and sum the ranks of the finance salaries (denoted W_2). Here we find that $W_1 = 149$ and $W_2 = 61$; see columns 4 and 5 of Table 20.9. To check that we have performed the calculations properly, we confirm that the sum of the rank sums, $W_1 + W_2$, equals $\frac{(n_1 + n_2)(n_1 + n_2 + 1)}{2}$, which is equivalent to the sum of the integers from 1 to $n_1 + n_2$. We first find that $W_1 + W_2 = 149 + 61 = 210$. Since $n_1 = 10$ and $n_2 = 10$, we then find that $\frac{(n_1 + n_2)(n_1 + n_2 + 1)}{2} = \frac{(10 + 10)(10 + 10 + 1)}{2} = 210$.

TABLE 20.9 Calculations for Wilcoxon Rank-Sum Test

Salary (1)	Sample of Origin (2)	Rank (3)	Computer Science Ranks (4)	Finance Ranks (5)
46	Finance	1		1
47	Finance	2		2
50	Finance	3		3
52	Finance	5		5
52	Finance	5		5
52	Finance	5		5
54	Finance	7		7
55	Finance	8		8
58	Computer Science	9	9	
59	Computer Science	10	10	
60	Computer Science	11	11	
61	Finance	12		12
62	Finance	13		13
64	Computer Science	14	14	
65	Computer Science	15	15	
66	Computer Science	16	16	
67	Computer Science	17	17	
68	Computer Science	18	18	
69	Computer Science	19	19	
70	Computer Science	20	20	
			$W_1 = 149$	$W_2 = 61$

If the median salary of computer science majors is equal to the median salary of finance majors, then we would expect each major to produce about as many low ranks as high ranks, so that both W_1 and W_2 are about equal to half of the total sum of ranks of 210, or about 105. However, if the median salaries are significantly different, then most of the higher ranks will be occupied by one major and most of the lower ranks will be occupied by the other major. For testing, we could analyze either W_1 or W_2. In what follows, we will base the Wilcoxon rank-sum test on W_1.

> ### THE TEST STATISTIC W FOR THE WILCOXON RANK-SUM TEST
>
> The test statistic W for the Wilcoxon rank-sum test is defined as $W = W_1$, where W_1 denotes the sum of the ranks of the values in sample 1.
>
> There are two scenarios when conducting the Wilcoxon rank-sum test:
>
> 1. If $n_1 \leq 10$ and $n_2 \leq 10$, then the p-value is found from the sampling distribution of W. Most statistical computer packages, including R, perform this calculation.
>
> 2. If $n_1 \geq 10$ and $n_2 \geq 10$, then W can be approximated by the normal distribution with mean $\mu_W = \frac{n_1(n_1 + n_2 + 1)}{2}$ and standard deviation $\sigma_W = \sqrt{\frac{n_1 n_2 (n_1 + n_2 + 1)}{12}}$, and hence the value of the resulting test statistic is computed as $z = \frac{W - \mu_W}{\sigma_W}$.

Using R to Test for Median Differences from Independent Samples

In Example 20.5, we show how R is used to implement the Wilcoxon rank-sum test for independent samples.

EXAMPLE 20.5

Use the salary data in Table 20.8 to determine whether the median computer science salary differs from the median finance salary at the 5% significance level.

SOLUTION: As discussed earlier, the competing hypotheses for the test are $H_0: m_1 - m_2 = 0$ versus $H_A: m_1 - m_2 \neq 0$.

a. Import the ***Undergrad_Salaries*** data into a data frame (table) in R.

b. As discussed in Section 20.1, we again use R's **wilcox.test** function with options *alternative* and *paired*. Enter

```
> wilcox.test(Undergrad_Salaries$'Computer Science',
  Undergrad_Salaries$'Finance', alternative="two.
  sided", paired=FALSE)
```

Table 20.10 reports the R output when testing whether the median salaries differ. We have put the value of the test statistic and the p-value in boldface.

TABLE 20.10 R's Output for Example 20.5

```
Wilcoxon rank-sum test with continuity correction

W = 94, p-value = 0.0009904
alternative hypothesis: true location shift is not equal to 0
```

Note that the value of the test statistic $W = 94$ reported by R is not the same as the value $W = W_1 = 149$ that we computed manually in Table 20.9. The value of W in Table 20.9 is often referred to as the unadjusted sum of ranks because it does not adjust for the sample size from which W is derived. To compute adjusted sum of ranks, we first compute $n_1(n_1 + 1)/2$ where n_1 is the number of observations in the first sample. We then subtract this value from W. In this example, since $n_1 = 10$, we find $10(10 + 1)/2 = 55$. So, the adjusted sum of ranks is equal to $149 - 55 = 94$. To avoid confusion, we refer to the adjusted sum of ranks derived by R as W^*. The p-values based on W or W^* are the same. The p-value for the two-tailed test reported by R is approximately equal to 0. Therefore, at $\alpha = 0.05$, we reject H_0. At the 5% significance level, we can conclude that the median computer science salary differs from the median finance salary.

Using a Normal Distribution Approximation for W

When n_1 and n_2 both have at least 10 observations, we can use the normal distribution approximation to implement a z test.

EXAMPLE 20.6

Assuming that the distribution of W is approximately normal, let's again determine whether the median computer science salary differs from the median finance salary at the 5% significance level.

SOLUTION: We specify the same competing hypotheses, $H_0: m_1 - m_2 = 0$ versus $H_A: m_1 - m_2 \neq 0$, and compute the value of the test statistic as $W = W_1 = 149$. We now compute the mean and the standard deviation as

$$\mu_W = \frac{n_1(n_1 + n_2 + 1)}{2} = \frac{10(10 + 10 + 1)}{2} = 105, \text{ and}$$

$$\sigma_W = \sqrt{\frac{n_1 n_2 (n_1 + n_2 + 1)}{12}} = \sqrt{\frac{(10 \times 10)(10 + 10 + 1)}{12}} = 13.2288.$$

The value of the test statistic is calculated as

$$z = \frac{W - \mu_W}{\sigma_W} = \frac{149 - 105}{13.2288} = 3.33.$$

Using the z table, we find the p-value as $2 \times P(Z \geq 3.33) = 0.0004$. Since the p-value is less than the significance level of $\alpha = 0.05$, we reject H_0 and conclude, as before, that the median computer science salary differs from the median finance salary.

EXERCISES 20.2

*For exercises marked with an asterisk, it is advised that you use a statistical software package that accommodates the Wilcoxon signed-rank test or the Wilcoxon rank-sum test.

Mechanics

12. A matched-pairs sample of 20 observations produced a test statistic of $T = 165$.

    a. Specify the competing hypotheses in order to determine whether the median difference is greater than zero.

    b. Determine the value of the test statistic using a normal approximation for T.

    c. Calculate the p-value.

    d. At the 5% significance level, what is the conclusion to the hypothesis test? Explain.

13. Consider the following competing hypotheses and accompanying sample data drawn from a matched-pairs sample.

    $$H_0: m_D = 0$$
    $$H_A: m_D \neq 0$$
    $\quad n = 50 \quad T^- = 400 \quad T^+ = 875$

    a. Determine the value of the test statistic using a normal approximation for T.

    b. Calculate the p-value.

    c. At the 5% significance level, what is the conclusion? Explain.

14.* **FILE** *Exercise_20.14.* The following table lists a portion of the data containing information on a matched-pairs sample.

Observation	Sample 1	Sample 2
1	18	21
2	12	11
⋮	⋮	⋮
8	18	22

a. Specify the competing hypotheses that determine whether the median difference between Population 1 and Population 2 is less than zero.

b. At the 5% significance level, what is the conclusion to the hypothesis test? Explain.

15. **FILE** *Exercise_20.15.* The following table lists a portion of the data derived from a matched-pairs sample.

Observation	Sample 1	Sample 2
1	120	125
2	156	160
⋮	⋮	⋮
10	190	182

a. Specify the competing hypotheses that determine whether the population median difference differs from zero.

b. Assuming that T is normally distributed, determine the value of the test statistic.

c. Calculate the p-value.

d. At the 1% significance level, what is the conclusion?

16. The following data were drawn from two independent populations.

Sample 1	15	23	19	34	30	
Sample 2	28	25	34	35	37	40

a. Specify the competing hypotheses to determine whether the median of Population 1 is less than the median of Population 2.

b. Find the unadjusted sum of ranks, W.

c. The p-value for the test is found to be equal to 0.034. At the 5% significance level, what is the conclusion to the hypothesis test? Explain.

17. The following data were drawn from two independent populations.

Sample 1	−2	0	4	−5	2	
Sample 2	−3	−8	−1	0	−10	3

a. Specify the competing hypotheses to determine whether the median of Population 1 is greater than the median of Population 2.

b. Find the unadjusted sum of ranks, W.

c. The p-value for the test is found to be equal to 0.180. At the 5% significance level, what is the conclusion to the hypothesis test? Explain.

18. The following data are provided for two samples drawn from independent populations: $W = 700$, $n_1 = 25$, and $n_2 = 20$. Suppose the distribution of W is approximately normal.

a. Calculate the mean and the standard deviation of the distribution of W.

b. Specify the competing hypotheses to determine whether the median of Population 1 is greater than the median of Population 2.

c. Calculate the value of the test statistic Z.

d. At the 5% significance level, what is the conclusion to the hypothesis test?

19. The following data are provided for two samples drawn from independent populations: $W = 545$, $n_1 = 25$, and $n_2 = 25$. Suppose the distribution of W is approximately normal.

a. Calculate the mean and the standard deviation of the distribution of W.

b. Specify the competing hypotheses to determine whether the median of Population 1 differs from the median of Population 2.

c. Calculate the value of the test statistic Z.

d. At the 10% significance level, what is the conclusion to the hypothesis test?

Applications

20.* **FILE** *Mock_SAT.* Suppose eight college-bound students take a mock SAT, complete a three-month test-prep course, and then take the real SAT. A portion of the data is shown in the accompanying table.

Student	Score on Mock SAT	Score on Real SAT
1	1830	1840
2	1760	1800
⋮	⋮	⋮
8	1710	1780

a. Specify the competing hypotheses to determine whether the median score on the real SAT is greater than the median score on the mock SAT.

b. At the 5% significance level, is there sufficient evidence to conclude that the median score on the real SAT is greater than the median score on the mock SAT? Explain.

21. A diet center claims that it has the most effective weight loss program in the region. Its advertisement says, "Participants in our program really lose weight." Five clients of this program are weighed on the first day of the diet and then three months later.

Client	Weight on First Day of Diet	Weight Three Months Later
1	155	151
2	205	203
3	167	168
4	186	183
5	194	195

a. Specify the null and alternative hypotheses to test whether the median difference for weight loss supports the diet center's claim.

b. Find the value of the test statistic, T.

c. The p-value for the test is found to be equal to 0.139. At the 5% significance level, do the data support the diet center's claim? Explain.

22. **FILE** *Appraisals.* A bank employs two appraisers. When approving borrowers for mortgages, it is imperative that the appraisers value the same types of properties consistently. To make sure that this is the case, the bank asks the appraisers to value 10 different properties (in $). A portion of the data is shown in the following table.

Property	Appraiser 1	Appraiser 2
1	235000	239000
2	195000	190000
⋮	⋮	⋮
10	575000	583000

a. Specify the competing hypotheses to determine whether the median difference between the values from appraiser 1 and appraiser 2 differs from zero.

b. Calculate the value of the test statistic T. Assume the normal approximation for T.

c. Calculate the p-value.

d. At the 5% significance level, is there sufficient evidence to conclude that the appraisers are not consistent in their appraisals? Explain.

23.* A professor teaches two sections of an introductory statistics course. He gives each section the same final and wonders if any significant differences exist between the medians of these sections. He draws a sample of seven scores from Section A and six scores from Section B.

Section A	75	62	87	93	74	77	65
Section B	64	95	72	78	85	80	

a. Set up the hypotheses to test the claim that the median test score in Section A differs from the median test score in Section B.

b. At the 5% significance level, do the median test scores differ? Explain.

24.* An analysis of census data suggests that married men have a higher median income than unmarried men (*The Boston Globe*, January 19, 2010). Suppose the incomes (in $1,000s) of six married men and seven unmarried men produce the following results:

Married	84	75	83	67	70	76	
Unmarried	67	63	62	66	71	64	68

a. Set up the hypotheses to test the claim that the median income of married men is greater than the median income of unmarried men.

b. At the 5% significance level, is the claim supported by the data? Explain.

25. **FILE** *South_Koreans.* According to the Organization of Economic Cooperation and Development, South Koreans spend more hours per year on the job than people in any other developed country (*The Wall Street Journal*, March 1, 2010). Suppose 10 workers in South Korea and 10 workers in the United States are asked to report the number of hours worked in the last year. A portion of the data is shown in the accompanying table.

South Korea	United States
2624	2132
1560	1432
⋮	⋮
2259	1041

a. Set up the hypotheses to test the claim that the median annual hours worked in South Korea is greater than the median annual hours worked in the United States.

b. Calculate the value of the test statistic W.

c. Assume the normal approximation for W. With $\alpha = 0.05$, is the claim supported by the data? Explain.

26.* **FILE** *Spending_Gender.* Researchers at the Wharton School of Business have found that men and women shop for different reasons. While women enjoy the shopping experience, men are on a mission to get the job done. Men do not shop as frequently, but when they do, they make big purchases like expensive electronics. The accompanying table shows a portion of the amount spent (in $) over the weekend by 40 men and 60 women at a local mall.

Men	Women
85	90
102	79
⋮	⋮

a. Specify the competing hypotheses to determine whether the median amount spent by men is more than the amount spent by women.

b. At the 5% significance level, is there sufficient evidence to conclude that the median amount spent by men is greater than the median amount spent by women? Explain.

20.3 TESTING THREE OR MORE POPULATION MEDIANS

Make inferences about the difference between three or more population medians.

In Chapter 13, we applied the one-way ANOVA F test to compare three or more population means. In order to implement this test, we assumed that for each population the variable of interest was normally distributed with the same variance. The **Kruskal-Wallis test** is a nonparametric alternative to the one-way ANOVA test that can be used when the assumptions of normality and/or equal population variances cannot be validated. It is based on ranks and is used for testing the equality of three or more population medians. Since the Kruskal-Wallis test is essentially an extension of the Wilcoxon rank-sum test, we discuss its application through an example.

The Kruskal-Wallis Test for Population Medians

An undergraduate admissions officer would like to examine whether SAT scores differ by ethnic background. She collects a representative sample of SAT scores from Blacks, Hispanics, Whites, and Asians. Her results are shown in Table 20.11. She decides not to pursue the one-way ANOVA F test because she does not believe that the population variances are equal. Instead she chooses to apply the Kruskal-Wallis test.

TABLE 20.11 SAT Scores by Ethnic Background

FILE
KW_SAT

Blacks	1246	1148	1300	1404	1396	1450	
Hispanics	1267	1228	1450	1351	1280		
Whites	1581	1649	981	1877	1629	1800	1423
Asians	1623	1550	1936	1800	1750		

Let m_1, m_2, m_3, and m_4 denote the median SAT scores for Blacks, Hispanics, Whites, and Asians, respectively. We formulate the competing hypotheses as

$$H_0: m_1 = m_2 = m_3 = m_4$$
$$H_A: \text{Not all population medians are equal.}$$

As in the Wilcoxon rank-sum test, we follow several steps to arrive at the value for the Kruskal-Wallis test statistic H.

A. First, we pool the k independent samples (here, $k = 4$) and then rank the observations from 1 to n. Since the total number of observations is 23, we rank the scores from 1 to 23. As before, if there are any ties, then we assign to each of the tied observations the mean of the ranks which they jointly occupy. In this sample, two individuals score 1450, and each is assigned the rank of 12.5, since the values jointly occupy the 12th and 13th ranks. Also, two individuals score 1800, and each is assigned the rank of 20.5. Table 20.12 shows the rank for each SAT score.

B. We then calculate a ranked sum, denoted R_i, for each of the k samples. For instance, the ranked sum for Blacks is calculated as $4 + 2 + 7 + 10 + 9 + 12.5 = 44.5$. These sums are shown in the second-to-last row of Table 20.12.

TABLE 20.12 Calculations for the Kruskal-Wallis Test

Blacks	Rank	Hispanics	Rank	Whites	Rank	Asians	Rank
1246	4	1267	5	1581	15	1623	16
1148	2	1228	3	1649	18	1550	14
1300	7	1450	12.5	981	1	1936	23
1404	10	1351	8	1877	22	1800	20.5
1396	9	1280	6	1629	17	1750	19
1450	12.5			1800	20.5		
				1423	11		
$R_1 = 44.5$		$R_2 = 34.5$		$R_3 = 104.5$		$R_4 = 92.5$	
$\dfrac{R_1^2}{n_1} = 330.0417$		$\dfrac{R_2^2}{n_2} = 238.05$		$\dfrac{R_3^2}{n_3} = 1560.0357$		$\dfrac{R_4^2}{n_4} = 1711.25$	

If median SAT scores across ethnic groups are the same, we expect the ranked sums to be relatively close to one another. However, if some sums deviate substantially from others, then this is evidence that not all population medians are the same. We determine whether the variability of some ranked sums differs significantly from others by first calculating the value of the test statistic H.

THE TEST STATISTIC H FOR THE KRUSKAL-WALLIS TEST

The test statistic H for the Kruskal-Wallis test is defined as

$$H = \left(\frac{12}{n(n+1)} \sum_{i=1}^{k} \frac{R_i^2}{n_i} \right) - 3(n+1),$$

where R_i and n_i are the rank sum and the size of the ith sample, $n = \sum_{i=1}^{k} n_i$, and k is the number of populations (independent samples). If $n_i \geq 5$ for $i = 1, 2, \ldots, k$, then H can be approximated by the χ^2 distribution with $k - 1$ degrees of freedom.

For small sample values ($n_i < 5$), the test may be based on special tables; however, we will not pursue that case. The Kruskal-Wallis test is always a right-tailed test.

EXAMPLE 20.7

Use the data in Table 20.12 to determine whether some median SAT scores differ by ethnic background at the 5% significance level.

SOLUTION: As discussed earlier, the appropriate hypotheses for the test are

$$H_0: m_1 = m_2 = m_3 = m_4$$
$$H_A: \text{Not all population medians are equal.}$$

We compute the value of the test statistic H as

$$H = \left(\frac{12}{n(n+1)} \sum_{i=1}^{k} \frac{R_i^2}{n_i} \right) - 3(n+1)$$

$$= \left(\frac{12}{23(23+1)} (330.0417 + 238.05 + 1560.0357 + 1711.25) \right) - 3(23+1)$$

$$= 11.465$$

With $k = 4$, degrees of freedom equal $df = k - 1 = 3$. We find the p-value as $P(\chi_3^2 \geq 11.465)$. Referencing the χ^2 table for $df = 3$, we see that 11.465 lies between the values 11.345 and 12.838, implying that the p-value is between 0.005 and 0.01. Using statistical software, we find the exact p-value as 0.009. Since the p-value is less than 0.05, we reject H_0. At the 5% significance level, not all median SAT scores across ethnic groups are the same.

We generally rely on computer software to perform the calculations involved in a Kruskal-Wallis test. In Example 20.8, we show how R is used to implement the Kruskal-Wallis test.

Using R to Conduct a Kruskal-Wallis Test

EXAMPLE 20.8

A sociologist suspects differences in median incomes in three major eastern cities. He randomly samples 100 workers from each city. Table 20.13 shows a portion of the data. Using R, he wants to implement the Kruskal-Wallis test at the 5% significance level to determine if some differences exist in the median incomes in these three cities.

TABLE 20.13 Data for Example 20.8

City 1	City 2	City 3
86.5	88.1	102.4
76.7	73.3	127.9
⋮	⋮	⋮
85	63.3	80.1

SOLUTION: We let $m_1, m_2,$ and m_3 denote the population median incomes for City 1, City 2, and City 3, respectively, and formulate the competing hypotheses as

$$H_0: m_1 = m_2 = m_3$$
$$H_A: \text{Not all population median incomes are equal.}$$

a. Import the ***City_Income*** data into a data frame (table) in R. Since many of the initial commands were presented in Chapter 13, we are brief here. We install and load the *reshape2* package. We use the **melt** function from this package to stack the city categories and salaries. We label the reconfigured data as Stacked. (Remember that we can ignore R's warning message.) For clarity, we then label the columns in Stacked as City and Income. Enter

```
> install.packages("reshape2")
> library(reshape2)
> Stacked <- melt(City_Income)
> colnames(Stacked) <- c("City", "Income")
```

FILE
City_Income

b. We then apply the **kruskal.test** function by referencing the City and Income variables from the Stacked data frame. Make sure that you first input the quantitative variable (Income), followed by the qualitative variable (City). Enter

```
> kruskal.test(Stacked$'Income', Stacked$'City')
```

Table 20.14 reports the R output when testing whether the median incomes differ between the three cities. We have put the value of the test statistic and the *p*-value in boldface.

TABLE 20.14 R's Output for Example 20.8

```
Kruskal-Wallis rank sum test

data: Stack$Income and Stack$City
Kruskal-Wallis chi-squared = 85.505, df = 2, p-value < 2.2e-16
```

The value of the test statistic computed by R is $H = 85.505$ with an associated *p*-value ≈ 0. Since the *p*-value is less than the significance level of $\alpha = 0.05$, we reject H_0 and conclude that not all median incomes across the three cities are the same.

It is important to note that if we reject the null hypothesis, we can only conclude that not all population medians are equal. The Kruskal-Wallis test does not allow us to infer which medians differ. Further analysis of the difference between population medians is beyond the scope of this text.

EXERCISES 20.3

*For exercises marked with an asterisk, it is advised that you use a statistical software package that accommodates the Kruskal-Wallis test.

Mechanics

27. Consider the following sample information: $k = 3$ and $H = 4.5$.
    a. Specify the competing hypotheses to test whether some differences exist between the medians.
    b. At the 10% significance level, do some medians differ? Explain.

28. Consider the following sample information: $k = 5$ and $H = 12.4$.
    a. Specify the competing hypotheses to test whether some differences exist between the medians.

    b. At the 5% significance level, do some medians differ? Explain.

29. **FILE** *Exercise_20.31.* Random samples were drawn from three independent populations. The results are shown in the accompanying table.

Sample 1	120	95	115	110	90	
Sample 2	100	85	105	80	75	90
Sample 3	72	65	100	76	66	55

    a. Specify the competing hypotheses to test whether some differences exist between the medians.

b. Calculate the value of the test statistic H.

c. At the 10% significance level, do some medians differ? Explain.

30.* **FILE** *Exercise_20.32.* Random samples were drawn from four independent populations. The results are shown in the accompanying table.

Sample 1	−10	−15	0	5	10
Sample 2	−2	−3	−4	−5	−6
Sample 3	2	4	6	8	10
Sample 4	5	7	9	11	13

a. Specify the competing hypotheses to test whether some differences exist between the medians.

b. At the 5% significance level, do some medians differ? Explain.

Applications

31. **FILE** *Unemployment.* A research analyst wants to test whether the median unemployment rate differs from one region of the country to another. She collects the unemployment rate (in percent) of similar-sized cities in three regions of the United States. The results are shown in the accompanying table.

Region A	12.5	13.0	8.5	10.7	9.3
Region B	9.0	9.5	7.0	6.7	8.2
Region C	8.2	7.4	10.9	11.1	10.4

a. Specify the competing hypotheses to test whether some differences exist in the median unemployment rates between the three regions.

b. Calculate the value of the test statistic H.

c. At the 10% significance level, do some unemployment rates differ by region? Explain.

32. **FILE** *Bulb.* A quality-control manager wants to test whether there is any difference in the median length of life of light bulbs between three different brands. Random samples were drawn from each brand, where the duration of each light bulb (in hours) was measured. The results are shown in the accompanying table.

Brand 1	Brand 2	Brand 3
375	280	350
400	290	415
425	300	425
410	325	380
420	350	405

a. Specify the competing hypotheses to test whether some differences exist in the median length of life of light bulbs between the three brands.

b. Calculate the value of the test statistic H.

c. At the 10% significance level, do some differences exist between the median length of life of light bulbs by brand? Explain.

33. **FILE** *Industry_Returns.* A research analyst examines annual returns (in percent) for Industry A, Industry B, and Industry C, as shown in the accompanying table.

Industry A	Industry B	Industry C
16.86	15.41	13.53
5.11	10.87	9.58
12.45	4.43	18.75
−32.44	−18.45	−28.77
32.11	20.96	32.17

a. Specify the competing hypotheses to test whether some differences exist in the median returns by industry.

b. Calculate the value of the test statistic H.

c. At the 10% significance level, do some differences exist between the median returns by industry. Explain.

34. **FILE** *Detergents.* A well-known conglomerate claims that its detergent "whitens and brightens better than all the rest." In order to compare the cleansing action of the top three detergents, 15 swatches of white cloth were soiled with red wine and grass stains and then washed in front-loading machines with the respective detergents. The following whiteness readings are shown in the accompanying table.

Detergent 1	Detergent 2	Detergent 3
84	78	87
79	74	80
87	81	91
85	86	77
94	86	78

a. Specify the competing hypotheses to test whether some differences exist in the median cleansing action of the three detergents.

b. Calculate the value of the test statistic H.

c. At the 1% significance level, do some differences exist between the median cleansing action by detergent? Explain.

35.* **FILE** *Exam_Scores.* A statistics instructor wonders whether significant differences exist in her students' median exam scores in her three different sections. She randomly selects scores from 10 different students in each section. A portion of the data is shown in the accompanying table.

Section 1	Section 2	Section 3
85	91	74
68	84	69
⋮	⋮	⋮
74	75	73

Do these data provide enough evidence at the 5% significance level to indicate that there are some differences in median scores in the three sections?

36.* **FILE** *Job_Satisfaction.* A human resource specialist wants to determine whether the median job satisfaction score (on a scale of 0 to 100) differs depending on a person's field of employment. She collects scores from 30 employees in three different fields. A portion of the data is shown in the accompanying table.

Field 1	Field 2	Field 3
80	76	81
76	73	77
⋮	⋮	⋮
79	67	80

At the 10% significance level, can the specialist conclude that there are some differences in job satisfaction depending on field of employment?

20.4 THE SPEARMAN RANK CORRELATION TEST

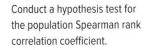

In earlier chapters, we used the correlation coefficient, also referred to as the **Pearson correlation coefficient**, to measure the strength and direction of the linear relationship between two random variables. Recall that the value of this correlation coefficient falls between −1 and +1; as its absolute value approaches one, the linear relationship becomes stronger. We used a *t* test to determine whether the population correlation coefficient differs from zero, which assumes that we sample from normal populations. Since this assumption breaks down in some situations, we need a nonparametric alternative. The Spearman rank correlation test serves as this option. The **Spearman rank correlation coefficient** measures the correlation between two random variables based on rank orderings. Its value also falls between −1 and +1 and is interpreted in the same way as the Pearson correlation coefficient.

Figure 20.2 shows a scatterplot of the return data for the Growth and the Value funds from the introductory case. Each point in the scatterplot represents a pairing of each fund's return for a given year. It appears that the two funds are positively related.

Conduct a hypothesis test for the population Spearman rank correlation coefficient.

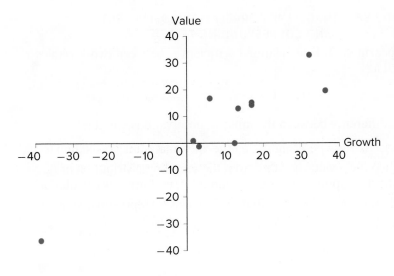

FIGURE 20.2
Scatterplot of return data for the Growth and the Value funds

Suppose we want to determine whether the observed relationship is real or due to chance. As we noted before, return data often do not follow the normal distribution. Therefore, using the t test to analyze the Pearson correlation coefficient is not appropriate. Instead, we let ρ_s denote the population Spearman rank correlation coefficient, and we formulate a two-tailed test as

$$H_0: \rho_s = 0$$
$$H_A: \rho_s \neq 0$$

To conduct the test, we first calculate the sample Spearman rank correlation coefficient r_S using the following steps.

A. We rank the observations from the Growth fund from smallest to largest. In the case of ties, we assign to each tied observation the average of the ranks that they jointly occupy. We perform the same procedure for the Value fund. Columns 2 and 3 of Table 20.15 show the original return data, and columns 4 and 5 show the funds' ranked values.

TABLE 20.15 Calculations for the Spearman Rank Correlation Coefficient

Year (1)	Growth x (2)	Value y (3)	Rank for Growth (4)	Rank for Value (5)	Difference d (6)	Difference Squared d^2 (7)
2007	12.56	0.09	5	3	2	4
2008	−38.32	−35.97	1	1	0	0
2009	36.29	19.58	10	9	1	1
2010	16.96	14.28	8	6	2	4
2011	1.71	1.00	2	4	−2	4
2012	16.89	15.00	7	7	0	0
2013	32.16	32.85	9	10	−1	1
2014	13.47	13.05	6	5	1	1
2015	3.17	−1.03	3	2	1	1
2016	5.99	16.75	4	8	−4	16
					$\Sigma d_i = 0$	$\Sigma d_i^2 = 32$

B. We calculate the difference d_i between the ranks of each pair of observations. See column 6 of Table 20.15. As a check, when we sum the differences, Σd_i, we should obtain zero.

C. We then sum the squared differences. The resulting value is shown in the last cell of column 7 in Table 20.15—that is, $\Sigma d_i^2 = 32$.

THE SPEARMAN RANK CORRELATION COEFFICIENT
AND CORRESPONDING TEST

The sample Spearman rank correlation coefficient r_S between two variables x and y is defined as

$$r_S = 1 - \frac{6 \, \Sigma d_i^2}{n(n^2 - 1)},$$

where d_i is the difference between the ranks of observations x_i and y_i.

There are two scenarios when conducting the Spearman rank correlation test:

1. If $n \leq 10$, then the p-value is found from the sampling distribution of r_S. Most statistical computer packages, including R, perform this calculation.

2. If $n \geq 10$, then the sampling distribution of r_S can be approximated by the normal distribution with zero mean and standard deviation of $\sqrt{\frac{1}{n-1}}$, and the value of the resulting test statistic is computed as $z = r_S \sqrt{n-1}$.

We calculate the sample Spearman correlation coefficient r_S between the Growth and the Value funds as

$$r_S = 1 - \frac{6 \, \Sigma d_i^2}{n(n^2 - 1)} = 1 - \frac{6 \times 32}{10 \times (10^2 - 1)} = 0.8061.$$

A value of $r_S = 0.8061$ implies that the Growth and the Value funds have a positive, rather strong, relationship.

Using R to Test the Spearman Rank Correlation Coefficient

EXAMPLE 20.9

At the 5% significance level, determine whether the Spearman rank correlation coefficient between the Growth and the Value funds differs from zero. Do not assume that the sampling distribution of r_S is normally distributed.

SOLUTION: For completeness, we repeat the competing hypotheses: $H_0: \rho_s = 0$ versus $H_A: \rho_s \neq 0$.

a. Import the ***Growth_Value*** data into a data frame (table) in R.

b. As discussed in Chapter 14, we again use the **cor.test** function—the only difference is that we include the option *method* in order to designate the correlation coefficient that is to be used. Enter

```
> cor.test(Growth_Value$'Growth', Growth_Value$'Value',
  alternative = "two.sided", method = "spearman")
```

FILE

Growth_Value

Table 20.16 shows a portion of the R output when conducting the Spearman rank correlation test. Note that the sum of the squared rank differences (see S = 32) and the Spearman rank correlation coefficient (see the value of 0.8060606 under rho) match the values that we calculated manually. We have put the value of the test statistic and the *p*-value in boldface. Since the *p*-value is less than $\alpha = 0.05$, we reject H_0. At the 5% significance level, we can conclude that the Spearman rank correlation coefficient between the Growth and the Value funds differs from zero.

TABLE 20.16 R's Output for Example 20.9

```
            Spearman's rank correlation rho

S = 32, p-value = 0.008236
alternative hypothesis: true rho is not equal to 0
sample estimates:
      rho
0.8060606
```

Using a Normal Distribution Approximation for r_S

As mentioned earlier, when $n \geq 10$, we can use the normal distribution approximation to implement a z test.

EXAMPLE 20.10

Assuming that the distribution of r_S is approximately normal, let's again determine whether the Spearman rank correlation coefficient between the Growth and Value funds differs from zero at the 5% significance level.

SOLUTION: We again repeat the competing hypotheses: $H_0: \rho_s = 0$ versus $H_A: \rho_s \neq 0$. We found that $r_S = 0.8061$. Under normality, the value of the corresponding test statistic is calculated as $z = 0.8061\sqrt{10 - 1} = 2.42$, which yields a p-value of $2 \times P(Z \geq 2.42) = 0.0156$. Since the p-value is less than $\alpha = 0.05$, we reject H_0 and again conclude that Spearman rank correlation coefficient between the Growth and the Value funds differs from zero.

Summary of Parametric and Nonparametric Tests

Table 20.17 summarizes the select parametric tests referenced in Section 20.1 and their nonparametric counterparts. Nonparametric tests use fewer and weaker assumptions than those associated with parametric tests and are especially attractive when the underlying population is markedly nonnormal. However, a nonparametric test ignores useful information since it focuses on the rank rather than the magnitude of sample values. Therefore, in situations when the parametric assumptions are valid, the nonparametric test is less powerful than its parametric counterpart. In general, when the assumptions for a parametric test are met, it is preferable to use a parametric test rather than a nonparametric test. Since the normality assumption for parametric tests is less stringent in large samples, the main appeal of nonparametric tests tends to be with relatively small samples.

TABLE 20.17 Parametric Test versus Nonparametric Alternative

Parametric Test	Nonparametric Alternative
t test concerning the population mean	Wilcoxon signed-rank test concerning the population median
t test to determine whether the population mean difference differs from zero based on matched-pairs sampling	Wilcoxon signed-rank test to determine whether the population median difference differs from zero based on matched-pairs sampling
t test to determine whether two population means differ based on independent sampling	Wilcoxon rank-sum test to determine whether two population medians differ based on independent sampling
F test to determine whether three or more population means differ	Kruskal-Wallis test to determine whether three or more population medians differ
t test to determine whether two variables are correlated	Spearman rank correlation test to determine whether two variables are correlated

SYNOPSIS OF INTRODUCTORY CASE

An analysis of annual return data for Vanguard's Growth Index mutual fund (Growth) and Vanguard's Value Index mutual fund (Value) for the years 2007 through 2016 provides important information for an investor trying to determine whether to invest in a growth mutual fund, a value mutual fund, or both types of mutual funds. Given that return data often have "fatter tails" than the normal distribution, the analysis focuses on nonparametric techniques. These techniques do not rely on the normality assumption concerning the underlying population.

When applying the Wilcoxon signed-rank test at the 5% significance level, it is found that the median return for the Growth fund is not greater than 5%. The same conclusion is also found for the Value fund. The Wilcoxon signed-rank test is also used

©Ken Reid/Photographer's Choice/Getty Images

to determine whether the median difference between the Growth and the Value returns differs from zero. At the 5% significance level, it is found that the median difference does not differ from zero. Finally, the sample Spearman rank correlation coefficient is calculated as 0.8061, implying a relatively strong, positive relationship between the returns of the two funds. A test conducted at the 5% significance level finds that the population Spearman rank correlation coefficient is different from zero. Interestingly, even though the approaches of growth and value investing use different fundamentals, the performance of the returns of these two funds is similar over the 2007–2016 time period.

EXERCISES 20.4

Mechanics

*For exercises marked with an asterisk, it is advised that you use a statistical software package that accommodates the Spearman rank correlation test.

37. Consider the following sample data:

x	12	18	20	22	25	15
y	15	20	25	22	27	19

   a. Specify the competing hypotheses to determine whether the Spearman rank correlation coefficient differs from zero.
   b. Calculate and interpret r_s.
   c. The p-value associated with the test statistic in part b is 0.017. At the 5% significance level, what is the conclusion to the hypothesis test?

38. Consider the following sample data:

x	−2	0	3	−1	4	7
y	−4	−3	−8	−5	−9	−10

   a. Specify the competing hypotheses to determine whether the Spearman rank correlation coefficient is less than zero.

   b. Calculate and interpret r_s.
   c. The p-value associated with the test statistic in part b is 0.029. At the 5% significance level, what is the conclusion to the hypothesis test?

39. Consider the following competing hypotheses and accompanying sample data.

$$H_0: \rho_S = 0 \qquad r_S = 0.85 \text{ and } n = 65$$
$$H_A: \rho_S \neq 0$$

   a. What is the value of the test statistic and its associated p-value? Assume the normal approximation for r_s.
   b. At the 10% significance level, what is the conclusion?

40. Consider the following competing hypotheses and accompanying sample data.

$$H_0: \rho_S \leq 0 \qquad r_S = 0.64 \text{ and } n = 50$$
$$H_A: \rho_S > 0$$

   a. What is the value of the test statistic and its associated p-value? Assume the normal approximation for r_s.
   b. At the 1% significance level, what is the conclusion?

Applications

41. The following table shows the ranks given by two judges to the performance of six finalists in a men's figure skating competition:

Skater	A	B	C	D	E	F
Judge 1	6	5	4	3	2	1
Judge 2	5	6	4	3	1	2

a. Specify the competing hypotheses to determine whether the Spearman rank correlation coefficient is different from zero.

b. Calculate and interpret the Spearman rank correlation coefficient r_s.

c. The p-value for the test is found to be equal to 0.033. At the 5% significance level, does the Spearman rank correlation coefficient differ from zero? Explain.

42. **FILE** *WB_Ranking.* The following table shows a portion of the World Bank's 2008 ranking of the richest countries, as measured by per capita GNP. In addition, it gives each country's respective rank with respect to infant mortality according to the Central Intelligence Agency. A higher rank indicates a lower mortality rate.

Country	GNP	Infant Mortality
Luxembourg	1	7
Norway	2	4
⋮	⋮	⋮
Iceland	10	3

a. Specify the competing hypotheses to determine whether the Spearman rank correlation coefficient is different from zero.

b. Calculate and interpret the Spearman rank correlation coefficient r_s.

c. At the 5% significance level, are GNP and the infant mortality rate correlated? Assume the normal distribution approximation.

43. You are interested in whether the returns on Asset A (in %) are negatively correlated with the returns on Asset B (in %). Consider the following annual return data on the two assets:

	Asset A	Asset B
Year 1	−20	8
Year 2	−5	5
Year 3	18	−1
Year 4	15	−2
Year 5	4	3
Year 6	−12	2

a. Specify the competing hypotheses to determine whether the Spearman rank correlation coefficient is less than zero.

b. Calculate and interpret the Spearman rank correlation coefficient r_s.

c. The p-value for the test is found to be equal to 0.051. At the 1% significance level, are the returns negatively correlated? Explain.

44.* **FILE** *Price_Days.* In an attempt to determine whether a relationship exists between the price of a home (in $1,000s) and the number of days it takes to sell the home, a real estate agent collected the relevant data from recent sales in his city. A portion of the data is shown in the accompanying table.

Price	Days
265	136
225	125
⋮	⋮
423	145

a. Specify the competing hypotheses to determine whether the Spearman rank correlation coefficient differs from zero.

b. At the 5% significance level, can you conclude that the price of a home and the number of days it takes to sell the home are correlated? Explain.

45.* **FILE** *GRE_GPA.* The director of graduate admissions at a local university is analyzing the relationship between scores on the Graduate Record Examination (GRE) and subsequent performance in graduate school, as measured by a student's grade point average (GPA). She uses a sample of seven students who graduated within the past five years. A portion of the data is shown in the accompanying table.

GRE	GPA
1500	3.4
1400	3.5
⋮	⋮
800	2.7

a. Specify the competing hypotheses to determine whether the Spearman rank correlation coefficient is greater than zero.

b. At the 5% significance level, are GRE and GPA positively correlated?

46. A social scientist analyzes the relationship between educational attainment and salary. For 65 individuals, he collects data on each individual's educational attainment (in years) and his/her salary (in $1,000s). He then calculates a Spearman rank correlation coefficient of 0.85.

a. Specify the competing hypotheses to determine whether the Spearman rank correlation coefficient differs from zero.

b. Assume that the distribution of r_s is approximately normal. Calculate the value of the test statistic and the p-value of the test.

c. At the 5% significance level, are educational attainment and salary correlated?

47. An engineer examines the relationship between the weight of a car and its average miles per gallon (MPG). For a sample of 100 cars, he calculates a Spearman rank correlation coefficient of −0.60.

a. Specify the competing hypotheses to determine whether the Spearman rank correlation coefficient is less than zero.

b. Assume that the distribution of r_s is approximately normal. Calculate the value of the test statistic and the p-value.

c. At the 5% significance level, does a negative relationship exist between a car's weight and its average MPG?

48.* **FILE** *Happiness.* Many attempts have been made to relate happiness with various factors. One such study relates happiness with age and finds that, holding everything else constant, people are least happy when they are in their mid-40s (*The Economist*, December 16, 2010). The accompanying table shows a portion of data on a respondent's age and his/her perception of well-being on a scale from 0 to 100.

Age	Happiness
49	62
51	66
⋮	⋮
69	72

Using the Spearman rank correlation coefficient, determine whether age and happiness are positively correlated at the 5% significance level.

49.* **FILE** *Gambling.* The accompanying table shows a portion of the number of cases of crime related to gambling and offenses against the family and children for the 50 states in the United States during 2010.

State	Gambling	Family Abuse
Alabama	47	1022
Alaska	10	315
⋮	⋮	⋮
Wyoming	0	194

Using the Spearman rank correlation coefficient, determine whether gambling and family abuse are correlated at the 5% significance level.

20.5 THE SIGN TEST

LO 20.7

In some applications, a matched-pairs sample originates from ordinal data rather than from interval- or ratio-scaled data. Let's review the definition of ordinal data first introduced in Chapter 1. With ordinal data, we are able to categorize and rank the data with respect to some characteristic or trait. The weakness with ordinal-scaled data is that we cannot interpret the difference between the ranked values because the actual numbers used are arbitrary. For example, suppose you are asked to classify the service at a particular hotel as excellent, good, fair, or poor. A standard way to record the ratings is

Make inferences about the difference between two populations of ordinal data based on matched-pairs sampling.

Category	Rating
Excellent	4
Good	3
Fair	2
Poor	1

Here the value attached to excellent (4) is higher than the value attached to good (3), indicating that the response of excellent is preferred to good. However, another representation of the ratings might be

Category	Rating
Excellent	100
Good	80
Fair	70
Poor	40

Excellent still receives a higher value than good, but now the difference between the two categories is 20 (100–80), as compared to a difference of 1 (4–3) when we use the first classification. In other words, differences between categories are meaningless with ordinal data.

If we have a matched-pairs sample of ordinal data, we can use the **sign test** to determine whether there are significant differences between the populations. When applying the sign test, we are only interested in whether the difference between two values in a pair is different from, greater than, or less than zero. The difference between each pairing is replaced by a plus sign (+) if the difference is positive (that is, the first value exceeds the second value) or by a minus sign (−) if the difference between the pair is negative. If the difference between the pair is zero, we discard that particular observation from the sample.

If significant differences do not exist between the two populations, then we expect just as many plus signs as minus signs. Equivalently, we should observe plus signs 50% of the time and minus signs 50% of the time. Suppose we let p denote the population proportion of plus signs. (We could just as easily allow p to represent the population proportion of minus signs without loss of generality.) The competing hypotheses for the sign test take one of the following forms.

Two-Tailed Test	Right-Tailed Test	Left-Tailed Test
$H_0: p = 0.50$	$H_0: p \leq 0.50$	$H_0: p \geq 0.50$
$H_A: p \neq 0.50$	$H_A: p > 0.50$	$H_A: p < 0.50$

A two-tailed test allows us to determine whether the proportion of plus signs differs from the proportion of minus signs. A right-tailed (left-tailed) test allows us to determine whether the proportion of plus signs is greater than (less than) the proportion of minus signs.

Let $\bar{P} = X/n$ be the estimator of the population proportion of plus signs. As discussed in Chapter 7, if np and $n(1 - p)$ are both 5 or more, then the distribution of $\bar{P}$ is approximately normal, with mean $E(\bar{P}) = p$ and standard error $se(\bar{P}) = \sqrt{p(1 - p)/n}$. Assuming a probability of success $p = 0.50$, $se(\bar{P}) = 0.5/\sqrt{n}$ and the normal distribution approximation is satisfactory as long as $n \geq 10$. When $n < 10$, we rely on the binomial distribution to conduct the sign test; we will not consider such cases.

THE TEST STATISTIC FOR THE SIGN TEST

The value of the test statistic for the sign test is computed as $z = \frac{\bar{p} - 0.5}{0.5/\sqrt{n}}$, where $\bar{p} = x/n$ is the sample proportion of plus signs. The test is valid when $n \geq 10$.

EXAMPLE 20.11

In December 2009, Domino's Pizza, Inc. released untraditional ads citing that its old recipe for pizza produced crust that tasted like cardboard and sauce that tasted like ketchup. Domino's Pizza claims that its reformulated pizza is a vast improvement over the old recipe; for instance, garlic and parsley are now baked into the crust and a new sweeter, bolder tomato sauce is used. Suppose 20 customers are asked to sample the old recipe and then sample the new recipe. Each person is asked to rate the pizzas on a 5-point scale, where 1 = inedible and 5 = very tasty. The ratings are shown in Table 20.18. Do these data provide sufficient evidence to allow us to conclude that the new recipe is preferred to the old recipe? Use $\alpha = 0.05$.

TABLE 20.18 Calculations for Sign Test in Example 20.11

Customer	Old Recipe	New Recipe	Sign	Customer	Old Recipe	New Recipe	Sign
1	3	4	−	11	3	4	−
2	3	2	+	12	4	5	−
3	2	5	−	13	1	2	−
4	4	4	0	14	3	3	0
5	2	5	−	15	5	3	+
6	1	3	−	16	3	4	−
7	3	2	+	17	1	5	−
8	1	2	−	18	4	2	+
9	2	4	−	19	3	4	−
10	4	5	−	20	2	5	−

SOLUTION: If customers feel that there is no difference between the old recipe and the new recipe, then we expect 50% of the customers to prefer the old recipe and 50% to prefer the new recipe. Let p denote the population proportion of consumers who prefer the old recipe. We want to specify the competing hypotheses such that rejection of the null hypothesis provides evidence that customers prefer the new recipe (implying that p is significantly less than 0.50). We set up the competing hypotheses as

$$H_0: p \geq 0.50$$
$$H_A: p < 0.50$$

Table 20.18 shows the signs for each customer. For example, customer 1 ranks the old recipe with the value 3 and the new recipe with the value 4, which yields a minus sign when the difference between the old recipe and the new recipe is calculated: $3 - 4 = -1$. This difference indicates that this customer prefers the new recipe. We find 4 positive signs, 14 negative signs, and 2 ties (ranks of zero). We then let n denote the number of matched-paired observations such that the sign between the rankings is nonzero; thus, n equals 18. We denote $\bar{p}$ as the sample proportion of plus signs. Given that there are four plus signs, the sample proportion is calculated as $\bar{p} = 4/18 = 0.22$. (Note that if we had calculated the sample proportion of minus signs, then $\bar{p} = 0.78$; the resulting value of the test statistic only differs in its sign. In this instance, we would conduct a right-tailed hypothesis test.) We calculate the value of the test statistic as

$$z = \frac{\bar{p} - 0.5}{0.5/\sqrt{n}} = \frac{0.22 - 0.5}{0.5/\sqrt{18}} = \frac{-0.28}{0.118} = -2.37.$$

Using the z table, we find the p-value for a left-tailed test as $P(Z \leq -2.37) = 0.0089$. Since the p-value is less than the significance level of $\alpha = 0.05$, we reject H_0 and conclude that customers prefer the reformulated version as compared to the old recipe at the 5% significance level.

The sign test can be used with quantitative as well as ordinal data. However, since the sign test ignores the magnitude in the difference between two observations, it is advisable to use the Wilcoxon signed-rank test if quantitative data are available.

EXERCISES 20.5

Mechanics

50. Consider the following competing hypotheses and sample data.

    $H_0: p = 0.50$
    $H_A: p \neq 0.50$ $n = 40$ $\bar{p} = 0.30$

    a. Calculate the value of the test statistic for the sign test.
    b. Calculate the p-value.
    c. At the 5% significance level, what is the conclusion? Explain.

51. Consider the following competing hypotheses and sample data.

    $H_0: p \leq 0.50$
    $H_A: p > 0.50$ $n = 25$ $\bar{p} = 0.64$

    a. Calculate the value of the test statistic for the sign test.
    b. Calculate the p-value.
    c. At the 1% significance level, what is the conclusion? Explain.

52. Consider the following sign data, produced from a matched-pairs sample of ordinal data.

+	+	+	−	+	+	−	+	+	+	+	−	+	+	−	−	+	+	+	+

    a. Specify the competing hypotheses to determine whether the proportion of negative signs differs from the proportion of positive signs.
    b. Calculate the value of the test statistic.
    c. Calculate the p-value.
    d. At the 5% significance level, what is the conclusion? Explain.

53. Consider the following sign data, produced from a matched-pairs sample of ordinal data.

+	−	−	+	−	−	+	−	+	−	+	−	−	−	+	−

    a. Specify the competing hypotheses to determine whether the proportion of negative signs is significantly greater than the proportion of positive signs.
    b. Calculate the value of the test statistic.
    c. Calculate the p-value.
    d. At the 1% significance level, what is the conclusion? Explain.

Applications

54. **FILE** *Water.* Concerned with the increase of plastic water bottles in landfills, a leading environmentalist wants to determine whether there is any difference in taste between the local tap water and the leading bottled water. She randomly selects 14 consumers and conducts a blind taste test. She asks the consumers to rank the taste on a scale of 1 to 5 (where a score of 5 indicates excellent taste). A portion of the sample results are shown in the accompanying table.

Consumer	Tap Water	Bottled Water
1	4	5
2	3	2
⋮	⋮	⋮
14	3	4

    a. Using the sign test, specify the competing hypotheses to determine whether there are significant differences in preferences between tap water and bottled water.
    b. Calculate the value of the test statistic.
    c. Calculate the p-value.
    d. At the 5% significance level, what is the conclusion? Do the results indicate that significant differences exist in preferences?

55. In March 2009, 100 registered voters were asked to rate the effectiveness of President Obama. In March 2010, these same people were again asked to make the same assessment. Seventy percent of the second ratings were lower than the first ratings and 30% were higher.

    a. Using the sign test, specify the competing hypotheses to determine whether the president's rating had significantly declined.
    b. Calculate the value of the test statistic.
    c. Calculate the p-value.
    d. At the 5% significance level, do the data suggest that the president's rating had significantly declined?

56. A new diet and exercise program claims that it significantly lowers a participant's cholesterol level. In order to test this claim, a sample of 60 participants is taken. Their cholesterol levels are measured before and after the three-month program. Forty of the participants recorded lower cholesterol levels at the end of the program, 18 participants recorded higher cholesterol levels, and 2 participants recorded no change.

    a. Using the sign test, specify the competing hypotheses to test the program's claim.
    b. Calculate the value of the test statistic.
    c. Calculate the p-value.
    d. At the 5% significance level, do the data support the program's claim? Explain.

57. **FILE** *PhD_Rating.* For scholarship purposes, two graduate faculty members rate 12 applicants to the PhD program on a

scale of 1 to 10 (with 10 indicating an excellent candidate). These ratings are shown in the following table.

Candidate	Faculty A's Rating	Faculty B's Rating
1	5	6
2	7	8
⋮	⋮	⋮
12	6	8

a. Using the sign test, specify the competing hypotheses to determine whether the ratings differ between the two faculty members.

b. Calculate the value of the test statistic.

c. Calculate the p-value.

d. At the 10% significance level, do the data suggest that faculty ratings differ? Explain.

20.6 TESTS BASED ON RUNS

LO 20.8

In many applications, we wish to determine whether some observed values occur in a truly random fashion or whether some form of a nonrandom pattern exists. In other words, we want to test if the elements of the sequence are mutually independent. The **Wald-Wolfowitz runs test**, or simply the **runs test**, is a procedure used to examine whether the elements in a sequence appear in a random order. It can be applied to either quantitative or qualitative data so long as we can separate the sample data into two categories.

Determine whether the elements of a sequence appear in a random order.

Suppose we observe a machine filling 16-ounce cereal boxes. Since a machine is unlikely to dispense exactly 16 ounces in each box, we expect the weight of each box to deviate from 16 ounces. We might conjecture that a machine is operating properly if the deviations from 16 ounces occur in a random order. Let's sample 30 cereal boxes and denote those boxes that are overfilled with the letter O and those that are underfilled with the letter U. The following sequence of Os and Us is produced:

Sequence: OOOOUUUOOOOUOOOUUUUOOOOUUOOOOO

One possible way to test whether or not a machine is operating properly is to determine if the elements of a particular sequence of Os and Us occur randomly. If we observe a long series of consecutive Os (or Us), then the machine is likely overfilling (or underfilling) the cereal boxes. Adjustment of the machine is necessary if this is the case. Given the observed sequence, can we conclude that the machine needs adjustment in the sense that the series of Os and Us do not occur randomly?

In general, when applying the runs test, we specify the competing hypotheses as

H_0: The elements occur randomly.

H_A: The elements do not occur randomly.

In this particular application, the null hypothesis implies that the machine properly fills the boxes, and the alternative hypothesis implies that it does not. Before deriving the test statistic, it is first necessary to introduce some terminology. We define a **run** as an uninterrupted sequence of one letter, symbol, or attribute, such as O or U. We rewrite the observed sequence but now include single horizontal lines below the letter O. The five single lines indicate that we observe five runs of O, or $R_O = 5$. Similarly, the double horizontal lines below the letter U show that we have four runs of U, or $R_U = 4$. Thus, the total number of runs R is equal to nine: $R = R_O + R_U = 5 + 4 = 9$. Also, note that we have a total of 30 observations, of which 20 are Os and 10 are Us, or $n = n_O + n_U = 20 + 10 = 30$.

Sequence: OOOO UUU OOOO U OOO UUUU OOOO UU OOOOO

We then ask: "Are nine runs consisting of 30 observations too few or too many compared with the number of runs expected in a strictly random sequence of 30 observations?"

In general, the runs test is a two-tailed test; that is, too many runs are deemed just as unlikely as too few runs. For example, consider the following two sequences:

Sequence A: OOOOOOOOOOOOO UUUUUU OOOOOOOOOOOO

Sequence B: O U O U O U O U O U O U O U O U O U O U O U O U O U O U O U

If the null hypothesis of randomness is true, Sequence A seems unlikely in the sense that there appear to be too few runs given a sample of 30 observations. Sequence B also seems unlikely since O and U alternate systematically, or equivalently, there appear to be too many runs. It is more readily apparent in the machine-filling application that a sequence that produces too few runs indicates a machine that is not operating properly; that is, the machine has a pattern of consistently overfilling and/or underfilling the cereal boxes. However, a machine that exhibits a perfect regularity of overfilling, underfilling, overfilling, underfilling, etc. (too many runs) may be just as problematic. If there are too many runs, then this may indicate some sort of repeated alternating pattern.

Let n_1 and n_2 denote the numbers of Os and Us in an n-element sequence. In general, the sampling distribution of R (the distribution for the runs test) is quite complex. However, if n_1 and n_2 are at least 10, then the distribution of R is approximately normal.

THE TEST STATISTIC R FOR THE WALD-WOLFOWITZ RUNS TEST

The value of the test statistic for the Wald-Wolfowitz runs test is computed as $z = \frac{R - \mu_R}{\sigma_R}$, where R represents the number of runs with mean $\mu_R = \frac{2n_1 n_2}{n} + 1$ and standard deviation $\sigma_R = \sqrt{\frac{2n_1 n_2(2n_1 n_2 - n)}{n^2(n - 1)}}$; n_1 and n_2 are the number of elements in a sequence possessing and not possessing a certain attribute; and $n = n_1 + n_2$. The test is valid when $n_1 \geq 10$ and $n_2 \geq 10$.

For the machine example, we found that $R = 9$; in addition, we have $n_1 = n_O = 20$ and $n_2 = n_U = 10$. We calculate the mean and the standard deviation of the distribution of R as

$$\mu_R = \frac{2n_1 n_2}{n} + 1 = \frac{2(20)(10)}{30} + 1 = 14.3333 \text{ and}$$

$$\sigma_R = \sqrt{\frac{2n_1 n_2(2n_1 n_2 - n)}{n^2(n - 1)}} = \sqrt{\frac{(2 \times 20 \times 10)(2 \times 20 \times 10 - 30)}{30^2(30 - 1)}} = \sqrt{\frac{148,000}{26,100}} = 2.3813.$$

Thus, the expected number of runs in a sample with 30 observations is 14.3333 and the standard deviation is 2.3813. We calculate the value of the test statistic as $z = \frac{R - \mu_R}{\sigma_R} = \frac{9 - 14.3333}{2.3813} = -2.24$. We find the p-value for a two-tailed test as $2 \times P(Z \leq -2.24) = 0.0250$. Since the p-value is less than $\alpha = 0.05$, we reject H_0 and conclude that the machine does not properly fill the boxes. At the 5% significance level, adjustment of the machine is necessary.

The Method of Runs Above and Below the Median

As mentioned earlier, the runs test can also be applied to quantitative data. For example, any sample with numerical values can be treated similarly by using letters, say A and B, to denote values falling above and below the median of the sample, respectively. The resulting As and Bs can be tested for nonrandomness by applying the **method of runs above and below the median**. This test is especially useful in detecting trends and cyclical patterns in economic data. A finding of too few runs is suggestive of a trend; that is, we first observe mostly As and later mostly Bs (or vice versa). In computing the value of the test statistic, we omit values that are equal to the median. A systematic alternation of As and Bs—that is, too many runs—implies a cyclical pattern. Consider the following example.

EXAMPLE 20.12

Table 20.19 shows the growth rate in the gross domestic product (GDP) for the United States from 1980 through 2009. Use the method of runs above and below the median with a significance level of 10% to test the null hypothesis of randomness against the alternative that a trend or cyclical pattern occurs.

TABLE 20.19 GDP Growth Rates (in percent) for the United States, 1980–2009

Year	GDP	Year	GDP	Year	GDP
1980	−0.24	1990	1.86	2000	3.69
1981	2.52	1991	−0.19	2001	0.76
1982	−1.97	1992	3.34	2002	1.61
1983	4.52	1993	2.69	2003	2.52
1984	7.20	1994	4.06	2004	3.65
1985	4.10	1995	2.54	2005	3.08
1986	3.43	1996	3.75	2006	2.87
1987	3.34	1997	4.55	2007	2.00
1988	4.12	1998	4.22	2008	1.10
1989	3.53	1999	4.49	2009	−2.40

Source: http://data.worldbank.org/indicator

FILE
US_GDP

SOLUTION: Since we are testing the null hypothesis of randomness against the alternative that there is a trend or cyclical pattern, we formulate the competing hypotheses as

H_0: The GDP growth rate is random.

H_A: The GDP growth rate is not random.

We first calculate the median GDP growth rate as 3.21%. Letting A and B denote an observation that falls above the median and below the median, respectively, we rewrite the data using the following sequence of As and Bs:

Sequence: BBB AAAAAAA BB A B A B AAAAA BBB A BBBBB

We see that the number of runs below the median R_B is 6, while the number of runs above the median R_A is 5, so the total number of runs R is 11. Also, since no values were discarded (no value was equal to the median), the total number of observations is $n = 30$, where the number of observations below the median and the number of observations above the median are $n_B = 15$ and $n_A = 15$, respectively. Using this information, we compute the mean and the standard deviation of the distribution of R as

$$\mu_R = \frac{2n_An_B}{n} + 1 = \frac{2(15)(15)}{30} + 1 = 16 \text{ and}$$

$$\sigma_R = \sqrt{\frac{2n_An_B(2n_An_B - n)}{n^2(n-1)}} = \sqrt{\frac{(2 \times 15 \times 15)(2 \times 15 \times 15 - 30)}{30^2(30 - 1)}} = \sqrt{\frac{189,000}{26,100}}$$

$$= 2.691.$$

Thus, the value of the test statistic is $z = \frac{R - \mu_R}{\sigma_R} = \frac{11 - 16}{2.691} = -1.86$. Using the z table, we find the p-value for this two-tailed test as $2 \times P(Z \le -1.86) = 0.0628$. Since the p-value is less than $\alpha = 0.10$, we reject H_0 and conclude that the values are not random. In fact, since the observed number of runs ($R = 11$) is significantly less than the expected number of runs ($\mu_R = 16$), there is evidence of a trend. The test results, however, do not enable us to determine whether there is an upward or downward trend in the data.

Using R to Conduct the Runs Test

EXAMPLE 20.13

Given the return data in Table 20.18, use R to replicate the findings in Example 20.12.

SOLUTION: For completeness, we repeat the competing hypotheses:

H_0: The GDP growth rate is random.

H_A: The GDP growth rate is not random.

FILE

US_GDP

a. Import the **US_GDP** data into a data frame (table) in R. In order to implement the runs test in R, we then install and load the *randtests* package. Enter

```
> install.packages("randtests")
> library(randtests)
```

b. We use R's **runs.test** function to find the value of the test statistic and the p-value. Enter

```
> runs.test(US_GDP$'GDP')
```

Table 20.20 shows a portion of the R output when conducting the runs test. We have put the value of the test statistic and the p-value in boldface; these values match those that we calculated by hand in Example 20.12. Thus, we arrive at the same conclusion. At the 10% significance level, the values are not random.

TABLE 20.20 R's Output for Example 20.13

```
                   Runs Test

statistic =-1.8581, runs = 11, n1 = 15, n2 = 15, n = 30,
p-value = 0.06316
alternative hypothesis: nonrandomness
```

EXERCISES 20.6

*For exercises marked with an asterisk, it is advised that you use a statistical software package that accommodates the runs test.

Mechanics

58. Consider the following information: $n_1 = 24$, $n_2 = 28$, and $R = 18$, where R is the number of runs, n_1 and n_2 are the number of elements in a sequence possessing and not possessing a certain attribute, and $n_1 + n_2 = n$.
    a. Specify the competing hypotheses to test for nonrandomness.
    b. Calculate the value of the test statistic.
    c. Calculate the p-value.
    d. At the 5% significance level, are the observations nonrandom?

59. Consider the following information: $n_1 = 10$, $n_2 = 13$, and $R = 8$, where R is the number of runs, n_1 and n_2 are the number of elements in a sequence possessing and not possessing a certain attribute, and $n_1 + n_2 = n$.
    a. Specify the competing hypotheses to test for nonrandomness.
    b. Calculate the value of the test statistic.
    c. Calculate the p-value.
    d. At the 5% significance level, are the observations nonrandom?

60. Let A and B be two possible outcomes of a single experiment. The sequence of the outcomes is as follows:

    BBAABAABBABABBBABBAAABABBABBABA

    At the 5% significance level, conduct a hypothesis test to determine if the outcomes are nonrandom.

61. Let D denote a desirable outcome and U denote an undesirable outcome. The sequence of the outcomes is as follows:

    DDDUUDUUUUUDDDUUDUUUDDDUUUUDDD

    At the 1% significance level, conduct a hypothesis test to determine if the outcomes are nonrandom.

Applications

62. Given the digits zero through nine, a computer program is supposed to generate even and odd numbers randomly. The computer produced the following sequence of numbers:

    5 3 4 6 8 0 2 9 7 7 1 6 8 3 1 5 2 4 3 3 9 2

    a. Specify the competing hypotheses to test for nonrandomness.
    b. What is the value of the test statistic?
    c. At the 1% significance level, is the program operating improperly? Explain.

63. A gambler suspects that a coin may be weighted more heavily toward the outcome of tails (T) over heads (H). He flips the coin 25 times and notes the following sequence:

    T T H T T T H H T H T T H T T T H H H T H T H T T H

a. Specify the competing hypotheses to test the gambler's belief on nonrandomness.
b. What is the value of the test statistic?
c. Calculate the p-value.
d. At the 5% significance level, is the gambler's belief supported by the data?

64.* **FILE** *India_GDP.* The following table shows a portion of the growth rate in the gross domestic product (GDP) for India from 1980 through 2008. Use the method of runs above and below the median with a significance level of 5% to test the null hypothesis of randomness against the alternative that there is a trend or cyclical pattern.

Year	GDP
1980	6.74
1981	6.00
⋮	⋮
2008	6.07

Source: http://data.worldbank.org/indicator.

65. **FILE** *Absenteeism.* The superintendent of a large suburban high school must decide whether to close the school for at least two days due to the spread of flu. If she can confirm a trend in absenteeism, then she will close the high school. The following are the number of students absent from the high school on 25 consecutive school days.

    44, 56, 55, 40, 42, 51, 50, 59, 58, 45, 44, 52, 52,
    43, 48, 58, 57, 42, 60, 65, 69, 75, 70, 72, 72

Use the method of runs above and below the median and $\alpha = 0.05$ to test the null hypothesis of randomness against the alternative hypothesis of nonrandomness.

66.* **FILE** *Amgen.* A research analyst follows the biotechnology industry and examines the daily stock price of Amgen, Inc. over the past year. The table below shows a portion of the daily stock price of Amgen (in $) for the 252 trading days in 2010. The research analyst wants to test the random walk hypothesis that suggests that stock prices move randomly over time with no discernible pattern.

Date	Price
1/4/2010	57.72
1/5/2010	57.22
⋮	⋮
12/31/2010	54.9

a. Use the method of runs above and below the median to test the null hypothesis of randomness against the alternative hypothesis of nonrandomness.
b. Can the research analyst conclude that the movement of Amgen's stock price is inconsistent with the random walk hypothesis?

WRITING WITH STATISTICS

©Lisovskaya Natalia/Shutterstock RF

Meg Suzuki manages a trendy sushi restaurant in Chicago, Illinois. She is planning an aggressive advertising campaign to offset the loss of business due to competition from other restaurants. She knows advertising costs increase overall costs, but she hopes this effort will positively affect sales, as it has done in the past under her tenure. She collects monthly data on sales (in $1,000s) and advertising costs (in $) over the past two years and produces the following regression equation:

$$\text{Estimated Sales} = 17.77 + 0.03\text{Advertising Costs}$$
$$t\text{-statistics} = (17.77) \quad (21.07)$$

At the 5% significance level, Meg initially concludes that advertising is significant in explaining sales. However, to estimate this regression model, she had to make certain assumptions that might not be valid. Specifically, with a time series analysis, the assumption maintaining the independence of the error terms often breaks down. In other words, the regression model often suffers from correlated observations. Table 20.21 shows a portion of the residuals from the regression.

TABLE 20.21 Values of Residuals

Observation	Residual
1	−0.31
2	−0.80
⋮	⋮
24	0.12

Meg would like to use the runs test to determine whether the positive and negative residuals occur randomly at the 5% significance level.

Sample Report— Testing the Independence of Residuals

One of the underlying assumptions of a linear regression model is that the error term is uncorrelated across observations. In a regression model relating sales to advertising costs, there is reason to believe that correlated observations may be a problem because the data are time series. Figure 20.A is a scatterplot of the residuals against time. If the residuals show no pattern around the horizontal axis, then the observations are not likely correlated. Given the wavelike movement in the residuals over time (clustering below the horizontal axis, then above the horizontal axis, and so on), the observations are likely correlated.

FIGURE 20.A Scatterplot of Residuals against Time

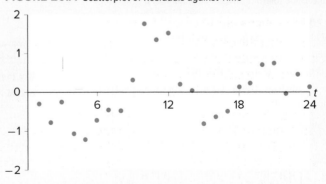

The above graphical analysis is supplemented with a runs test to determine if the residuals fail to follow a random pattern. A residual is given a + symbol if the residual is positive and a − symbol if the residual is negative. There are 12 positive residuals and 12 negative residuals, or $n_+ = 12$ and $n_- = 12$, respectively. A run is then defined as an uninterrupted sequence of a + or a − sign. The sample data exhibit three positive runs, $R_+ = 3$, and three negative runs, $R_- = 3$, for a total number of runs equal to six, $R = 6$.

Are six runs consisting of 24 observations too few or too many compared with the number of runs expected in a strictly random sequence of 24 observations? To answer this question, the mean and the standard deviation for the distribution of R are calculated. The mean number of runs in a sample of 24 observations is 13 with a standard deviation of 2.4. Table 20.A provides summary data to conduct the runs test.

TABLE 20.A Data for Runs Test, $n = 24$

• Mean number of runs, $\mu_R = 13$, versus actual number of runs, $R = 6$.
• Standard deviation of the sampling distribution of R: $\sigma_R = 2.4$.
• z-statistic = −2.92; the p-value (two-tailed) = 0.0036.

The sample value of the test statistic is $z = -2.92$ with an associated p-value of 0.0036. The null hypothesis of the randomness of the residuals is rejected at the 5% level; the pattern of the residuals is nonrandom. Corrective measures should be taken before statistical inference is conducted on the estimated model.

CONCEPTUAL REVIEW

LO 20.1 **Distinguish between parametric and nonparametric tests.**

Nonparametric tests, also referred to as distribution-free tests, do not require the stringent assumptions of parametric tests and are especially attractive when the underlying population is markedly nonnormal. Also, while parametric tests require data of interval or ratio scale, nonparametric tests can be performed on data of nominal or ordinal scale.

A nonparametric test, however, ignores useful information since it often focuses on the rank rather than the magnitude of sample values. Therefore, in situations when the parametric assumptions are valid, the nonparametric test is less powerful (more prone to Type II error) than its parametric counterpart. In general, when the assumptions for a parametric test are met, it is preferable to use a parametric test rather than a nonparametric test. Since the normality assumption for parametric tests is less stringent in large samples, the main appeal of rank-based nonparametric tests tends to be with relatively small samples.

LO 20.2 **Make inferences about a population median.**

If we cannot assume that the data are normally distributed and/or we want to test the population median, we apply the **Wilcoxon signed-rank test**. The value of the test statistic T for the Wilcoxon signed-rank test is $T = T^+$, where T^+ denotes the sum of the ranks of the positive differences from the hypothesized median m_0.

If the sample size $n \leq 10$, then the p-value for the resulting test statistic is found from the sampling distribution of T. Most statistical computer packages, including R, perform this calculation. The sampling distribution of T can also be approximated by the normal distribution if $n \geq 10$. With the normal approximation, the value of the test statistic is calculated as $z = \frac{T - \mu_T}{\sigma_T}$, where $\mu_T = \frac{n(n+1)}{4}$ and $\sigma_T = \sqrt{\frac{n(n+1)(2n+1)}{24}}$.

LO 20.3 Make inferences about the population median difference based on matched-pairs sampling.

We can also apply the **Wilcoxon signed-rank test** as the nonparametric counterpart to the t test that was used to determine whether the population mean difference differs from zero based on matched-pairs sampling. The measurement of interest is the difference between paired observations, or $d_i = x_i - y_i$. We conduct the test by following steps analogous to those applied for a one-sample Wilcoxon signed-rank test.

LO 20.4 Make inferences about the difference between two population medians based on independent sampling.

We use the **Wilcoxon rank-sum test** to determine whether two populations have different medians based on independent sampling. We pool the data and calculate the rank sum of sample 1, W_1, and the rank sum of sample 2, W_2. The test statistic W for the Wilcoxon rank-sum test is defined as $W = W_1$.

If either sample is less than or equal to 10, the p-value for the resulting W test statistic is found from the sampling distribution of W. Most statistical computer packages, including R, perform this calculation. The sampling distribution of W can be approximated by the normal distribution if both sample sizes are greater than or equal to 10. The value of the test statistic is calculated as $z = \frac{W - \mu_W}{\sigma_W}$, where $\mu_W = \frac{n_1(n_1 + n_2 + 1)}{2}$ and $\sigma_W = \sqrt{\frac{n_1 n_2(n_1 + n_2 + 1)}{12}}$.

LO 20.5 Make inferences about the difference between three or more population medians.

We employ the **Kruskal-Wallis test** as the nonparametric alternative to the one-way ANOVA F test. It is based on ranks and is used for testing the differences between the medians of k populations. The value of the test statistic for the Kruskal-Wallis test is $H = \left(\frac{12}{n(n + 1)} \sum_{i=1}^{k} \frac{R_i^2}{n_i} \right) - 3(n + 1)$, where R_i and n_i are the rank sum and the size of the ith sample, $n = \sum_{i=1}^{k} n_i$, and k is the number of populations (independent samples). So long as $n_i \geq 5$, the test statistic H follows the χ^2 distribution with $k - 1$ degrees of freedom.

LO 20.6 Conduct a hypothesis test for the population Spearman rank correlation coefficient.

The **Spearman rank correlation coefficient r_S** measures the sample correlation between two random variables. We compute it as $r_S = 1 - \frac{6\Sigma d_i^2}{n(n^2 - 1)}$, where d_i is the difference between the ranks assigned to the variables. If $n \leq 10$, then the p-value for the resulting test statistic is found from the sampling distribution of r_S. Most statistical computer packages, including R, perform this calculation. If $n \geq 10$, then it is reasonable to assume that the distribution of r_S is approximately normal. The resulting value of the test statistic is calculated as $z = r_S\sqrt{n - 1}$.

LO 20.7 Make inferences about the difference between two populations of ordinal data based on matched-pairs sampling.

We use the **sign test** to determine whether significant differences exist between two matched-pairs populations of ordinal data. The value of the test statistic is computed as $z = \frac{\bar{p} - 0.5}{0.5/\sqrt{n}}$, where $\bar{p}$ is the sample proportion of positive signs. The test is valid when $n \geq 10$.

Determine whether the elements of a sequence appear in a random order.

We apply the **Wald-Wolfowitz runs test** to examine whether or not the attributes in a sequence appear in a random order. The sampling distribution of R, representing the number of runs, can be approximated by the normal distribution if $n_1 \geq 10$ and $n_2 \geq 10$. The value of the test statistic is computed as $z = \frac{R - \mu_R}{\sigma_R}$, where $\mu_R = \frac{2n_1 n_2}{n} + 1$ and $\sigma_R = \sqrt{\frac{2n_1 n_2 (2n_1 n_2 - n)}{n^2(n-1)}}$. We can use the runs test with quantitative data to investigate whether the values randomly fall above and below the sample's median. This test is especially useful in detecting trends and cyclical patterns in economic data.

ADDITIONAL EXERCISES AND CASE STUDIES

Exercises

*For exercises marked with an asterisk, it is advised to use a statistical software package that accommodates the relevant nonparametric test.

67. The following are the closing stock prices for a pharmaceutical firm over the past five days.

Day	1	2	3	4	5
Price ($)	61.22	60.99	61.91	61.59	61.76

a. Specify the competing hypotheses to determine whether the median stock price is greater than $61.25.

b. Calculate the value of the Wilcoxon signed-rank test statistic T.

c. The p-value for the test is found to be equal to 0.156. At the 5% significance level, is the median stock price greater than $61.25? Explain.

68. A farmer is concerned that a change in fertilizer to an organic variant might change his crop yield. He subdivides six lots and uses the old fertilizer on one half of each lot and the new fertilizer on the other half. The following table shows the results.

Lot	Old	New
1	10	12
2	11	10
3	10	13
4	12	9
5	12	11
6	11	12

a. Specify the competing hypotheses to determine whether the median difference between the crop yields differs from zero.

b. Calculate the value of the Wilcoxon signed-rank test statistic T.

c. The p-value for the test is found to be equal to 0.915. At the 5% significance level, is there sufficient evidence to conclude that the median difference between the crop yields differs from zero? Should the farmer be concerned? Explain.

69. **FILE** *Comparison.* The table below shows a portion of the returns for Fidelity's Equity Income mutual fund and Vanguard's Equity Income mutual fund from 2000 through 2010.

Year	Fidelity	Vanguard
2000	3.88	13.57
2001	−5.02	−2.34
⋮	⋮	⋮
2010	15.13	14.88

Source: http://finance.yahoo.com.

a. Specify the competing hypotheses to determine whether the median difference between the returns differs from zero.

b. Calculate the value of the Wilcoxon signed-rank test statistic T. Assume normality of T.

c. At the 5% significance level, does the median difference between the returns differ from zero? Explain.

70.* **FILE** *Refrigerator.* A consumer advocate researches the length of life between two brands of refrigerators, Brand A and Brand B. He collects data on the longevity of 40 refrigerators for Brand A and repeats the sampling for Brand B. A portion of the data is shown in the accompanying table.

Brand A	Brand B
16	16
14	20
⋮	⋮
18	17

a. Specify the competing hypotheses to test whether the median length of life differs between the two brands.
b. With $\alpha = 0.05$, does median longevity differ between the two brands? Explain.

71.* **FILE** **Test_Centers.** A psychiatrist believes that the location of a test center may influence a test taker's performance. To test his claim, he collects SAT scores from four different locations.

Location 1	Location 2	Location 3	Location 4
1350	1300	1000	1450
1275	1320	1350	1700
1200	1260	1100	1600
1450	1400	1050	1325
1150	1425	1025	1200

a. Specify the competing hypotheses to test whether some median test scores differ by location.
b. At the 5% significance level, do the data support the psychiatrist's belief? Explain.

72. **FILE** **PE_Ratio.** An economist wants to determine whether the Price/Earnings (P/E) ratio is the same for firms in three industries. Five firms were randomly selected from each industry. Their P/E ratios are shown in the accompanying table.

Industry A	12.19	12.44	7.28	9.96	10.51
Industry B	14.34	17.80	9.32	14.90	9.41
Industry C	26.38	24.75	16.88	16.87	16.70

a. Specify the competing hypotheses to test whether some median P/E ratios differ by industry.
b. Calculate the value of the test statistic H.
c. At the 5% significance level, do some P/E ratios differ by industry? Explain.

73. **FILE** **Electronics_Utilities.** The following table shows a portion of the annual returns (in percent) for two of Fidelity's mutual funds: the Fidelity Advisor's Electronic Fund and the Fidelity Advisor's Utilities Fund.

Year	Electronics	Utilities
2001	47.41	−15.28
2002	20.74	−29.48
⋮	⋮	⋮
2010	16.84	11.08

Source: http://finance.yahoo.com.

a. Specify the competing hypotheses to determine whether the Spearman rank correlation coefficient differs from zero.
b. Calculate and interpret the Spearman correlation coefficient.
c. At the 5% significance level, are the returns correlated? Explain. Assume the sampling distribution of r_S is approximately normal.

74. A research analyst believes that a positive relationship exists between a firm's advertising expenditures and its sales. For 65 firms, she collects data on each firm's yearly advertising expenditures and subsequent sales. She calculates a Spearman rank correlation coefficient of 0.45.
a. Specify the competing hypotheses to determine whether the Spearman rank correlation coefficient is greater than zero.
b. Assume that the sampling distribution of r_S is approximately normal. Calculate the value of the test statistic and the p-value.
c. At the 5% significance level, are advertising and sales positively correlated? Explain.

75. **FILE** **Inspectors.** In order to ensure the public's health and safety, state health inspectors are required to rate the cleanliness and quality of all restaurants in the state. Restaurants that consistently score below a certain level often lose their licenses to operate. From a sample of 10 restaurants, two health inspectors give the ratings where a score of 10 denotes excellence in cleanliness and quality. A portion of the data is shown in the accompanying table.

Restaurant	Inspector A's Rating	Inspector B's Rating
1	9	8
2	5	6
⋮	⋮	⋮
10	8	9

a. Using the sign test, specify the competing hypotheses to determine whether the ratings differ between the two health inspectors.
b. Calculate the value of the test statistic.

c. Calculate the *p*-value.

d. At the 5% significance level, do the data suggest that the ratings differ?

76.* **FILE** *China_GDP.* The following table shows a portion of the growth rate in the gross domestic product (GDP) for China from 1980 through 2008. Use the method of runs above and below the median with a significance level of 5% to test the null hypothesis of randomness against the alternative that there is a trend or cyclical pattern.

Year	GDP
1980	7.8
1981	5.2
⋮	⋮
2008	9.0

Source: http://data.worldbank.org/indicator.

77.* **FILE** *Dow_Jones.* A research analyst follows the monthly price data for the Dow Jones Industrial Average for the years 2008–2010. The accompanying table shows a portion of the price data. The analyst wants to test the random-walk hypothesis that suggests that prices move randomly over time with no discernible pattern.

Date	Price
1/2/2008	12650.36
2/1/2008	12266.39
⋮	⋮
12/1/2010	11577.51

Source: http://finance.yahoo.com.

Use the method-of-runs above and below the median to test the null hypothesis of randomness against the alternative hypothesis of nonrandomness at the 5% significance level. Can the research analyst conclude that the movement of the Dow Jones Industrial Average is inconsistent with the random walk hypothesis?

78.* **FILE** *US_CPI.* The following table shows a portion of the percent change in the consumer price index (CPI) for the United States from 1980 through 2008. Use the method of runs above and below the median with a significance level of 5% to test the null hypothesis of randomness against the alternative hypothesis of nonrandomness.

Year	CPI
1980	12.5
1981	8.9
⋮	⋮
2008	0.1

Source: http://data.worldbank.org/indicator.

CASE STUDIES

CASE STUDY 20.1 In order to analyze differences in home prices between coastal and inland areas in California, an economist gathers 20 recent home sales (in $1,000s) in Southern California and 20 recent home sales (in $1,000s) in the Inland Empire. A portion of the results are shown in the accompanying table.

Data for Case Study 20.1 California Home Prices

Home	Southern California	Inland Empire
1	618	367
2	691	386
⋮	⋮	⋮
20	1075	472

FILE

California

In a report, use the sample information to

1. Calculate and interpret relevant summary measures for California home prices in these two regions.

2. Explain why the *t* test for comparing means from independent samples might be inappropriate in this case.

3. Use the Wilcoxon rank-sum test to determine whether the median home price in Southern California is greater than the median home price in the Inland Empire.

CASE STUDY 20.2   There has been a lot of discussion lately surrounding the levels and structure of executive compensation. It is well documented that in general, compensation received by senior executives has risen steeply in recent years. The accompanying table lists a portion of total compensation for the top 10 CEOs in four industry classifications: Manufacturing (technology); Manufacturing (other); Services (financial); Services (other). Total compensation for 2006 is measured in millions of dollars.

Data for Case Study 20.2   Top Executive Compensation (in $ millions), 2006

Compensation

Manufacturing (Technology)	Manufacturing (Other)	Services (Financial)	Services (Other)
39.82	64.63	91.38	24.02
32.85	60.73	48.13	21.51
⋮	⋮	⋮	⋮
24.08	30.80	25.75	13.04

Source: Compustat.

In a report, use the sample information to

1. Calculate and interpret relevant summary measures for executive compensation in these four industries.

2. Explain why the one-way ANOVA *F* test for comparing three or more population means may be inappropriate in this case.

3. Use the Kruskal-Wallis test to determine whether some median compensations vary across classifications at the 5% significance level.

CASE STUDY 20.3   The consumption function, developed by John Maynard Keynes, captures one of the key relationships in economics. It expresses consumption as a function of disposable income, where disposable income is defined as income after taxes. For the years 2000–2016, quarterly observations are collected on U.S. per-capita consumption (in $) and U.S. per-capita disposable income (in $). The accompanying table shows a portion of the data.

Data for Case Study 20.3   Consumption and Disposable Income (in $), 2000–2016

Consumption_Function

Time	Consumption	Disposable Income
Quarter 1, 2000	28634	31192
Quarter 2, 2000	28837	31438
⋮	⋮	⋮
Quarter 4, 2016	35987	39254

Source: www.fred.stlouisfed.org; data retrieved June 3, 2017.

In a report, use the sample information to

1. Estimate and interpret the model: Consumption $= \beta_0 + \beta_1$Disposable Income $+ \varepsilon$.

2. Indicate which assumption might be violated, given that the analysis uses time series data.

3. Use the runs test to determine whether the pattern of the residuals is nonrandom at the 5% significance level.

APPENDIX 20.1 Guidelines for Other Software Packages

The following section provides brief commands for Minitab, SPSS, and JMP. Copy and paste the specified data file into the relevant software spreadsheet prior to following the commands.

Minitab

The Wilcoxon Signed-Rank Test

(Replicating Example 20.3) From the menu, choose **Stat > Nonparametrics > 1-Sample Wilcoxon**. After **Variables**, select Value. Select **Test median** and enter the value 5. After **Alternative**, select "greater than."

FILE
Growth_Value

The Wilcoxon Rank-Sum Test

(Replicating Example 20.5) From the menu, choose **Stat > Nonparametrics > Mann-Whitney**. Select Computer Science for the **First Sample**, and then select Finance for the **Second Sample**. After **Alternative**, select "not equal."

FILE
Undergrad_Salaries

The Kruskal-Wallis Test

A. (Replicating Example 20.8) Pool the data into one column, labeled Income. In an adjacent column, labeled Category, denote all City 1 observations with the value 1, all City 2 observations with the value 2, and all City 3 observations with the value 3.

FILE
City_Income

B. From the menu, choose **Stat, > Nonparametrics > Kruskal-Wallis**.

C. After **Response**, select Income, and after **Factor**, select Category.

The Spearman Rank Correlation Test

(Replicating Example 20.9) From the menu, choose **Stat > Basic Statistics > Correlation**. Under **Variables**, select Growth and Value. Next to **Method**, select Spearman rho.

FILE
Growth_Value

The Runs Test

(Replicating Example 20.12) From the menu, choose **Stat > Nonparametrics > Runs Test**. Under **Variables**, select GDP. Select **Above and below**, and enter the value 3.21.

FILE
US_GDP

SPSS

The Wilcoxon Signed-Rank Test

A. (Replicating Example 20.3) From the menu, select **Analyze > Nonparametric Tests > One-Sample**.

FILE
Growth_Value

B. Choose the **Objective** tab and after "**What is your objective?**" select **Custom Analysis**. Choose the **Fields** tab and after **Test Fields**, select Value. Choose the **Settings** tab, select **Customize tests**, and select **Compare median to hypothesized (Wilcoxon signed-rank test)**. Enter 5 after **Hypothesized Mean**.

The Wilcoxon Rank-Sum Test

A. (Replicating Example 20.5) Pool the data into one column, labeled Salary. In an adjacent column, labeled Major, input the corresponding major with each salary.

FILE
Undergrad_Salaries

B. In the menu, select **Analyze > Nonparametric Tests > Independent Samples**.

C. Choose the **Objective** tab and after **"What is your objective?"** select **Custom Analysis**. Choose the **Field** tab, after **Test Field** select Salary, and after **Groups** select Major. Choose the **Settings** tab, select **Customize settings**, and select **Mann-Whitney U (2 samples)**.

The Kruskal-Wallis Test

City_Income

A. (Replicating Example 20.8) To arrange the data, follow step A under the Minitab section for the Kruskal-Wallis Test.

B. In the menu, select **Analyze > Nonparametric Tests > Independent Samples**.

C. Choose the **Objective** tab and after **"What is your objective?"** select **Custom Analysis**. Choose the **Field** tab, after **Test Field** select Income, and after **Groups** select Category. Choose the **Settings** tab, select **Customize settings**, and select **Kruskal-Wallis 1-Way Anova (k samples)**.

The Spearman Rank Correlation Test

Growth_Value

A. (Replicating Example 20.9) From the menu, choose **Analyze > Correlate > Bivariate**.

B. Under **Variables**, select Growth and Value. Under **Correlation Coefficients**, select Spearman.

The Runs Test

US_GDP

A. (Replicating Example 20.12) From the menu, select **Analyze > Nonparametric Tests > Legacy Dialogs > Runs**.

B. Under **Test Variable List**, select GDP. Under **Cut Point**, select **Custom** and enter 3.21.

JMP

The Wilcoxon Signed-Rank Test

Growth_Value

A. (Replicating Example 20.3) Create a column of differences between the returns (Growth − Value), labeled Difference.

B. From the menu, choose **Analyze > Distribution**.

C. Under **Select Columns**, select Difference, then under **Cast Selected Columns into Roles**, select **Y, Columns**.

D. Click on the red triangle next to **Difference**, and select **Test Mean**. After **Specify Hypothesized Mean**, enter 0, and check the box before **Wilcoxon Signed Rank**.

The Wilcoxon Rank-Sum Test

Undergrad_Salaries

A. (Replicating Example 20.5) To arrange the data, follow step A under the SPSS section for the Wilcoxon Rank-Sum Test.

B. From the menu, select **Analyze > Fit Y by X**.

C. Under **Select Columns**, select Salary, then under **Cast Selected Columns into Roles**, select **Y, Columns**. Under **Select Columns**, select Major, and then under **Cast Selected Columns into Roles**, select **X, Factor**.

D. Click on the red triangle next to **Oneway Analysis of Salary By Major** and select **Nonparametric > Wilcoxon Test**.

The Kruskal-Wallis Test

A. (Replicating Example 20.8) To arrange the data, follow step A under the Minitab section for the Kruskal-Wallis Test.

B. From the menu, select **Analyze > Fit Y by X**.

C. Under **Select Columns**, select Income, then under **Cast Selected Columns into Roles**, select **Y, Columns**. Under **Select Columns**, select Category, and then under **Cast Selected Columns into Roles**, select **X, Factor**.

D. Click on the red triangle next to **Oneway Analysis of All By Category** and select **Nonparametric > Wilcoxon Test**.

The Spearman Rank Correlation Test

A. (Replicating Example 20.9) From the menu, choose **Analyze > Multivariate Methods > Multivariate**.

B. Under **Select Columns**, select Growth and Value, and under **Cast Selected Columns into Roles**, select **Y, Columns**.

C. Click the red triangle beside **Multivariate**. Select **Nonparametric Correlations > Spearman's ρ**.

Getting Started with R

What is R?

R is powerful software that merges the convenience of statistical packages with the power of coding. It is open source as well as cross-platform compatible. This means that there is zero cost to download R, and it can be run on Windows, Mac OS X, or Linux. In this appendix, we will introduce you to some fundamental features of R and provide instructions on how to obtain solutions for many of the exercises in the text.

What is RStudio?

RStudio is a program that makes R easier to use. On its own, R acts like a programming language and, as such, comes with a minimal user interface. As standalone software, R shows a single prompt for you to enter commands; this is called the Console. While everything we will ever need from R can be done through combining Console commands with other programs, things can quickly get messy. Instead, we "clean up" by running R through an integrated development environment (IDE). IDEs are programs that combine in one place many common features needed in programming and give them a graphical representation.[1] Here, we will use an open source version of an IDE called RStudio, which is very popular among students, professionals, and researchers who use R.

Installation

Installation of both R and RStudio is straightforward and requires no special modifications to your system. However, it should be noted that RStudio does not come with R; *therefore, both pieces of software need to be installed separately.* Also, these instructions were written in July 2017. Given the constant innovation in technology, you may need to refer to the Internet if some of the steps provided below do not work.

Installing R

A. Navigate to https://cran.r-project.org/.
B. In the *Download and Install R* box, select the link that corresponds with your operating system (Linux, Mac, or Windows). After installation, the instructions provided in the text work the same regardless of your operating system.
C. Select the link *install R for the first time*.
D. Download the latest version of R, then select *Open* or *Run*.
E. Select *Yes* when asked about verifying the software publisher, and then select the language that you prefer. We will use English.
F. Follow the instructions in the R Setup window.

Installing RStudio

A. Navigate to https://www.rstudio.com/products/rstudio/.
B. Select *RStudio Desktop,* then select *Download RStudio Desktop.*

---

[1]More formally, this is called a "graphical user interface," or a GUI. In practice, this means that charts, graphs, and buttons can be seen and used.

C. Scroll down to the *Installers for Supported Platforms* section, select the link that corresponds to your operating system, and then select *Open* or *Run*.

D. Select *Yes* when asked about verifying the software publisher.

E. Follow the instructions in the RStudio Setup window.

The Interface

Installation should now be complete. You can close all windows and then double-click on the RStudio icon.

The RStudio interface consists of several panes. By default, three panes are visible. We will refer to these by the names of the default tab shown in each: Console, Environment, and Help. We will also briefly discuss the Source pane, which is hidden until you open it. Figure A.1 shows what you should see when you open RStudio for the first time.

FIGURE A.1 The Console, Environment, and Help Panes

- **Console pane:** The Console pane is the primary way that you interact with R. It is here that you input commands (at the > prompt) and then view most of your output.

- **Environment pane:** The Environment pane has two tabs: Environment and History. A common feature between them is the broom icon, which clears the content of each tab. The Environment tab shows the data, objects, and variables in the current R session. The History tab provides a list of all console commands issued in the session.

- **Help pane:** The help section has five tabs. We discuss two of these here: Help and Plots.

  - The Help tab is where you can view R documentation (help files). For example, to learn about the **print** function, select the Help tab and then enter `print` next to the magnifying glass icon. (You can also view R documentation by entering a question mark followed immediately by the topic of interest in the Console pane; so, for this example, you would enter `?print` after the prompt.)

  - The Plots tab is where you can see all graphs and charts. Any graph or chart can be cleared with the broom icon.

- **The Source pane:** The Source pane is hidden by default in R. This is where you can write your own scripts. As you will see, most of what we do in this text can be accomplished by importing a data set and then using a single command in the Console. Nonetheless, here is an example of how you would write a simple script:

A. Open a new script file in the Source pane by navigating
File > New File > R Script

B. In the new window, enter the following:

```
print("This is my first script.")
print("This is easy!")
```

• Save the script with **File > Save As**. Name your script `Script1`. Figure A.2 shows what you should see in the Source pane.

FIGURE A.2 The Source Pane After Writing First Script

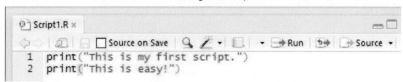

C. Now, select the Source button from the menu on the Source pane; this tells R to read and execute the script. Figure A.3 shows what you should see in the Console pane after executing your first script.

FIGURE A.3 The Console Pane After Executing First Script

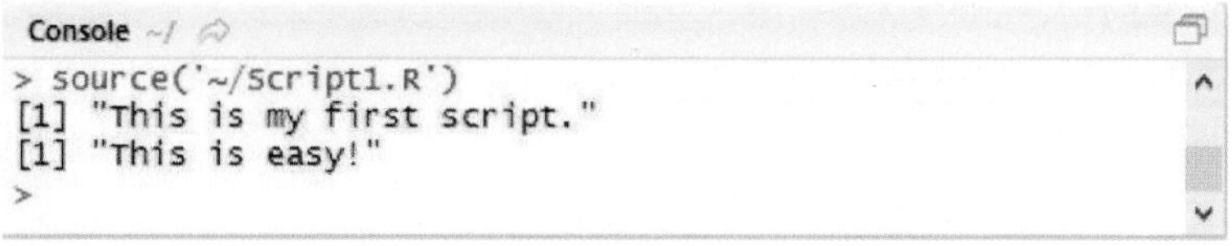

```
Console ~/
> source('~/Script1.R')
[1] "This is my first script."
[1] "This is easy!"
>
```

R executes complete statements in the order that they appear. Unique to RStudio, there is also a way to run specific sections of scripts. This is done by highlighting the desired section of the script in RStudio and selecting the Run button from the menu on the Source pane.

Entering Data and Using Functions

Throughout this text, our goal is to provide the simplest way to obtain the relevant output. Seasoned users of R might argue that there are "better" approaches than the ones we suggest, but we feel that they may distract from learning the important statistical concepts.

Like Excel and other statistical packages, R has many built-in formulas or functions. In the text, we denote all function names in **boldface**. Within each function, R also provides various options, such as labeling the axes of a graph, inserting colors in a chart, and so on. We will not use every option within a function; rather, we use those that we feel are most useful and least cumbersome. We denote all option names in *italics*.

Most of the time we will be importing data files, as we explain in the next section. However, suppose we want to use R to verify some of our manual calculations. Consider Exercise 3.2 in Chapter 3, where we are asked to calculate the mean given the following data: −4, 0, 6, 1, −3, −4. In order to input these values into R, we use the **c** function, which combines the values to form a list; or, perhaps more mathematically precise, the **c** function combines the values to form a vector. We label this data as

Exercise_3.2 and then use the expression "<-", implying that it equals to, which is then followed by the **c** function. We enter

```
> Exercise_3.2 <- c(-4, 0, 6, 1, -3, -4)
```

You should now see that this data is listed as a variable in the Environment pane. You can also view the data by entering Exercise_3.2 at the prompt or using the **list** function. We use the **list** function:

```
> list(Exercise_3.2)
```

As we discuss in more detail in Chapter 3, we use the **mean** function to calculate the mean of a data set. We enter

```
> mean(Exercise_3.2)
```

And R returns: −0.6666667.

Importing Data and Using Functions

FILE
Wage

All the data for *Business Statistics—Communicating with Numbers* have been stored in Excel spreadsheets. We will assume that you have stored all the relevant spreadsheets in a Data folder. When we import a spreadsheet into R, it is referred to as a data frame. A data frame is a table, or two-dimensional array-like structure, in which each column contains measurements on one variable and each row contains one case. A data frame is used for storing data tables.

We illustrate the mechanics of importing an Excel file using the **Wage** data from Chapter 14. For 50 individuals, the data show each individual's hourly wage (Wage in $), years of experience (EXPER), years of education (EDUC), age, and sex (Male equals 1 if male, 0 otherwise). Figure A.4 shows a portion of the **Wage** data after it is opened in Excel.

FIGURE A.4 Portion of the Wage Data

A1		f_x	Wage	
	A	**B**	**C**	**D**	**E**
	Wage	EDUC	EXPER	Age	Male
1	Wage	EDUC	EXPER	Age	Male
2	37.85	11	2	40	1
3	21.72	4	1	39	0
4	14.34	4	2	38	0
5	21.26	5	9	53	1
6	24.65	6	15	59	1

In order to import this data file into R, we select **File > Import Dataset > From Excel**, as shown in Figure A.5.[2] (The first time you import data, R might prompt you to add updates. Simply follow the steps to add the relevant updates.)

---

[2]We should note that if you want to import Excel spreadsheets using scripts, then the menu-driven option of importing data will not work. One way to write a script in this instance is to first save the Excel file in a tab-delimited text file (.txt file) and then use the **read.table** function. Prior to using the **read.table** function, you first need to find out where your working directory is set by entering getwd() at the prompt sign. Suppose that when you enter this command, R returns "C:/Users/Documents". If your Data folder is stored on this path, then you are ready to use the **read.table** function. For instance, in order to import the Wage data (after saving it as a .txt file), you would enter Wage <- read.table("C:/Users/Documents/Data/Wage.txt", header=TRUE). If you would like to set a different working directory, then enter setwd("<location of your Data folder>").

FIGURE A.5 Importing the Wage Data into R

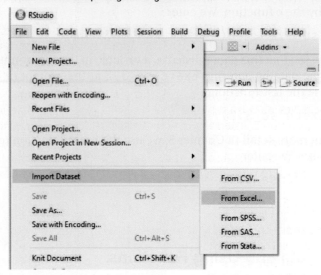

We select the Browse button and then navigate to the **Wage** data in the Data folder. Once we select the **Wage** data, we should see the data in the *Data Preview* dialog box, as shown in Figure A.6.

FIGURE A.6 Viewing the Wage Data Prior to Importing

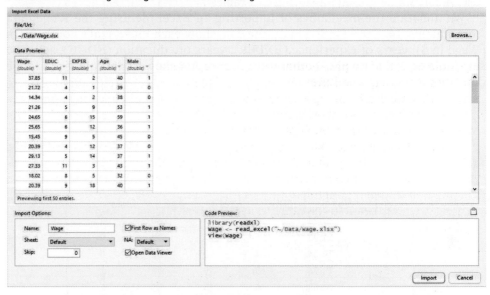

Once you select the *Import* button (see the bottom of Figure A.6), you have successfully imported the data. You can verify this in a couple of ways: (1) in the Environment pane, you should now see Wage under *Data*, and (2) in the Console pane, you can enter `list(Wage)` and R returns a portion of the data.

Suppose we want to calculate the mean age in the Wage data frame. In order to select a variable from a data frame, we attach the expression `$'variable name'` to the name of the data frame. Here we enter

> `mean(Wage$'Age')`

And R returns: `42.26`.

If the variable name in the data frame is a single word, as it is here, it is not necessary to enclose the variable name with single quotation marks after the dollar sign. So in this example, we could have entered `mean(Wage$Age)` and R would have returned the same value of 42.26.

If we are confronted with a variable name that consists of more than one word or a variable name that is numeric, such as the year, then we need to enclose the variable name with single quotation marks. For these reasons and for consistency purposes, we will always enclose variable names with single quotation marks. Another function that we discuss in Chapter 3 is the **summary** function. This function provides various summary measures for all variables in a data frame. We could input `summary(Wage)` and R would return summary measures for all the variables in the Wage data frame, including the categorical variable Male. Suppose we would like summary measures on all variables except the Male variable. In this case, we attach square brackets to the name of the data frame, and within the brackets we indicate the columns that should be included in the calculations. In order to obtain summary measures of the first four variables, thus excluding Male, we enter

```
> summary(Wage[,1:4])
```

Notice in the above command that we enter a comma directly after the left square bracket. This implies that we are including all 50 observations (all 50 rows) of the data in the calculations. If for some reason we only wanted to include the first 25 observations in the calculations, we would have entered `summary(Wage[1:25, 1:4])`.

Finally, suppose we want to delete the Wage data frame. We use the **rm** function and enter

```
> rm(Wage)
```

You will find that Wage no longer appears under *Data* in the Environment pane.

A Note on Line Breaks

The commands that we have outlined here have been relatively short. There are some instances, however, when the commands get long and become difficult to read. To mitigate this, we can break up a command into parts. R will prompt you to finish the command with plus + symbols in lines following the first line. For example, in Chapter 2 we discuss a scatterplot. Suppose we want to construct a scatterplot of Hourly Wage against Experience using R's **plot** function. In addition to constructing the scatterplot, we use the *ylab* and *xlab* options to add titles on the *y*-axis and the *x*-axis. Two entries for constructing a scatterplot are shown below. Entry 1 uses a single line in R (even though two lines are shown on the page). Entry 2 uses three lines. Both entries result in the same scatterplot, as shown in Figure A.7.

Entry 1:

```
> plot(Wage$'EXPER', Wage$'Wage', ylab="Hourly Wages",
  xlab="Experience")
```

Entry 2:

```
> plot(Wage$'EXPER', Wage$'Wage',
  + ylab="Hourly Wages",
  + xlab="Experience")
```

FIGURE A.7 Scatterplot of Hourly Wage against Experience

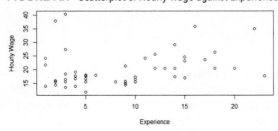

Packages

Part of what makes R so powerful is its large collection of packages, or collections of objects not included in the base version. Packages greatly expand what can be done with R by adding custom functions and data structures. To use a package, you must install it and then load it. We use the *qcc* package, which stands for quality control chart and is introduced in Chapter 7, to demonstrate how this is done:

```
> install.packages("qcc")
> library(qcc)
```

The **install.packages** function opens a connection to the official R servers (CRAN), downloads the specified package(s) and those it depends on, and installs it. This must be done with each package only once on each computer used. The **library** function loads the installed package(s). Note that each package only needs to be loaded once per R session. Once the package is downloaded and loaded, documentation for commands it contains can be viewed in R using the help feature discussed earlier. Documentation files for an entire package can be viewed online. All information associated with available packages can be found at https://cran.r-project.org/web/packages/.

Tables

TABLE 1 Standard Normal Curve Areas

Entries in this table provide cumulative probabilities, that is, the area under the curve to the left of $-z$. For example, $P(Z \le -1.52) = 0.0643$.

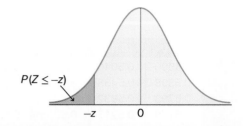

$P(Z \le -z)$

z	0.00	0.01	0.02	0.03	0.04	0.05	0.06	0.07	0.08	0.09
−3.9	0.0000	0.0000	0.0000	0.0000	0.0000	0.0000	0.0000	0.0000	0.0000	0.0000
−3.8	0.0001	0.0001	0.0001	0.0001	0.0001	0.0001	0.0001	0.0001	0.0001	0.0001
−3.7	0.0001	0.0001	0.0001	0.0001	0.0001	0.0001	0.0001	0.0001	0.0001	0.0001
−3.6	0.0002	0.0002	0.0001	0.0001	0.0001	0.0001	0.0001	0.0001	0.0001	0.0001
−3.5	0.0002	0.0002	0.0002	0.0002	0.0002	0.0002	0.0002	0.0002	0.0002	0.0002
−3.4	0.0003	0.0003	0.0003	0.0003	0.0003	0.0003	0.0003	0.0003	0.0003	0.0002
−3.3	0.0005	0.0005	0.0005	0.0004	0.0004	0.0004	0.0004	0.0004	0.0004	0.0003
−3.2	0.0007	0.0007	0.0006	0.0006	0.0006	0.0006	0.0006	0.0005	0.0005	0.0005
−3.1	0.0010	0.0009	0.0009	0.0009	0.0008	0.0008	0.0008	0.0008	0.0007	0.0007
−3.0	0.0013	0.0013	0.0013	0.0012	0.0012	0.0011	0.0011	0.0011	0.0010	0.0010
−2.9	0.0019	0.0018	0.0018	0.0017	0.0016	0.0016	0.0015	0.0015	0.0014	0.0014
−2.8	0.0026	0.0025	0.0024	0.0023	0.0023	0.0022	0.0021	0.0021	0.0020	0.0019
−2.7	0.0035	0.0034	0.0033	0.0032	0.0031	0.0030	0.0029	0.0028	0.0027	0.0026
−2.6	0.0047	0.0045	0.0044	0.0043	0.0041	0.0040	0.0039	0.0038	0.0037	0.0036
−2.5	0.0062	0.0060	0.0059	0.0057	0.0055	0.0054	0.0052	0.0051	0.0049	0.0048
−2.4	0.0082	0.0080	0.0078	0.0075	0.0073	0.0071	0.0069	0.0068	0.0066	0.0064
−2.3	0.0107	0.0104	0.0102	0.0099	0.0096	0.0094	0.0091	0.0089	0.0087	0.0084
−2.2	0.0139	0.0136	0.0132	0.0129	0.0125	0.0122	0.0119	0.0116	0.0113	0.0110
−2.1	0.0179	0.0174	0.0170	0.0166	0.0162	0.0158	0.0154	0.0150	0.0146	0.0143
−2.0	0.0228	0.0222	0.0217	0.0212	0.0207	0.0202	0.0197	0.0192	0.0188	0.0183
−1.9	0.0287	0.0281	0.0274	0.0268	0.0262	0.0256	0.0250	0.0244	0.0239	0.0233
−1.8	0.0359	0.0351	0.0344	0.0336	0.0329	0.0322	0.0314	0.0307	0.0301	0.0294
−1.7	0.0446	0.0436	0.0427	0.0418	0.0409	0.0401	0.0392	0.0384	0.0375	0.0367
−1.6	0.0548	0.0537	0.0526	0.0516	0.0505	0.0495	0.0485	0.0475	0.0465	0.0455
−1.5	0.0668	0.0655	0.0643	0.0630	0.0618	0.0606	0.0594	0.0582	0.0571	0.0559
−1.4	0.0808	0.0793	0.0778	0.0764	0.0749	0.0735	0.0721	0.0708	0.0694	0.0681
−1.3	0.0968	0.0951	0.0934	0.0918	0.0901	0.0885	0.0869	0.0853	0.0838	0.0823
−1.2	0.1151	0.1131	0.1112	0.1093	0.1075	0.1056	0.1038	0.1020	0.1003	0.0985
−1.1	0.1357	0.1335	0.1314	0.1292	0.1271	0.1251	0.1230	0.1210	0.1190	0.1170
−1.0	0.1587	0.1562	0.1539	0.1515	0.1492	0.1469	0.1446	0.1423	0.1401	0.1379
−0.9	0.1841	0.1814	0.1788	0.1762	0.1736	0.1711	0.1685	0.1660	0.1635	0.1611
−0.8	0.2119	0.2090	0.2061	0.2033	0.2005	0.1977	0.1949	0.1922	0.1894	0.1867
−0.7	0.2420	0.2389	0.2358	0.2327	0.2296	0.2266	0.2236	0.2206	0.2177	0.2148
−0.6	0.2743	0.2709	0.2676	0.2643	0.2611	0.2578	0.2546	0.2514	0.2483	0.2451
−0.5	0.3085	0.3050	0.3015	0.2981	0.2946	0.2912	0.2877	0.2843	0.2810	0.2776
−0.4	0.3446	0.3409	0.3372	0.3336	0.3300	0.3264	0.3228	0.3192	0.3156	0.3121
−0.3	0.3821	0.3783	0.3745	0.3707	0.3669	0.3632	0.3594	0.3557	0.3520	0.3483
−0.2	0.4207	0.4168	0.4129	0.4090	0.4052	0.4013	0.3974	0.3936	0.3897	0.3859
−0.1	0.4602	0.4562	0.4522	0.4483	0.4443	0.4404	0.4364	0.4325	0.4286	0.4247
−0.0	0.5000	0.4960	0.4920	0.4880	0.4840	0.4801	0.4761	0.4721	0.4681	0.4641

Source: Probabilities calculated with Excel.

TABLE 1 (*Continued*)

Entries in this table provide cumulative probabilities, that is, the area under the curve to the left of *z*. For example, $P(Z \le 1.52) = 0.9357$.

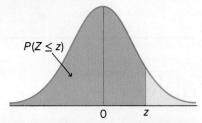

$P(Z \le z)$

z	0.00	0.01	0.02	0.03	0.04	0.05	0.06	0.07	0.08	0.09
0.0	0.5000	0.5040	0.5080	0.5120	0.5160	0.5199	0.5239	0.5279	0.5319	0.5359
0.1	0.5398	0.5438	0.5478	0.5517	0.5557	0.5596	0.5636	0.5675	0.5714	0.5753
0.2	0.5793	0.5832	0.5871	0.5910	0.5948	0.5987	0.6026	0.6064	0.6103	0.6141
0.3	0.6179	0.6217	0.6255	0.6293	0.6331	0.6368	0.6406	0.6443	0.6480	0.6517
0.4	0.6554	0.6591	0.6628	0.6664	0.6700	0.6736	0.6772	0.6808	0.6844	0.6879
0.5	0.6915	0.6950	0.6985	0.7019	0.7054	0.7088	0.7123	0.7157	0.7190	0.7224
0.6	0.7257	0.7291	0.7324	0.7357	0.7389	0.7422	0.7454	0.7486	0.7517	0.7549
0.7	0.7580	0.7611	0.7642	0.7673	0.7704	0.7734	0.7764	0.7794	0.7823	0.7852
0.8	0.7881	0.7910	0.7939	0.7967	0.7995	0.8023	0.8051	0.8078	0.8106	0.8133
0.9	0.8159	0.8186	0.8212	0.8238	0.8264	0.8289	0.8315	0.8340	0.8365	0.8389
1.0	0.8413	0.8438	0.8461	0.8485	0.8508	0.8531	0.8554	0.8577	0.8599	0.8621
1.1	0.8643	0.8665	0.8686	0.8708	0.8729	0.8749	0.8770	0.8790	0.8810	0.8830
1.2	0.8849	0.8869	0.8888	0.8907	0.8925	0.8944	0.8962	0.8980	0.8997	0.9015
1.3	0.9032	0.9049	0.9066	0.9082	0.9099	0.9115	0.9131	0.9147	0.9162	0.9177
1.4	0.9192	0.9207	0.9222	0.9236	0.9251	0.9265	0.9279	0.9292	0.9306	0.9319
1.5	0.9332	0.9345	0.9357	0.9370	0.9382	0.9394	0.9406	0.9418	0.9429	0.9441
1.6	0.9452	0.9463	0.9474	0.9484	0.9495	0.9505	0.9515	0.9525	0.9535	0.9545
1.7	0.9554	0.9564	0.9573	0.9582	0.9591	0.9599	0.9608	0.9616	0.9625	0.9633
1.8	0.9641	0.9649	0.9656	0.9664	0.9671	0.9678	0.9686	0.9693	0.9699	0.9706
1.9	0.9713	0.9719	0.9726	0.9732	0.9738	0.9744	0.9750	0.9756	0.9761	0.9767
2.0	0.9772	0.9778	0.9783	0.9788	0.9793	0.9798	0.9803	0.9808	0.9812	0.9817
2.1	0.9821	0.9826	0.9830	0.9834	0.9838	0.9842	0.9846	0.9850	0.9854	0.9857
2.2	0.9861	0.9864	0.9868	0.9871	0.9875	0.9878	0.9881	0.9884	0.9887	0.9890
2.3	0.9893	0.9896	0.9898	0.9901	0.9904	0.9906	0.9909	0.9911	0.9913	0.9916
2.4	0.9918	0.9920	0.9922	0.9925	0.9927	0.9929	0.9931	0.9932	0.9934	0.9936
2.5	0.9938	0.9940	0.9941	0.9943	0.9945	0.9946	0.9948	0.9949	0.9951	0.9952
2.6	0.9953	0.9955	0.9956	0.9957	0.9959	0.9960	0.9961	0.9962	0.9963	0.9964
2.7	0.9965	0.9966	0.9967	0.9968	0.9969	0.9970	0.9971	0.9972	0.9973	0.9974
2.8	0.9974	0.9975	0.9976	0.9977	0.9977	0.9978	0.9979	0.9979	0.9980	0.9981
2.9	0.9981	0.9982	0.9982	0.9983	0.9984	0.9984	0.9985	0.9985	0.9986	0.9986
3.0	0.9987	0.9987	0.9987	0.9988	0.9988	0.9989	0.9989	0.9989	0.9990	0.9990
3.1	0.9990	0.9991	0.9991	0.9991	0.9992	0.9992	0.9992	0.9992	0.9993	0.9993
3.2	0.9993	0.9993	0.9994	0.9994	0.9994	0.9994	0.9994	0.9995	0.9995	0.9995
3.3	0.9995	0.9995	0.9995	0.9996	0.9996	0.9996	0.9996	0.9996	0.9996	0.9997
3.4	0.9997	0.9997	0.9997	0.9997	0.9997	0.9997	0.9997	0.9997	0.9997	0.9998
3.5	0.9998	0.9998	0.9998	0.9998	0.9998	0.9998	0.9998	0.9998	0.9998	0.9998
3.6	0.9998	0.9998	0.9999	0.9999	0.9999	0.9999	0.9999	0.9999	0.9999	0.9999
3.7	0.9999	0.9999	0.9999	0.9999	0.9999	0.9999	0.9999	0.9999	0.9999	0.9999
3.8	0.9999	0.9999	0.9999	0.9999	0.9999	0.9999	0.9999	0.9999	0.9999	0.9999
3.9	1.0000	1.0000	1.0000	1.0000	1.0000	1.0000	1.0000	1.0000	1.0000	1.0000

Source: Probabilities calculated with Excel.

TABLE 2 Student's *t* Distribution

Entries in this table provide the values of $t_{\alpha,df}$ that correspond to a given upper-tail area α and a specified number of degrees of freedom *df*. For example, for $\alpha = 0.05$ and $df = 10$, $P(T_{10} \geq 1.812) = 0.05$.

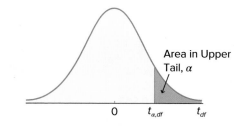

Area in Upper Tail, α

	α					
df	0.20	0.10	0.05	0.025	0.01	0.005
1	1.376	3.078	6.314	12.706	31.821	63.657
2	1.061	1.886	2.920	4.303	6.965	9.925
3	0.978	1.638	2.353	3.182	4.541	5.841
4	0.941	1.533	2.132	2.776	3.747	4.604
5	0.920	1.476	2.015	2.571	3.365	4.032
6	0.906	1.440	1.943	2.447	3.143	3.707
7	0.896	1.415	1.895	2.365	2.998	3.499
8	0.889	1.397	1.860	2.306	2.896	3.355
9	0.883	1.383	1.833	2.262	2.821	3.250
10	0.879	1.372	1.812	2.228	2.764	3.169
11	0.876	1.363	1.796	2.201	2.718	3.106
12	0.873	1.356	1.782	2.179	2.681	3.055
13	0.870	1.350	1.771	2.160	2.650	3.012
14	0.868	1.345	1.761	2.145	2.624	2.977
15	0.866	1.341	1.753	2.131	2.602	2.947
16	0.865	1.337	1.746	2.120	2.583	2.921
17	0.863	1.333	1.740	2.110	2.567	2.898
18	0.862	1.330	1.734	2.101	2.552	2.878
19	0.861	1.328	1.729	2.093	2.539	2.861
20	0.860	1.325	1.725	2.086	2.528	2.845
21	0.859	1.323	1.721	2.080	2.518	2.831
22	0.858	1.321	1.717	2.074	2.508	2.819
23	0.858	1.319	1.714	2.069	2.500	2.807
24	0.857	1.318	1.711	2.064	2.492	2.797
25	0.856	1.316	1.708	2.060	2.485	2.787
26	0.856	1.315	1.706	2.056	2.479	2.779
27	0.855	1.314	1.703	2.052	2.473	2.771
28	0.855	1.313	1.701	2.048	2.467	2.763
29	0.854	1.311	1.699	2.045	2.462	2.756
30	0.854	1.310	1.697	2.042	2.457	2.750

TABLE 2 (*Continued*)

df	α					
	0.20	0.10	0.05	0.025	0.01	0.005
31	0.853	1.309	1.696	2.040	2.453	2.744
32	0.853	1.309	1.694	2.037	2.449	2.738
33	0.853	1.308	1.692	2.035	2.445	2.733
34	0.852	1.307	1.691	2.032	2.441	2.728
35	0.852	1.306	1.690	2.030	2.438	2.724
36	0.852	1.306	1.688	2.028	2.434	2.719
37	0.851	1.305	1.687	2.026	2.431	2.715
38	0.851	1.304	1.686	2.024	2.429	2.712
39	0.851	1.304	1.685	2.023	2.426	2.708
40	0.851	1.303	1.684	2.021	2.423	2.704
41	0.850	1.303	1.683	2.020	2.421	2.701
42	0.850	1.302	1.682	2.018	2.418	2.698
43	0.850	1.302	1.681	2.017	2.416	2.695
44	0.850	1.301	1.680	2.015	2.414	2.692
45	0.850	1.301	1.679	2.014	2.412	2.690
46	0.850	1.300	1.679	2.013	2.410	2.687
47	0.849	1.300	1.678	2.012	2.408	2.685
48	0.849	1.299	1.677	2.011	2.407	2.682
49	0.849	1.299	1.677	2.010	2.405	2.680
50	0.849	1.299	1.676	2.009	2.403	2.678
51	0.849	1.298	1.675	2.008	2.402	2.676
52	0.849	1.298	1.675	2.007	2.400	2.674
53	0.848	1.298	1.674	2.006	2.399	2.672
54	0.848	1.297	1.674	2.005	2.397	2.670
55	0.848	1.297	1.673	2.004	2.396	2.668
56	0.848	1.297	1.673	2.003	2.395	2.667
57	0.848	1.297	1.672	2.002	2.394	2.665
58	0.848	1.296	1.672	2.002	2.392	2.663
59	0.848	1.296	1.671	2.001	2.391	2.662
60	0.848	1.296	1.671	2.000	2.390	2.660
80	0.846	1.292	1.664	1.990	2.374	2.639
100	0.845	1.290	1.660	1.984	2.364	2.626
150	0.844	1.287	1.655	1.976	2.351	2.609
200	0.843	1.286	1.653	1.972	2.345	2.601
500	0.842	1.283	1.648	1.965	2.334	2.586
1000	0.842	1.282	1.646	1.962	2.330	2.581
∞	0.842	1.282	1.645	1.960	2.326	2.576

Source: *t* values calculated with Excel.

TABLE 3 χ^2 (Chi-Square) Distribution

Entries in this table provide the values of $\chi^2_{\alpha,df}$ that correspond to a given upper-tail area α and a specified number of degrees of freedom df. For example, for $\alpha = 0.05$ and $df = 10$, $P(\chi^2_{10} \geq 18.307) = 0.05$.

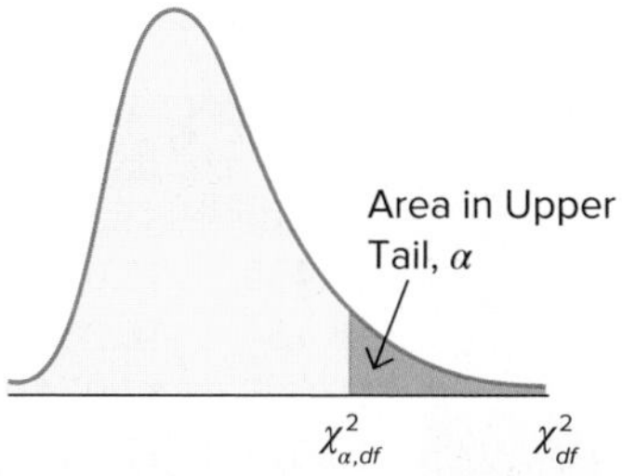

	α									
df	**0.995**	**0.990**	**0.975**	**0.950**	**0.900**	**0.100**	**0.050**	**0.025**	**0.010**	**0.005**
1	0.000	0.000	0.001	0.004	0.016	2.706	3.841	5.024	6.635	7.879
2	0.010	0.020	0.051	0.103	0.211	4.605	5.991	7.378	9.210	10.597
3	0.072	0.115	0.216	0.352	0.584	6.251	7.815	9.348	11.345	12.838
4	0.207	0.297	0.484	0.711	1.064	7.779	9.488	11.143	13.277	14.860
5	0.412	0.554	0.831	1.145	1.610	9.236	11.070	12.833	15.086	16.750
6	0.676	0.872	1.237	1.635	2.204	10.645	12.592	14.449	16.812	18.548
7	0.989	1.239	1.690	2.167	2.833	12.017	14.067	16.013	18.475	20.278
8	1.344	1.646	2.180	2.733	3.490	13.362	15.507	17.535	20.090	21.955
9	1.735	2.088	2.700	3.325	4.168	14.684	16.919	19.023	21.666	23.589
10	2.156	2.558	3.247	3.940	4.865	15.987	18.307	20.483	23.209	25.188
11	2.603	3.053	3.816	4.575	5.578	17.275	19.675	21.920	24.725	26.757
12	3.074	3.571	4.404	5.226	6.304	18.549	21.026	23.337	26.217	28.300
13	3.565	4.107	5.009	5.892	7.042	19.812	22.362	24.736	27.688	29.819
14	4.075	4.660	5.629	6.571	7.790	21.064	23.685	26.119	29.141	31.319
15	4.601	5.229	6.262	7.261	8.547	22.307	24.996	27.488	30.578	32.801
16	5.142	5.812	6.908	7.962	9.312	23.542	26.296	28.845	32.000	34.267
17	5.697	6.408	7.564	8.672	10.085	24.769	27.587	30.191	33.409	35.718
18	6.265	7.015	8.231	9.390	10.865	25.989	28.869	31.526	34.805	37.156
19	6.844	7.633	8.907	10.117	11.651	27.204	30.144	32.852	36.191	38.582
20	7.434	8.260	9.591	10.851	12.443	28.412	31.410	34.170	37.566	39.997
21	8.034	8.897	10.283	11.591	13.240	29.615	32.671	35.479	38.932	41.401
22	8.643	9.542	10.982	12.338	14.041	30.813	33.924	36.781	40.289	42.796
23	9.260	10.196	11.689	13.091	14.848	32.007	35.172	38.076	41.638	44.181
24	9.886	10.856	12.401	13.848	15.659	33.196	36.415	39.364	42.980	45.559
25	10.520	11.524	13.120	14.611	16.473	34.382	37.652	40.646	44.314	46.928
26	11.160	12.198	13.844	15.379	17.292	35.563	38.885	41.923	45.642	48.290
27	11.808	12.879	14.573	16.151	18.114	36.741	40.113	43.195	46.963	49.645
28	12.461	13.565	15.308	16.928	18.939	37.916	41.337	44.461	48.278	50.993
29	13.121	14.256	16.047	17.708	19.768	39.087	42.557	45.722	49.588	52.336
30	13.787	14.953	16.791	18.493	20.599	40.256	43.773	46.979	50.892	53.672

TABLE 3 (*Continued*)

df	α									
	0.995	0.990	0.975	0.950	0.900	0.100	0.050	0.025	0.010	0.005
31	14.458	15.655	17.539	19.281	21.434	41.422	44.985	48.232	52.191	55.003
32	15.134	16.362	18.291	20.072	22.271	42.585	46.194	49.480	53.486	56.328
33	15.815	17.074	19.047	20.867	23.110	43.745	47.400	50.725	54.776	57.648
34	16.501	17.789	19.806	21.664	23.952	44.903	48.602	51.966	56.061	58.964
35	17.192	18.509	20.569	22.465	24.797	46.059	49.802	53.203	57.342	60.275
36	17.887	19.233	21.336	23.269	25.643	47.212	50.998	54.437	58.619	61.581
37	18.586	19.960	22.106	24.075	26.492	48.363	52.192	55.668	59.893	62.883
38	19.289	20.691	22.878	24.884	27.343	49.513	53.384	56.896	61.162	64.181
39	19.996	21.426	23.654	25.695	28.196	50.660	54.572	58.120	62.428	65.476
40	20.707	22.164	24.433	26.509	29.051	51.805	55.758	59.342	63.691	66.766
41	21.421	22.906	25.215	27.326	29.907	52.949	56.942	60.561	64.950	68.053
42	22.138	23.650	25.999	28.144	30.765	54.090	58.124	61.777	66.206	69.336
43	22.859	24.398	26.785	28.965	31.625	55.230	59.304	62.990	67.459	70.616
44	23.584	25.148	27.575	29.787	32.487	56.369	60.481	64.201	68.710	71.893
45	24.311	25.901	28.366	30.612	33.350	57.505	61.656	65.410	69.957	73.166
46	25.041	26.657	29.160	31.439	34.215	58.641	62.830	66.617	71.201	74.437
47	25.775	27.416	29.956	32.268	35.081	59.774	64.001	67.821	72.443	75.704
48	26.511	28.177	30.755	33.098	35.949	60.907	65.171	69.023	73.683	76.969
49	27.249	28.941	31.555	33.930	36.818	62.038	66.339	70.222	74.919	78.231
50	27.991	29.707	32.357	34.764	37.689	63.167	67.505	71.420	76.154	79.490
55	31.735	33.570	36.398	38.958	42.060	68.796	73.311	77.380	82.292	85.749
60	35.534	37.485	40.482	43.188	46.459	74.397	79.082	83.298	88.379	91.952
65	39.383	41.444	44.603	47.450	50.883	79.973	84.821	89.177	94.422	98.105
70	43.275	45.442	48.758	51.739	55.329	85.527	90.531	95.023	100.425	104.215
75	47.206	49.475	52.942	56.054	59.795	91.061	96.217	100.839	106.393	110.286
80	51.172	53.540	57.153	60.391	64.278	96.578	101.879	106.629	112.329	116.321
85	55.170	57.634	61.389	64.749	68.777	102.079	107.522	112.393	118.236	122.325
90	59.196	61.754	65.647	69.126	73.291	107.565	113.145	118.136	124.116	128.299
95	63.250	65.898	69.925	73.520	77.818	113.038	118.752	123.858	129.973	134.247
100	67.328	70.065	74.222	77.929	82.358	118.498	124.342	129.561	135.807	140.169

Source: χ^2 values calculated with Excel.

TABLE 4 F Distribution

Entries in this table provide the values of $F_{\alpha,(df_1, df_2)}$ that correspond to a given upper-tail area α and a specified number of degrees of freedom in the numerator df_1 and degrees of freedom in the denominator df_2. For example, for $\alpha = 0.05$, $df_1 = 8$, and $df_2 = 6$, $P(F_{(8,6)} \geq 4.15) = 0.05$.

Area in Upper Tail, α

$F_{\alpha,(df1, df2)}$

df_2	α	1	2	3	4	5	6	7	8	9	10	15	25	50	100	500
1	0.10	39.86	49.50	53.59	55.83	57.24	58.2	58.91	59.44	59.86	60.19	61.22	62.05	62.69	63.01	63.26
	0.05	161.45	199.50	215.71	224.58	230.16	233.99	236.77	238.88	240.54	241.88	245.95	249.26	251.77	253.04	254.06
	0.025	647.79	799.50	864.16	899.58	921.85	937.11	948.22	956.66	963.28	968.63	984.87	998.12	1008.12	1013.17	1017.24
	0.01	4052.18	4999.50	5403.35	5624.58	5763.65	5858.99	5928.36	5981.07	6022.47	6055.85	6157.28	6239.83	6302.52	6334.11	6359.50
2	0.10	8.53	9.00	9.16	9.24	9.29	9.33	9.35	9.37	9.38	9.39	9.42	9.45	9.47	9.48	9.49
	0.05	18.51	19.00	19.16	19.25	19.30	19.33	19.35	19.37	19.38	19.40	19.43	19.46	19.48	19.49	19.49
	0.025	38.51	39.00	39.17	39.25	39.30	39.33	39.36	39.37	39.39	39.40	39.43	39.46	39.48	39.49	39.50
	0.01	98.50	99.00	99.17	99.25	99.30	99.33	99.36	99.37	99.39	99.40	99.43	99.46	99.48	99.49	99.50
3	0.10	5.54	5.46	5.39	5.34	5.31	5.28	5.27	5.25	5.24	5.23	5.20	5.17	5.15	5.14	5.14
	0.05	10.13	9.55	9.28	9.12	9.01	8.94	8.89	8.85	8.81	8.79	8.70	8.63	8.58	8.55	8.53
	0.025	17.44	16.04	15.44	15.10	14.88	14.73	14.62	14.54	14.47	14.42	14.25	14.12	14.01	13.96	13.91
	0.01	34.12	30.82	29.46	28.71	28.24	27.91	27.67	27.49	27.35	27.23	26.87	26.58	26.35	26.24	26.15
4	0.10	4.54	4.32	4.19	4.11	4.05	4.01	3.98	3.95	3.94	3.92	3.87	3.83	3.80	3.78	3.76
	0.05	7.71	6.94	6.59	6.39	6.26	6.16	6.09	6.04	6.00	5.96	5.86	5.77	5.70	5.66	5.64
	0.025	12.22	10.65	9.98	9.60	9.36	9.20	9.07	8.98	8.90	8.84	8.66	8.50	8.38	8.32	8.27
	0.01	21.20	18.00	16.69	15.98	15.52	15.21	14.98	14.80	14.66	14.55	14.20	13.91	13.69	13.58	13.49
5	0.10	4.06	3.78	3.62	3.52	3.45	3.40	3.37	3.34	3.32	3.30	3.24	3.19	3.15	3.13	3.11
	0.05	6.61	5.79	5.41	5.19	5.05	4.95	4.88	4.82	4.77	4.74	4.62	4.52	4.44	4.41	4.37
	0.025	10.01	8.43	7.76	7.39	7.15	6.98	6.85	6.76	6.68	6.62	6.43	6.27	6.14	6.08	6.03
	0.01	16.26	13.27	12.06	11.39	10.97	10.67	10.46	10.29	10.16	10.05	9.72	9.45	9.24	9.13	9.04
6	0.10	3.78	3.46	3.29	3.18	3.11	3.05	3.01	2.98	2.96	2.94	2.87	2.81	2.77	2.75	2.73
	0.05	5.99	5.14	4.76	4.53	4.39	4.28	4.21	4.15	4.10	4.06	3.94	3.83	3.75	3.71	3.68
	0.025	8.81	7.26	6.60	6.23	5.99	5.82	5.70	5.60	5.52	5.46	5.27	5.11	4.98	4.92	4.86
	0.01	13.75	10.92	9.78	9.15	8.75	8.47	8.26	8.10	7.98	7.87	7.56	7.30	7.09	6.99	6.90
7	0.10	3.59	3.26	3.07	2.96	2.88	2.83	2.78	2.75	2.72	2.70	2.63	2.57	2.52	2.50	2.48
	0.05	5.59	4.74	4.35	4.12	3.97	3.87	3.79	3.73	3.68	3.64	3.51	3.40	3.32	3.27	3.24
	0.025	8.07	6.54	5.89	5.52	5.29	5.12	4.99	4.90	4.82	4.76	4.57	4.40	4.28	4.21	4.16
	0.01	12.25	9.55	8.45	7.85	7.46	7.19	6.99	6.84	6.72	6.62	6.31	6.06	5.86	5.75	5.67

df_1

TABLE 4 (Continued)

df_2	α	1	2	3	4	5	6	7	8	9	10	15	25	50	100	500
8	0.10	3.46	3.11	2.92	2.81	2.73	2.67	2.62	2.59	2.56	2.54	2.46	2.40	2.35	2.32	2.30
	0.05	5.32	4.46	4.07	3.84	3.69	3.58	3.50	3.44	3.39	3.35	3.22	3.11	3.02	2.97	2.94
	0.025	7.57	6.06	5.42	5.05	4.82	4.65	4.53	4.43	4.36	4.30	4.10	3.94	3.81	3.74	3.68
	0.01	11.26	8.65	7.59	7.01	6.63	6.37	6.18	6.03	5.91	5.81	5.52	5.26	5.07	4.96	4.88
9	0.10	3.36	3.01	2.81	2.69	2.61	2.55	2.51	2.47	2.44	2.42	2.34	2.27	2.22	2.19	2.17
	0.05	5.12	4.26	3.86	3.63	3.48	3.37	3.29	3.23	3.18	3.14	3.01	2.89	2.80	2.76	2.72
	0.025	7.21	5.71	5.08	4.72	4.48	4.32	4.20	4.10	4.03	3.96	3.77	3.60	3.47	3.40	3.35
	0.01	10.56	8.02	6.99	6.42	6.06	5.80	5.61	5.47	5.35	5.26	4.96	4.71	4.52	4.41	4.33
10	0.10	3.29	2.92	2.73	2.61	2.52	2.46	2.41	2.38	2.35	2.32	2.24	2.17	2.12	2.09	2.06
	0.05	4.96	4.10	3.71	3.48	3.33	3.22	3.14	3.07	3.02	2.98	2.85	2.73	2.64	2.59	2.55
	0.025	6.94	5.46	4.83	4.47	4.24	4.07	3.95	3.85	3.78	3.72	3.52	3.35	3.22	3.15	3.09
	0.01	10.04	7.56	6.55	5.99	5.64	5.39	5.20	5.06	4.94	4.85	4.56	4.31	4.12	4.01	3.93
11	0.10	3.23	2.86	2.66	2.54	2.45	2.39	2.34	2.30	2.27	2.25	2.17	2.10	2.04	2.01	1.98
	0.05	4.84	3.98	3.59	3.36	3.20	3.09	3.01	2.95	2.90	2.85	2.72	2.60	2.51	2.46	2.42
	0.025	6.72	5.26	4.63	4.28	4.04	3.88	3.76	3.66	3.59	3.53	3.33	3.16	3.03	2.96	2.90
	0.01	9.65	7.21	6.22	5.67	5.32	5.07	4.89	4.74	4.63	4.54	4.25	4.01	3.81	3.71	3.62
12	0.10	3.18	2.81	2.61	2.48	2.39	2.33	2.28	2.24	2.21	2.19	2.10	2.03	1.97	1.94	1.91
	0.05	4.75	3.89	3.49	3.26	3.11	3.00	2.91	2.85	2.80	2.75	2.62	2.50	2.40	2.35	2.31
	0.025	6.55	5.10	4.47	4.12	3.89	3.73	3.61	3.51	3.44	3.37	3.18	3.01	2.87	2.80	2.74
	0.01	9.33	6.93	5.95	5.41	5.06	4.82	4.64	4.50	4.39	4.30	4.01	3.76	3.57	3.47	3.38
13	0.10	3.14	2.76	2.56	2.43	2.35	2.28	2.23	2.20	2.16	2.14	2.05	1.98	1.92	1.88	1.85
	0.05	4.67	3.81	3.41	3.18	3.03	2.92	2.83	2.77	2.71	2.67	2.53	2.41	2.31	2.26	2.22
	0.025	6.41	4.97	4.35	4.00	3.77	3.60	3.48	3.39	3.31	3.25	3.05	2.88	2.74	2.67	2.61
	0.01	9.07	6.70	5.74	5.21	4.86	4.62	4.44	4.30	4.19	4.10	3.82	3.57	3.38	3.27	3.19
14	0.10	3.10	2.73	2.52	2.39	2.31	2.24	2.19	2.15	2.12	2.10	2.01	1.93	1.87	1.83	1.80
	0.05	4.60	3.74	3.34	3.11	2.96	2.85	2.76	2.70	2.65	2.60	2.46	2.34	2.24	2.19	2.14
	0.025	6.30	4.86	4.24	3.89	3.66	3.50	3.38	3.29	3.21	3.15	2.95	2.78	2.64	2.56	2.50
	0.01	8.86	6.51	5.56	5.04	4.69	4.46	4.28	4.14	4.03	3.94	3.66	3.41	3.22	3.11	3.03
15	0.10	3.07	2.70	2.49	2.36	2.27	2.21	2.16	2.12	2.09	2.06	1.97	1.89	1.83	1.79	1.76
	0.05	4.54	3.68	3.29	3.06	2.90	2.79	2.71	2.64	2.59	2.54	2.40	2.28	2.18	2.12	2.08
	0.025	6.20	4.77	4.15	3.80	3.58	3.41	3.29	3.20	3.12	3.06	2.86	2.69	2.55	2.47	2.41
	0.01	8.68	6.36	5.42	4.89	4.56	4.32	4.14	4.00	3.89	3.80	3.52	3.28	3.08	2.98	2.89
16	0.10	3.05	2.67	2.46	2.33	2.24	2.18	2.13	2.09	2.06	2.03	1.94	1.86	1.79	1.76	1.73
	0.05	4.49	3.63	3.24	3.01	2.85	2.74	2.66	2.59	2.54	2.49	2.35	2.23	2.12	2.07	2.02
	0.025	6.12	4.69	4.08	3.73	3.50	3.34	3.22	3.12	3.05	2.99	2.79	2.61	2.47	2.40	2.33
	0.01	8.53	6.23	5.29	4.77	4.44	4.20	4.03	3.89	3.78	3.69	3.41	3.16	2.97	2.86	2.78

df_1

df_2	α	1	2	3	4	5	6	7	8	9	10	15	25	50	100	500
17	0.10	3.03	2.64	2.44	2.31	2.22	2.15	2.10	2.06	2.03	2.00	1.91	1.83	1.76	1.73	1.69
	0.05	4.45	3.59	3.20	2.96	2.81	2.70	2.61	2.55	2.49	2.45	2.31	2.18	2.08	2.02	1.97
	0.025	6.04	4.62	4.01	3.66	3.44	3.28	3.16	3.06	2.98	2.92	2.72	2.55	2.41	2.33	2.26
	0.01	8.40	6.11	5.18	4.67	4.34	4.10	3.93	3.79	3.68	3.59	3.31	3.07	2.87	2.76	2.68
18	0.10	3.01	2.62	2.42	2.29	2.20	2.13	2.08	2.04	2.00	1.98	1.89	1.80	1.74	1.70	1.67
	0.05	4.41	3.55	3.16	2.93	2.77	2.66	2.58	2.51	2.46	2.41	2.27	2.14	2.04	1.98	1.93
	0.025	5.98	4.56	3.95	3.61	3.38	3.22	3.10	3.01	2.93	2.87	2.67	2.49	2.35	2.27	2.20
	0.01	8.29	6.01	5.09	4.58	4.25	4.01	3.84	3.71	3.60	3.51	3.23	2.98	2.78	2.68	2.59
19	0.10	2.99	2.61	2.40	2.27	2.18	2.11	2.06	2.02	1.98	1.96	1.86	1.78	1.71	1.67	1.64
	0.05	4.38	3.52	3.13	2.90	2.74	2.63	2.54	2.48	2.42	2.38	2.23	2.11	2.00	1.94	1.89
	0.025	5.92	4.51	3.90	3.56	3.33	3.17	3.05	2.96	2.88	2.82	2.62	2.44	2.30	2.22	2.15
	0.01	8.18	5.93	5.01	4.50	4.17	3.94	3.77	3.63	3.52	3.43	3.15	2.91	2.71	2.60	2.51
20	0.10	2.97	2.59	2.38	2.25	2.16	2.09	2.04	2.00	1.96	1.94	1.84	1.76	1.69	1.65	1.62
	0.05	4.35	3.49	3.10	2.87	2.71	2.60	2.51	2.45	2.39	2.35	2.20	2.07	1.97	1.91	1.86
	0.025	5.87	4.46	3.86	3.51	3.29	3.13	3.01	2.91	2.84	2.77	2.57	2.40	2.25	2.17	2.10
	0.01	8.10	5.85	4.94	4.43	4.10	3.87	3.70	3.56	3.46	3.37	3.09	2.84	2.64	2.54	2.44
21	0.10	2.96	2.57	2.36	2.23	2.14	2.08	2.02	1.98	1.95	1.92	1.83	1.74	1.67	1.63	1.60
	0.05	4.32	3.47	3.07	2.84	2.68	2.57	2.49	2.42	2.37	2.32	2.18	2.05	1.94	1.88	1.83
	0.025	5.83	4.42	3.82	3.48	3.25	3.09	2.97	2.87	2.80	2.73	2.53	2.36	2.21	2.13	2.06
	0.01	8.02	5.78	4.87	4.37	4.04	3.81	3.64	3.51	3.40	3.31	3.03	2.79	2.58	2.48	2.38
22	0.10	2.95	2.56	2.35	2.22	2.13	2.06	2.01	1.97	1.93	1.90	1.81	1.73	1.65	1.61	1.58
	0.05	4.30	3.44	3.05	2.82	2.66	2.55	2.46	2.40	2.34	2.30	2.15	2.02	1.91	1.85	1.80
	0.025	5.79	4.38	3.78	3.44	3.22	3.05	2.93	2.84	2.76	2.70	2.50	2.32	2.17	2.09	2.02
	0.01	7.95	5.72	4.82	4.31	3.99	3.76	3.59	3.45	3.35	3.26	2.98	2.73	2.53	2.42	2.33
23	0.10	2.94	2.55	2.34	2.21	2.11	2.05	1.99	1.95	1.92	1.89	1.80	1.71	1.64	1.59	1.56
	0.05	4.28	3.42	3.03	2.80	2.64	2.53	2.44	2.37	2.32	2.27	2.13	2.00	1.88	1.82	1.77
	0.025	5.75	4.35	3.75	3.41	3.18	3.02	2.90	2.81	2.73	2.67	2.47	2.29	2.14	2.06	1.99
	0.01	7.88	5.66	4.76	4.26	3.94	3.71	3.54	3.41	3.30	3.21	2.93	2.69	2.48	2.37	2.28
24	0.10	2.93	2.54	2.33	2.19	2.10	2.04	1.98	1.94	1.91	1.88	1.78	1.70	1.62	1.58	1.54
	0.05	4.26	3.40	3.01	2.78	2.62	2.51	2.42	2.36	2.30	2.25	2.11	1.97	1.86	1.80	1.75
	0.025	5.72	4.32	3.72	3.38	3.15	2.99	2.87	2.78	2.70	2.64	2.44	2.26	2.11	2.02	1.95
	0.01	7.82	5.61	4.72	4.22	3.90	3.67	3.50	3.36	3.26	3.17	2.89	2.64	2.44	2.33	2.24

df_1

TABLE 4 (Continued)

df_2	α	1	2	3	4	5	6	7	8	9	10	15	25	50	100	500
25	0.10	2.92	2.53	2.32	2.18	2.09	2.02	1.97	1.93	1.89	1.87	1.77	1.68	1.61	1.56	1.53
	0.05	4.24	3.39	2.99	2.76	2.60	2.49	2.40	2.34	2.28	2.24	2.09	1.96	1.84	1.78	1.73
	0.025	5.69	4.29	3.69	3.35	3.13	2.97	2.85	2.75	2.68	2.61	2.41	2.23	2.08	2.00	1.92
	0.01	7.77	5.57	4.68	4.18	3.85	3.63	3.46	3.32	3.22	3.13	2.85	2.60	2.40	2.29	2.19
26	0.10	2.91	2.52	2.31	2.17	2.08	2.01	1.96	1.92	1.88	1.86	1.76	1.67	1.59	1.55	1.51
	0.05	4.23	3.37	2.98	2.74	2.59	2.47	2.39	2.32	2.27	2.22	2.07	1.94	1.82	1.76	1.71
	0.025	5.66	4.27	3.67	3.33	3.10	2.94	2.82	2.73	2.65	2.59	2.39	2.21	2.05	1.97	1.90
	0.01	7.72	5.53	4.64	4.14	3.82	3.59	3.42	3.29	3.18	3.09	2.81	2.57	2.36	2.25	2.16
27	0.10	2.90	2.51	2.30	2.17	2.07	2.00	1.95	1.91	1.87	1.85	1.75	1.66	1.58	1.54	1.50
	0.05	4.21	3.35	2.96	2.73	2.57	2.46	2.37	2.31	2.25	2.20	2.06	1.92	1.81	1.74	1.69
	0.025	5.63	4.24	3.65	3.31	3.08	2.92	2.80	2.71	2.63	2.57	2.36	2.18	2.03	1.94	1.87
	0.01	7.68	5.49	4.60	4.11	3.78	3.56	3.39	3.26	3.15	3.06	2.78	2.54	2.33	2.22	2.12
28	0.10	2.89	2.50	2.29	2.16	2.06	2.00	1.94	1.90	1.87	1.84	1.74	1.65	1.57	1.53	1.49
	0.05	4.20	3.34	2.95	2.71	2.56	2.45	2.36	2.29	2.24	2.19	2.04	1.91	1.79	1.73	1.67
	0.025	5.61	4.22	3.63	3.29	3.06	2.90	2.78	2.69	2.61	2.55	2.34	2.16	2.01	1.92	1.85
	0.01	7.64	5.45	4.57	4.07	3.75	3.53	3.36	3.23	3.12	3.03	2.75	2.51	2.30	2.19	2.09
29	0.10	2.89	2.50	2.28	2.15	2.06	1.99	1.93	1.89	1.86	1.83	1.73	1.64	1.56	1.52	1.48
	0.05	4.18	3.33	2.93	2.70	2.55	2.43	2.35	2.28	2.22	2.18	2.03	1.89	1.77	1.71	1.65
	0.025	5.59	4.20	3.61	3.27	3.04	2.88	2.76	2.67	2.59	2.53	2.32	2.14	1.99	1.90	1.83
	0.01	7.60	5.42	4.54	4.04	3.73	3.50	3.33	3.20	3.09	3.00	2.73	2.48	2.27	2.16	2.06
30	0.10	2.88	2.49	2.28	2.14	2.05	1.98	1.93	1.88	1.85	1.82	1.72	1.63	1.55	1.51	1.47
	0.05	4.17	3.32	2.92	2.69	2.53	2.42	2.33	2.27	2.21	2.16	2.01	1.88	1.76	1.70	1.64
	0.025	5.57	4.18	3.59	3.25	3.03	2.87	2.75	2.65	2.57	2.51	2.31	2.12	1.97	1.88	1.81
	0.01	7.56	5.39	4.51	4.02	3.70	3.47	3.30	3.17	3.07	2.98	2.70	2.45	2.25	2.13	2.03
50	0.10	2.81	2.41	2.20	2.06	1.97	1.90	1.84	1.80	1.76	1.73	1.63	1.53	1.44	1.39	1.34
	0.05	4.03	3.18	2.79	2.56	2.40	2.29	2.20	2.13	2.07	2.03	1.87	1.73	1.60	1.52	1.46
	0.025	5.34	3.97	3.39	3.05	2.83	2.67	2.55	2.46	2.38	2.32	2.11	1.92	1.75	1.66	1.57
	0.01	7.17	5.06	4.20	3.72	3.41	3.19	3.02	2.89	2.78	2.70	2.42	2.17	1.95	1.82	1.71
100	0.10	2.76	2.36	2.14	2.00	1.91	1.83	1.78	1.73	1.69	1.66	1.56	1.45	1.35	1.29	1.23
	0.05	3.94	3.09	2.70	2.46	2.31	2.19	2.10	2.03	1.97	1.93	1.77	1.62	1.48	1.39	1.31
	0.025	5.18	3.83	3.25	2.92	2.70	2.54	2.42	2.32	2.24	2.18	1.97	1.77	1.59	1.48	1.38
	0.01	6.90	4.82	3.98	3.51	3.21	2.99	2.82	2.69	2.59	2.50	2.22	1.97	1.74	1.60	1.47
500	0.10	2.72	2.31	2.09	1.96	1.86	1.79	1.73	1.68	1.64	1.61	1.50	1.39	1.28	1.21	1.12
	0.05	3.86	3.01	2.62	2.39	2.23	2.12	2.03	1.96	1.90	1.85	1.69	1.53	1.38	1.28	1.16
	0.025	5.05	3.72	3.14	2.81	2.59	2.43	2.31	2.22	2.14	2.07	1.86	1.65	1.46	1.34	1.19
	0.01	6.69	4.65	3.82	3.36	3.05	2.84	2.68	2.55	2.44	2.36	2.07	1.81	1.57	1.41	1.23

df_1

Source: *F*-values calculated with Excel.

TABLE 5 Studentized Range Values $q_{\alpha,(c,n_T-c)}$ for Tukey's HSD Method

		The number of means, c										
$n_T - c$	α	2	3	4	5	6	7	8	9	10	11	12
5	0.05	3.64	4.60	5.22	5.67	6.03	6.33	6.58	6.80	6.99	7.17	7.32
5	0.01	5.70	6.98	7.80	8.42	8.91	9.32	9.67	9.97	10.24	10.48	10.70
6	0.05	3.46	4.34	4.90	5.30	5.63	5.90	6.12	6.32	6.49	6.65	6.79
6	0.01	5.24	6.33	7.03	7.56	7.97	8.32	8.61	8.87	9.10	9.30	9.48
7	0.05	3.34	4.16	4.68	5.06	5.36	5.61	5.82	6.00	6.16	6.30	6.43
7	0.01	4.95	5.92	6.54	7.01	7.37	7.68	7.94	8.17	8.37	8.55	8.71
8	0.05	3.26	4.04	4.53	4.89	5.17	5.40	5.60	5.77	5.92	6.05	6.18
8	0.01	4.75	5.64	6.20	6.62	6.96	7.24	7.47	7.68	7.86	8.03	8.18
9	0.05	3.20	3.95	4.41	4.76	5.02	5.24	5.43	5.59	5.74	5.87	5.98
9	0.01	4.60	5.43	5.96	6.35	6.66	6.91	7.13	7.33	7.49	7.65	7.78
10	0.05	3.15	3.88	4.33	4.65	4.91	5.12	5.30	5.46	5.60	5.72	5.83
10	0.01	4.48	5.27	5.77	6.14	6.43	6.67	6.87	7.05	7.21	7.36	7.49
11	0.05	3.11	3.82	4.26	4.57	4.82	5.03	5.20	5.35	5.49	5.61	5.71
11	0.01	4.39	5.15	5.62	5.97	6.25	6.48	6.67	6.84	6.99	7.13	7.25
12	0.05	3.08	3.77	4.20	4.51	4.75	4.95	5.12	5.27	5.39	5.51	5.61
12	0.01	4.32	5.05	5.50	5.84	6.10	6.32	6.51	6.67	6.81	6.94	7.06
13	0.05	3.06	3.73	4.15	4.45	4.69	4.88	5.05	5.19	5.32	5.43	5.53
13	0.01	4.26	4.96	5.40	5.73	5.98	6.19	6.37	6.53	6.67	6.79	6.90
14	0.05	3.03	3.70	4.11	4.41	4.64	4.83	4.99	5.13	5.25	5.36	5.46
14	0.01	4.21	4.89	5.32	5.63	5.88	6.08	6.26	6.41	6.54	6.66	6.77
15	0.05	3.01	3.67	4.08	4.37	4.59	4.78	4.94	5.08	5.20	5.31	5.40
15	0.01	4.17	4.84	5.25	5.56	5.80	5.99	6.16	6.31	6.44	6.55	6.66
16	0.05	3.00	3.65	4.05	4.33	4.56	4.74	4.90	5.03	5.15	5.26	5.35
16	0.01	4.13	4.79	5.19	5.49	5.72	5.92	6.08	6.22	6.35	6.46	6.56
17	0.05	2.98	3.63	4.02	4.30	4.52	4.70	4.86	4.99	5.11	5.21	5.31
17	0.01	4.10	4.74	5.14	5.43	5.66	5.85	6.01	6.15	6.27	6.38	6.48
18	0.05	2.97	3.61	4.00	4.28	4.49	4.67	4.82	4.96	5.07	5.17	5.27
18	0.01	4.07	4.70	5.09	5.38	5.60	5.79	5.94	6.08	6.20	6.31	6.41
19	0.05	2.96	3.59	3.98	4.25	4.47	4.65	4.79	4.92	5.04	5.14	5.23
19	0.01	4.05	4.67	5.05	5.33	5.55	5.73	5.89	6.02	6.14	6.25	6.34
20	0.05	2.95	3.58	3.96	4.23	4.45	4.62	4.77	4.90	5.01	5.11	5.20
20	0.01	4.02	4.64	5.02	5.29	5.51	5.69	5.84	5.97	6.09	6.19	6.28

TABLE 5 (*Continued*)

		The number of means, c										
$n_T - c$	α	2	3	4	5	6	7	8	9	10	11	12
24	0.05	2.92	3.53	3.90	4.17	4.37	4.54	4.68	4.81	4.92	5.01	5.10
	0.01	3.96	4.55	4.91	5.17	5.37	5.54	5.69	5.81	5.92	6.02	6.11
30	0.05	2.89	3.49	3.85	4.10	4.30	4.46	4.60	4.72	4.82	4.92	5.00
	0.01	3.89	4.45	4.80	5.05	5.24	5.40	5.54	5.65	5.76	5.85	5.93
40	0.05	2.86	3.44	3.79	4.04	4.23	4.39	4.52	4.63	4.73	4.82	4.90
	0.01	3.82	4.37	4.70	4.93	5.11	5.26	5.39	5.50	5.60	5.69	5.76
60	0.05	2.83	3.40	3.74	3.98	4.16	4.31	4.44	4.55	4.65	4.73	4.81
	0.01	3.76	4.28	4.59	4.82	4.99	5.13	5.25	5.36	5.45	5.53	5.60
120	0.05	2.80	3.36	3.68	3.92	4.10	4.24	4.36	4.47	4.56	4.64	4.71
	0.01	3.70	4.20	4.50	4.71	4.87	5.01	5.12	5.21	5.30	5.37	5.44
∞	0.05	2.77	3.31	3.63	3.86	4.03	4.17	4.29	4.39	4.47	4.55	4.62
	0.01	3.64	4.12	4.40	4.60	4.76	4.88	4.99	5.08	5.16	5.23	5.29

Source: E. S. Pearson and H. O. Hartley, *Biometrika Tables for Statisticians,* vol. 1 (Cambridge: Cambridge University Press, 1966).

Answers to Selected Even-Numbered Exercises

Chapter 1

1.2 35 is likely the estimated average age. It would be rather impossible to reach all video game players.

1.4 a. The population consists of all marketing managers.

b. No, the average salary was likely computed from a sample in order to save time and money.

1.6 Answers will vary depending on when data are retrieved. The numbers represent time series data.

1.8 Answers will vary depending on when data are retrieved. The numbers represent cross-sectional data.

1.10 Answers will vary depending on when data are retrieved. The numbers represent cross-sectional data.

1.12 Structured

1.14 Structured; time series

Chapter 2

2.4 a.

Delays	Frequency	Relative Frequency
PM Delays	1	0.056
All Day Delays	6	0.333
AM Delays	4	0.222
None	7	0.389

b.

Air Travel Delays

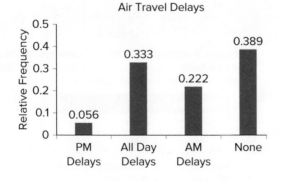

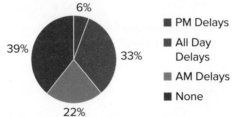

Air Travel Delays

2.8 a.

Company	Market Share
Enterprise	0.489
Hertz	0.215
Avis Budget	0.183
Dollar Thrifty	0.068
Other	0.046

b. Hertz accounted for 21.5% of sales.

c.

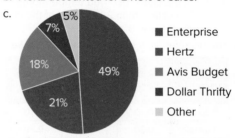

2.12 It does not. With a relatively high upper limit on the vertical axis ($500), the rise in stock price appears dampened.

2.14 It does not. The vertical axis has been stretched and the increase in sales appears more pronounced than warranted.

2.22 a.

Assets (in billions)	Frequency
40 up to 70	9
70 up to 100	8
100 up to 130	2
130 up to 160	0
160 up to 190	1

b.

Assets (in billions)	Relative Frequency	Cumulative Frequency	Cumulative Relative Frequency
40 up to 70	0.45	9	0.45
70 up to 100	0.40	17	0.85
100 up to 130	0.10	19	0.95
130 up to 160	0.00	19	0.95
160 up to 190	0.05	20	1.00

c. Two funds had assets of at least 100 but less than 130 (in $ billions); 19 funds had assets less than $160 billion.

d. 40% of the funds had assets of at least $70 but less than $100 (in billions); 95% of the funds had assets less than $130 billion.

e. The distribution is positively skewed.

2.24 a.

Temperature	Frequency
60 up to 70	2
70 up to 80	7
80 up to 90	14
90 up to 100	10

b.

Temperature	Relative Frequency	Cumulative Frequency	Cumulative Relative Frequency
60 up to 70	0.061	2	0.061
70 up to 80	0.212	9	0.273
80 up to 90	0.424	23	0.697
90 up to 100	0.303	33	1.000

c. 9 cities had temperatures less than 80°.

d. 42.4% of the cities recorded temperatures of at least 80° but less than 90°; 69.7% of the cities had temperatures less than 90°.

e. The distribution is slightly negatively skewed.

2.26 a.

Vacancy Rate (%)	Relative Frequency	Cumulative Frequency	Cumulative Relative Frequency
0 up to 3	0.10	5	0.10
3 up to 6	0.20	15	0.30
6 up to 9	0.40	35	0.70
9 up to 12	0.20	45	0.90
12 up to 15	0.10	50	1.00

b. 45 cities had a vacancy rate of less than 12%; 40% of the cities had a vacancy rate of at least 6% but less than 9%; 70% of the cities had a vacancy rate of less than 9%.

c. The distribution is symmetric.

2.30 a. No, it is positively skewed

b. Minimum is at least 50; maximum is at most 450.

c. 50–150 class

2.32 a. 70%

b. 85%

2.38

Stem	Leaf
−8	7 5 5 3 2 0 0 0
−7	9 7 5 3 3 2 1
−6	5 5 4
−5	2 0

No, it is positively skewed. Most of the numbers are in the lower stems of −8 and −7.

2.40

Stem	Leaf
7	3 4 6 7 8 8
8	0 1 2 3 4 4 4 4 7 8
9	0 0 0 1 1 2 2 2 3 3 4 4 4 4 4 5 6 6 6 8 8 9
10	6 7

Temperatures ranged between 73 and 107. The distribution is negatively skewed, with most temperatures in the 90s.

2.42 Spain

Stem	Leaf
2	1 1 1 2 3 3 4 4 5 5 5 6 7 8 9 9 9
3	0 0 2

Netherlands

Stem	Leaf
2	2 3 3 4 5 5 5 6 6 6 7 7 7 7 9
3	0 3 5 5 9

Spain has a relatively younger team compared to the Netherlands. The majority of players on both teams are in their 20s.

2.44

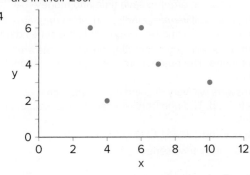

There is no evident relationship between *x* and *y*.

2.46

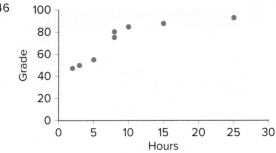

There is a positive relationship between number of hours spent studying and grades.

2.48

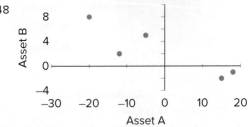

There is a negative relationship between the two asset returns. For diversification, the investor should include both assets in her portfolio.

2.50 a.

Responses	Utah	Kentucky
Yes	0.10	0.45
No	0.90	0.55

Relative to Utah, Kentucky is more lenient in allowing smoking at home.

b.

Smoking Behavior

2.58 a. Percentage of People in Each Region

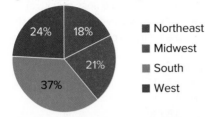

The highest percentage of people live in the South and the lowest percentage live in the Northeast.

b. Percentage of People Below Poverty Level

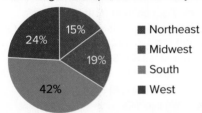

The percentage of people living in poverty is highest in the South and lowest in the Northeast. Furthermore, relative to the population, there are more (less) people living in poverty in the South (Northeast).

2.62 a. 16%
     b. 76%
     c.

Stem	Leaf
3	6 6
4	4 7
5	3 3 4 6
6	0 1 5 5 6 7 7 9
7	0 1 3 3 3 7 8 9 9

The distribution is negatively skewed. The majority of ages range between 60s and 70s.

2.64 a.

Type of House	Frequency
Colonial	6
Contemporary	4
Ranch	6
Other	4

The majority (60%) of houses were either Ranch or Colonial.

b.

Classes	Frequency
300 up to 350	4
350 up to 400	6
400 up to 450	4
450 up to 500	2
500 up to 550	3
550 up to 600	1

The most frequent house price is in the $350,000 up to $400,000 range. The distribution is positively skewed.

2.66
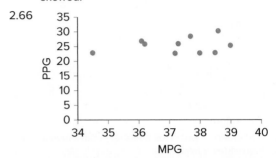

The scatterplot reveals a mild positive relationship between PPG and MPG.

Chapter 3

3.2   Mean = −2.67; Median = −3.5; Mode = −4
3.4   Mean = 18.33; Median = 20; Two Modes: 15 and 20
3.6   a. Mean = 3.4; Median = 3.5; Mode = 3
      b. Mode
3.10 a. 101.27
      b. 107.42
3.12 a. Market capitalization: Mean = 164.10; Median = 167.50.
      b. Total return: Mean = 40.71%; Median = 6.05%.
      c. Either of the two for market capitalization; median for total return.
3.14 Mean = 3.90; Median = 3.87; Mode = 3.89
3.20 a. 25% (75%) of the observations are less than 54 (78).
      b. IQR = 24; no outliers
      c. Relatively symmetric
3.22 a. 25th Percentile = −0.19; 50th Percentile = 13.67; 75th Percentile = 17.46
      b. IQR = 26.48; Lower limit = −26.67; Upper limit = 43.94; −35.97 is an outlier.
      c. No, it is negatively skewed.
3.26 G_g = 0.0313, or 3.13%.
3.28 G_R = −0.006, or −0.6%.
3.30 G_R = 0.0647, or 6.47%.
3.32 a. Year 1-2: 0.0667; Year 2-3: 0.0781; Year 3-4: 0.1014
      b. G_g = 0.082, or 8.2%.
3.34 a. 12.98%
      b. G_R = 0.1284, or 12.84%
      c. $1,621.26

3.36 a. 3.56%
    b. 3.00%
    c. $23,185.48
3.40 a. 18
    b. 4.8
    c. 36.80
    d. 6.07
3.42 a. 22
    b. 7.33
    c. $s^2 = 81.2$; $s = 9.01$
3.44 a. For Starbucks, $s^2 = 4.57$; $s = 2.14$.
       For Panera Bread Co, $s^2 = 77.87$; $s = 8.82$.
    b. Panera (8.82 against 2.14)
    c. Panera (0.042 against 0.037)
3.46 a. $CV_{MKT} = \dfrac{74.01}{164.10} = 0.45.$

    b. $CV_{Return} = \dfrac{105.07}{40.71} = 2.58.$

    c. Total return
3.48 a. Investment B provides a higher return. Investment A provides a lower risk.
    b. $Sharpe_A = \dfrac{10 - 1.4}{5} = 1.72;$

       $Sharpe_B = \dfrac{15 - 1.4}{10} = 1.36.$

       Investment A provides a higher reward per unit of risk.
3.50 a. Investment 2
    b. Investment 1
    c. $Sharpe_1 = \dfrac{3 - 1.2}{5.29} = 0.34$; $Sharpe_2 = \dfrac{5 - 1.2}{9} = 0.42.$
       Investment 2 performs better because it offers more reward per risk.
3.54 a. At least 75%
    b. At least 89%
3.56 a. 450 to 550
    b. 425 to 575
3.58 a. 16%
    b. 80
3.64 a. At least 75%
    b. At least 89%
3.66 a. 68%
    b. 95%
    c. 16%
3.68 a. At least 75%
    b. About 95%
3.70 a. No outliers
    b. No outliers
3.72 a. $\bar{x} = 65.86$
    b. $s^2 = 88.95$; $s = 9.43$
3.74 a. $\bar{x} = 3.36$
    b. $s^2 = 3.87$; $s = 1.97.$
3.80 a. −12.3.
    b. −0.96; strong negative linear relationship

3.82 a. 631.39; positive linear relationship
    b. 0.45; moderate, positive linear relationship
3.84 a. 35; positive linear relationship
    b. 0.95; strong positive linear relationship
3.88 Mean = 809.14; Median = 366; Mode = *not available*. The median best reflects the typical sales as the value 3,300 is clearly an outlier that pulls the mean up.
3.90 a. 1,817
    b. $s^2 = 113,065$; $s = 336.25$
3.92 a. $G_g(Gap) = -0.050$, or −5%; $G_g(AE) = -0.012$, or −1.2%
    b. American Eagle (less negative)
3.96 a. 136.62; positive linear relationship
    b. 0.81; strong positive linear relationship

Chapter 4

4.2 a. 1 to 1
    b. 9 to 1
    c. 0.67 to 1
4.6 Empirical probability. It is considered accurate since it is based on a very large sample of 65,000 subscribers.
4.10 a. You may not get an offer from either firm.
    b. You may get an offer from both firms.
4.14 a. Since Spain won, net gain is $533.33. If Spain had lost, net loss would have been $1,000.
    b. $P(\{Spain\ wins\}) = 0.652$
4.20 a. No, because $P(A|B) \neq (A)$
    b. No, because $P(A \cap B) \neq 0.$
    c. $P((A \cup B)^C) = 0.185$
4.22 a. $P(B) = 0.60$
    b. $P(A|B) = 0.133$
    c. $P(B|A) = 0.32$
4.24 a. $P(A^C|B^C) = 0.48$
    b. $P(A^C \cup B^C) = 0.86$
    c. $P(A^C \cap B^C) = 0.76$
4.26 Let event O correspond to "students who ever go to their professor during office hours" and events MI and MA to "minor clarification" and "major clarification," respectively. We have $P(O) = 0.20$, $P(MI|O) = 0.3$, $P(MA|O) = 0.7$
    a. $P(MI \cap O) = 0.06$
    b. $P(MA \cap O) = 0.14$
4.28 Let event R correspond to "Reduction in unemployment in the US" and event E to "Recession in Europe." We have $P(R) = 0.18$, $P(R|E) = 0.06$
    a. $P(R^C) = 0.82$
    b. $P(R^C \cap E) = 0.0752$
4.30 Let F correspond to "Foreign student" and S to "Smoke." We have $P(F \cap S) = 0.05$ and $P(S|F) = 0.50$. $P(F) = 0.10$, or 10%
4.32 a. $P(A) = 0.70$, $P(A^C) = 0.30$, $P(B) = 0.50$
    b. No, because only 6 shirts are neither white or blue.
    c. $A \cap B$

4.36 For $i = 1,2$, let event A_i be "the i-th selected member is in favor of the bonus."

   a. $P(A_1 \cap A_2) = \frac{10}{15} \times \frac{9}{14} = 0.4286$

   b. $P(A_1^c \cap A_2^c) = \frac{5}{15} \times \frac{4}{14} = 0.0952$

4.40 Let event H correspond to "Woman faces sexual harassment" and event T to "Woman uses public transportation." We have $P(H) = 0.6667$, $P(H \mid T) = 0.82$, and $P(T) = 0.28$.

   a. $P(H \cap T) = 0.2296$

   b. $P(T \mid H) = 0.3444$

4.48 a. Joint probability table:

Global Warming	Political Affiliation		Total
	Democrat (D)	Republican (R)	
Yes (Y)	280	120	400
No (N)	120	280	400
Total	400	400	800

   b. $P(R \cap Y) = 0.15$

   c. $P(N) = 0.50$

   d. $P(D \mid Y) = 0.70$

4.52 a. $P(B^c) = 0.40$

   b. $P(A \cap B) = 0.48$

      $P(A \cap B^c) = 0.04$

   c. $P(A) = 0.52$

   d. $P(B \mid A) = 0.9231$

4.58 Let event D correspond to "Experience a decline" and event N to "Ratio is negative." We have $P(D) = 0.20$, $P(N \mid D) = 0.70$, and $P(N \mid D^c) = 0.15$.

   $P(D \mid N) = \frac{P(N \cap D)}{P(N)} = 0.54$.

4.60 Let event O correspond to "Teen owns a cell phone" and event T to "Older teens." We have $P(O \mid T) = 0.90$, $P(O \mid T^c) = 0.60$, and $P(T) = 0.70$.

   a. $P(O) = 0.81$

   b. $P(T \mid O) = 0.7778$

   c. $P(T^c \mid O) = 0.2222$

4.62 Let F = "Player is fully fit to play," S = "Player is somewhat fit to play," N = "Player is not able to play," and W = "The Lakers win the game."

   a. $P(W) = P(W \cap F) + P(W \cap S) + P(W \cap N) = 0.62$

   b. $P(F \mid W) = 0.52$

4.64 a. $8! = 40,320$

      $6! = 720$

   b. $\frac{8!}{(8-6)6!} = 28$

   c. $\frac{8!}{(8-6)!} = 20,160$

4.66 $8! = 40,320$

4.68 a. $\frac{10!}{(10-5)!5!} = 252$

   b. $\frac{10!}{(10-5)!} = 30,240$

4.72 a. Empirical Probabilities: $P(A) = 0.10$, $P(B) = 0.44$, and $P(B \mid A) = 0.60$

   b. Not mutually exclusive since $P(A \cap B) > 0$
      Not exhaustive since $P(A \cup B) < 1$

   c. Not independent since $P(B \mid A) \neq P(B)$

   d. $P(A \mid B) = 0.136$

4.74 Let event A correspond to "own a mobile phone" and B to "own a smartphone." We have $P(A) = 0.883$ and $P(B \mid A) = 0.84$. $P(B) = P(B \cap A) = 0.742$

4.78 Let event S correspond to "Biggest smilers," F to "Biggest frowners," and D to "Divorced." We have $P(D \mid S) = 0.11$ and $P(D \mid F) = 0.31$.

   a. $P(S) = 0.1818$

   b. $P(F \cap D) = 0.0775$

4.80 a. $\frac{17}{20} = 0.85$

   b. $\frac{17}{20} \times \frac{16}{19} = 0.7158$

   c. $\frac{3}{20} \times \frac{2}{19} = 0.0158$

4.82 Let event O correspond to "Optimism about the global economy," U to "Respondents from the U.S.," and A to "Respondents from Asia." We have $P(O) = 0.18$, $P(O \mid U) = 0.22$, and $P(O \mid A) = 0.09$.

   a. $P(O^c \mid A) = 0.91$.

   b. $P(O \cap U) = 0.0616$

   c. $P(A \mid O) = 0.11$

4.86

	Survived for Discharge (S)	Did not Survive for Discharge (S^c)	Total
Day or Evening (D)	0.1338	0.5417	0.6755
Graveyard Shift (G)	0.0477	0.2768	0.3245
Total	0.1815	0.8185	1.00

   a. $P(G) = 0.3245$

   b. $P(S) = 0.1815$

   c. $P(S \mid G) = 0.1470$

   d. $P(G \mid S) = 0.2628$

   e. No since $P(S \mid G) \neq P(S)$

4.88 Let event A correspond to "US economy performs well" and B to "Asian countries perform well." We have $P(A) = 0.40$, $P(B \mid A) = 0.80$, and $P(B \mid A^c) = 0.30$.

   a. $P(A \cap B) = 0.32$

   b. $P(B) = P(B \cap A) + P(B \cap A^c) = 0.50$

   c. $P(A \mid B) = 0.64$

4.90 Let event M correspond to "Men," W to "Women," and H to "Healthy weight." We have $P(H \mid W) = 0.365$, $P(H \mid M) = 0.266$, and $P(W) = 0.5052$.

   a. $P(H) = P(H \cap W) + P(H \cap M) = 0.3160$

   b. $P(W \mid H) = 0.5835$

   c. $P(M \mid H) = 0.4165$

4.92 Let event R correspond to "Republican," D to "Democrat," I to "Independent," and S to "Support marijuana legalization." We have $P(R) = 0.27$, $P(D) = 0.30$, $P(I) = 0.43$, $P(S \mid R) = 0.41$, $P(S \mid D) = 0.66$, $P(S \mid I) = 0.63$.

   a. $P(S \cap R) = 0.1107$

   b. $P(S \cap D) = 0.1980$

   c. $P(S \cap I) = 0.2709$

   d. $P(S) = P(S \cap R) + P(S \cap D) + P(S \cap I) = 0.5796$

   e. $P(R \mid S) = 0.1910$

4.96 a. $\frac{7!}{4!3!} = 35$

   b. $\frac{7!}{4!} = 210$

   c. $\frac{6!}{3!3!} = 20$

Chapter 5

5.4 a. $P(X \le 0) = 0.5$
     b. $P(X = 50) = 0.25$
     c. Yes

5.8 Let X represent performance.
     a. The analyst has a somewhat pessimistic view. There is a 57% chance that the performance will be poor or very poor.
     b.

x	$P(X \le x)$
1 (Very poor)	0.14
2 (Poor)	0.57
3 (Neutral)	0.79
4 (Good)	0.95
5 (Very good)	1

     c. $P(X \ge 4) = 0.21$.

5.10 Let X represent confidence score.
     a. $P(X = 2) = 0.20$.
     b. $P(2 \le X \le 3) = 0.25$.

5.14 $\mu = 10.75$
     $\sigma^2 = 28.19$ $\sigma = 5.31$

5.16 a. $\mu = 0.95$
     b. $\sigma = 0.80$

5.20 2.2

5.22 $3,600

5.28 $w_X = 0.45$ and $w_Y = 0.55$

5.30 a. $w_X = 0.40$; $w_Y = 0.60$
     b. $E(R_p) = 10.4\%$
     c. $SD(R_P) = 14.60$

5.34 a. $P(X = 0) = 0.1160$
     b. $P(X = 1) = 0.3124$
     c. $P(X \le 1) = 0.4284$

5.36 a. $P(3 < X < 5) = 0.1569$
     b. $P(3 < X \le 5) = 0.2160$
     c. $P(3 \le X \le 5) = 0.4828$

5.42 a. $P(X < 2) = 0.7213$
     b. $P(X < 2) = 0.4580$

5.44 a. $E(X) = 2,850$; $SD(X) = 35.01$
     b. $E(X) = 2,150$; $SD(X) = 35.01$
     c. $P(X = 6) = 0.1780$

5.46 a. $P(X > 2) = 0.3125$
     b. $P(X > 2) = 0.5276$
     c. $P(X > 2) = 0.1362$

5.48 a. $P(X \ge 1) = 0.4375$; her statement is not correct
     b. $P(X \ge 1) = 0.5781$; her statement is correct

5.50 a. $P(X = 10) = 0.1171$
     b. $P(X \le 10) = 0.8725$
     c. $P(X \ge 15) = 0.0016$

5.52 a. $P(X = 1) = 0.3347$
     b. $P(X = 2) = 0.2510$
     c. $P(X \ge 2) = 0.4422$

5.56 a. $P(X < 14) = 0.0661$
     b. $P(X \ge 20) = 0.5297$
     c. $P(X = 25) = 0.0446$
     d. $P(18 \le X \le 23) = 0.4905$

5.58 a. Poisson
     b. Not Poisson
     c. Poisson
     d. Not Poisson

5.60 a. $\mu = 6$; $P(X = 2) = 0.0446$
     b. $\mu = 6$; $P(X \ge 2) = 0.9826$
     c. $\mu = 60$; $P(X = 40) = 0.001$

5.64 a. $P(X \le 425) = 0.8980$
     b. $P(X \ge 375) = 0.8998$

5.66 a. $\mu = 304$; $P(X > 320) = 0.1717$
     b. $\mu = 2,128$; $P(X > 2,200) = 0.0586$

5.68 a. $P(X = 0) = 0.5783$
     b. $P(X = 1) = 0.3652$
     c. $P(X \le 1) = 0.9435$

5.72 $P(X \ge 8) = 0.0777$
     $E(X) = 5$; $SD(X) = 1.7408$

5.76 a. $P(X = 3) = 0.2696$
     b. $P(X \ge 2) = 0.7549$

5.78 $P(X = 2) = 0.0316$

5.80 a. $P(X = 2) = 0.0495$
     b. $P(X = 5) = 0.0000002$
     c. $P(X = 1) = 0.0256$
     d. $0.0000002 \times 0.0256 = 0.00000000512$

5.82 a. $E(X) = -\$700,000$

5.84 a. $P(X = 3) = 0.45$
     b. $P(X \ge 2) = 0.90$
     c. $E(X) = 2.6$; $SD(X) = 0.97$

5.86 a. $E(X) = 2.79$; $SD(X) = 1.3137$
     b. $120 \times 41.85 = 5,022$

5.90 a. $P(X = 2) = 0.3747$
     b. $P(X = 4) = 0.0677$
     c. $E(X) = 51$; $SD(X) = 4.999$

5.92 a. $P(X = 10) = 0.0272$
     b. $P(10 \le X \le 20) = 0.0451$
     c. $P(X \le 8) = 0.8996$

5.96 a. $P(X = 3) = 0.0129$
     b. $P(X \le 2) = 0.9871$
     c. $2P(X = 3) = 0.0258$

5.100 a. $P(X = 6) = 0.0115$
      b. $P(X \ge 5) = 0.0647$
      c. $P(X \le 2) = 0.5206$
      d. $E(X) = 2.5$

Chapter 6

6.2 a. 0.30
     b. 0.16
     c. 0.70

6.4 a. $f(x) = 0.0333$
     b. $\mu = 20$; $\sigma = 8.66$
     c. $P(X > 10) = 0.8325$

6.6 a. $\mu = 20$; $\sigma = 5.77$
     b. $P(X > 22) = 0.4$
     c. $P(15 \le X \le 23) = 0.4$

6.8 a. $\mu = 16$
     b. $P(X < 15.5) = 0.4375$
     c. $P(X > 14) = 0.75$

6.12 a. $P(X \geq 25) = 0.4167$
 b. $P(X \leq 20) = 0.1667$
6.14 a. $P(Z > 1.32) = 0.0934$
 b. $P(Z \leq -1.32) = 0.0934$
 c. $P(1.32 \leq Z \leq 2.37) = 0.0845$
 d. $P(-1.32 \leq Z \leq 2.37) = 0.8977$
6.20 a. $P(X \leq 0) = P(Z \leq -2.5) = 0.0062$
 b. $P(X > 2) = P(Z > -2) = 0.9772$
 c. $P(4 \leq X \leq 10) = P(-1.5 \leq Z \leq 0) = 0.4332$
 d. $P(6 \leq X \leq 14) = P(-1 \leq Z \leq 1) = 0.6826$
6.26 a. $P(X > -12) = P(Z > 0.33) = 0.3707$
 b. $P(0 \leq X \leq 5) = P(1.67 \leq Z \leq 2.22) = 0.0343$
 c. Given $P(X \leq x) = 0.25$, $x = -21.07$
 d. Given $P(X > x) = 0.25$, $x = -8.93$
6.28 a. $P(84 < X < 116) = P(-1 < Z < 1) = 0.6826$
 b. $P(X < 68) = P(Z < -2) = 0.0228$
 c. Given $P(X > x) = 0.01$, $x = 137.22$
6.30 a. $P(60 < X < 100) = P(-2 < Z < 2) = 0.9544$
 b. $P(X > 100) = P(Z > 2) = 0.0228$; 1.87 games
6.34 a. $P(X \geq 40) = P(Z \geq 1.77) = 0.0384$
 b. $P(30 \leq X \leq 35) = P(-1.09 \leq Z \leq 0.34) = 0.4952$
 c. Given $P(X \leq x) = 0.99$, $x = 41.94$
6.36 No, since $P(X > 16) = P(Z > 0.67) = 0.2514 \neq 0.15$
6.38 a. $P(X > 19) = P(Z > -1.5) = 0.9332$
 b. $P(X > 19) = P(Z > 1.5) = 0.0668$
 c. $P(23 \leq X \leq 25) = P(0.5 \leq Z \leq 1.5) = 0.2417$
 d. $P(23 \leq X \leq 25) = P(3.5 \leq Z \leq 4.5) = 0.0002$
6.44 a. $P(50 \leq X \leq 80) = P(-0.5 \leq Z \leq 1) = 0.5328$
 b. $P(20 \leq X \leq 40) = P(-2 \leq Z \leq -1) = 0.1359$
 c. Given $P(X \geq x) = 0.15$, $x = 80.72$
 d. Given $P(X < x) = 0.10$, $x = 34.36$
6.48 a. Riskier Fund: $P(X < 0) = P(Z < -0.57) = 0.2843$
 Less Risky Fund: $P(X < 0) = P(Z < -0.8) = 0.2119$
 Pick the less risky fund.
 b. Riskier Fund: $P(X > 8) = P(Z > 0) = 0.5$
 Less Risky Fund: $P(X > 8) = P(Z > 0.8) = 0.2119$
 Pick the riskier fund.
6.50 a. $P(X < 200) = P(Z < -0.58) = 0.2810$
 b. $P(X \geq 266.5) = P(Z \geq 2.74) = 0.0031$
 c. Given $P(X < x) = 0.10$, $x = 186.06$
 d. Given $P(X < x) = 0.99$, $x = 258.22$
6.54 a. $\mu = 2.5$
 b. $\lambda = 0.4$
 c. $P(1 \leq X \leq 2) = 0.2210$
6.56 $E(X) = SD(X) = 0.20$
6.58 a. $P(X \leq 1) = 0.3935$
 b. $P(2 < X < 4) = 0.2326$
 c. $P(X > 10) = 0.0067$
6.60 a. $\mu_Y = 54.60$; $\sigma_Y^2 = 19,046$
 b. $\mu_Y = 403.42$; $\sigma_Y^2 = 1,039,849$
 c. $\mu_Y = 665.14$; $\sigma_Y^2 = 8,443,697$
6.62 a. $\mu = 2.5859$; $\sigma^2 = 0.1064$
 b. $\mu = 2.9690$; $\sigma^2 = 0.0535$
 c. $\mu = 2.8646$; $\sigma^2 = 0.2624$

6.64 a. $\mu = 6$
 b. $P(X > 15) = 0.0820$
 c. $P(15 \leq X \leq 20) = 0.0463$
6.66 a. $\mu = 0.0028$ (in hours)
 b. $P\left(X < \frac{10}{3600}\right) = 0.6321$
6.68 a. $P(X \leq 24) = 0.0469$
 b. $(P(X \leq 24))^2 = 0.0022$
6.72 a. $P(X < 1) = 0.8647$
 b. $P(X > 5) = 0.0001$
6.74 a. $E(X) = 3$; $Var(X) = 1.3333$
 b. $P(X > 4) = 0.25$
 c. $P(X < 2.5) = 0.375$
6.76 a. $P(80 \leq X \leq 90) = P(0.1 \leq Z \leq 1.1) = 0.3245$
 b. $P(120 \leq X \leq 139) = P(-0.29 \leq Z \leq 0.82) = 0.4080$
6.80 Given $P(X > x) = 0.03$, $x = 100.22$
6.82 $Q_1 = 5.99$; $Q_2 = 6.00$; $Q_3 = 6.01$
6.84 a. $P(X \leq 10) = P(Z \leq -1.2) = 0.1151$
 b. $1,000 \times 271.225 = \$271,225$
6.88 a. $\mu = 7.5$
 b. $P(X \leq 5) = 0.4865$
6.90 a. $\mu = 0.365$
 b. $\lambda = 2.7397$
 c. $P(X \leq 1) = 0.9354$
6.92 a. $\mu = 0.8333$
 b. $P(X \leq 1) = 0.6988$
 c. $P(1 \leq X \leq 2) = 0.2105$
6.96 a. $P(Y < 50,000) = P(X < 10.8198) =$
 $P(Z < -0.70) = 0.2420$
 b. $P(Y > 60,000) = P(X > 11.0021) =$
 $P(Z > -0.24) = 0.5948$
 c. Given $P(Y > y) = 0.99$, $x = 12.0304$ and $y = 167,779$
 d. Given $P(Y < y) = 0.10$, $x = 10.588$ and $y = 39,656$

Chapter 7

7.2 Nonresponse bias if some people are less likely to stop at the booth. Selection bias since the booth is only open on the weekend.
7.4 a. Nonresponse bias if the people who respond are systematically different from those who do not respond.
 b. Selection bias since those who frequent the store in the morning are likely to prefer an earlier opening time.
 c. Selection bias since not everyone reads a newspaper. Nonresponse bias if the people who respond are systematically different from those who do not respond.
7.8 a. $E(\bar{X}) = 80$; $SE(\bar{X}) = 1.4$
 b. $P(77 \leq \bar{X} \leq 85) = P(-2.14 \leq Z \leq 3.57) = 0.9836$
 c. $P(\bar{X} > 84) = P(Z > 2.86) = 0.0021$
7.12 a. $P(\bar{X} \geq 18) = P(Z \geq 1.85) = 0.0322$
 b. $P(\bar{X} \geq 17.5) = P(Z \geq 2.03) = 0.0212$
 c. Janice; her findings are more likely if a representative sample is used.

7.14 a. The sample mean has a normal distribution because the population is normally distributed.
     b. $P(\overline{X} > 25) = P(Z > 2.4) = 0.0082$
     c. $P(18 \le \overline{X} \le 24) = P(-3.20 \le Z \le 1.60) = 0.9445$

7.18 a. $P(X > 1{,}000{,}000) = P(Z > 0.80) = 0.2119$
     b. $P(\overline{X} > 1{,}000{,}000) = P(Z > 1.60) = 0.0548$

7.20 a. $P(X < 90) = P(Z < -0.63) = 0.2643$
     b. $P(\overline{X} < 90) = P(Z < -1.25) = 0.1056$
     c. $(0.2643)^4 = 0.0049$

7.24 a. $P(\overline{P} < 0.30) = P(Z < 1.29) = 0.9015$
     b. $p = 0.74; P(\overline{P} > 0.75) = P(Z > 0.32) = 0.3745$

7.26 a. $E(\overline{P}) = 0.17$ and $se(\overline{P}) = 0.0266$; the normal approximation criteria are met because $np = 34 > 5$ and $n(1 - p) = 166 > 5$.
     b. $P(\overline{P} > 0.20) = P(Z > 1.13) = 0.1292$

7.34 $n = 120, N = 1{,}000$; apply the finite population correction; $E(\overline{P}) = 0.6667$ and $se(\overline{P}) = 0.0404$; $P(\overline{P} > 0.625) = P(Z > -1.03) = 0.8485$

7.36 a. No, since n is less than 5% of N.
     b. No because we do not know if the population has a normal distribution and $n < 30$.
     c. $E(\overline{X}) = 10.32; se(\overline{X}) = 2.8232$
     d. The normal approximation is not justified (see part b).

7.40 a. Centerline: $\mu = 20$
     UCL = 26
     LCL = 14
     b.

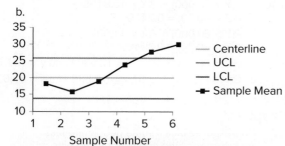

     c. The last two points are outside the upper control limit. There is also an upward trend, suggesting the process is becoming increasingly out of control. The process should be adjusted.

7.42 a. Centerline: $p = 0.34$
     UCL = 0.404
     LCL = 0.276
     b.

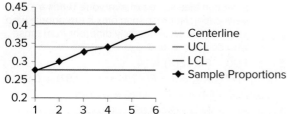

     c. Although there are no points outside the control limits, the positive trend suggests that the process may become out of control if the upward trend continues.

7.44 a.

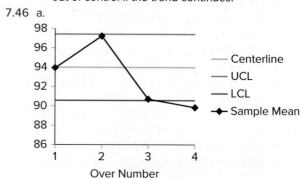

     Centerline: $\mu = 5.125$
     UCL = 5.25
     LCL = 5
     b. There are no points outside the control limits. It appears that the process is under control, but the positive trend suggests the process may become out of control if the trend continues.

7.46 a.

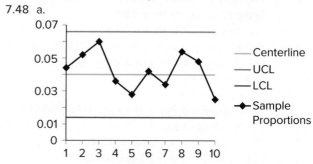

     b. Kalwant's average speed is out of control; the coach's concern is justified.

7.48 a.

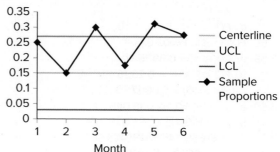

     b. Yes since all sample proportions are within the control limits and there is no apparent trend.

7.50 a.

     b. 3 out of 6 months were out of the control limits, which is a good justification for why Dell chose to direct customers away from India call centers.

7.54 a. $P(\overline{P} > 0.50) = P(Z > 0.71) = 0.2389$
    b. $P(\overline{P} > 0.50) = P(Z > 0.28) = 0.3897$
7.56 a. $P(X < 79) = P(Z < -0.5) = 0.3085$
    b. $P(\overline{X} < 79) = P(Z < -1.58) = 0.0571$
    c. $P(\overline{X} < 79) = P(Z < -2.74) = 0.0031$
7.58 a. $P(X > 500) = P(Z > 0.59) = 0.2776$
    b. $P(\overline{X} > 500) = P(Z > 1.17) = 0.1210$
    c. $(0.2776)^4 = 0.0059$
7.60 a. $P(\overline{P} > 0.80) = P(Z > 0.87) = 0.1922$
    b. $P(\overline{P} < 0.70) = P(Z < -2.04) = 0.0207$
7.62 a.

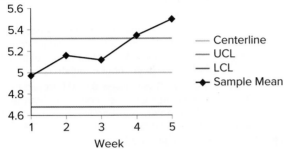

Week

    b. The last two points are outside the upper control limit, and there is a positive trend, suggesting that the process is out of control.

Chapter 8

8.2 a. For 89%, $z_{\alpha/2} = 1.598$
    b. For 92%, $z_{\alpha/2} = 1.751$
    c. For 96%, $z_{\alpha/2} = 2.054$
8.6 a. $\overline{x} = 78.1$
    b. $1.645 \frac{4.5}{\sqrt{50}} = 1.05$
    c. 78.1 ± 1.05 or [77.05, 79.15]
8.10 a. $2.576 \frac{500}{\sqrt{100}} = 128.80$
    b. $7{,}790 \pm 128.80$ or [7,661.20, 7,918.80]
8.14 90%: [18.81, 21.61]
    99%: [18.02, 22.40]
    The 99% confidence interval is wider.
8.22 a. $2.11 \frac{9.2}{\sqrt{18}} = 4.58$
    b. 12.5 ± 4.58 or [7.92, 17.08]
8.24 a. $2.724 \frac{10}{\sqrt{36}} = 4.54$
    b. 100 ± 4.54 or [95.46, 104.54]
8.26 a. $17.25 \pm 3.499 \frac{5.95}{\sqrt{8}}$ or [9.89, 24.61].
    b. The population is normally distributed.
8.30 a. Electronic: $18 \pm 4.604 \frac{20.70}{\sqrt{5}}$ or [−24.62, 60.62]
    Utilities: $14.8 \pm 4.604 \frac{6.50}{\sqrt{5}}$ or [1.42, 28.18]
    b. Annual return of each fund has a normal distribution
8.34 $1{,}080 \pm 2.032 \frac{260}{\sqrt{35}}$ or [990.70, 1,169.30]
    The manager is wrong since 1,200 is not within the 95% confidence interval.
8.36 a. Microeconomics: [68.74, 74.91]
    Macroeconomics: [66.16, 74.64]
    b. The widths are different because of the differences in the sample standard deviations for microeconomics and macroeconomics.

8.40 a. $0.6 \pm 1.960 \sqrt{\frac{0.6(1 - 0.6)}{50}}$ or [0.464, 0.736]
    b. $0.6 \pm 1.960 \sqrt{\frac{0.6(1 - 0.6)}{200}}$ or [0.532, 0.668]. With larger n, the interval is narrower.
8.42 a. $\overline{p} = 0.40$.
    b. 90%: $0.40 \pm 1.645 \sqrt{\frac{0.40(1 - 0.40)}{100}}$ or [0.319, 0.481]
    99%: $0.40 \pm 2.576 \sqrt{\frac{0.40(1 - 0.40)}{100}}$ or [0.274, 0.526]
    c. Yes, since the value 0.5 does not fall within the interval.
    d. No, since the value 0.5 falls within the interval.
8.44 $0.51 \pm 1.960 \sqrt{\frac{0.51(1 - 0.51)}{1.079}}$ or [0.480, 0.540].
8.46 a. $0.37 \pm 1.645 \sqrt{\frac{0.37(1 - 0.37)}{5.324}}$ or [0.359, 0.381]
    b. $0.37 \pm 2.576 \sqrt{\frac{0.37(1 - 0.37)}{5.324}}$ or [0.353, 0.387]
    c. The margin of error in part b is greater because it uses a higher confidence level.
8.50 a. $0.275 \pm 1.645 \sqrt{\frac{0.275(1 - 0.275)}{400}}$ or [0.238, 0.312]
    b. No, because the value 0.30 falls in the interval.
8.52 a. $0.30 \pm 1.645 \sqrt{\frac{0.30(1 - 0.30)}{1.026}}$ or [0.276, 0.324]
    b. $0.10 \pm 1.645 \sqrt{\frac{0.10(1 - 0.10)}{1.026}}$ or [0.085, 0.115]
8.56 $n = 61.47$, rounded up to 62
8.58 With $E = 1.2$, $n = 23.02$, rounded up to 24.
    With $E = 0.7$, $n = 67.65$, rounded up to 68.
8.60 With $E = 0.08$, $n = 138.3$, rounded up to 139.
    With $E = 0.12$, $n = 61.47$, rounded up to 62.
8.64 a. $n = 101.89$, rounded up to 102.
    b. $n = 39.34$, rounded up to 40.
    c. With higher standard deviation, Fund A requires a larger sample size to achieve the same margin of error.
8.68 $n = 1{,}680.44$, rounded up to 1,681.
8.72 $10 \pm 2.262 \frac{15}{\sqrt{10}}$ or [−0.73, 20.73]
8.74 a. $16 \pm 1.971 \frac{12}{\sqrt{225}}$ or [14.42, 17.58]
    b. Yes, because the interval does not include the value 14.
8.82 a. [77.04, 79.81]
    b. It differs since the value 81.84 is not contained in the interval.
8.84 a. 7.89 (Monday), 4.41 (Tuesday)
    b. [214.48, 230.25] (Monday), [185.65, 194.48] (Tuesday)
    c. For both Monday and Tuesday, the population mean differs because the value 200 does not belong to either of the two confidence intervals.
8.86 a. 0.018
    b. 0.121 ± 0.018 or [0.103, 0.139].
8.92 $n = 259.35$, rounded up to 260

Chapter 9

9.4 a. Incorrect; we never accept the null hypothesis.
    b. Correct
    c. Incorrect; we establish a claim only if the null hypothesis is rejected.
    d. Correct

9.10 a. Type I error; the new software is purchased even though it does not reduce assembly costs.

b. Type II error; the new software is not purchased even though it reduces assembly costs.

9.12 a. Type I error; the restaurant is incorrectly implicated for using higher fat content.

b. Type II error; the restaurant escapes being implicated for using higher fat content.

9.14 a. $z = -2$

b. p-value $= 0.0456$

c. Reject H_0; at the 10% significance level, we conclude that the population mean differs from 100.

9.16 a. $H_0: \mu \leq 45; H_A: \mu > 45$

b. $z = 1.50$

c. p-value $= 0.0668$

d. Do not reject H_0; at the 5% significance level, we cannot conclude that the population mean is greater than 45.

9.18 $z = 1.41$; p-value $= 0.0793$. Do not reject H_0; at the 5% significance level, we cannot conclude that the population mean is greater than -5.

9.20 $z = -3.57$; p-value $= 0.0004$. Reject H_0; at the 1% significance level, we conclude that the population mean differs from -100.

9.24 a. $H_0: \mu \leq 90; H_A: \mu > 90$

b. $z = 1.58$; p-value $= 0.0571$

c. Do not reject H_0; the manager's claim is not supported at the 1% significance level.

9.28 a. $H_0: \mu = 30; H_A: \mu \neq 30$

b. $z = 2.40$; p-value $= 0.0164$

c. Reject H_0; at the 5% significance level, we conclude that the average weekly price differs from $30.

9.36 $H_0: \mu = 16; H_A: \mu \neq 16; t_{31} = -7.54$; p-value $= 0$ (approximately). Reject H_0; at the 1% significance level, we conclude that the population mean differs from 16.

9.42 a. $H_0: \mu \leq 5; H_A: \mu > 5$

b. $t_6 = 0.643$; p-value $= 0.272$; population normally distributed

c. Do not reject H_0; at the 10% significance level, we cannot conclude that the average waiting time is more than 5 minutes.

9.44 a. $H_0: \mu = 12; H_A: \mu \neq 12$

b. No, since $n > 30$

c. $t_{47} = -1.732$; p-value $= 0.09$

d. Do not reject H_0; at the 5% significance level, we cannot conclude that the bottling process has fallen out of adjustment.

9.46 $H_0: \mu \leq 7; H_A: \mu > 7; t_{33} = 2.915$; p-value $= 0.003$; reject H_0. At the 1% significance level, we conclude that the mean drop of home prices in San Diego is greater than the 7% drop in Los Angeles.

9.50 a. $H_0: \mu = 95; H_A: \mu \neq 95$

b. $t_{24} = 0.71$; p-value $= 0.484$

c. Do not reject H_0; at the 5% significance level, we cannot conclude that the average MPG differs from 95.

9.56 a. $z = -0.30$; p-value $= 0.7642$

b. $z = 2.05$; p-value $= 0.0404$

c. $z = 1.08$; p-value $= 0.2802$

d. $z = 1.73$; p-value $= 0.0836$

9.64 a. $H_0: p \leq 0.20; H_A: p > 0.20$

b. $z = 2.18$; p-value $= 0.0146$

c. Reject H_0; at the 5% significance level, the economist's concern is supported.

9.66 $H_0: p \leq 0.75; H_A: p > 0.75; z = 1.01$; p-value $= 0.1562$. Do not reject H_0; at the 5% significance level, we cannot conclude that more than 75% of financial institutions are prone to fraud.

9.78 $H_0: p \geq 0.35; H_A: p < 0.35$

Case 1: $z = -1.33$; p-value $= 0.0918$. Do not reject H_0; at the 5% significance level, we cannot conclude that the percentage of Americans who feel that the country is headed in the right direction is below 35%.

Case 2: $z = -1.88$; p-value $= 0.0301$. Reject H_0; at the 5% significance level, we conclude that the percentage of Americans who feel that the country is headed in the right direction is below 35%.

9.82 a. $H_0: p = 0.17; H_A: p \neq 0.17$

b. $z = 2.07$; p-value $= 0.0384$

c. Reject H_0; at the 5% significance level, we conclude that the proportion of households in the rural South is not representative of the national proportion.

9.84 a. $H_0: \mu = 13,500; H_A: \mu \neq 13,500$

b. $t_{49} = 2.593$; p-value $= 0.012$

c. Reject H_0; at the 10% significance level, we conclude that the average number of miles driven by Midwesterners differs from the U.S. average.

Chapter 10

10.4 a. $t_{20} = 1.719$; p-value $= 0.051$. Do not reject H_0; at the 5% significance level, we cannot conclude that μ_1 is greater than μ_2.

b. At the 10% significance level, we conclude that μ_1 is greater than μ_2.

10.8 a. $H_0: \mu_1 - \mu_2 = 0; H_A: \mu_1 - \mu_2 \neq 0$

b. $t_8 = \dfrac{98.3333 - 111.6667}{\sqrt{\dfrac{16.2686^2}{6} + \dfrac{10.9118^2}{6}}} = -1.667$;

p-value $= 0.134$

c. Do not reject H_0; at the 10% significance level, we cannot conclude that the population means differ.

10.10 a. $H_0: \mu_1 - \mu_2 \geq 0; H_A: \mu_1 - \mu_2 < 0$

b. $z = -5.81$; p-value $= 0$ (approximately)

c. Reject H_0; at the 5% significance level, we conclude that there is a "community college penalty" at Lucille's university.

10.12 a. $H_0: \mu_1 - \mu_2 = 0; H_A: \mu_1 - \mu_2 \neq 0$

b. $z = 1.53$; p-value $= 0.126$

c. Do not reject H_0; at the 5% or the 10% significance levels, we cannot conclude the mean profitability differs between condominiums and apartment buildings.

10.14 a. $H_0: \mu_1 - \mu_2 \leq 0; H_A: \mu_1 - \mu_2 > 0$ (Population 1 = New Process and Population 2 = Old Process)

b. $t_{16} = \dfrac{(2613.63 - 2485.10) - 0}{\sqrt{15{,}963.10\left(\frac{1}{8} + \frac{1}{10}\right)}} = 2.145;$

p-value $= 0.024$

c. Reject H_0; at the 5% significance level, we conclude that the mean output rate of the new process exceeds that of the old process.

d. Do not reject H_0; at the 1% significance level, we cannot conclude that the mean output rate of the new process exceeds that of the old process.

10.18 a. $H_0: \mu_1 - \mu_2 = 0; H_A: \mu_1 - \mu_2 \neq 0$ (Population 1 = Day Searches and Population 2 = Evening Searches)

b. $t_{16} = \dfrac{(98{,}817.30 - 110{,}204.17) - 0}{1{,}570.7702} = -7.249;$

p-value $= 0$ (approximately)

c. Reject H_0; at the 5% significance level, we conclude that the mean number of website searches differs between the day and evening advertisements.

10.20 a. $H_0: \mu_1 - \mu_2 \geq 0; H_A: \mu_1 - \mu_2 < 0$ (Population 1 = New Method and Population 2 = Old Method)

b. $t_{66} = \dfrac{(32.0938 - 32.7500) - 0}{0.4571} = -1.436;$

p-value $= 0.078$

c. We conclude that the mean assembly time using the new method is less than the old method only at the 10% significance level.

10.28 a. $H_0: \mu_D \leq 0; H_A: \mu_D > 0$

b. $t_{34} = 1.868; p$-value $= 0.035$

c. Reject H_0; at the 5% significance level, we conclude that there is a positive mean difference.

10.30 a. $H_0: \mu_D = 0; H_A: \mu_D \neq 0$ (Mean difference between Method A and Method B)

b. $t_6 = \dfrac{-1.8571 - 0}{2.3401/\sqrt{7}} = -2.10$

c. p-value $= 0.08$

d. Reject H_0; at the 10% significance level, the manager's assertion is supported by the data.

10.34 a. $H_0: \mu_D \geq 0; H_A: \mu_D < 0$ (Mean time difference between New Processor and Existing Processor)

b. $t_6 = \dfrac{-0.2771 - 0}{0.1991/\sqrt{7}} = -3.682; p$-value $= 0.005$

c. Reject H_0; at the 5% significance level, we conclude that the mean difference between the new and the existing processing time is less than zero. Yes, there is evidence the new processor is faster than the old processor.

10.36 a. $H_0: \mu_D \leq 100; H_A: \mu_D > 100$ (Mean difference between the competitor's and Insure-Me premiums)

b. $t_{49} = \dfrac{197.06 - 100}{443.9387/\sqrt{50}} = 1.546; p$-value $= 0.064$

c. We conclude, only at the 10% significance level, that the mean premium difference between the competitor and Insure-Me is more than \$100.

10.42 $(0.25 - 0.28) \pm 1.96\sqrt{\dfrac{0.25(1 - 0.25)}{200} + \dfrac{0.28(1 - 0.28)}{250}},$

or $[-0.112, 0.052]$

At the 5% significance level, we cannot conclude that the population proportions differ.

10.44 a. $z = \dfrac{0.40 - 0.43}{\sqrt{0.4185(1 - 0.4185)\left(\frac{1}{250} + \frac{1}{400}\right)}} = -0.75$

b. p-value $= 0.453$

c. Do not reject H_0; at the 5% significance level, we cannot conclude that the population proportions differ.

10.50 a. $H_0: p_1 - p_2 \leq 0; H_A: p_1 - p_2 > 0$ (Population 1 = Boys and Population 2 = Girls)

b. $z = \dfrac{0.27 - 0.14}{\sqrt{0.205(1 - 0.205)\left(\frac{1}{500} + \frac{1}{500}\right)}} = 5.09;$

p-value $= 0$ (approximately)

Reject H_0; at the 5% significance level, we conclude that the proportion of boys growing out of asthma is more than that of girls.

c. $H_0: p_1 - p_2 \leq 0.10; H_A: p_1 - p_2 > 0.10;$

$z = \dfrac{(0.27 - 0.14) - 0.10}{\sqrt{\frac{0.27(1 - 0.27)}{500} + \frac{0.14(1 - 0.14)}{500}}} = 1.19;$

p-value $= 0.117$

Do not reject H_0; at the 5% significance level, we cannot conclude that the proportion of boys who grow out of asthma exceeds that of girls by more than 0.10.

10.54 a. $H_0: p_1 - p_2 \geq 0; H_A: p_1 - p_2 < 0$ (Population 1 = African American Men and Population 2 = Caucasian Men)

$z = \dfrac{0.2769 - 0.3444}{\sqrt{0.3161(1 - 0.3161)\left(\frac{1}{130} + \frac{1}{180}\right)}} = -1.26;$

p-value $= 0.1038$; do not reject H_0. At the 5% significance level, we cannot conclude that the proportion of obese African American men is less than their Caucasian counterparts.

b. $H_0: p_1 - p_2 \leq 0; H_A: p_1 - p_2 > 0$ (Population 1 = African American Women and Population 2 = Caucasian Women)

$z = \dfrac{0.3889 - 0.2583}{\sqrt{0.3143(1 - 0.3143)\left(\frac{1}{90} + \frac{1}{120}\right)}} = 2.02;$

p-value $= 0.0217$; reject H_0.

At the 5% significance level, we conclude that the proportion of obese African American women is greater than their Caucasian counterparts.

c. $H_0: p_1 - p_2 = 0; H_A: p_1 - p_2 \neq 0$ (Population 1 = African American Adults and Population 2 = Caucasian Adults)

$z = \dfrac{0.3227 - 0.3100}{\sqrt{0.3154(1 - 0.3154)\left(\frac{1}{220} + \frac{1}{300}\right)}} = 0.31;$

p-value $= 0.7566$; do not reject H_0.

At the 5% significance level, we cannot conclude that the proportion of obese African American adults differs from their Caucasian counterparts.

10.58 $H_0: p_1 - p_2 \leq 0.10; H_A: p_1 - p_2 > 0.10$ (Population 1 = Male Students and Population 2 = Female Students)

$$z = \frac{(0.57 - 0.32) - 0.10}{\sqrt{\frac{0.57(1 - 0.57)}{100} + \frac{0.32(1 - 0.32)}{100}}} = 2.21;$$

p-value = 0.0136; reject H_0.

At the 5% significance level, we conclude that there is a greater than 10 percentage point difference between the proportion of male and female students who think it is not feasible for men and women to be just friends.

10.60 a. $H_0: \mu_1 - \mu_2 \leq 0; H_A: \mu_1 - \mu_2 > 0$ (Population 1 = Men and Population 2 = Women)

b. $z = 3.53$

c. p-value = 0.0002

d. Reject H_0; at the 1% significance level, we conclude that men spend more money than women on St. Patrick's Day.

10.62 $H_0: \mu_1 - \mu_2 = 0; H_A: \mu_1 - \mu_2 \neq 0$ (Population 1 = Men and Population 2 = Women)

$$t_{28} = \frac{(194.48 - 188.88) - 0}{1.7045} = 3.285; p\text{-value} = 0.002$$

At the 1% significance level, we conclude that the mean cholesterol levels for men and women are different.

10.64 a. $H_0: \mu_D \leq 30; H_A: \mu_D > 30$ (Mean difference between after and before pregnancy weight)

$$t_{39} = \frac{36 - 30}{9.6503/\sqrt{40}} = 3.932; p\text{-value} = 0$$

(approximately); reject H_0. At the 5% significance level, we conclude that the mean weight gain of women due to pregnancy is more than 30 pounds.

b. $H_0: \mu_D \leq 35; H_A: \mu_D > 35$ (Mean difference between after and before pregnancy weight)

$$t_{39} = \frac{36 - 35}{9.6503/\sqrt{40}} = 0.655; p\text{-value} = 0.258;$$ do not reject H_0. At the 5% significance level, we cannot conclude that the mean weight gain of women due to pregnancy is more than 35 pounds.

10.66 a. $H_0: p_1 - p_2 \leq 0; H_A: p_1 - p_2 > 0$ (Population 1 = Young Adults and Population 2 = Older Adults)

b. $$z = \frac{0.109 - 0.068}{\sqrt{0.0885(1 - 0.0885)\left(\frac{1}{1,000} + \frac{1}{1,000}\right)}} = 3.23;$$

p-value = 0.0006

c. Reject H_0; at the 5% significance level, we conclude that the proportion of young adults suffering from depression is greater than that of older adults.

10.68 a. $H_0: p_1 - p_2 \leq 0.05; H_A: p_1 - p_2 > 0.05$ (Population 1 = JFK and Population 2 = O'Hare)

b. $$z = \frac{(0.70 - 0.63) - 0.05}{\sqrt{\frac{0.70(1 - 0.70)}{200} + \frac{0.63(1 - 0.63)}{200}}} = 0.42;$$

p-value = 0.3372

c. Do not reject H_0; at the 5% significance level, we cannot conclude that the proportion of on-time flights at JFK is more than 5 percentage points higher than that of O'Hare.

Chapter 11

11.8 $H_0: \sigma^2 \leq 2; H_A: \sigma^2 > 2; \chi_9^2 = 13; p\text{-value} = 0.163$. Do not reject H_0; at the 10% significance level, we cannot conclude that the variance is more than 2.

11.10 a. $\left[\frac{19 \times 0.03}{32.852}, \frac{19 \times 0.03}{8.907}\right] = [0.02, 0.06]$

b. At the 5% significance level, we cannot conclude that the specification is violated.

11.14 a. $H_0: \sigma^2 \geq 90,000; H_A: \sigma^2 < 90,000$

b. $\chi_6^2 = \frac{6 \times 30,696.8095}{90,000} = 2.046$ p-value = 0.085

c. Do not reject H_0; at the 1% significance level, we cannot support the owner's hope that the standard deviation is less than 300.

d. Reject H_0; at the 10% significance level, we support the owner's hope that the standard deviation is less than 300.

11.16 a. $H_0: \sigma^2 = 0.002^2; H_A: \sigma^2 \neq 0.002^2$

b. $\chi_{24}^2 = \frac{24 \times 0.0025^2}{0.002^2} = 37.50$; assume that the population is normally distributed.

c. p-value = 0.078; do not reject H_0. At the 5% significance level, we cannot conclude that the standard deviation of the bearing diameters differs from 0.002 inches.

d. Reject H_0; at the 10% significance level, we conclude that the standard deviation of the bearing diameters differs from 0.002 inches.

11.18 a. $H_0: \sigma^2 \leq 81; H_A: \sigma^2 > 81$

b. $\chi_{29}^2 = \frac{29 \times 133.4437}{81} = 47.775$

c. p-value = 0.016

d. At the 1% significance level, we cannot conclude that the standard deviation of the dexterity scores exceeds 9. At the 5% and 10% significance levels, we conclude that the standard deviation of the dexterity scores exceeds 9.

11.22 a. Ann Arbor: $s = 176.1136$

Davis: $s = 297.6443$

b. Ann Arbor: $\left[\sqrt{\frac{9 \times 176.1136^2}{19.023}}, \sqrt{\frac{9 \times 176.1136^2}{2.700}}\right]$

$= [121.14, 321.54]$

Davis: $\left[\sqrt{\frac{9 \times 297.6443^2}{19.023}}, \sqrt{\frac{9 \times 297.6443^2}{2.700}}\right]$

$= [204.73, 543.42]$

c. At the 5% significance level, we conclude that the standard deviation of rent differs from 200 for Davis, California, but not Ann Arbor, Michigan.

11.30 a. $H_0: \sigma_2^2/\sigma_1^2 = 1; H_A: \sigma_2^2/\sigma_1^2 \neq 1$

b. $F_{(25,25)} = 1.714; p\text{-value} = 0.185$

c. Do not reject H_0; at the 5% significance level, we cannot conclude that the population variances differ. The company can adopt the new cost-cutting technology.

11.32 $H_0: \sigma_1^2/\sigma_2^2 = 1, H_A: \sigma_1^2/\sigma_2^2 \neq 1; F_{(4,4)} = 10.154$ (assume that the samples are drawn independently from normally distributed populations); p-value = 0.045. Reject H_0; at the 5% significance level, we conclude that the population variances differ.

11.34 a. $H_0: \sigma_2^2/\sigma_1^2 \leq 1$, $H_A: \sigma_2^2/\sigma_1^2 > 1$ (Population 1 = Lithium-ion and Population 2 = Nickel-Cadmium)

b. $F_{(25,15)} = 2.023$ (assume that the samples are drawn independently from normally distributed populations)

c. p-value = 0.058

d. Do not reject H_0; at the 5% significance level, we cannot conclude that the variance in discharge time for the lithium-ion battery is less than it is for the nickel-cadmium battery.

e. Reject H_0; at the 10% significance level we conclude that the variance in discharge time for the lithium-ion battery is less than it is for the nickel-cadmium battery.

11.36 a. $H_0: \sigma_2^2/\sigma_1^2 = 1$, $H_A: \sigma_2^2/\sigma_1^2 \neq 1$ (Population 1 = Starbucks and Population 2 = Panera)

b. The samples are drawn independently from normally distributed populations.

c. $F_{(47,47)} = 4.43$; p-value = 0 (approximately)

d. Reject H_0; at the 5% significance level, we conclude that the variances differ.

11.40 a. $H_0: \sigma^2 \leq 5$; $H_A: \sigma^2 > 5$; $\chi_6^2 = \frac{6 \times 11.5714}{5} = 13.886$; p-value = 0.031

Do not reject H_0; at the 1% significance level, we cannot conclude that the variance exceeds 5. There is no cause for concern for the advocacy group.

b. Assume that the generic drug prices are normally distributed.

11.42 a. $\left[\sqrt{\frac{11 \times 35.8788}{21.920}}, \sqrt{\frac{11 \times 35.8788}{3.816}}\right] = [4.24, 10.17]$

b. At the 5% significance level, we cannot conclude that the standard deviation differs from the required level of 5 milliliters.

11.46 a. $H_0: \sigma_1^2/\sigma_2^2 = 1$, $H_A: \sigma_1^2/\sigma_2^2 \neq 1$ (Population 1 = Hasbro and Population 2 = Mattel)

b. The samples are drawn independently from normally distributed populations.

c. $F_{(4,4)} = 1.725$; p-value = 0.610

Do not reject H_0; at the 5% significance level, we cannot conclude that the variances differ.

11.48 a. $H_0: \sigma_1^2/\sigma_2^2 = 1$, $H_A: \sigma_1^2/\sigma_2^2 \neq 1$ (Population 1 = Part A and Population 2 = Part B)

b. $F_{(29,29)} = 1.105$; p-value = 0.789

c. Do not reject H_0; at the 5% significance level, we cannot conclude that the variances are different. Carrying the same safety stock level for each part is reasonable.

Chapter 12

12.8 a. $H_0: p_1 = p_2 = p_3 = 1/3$; H_A: Not all population proportions are equal to $1/3$.

b. $\chi_2^2 = 6.968$; p-value = 0.031; reject H_0. At the 5% significance level, we conclude that Zimbabwe visitors are not equally represented by Europe, North America, and the rest of the world.

12.10 $H_0: p_1 = 0.38$, $p_2 = 0.33$, $p_3 = 0.29$; H_A: At least one of the p_i ($i = 1,2,3$) differs from its hypothesized value

$\chi_2^2 = 2.179$; p-value = 0.336; do not reject H_0. At the 5% significance level, the researcher cannot conclude that car preferences have changed since the Associated Press-GfK Poll.

12.12 a. $H_0: p_1 = p_2 = p_3 = p_4 = 0.25$; H_A: At least one p_i ($i = 1,2,3,4$) differs from 0.25.

b. $\chi_3^2 = 7.720$; p-value = 0.052

c. At the 10% significance level, we conclude that the proportion of bags filled by at least one chute differs from 0.25.

12.14 H_0: The two categories are independent.
H_A: The two categories are dependent.

$\chi_6^2 = 1.249$; p-value = 0.974; do not reject H_0. At the 1% significance level, we cannot conclude that Category 1 and Category 2 are dependent.

12.18 a. H_0: Vehicle brand and union membership are independent.
H_A: Vehicle brand and union membership are dependent.

b. $\chi_2^2 = 14.915$; p-value = 0 (approximately); reject H_0. At the 10% significance level, we conclude that vehicle brand and union membership are dependent.

c. The conclusion in part b is not sensitive to the choice of significance level.

12.22 H_0: Breakup reasons and one's sex are independent.
H_A: Breakup reasons and one's sex are dependent.

$\chi_4^2 = 19.463$; p-value = 0 (approximately); reject H_0. At the 1% significance level, we conclude that breakup reason and one's sex are dependent.

12.24 H_0: The data are normally distributed with a mean of -3.5 and a standard deviation of 9.7.
H_A: The data are not normally distributed with a mean of -3.5 and a standard deviation of 9.7.

$\chi_1^2 = 39.566$; p-value = 0 (approximately); reject H_0. At the 1% significance level, we conclude that the data are not normally distributed.

12.28 a. H_0: Resistance is normally distributed with a mean of 4,790 and a standard deviation of 40.
H_A: Resistance is not normally distributed with a mean of 4,790 and a standard deviation of 40.

b. $\chi_2^2 = 5.579$; p-value = 0.061; do not reject H_0. At the 5% significance level, we cannot conclude that the resistance is not normally distributed.

c. At the 10% significance level, the conclusion in part b would change.

12.30 a. H_0: CEO compensation is normally distributed with a mean of $19.03 million and a standard deviation of $27.61 million.
H_A: CEO compensation is not normally distributed with a mean of $19.03 million and a standard deviation of $27.61 million.

$\chi_2^2 = 230.907$; p-value = 0 (approximately); reject H_0. At the 1% significance level, we conclude that CEO compensation is not normally distributed.

b. $H_0: S = 0$ and $K = 0$; $H_A: S \neq 0$ or $K \neq 0$
$\chi_2^2 = (238/6)[5.26^2 + 35.53^2/4] = 13,616.092$; p-value = 0 (approximately). Both tests show that at the 5% significance level, total compensation of CEOs is not normally distributed.

12.34 a. $H_0: p_1 = 0.40, p_2 = 0.30, p_3 = 0.20, p_4 = 0.10$
H_A: At least one of the p_i (i = 1,2,3,4) differs from its hypothesized value.
b. $\chi_3^2 = 8.182$
c. p-value = 0.042; do not reject H_0. At the 1% significance level, we cannot conclude that the market shares have changed.

12.36 $H_0: p_1 = 0.47, p_2 = 0.30, p_3 = 0.04,$
$p_4 = 0.05, p_5 = 0.14$
H_A: At least one of the p_i (i = 1,2,3,4,5) differs from its hypothesized value.
$\chi_4^2 = 9.961$; p-value = 0.041; reject H_0. At the 5% significance level, we conclude that the researcher's results are inconsistent with the survey results conducted by Facebook.

12.38 a. H_0: Surviving a cardiac arrest is independent of the time of the cardiac arrest.
H_A: Surviving a cardiac arrest is dependent on the time of the cardiac arrest.
b. $\chi_1^2 = 333.462$; p-value = 0 (approximately)
c. Reject H_0; at the 1% significance level, we conclude that a patient surviving a cardiac arrest is dependent on the time that it happens. Hospitals need to ensure that patients have equal chances of surviving a cardiac arrest, regardless of when it happens.

12.42 H_0: A household's delinquency in payment is independent of the type of heating.
H_A: A household's delinquency in payment is dependent on the type of heating.
$\chi_3^2 = 23.82$; p-value = 0 (approximately); reject H_0. At the 5% significance level, we conclude that a household's delinquency in payments and the type of heating it uses are dependent.

12.46 a. $H_0: p_1 = 0.80, p_2 = 0.09, p_3 = 0.09, p_4 = 0.02$
H_A: At least one of the p_i (i = 1,2,3,4) differs from its hypothesized value.
b. $\chi_3^2 = 8.436$; p-value = 0.038
c. At the 5% significance level, we conclude that the management's goals are not being met. Yes, the conclusion changes at the 1% significance level.

12.50 a. $H_0: S = 0$ and $K = 0$; $H_A: S \neq 0$ or $K \neq 0$
b. $\chi_2^2 = \left(\frac{52}{6}\right)\left[0.1622^2 + \frac{0.8681^2}{4}\right] = 1.861$;
p-value = 0.394
c. At the 5% significance level, we cannot conclude that weekly demand values are not normally distributed. The conclusion is not sensitive to the choice of the significance level.

Chapter 13

13.6 a. $H_0: \mu_1 = \mu_2 = \mu_3 = \mu_4 = \mu_5 = \mu_6$
H_A: Not all population means are equal.
c. $F_{(5,54)} = 1.371$; p-value = 0.250; do not reject H_0. At the 5% significance level, we cannot conclude that not all population means are equal.

13.8 a. $H_0: \mu_1 = \mu_2 = \mu_3$
H_A: Not all population means are equal.

c. $F_{(2,21)} = 2.804$; p-value = 0.083; do not reject H_0. At the 5% significance level, we cannot conclude that there are differences in the effectiveness of the three detergents.

13.14 a. $H_0: \mu_{Low} = \mu_{Medium} = \mu_{High}$
H_A: Not all population means are equal.
c. $F_{(2,117)} = 10.591$; p-value = 0 (approximately). At the 1% and 5% significance levels, we conclude that the mean fill volumes are not equal.

13.18 $H_0: \mu_1 = \mu_2 = \mu_3$
H_A: Not all population means are equal.
$F_{(2,117)} = 10.591$; p-value = 0 (approximately); reject H_0. At the 10% significance level, we conclude that the average job satisfaction differs by field.

13.24 a. $\mu_1 - \mu_2$: $[-12.10, -7.90]$
$\mu_1 - \mu_3$: $[-9.01, -4.99]$
$\mu_2 - \mu_3$: $[0.78, 5.22]$
b. $\mu_1 - \mu_2$: $[-12.53, -7.47]$
$\mu_1 - \mu_3$: $[-9.42, -4.58]$
$\mu_2 - \mu_3$: $[0.33, 5.67]$
c. Tukey's HSD approach is more reliable because it protects against an inflated risk of Type I error.

13.26 a. $H_0: \mu_{Day1} = \mu_{Day2} = \mu_{Day3} = \mu_{Day4}$
H_A: Not all population means are equal.
Reject H_0; at the 1% significance level, we conclude that the mean hardness is not the same.
b.

Mean Differences	Tukey's Interval
$\mu_1 - \mu_2$	$[1.76, 13.74]^*$
$\mu_1 - \mu_3$	$[-11.44, 0.16]$
$\mu_1 - \mu_4$	$[-9.67, 2.11]$
$\mu_2 - \mu_3$	$[-19.53, -7.25]^*$
$\mu_2 - \mu_4$	$[-17.75, -5.31]^*$
$\mu_3 - \mu_4$	$[-4.18, 7.90]$

*indicates significance at the 1% level.

At the 1% significance level, we conclude that the mean hardness of the Day 2 batch differs from those of the Day 1, 3, and 4 batches.

13.28 a. $H_0: \mu_{First} = \mu_{Second} = \mu_{Third}$
H_A: Not all population means are equal.
$F_{(2,72)} = 2.759$; p-value = 0.07; do not reject H_0. We conclude only at the 10% significance level (not at 5%) that the mean absenteeism differs across the three work shifts.
b.

Mean Differences	Fisher's Interval
$\mu_1 - \mu_2$	$[-5.81, 0.13]$
$\mu_1 - \mu_3$	$[-7.05, -1.11]^*$
$\mu_2 - \mu_3$	$[-4.21, 1.73]$

*indicates significance at the 10% level.

At the 10% significance level, we conclude that the mean absenteeism differs between the first and third shift workers.

13.30 a. $SST = 176.25$; $SSA = 51.5$;
        $SSB = 74.25$; $SSE = 50.5$
    b. $MSA = 25.75$; $MSB = 24.75$; $MSE = 8.4167$
    d. p-value = 0.1214; do not reject H_0. At the 5% significance level, we cannot conclude that the Factor A means differ.
    e. p-value = 0.1209; do not reject H_0. At the 5% significance level, we cannot conclude that the Factor B means differ.

13.34 b. p-value = 0.900; do not reject H_0. At the 5% significance level, we cannot conclude that the column means differ.
    c. p-value = 0.006; reject H_0. At the 5% significance level, we conclude that the row means differ.

13.36 b. p-value = 0.233; do not reject H_0. At the 5% significance level, we cannot conclude that average scores differ between rounds.
    c. p-value = 0.132; do not reject H_0. At the 5% significance level, we cannot conclude that the average scores differ across players.

13.38 a. H_0: $\mu_1 = \mu_2 = \mu_3$
        H_A: Not all population means are equal.
        p-value = 0.593; do not reject H_0. At the 5% significance level, we cannot conclude the mean output rate is not the same for each shift.
    b. H_0: $\mu_A = \mu_B = \mu_C = \mu_D$
        H_A: Not all population means are equal.
        p-value = 0.013; reject H_0. At the 5% significance level, we conclude that the mean output rate is not the same for each machine.
    c.

Mean Differences	Tukey's Interval
$\mu_A - \mu_B$	[−12.33, 291.00]
$\mu_A - \mu_C$	[22.67, 326.00]*
$\mu_A - \mu_D$	[−175.00, 128.33]
$\mu_B - \mu_C$	[−116.67, 186.67]
$\mu_B - \mu_D$	[−314.33, −11.00]*
$\mu_C - \mu_D$	[−349.33, −46.00]*

*indicates significance at the 1% level.

At the 5% significance level, the mean output rate differs between machines A and C, B and D, and C and D.

13.42 b. p-value = 0.751; do not reject H_0. At the 5% significance level, we cannot conclude that there is interaction between factors A and B.
    c. p-value = 0 (approximately); reject H_0. At the 5% significance level, the means differ for factor A.
    d. p-value = 0 (approximately); reject H_0. At the 5% significance level, the means differ for factor B.

13.44 a. p-value = 0.463; do not reject H_0. At the 1% significance level, we cannot conclude that there is interaction between the two factors.
    b. Yes. At the 1% significance level, the column means as well as the row means differ.

13.48 a. p-value = 0.296; do not reject H_0. At the 5% significance level, we cannot conclude that there is interaction between the two factors.
    b. Yes. At the 5% significance level, we conclude that differences in the mean weekly sales depend on the time of day used for advertising. At the 5% significance level, we cannot conclude that differences in the mean weekly sales depend on the local channel used for advertising.

13.52 a. H_0: $\mu_1 = \mu_2 = \mu_3 = \mu_4$
        H_A: Not all population means are equal.
    b. p-value = 0 (approximately); reject H_0. At the 5% significance level, we conclude that the average salaries of the four different transportation operators differ.

13.56 H_0: $\mu_1 = \mu_2 = \mu_3$
    H_A: Not all population means are equal.
    p-value = 0.020; reject H_0. At the 5% significance level, we conclude that the average strength of the plywood boards differs by the type of glue used.

13.58 a. H_0: $\mu_A = \mu_B = \mu_C$
        H_A: Not all population means are equal.
        p-value = 0.003; reject H_0. At the 5% significance level, we conclude that the mean P/E ratios of these three industries differ.
    b.

Mean Differences	Tukey's Interval
$\mu_A - \mu_B$	[−8.93, 3.58]
$\mu_A - \mu_C$	[−16.10, −3.58]*
$\mu_B - \mu_C$	[−13.42, −0.91]*

*indicates significance at the 5% level.

At the 5% significance level, the mean P/E ratio differs between A and C, and between B and C.

13.60 a. H_0: $\mu_{Internet} = \mu_{Phone} = \mu_{Mail\text{-}in}$
        H_A: Not all population means are equal.
        p-value = 0.651; do not reject H_0. At the 5% significance level, we cannot conclude that the mean purchase amounts differ across the three purchase sources.
    b. Fisher's LSD method is not necessary since we did not find differences in means.

13.62 H_0: $\mu_1 = \mu_2 = \mu_3 = \mu_4 = \mu_5 = \mu_6 = \mu_7$
    H_A: Not all population means are equal.
    p-value = 0 (approximately); reject H_0. At the 5% significance level, we conclude that the mean visits to the website differ by day of the week.

13.66 a. p-value = 0.456; do not reject H_0. At the 5% significance level, we cannot conclude that the mean nighttime viewing distance differs among the three headlight designs. This implies that no single headlight design is superior.
    b. p-value = 0.009; reject H_0. At the 5% significance level, we conclude that the mean nighttime viewing distance differs across the driver age groups.

13.68 a. p-value = 0.221; do not reject H_0. At the 5% significance level, we cannot conclude that there is interaction between fuel type and hybrid type.

b. p-value = 0.010; reject H_0. At the 5% significance level, we conclude that average fuel consumption differs by fuel type.

c. p-value = 0.160; do not reject H_0. At the 5% significance level, we cannot conclude that average fuel consumption differs by type of hybrid.

13.70 a. p-value = 0.001; reject H_0. At the 5% significance level, we conclude that there is interaction between the training method and operator experience level.

b. Given significant interaction, it is not necessary to conduct tests on the main effects.

Chapter 14

14.6 a. $r_{xy} = -0.175$; negative linear relationship

b. $H_0: \rho_{xy} = 0; H_A: \rho_{xy} \neq 0$

c. $t_{23} = -0.852$; p-value = 0.402; do not reject H_0. At the 5% significance level, we cannot conclude that the population correlation coefficient differs from zero.

14.8 a. $r_{MC} = 0.5662$; $r_{MB} = 0.6264$; $r_{MG} = 0.8231$; $r_{CB} = 0.0445$; $r_{CG} = 0.6278$; $r_{BG} = 0.4594$ (M = Microsoft, C = Coca Cola, B = BOA, and G = GE)

b. Coca Cola

c. Coca Cola and Bank of America

14.12 a. $\hat{y} = 40$

b. $\hat{y}$ increases by 25

14.14 a. $\hat{y} = 568$

b. If x_2 increases by 1 unit, $\hat{y}$ decreases by 47.2 units, holding x_1 constant.

14.18 a. $b_1 = 30$; if x_1 increases by 1 unit, $\hat{y}$ increases by 30 units, holding x_2 as constant.

b. $\hat{y} = 21.97 + 30x_1 - 1.88x_2$

c. $\hat{y} = 884.37$

14.24 a. The positive sign for the Poverty coefficient is as expected; the slope coefficient for Income is not as expected.

b. As Poverty increases by 1%, Crime is predicted to rise by 53.16, holding Income constant.

c. $\widehat{Crime} = 1009.08$

14.26 a. $\widehat{GPA} = 0.4256 + 0.0041GRE$

b. $\widehat{GPA} = 3.34$

14.28 a. $\widehat{Consumption} = 8550.675 + 0.686Disposable\ Income$

b. Consumers spend 68.6% of an increase in income on consumption.

c. $\widehat{Consumption} = 47,652.68$

14.32 a. $\widehat{Final} = 27.58 + 0.68Midterm$

b. $\widehat{Final} = 81.98$

14.40 a. $\widehat{Rent} = 300.4116 + 225.81Bed + 89.2661Bath + 0.2096Sqft$

b. For every additional bathroom, the predicted rent increases by $89.27, holding number of bedrooms and square feet constant.

c. $\widehat{Rent} = 1155.70$

14.42 a. $s_e^2 = 54.3478$; $s_e = 7.3721$

b. $R^2 = 0.1667$

14.44 a. $s_e = 0.8629$

b. $R^2 = 0.6111$

14.46 Model 2, since it has a smaller s_e and a higher R^2. We need not use adjusted R^2 since both models have the same number of explanatory variables.

14.48 Model 2, since it has a smaller s_e and a higher adjusted R^2.

14.50 a. 82.99% of the sample variability in sales is explained.

b. 17.01% of the sample variability in sales is not explained.

14.54 Model 2, since it has a smaller s_e (1475 versus 1509) and a higher adjusted R^2 (0.8283 versus 0.8204).

14.56 a. $s_e = 12.7697$

b. $R^2 = 0.1726$

c. Adjusted $R^2 = 0.1113$

14.64 a. $\widehat{Startups} = 0.4190 + 0.0087Research + 0.0517Patents - 0.0194Duration$

b. $\widehat{Startups} = 1.49$

c. $114.94 million

Chapter 15

15.8 a. $H_0: \beta_1 \leq 0; H_A: \beta_1 > 0$

b. $t_{18} = 8.40$; p-value = 0 (approximately)

c. Reject H_0; at the 5% significance level, we conclude that advertising expenditures and sales have a positive linear relationship.

15.10 a. $\widehat{Time} = 13.353 - 0.0477Height$

b. $H_0: \beta_1 = 0; H_A: \beta_1 \neq 0$

c. $t_5 = -2.926$

d. p-value = 0.033; reject H_0. At the 5% significance level, Height is significant.

15.14 a. $\widehat{Return} = -12.0243 + 0.1459P/E + 5.4417P/S$

b. $H_0: \beta_1 = \beta_2 = 0; H_A$: At least one $\beta_j \neq 0$
$F_{(2,27)} = 2.817$; p-value = 0.077; reject H_0. At the 10% significance level, the two explanatory variables are jointly significant.

c. At the 10% significance level, P/E is not significant but P/S is significant.

15.16 $\widehat{Taxes} = 6,499.4126 + 6.8063Size$
$H_0: \beta_1 = 0$ and $H_A: \beta_1 \neq 0$
p-value = 0 (approximately); reject H_0. At the 5% significance level, home size is significant.

15.20 a. $\widehat{Cost} = 14,039.1873 + 92.7827Temp + 446.1406Days - 27.0033Tons$

b. $H_0: \beta_1 = \beta_2 = \beta_3 = 0; H_A$: At least one $\beta_j \neq 0$
p-value = 0.026; reject H_0. At the 10% significance level, the explanatory variables are jointly significant.

c. At the 10% significance level, the average temperature is significant, the number of work days is not significant, and the tons produced is not significant.

15.22 a. $\widehat{Price} = 153{,}348.2664 + 95.8559\text{Sqft} + 556.8907\text{Beds} + 92{,}022.9126\text{Baths}$

b. At the 5% significance level, the explanatory variables are jointly significant.

c. At the 5% significance level, square footage is significant, number of beds is not significant, and number of baths is significant.

15.24 Restricted Model: $y = \beta_0 + \beta_2 x_2 + \varepsilon$
Unrestricted Model: $y = \beta_0 + \beta_1 x_1 + \beta_2 x_2 + \beta_3 x_3 + \varepsilon$

15.26 Restricted Model: $(y - x_2) = \beta_0 + \beta_1(x_1 - x_2) + \varepsilon$
Unrestricted Model: $y = \beta_0 + \beta_1 x_1 + \beta_2 x_2 + \varepsilon$

15.30 $H_0: \beta_2 = \beta_3 = 0$; H_A: At least one of the coefficients is nonzero.
$F_{(2,139)} = 3.385$; p-value $= 0.037$; reject H_0.
At the 5% level, Patents and Duration are jointly significant. Lisa should add both variables for predicting Startups.

15.32 a. $\widehat{Sale} = 23.3045 + 0.5184\text{MaleHours} + 0.6779\text{FemaleHours}$

b. At the 5% significance level, both explanatory variables are jointly significant.

At the 5% significance level, both explanatory variables are individually significant.

c. $H_0: \beta_1 = \beta_2$; $H_A: \beta_1 \neq \beta_2$
$F_{(1,49)} = 2.260$; p-value $= 0.139$; do not reject H_0. At the 5% significance level, we cannot conclude that there is a difference in productivity between male and female employees.

15.36 a. $28.46 \le E(y^0) \le 33.64$

b. $24.02 \le y^0 \le 38.08$

c. The prediction interval because it incorporates the non-zero error term.

15.38 a. $45.51 \le E(y^0) \le 56.71$

b. $37.81 \le y^0 \le 64.41$

c. The confidence interval because the prediction interval incorporates the non-zero error term.

15.40 a. $\hat{y}^0 = 34.2632$

b. $31.60 \le E(y^0) \le 36.93$

c. $19.49 \le y^0 \le 49.03$

15.44 a. $\hat{y}^0 = 6.1871$

b. $5.83 \le E(y^0) \le 6.55$

c. $4.75 \le y^0 \le 7.63$

15.46 b. Since the residuals fan out when plotted against x, it suggests a problem of changing variability (heteroskedasticity). This means that the estimators are not efficient and the significance tests are not valid. A common solution is to use robust standard errors for conducting significance tests.

15.48 The scatterplot shows that a simple linear regression model is not appropriate as GPA is positively related to Hours at lower levels but negatively related at higher levels of Hours.

15.50 a. Perfect multicollinearity, since Study + Sleep + Leisure = 24; the proposed model cannot be estimated.

b. Drop the Sleep variable.

15.52 a. Experienced (older) employees are likely to have more variability in salaries because not all employees reach the same level of success over time.

b. The residuals fan out when plotted against experience, confirming the changing variability (heteroskedasticity) problem.

15.54 There does not appear to be an issue with correlated observations, as the residuals do not show any pattern around the horizontal axis.

15.58 a. $\widehat{Time} = 0.0357 + 0.0079\text{Machine Parts} + 0.6465\text{Manual Parts}$

b. $\widehat{Time} = 14.1322$ minutes

c. 85.30%

d. At the 5% significance level, the explanatory variables are jointly significant.

In addition, at the 5% significance level, the explanatory variables are individually significant.

15.60 a. $\widehat{Ownership} = 78.9791 - 0.0002\text{Income}$

b. At the 5% significance level, we cannot conclude that Ownership is linearly related to Income.

c. $67.58 \le E(y^0) \le 70.82$

d. $57.49 \le y^0 \le 80.91$; the prediction interval is wider since it accounts for the non-zero random error term.

15.62 a. $\widehat{Return} = 7.2359 + 0.1074\text{Turnover} - 3.1338\text{Expense}$

At the 5% significance level, the explanatory variables are not jointly or individually significant. George's theory is not valid.

b. Multicollinearity is not likely a problem since the sample correlation coefficient between Turnover and Expense is only -0.247. There does not seem to be a problem of changing variability since the residuals appear randomly dispersed around zero when plotted against Turnover and Expense.

Chapter 16

16.4 a. Quadratic model, with a higher adjusted R^2, provides a better fit.

b. $x = 4: \hat{y} = 3.82$; $x = 6: \hat{y} = 2.75$; $x = 12: \hat{y} = 11.83$

16.8 a. From the scatterplot, crew sizes between 6 and 7 seem optimal.

b. Linear Model: $\widehat{Jobs} = 13.0741 + 0.1111(\text{Crew Size})$

Quadratic Model: $\widehat{Jobs} = 2.1111 + 4.5960(\text{Crew Size}) - 0.3737(\text{Crew Size})^2$

The quadratic model provides a better fit than the linear model. It has a higher adjusted R^2 ($0.6307 > -0.0284$) and also has statistically significant explanatory variables.

c. $\widehat{Jobs} = 15.75$ jobs/week

d. $\widehat{Jobs} = 0.6852 + 5.5407(\text{Crew Size}) - 0.5505(\text{Crew Size})^2 + 0.0098(\text{Crew Size})^3$

The quadratic model, with a higher adjusted R^2 ($0.6307 > 0.6170$), provides a better fit than the cubic model.

16.14 Model 1: $\hat{y} = 708.42$
Model 2: $\hat{y} = 678.64$
Model 3: $\hat{y} = 725.75$
Model 4: $\hat{y} = 685.75$

16.16 a. The logarithmic model, with a higher R^2 (0.9341 > 0.8233), provides a better fit than the linear model.
b. $\hat{y} = 18.61$

16.22 a. $\widehat{Cost} = 14,039.1873 + 92.7827 \times 65 + 446.1406 \times 23 - 27.0033 \times 76 = \$28,279.05$
b. $\widehat{Cost} = exp(9.7004 + 0.0034 \times 65 + 0.0181 \times 23 - 0.0012 \times 76 + (0.0587^2/2) = \$28,232.32$
c. The linear model, with a higher R^2 (0.6659 > 0.6543), provides a better fit than the exponential model.

16.24 a. The scatterplot suggests that the logarithmic model provides a better fit than the linear model.
b. As people-to-physician ratio decreases by 500, the predicted life expectancy of females increases by 0.40 year.
c. As people-to-physician ratio decreases by 500, the predicted life expectancy of females increases by 3.84 years.
d. The logarithmic model, with a higher R^2 (0.6967 > 0.4126), provides a better fit.

16.30 a. Linear Model: $\widehat{Time} = -14.4886 + 0.7502Parts$
Quadratic Model: $\widehat{Time} = -6.7165 + 0.4476Parts + 0.0025Parts^2$
b. All the explanatory variables are significant in both models. The quadratic model, with a higher adjusted R^2 (0.9966 > 0.9916), provides a better fit than the linear model.
c. $\widehat{Time} = 20.53$ minutes

16.32 a. Linear Model: $\widehat{Savings} = -40.8632 + 0.0041Income$
Log-log Model: $\ln(\widehat{Savings}) = -112.0910 + 12.2033\ln(Income)$
b. The linear model, with a higher R^2 (0.7001 > 0.6498), provides a better fit than the log-log model.

Chapter 17

17.2 a. $\hat{y} = 160 + 15 \times 1 + 32 \times 1 = 207$
b. $\hat{y} = 160 + 15 \times 0 + 32 \times 0 = 160$

17.4 a. Female employees
b. Female employees without an MBA
c. No

17.6 a. $\widehat{Consumption} = 13,007.2568 + 0.4444Income + 6,544.4264Urban$
Urban: = \$55,103.68.
Rural: = \$48,559.26.
b. $\widehat{Consumption} = 19,551.6832 + 0.4444Income - 6,544.4264Rural$
Urban: = \$55,103.68.
Rural: = \$48,559.26.

17.8 a. $\widehat{Salary} = 62.3383 - 0.9605BMI + 4.4855White$
At the 5% significance level, we conclude that BMI influences Salary.
b. White man: $\widehat{Salary} = 38.01$
c. Non-white man: $\widehat{Salary} = 33.52$

17.16 a. $\widehat{Vehicles} = 135.3913 + 23.5056Garage Bays + 0.5955Population + 84.5998Access + 77.4646Winter$
c. At the 5% (and 10%) significance level, we conclude the explanatory variables are jointly significant.
At the 5% significance level, only the interstate access and the winter dummy variable are significant.
At the 10% significance level, the number of bays, the interstate access, and the winter dummy variable are significant.
d. 87.39%
e. $\widehat{Vehicles} = 361.34$

17.20 a. 5 years: $\widehat{Salary} = 61.8$, or \$61,800
15 years: $\widehat{Salary} = 93.8$, or \$93,800
b. 5 years: $\widehat{Salary} = 36.3$, or \$36,300
15 years: $\widehat{Salary} = 48.3$, or \$48,300
c. Higher salary, where the salary gap increases with experience.

17.24 a. Model 1: $\widehat{Errors} = 37.9305 - 1.2814Exper - 7.4241Train$
Model 2: $\widehat{Errors} = 42.7765 - 1.6991Exper - 23.1111Train + 0.9785(Exper \times Train)$
b. Model 2; higher adjusted R^2 (0.6035 > 0.5621) and the explanatory variables are significant.
c. 10 years, training: $\widehat{Errors} = 12.46$; 20 years, no training: $\widehat{Errors} = 8.79$
d. Less experienced employees benefit more from the training program than more experienced employees.

17.28 a. $x = 25$: $\hat{y} = 0.42$; $x = 40$: $\hat{y} = 0.12$
b. $46 < x \leq 50$

17.30 a.

x	LPM	Logit
1	−0.08	0.05
2	0.24	0.19
3	0.56	0.53
4	0.88	0.84
5	1.20	0.96

b. The LPM model doesn't constrain the probabilities between 0 and 1.

17.32 a. $\hat{y} = 0.51$
b. At the 5% level, x is significant.

17.34 a. $\hat{y} = 0.57$
b. At the 5% level, x_3 is the only variable that is significant.

17.40 a. $H_0: \beta_1 \leq 0$, $H_A: \beta_1 > 0$; p-value $= 0.015$, reject H_0. At the 5% significance level, we conclude that the divorce rate is higher for this age group.

b. $\hat{y} = \dfrac{\exp(-0.8103 + 2.5615x_1 + 0.0094x_2 - 1.2436x_3)}{1 + \exp(-0.8103 + 2.5615x_1 + 0.0094x_2 - 1.2436x_3)}$

$\hat{y} = 0.74$ (1 child); $\hat{y} = 0.20$ (3 children)

17.44 a. At the 5% significance level, we conclude that the students study more in the fall quarter and the winter quarter than in the spring quarter.

b. Study Hours $= 13.7647 + 4.5144$Fall $+ 1.6074$Winter

Fall quarter: Study Hours $= 18.28$

Winter quarter: Study Hours $= 15.37$

Spring quarter: Study Hours $= 13.76$

17.48 a. Compensation $= 2{,}677.1892 + 10.3154$Profit $+ 1{,}227.6866$Years $+ 36{,}655.1363$Grad $- 0.5227$(Profit $\times$ Grad) $- 193.1612$(Years $\times$ Grad)

b. At the 5% significance level, we conclude that the explanatory variables are jointly significant.

c. At the 5% significance level, we conclude that the explanatory variables are individually significant, except for the two interaction terms, Profit $\times$ Grad and Years $\times$ Grad.

d. Compensation $= \$101{,}855$

Chapter 18

18.2 a. The plot displays a jagged appearance, whereas the plot of the 5-period moving average appears smoother.

b. $MSE = 29.54$ and $MAD = 4.59$

c. $\hat{y}_{21} = 37.00$

18.4 a. $MSE = 9.14$ and $MAD = 2.63$

b. $MSE = 8.23$ and $MAD = 2.41$

c. Use the exponential smoothing method to forecast $\hat{y}_{21} = 22.13$.

18.6 a. $\hat{y}_{2009} = 31.32$

b. $\hat{y}_{2009} = 31.95$

c. Use $\alpha = 0.6$ because it provides a lower MSE ($10.52 < 12.89$).

18.14 a. The plot exhibits an inverted U-shape. A quadratic trend seems more suitable than a linear trend.

b. The quadratic model is preferred, as it has an overwhelmingly greater adjusted R^2 ($0.5342 > -0.0643$).

c. $\hat{y} = 153.7000 + 884.2106 \times 11 - 75.1288 \times 11^2 = 789.43$

18.18 a. From the plots, the linear trend model is inappropriate.

b. Select the cubic model, as it has a higher adjusted R^2 than the quadratic model ($0.9886 > 0.9741$).

c. $\hat{y} = 2{,}953.7899 + 0.6775 \times 85 - 0.0331 \times 85^2 + 0.0007 \times 85^3 = 3{,}197.89$

18.20 a. The linear and the exponential trends are almost indiscernible.

b. The exponential model performs better than the linear model, as it has a lower MSE ($22.24 < 27.77$).

c. $\hat{y} = \exp(4.5347 + 0.0091 \times 54 + 0.0405^2/2) = 152.72$

18.24 0.7567 (Qtr 1), 0.9183 (Qtr 2), 0.8315 (Qtr 3), 1.4935 (Qtr 4)

The series in the 1st, 2nd, and 3rd quarter is about 24%, 8%, and 17% below the average quarterly level, respectively, whereas it is about 49% above its average quarterly level in the 4th quarter.

18.26 a. An upward trend with a sharp spike in the fourth quarter of each year. Seasonality with an exponential trend seems appropriate.

b. Seasonal Indices:

0.8487 (Qtr 1), 0.9348 (Qtr 2), 0.8883 (Qtr 3), 1.3282 (Qtr 4)

Exponential Trend: $\hat{T}_t = \exp(2.0175 + 0.0199t + 0.0019^2/2)$

$MSE = \dfrac{0.0041}{20} = 0.0002$

c. Seasonal dummy variables:

$\hat{y}_t = \exp(2.3014 - 0.4500d_1 - 0.3503d_2 - 0.4001d_3 + 0.0199t + 0.0010^2/2)$.

$MSE = 0.00005$

d. Year 6 forecasts with seasonal dummy variables:

9.68 (Qtr 1), 10.91 (Qtr 2), 10.59 (Qtr 3), 16.11 (Qtr 4)

18.30 b. Seasonal Indices:

0.9550 (Jan), 0.9902 (Feb), . . . 0.9798 (Nov), 0.9290 (Dec)

c. Linear trend model: $\hat{T}_t = 5.1605 - 0.0223t$

Forecasts: 3.6306 (Jan 11), 3.7422 (Feb 11), 3.6892 (Mar 11)

18.32 a. Linear Model:

$\hat{y}_t = 1{,}947.5250 + 196.9188d_1 + 324.6125d_2 + 55.7063d_3 + 64.9063t$

$MSE = 5{,}771.92$ and $MAD = 58.24$

b. Exponential Model:

$\hat{y}_t = \exp(7.6159 + 0.0694d_1 + 0.1129d_2 + 0.0201d_3 + 0.0239t + 0.0371^2/2)$

$MSE = 7{,}358.85$ and $MAD = 68.61$

c. The linear trend model is selected to make forecasts for 2011:

3,507.48 (Qtr 1), 3,700.08 (Qtr 2), 3,496.08 (Qtr 3), 3,505.28 (Qtr 4)

18.42 a. No, since the explanatory variables are insignificant. Also, adjusted R^2 is negative for both models.

b. Autoregressive model of order 1, as it has a higher adjusted R^2 ($0.8902 > 0.7987$).

Unemployment$_{24} = 2.7465 + 0.7193 \times 9.80 = 9.80$

18.48
a. Real estate loans have been rising exponentially, with a slight boom around 1990.
b. MSE for Linear Model = 113,356.64
MSE for Exponential Model = 35,419.65 (preferred model)
$\hat{y}_{2008} = \exp(6.0545 + 0.0543 \times 37 + 0.1082^2/2)$
= \$3,189.63 billion
c. MSE for AR (1) = 4,104.42 (best model)
$\hat{y}_{2008} = -37.2161 + 1.0961(3604.03)$
= \$3,913.21 billion

18.50
a. A flat trend with spikes in July of each year.
b. Seasonal Indices:
0.8933 (Jan), 0.8480 (Feb), . . . 0.9313 (Nov), 0.9667 (Dec)
c. The cubic trend model with adjusted R^2 of 0.6924 is selected.
$\hat{T}_t = 45.849 + 0.594t - 0.0271t^2 + 0.0003t^3$
d. Forecasts for the last three months of 2010:
46.80 (October), 44.62 (November), 46.84 (December)

18.52
a. Linear Trend: $MSE = 481,710.35$ and $MAD = 562.90$
b. Exponential Trend: $MSE = 454,956.07$ and $MAD = 547.70$
c. Choose the exponential model to make forecasts for 2009.
$\hat{y}_t = \exp(9.0170 + 0.0161t + 0.1340d_1 + 0.2739d_2 + 0.0924d_3 + (0.0730)^2/2)$
\$13,237 (Qtr 1), \$15,472 (Qtr 2), \$13,113 (Qtr 3), \$12,148 (Qtr 4)

Chapter 19

19.2
a. 6.12%
b. 1.02%
c. 7.14%

19.4
a. 5.00%
b. 45.83%
c. 50.83%

19.8 −1.68% (January); −0.36% (February)

19.10
a. For 2004, the updated price index = 91.41; others are updated similarly.
b. 14.7% increase
c. 4.84% increase

19.14
a.

Jan	Feb	...	Nov	Dec
3.25	3.18	...	2.46	1.82
100.00	97.85	...	75.69	56.00

b. 37.85% increase

19.16

	Month				
Price Index	Jan	Feb	...	Nov	Dec
Laspeyres	100	93.99	...	123.99	124.97
Paasche	100	94.88	...	121.86	122.62

a. The Laspeyres price index suggests that the prices in December were 24.97% higher than what they were in January.
b. The Paasche price index suggests that the prices in December were 22.62% higher than what they were in January.
c. The base year quantities (16.93 and 55.93) are higher than the current year quantities (11.91 and 51.87), resulting in the higher value of the Laspeyres price index as compared to the Paasche price index.

19.20
a.

Region	2007	2008	2009
Northeast	100.00	94.24	83.55
Midwest	100.00	93.25	88.29
South	100.00	94.74	86.47
West	100.00	80.61	65.46

b. Relative to 2007 home prices, the most severe drop was in the West, and the least severe drop was in the Midwest.

19.22

Nominal Value	Real Value
32	32.00
37	36.27
39	37.86
42	38.89

19.24 5.77% increase

19.26
a. Nominal values increased by 5.26%, compared to 2.18% increase in real values.
b. Nominal values increased by 5.00%, compared to 3.43% decrease in real values.
c. The inflation rate is 3.00% for 2010 and 8.74% in 2011.

19.34 a and b.

Date	Base = Oct 09	Base = Jan 10
Oct-09	100.00	102.46
Nov-09	99.56	102.00
Dec-09	106.68	109.30
Jan-10	97.60	100.00
Feb-10	94.85	97.19
Mar-10	100.85	103.33

c. 6.68% increase
d. 3.33% increase

19.40 a and b.

Year	Real Net Revenue	Real Net Income
2006	88.96	10.52
2007	92.18	1.74
2008	55.80	−12.87
2009	64.20	−0.75

19.42 a. −6.76%
  b. −0.35%
  c. −6.43%

Chapter 20

20.2 a. $H_0: m \leq 140; H_A: m > 140$
  b. $T = T^+ = 19$
  c. At the 5% significance level, we conclude that the median is greater than 140.

20.6 a. $H_0: m \geq 6; H_A: m < 6$
  b. $T = T^+ = 1.5$
  c. At the 5% significance level, we conclude that the median price is less than \$6.

20.8 a. $H_0: m \leq 25; H_A: m > 25$
  b. $z = \frac{35 - 27.5}{9.8107} = 0.76$
  c. p-value = 0.2236
  d. Do not reject H_0; at the 1% significance level we cannot conclude that the median rent exceeds \$25 per square foot.

20.10 a. $H_0: m \leq 500; H_A: m > 500$
  b. Using R, p-value = 0.313; do not reject H_0. At the 5% significance level, the realtor's claim is not supported by the data.

20.12 a. $H_0: m_D \leq 0; H_A: m_D > 0$
  b. $z = \frac{165 - 105}{26.7862}$
  c. p-value = 0.0125
  d. At the 5% significance level, we conclude that the median difference is greater than zero.

20.14 a. $H_0: m_D \geq 0; H_A: m_D < 0$
  b. Using R, p-value = 0.045; reject H_0. At the 5% significance level, we conclude that the median difference is less than 0.

20.18 a. $\mu_W = 575; \sigma_W = 43.7798$
  b. $H_0: m_1 - m_2 \leq 0; H_A: m_1 - m_2 > 0$
  c. $z = 2.86; p$-value = 0.0021
  d. Reject H_0; at the 5% significance level, we conclude that the median of Population 1 is greater than the median of Population 2.

20.20 a. $H_0: m_D \leq 0; H_A: m_D > 0$
  b. Using R, p-value = 0.069; do not reject H_0. At the 5% significance level, we cannot conclude that the median score on the real SAT is greater than the median score on the mock SAT.

20.22 a. $H_0: m_D = 0; H_A: m_D \neq 0$
  b. $z = \frac{14 - 27.5}{9.8107} = -1.38$
  c. p-value = 0.1676
  d. Do not reject H_0; at the 5% significance level, we cannot conclude that the medians of the two appraisal values differ.

20.30 a. $H_0: m_1 = m_2 = m_3 = m_4; H_A:$ Not all population medians are equal.
  b. Using R, p-value = 0.015; reject H_0. At the 5% significance level, we conclude that some medians differ.

20.34 a. $H_0: m_1 = m_2 = m_3; H_A:$ Not all population medians are equal.
  b. $H = \left(\frac{12}{15 \times (15 + 1)} \times 990.10\right) - 3 \times (15 + 1) = 1.505$
  c. p-value = 0.471; do not reject H_0. At the 1% significance level, we cannot conclude that some medians differ. This suggests that the cleansing action does not differ by the type of detergent.

20.36 $H_0: m_1 = m_2 = m_3; H_A:$ Not all population medians are equal.
  Using R, p-value = 6.649e-05; reject H_0. At the 10% significance level, we conclude that there are differences in the median job satisfaction scores.

20.38 a. $H_0: \rho_S \geq 0; H_A: \rho_S < 0$
  b. $r_S = 1 - \frac{6 \times 64}{6 \times (6^2 - 1)} = -0.829$; relatively strong negative relationship
  c. At the 5% significance level, we conclude that the correlation is negative.

20.42 a. $H_0: \rho_S = 0; H_A: \rho_S \neq 0$
  b. $r_S = 1 - \frac{6 \times 200}{10 \times (10^2 - 1)} = -0.212$; relatively weak negative relationship
  c. $z = -0.212 \times \sqrt{(10 - 1)} = -0.64; p$-value = 0.5222. Do not reject H_0. At the 5% significance level, we cannot conclude that the Per Capita GNP and Infant Mortality rankings are correlated.

20.44 a. $H_0: \rho_S = 0; H_A: \rho_S \neq 0$
  b. Using R, p-value = 0.217; do not reject H_0. At the 5% significance level, we cannot conclude that the price of a home and the number of days it takes to sell the home are correlated.

20.48 $H_0: \rho_S \leq 0; H_A: \rho_S > 0$
  Using R, $r_S = 0.5464; p$-value = 0.003; reject H_0. At the 5% significance level, we conclude that age and happiness are positively correlated.

20.50 a. $z = -2.53$
  b. p-value = 0.0114
  c. Reject H_0; at the 5% significance level, we conclude that the population proportions differ.

20.52 a. $H_0: p = 0.50$; $H_A: p \neq 0.50$ (p represents the proportion of plus signs)

b. $z = \frac{0.75 - 0.50}{0.5/\sqrt{20}} = 2.24$

c. p-value $= 0.0250$

d. Reject H_0; at the 5% significance level, the proportion of positive signs is different from the proportion of negative signs.

20.62 a. H_0: Even and odd numbers occur randomly.

H_A: Even and odd numbers do not occur randomly.

b. $z = \frac{8 - 11.9091}{2.2688} = -1.72$

c. p-value $= 0.0854$; do not reject H_0. At the 1% significance level, we cannot conclude that the computer program is operating improperly.

20.64 H_0: GDP growth rate is random; H_A: GDP growth rate is not random.

Using R, p-value $= 0.123$; do not reject H_0. At the 5% significance level, we cannot conclude that India GDP growth rate is non-random.

20.72 a. $H_0: m_1 = m_2 = m_3$; H_A: Not all population medians are equal.

b. $H = \left(\frac{12}{15 \times (15 + 1)} \times 1{,}119.60\right) - 3 \times (15 + 1) = 7.98$

c. p-value $= 0.019$; reject H_0. At the 5% significance level, we conclude that some median P/E ratios differ.

A

Acceptance sampling   A statistical quality control technique in which a portion of the completed products is inspected.

Addition rule   The probability that A or B occurs, or that at least one of these events occurs, is $P(A \cup B) = P(A) + P(B) - P(A \cap B)$.

Adjusted closing price   Stock price data adjusted using appropriate dividend and split multipliers.

Adjusted R^2   A modification of the coefficient of determination that imposes a penalty for using additional explanatory variables in the linear regression model.

Aggregate price index   A representation of relative price movements for a group of items.

Alpha   In the capital asset pricing model (CAPM), it measures whether abnormal returns exist.

Alternative hypothesis (H_A)   In a hypothesis text, the alternative hypothesis contradicts the default state or status quo specified in the null hypothesis.

Analysis of variance (ANOVA)   A statistical technique used to determine if differences exist between three or more population means.

Annualized return   A measure equivalent to the geometric mean return.

Arithmetic mean   The average value of a data set; the most commonly used measure of central location, also referred to as the mean or the average.

Assignable variation   In a production process, the variation that is caused by specific events or factors that can usually be identified and eliminated.

Autoregressive model   A regression model where lagged values of the response variable are used as explanatory variables.

Average   See *Arithmetic mean.*

Average growth rate   For growth rates $g_1, g_2 \ldots, g_n$, the average growth rate G_g is computed as

$G_g = \sqrt[n]{(1 + g_1)(1 + g_2) \cdots (1 + g_n)} - 1$, where n is the number of multi-period growth rates.

B

Balanced data   A completely randomized ANOVA design with an equal number of observations in each sample.

Bar chart   A graph that depicts the frequency or relative frequency of each category of qualitative data as a series of horizontal or vertical bars, the lengths of which are proportional to the values that are to be depicted.

Bayes' theorem   The rule for updating probabilities is
$$P(B|A) = \frac{P(A|B)P(B)}{P(A|B)P(B) + P(A|B^c)P(B^c)},$$ where $P(B)$ is the prior probability and $P(B|A)$ is the posterior probability.

Bell curve   See *Normal curve.*

Bell-shaped distribution   See *Normal distribution.*

Bernoulli process   A series of n independent and identical trials of an experiment such that each trial has only two possible outcomes, and each time the trial is repeated, the probabilities of success and failure remain the same.

Beta   In the capital asset pricing model (CAPM), it measures the sensitivity of the stock's return to changes in the level of the overall market.

Between-treatments variance   In ANOVA, a measure of the variability between sample means.

Bias   The tendency of a sample statistic to systematically overestimate or underestimate a population parameter.

Big data   A massive volume of both structured and unstructured data that are often difficult to manage, process, and analyze using traditional data processing tools.

Binary choice models   Regression models that use a dummy (binary) variable as the response variable. Also called discrete choice or qualitative response models.

Binomial distribution   A description of the probabilities associated with the possible values of a binomial random variable.

Binomial random variable   The number of successes achieved in the n trials of a Bernoulli process.

Box plot   A graphical display of the minimum value, quartiles, and the maximum value of a data set.

C

***c* chart**   A control chart that monitors the count of defects per item in statistical quality control.

Capital asset pricing model (CAPM)   A regression model used in finance to examine an investment return.

Capital gains yield   The gain or loss resulting from the increase or decrease in the value of an asset.

Causal (forecasting) models   Quantitative forecasts based on a regression framework, where the variable of interest is related to a single or multiple explanatory variables.

Centered moving averages (CMA)   In time series analysis, a smoothing technique based on computing the average from a fixed number m of the most recent observations, where m is even.

Centerline   In a control chart, the centerline represents a variable's expected value when the production process is in control.

Central limit theorem (CLT)   The CLT states that the sum or mean of a large number of independent observations from the same underlying distribution has an approximate normal distribution.

Chance variation   In a production process, the variation that is caused by a number of randomly occurring events that are part of the production process.

Changing variability   In regression analysis, a violation of the assumption that the variance of the error term is the same for all observations. It is also referred to as heteroskedasticity.

Chebyshev's theorem   For any data set, the proportion of observations that lie within k standard deviations from the mean will be at least $1 - 1/k^2$, where k is any number greater than 1.

Chi-square test of a contingency table   See *Test for independence.*

Chi-square (X^2) distribution   A family of distributions where each distribution depends on its particular degrees of freedom df. It is positively skewed, with values ranging from zero to infinity, but becomes increasingly symmetric as df increase.

Classes   Intervals for a frequency distribution of quantitative data.

Classical probability   A probability often used in games of chance. It is based on the assumption that all outcomes are equally likely.

Cluster sampling   A population is first divided up into mutually exclusive and collectively exhaustive groups of observations, called clusters. A cluster sample includes observations from randomly selected clusters.

Coefficient of determination (R^2)   The proportion of the sample variation in the response variable that is explained by the sample regression equation.

Coefficient of variation (CV)   The ratio of the standard deviation of a data set to its mean; a relative measure of dispersion.

Combination formula   The number of ways to choose x objects from a total of n objects, where the order in which the x objects is listed *does not matter*, is

$$ _nC_x = \binom{n}{x} = \frac{n!}{(n-x)!x!}. $$

Complement   The complement of event A, denoted A^c, is the event consisting of all outcomes in the sample space that are not in A.

Complement rule   The probability of the complement of an event is $P(A^c) = 1 - P(A)$.

Conditional probability   The probability of an event given that another event has already occurred.

Confidence coefficient   The probability that the estimation procedure will generate an interval that contains the population parameter of interest.

Confidence interval   A range of values that, with a certain level of confidence, contains the population parameter of interest.

Consistency   An estimator is consistent if it approaches the unknown population parameter being estimated as the sample size grows larger.

Consumer price index (CPI)   A monthly weighted aggregate price index, computed by the U.S. Bureau of Labor Statistics, based on the prices paid by urban consumers for a representative basket of goods and services.

Contingency table   A table that shows frequencies for two qualitative (categorical) variables, x and y, where each cell represents a mutually exclusive combination of the pair of x and y values.

Continuous (random) variable   A variable that assumes uncountable values in an interval.

Continuous uniform distribution   A distribution describing a continuous random variable that has an equally likely chance of assuming a value within a specified range.

Control chart   A plot of statistics of a production process over time.

Correlated observations   In regression analysis, a violation of the assumption that the observations are uncorrelated. It is also referred to as serial correlation.

Correlation coefficient   A measure that describes the direction and strength of the linear relationship between two variables.

Covariance   A measure that describes the direction of the linear relationship between two variables.

Critical value   In a hypothesis test, the critical value is a point that separates the rejection region from the nonrejection region.

Cross-sectional data   Values of a characteristic of many subjects at the same point in time or approximately the same point in time.

Cubic regression model   In regression analysis, a model that allows two sign changes of the slope capturing the influence of the explanatory variable on the response variable.

Cubic trend model   In time series analysis, a model that allows for two changes in the direction of the series.

Cumulative distribution function   A probability that the value of a random variable X is less than or equal to a particular value x, $P(X \leq x)$.

Cumulative frequency distribution   A distribution of quantitative data recording the number of observations that falls below the upper limit of each class.

Cumulative relative frequency distribution   A distribution of quantitative data recording the fraction (proportion) of observations that falls below the upper limit of each class.

Cyclical component   Wave-like fluctuations or business cycles of a time series, often caused by expansion and contraction of the economy.

D

Decomposition analysis   A method of estimating trend and seasonal components from a time series and then recomposing them to make forecasts.

Deflated time series   An economic time series that has been adjusted for changes in prices, or inflation.

Degrees of freedom   The number of independent pieces of information that go into the calculation of a given statistic. Many probability distributions are identified by the degrees of freedom.

Dependent events   The occurrence of one event is related to the probability of the occurrence of the other event.

Descriptive statistics   The summary of a data set in the form of tables, graphs, or numerical measures.

Detection approach   A statistical quality control technique that determines at which point the production process does not conform to specifications.

Deterministic relationship   A relationship in which the value of the response variable is uniquely determined by the values of the explanatory variables.

Discrete choice models   See *Binary choice models*.

Discrete uniform distribution A symmetric distribution where the random variable assumes a finite number of values and each value is equally likely.

Discrete (random) variable A variable that assumes a countable number of values.

Dummy variable A variable that takes on values of 0 or 1.

Dummy variable trap A regression model where the number of dummy variables equals the number of categories of a qualitative variable; the resulting model cannot be estimated.

E

Efficiency An unbiased estimator is efficient if its standard error is lower than that of other unbiased estimators.

Empirical probability A probability value based on observing the relative frequency with which an event occurs.

Empirical rule Given a sample mean $\bar{x}$, a sample standard deviation s, and a relatively symmetric and bell-shaped distribution, approximately 68% of all observations fall in the interval $\bar{x} \pm s$; approximately 95% of all observations fall in the interval $\bar{x} \pm 2s$; and almost all observations fall in the interval $\bar{x} \pm 3s$.

Endogeneity See *Excluded variables*.

Error sum of squares (SSE) In ANOVA, a measure of the degree of variability that exists even if all population means are the same. In regression analysis, it measures the unexplained variation in the response variable.

Estimate A particular value of an estimator.

Estimator A statistic used to estimate a population parameter.

Event A subset of a sample space.

Excluded variables In regression analysis, a situation where important explanatory variables are excluded from the regression. It often leads to the violation of the assumption that the error term is uncorrelated with the (included) explanatory variables.

Exhaustive events When all possible outcomes of an experiment are included in the events.

Expected return of a portfolio A weighted average of the expected returns of the assets comprising the portfolio.

Expected value A weighted average of all possible values of a random variable.

Experiment A process that leads to one of several possible outcomes.

Explanatory variables In regression analysis, the variables that influence the response variable. They are also called the independent variables, predictor variables, control variables, or regressors.

Exponential distribution A continuous, nonsymmetric probability distribution used to describe the time that has elapsed *between* occurrences of an event.

Exponential regression model A regression model in which only the response variable is transformed into natural logs.

Exponential smoothing In time series analysis, a smoothing technique based on a weighted average where

the weights decline exponentially as they become more distant.

Exponential trend model A regression model used for a time series that is expected to grow by an increasing amount each period.

F

F distribution A family of distributions where each distribution depends on two degrees of freedom: the numerator degrees of freedom df_1 and the denominator degrees of freedom df_2. It is positively skewed, with values ranging from zero to infinity, but becomes increasingly symmetric as df_1 and df_2 increase.

Factorial formula The number of ways to assign every member of a group of size n to n slots is $n! = n \times (n-1) \times (n-2) \times (n-3) \times \cdots \times 1$.

Finite population correction factor A correction factor that accounts for the added precision gained by sampling a larger percentage of the population. It is implemented when the sample constitutes at least 5% of the population.

Fisher equation A theoretical relationship between the nominal return, the real return, and the expected inflation rate.

Fisher's least significant difference (LSD) method In ANOVA, a test that determines which means significantly differ by computing all pairwise differences of the means.

Frequency distribution A table that groups qualitative data into categories, or quantitative data into intervals called classes, where the number of observations that fall into each category or class is recorded.

G

Geometric mean The geometric mean is a multiplicative average of the data set.

Geometric mean return For multiperiod returns R_1, $R_2 \cdots, R_n$, the geometric mean return G_R is computed as $G_R = \sqrt[n]{(1 + R_1)(1 + R_2) \cdots (1 + R_n)} - 1$, where n is the number of multiperiod returns.

Goodness-of-fit test A chi-square test used to determine if the sample proportions resulting from a multinomial experiment differ from the hypothesized population proportions specified in the null hypothesis.

Goodness-of-fit test for normality A chi-square test used to determine if sample data are drawn from a normally distributed population.

Grand mean In ANOVA, the sum of all observations in a data set divided by the total number of observations.

H

Heteroskedasticity See *Changing variability*.

Histogram A graphical depiction of a frequency or relative frequency distribution; it is a series of rectangles where the width and height of each rectangle represent the class width and frequency (or relative frequency) of the respective class.

Hypergeometric distribution   A description of the probabilities associated with the possible values of a hypergeometric random variable.

Hypergeometric random variable   The number of successes achieved in the n trials of a two-outcome experiment, where the trials are not assumed to be independent.

Hypothesis test   A statistical procedure to resolve conflicts between two competing claims (hypotheses) on a particular population parameter of interest.

I

Income yield   The direct cash payments from an underlying asset, such as dividends, interest, or rental income.

Independent events   The occurrence of one event does not affect the probability of the occurrence of the other event.

Independent random samples   Two (or more) random samples are considered independent if the process that generates one sample is completely separate from the process that generates the other sample.

Index number   A numerical value that reflects a percentage change in price or quantity from a base value.

Indicator variable   See *dummy variable*.

Inferential statistics   The practice of extracting useful information from a sample to draw conclusions about a population.

Inflation rate   The percentage rate of change of a price index over time.

Interaction variable   In a regression model, a product of two explanatory variables. For example, xd captures the interaction between a quantitative variable x and a dummy variable d.

Interquartile range (IQR)   The difference between the third and first quartiles.

Intersection   The intersection of two events A and B, denoted $A \cap B$, is the event consisting of all outcomes in A and B.

Interval (scale) data   Values of a quantitative variable that can be categorized and ranked, and in which differences between values are meaningful.

Interval estimate   See *Confidence interval*.

Inverse transformation   A standard normal variable Z can be transformed to the normally distributed random variable X with mean μ and standard deviation σ as $X = \mu + Z\sigma$.

Investment return   The net gain or loss in value of an investment over a time period.

J

Jarque–Bera test   Uses the skewness and kurtosis coefficients to determine if sample data are drawn from a normally distributed population.

Joint probabilities   The values in the interior of a joint probability table, representing the probabilities of the intersection of two events.

Joint probability table   A contingency table whose frequencies have been converted to relative frequencies.

K

Kruskal–Wallis test   A nonparametric test to determine whether differences exist between several population medians.

Kurtosis coefficient   A measure of whether data is more or less peaked than a normal distribution.

L

Laspeyres price index   A weighted aggregate price index based on quantities evaluated in the base period.

Law of large numbers   In probability theory, if an experiment is repeated a large number of times, its empirical probability approaches its classical probability.

Left-tailed test   In hypothesis testing, when the null hypothesis is rejected on the left side of the hypothesized value of the population parameter.

Linear probability model (LPM)   A linear regression model applied to a binary response variable.

Linear trend model   A regression model used for a time series that is expected to grow by a fixed amount each time period.

Logarithmic regression model   A regression model in which only the explanatory variable is transformed into natural logs.

Logit model   A nonlinear regression model that ensures that the predicted probability of the binary response variable falls between zero and one.

Log-log regression model   A regression model in which both the response variable and the explanatory variable(s) are transformed into natural logs.

Lognormal distribution   A continuous nonsymmetric probability distribution used to describe random variables that are known to be positively skewed.

Lower control limit   In a control chart, the lower control limit indicates excessive deviation below the expected value of the variable of interest.

M

Mann–Whitney test   See *Wilcoxon rank-sum test*.

Margin of error   A value that accounts for the standard error of the estimator and the desired confidence level of the interval.

Marginal probabilities   The values in the margins of a joint probability table that represent unconditional probabilities.

Matched-pairs sample   When a sample is matched or paired in some way.

Maximum likelihood estimation (MLE)   An estimation technique used to estimate models such as the logit models.

Mean   See *Arithmetic mean*.

Mean absolute deviation (MAD)   The average of the absolute differences between the observations and the mean.

Mean square error (MSE)   The average of the error (residual) sum of squares, where the residual is the difference between the observed and the predicted value of a variable.

Mean square regression   The average of the sum of squares due to regression.

Mean-variance analysis   The idea that the performance of an asset is measured by its rate of return, and this rate of return is evaluated in terms of its reward (mean) and risk (variance).

Median   The middle value of a data set.

Method of least squares   See *Ordinary least squares (OLS)*.

Method of runs above and below the median   A nonparametric test to determine randomness with quantitative data.

Mode   The most frequently occurring value in a data set.

Moving average (MA) method   In time series analysis, a smoothing technique based on computing the average from a fixed number m of the most recent observations.

Multicollinearity   In regression analysis, a situation where two or more explanatory variables are correlated.

Multinomial experiment   A series of n independent and identical trials, such that on each trial there are k possible outcomes, called categories; the probability p_i associated with the ith category remains the same; and the sum of the probabilities is one.

Multiple linear regression model   In regression analysis, more than one explanatory variable is used to explain the variability in the response variable.

Multiplication rule   The probability that A and B both occur is $P(A \cap B) = P(A \,|\, B)P(B)$.

Mutually exclusive events   Events that do not share any common outcome of an experiment.

N

Negatively skewed (left-skewed) distribution   A distribution in which extreme values are concentrated in the left tail of the distribution.

Nominal (scale) data   Values of a qualitative variable that differ merely by name or label.

Nominal return   Investment return that has not been adjusted for a change in purchasing power due to inflation.

Nominal terms   A representation of a time series that is not adjusted for inflation.

Noncausal (forecasting) models   Quantitative forecasts that do not present any explanation of the mechanism generating the variable of interest and simply provide a method for projecting historical data.

Nonparametric tests   Statistical tests that rely on fewer assumptions concerning the distribution of the underlying population. These tests are often used when the underlying distribution is not normal and the sample size is small.

Nonresponse bias   A systematic difference in preferences between respondents and nonrespondents of a survey or a poll.

Normal curve   A graph depicting the normal probability density function; also referred to as the bell curve.

Normal (probability) distribution   The most extensively used probability distribution in statistical work and the cornerstone of statistical inference. It is symmetric and bell-shaped and is completely described by the mean and the variance.

Null hypothesis (H_0)   In a hypothesis test, the null hypothesis corresponds to a presumed default state of nature or status quo.

O

Ogive   A graph of the cumulative frequency or cumulative relative frequency distribution in which lines connect a series of neighboring points, where each point represents the upper limit of each class and its corresponding cumulative frequency or cumulative relative frequency.

One-tailed hypothesis test   A test in which the null hypothesis is rejected only on one side of the hypothesized value of the population parameter.

One-way ANOVA   A statistical technique that analyzes the effect of one categorical variable (factor) on the mean.

Ordinal (scale) data   Values of a qualitative variable that can be categorized and ranked.

Ordinary least squares (OLS)   A regression technique for fitting a straight line whereby the error (residual) sum of squares is minimized.

Outliers   Extreme small or large data values.

P

$\bar{p}$ chart   A control chart that monitors the proportion of defectives (or some other characteristic) of a production process.

p-value   In a hypothesis test, the likelihood of observing a sample mean that is at least as extreme as the one derived from the given sample, under the assumption that the null hypothesis is true.

Paasche price index   A weighted aggregate price index based on quantities evaluated in the current period.

Parameter   See *Population parameter*.

Partial F test   See *test of linear restrictions*.

Percentile   The pth percentile divides a data set into two parts: approximately p percent of the observations have values less than the pth percentile and approximately $(100 - p)$ percent of the observations have values greater than the pth percentile.

Permutation formula   The number of ways to choose x objects from a total of n objects, where the order in which the x objects is listed *does matter*, is $_nP_x = \dfrac{n!}{(n - x)!}$.

Pie chart   A segmented circle portraying the categories and relative sizes of some qualitative variable.

Point estimate   The value of the point estimator derived from a given sample.

Point estimator   A function of the random sample used to make inferences about the value of an unknown population parameter.

Poisson distribution   A description of the probabilities associated with the possible values of a Poisson random variable.

Poisson process   An experiment in which the number of successes within a specified time or space interval equals any integer between zero and infinity; the numbers of successes counted in nonoverlapping intervals are independent from one another; and the probability that success occurs in any interval is the same for all intervals of equal size and is proportional to the size of the interval.

Poisson random variable   The number of successes over a given interval of time or space in a Poisson process.

Polygon   A graph of a frequency or relative frequency distribution in which lines connect a series of neighboring points, where each point represents the midpoint of a particular class and its associated frequency or relative frequency.

Polynomial regression model   In regression analysis, a model that allow sign changes of the slope capturing the influence of an explanatory variable on the response variable.

Population   The complete collection of items of interest in a statistical problem.

Population parameter   A characteristic of a population.

Portfolio   A collection of assets.

Positively skewed (right-skewed) distribution   A distribution in which extreme values are concentrated in the right tail of the distribution.

Posterior probability   The updated probability, conditional on the arrival of new information.

Prediction interval   In regression analysis, an interval that pertains to the individual value of the response variable defined for specific values of the explanatory variables.

Prior probability   The unconditional probability before the arrival of new information.

Probability   A numerical value between 0 and 1 that measures the likelihood that an event occurs.

Probability density function   The probability density function provides the probability that a continuous random variable falls within a particular range of values.

Probability distribution   Every random variable is associated with a probability distribution that describes the variable completely. It is used to compute probabilities associated with the variable.

Probability mass function   The probability mass function provides the probability that a discrete random variable takes on a particular value.

Probability tree   A graphical representation of the various possible sequences of an experiment.

Producer price index (PPI)   A monthly weighted aggregate price index, computed by the U.S. Bureau of Labor Statistics, based on prices measured at the wholesale or producer level.

Q

Quadratic regression model   In regression analysis, a model that allows one sign change of the slope capturing the influence of the explanatory variable on the response variable.

Quadratic trend model   In time series analysis, a model that captures either a U-shaped trend or an inverted U-shaped trend.

Qualitative forecasts   Forecasts based on the judgment of the forecaster using prior experience and expertise.

Qualitative response models   See *Binary choice models*.

Qualitative variable   A variable that uses labels or names to identify the distinguishing characteristics of observations.

Quantitative forecasts   Forecasts based on a formal model using historical data for the variable of interest.

Quantitative variable   A variable that assumes meaningful numerical values for observations.

Quartiles   Any of the three values that divide the ordered data into four equal parts, where the first, second, and third quartiles refer to the 25th, 50th, and 75th percentiles, respectively.

R

***R* chart**   A control chart that monitors the variability of a production process.

Random error   In regression analysis, random error is due to the omission of factors that influence the response variable.

Random variable   A function that assigns numerical values to the outcomes of an experiment.

Randomized block design   In ANOVA, allowing the variation in the means to be explained by two factors.

Range   The difference between the maximum and the minimum values in a data set.

Ratio (scale) data   Values of a quantitative variable that can be categorized and ranked, and in which differences between values are meaningful; in addition, a true zero point (origin) exists.

Ratio-to-moving average   In time series analysis, a method used to isolate seasonal variations of a time series.

Real return   Investment return that is adjusted for the change in purchasing power due to inflation.

Real terms   A representation of a time series that is adjusted for inflation.

Regression analysis   A statistical method for analyzing the relationship between variables.

Rejection region   In a hypothesis test, a range of values such that if the value of the test statistic falls into this range, then the decision is to reject the null hypothesis.

Relative frequency distribution   A frequency distribution that shows the fraction (proportion) of observations in each category of qualitative data or class of quantitative data.

Residual (*e*) In regression analysis, the difference between the observed value and the predicted value of the response variable, that is, $e = y - \hat{y}$.

Residual plots In regression analysis, the residuals are plotted sequentially or against an explanatory variable to identify model inadequacies. The model is adequate if the residuals are randomly dispersed around the zero value.

Response variable In regression analysis, the variable that is influenced by the explanatory variable(s). It is also called the dependent variable, the explained variable, the predicted variable, or the regressand.

Restricted model A regression model that imposes restrictions on the coefficients.

Right-tailed test In hypothesis testing, when the null hypothesis is rejected on the right side of the hypothesized value of the population parameter.

Risk-averse consumer Someone who takes risk only if it entails a suitable compensation and may decline a risky prospect even if it offers a positive expected gain.

Risk-loving consumer Someone who may accept a risky prospect even if the expected gain is negative.

Risk-neutral consumer Someone who is indifferent to risk and makes his/her decisions solely on the basis of the expected gain.

Run In the Wald–Wolfowitz runs test, a run is as an uninterrupted sequence of one letter, symbol, or attribute.

Runs test See the *Wald–Wolfowitz runs test*.

S

***s* chart** A control chart that monitors the variability of a production process.

Sample A subset of a population of interest.

Sample correlation coefficient A sample measure that describes both the direction and strength of the linear relationship between two variables.

Sample covariance A sample measure that describes the direction of the linear relationship between two variables.

Sample space A record of all possible outcomes of an experiment.

Sample statistic A random variable used to estimate the unknown population parameter of interest.

Sampling distribution The probability distribution of an estimator.

Scatterplot A graphical tool that helps in determining whether or not two variables are related in some systematic way. Each point in the diagram represents a pair of known or observed values of the two variables.

Seasonal component Repetitions of a time series over a one-year period.

Seasonal dummy variables Dummy variables used to capture the seasonal component from a time series.

Seasonal index A measure of the seasonal variation within a time series used to deseasonalize time series data.

Seasonally adjusted series A time series that is free of seasonal variations.

Selection bias A systematic underrepresentation of certain groups from consideration for a sample.

Serial correlation See *Correlated observations*.

Sharpe ratio A ratio calculated by dividing the difference of the mean return from the risk-free rate by the asset's standard deviation.

Sign test A nonparametric test to determine whether significant differences exist between two populations using matched-pairs sampling with ordinal data.

Significance level The allowed probability of making a Type I error.

Simple linear regression model In regression analysis, one explanatory variable is used to explain the variability in the response variable.

Simple price index For any item, the ratio of the price in a given time period to the price in the base period, expressed as a percentage.

Simple random sample A sample of *n* observations that has the same probability of being selected from the population as any other sample of *n* observations.

Skewness When the distribution is not symmetric.

Skewness coefficient A measure that determines if the data are symmetric about the mean. Symmetric data have a skewness coefficient of zero.

Smoothing techniques In time series analysis, methods to provide forecasts if short-term fluctuations represent random departures from the structure with no discernible systematic patterns.

Social-desirability bias A systematic difference between a group's "socially acceptable" responses to a survey or poll and this group's ultimate choice.

Spearman rank correlation coefficient Measures the correlation between two variables based on rank orderings.

Standard deviation The positive square root of the variance; a common measure of dispersion.

Standard error The standard deviation of an estimator.

Standard error of the estimate The standard deviation of the residual; used as a goodness-of-fit measure for regression analysis.

Standard normal distribution A special case of the normal distribution with a mean equal to zero and a standard deviation (or variance) equal to one.

Standard normal table See *z table*.

Standard transformation A normally distributed random variable X with mean μ and standard deviation σ can be transformed into the standard normal random variable Z as $Z = (X - \mu)/\sigma$.

Standardize A technique used to convert a value into its corresponding *z*-score.

Statistic See *Sample statistic*.

Statistical quality control Statistical techniques used to develop and maintain a firm's ability to produce high-quality goods and services.

Stem-and-leaf diagram A visual method of displaying quantitative data where each value of a data set is separated into two parts: a stem, which consists of the leftmost digits, and a leaf, which consists of the last digit.

Stochastic relationship A relationship in which the value of the response variable is not uniquely determined by the values of the explanatory variables.

Stratified random sampling A population is first divided up into mutually exclusive and collectively exhaustive groups, called strata. A stratified sample includes randomly selected observations from each stratum. The number of observations per stratum is proportional to the stratum's size in the population. The data for each stratum are eventually pooled.

Structured data Data that conform to a predefined row-column format.

Student's *t* distribution See *t distribution*.

Studentized range distribution A distribution used in Tukey's HSD method that has broader, flatter, and thicker tails than the *t* distribution.

Subjective probability A probability value based on personal and subjective judgment.

Sum of squares due to regression (SSR) In regression analysis, it measures the explained variation in the response variable.

Sum of squares due to treatments (SSTR) In ANOVA, a weighted sum of squared differences between the sample means and the overall mean of the data.

Symmetry When one side of a distribution is a mirror image of the other side.

Systematic patterns In time series, patterns caused by a set of identifiable components: the trend, the seasonal, and the cyclical components.

T

***t* distribution** A family of distributions that are similar to the *z* distribution except that they have broader tails. They are identified by their degrees of freedom *df*.

Test for independence A goodness-of-fit test analyzing the relationship between two qualitative variables. Also called a chi-square test of a contingency table.

Test of individual significance In regression analysis, a test that determines whether an explanatory variable has an individual statistical influence on the response variable.

Test of joint significance In regression analysis, a test to determine whether the explanatory variables have a joint statistical influence on the response variable.

Test of linear restrictions In regression analysis, a test to determine if the restrictions specified in the null hypothesis are invalid.

Test statistic A sample-based measure used in hypothesis testing.

Time series A set of sequential observations of a variable over time.

Total probability rule A rule that expresses the unconditional probability of an event, $P(A)$, in terms of probabilities conditional on various mutually exclusive and exhaustive events. The total probability rule conditional on two events B and B^c is $P(A) = P(A \cap B) + P(A \cap B^c) = P(A \mid B)P(B) + P(A \mid B^c)P(B^c)$.

Total sum of squares (SST) In regression analysis, it measures the total variation in the response variable.

Trend A long-term upward or downward movement of a time series.

Tukey's honestly significant difference (HSD) method In ANOVA, a method that determines which means significantly differ by comparing all pairwise differences of the means.

Two-tailed hypothesis test A test in which the null hypothesis can be rejected on either side of the hypothesized value of the population parameter.

Two-way ANOVA test A test that simultaneously examines the effect of two factors on the mean. A two-way ANOVA test can be conducted with or without interaction between the factors.

Type I error In a hypothesis test, this error occurs when the decision is to reject the null hypothesis when the null hypothesis is actually true.

Type II error In a hypothesis test, this error occurs when the decision is to not reject the null hypothesis when the null hypothesis is actually false.

U

Unbalanced data A completely randomized ANOVA design where the number of observations are not the same for each sample.

Unbiased An estimator is unbiased if its expected value equals the unknown population parameter being estimated.

Unconditional probability The probability of an event without any restriction.

Union The union of two events A and B, denoted $A \cup B$, is the event consisting of all outcomes in A or B.

Unrestricted model A regression model that imposes no restrictions on the coefficients.

Unstructured data Data that do not conform to a predefined row-column format.

Unsystematic patterns In time series, patterns caused by the presence of a random error term.

Unweighted aggregate price index An aggregate price index based entirely on aggregate prices with no emphasis placed on quantity.

Upper control limit In a control chart, the upper control limit indicates excessive deviation above the expected value of the variable of interest.

V

Variable A general characteristic being observed on a set of people, objects, or events, where each observation varies in kind or degree.

Variance The average of the squared differences from the mean; a common measure of dispersion.

W

Wald–Wolfowitz runs test A nonparametric test to determine whether the elements in a sequence appear in a random order.

Weighted aggregate price index An aggregate price index that gives higher weight to the items sold in higher quantities.

Weighted mean When some observations contribute more than others in the calculation of an average.

Wilcoxon rank-sum test A nonparametric test to determine whether two population medians differ under independent sampling. Also known as the Mann–Whitney test.

Wilcoxon signed-rank test A nonparametric test to determine whether a sample could have been drawn from a population having a hypothesized value as its median; this test can also be used to determine whether the median difference differs from zero under matched-pairs sampling.

Within-treatments variance In ANOVA, a measure of the variability within each sample.

X

$\bar{x}$ chart A control chart that monitors the central tendency of a production process.

Z

z-score The relative position of a value within a data set; it is also used to detect outliers.

z table A table providing cumulative probabilities for positive or negative values of the standard normal random variable Z.

n refers to notes at the bottom of the page

A

Acceptance sampling, 268
Addition rule, 126–128, 152
Adidas Group, 115, 138, 427, 436, 439
Adjusted closing price, 705–706, 723
Adjusted coefficient of determination, 529, 533
Adjusted R^2, 533, 539
Adjusted seasonal index, 680–681
Aggregate price indices
   unweighted, 710–711
   weighted, 711–713
Alpha, 550
Alstead, Troy, 4
Alternative hypothesis, 324–325, 350
American Public Transportation Association, 473
Analysis of variance (ANOVA). *See also* One-way
   ANOVA; Two-way ANOVA
   ANOVA table, 466
   Fisher's Least Significant Difference (LSD)
     Method, 472–475, 499
   Tukey's honestly significant differences (HSD)
     method, 472, 474–476, 499
   uses of, 460, 462
Annualized return, 80
ANOVA. *See* Analysis of variance (ANOVA)
Anti-log function, 601–602
Arithmetic mean, 64–66
Arizona Cardinals, 122
Assignable variation, 268–269
Association measures, 100–103
   correlation coefficient, 100–101, 106
   covariance, 16, 100
   Excel calculations, 102
   R and RStudio, 102
Asymptotic distribution, 211
Autoregressive model, 689
Average growth rates, 81–82, 106
Averages. *See* Mean

B

Balanced data, 474–476, 499
Bar charts, 23, 25, 52
Baseball
   analyzing winning percentage in,
     545, 554
   major league disparities, 110
   player salaries, 620
   player value assessments, 580–582
Bayes, Thomas, 143
Bayes' theorem, 140, 143–146, 153

Beer price changes, 703, 715
Bell curve, 211. *See also* Symmetric distributions
Bell-shaped distribution, 210
Bell Telephone Laboratories, 269
Bernoulli, James, 176
Bernoulli process, 176, 190, 196, 428
Beta, 550
Betting, 122
Between-treatments estimate of population
   variance, 463–464
Between-treatments variance, 463
Bias, in sampling, 248
   nonresponse bias, 249, 277
   selection bias, 249, 277
   social-desirability bias, 250
Big data, 8, 17
Binary choice models
   defined, 641
   linear probability model (LPM), 641–643, 651
   logit model, 643–646, 651
Binomial distribution, 176–182, 221
   defined, 176
   with Excel, 181–182
   formula, 178–179
   with R, 182
Binomial experiments, 176, 428
Binomial random variable, 176, 178–182, 196
Blocked outcomes, 482
Bloomberg Businessweek, 264
Boston Globe, 4, 342
Box-and-whisker plot. *See* Boxplots
Boxplots, 76–78, 105
Brady, Tom, 439
Brown, Scott, 4
Bureau of Economic Analysis (BEA), 8
Bureau of Labor Statistics (BLS), 6, 8, 718
Business Week, 9

C

Caloric information on menus, 361, 379
Capital asset pricing model (CAPM), 549–550
Capital gains yield, 704, 723
Case studies
   Advanced Placement test financial
     incentives, 355
   annual return data, 394–395
   annual stock return data, 504–505
   Apple Inc. stock analysis, 586
   body mass index percentiles, 240–241
   campaign polls, 320
   Chartered Financial Analyst exam success,
     656–657

Notes

Notes

Notes

Notes

Notes

Notes

Notes